Mathematics, Structure and Method, Course 2, New E...

Comprehensive content developed for the academically oriented eighth grade student emphasizes pre-algebra skills and concepts, such as variables, equation solving, and problem solving. The full range of topics needed for the successful study of algebra is presented. See the Table of Contents.

Class Exercises, Written Exercises, and **Review Exercises** often develop the theory behind lesson concepts as well as basic pre-algebra skills. See pages 42, 43, 124, 125, and 273–275.

Precision in the use of **mathematical terminology** and **concepts** is emphasized in lesson narratives and in special features like **Reading Mathematics.** See pages 2, 3, and 182–184.

Review and testing features at the ends of lessons and chapters measure student progress, reinforce basic skills, and aid retention of frequently used fundamental concepts. See pages 325, 347, and 350–353.

A unique collection of **supplementary materials** accompanies a **comprehensive teacher's edition** that features side-column notes along with annotated versions of the student book pages, teaching commentary, chalkboard examples, additional exercises, and quick quizzes. The supplementary materials consist of the following:

Solution Key (includes worked-out solutions to all exercises)

Resource Book (includes extra testing, practice, enrichment, and review sheets; on blackline copying masters)

Tests (different from Resource Book tests; on duplicating masters)

Practice Masters (different from Resource Book practice sheets; on duplicating masters)

Computer Activities (diskettes are available to accompany this item; on duplicating masters)

In addition to the **Computer Activities** on duplicating masters described above, short features in the student book called **Calculator Key-In** and **Computer Byte** extend and apply pre-algebra concepts by means of calculators and computers. See references under *Calculator* and *Computer* in the Index.

Teacher's Edition

MATHEMATICS
Structure and Method

Course 2   New Edition

Mary P. Dolciani
Robert H. Sorgenfrey
John A. Graham

Editorial Advisers

Richard G. Brown
Robert B. Kane

HOUGHTON MIFFLIN COMPANY · **Boston**
Atlanta Dallas Geneva, Ill. Lawrenceville, N.J. Palo Alto Toronto

AUTHORS

Mary P. Dolciani Professor of Mathematical Sciences, Hunter College of the City University of New York

Robert H. Sorgenfrey Professor of Mathematics, University of California, Los Angeles

John A. Graham Mathematics Teacher, Buckingham Browne and Nichols School, Cambridge, Massachusetts

Editorial Advisers

Richard G. Brown Mathematics Teacher, The Phillips Exeter Academy, Exeter, New Hampshire

Robert B. Kane Director of Teacher Education and Head of the Department of Education, Purdue University

Teacher Consultants

Jimmie B. Jenkins Mathematics and Science Teacher, Conyers Middle School, Conyers, Georgia

Steven P. Meiring State Mathematics Consultant, Ohio Department of Education

Sharon A. Sandhu Mathematics Teacher and Department Chairman, El Dorado Middle Intermediate School, Concord, California

Acknowledgments

The authors wish to thank Joan MacDonald, Mathematics Teacher and Department Chairman, Milton Academy, Milton, Massachusetts, for her valuable contribution to this edition of the student textbook. The authors also wish to thank Rebecca Cook and James Sconyers for their valuable contributions to this teacher's edition. Rebecca Cook is Department Chairman and Mathematics Teacher, Gifted and Talented Grades 7 and 8, Wiley Junior High School, Winston-Salem, North Carolina. James Sconyers is Mathematics Teacher at Terra Alta High School, Terra Alta, West Virginia.

Contents

Each chapter of the student book is preceded by a section of Lesson Commentary, including reduced facsimiles of most Resource Book pages designed for use with the chapter. (See Student Book Contents, page T27.) Answer annotations appear on student pages. Side columns present Chalkboard Examples, Additional A Exercises, Reading Mathematics, Additional Answers, Suggested Assignments, Supplementary Materials (references), Quizzes, Reviews for Retention, and Enrichment Notes.

TEACHING THE COURSE

The Teacher's Edition, Resource Book, and Solution Key are designed to help teach the course. For each chapter the Teacher's Edition provides Lesson Commentary and slightly reduced reproductions of student pages with answer annotations. The Lesson Commentary precedes the student pages for each chapter and includes Teaching Suggestions, designed to help in lesson planning, and Related Activities, which can be used to add variety to the presentation. The Lesson Commentary also includes reduced facsimiles of the appropriate Resource Book pages with answer annotations.

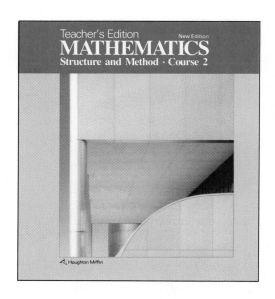

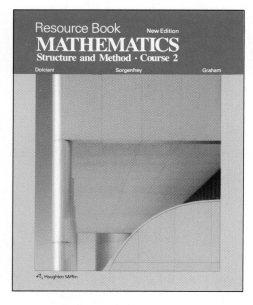

The Resource Book is a book of blackline masters that includes quizzes, tests, reviews, problem solving, enrichment, practice, and calculator or computer pages for each chapter. Four cumulative tests and some teaching aids are also provided. Answers to exercises are printed at the back of the book, as well as in the Teacher's Edition.

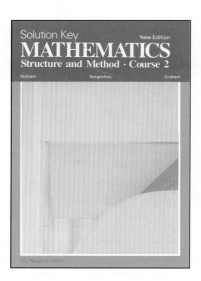

The Solution Key provides worked-out solutions and all necessary artwork for the exercises in the student book.

SUPPLEMENTARY MATERIALS

The supplementary materials on duplicating masters include Tests, Practice Masters, and Computer Activities. Each set of masters is keyed to the student textbook and has a separate answer key with answers annotated on facsimiles of the masters.

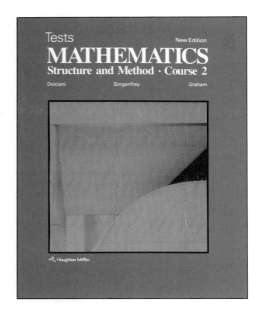

The Tests offer a simple way to measure achievement and keep track of progress.

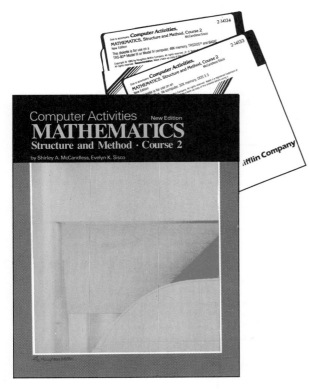

The Computer Activities consist of twenty-four activities in the BASIC computer language. They explore related mathematical topics and are designed to be used independently by the student. Diskettes for the TRS-80 (Model III and Model IV) and Apple II microcomputers are available to be used with the activities. They save students' time by making it unnecessary to type in the programs.

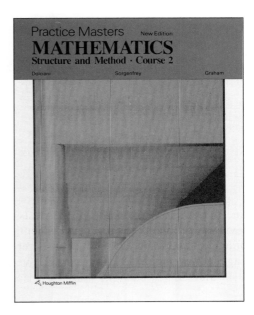

The Practice Masters offer additional practice on the material presented in the student textbook.

USING THE TEACHER'S EDITION

This teacher's edition shows nearly full-sized student textbook pages annotated with answers. Time-saving suggestions and additional materials appear in the adjacent margins, where they will be most useful. Sample teacher's edition pages are shown here to explain the material in the side columns. (These are not actual pages.)

Featured are references to the Teaching Suggestions and Related Activities that appear in the Teaching Commentary prior to each chapter.

Reading Mathematics lists vocabulary words and gives suggestions for helping students read and study mathematics.

Chalkboard Examples illustrate each lesson.

Additional A Exercises assure that students proceed with the Written Exercises on their own.

Reviews for Retention keep previously learned material alive in students' minds.

Teaching Suggestions p. 39b

Related Activities p. 39c

Reading Mathematics
Students will learn the meaning of the following mathematical terms in this lesson: *approximation, rounding, estimate.*

Chalkboard Examples
Round to the nearest tenth.
1. 42.92 42.9
2. 42.96 43.0
Round to the nearest hundredth.
3. 3.984 3.98
4. 3.9807 3.98
Find an estimated answer for each operation.
5. 6.7 + 5.2 12
6. 51.723 − 29.518 22
7. 4.87 × 25.1 125
8. 276 ÷ 19 14

Additional A Exercises
Round to the nearest ten.
1. 27.8 30
2. 13.2 10
Round to the nearest hundredth.
3. 112.347 112.35
4. 77.012 77.01
Round to the nearest thousandth.
5. 0.3452 0.345
6. 12.10103 12.101

Review for Retention
Evaluate the expression when $a = 5$ and $b = 2$.
1. $8a − 24$ 16
2. $6ab$ 60
3. $a + 3b$ 11
4. $(a − b)(3b − a)$ 3
5. $4(2a − 3b)$ 16
6. $a(5b − 5)$ 25

2-3 Rounding

When we use an *approximation* for a number, we say that we are **rounding** the number. For example, suppose that a distance is 6.7 km. We know that 6.7 is between 6 and 7. If we round 6.7 to the nearest whole number, we say that the distance is about 7 km.

We can see that 6.7 is closer to 7 than to 6 by graphing 6.7 on the number line. First we divide the portion of the number line between 6 and 7 into ten equal parts. Then we graph 6.7 on the number line as shown.

Since 6.7 rounded to the nearest whole number is 7, we can write $6.7 \simeq 7$. The symbol $\simeq$ means *is approximately equal to.*

The rule for rounding decimal numbers can be stated as follows:

> 1. Find the decimal place to which you wish to round, and mark it with a caret ($_\wedge$). Look at the digit to the right.
>
> 2. If the digit to the right is 5 or greater, add 1 to the marked digit. If the digit to the right is less than 5, leave the marked digit unchanged.
>
> 3. If the marked digit is to the left of the decimal point, replace each digit to the right of the marked place with "0," and drop all digits to the right of the decimal point.
>   If the marked digit is to the right of the decimal point, drop all digits to the right of the marked place.

EXAMPLE 1 Round 16.0973 to the nearest

  a. ten   **b.** tenth   **c.** hundredth

Solution
a. 16.0973 $_\wedge$ **b.** 16.0973 $_\wedge$ **c.** 16.0973 $_\wedge$
20   16.1   16.10

$16.0973 \simeq 20$ $16.0973 \simeq 16.1$ $16.0973 \simeq 16.10$

Rounding is often used as a quick check on calculations. In general, we **estimate** by rounding to the highest place value of the smaller number for all operations. As a result, our estimated answer should be reasonably close to the exact answer.

48 *Chapter 2*

48

T6

EXAMPLE 2 Find an estimated answer for each operation.

a. $\begin{array}{r} 386 \\ +\ 54 \end{array}$ **b.** $\begin{array}{r} 2.849 \\ -\ 0.154 \end{array}$ **c.** $\begin{array}{r} 32.9 \\ \times\ 8.7 \end{array}$ **d.** $13\overline{)247}$

Solution **a.** $\begin{array}{r} 386 \\ +\ 54 \end{array} \longrightarrow \begin{array}{r} 390 \\ +\ 50 \\ \hline 440 \end{array}$ **b.** $\begin{array}{r} 2.849 \\ -\ 0.154 \end{array} \longrightarrow \begin{array}{r} 2.8 \\ -\ 0.2 \\ \hline 2.6 \end{array}$

c. $\begin{array}{r} 32.9 \\ \times\ 8.7 \end{array} \longrightarrow \begin{array}{r} 33 \\ \times\ 9 \\ \hline 297 \end{array}$ **d.** $12\overline{)253} \longrightarrow 10\overline{)250}\ \ ^{25}$

Class Exercises

Round to the place underlined.

1. 8.0<u>3</u>9 8.04   **2.** 2<u>9</u>4.65 290   **3.** 7<u>5</u>,452 75,000   **4.** 1<u>0</u>.988 11

5. 0.9<u>9</u>6 1.00   **6.** 1.35<u>4</u>7 1.355   **7.** <u>3</u>19.84 300   **8.** 0.<u>3</u>828 0.4

Round to the highest place value.

9. 43 40   **10.** 127.14 100   **11.** 0.036 0.04   **12.** 0.8981 0.9

13. 1986 2000   **14.** 532.3 500   **15.** 0.073 0.07   **16.** 0.0249 0.02

Written Exercises

Round to the nearest ten.

A **1.** 27.5149 30   **2.** 82.604 80   **3.** 293.4 290   **4.** 70.76

5. 648.01 650   **6.** 108.3 110   **7.** 159.62344 160   **8.** 97.23

Round to the nearest hundredth.

9. 72.459 72.46   **10.** 26.804 26.80   **11.** 0.0643 0.06   **12.** 12.395

13. 0.0103 0.01   **14.** 8.142 8.14   **15.** 18.1657 18.17   **16.** 0.70605

Round to the nearest thousandth.

17. 0.0006 0.001   **18.** 12.3568 12.357   **19.** 401.0904 401.090   **20.** 30.0317

21. 250.3407 250.341   **22.** 7.0063 7.006   **23.** 8.0995 8.100   **24.** 0.9996

The Decimal System **49**

Suggested Assignments

Minimum
49/1–24
50/26–32 even
50/Self-Test A

Average
49/2–24 even
50/25–32
50/Self-Test A
50/Calculator Key-In

Maximum
49/2–24 even
50/25–32
50/Self-Test A
50/Calculator Key-In

Supplementary Materials

Practice Masters, p. 8
Test 2A, pp. 9–10
Computer Activity 3

**Additional Answers
Written Exercises**

4. 70 **8.** 100 **12.** 12.40
16. 0.71 **20.** 30.032
24. 1.000

Quick Quiz A

Simplify the expression.
1. 4^3 64
2. 12^1 12
3. 3^4 81
4. $2^4 + 5^2$ 41
5. $g^5 + g^3$ g^8

Replace __?__ with $>$ or $<$
to make a true statement.
6. 83.50 _$>$_ 79.86
7. 0.0842 _$<$_ 0.131
8. 0.5 _$>$_ 0.38467
Round to the place specified.
9. tens: 483.2 480
10. tenths: 0.853 0.9
11. hundredths: 1.603 1.60

Suggested Assignments are
provided for minimum, average, and maximum courses.

Supplementary Materials provides references to the duplicating masters available to
accompany the lesson.

Additional Answers supple-
ment the annotations.

Quick Quizzes check stu-
dents' understanding of the
previous groups of lessons.

Assignment Guide/Management System

To make your planning easier, the following table outlines suggested schedules and assignments for minimum, average, and maximum courses. The minimum course provides more review; the maximum course provides more challenging work and less drill. You can adapt the three courses to fit the needs of your students. For your convenience, reference is made after Chapter 6 to the Mid-Year Test in the Tests booklet.

KEY

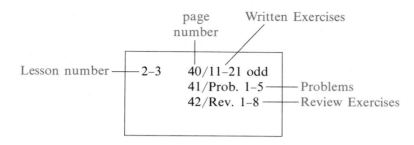

SUMMARY SUGGESTED TIME SCHEDULE

Chapter	1	2	3	4	5	6	7	8	9	10	11	12	Total
Minimum	15	12	14	12	16	13	13	14	15	15	11	10	160
Average	14	12	14	12	14	13	13	15	15	15	12	11	160
Maximum	11	10	13	11	13	12	12	16	16	16	16	14	160

Trimester   Semester   Trimester

Day	Minimum Course	Average Course	Maximum Course
1	**1-1** 4/1–28 4/Rev. 1–8	**1-1** 4/2–24 even; 25–36 4/Rev. 2–8 even	**1-1** 4/2–24 even; 25–38
2	**1-2** 7/1–6; 7–33 odd 8/Rev. 1–10	**1-2** 7/1–23 odd; 25–33 8/34–36 8/Rev. 1–9 odd 8/Calculator Key-In	**1-2** 7/1–23 odd; 25–33 8/34–39 8/Calculator Key-In

Day	Minimum Course		Average Course		Maximum Course	
3	**1-3**	10/1–22	**1-3**	10/1–22 11/23–26	**1-3**	10/6–16 even 11/28–34 even; 37–50
4	**1-3**	11/23–32 11/Rev. 1–8	**1-3**	11/27–41; 45–46 11/Rev. 2–8 even	**1-4**	13/3, 6 14/16–52 even 15/63–68; Challenge
5	**1-4**	13/2–6 even 14/8–36 even	**1-4**	13/2–6 even 14/8–44 even	**1-5**	18/25–55 odd 19/60–65 19/Self-Test A
6	**1-4**	14/25–55 odd 15/Rev. 1–9	**1-4**	14/45–56 15/57–62 15/Rev. 1–9 odd 15/Challenge	**1-6**	22/12–24 23/25–36 23/Challenge
7	**1-5**	18/2–40 even	**1-5**	18/8–56 even	**1-7**	25/1–14 26/15–26
8	**1-5**	18/17–55 odd 19/Self-Test A	**1-5**	18/27–55 odd 19/57–61 19/Self-Test A	**1-8**	29/Prob. 1–6 30/Prob. 7–14
9	**1-6**	22/1–20	**1-6**	22/12–24 23/25–36 23/Rev. 2–8 even 23/Challenge	**1-8**	31/Prob. 15–17 31/Self-Test B
10	**1-6**	22/21–24 23/25–34 23/Rev. 1–8	**1-7**	25/2–10 even; 11–14 26/15–24 26/Rev. 2–8 even	Prepare for Chapter Test 34/Chapter Review 32–33/Enrichment	
11	**1-7**	25/1–14 26/15–22 26/Rev. 1–9	**1-8**	29/Prob. 1–6 30/Prob. 7–14	Administer Chapter 1 Test Resource Book pp. 15–16 36–37/Cumulative Review	
12	**1-8**	29/Prob. 1–6 30/Prob. 7–10	**1-8**	31/Prob. 15–17 31/Self-Test B	**2-1**	43/1–31 odd; 32–48
13	**1-8**	30/Prob. 11–14 31/Prob. 15 31/Self-Test B	Prepare for Chapter Test 34/Chapter Review 32–33/Enrichment		**2-2**	46/2–38 even 47/40–64 even
14	Prepare for Chapter Test 34/Chapter Review		Administer Chapter 1 Test Resource Book pp. 15–16 36–37/Cumulative Review		**2-3**	49/2–24 even 50/25–32 50/Self-Test A 50/Calculator Key-In

Day	Minimum Course	Average Course	Maximum Course
15	Administer Chapter 1 Test Resource Book pp. 15–16 36–37/Cumulative Review	**2-1** 43/1–31 odd; 32–46 43/Rev. 1–7 odd	**2-4** 54/1–27 odd 55/29–33 odd; 35–43 55/Challenge
16	**2-1** 43/1–21; 23–37 odd 43/Rev. 1–8	**2-2** 46/2–38 even 47/40–49	**2-5** 57/1–25
17	**2-2** 46/2–38 even 47/44–49	**2-2** 46/1–39 odd 47/50–59 47/Rev. 2–8 even	**2-5** 57/26–29 58/30–35 58/Computer Byte
18	**2-2** 46/1–39 odd 47/53–57 47/Rev. 1–9	**2-3** 49/2–24 even 50/25–32 50/Self-Test A 50/Calculator Key-In	**2-6** 62/1–7
19	**2-3** 49/1–24 50/26–32 even 50/Self-Test A	**2-4** 54/1–28	**2-6** 63/8–12 63/Self-Test B
20	**2-4** 54/1–18	**2-4** 55/29–40 55/Rev. 1–7 odd 55/Challenge	Prepare for Chapter Test 66/Chapter Review 64–65/Enrichment
21	**2-4** 54/19–28 55/29–40 55/Rev. 1–8	**2-5** 57/1–25	Administer Chapter 2 Test Resource Book pp. 27–28 68–69/Cumulative Review
22	**2-5** 57/1–20	**2-5** 57/26–29 58/30–35 58/Rev. 2–8 even 58/Computer Byte	**3-1** 73/2–10 even 74/12–30 even; 31–45
23	**2-5** 57/21–29 58/30–33; Rev. 1–8	**2-6** 62/1–7	**3-2** 77/1–33 odd 78/35–39 odd; 41–54
24	**2-6** 62/1–7	**2-6** 63/8–12 63/Self-Test B	**3-3** 82/1–48
25	**2-6** 63/8–12 63/Self-Test B	Prepare for Chapter Test 66/Chapter Review 64–65/Enrichment	**3-3** 82/49–53 83/Prob. 1–5
26	Prepare for Chapter Test 66/Chapter Review	Administer Chapter 2 Test Resource Book pp. 27–28 68–69/Cumulative Review	**3-4** 85/1–31 odd 86/33–53 odd; 54–58

Day	Minimum Course	Average Course	Maximum Course
27	Administer Chapter 2 Test Resource Book pp. 27–28 68–69/Cumulative Review	**3-1** 73/2–10 even 74/12–30 even; 31–44 74/Rev. 2–8 even	**3-4** 86/59–66 86/Prob. 1–4 87/Prob. 5–8 87/Self-Test A
28	**3-1** 73/1–10 74/11–30; 32–38 even 74/Rev. 1–9	**3-2** 77/1–33 odd 78/34–43	**3-5** 91/14–54 even; 55–66
29	**3-2** 77/1–33 odd 78/34–40	**3-2** 77/2–32 even 78/44–54 78/Rev. 1–9 odd	**3-6** 93/1–49 odd 94/51–52
30	**3-2** 77/2–32 even 78/41–50 78/Rev. 1–9	**3-3** 82/1–48	**3-6** 93/2–50 even 94/Calculator Key-In
31	**3-3** 82/1–40	**3-3** 82/49–52 83/Prob. 1–5 83/Rev. 2–8 even	**3-7** 96/1–35
32	**3-3** 82/41–46 83/Prob. 1–5 83/Rev. 1–9	**3-4** 85/1–31 odd 86/33–53 odd; 54–58	**3-7** 96/36–48 97/Self-Test B 97/Challenge
33	**3-4** 85/1–32 86/33–57 odd	**3-4** 86/59–65 86/Prob. 1–4 87/Prob. 5–8 87/Self-Test A	Prepare for Chapter Test 100/Chapter Review 98–99/Enrichment
34	**3-4** 86/34–58 even 86/Prob. 1–4 87/Prob. 5–6 87/Self-Test A	**3-5** 90/2–12 even 91/14–38 even; 39–57 91/Rev. 2–8 even	Administer Chapter 3 Test Resource Book pp. 39–40 102–103/Cumulative Review
35	**3-5** 90/1–12 91/13–42 91/Rev. 1–8	**3-6** 93/1–49 odd 94/51–52	**4-1** 108/1–15 odd 109/17–43
36	**3-6** 93/1–49 odd	**3-6** 93/2–50 even 94/Rev. 2–10 even 94/Calculator Key-In	**4-2** 112/2–10 even 113/12–40 even; 41–56
37	**3-6** 93/2–50 even 94/Rev. 1–10	**3-7** 96/1–35	**4-2** 113/Prob. 1–3 114/Prob. 4–9

Day	Minimum Course	Average Course	Maximum Course
38	**3-7** 96/1–28	**3-7** 96/36–48 97/Self-Test B 97/Challenge	**4-3** 116/1–15 odd; 17–32 117/33–45 117/Calculator Key-In
39	**3-7** 96/29–43 97/Self-Test B	Prepare for Chapter Test 100/Chapter Review 98–99/Enrichment	**4-4** 119/20–26 even 120/28–40 even; 42–51 120/Prob. 1–3 121/Prob. 4–7 121/Self-Test A
40	Prepare for Chapter Test 100/Chapter Review	Administer Chapter 3 Test Resource Book pp. 39–40 102–103 Cumulative Review	**4-5** 124/1–15 odd 125/17, 19, 21–44
41	Administer Chapter 3 Test Resource Book pp. 39–40 102–103/Cumulative Review	**4-1** 108/1–16 109/17–37 109/Rev. 1–6	**4-6** 128/2–24 even 129/26, 28; 30–39
42	**4-1** 108/1–16 109/17–30 109/Rev. 1–6	**4-2** 112/2–10 even 113/12–40 even; 41–56	**4-6** 129/Prob. 1–7 130/Prob. 8–14 130/Challenge
43	**4-2** 112/1–10 113/11–30; 31–47 odd	**4-2** 113/Prob. 1–3 114/Prob. 4–8 114/Rev. 2–10 even	**4-7** 134/17–59 odd; 61–64 135/Self-Test B 135/Computer Byte
44	**4-2** 113/Prob. 1–3 114/Prob. 4–7 114/Rev. 1–10	**4-3** 116/1–15 odd; 17–32 117/33–44 117/Rev. 1–9 odd 117/Calculator Key-In	Prepare for Chapter Test 138/Chapter Review 136–137/Enrichment
45	**4-3** 116/1–16; 18–32 even 117/34–44 even 117/Rev. 1–9	**4-4** 119/2–26 even 120/28–45	Administer Chapter 4 Test Resource Book pp. 53–54 140–141/Cumulative Review
46	**4-4** 119/1–24; 26 120/28–40 even	**4-4** 120/Prob. 1–3 121/Prob. 4–6 121/Self-Test A	**5-1** 145/1–28
47	**4-4** 120/Prob. 1–3 121/Prob. 4–5 121/Self-Test A	**4-5** 124/1–15 odd 125/17, 19; 21–42 125/Rev. 1–7 odd	**5-2** 147/1–19 odd 148/21–25 odd; 27–44 148/Challenge
48	**4-5** 124/1–16 125/17–20; 21–37 odd 125/Rev. 1–8	**4-6** 128/2–16 even; 17–25 129/26–29; 30–36 even	**5-3** 151/2–24 even; 25–40

Day	Minimum Course		Average Course		Maximum Course	
49	**4-6**	128/1–16; 18–24 even 129/26, 28	**4-6**	129/Prob. 1–7 130/Prob. 8–12 130/Rev. 2–8 even 130/Challenge	**5-4**	154/1–27 odd; 29–40
50	**4-6**	129/Prob. 1–7 130/Prob. 8–10 130/Rev. 1–8	**4-7**	134/17–59 odd 135/Self-Test B 135/Computer Byte	**5-5**	157/7–33 odd 158/35–51 odd
51	**4-7**	134/1–49 odd; 55–60 135/Self-Test B		Prepare for Chapter Test 138/Chapter Review 136–137/Enrichment	**5-5**	157/8–32 even 158/34–52 even 158/Self-Test A
52		Prepare for Chapter Test 138/Chapter Review		Administer Chapter 4 Test Resource Book pp. 53–54 140–141/Cumulative Review	**5-6**	161/1–17 odd 162/19–47 odd; 49–52
53		Administer Chapter 4 Test Resource Book pp. 53–54 140–141/Cumulative Review	**5-1**	145/1–26 145/Rev. 1–6	**5-7**	165/2–26 even 166/27–33
54	**5-1**	145/1–20 145/Rev. 1–6	**5-2**	147/1–19 odd 148/21–25 odd; 27–38 148/Rev. 1–9 odd 148/Challenge	**5-7**	166/34–40 166/Calculator Key-In
55	**5-2**	147/1–20 148/21–30 148/Rev. 1–9	**5-3**	151/2–24 even; 25–36 151/Rev. 1–6	**5-8**	168/2–12 even; 13–21
56	**5-3**	151/1–30 151/Rev. 1–6	**5-4**	154/1–27 odd; 29–38 154/Rev. 2–8 even	**5-9**	172/Prob. 1–8 173/Prob. 9–13 173/Self-Test B
57	**5-4**	154/1–20	**5-5**	157/1–33 odd 158/35–43 odd		Prepare for Chapter Test 176/Chapter Review 174–175/Enrichment
58	**5-4**	154/21–36 154/Rev. 1–8	**5-5**	157/2–32 even 158/34–44 even 158/Self-Test A		Administer Chapter 5 Test Resource Book pp. 65–66 178–179/Cumulative Review
59	**5-5**	157/1–25	**5-6**	161/1–17 odd 162/19–47 odd 162/Rev. 1–7 odd	**6-1**	185/1–16 186/17–32

Day	Minimum Course	Average Course	Maximum Course
60	**5-5** 157/26–33 158/34–40 158/Self-Test A	**5-7** 165/1–24	**6-2** 189/1–18 190/19–24 190/Calculator Key-In
61	**5-6** 161/1–18 162/19–24	**5-7** 165/25–26 166/27–38 166/Rev. 1–8 166/Calculator Key-In	**6-3** 194/1–15
62	**5-6** 162/25–47 odd 162/Rev. 1–8	**5-8** 168/2–12 even; 13–21 168/Rev. 2–8 even	**6-4** 198/1–23 199/24–30
63	**5-7** 165/1–20	**5-9** 172/Prob. 1–8	**6-5** 202/1–23
64	**5-7** 165/21–26 166/27–30 166/Rev. 1–8	**5-9** 173/Prob. 9–13 173/Self-Test B	**6-5** 203/24–27 203/Self-Test A
65	**5-8** 168/2–14 even; 17–21 168/Rev. 1–8	Prepare for Chapter Test 176/Chapter Review 174–175/Enrichment	**6-6** 206/1–6 207/7–20 208/21–28
66	**5-9** 172/Prob. 1–8	Administer Chapter 5 Test Resource Book pp. 65–66 178–179/Cumulative Review	**6-7** 211/1–16 212/17–25
67	**5-9** 173/Prob. 9–12 173/Self-Test B	**6-1** 185/1–16 186/17–28 186/Rev. 2–10 even	**6-8** 214/1–3 215/4–18 216/19–22; Challenge
68	Prepare for Chapter Test 176/Chapter Review	**6-2** 189/1–18 190/19–22 190/Rev. 1–7 odd 190/Calculator Key-In	**6-9** 219/1–4 220/5–16 221/17–20 221/Self-Test B
69	Administer Chapter 5 Test Resource Book pp. 65–66 178–179/Cumulative Review	**6-3** 194/1–14 194/Rev. 2–12 even	Prepare for Chapter Test 224/Chapter Review 222–223/Enrichment
70	**6-1** 185/1–16 186/17–22 186/Rev. 1–10	**6-4** 198/1–23 199/24–28 199/Rev. 1–9 odd	Administer Chapter 6 Test Resource Book pp. 77–78 226–227/Cumulative Review (Mid-Year Test, pp. 43–46)
71	**6-2** 189/1–18 190/19–20 190/Rev. 1–8	**6-5** 202/1–23	**7-1** 232/2–20 even; 21–28 233/Prob. 1–10

Day	Minimum Course	Average Course	Maximum Course
72	**6-3** 194/1–12 194/Rev. 1–12	**6-5** 203/24–26 203/Self-Test A	**7-2** 236/Prob. 1–12 237/Prob. 13–17
73	**6-4** 198/1–23 199/24–25 199/Rev. 1–9	**6-6** 206/1–6 207/7–20 208/21–24; Rev. 2–8 even	**7-3** 239/1–13 240/14 240/Computer Byte
74	**6-5** 202/1–22	**6-7** 211/1–16 212/17–24 212/Rev. 1–9 odd	**7-4** 243/2–44 even; 45–47 244/48–53; Prob. 1–6 244/Challenge
75	**6-5** 202/23 203/24–25 203/Self-Test A	**6-8** 214/1–3 215/4–18 216/19–20 216/Rev. 2–8 even 216/Challenge	**7-5** 246/2–8 even 247/10–18 even; Prob. 1–10 248/Prob. 11–12 248/Self-Test A
76	**6-6** 206/1–6 207/7–20 208/Rev. 1–8	**6-9** 219/1–4 220/5–16	**7-6** 250/Prob. 1–3 251/Prob. 4–12
77	**6-7** 211/1–16 212/17–18 212/Rev. 1–9	**6-9** 221/17–20 221/Self-Test B	**7-7** 253/Prob. 1–6 254/Prob. 7–16 254/Calculator Key-In
78	**6-8** 214/1–3 215/4–18 216/Rev. 1–8	Prepare for Chapter Test 224/Chapter Review 222–223/Enrichment	**7-8** 257/2, 4, 6; Prob. 1–4 258/Prob. 5–10 259/Prob. 11–13 259/Computer Byte
79	**6-9** 219/1–4 220/5–16	Administer Chapter 6 Test Resource Book pp. 77–78 226–227/Cumulative Review (Mid-Year Test, pp. 43–46)	**7-9** 261/Prob. 1–6 262/Prob. 7–14
80	**6-9** 221/Self-Test B	**7-1** 232/2–20 even; 21–28 233/Prob. 1–8 233/Rev. 2–8 even	**7-9** 262/Prob. 15–17 263/Prob. 18–19 263/Self-Test B
81	Prepare for Chapter Test 224/Chapter Review	**7-2** 236/Prob. 1–12 237/Prob. 13–16 237/Rev. 1–7 odd	Prepare for Chapter Test 266/Chapter Review 264–265/Enrichment
82	Administer Chapter 6 Test Resource Book pp. 77–78 226–227/Cumulative Review (Mid-Year Test, pp. 43–46)	**7-3** 239/1–13 240/14 240/Rev. 2–8 even 240/Computer Byte	Administer Chapter 7 Test Resource Book pp. 91–92 268–269/Cumulative Review

Day	Minimum Course	Average Course	Maximum Course
83	**7-1** 232/1–20 233/Prob. 1–8 233/Rev. 1–8	**7-4** 243/2–44 even; 45–47 244/48–53; Prob. 1–6 244/Rev. 1–7 odd 244/Challenge	**8-1** 274/1–22 275/23–24
84	**7-2** 236/Prob. 1–12 237/Prob. 13–14 237/Rev. 1–8	**7-5** 246/1–8 247/9–18; Prob. 1–4	**8-1** 275/25–28 275/Challenge
85	**7-3** 239/1–13 240/Rev. 1–8	**7-5** 247/Prob. 5–10 248/Self-Test A	**8-2** 278/1–23 odd 279/25–47 odd
86	**7-4** 243/2–44 even 244/Prob. 1–6 244/Rev. 1–8	**7-6** 250/Prob. 1–3 251/Prob. 4–10 251/Rev. 1–9 odd	**8-2** 278/2–24 even 279/26–46 even
87	**7-5** 246/1–8 247/9–18	**7-7** 253/Prob. 1–6 254/Prob. 7–14 254/Rev. 1–8 254/Calculator Key-In	**8-3** 281/1–9 282/10–18
88	**7-5** 247/Prob. 1–6 248/Self-Test A	**7-8** 257/1–6 257/Prob. 1–4 258/Prob. 5–10 259/Rev. 2–8 even 259/Computer Byte	**8-3** 282/19–33
89	**7-6** 250/Prob. 1–3 251/Prob. 4–8 251/Rev. 1–9	**7-9** 261/Prob. 1–6 262/Prob. 7–14	**8-3** 282/34–40 283/41–47 283/Self-Test A
90	**7-7** 253/Prob. 1–6 254/Prob. 7–8 254/Rev. 1–8	**7-9** 262/Prob. 15–17 263/Prob. 18 263/Self-Test B	**8-4** 286/1–6 287/7–12
91	**7-8** 257/1–6 257/Prob. 1–4 258/Prob. 5–8 259/Rev. 1–8	Prepare for Chapter Test 266/Chapter Review 264–265/Enrichment	**8-4** 287/13–20 287/Calculator Key-In
92	**7-9** 261/Prob. 1–6 262/Prob. 7–12	Administer Chapter 7 Test Resource Book pp. 91–92 268–269/Cumulative Review	**8-5** 291/1–2 292/3–6
93	**7-9** 262/Prob. 13–15 263/Self-Test B	**8-1** 274/1–22	**8-5** 292/7–8 293/9–11 293/Calculator Key-In

Day	Minimum Course	Average Course	Maximum Course
94	Prepare for Chapter Test 266/Chapter Review	**8-1** 275/23–26 275/Rev. 1–7 odd 275/Challenge	**8-6** 296/1–18
95	Administer Chapter 7 Test Resource Book pp. 91–92 268–269/Cumulative Review	**8-2** 278/1–23 odd 279/25–43 odd	**8-6** 296/19–27 297/28–29
96	**8-1** 274/1–18	**8-2** 278/2–24 even 279/26–44 even 279/Rev. 2–8 even	**8-6** 297/30–31 297/Self-Test B
97	**8-1** 274/19–22 275/23–24 275/Rev. 1–8	**8-3** 281/1–9 282/10–18	Prepare for Chapter Test 300/Chapter Review 298–299/Enrichment
98	**8-2** 278/1–22	**8-3** 282/19–33	Administer Chapter 8 Test Resource Book pp. 103–104 302–303/Cumulative Review
99	**8-2** 278/23–24 279/25–40 279/Rev. 1–9	**8-3** 282/34–40 283/42–45 283/Self-Test A	**9-1** 308/1–3 309/4–16 310/17–22
100	**8-3** 281/1–9 282/10–15	**8-4** 286/1–6 287/7–12	**9-1** 310/Prob. 1–4 311/Prob. 5–11
101	**8-3** 282/16–25; 34–38 283/Self-Test A	**8-4** 287/13–18 287/Rev. 1–7 odd 287/Calculator Key-In	**9-2** 314/2–8 even 315/10, 12–18 316/19–24
102	**8-4** 286/1–6 287/7–10	**8-5** 291/1–2 292/3–6	**9-3** 318/1, 3 319/5–17 odd; 19–24 320/Prob. 1–8
103	**8-4** 287/11–15 287/Rev. 1–8	**8-5** 292/7–8 293/9–10 293/Rev. 2–8 even 293/Calculator Key-In	**9-4** 323/1–9 odd 324/10–15
104	**8-5** 291/1–2 292/3–5	**8-6** 296/1–18	**9-4** 324/16–18 324/Challenge 325/Self-Test A
105	**8-5** 292/6–8 293/Rev. 1–9	**8-6** 296/19–27 297/28–29 297/Self-Test B	**9-5** 328/2–6 even 329/8–12 even; 13–22

Day	Minimum Course	Average Course	Maximum Course
106	**8-6** 296/1–15	Prepare for Chapter Test 300/Chapter Review 298–299/Enrichment	**9-5** 330/23–24 330/Prob. 1–5
107	**8-6** 296/16–27 297/Self-Test B	Administer Chapter 8 Test Resource Book pp. 103–104 302–303/Cumulative Review	**9-6** 333/1–16 334/17–20
108	Prepare for Chapter Test 300/Chapter Review	**9-1** 308/1–3 309/4–16 310/17–20	**9-6** 334/21–22 334/Prob. 1–4
109	Administer Chapter 8 Test Resource Book pp. 103–104 302–303/Cumulative Review	**9-1** 310/Prob. 1–4 311/Prob. 5–10 311/Rev. 2–8 even	**9-7** 337/1–9 odd 338/11–19 339/20; Challenge
110	**9-1** 308/1–3 309/4–16 310/17–18	**9-2** 314/2–8 even 315/10, 12–18 316/19–23 316/Rev. 1–9 odd	**9-8** 342/7–20 343/21–22 343/Calculator Key-In
111	**9-1** 310/Prob. 1–4 311/Prob. 5–8 311/Rev. 1–8	**9-3** 318/1, 3 319/5–11 odd; 13–22 320/Prob. 1–6 320/Rev. 1–6	**9-9** 345/1–12 346/13–18
112	**9-2** 314/1–9 315/10–12 316/Rev. 1–10	**9-4** 323/1–9 324/10–11	**9-9** 346/Prob. 1–5 347/Prob. 6 347/Self-Test B
113	**9-3** 318/1–4 319/5–14, 21 320/Prob. 1–2 320/Rev. 1–6	**9-4** 324/12–15 324/Challenge 325/Self-Test A	Prepare for Chapter Test 350/Chapter Review 348–349/Enrichment
114	**9-4** 323/1–9	**9-5** 328/2–6 even 329/8–12 even; 13–20 330/Prob. 1–4 330/Rev. 2–8 even	Administer Chapter 9 Test Resource Book pp. 115–116 352–353/Cumulative Review
115	**9-4** 324/10–12 325/Self-Test A	**9-6** 333/1–16 334/17–20	**10-1** 357/1–34
116	**9-5** 328/1–6 329/7–12 330/Prob. 1–2; Rev. 1–8	**9-6** 334/Prob. 1–4 334/Rev. 1–8	**10-2** 360/1–19 odd; 21–24

Day	Minimum Course		Average Course		Maximum Course	
117	9-6	333/1–16	9-7	337/1–9 odd 338/11–19 339/Rev. 1–7 odd 339/Challenge	10-2	360/25–36 360/Calculator Key-In
118	9-6	334/17–20 334/Prob. 1–2 334/Rev. 1–8	9-8	342/7–20 343/Rev. 2–8 even 343/Calculator Key-In	10-3	362/2–30 even 363/32–37 363/Prob. 1–8
119	9-7	337/1–10 338/13, 16 339/Rev. 1–8	9-9	345/1–12 346/13–18	10-4	366/1–24
120	9-8	341/1–6 342/7–10, 17 343/Rev. 1–8	9-9	346/Prob. 1–5 347/Prob. 6 347/Self-Test B	10-4	366/Prob. 1 367/Prob. 2–8 367/Self-Test A
121	9-9	345/1–12 346/13–15		Prepare for Chapter Test 350/Chapter Review 348–349/Enrichment	10-5	371/1–13 odd; 14–16 372/17–25
122	9-9	346/Prob. 1–4 347/Self-Test B		Administer Chapter 9 Test Resource Book pp. 115–116 352–353/Cumulative Review	10-6	375/1–11 odd 376/13–24
123		Prepare for Chapter Test 350/Chapter Review	10-1	357/1–32 357/Rev. 1–7 odd	10-6	376/Prob. 1–3 377/Prob. 4–12
124		Administer Chapter 9 Test Resource Book pp. 115–116 352–353/Cumulative Review	10-2	360/1–19 odd; 21–24	10-7	380/1–10 381/11–12
125	10-1	357/1–25 357/Rev. 1–8	10-2	360/25–34 360/Rev. 2–8 even 360/Calculator Key-In	10-7	381/13–17 381/Challenge
126	10-2	360/1–12	10-3	362/2–14 even; 16–31 363/Prob. 1–6 363/Rev. 1–7 odd	10-8	384/1–30
127	10-2	360/13–22 360/Rev. 1–8	10-4	366/1–21	10-8	384/25–40 385/Prob. 1–6
128	10-3	362/1–21 363/Prob. 1–5 363/Rev. 1–8	10-4	366/Prob. 1 367/Prob. 2–7 367/Self-Test A	10-8	385/Prob. 7–8 386/Prob. 9–10; Self-Test B 387/Computer Byte 387/Challenge

Day	Minimum Course		Average Course		Maximum Course	
129	10-4	366/1–17	10-5	371/1–16 372/17–20 372/Rev. 2–8 even	Prepare for Chapter Test 390/Chapter Review 388–389/Enrichment	
130	10-4	366/Prob. 1 367/Prob. 2–5 367/Self-Test A	10-6	375/1–11 odd 376/13–20; 23–24	Administer Chapter 10 Test Resource Book pp. 129–130 392–393/Cumulative Review	
131	10-5	371/1–13 372/17 372/Rev. 1–9	10-6	376/Prob. 1–3 377/Prob. 4–10 377/Rev. 1–7 odd	11-1	398/1–11 odd 398/Prob. 1–4 399/Prob. 5–17 400/Prob. 18–20 400/Challenge
132	10-6	375/1–12 376/13–19 odd	10-7	380/1–10 381/11–15 381/Rev. 2–8 even 381/Challenge	11-2	402/Prob. 1–3 403/Prob. 4–12
133	10-6	376/Prob. 1–3 377/Prob. 4–8 377/Rev. 1–8	10-8	384/1–30	11-3	407/1–27 odd; 29–36 408/37–39
134	10-7	380/1–10 381/11–12 381/Rev. 1–8	10-8	384/25–40 385/Prob. 1–6	11-4	411/1–24 412/25–30
135	10-8	384/1–24	10-8	385/Prob. 7–8 386/Prob. 9 386/Self-Test B 387/Computer Byte 387/Challenge	11-4	412/31–32 412/Self-Test A
136	10-8	384/25–34 385/Prob. 1–6	Prepare for Chapter Test 390/Chapter Review 388–389/Enrichment		11-5	414/1–10 415/11–20
137	10-8	386/Self-Test B	Administer Chapter 10 Test Resource Book pp. 129–130 392–393/Cumulative Review		11-6	418/1–16 419/17–18
138	Prepare for Chapter Test 390/Chapter Review		11-1	398/1–12 398/Prob. 1–4 399/Prob. 5–17 400/Rev. 2–8 even 400/Challenge	11-6	419/Prob. 1–5

Day	Minimum Course	Average Course	Maximum Course
139	Administer Chapter 10 Test Resource Book pp. 129–130 392–393/Cumulative Review	**11-2** 402/Prob. 1–3 403/Prob. 4–11 403/Rev. 1–8	**11-7** 422/1–8 423/9–10
140	**11-1** 398/1–12 398/Prob. 1–4 399/Prob. 5–12 399/Rev. 1–8	**11-3** 407/1–27 odd; 29–36 408/37–38 408/Rev. 1–7 odd	**11-7** 423/11–16
141	**11-2** 402/Prob. 1–3 403/Prob. 4–10 403/Rev. 1–8	**11-4** 411/1–24 412/25–30 412/Self-Test A	**11-8** 426/1–9 427/10–12
142	**11-3** 407/1–30 408/37 408/Rev. 1–8	**11-5** 414/1–10 415/11–18 415/Rev. 2–8 even	**11-8** 427/13–20
143	**11-4** 411/1–22 412/25–28 412/Self-Test A	**11-6** 418/1–14 419/Prob. 1–4 419/Rev. 1–7 odd	**11-9** 429/Prob. 1–8 430/Prob. 9–14
144	**11-5** 414/1–10 415/11–14 415/Rev. 1–9	**11-7** 422/2–8 even 423/9–14 423/Rev. 2–8 even	**11-9** 431/Prob. 15–16 431/Self-Test B
145	**11-6** 418/1–10 419/Prob. 1–3 419/Rev. 1–8	**11-8** 426/1–9 427/10–18 427/Rev. 1–9 odd	Prepare for Chapter Test 434/Chapter Review 432–433/Enrichment
146	**11-7** 422/1–8 423/9–10 423/Rev. 1–8	**11-9** 429/Prob. 1–8 430/Prob. 9–14	Administer Chapter 11 Test Resource Book pp. 141–142 436–437/Cumulative Review
147	**11-8** 426/1–9 427/10–15; Rev. 1–10	**11-9** 431/Prob. 15–16 431/Self-Test B	**12-1** 442/1–6 443/7–10
148	**11-9** 429/Prob. 1–8 430/Prob. 9–12 431/Self-Test B	Prepare for Chapter Test 434/Chapter Review 432–433/Enrichment	**12-1** 443/11–12 444/13–14 444/Challenge
149	Prepare for Chapter Test 434/Chapter Review	Administer Chapter 11 Test Resource Book pp. 141–142 436–437/Cumulative Review	**12-2** 447/1–8
150	Administer Chapter 11 Test Resource Book pp. 141–142 436–437/Cumulative Review	**12-1** 442/1–6 443/7–10	**12-2** 448/9–11 448/Challenge

Day	Minimum Course	Average Course	Maximum Course
151	**12-1** 442/1–6 443/7–9	**12-1** 443/11–12 444/Rev. 1–9 odd 444/Challenge	**12-3** 451/1–14
152	**12-1** 443/10–12 444/Rev. 1–10	**12-2** 447/1–8	**12-3** 452/15–20 452/Self-Test A
153	**12-2** 447/1–7	**12-2** 448/9–10 448/Rev. 1–6 448/Challenge	**12-4** 455/1–12
154	**12-2** 447/8 448/9 448/Rev. 1–6	**12-3** 451/1–13 odd 452/15–18 452/Self-Test A	**12-4** 455/13–14 456/15–22
155	**12-3** 451/1–12 452/15–16 452/Self-Test A	**12-4** 455/2–14 even 456/16–20 456/Rev. 2–8 even	**12-5** 459/1–14
156	**12-4** 455/2–14 even 456/16, 18 456/Rev. 1–8	**12-5** 459/1–12	**12-5** 460/15–19
157	**12-5** 459/1–11, 13 460/15 460/Rev. 1–8	**12-5** 459/13–14 460/15–16 460/Rev. 1–7 odd	**12-6** 463/1–5
158	**12-6** 463/1–5 463/Self-Test B	**12-6** 463/1–6 463/Self-Test B	**12-6** 463/6–7 463/Self-Test B
159	Prepare for Chapter Test 466/Chapter Review	Prepare for Chapter Test 466/Chapter Review 464–465/Enrichment	Prepare for Chapter Test 466/Chapter Review 464–465/Enrichment
160	Administer Chapter 12 Test Resource Book pp. 153–154 468–469/Cumulative Review	Administer Chapter 12 Test Resource Book pp. 153–154 468–469/Cumulative Review	Administer Chapter 12 Test Resource Book pp. 153–154 468–469/Cumulative Review

Supplementary Materials Guide

For use after Lesson	Resource Book page	Practice Masters page	Tests	Computer Activities
(Diagnostic Tests)	1–6	1–2	Diagnostic Test	
1-1		3		
1-2	7	3		Activity 1
1-3	8	4		
1-4	9	4		Activity 2
1-5	10	4	1A	
1-6		5		
1-7		5		
1-8	11–13	6	1B	
Chapter 1	14–16		Chapter 1 Test	
Cumulative Review	17–18			
2-1	19–20	7		
2-2	21	8		Activity 3
2-3	22	8	2A	Activity 4
2-4		9		
2-5		9		
2-6	23–25	10	2B	
Chapter 2	26–28		Chapter 2 Test	
Cumulative Review	29–30			
3-1	31	11		
3-2		11		

For use after Lesson	Resource Book page	Practice Masters page	Tests	Computer Activities
3-3		12		
3-4	32–33	12	3A	
3-5		13		Activity 5
3-6		14		
3-7	34–37	14	3B	Activity 6
Chapter 3	38–40		Chapter 3 Test	
Cumulative Review	41–44	15–16	Cumulative Test	
4-1	45	17		
4-2		17		
4-3		18		Activity 7
4-4	46–47	18	4A	
4-5		19		
4-6	48–49	19		
4-7	50–51	20	4B	Activity 8
Chapter 4	52–54		Chapter 4 Test	
Cumulative Review	55–56			
5-1	57	21		
5-2		21		
5-3		22		
5-4		22		
5-5	58–60	22	5A	Activity 9

For use after Lesson	Resource Book page	Practice Masters page	Tests	Computer Activities
5-6		23		
5-7	61–62	23		
5-8		24		
5-9	63	24	5B	Activity 10
Chapter 5	64–66		Chapter 5 Test	
Cumulative Review	67–68			
6-1	69	25		
6-2		25		
6-3		26		
6-4		26		
6-5	70	26	6A	
6-6		27		Activity 11
6-7		27		
6-8	71–73	28		Activity 12
6-9	74–75	28	6B	
Chapter 6	76–78		Chapter 6 Test	
Cumulative Review	79–82	29–30	Cumulative Test	
Mid-Year			Chapters 1–6	
7-1	83	31		Activity 13
7-2		32		
7-3		32		
7-4	84	33		
7-5	85–86	33	7A	
7-6		33		
7-7		34		Activity 14

For use after Lesson	Resource Book page	Practice Masters page	Tests	Computer Activities
7-8		34		
7-9	87–89	34	7B	
Chapter 7	90–92		Chapter 7 Test	
Cumulative Review	93–94			
8-1	95–96	35		
8-2		35		
8-3	97–98	36	8A	Activity 15
8-4		37		
8-5	99–100	38		
8-6	101	38	8B	Activity 16
Chapter 8	102–104		Chapter 8 Test	
Cumulative Review	105–106			
9-1	107	39		Activity 17
9-2		39		
9-3		40		Activity 18
9-4	108	40	9A	
9-5		41		
9-6	109	41		
9-7	110	42		
9-8	111–112	42		
9-9	113	42	9B	
Chapter 9	114–116		Chapter 9 Test	
Cumulative Review	117–120	43–44	Cumulative Test	

For use after Lesson	Resource Book page	Practice Masters page	Tests	Computer Activities
10-1	121–122	45		
10-2		45		Activity 19
10-3		46		
10-4	123–124	47	10A	Activity 20
10-5		47		
10-6		48		
10-7		48		
10-8	125–127	48	10B	
Chapter 10	128–130		Chapter 10 Test	
Cumulative Review	131–132			
11-1	133	49		
11-2		49		Activity 21
11-3	134–135	50		
11-4	136	50	11A	
11-5		51		

For use after Lesson	Resource Book page	Practice Masters page	Tests	Computer Activities
11-6		51		
11-7		52		Activity 22
11-8	137–138	52		
11-9	139	52	11B	
Chapter 11	140–142		Chapter 11 Test	
Cumulative Review	143–144			
12-1	145	53		
12-2		54		
12-3	146–147	54	12A	
12-4	148	55		
12-5	149	55		
12-6	150–151	56	12B	
Chapter 12	152–154		Chapter 12 Test	Activities 23 and 24
Cumulative Review	155–158	57–58	Cumulative Test	
Final			Chapters 7–12	

New Edition

MATHEMATICS

Structure and Method

Course 2

Mary P. Dolciani
Robert H. Sorgenfrey
John A. Graham

Editorial Advisers

Richard G. Brown
Robert B. Kane

HOUGHTON MIFFLIN COMPANY · Boston
Atlanta   Dallas   Geneva, Ill.   Hopewell, N.J.   Palo Alto   Toronto

Contents

iv

v

vi

Reading Mathematics

This page shows many of the metric measures and symbols that are used in this book. Use this page as a reference when you read the book.

Symbols

		Page			Page
$\cdot$	times	3	$\angle A$	angle A	191
$\dots$	and so on	9	$m\angle A$	measure of angle A	191
$<$	is less than	12	$60°$	sixty degrees	191
$>$	is greater than	12	$\cong$	is congruent to	192
$\approx$	is approximately equal to	48	$\rceil$	is a right angle	195
$^-4$	negative 4	72	$\perp$	is perpendicular to	195
$\lvert n \rvert$	absolute value of n	72	$\parallel$	is parallel to	200
$-n$	opposite of n	84	$\triangle ABC$	triangle ABC	204
$0.6\overline{81}$	81 repeats without end	131	$1:5$	1 to 5	230
$\overleftrightarrow{PQ}$	line PQ	182	$(6, 8)$	ordered pair 6, 8	272
$\overline{FG}$	segment FG	182	$\sqrt{n}$	positive square root of n	356
$\overrightarrow{BA}$	ray BA	182	$\sim$	is similar to	368
FG	length of $\overline{FG}$	182	$4!$	4 factorial	396
π	pi	188	$P(A)$	probability of A	404

Metric Measures

Prefixes

Prefix	kilo	centi	milli
Factor	1000	0.01	0.001
Symbol	k	c	m

Base Units

Length: **meter** (m)
Mass: **kilogram** (kg)
Capacity: **liter** (L)

Temperature   **Degree Celsius** (°C)

Length   1 mm = 0.001 m   1 cm = 0.01 m   1 km = 1000 m
              1 m = 1000 mm   1 m = 100 cm   1 cm = 10 mm

Mass   1 kg = 1000 g   1 mg = 0.001 g   1 g = 0.001 kg

Capacity 1 mL = 0.001 L   1 L = 1000 mL   1 L = 1000 cm³

Time   60 s = 1 min   60 min = 1 h   3600 s = 1 h

Examples of compound units   kilometers per hour: km/h
                               square centimeters: cm²   cubic meters: m³

Review of Decimal Number Skills

OVERVIEW

The Diagnostic Test of Decimal Number Skills appears on pages viii–ix of the student textbook. Answers appear on pages T34–T35. This test is designed to help you gauge your students' knowledge of decimal number arithmetic skills before starting the course. Students who need extensive review or reteaching may belong in a less demanding program. For students who need moderate review, pages 470–473 of the student textbook provide additional practice in the four basic skills.

An alternate version of the Diagnostic Test, shown below, is in the Resource Book; you may wish to use it for retesting after any necessary review. The Resource Book also contains four more pages of practice exercises; these are shown at the right, on page T33.

Resource Book: Pages 1–2

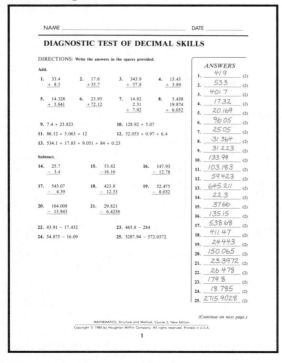

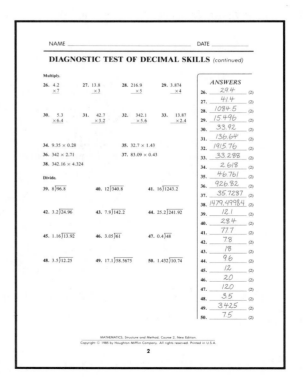

Resource Book: Pages 3–6

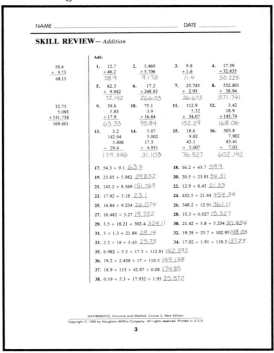

NAME _____ DATE _____

SKILL REVIEW — Addition

```
  58.4
+ 9.73
 68.13

  32.75
   5.093
+531.758
 569.601
```

Add.

1. 12.7 + 46.2 = 58.9
2. 3.469 + 5.706 = 9.175
3. 9.8 + 1.6 = 11.4
4. 17.59 + 32.635 = 50.225
5. 62.3 + 9.842 = 72.142
6. 17.2 + 248.83 = 266.03
7. 23.743 + 2.93 = 26.673
8. 532.801 + 38.94 = 571.741
9. 39.6 + 5.83 + 17.9 = 63.33
10. 75.1 + 3.9 + 16.84 = 95.84
11. 112.9 + 5.32 + 34.07 = 152.29
12. 3.42 + 18.9 + 145.74 = 168.06

```
13.  3.2      14.  5.87     15. 18.6     16. 503.8
     3.806         3.002         9.82         7.902
   142.94         17.3          43.1         83.41
  + 29.4        + 4.931       + 5.007       + 7.03
  179.346        31.103        76.527       602.142
```

17. 54.3 + 9.1 = 63.4
18. 16.2 + 43.7 = 59.9
19. 23.85 + 5.982 = 29.832
20. 30.5 + 23.81 = 54.31
21. 143.2 + 8.569 = 151.769
22. 12.9 + 8.43 = 21.33
23. 17.92 + 5.18 = 23.1
24. 432.5 + 21.84 = 454.34
25. 16.84 + 9.234 = 26.074
26. 348.2 + 12.91 = 361.11
27. 16.482 + 3.27 = 19.752
28. 15.3 + 0.027 = 15.327
29. 3.5 + 18.21 + 302.4 = 324.11
30. 21.42 + 3.8 + 5.234 = 30.454
31. 5 + 1.3 + 21.84 = 28.14
32. 19.38 + 25.7 + 102.95 = 148.03
33. 2.3 + 18 + 5.43 = 25.73
34. 17.02 + 1.91 + 118.3 = 137.23
35. 6.982 + 5.3 + 17.3 + 112.81 = 142.392
36. 19.2 + 2.438 + 17 + 110.5 = 149.138
37. 18.9 + 113 + 42.87 + 0.08 = 174.85
38. 0.19 + 5.3 + 17.932 + 1.95 = 25.372

3

NAME _____ DATE _____

SKILL REVIEW — Subtraction

```
 743.841
- 61.570
 682.271

 507.830
- 29.007
 478.823
```

Subtract.

1. 14.932 − 9.521 = 5.411
2. 347.26 − 8.15 = 339.11
3. 79.385 − 18.73 = 60.655
4. 645.9267 − 23.005 = 622.9217
5. 47.9 − 12.6 = 35.3
6. 84.71 − 32.65 = 52.06
7. 19.436 − 7.524 = 11.912
8. 61.0532 − 7.326 = 53.7272
9. 22.905 − 17.063 = 5.842
10. 648.29 − 299.9 = 348.39
11. 217.008 − 64.32 = 152.688
12. 65.27 − 53.88 = 11.39
13. 251.07 − 3.4 = 247.67
14. 93.42 − 5.8 = 87.62
15. 793.84 − 69.25 = 724.59
16. 3247.93 − 658.97 = 2588.96
17. 0.047 − 0.009 = 0.038
18. 36.05 − 3.724 = 32.326
19. 16.7 − 3.923 = 12.777
20. 792 − 18.37 = 773.63
21. 9.8 − 6.4 = 3.4
22. 23.87 − 16.52 = 7.35
23. 379.5 − 85.9 = 293.6
24. 823.64 − 35.96 = 787.68
25. 0.075 − 0.009 = 0.066
26. 72.842 − 18.35 = 54.492
27. 2743.9 − 184.65 = 2559.25
28. 3.7847 − 0.1254 = 3.6593
29. 78 − 12.8 = 65.2
30. 385.3 − 297.8 = 87.5
31. 43.9 − 8.67 = 35.23
32. 587.32 − 94.675 = 492.645
33. 843.92 − 537.768 = 306.152
34. 541 − 68.7 = 472.3
35. 321.8 − 76.562 = 245.238
36. 643.1 − 0.016 = 643.084
37. 16.83 − 9.978 = 6.852
38. 48.09 − 29.9 = 18.19
39. 72.1 − 42.16 = 29.94
40. 37.8 − 16.87 = 20.93
41. 5421.92 − 735.8 = 4686.12
42. 7432 − 83.53 = 7348.47

4

NAME _____ DATE _____

SKILL REVIEW — Multiplication

```
  43.8   1 place
× 0.36   2 places
  2628
  1314
15.768   3 places

  6.82    2 places
× 0.013   3 places
  2046
   682
0.08866   5 places
```

Multiply.

1. 64 × 1.3 = 83.2
2. 634 × 3.2 = 2028.8
3. 507 × 8.4 = 4258.8
4. 38.5 × 12.6 = 485.1
5. 31.07 × 4.2 = 130.494
6. 18.7 × 61.2 = 1144.44
7. 314.6 × 0.3 = 94.38
8. 29.05 × 8.07 = 234.4335
9. 40.9 × 18.2 = 744.38
10. 312.6 × 12.83 = 4010.658
11. 24.16 × 0.05 = 1.208
12. 162.3 × 3.8 = 616.74
13. 22.8 × 0.4 = 9.12
14. 131.27 × 46 = 6038.42
15. 291.06 × 0.16 = 46.5696
16. 301.5 × 0.016 = 4.824
17. 43.872 × 4.31 = 189.08832
18. 2346.8 × 3.52 = 8260.736
19. 0.003 × 0.402 = 0.001206
20. 0.0006 × 0.0134 = 0.0000804
21. 2.6 × 33.1 = 86.06
22. 35.2 × 12.4 = 436.48
23. 63.7 × 0.23 = 14.651
24. 18.7 × 0.37 = 6.919
25. 287.4 × 1.3 = 373.62
26. 5.6 × 0.003 = 0.0168
27. 16.7 × 0.04 = 0.668
28. 23.25 × 16.2 = 376.65
29. 1.875 × 0.3 = 0.5625
30. 543 × 18.74 = 10,175.82
31. 0.643 × 1.7 = 1.0931
32. 43.82 × 19.274 = 844.58668
33. 2.038 × 0.14 = 0.28532
34. 0.0503 × 0.08 = 0.004024
35. 73.92 × 4.16 = 307.5072
36. 8.3142 × 0.6 = 4.98852
37. 19.75 × 0.001 = 0.01975
38. 2.9 × 1.632 = 4.7328
39. 238.65 × 52 = 12,409.8
40. 17.93 × 4.321 = 77.47553
41. 0.083 × 0.04 = 0.00332
42. 7.941 × 14.3 = 113.5563

5

NAME _____ DATE _____

SKILL REVIEW — Division

```
      126.2
3.6)454.32
    36
    94
    72
    223
    216
     72
     72
      0
```

Divide.

1. 6)224.4 = 37.4
2. 3)703.2 = 234.4
3. 2.4)35.52 = 14.8
4. 3.12)56.784 = 18.2
5. 2.9)10.034 = 3.46
6. 6.8)177.48 = 26.1
7. 2.5)112.5 = 45
8. 0.3)1.563 = 5.21
9. 3.46)22.49 = 6.5
10. 16.2)13.608 = 0.84
11. 0.06)1.65 = 27.5
12. 9.1)0.546 = 0.06

Divide. Round to the nearest tenth.

13. 12)200.6 = 16.7
14. 7.2)45.316 = 6.3
15. 0.34)19.5 = 57.4
16. 243 ÷ 12.2 = 19.9
17. 8.4 ÷ 5.1 = 1.6
18. 96.82 ÷ 0.3 = 322.9
19. 53.9 ÷ 1.8 = 29.9
20. 342.6 ÷ 1.32 = 259.5
21. 3.4708 ÷ 0.26 = 13.3
22. 28.7 ÷ 3.18 = 9.0
23. 160.2 ÷ 0.48 = 33.8
24. 5.0802 ÷ 1.7 = 3.0
25. 3.4 ÷ 0.18 = 18.9
26. 22.08 ÷ 16.2 = 1.4
27. 4.61 ÷ 3.8 = 1.2

To round a quotient, divide to one place beyond the place specified and then round.

```
         31.259
5.32)166.3000
     159 6
       6 70
       5 32
       1 380
       1 064
         3160
         2660
         5000
         4788
          212
```

Rounded to the nearest hundredth, the quotient is 31.26

Divide. Round to the nearest hundredth.

28. 3642 ÷ 6.5 = 560.31
29. 4.682 ÷ 3.1 = 1.51
30. 17.43 ÷ 0.8 = 21.79
31. 0.432 ÷ 9.3 = 0.05
32. 5.008 ÷ 4.5 = 1.11
33. 69.38 ÷ 0.018 = 3854.44
34. 0.046 ÷ 1.7 = 0.03
35. 0.0387 ÷ 0.065 = 0.60

6

Teaching Suggestions

The exercises in the Diagnostic Test are equally distributed for each operation. Depending on time, you may assign only the even- or odd-numbered exercises.

Supplementary Materials

Diagnostic Test, pp. 1–2
Practice Masters, pp. 1–2

Diagnostic Test of Decimal Skills

This test reviews the skills of addition, subtraction, multiplication, and division necessary to begin Chapter 1. More practice of these skills can be found on pages 470–473.

Addition

Add.

1. 5.246 + 6.38 11.626	**2.** 16.439 + 28.32 44.759	**3.** 9.85 + 3.7647 13.6147	**4.** 34.62 + 17.9903 52.6103	**5.** 218.951 + 0.006 218.957
6. 35.046 + 17.923 52.969	**7.** 3.84 2.07 + 9.39 15.30	**8.** 72.8 6.349 + 0.76 79.909	**9.** 67.4 2.0051 6.28 + 7.3 82.9851	**10.** 0.16 54.3 119.057 + 2.0918 175.6088

11. $18.7 + 5.394$ 24.094

12. $0.06 + 19.803$ 19.863

13. $254.81 + 93$ 347.81

14. $126 + 9.4078$ 135.4078

15. $11.882 + 6.49 + 0.083$ 18.455

16. $583.117 + 72.5 + 3.76824$ 659.38524

17. $26.5 + 180.1 + 0.39 + 5.18$ 212.17

18. $0.05 + 11.026 + 9.38 + 4.7829$ 25.2389

19. $35.402 + 17.6 + 5.28 + 0.314$ 58.596

20. $3.4289 + 5.005 + 3.1 + 8.57$ 20.1039

Subtraction

Subtract.

1. 6.75 − 3.81 2.94	**2.** 14.90 − 7.88 7.02	**3.** 675.01 − 25.312 649.698	**4.** 31.801 − 6.03 25.771	**5.** 22.008 − 5.911 16.097
6. 388.6 − 97.86 290.74	**7.** 2008.11 − 487.8 1520.31	**8.** 705.56 − 314.6 390.96	**9.** 0.615 − 0.038 0.577	**10.** 0.986 − 0.097 0.889

11. $12.6 - 3.9$ 8.7

12. $9.5 - 4.8$ 4.7

13. $567 - 199.1$ 367.9

14. $379 - 65.7$ 313.3

15. $46.71 - 22.52$ 24.19

16. $853.7 - 139.8$ 713.9

17. $0.551 - 0.493$ 0.058

18. $0.877 - 0.098$ 0.779

19. $0.039 - 0.0271$ 0.0119

20. $0.8743 - 0.33591$ 0.53839

21. $4.00682 - 2.01985$ 1.98697

22. $5.04876 - 2.29$ 2.75876

viii

Multiplication

Multiply.

1. 473
$\times$ 0.3
141.9

2. 846
$\times$ 2.5
2115

3. 127.3
$\times$ 6.6
840.18

4. 885.1
$\times$ 4.5
3982.95

5. 0.061
$\times$ 0.02
0.00122

6. 3.08
$\times$ 0.007
0.02156

7. 0.681
$\times$ 14.7
10.0107

8. 0.263
$\times$ 8.08
2.12504

9. 288.86
$\times$ 31.3
9041.318

10. 810.95
$\times$ 1.35
1094.7825

11. 67.05
$\times$ 2.39
160.2495

12. 99.7
$\times$ 10.06
1002.982

13. 621.82 $\times$ 4.3 **2673.826**

14. 63.71 $\times$ 2.5 **159.275**

15. 18.7 $\times$ 16 **299.2**

16. 46 $\times$ 86.91 **3997.86**

17. 0.08 $\times$ 58.6 **4.688**

18. 0.75 $\times$ 0.69 **0.5175**

19. 27.9 $\times$ 33.3 **929.07**

20. 10.29 $\times$ 4.79 **49.2891**

21. 17.003 $\times$ 0.301 **5.117903**

22. 0.473 $\times$ 86.11 **40.73003**

23. 6.0810 $\times$ 148.3 **901.8123**

24. 5.62 $\times$ 83.109 **467.07258**

Division

Divide.

1. $5\overline{)37.60}$ **7.52**

2. $81\overline{)108.54}$ **1.34**

3. $5.4\overline{)3348}$ **620**

4. $0.8\overline{)168}$ **210**

5. $4.1\overline{)37.761}$ **9.21**

6. $1.6\overline{)99.68}$ **62.3**

7. $2.9\overline{)279.27}$ **96.3**

8. $8.3\overline{)5.6025}$ **0.675**

9. $38.4\overline{)0.192}$ **0.005**

10. $36.1\overline{)0.722}$ **0.02**

11. $2.86\overline{)247.39}$ **86.5**

12. $1.13\overline{)1006.83}$ **891**

Divide. Round to the nearest tenth.

13. 798.06 $\div$ 98.7 **8.1**

14. 486.09 $\div$ 17.3 **28.1**

15. 0.851 $\div$ 0.33 **2.6**

16. 0.268 $\div$ 0.59 **0.5**

17. 0.909 $\div$ 1.35 **0.7**

18. 0.284 $\div$ 7.31 **0.0**

19. 486 $\div$ 0.391 **1243.0**

20. 276 $\div$ 0.106 **2603.8**

21. 81.69 $\div$ 73.12 **1.1**

22. 5.005 $\div$ 0.095 **52.7**

23. 37.076 $\div$ 55.619 **0.7**

24. 43.761 $\div$ 27.515 **1.6**

1

Introduction to Algebra

All of the many pieces of information handled by computers are stored and processed by means of tiny microchips, such as the one shown at the right. Each microchip is about 2 mm square and is made up of thin layers of silicon crystals. Each layer is treated chemically and etched photographically with different patterns containing tens of thousands of microscopic switches. Information on the microchip is represented by a code made up of a series of "on" or "off" switches.

Although we use words and numbers to communicate with a computer, the machine does not work directly with those words and numbers. A program within the computer automatically translates the information that we use into the special code that the machine understands. In a similar way, when we work with algebra, we translate our words and ideas into the language of mathematics. In this chapter, you will learn many of the symbols that we use to express mathematical ideas.

Career Note

Consider how intricate the design of a single microchip is. Electrical engineers are involved in designing and testing new electrical equipment such as the microchip. Electrical engineers must therefore be qualified in both mathematics and science. Most, in fact, specialize in a major field such as communications, industrial equipment, or computers.

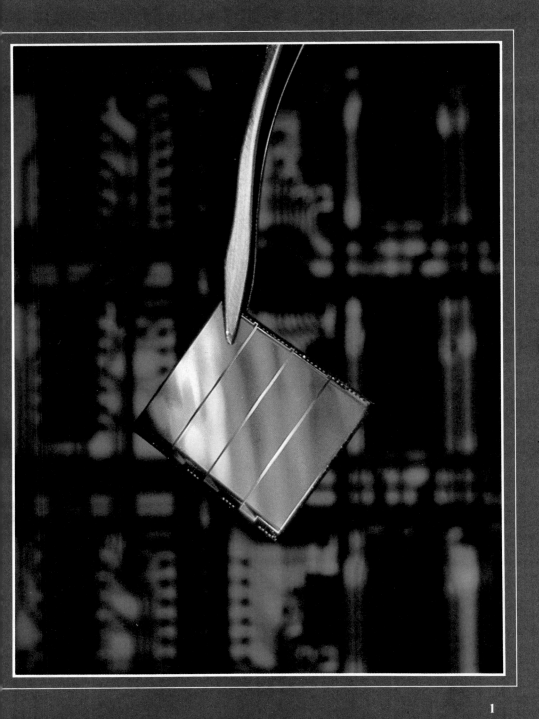

Lesson Commentary
Chapter 1   Introduction to Algebra

Overview

As it should, the first chapter sets a pace and tone for the entire book. A groundwork is established for future work in algebra, both in this course and in any later study of algebra. The introductory material sharpens students' ideas of what variables are and how they can be used in open sentences. The approach to equations and inequalities is not yet completely rigorous; rigor will come in later chapters. The approach is, however, mathematically correct and will have students solving equations and inequalities early. The solving skills, which are based on inverse operations, build on students' background in arithmetic.

The purpose of the study of algebra is to be able to solve problems. The ability to organize a problem and to reduce it to a concise mathematical statement is the basis of applied mathematics. Students begin to use their algebra skills to translate problems into open sentences and to solve them. This emphasizes the connection between abstract mathematics and the concrete "real" world.

USING VARIABLES

1-1 Mathematical Expressions

Objective *for pages 2–4*

■ To evaluate a variable expression for given values of the variables.

Teaching Suggestions

The expressions used here can contain only certain operation signs, because an order of operations has yet to be adopted. Students should have no difficulty with the material, finding it very natural to substitute a value for each variable. The only real prerequisite for success here is a good grasp of arithmetic.

Emphasize that if an expression contains several variables, as in $3abc$, we need a value for each one. If the same variable is used more than once, as in $a + a + 2$, the same value must be used each time that variable occurs.

Some students may be so accustomed to working with expressions in vertical form that they are confused by an expression such as $a - b$. Show them that $a - b$ is equivalent to

$$\begin{array}{c} a \\ -\,b, \end{array} \qquad \text{not} \qquad \begin{array}{c} b \\ -\,a. \end{array}$$

Similarly, $a \div b$ is equivalent to $b\overline{)a}$, not $a\overline{)b}$.

Related Activities

To reinforce understanding of variable expressions, reverse the usual process. Give the value of the expression, and ask what value of the variable will produce this value.

a. If the value of $100 - x$ is 36, then $x =$ __?__. **64**
b. If the value of $3 \times c \times c$ is 147, then $c =$ __?__. **7**
c. If the value of $7 \times a \times b$ is 154 and $b = 2$, then $a =$ __?__. **11**

To prepare for later work with equations, have students find values of the variables so that the two expressions have the same value.

1. $3h, h + 12$ **6**   **2.** $j - 4, j \div 2$ **8**
3. $4d, d + 9$ **3**   **4.** $k - 8, k \div 5$ **10**

1-2 Order of Operations

Objective *for pages 5–8*

■ To use the order of operations to simplify numerical expressions and to evaluate variable expressions.

Teaching Suggestions

In mathematics, more than in some other forms of written expression, ambiguity must be reduced or eliminated. Otherwise, different people may ascribe different meanings to the same symbols, and communication is faulty. Precision of expression is facilitated by grouping symbols and the order of operations rules. To show that expressions would be confusingly ambiguous without grouping symbols and rules, present the expression below and ask students to insert parentheses to make as many different values as possible.

$$4 \times 8 - 6 \div 2 + 1$$

Some possible values are:

$$29 = (4 \times 8) - (6 - 2) + 1$$
$$= (4 \times 8) - (6 - (2 + 1))$$
$$7 = ((4 \times (8 - 6)) - 2) + 1$$
$$17 = (4 \times (8 - (6 - 2))) + 1$$
$$12 = 4 \times (8 - ((6 - 2) + 1))$$

To provide a note of humor, write on the board the following statement:

SLOW CHILDREN PLAYING

This is a common warning sign along streets. Ask if students can explain why the sign is ambiguous. Do the same with

SAVE RAGS AND WASTE PAPER,

a sign that might be found in a factory.

The order of operations convention requires practice to master. Students will need it throughout their work in math, and will need occasional reminders not to backslide into doing all operations from left to right. They might enjoy knowing that the rule on page 6 is the same as that followed by computers operating in BASIC.

Related Activities

To provide practice in a different way, let students play "Four Fours." Using the symbols $+$, $-$, $\times$, and $\div$, and four fours, write expressions for as many different integers as possible. Insert parentheses as needed. Possible expressions include:

$$\frac{4 \times 4}{4 + 4} = 2 \qquad \frac{(4 \times 4) + 4}{4} = 5$$

To increase awareness of ambiguity in expression, have students find examples of ambiguous expressions in advertising, news reporting, and so on.

Resource Book: Page 7 (Use After Page 8)

NAME _____ DATE _____

CALCULATOR—For use after Lesson 1-2
Calculator Messages

You can use a calculator to write coded messages. When you hold the calculator right side up, you see numbers. But when you hold the calculator upside-down, you can see letters.

| number | 0 1 2 3 4 5 7 8 9 |
| letter | 0 1 2 E h S L B G |

EXAMPLE Write a mathematical expression for the code word SIZE.

SOLUTION The code number for SIZE is 3215.
$$3215 = 5(8 \times 8 + 3)$$

Write a mathematical expression for each code word. *Other answers are possible.*

1. HIS $2(5 \times 50 + 7)$
2. BIG $9 \times 2 \times 17 \times 3$
3. LOG $100 \times 27 - 3 + 7$
4. GOSH $(1000 - 4 + 251) \times 9$
5. GIBE $366 - 6 + 89 \times 42 + 20$
6. ZOOS $2 + (20 \times 20 + 100) \times 10$
7. LIEGE $1709 \times 23 + 10$
8. BEZEL $54 \times 82 \times 16 + 478 \times 5$
9. SHELL $(2209 \times 7 + 6) \times 5$
10. GHILLIE $4068 \times 781 + 41$

Write 5 other code words. Then write a mathematical expression for each. Use a dictionary to find the words. *answers will vary.*

11. _____
12. _____
13. _____
14. _____
15. _____

MATHEMATICS, Structure and Method, Course 2, New Edition.
Copyright © 1985 by Houghton Mifflin Company. All rights reserved. Printed in U.S.A.

7

1-3 Equations

Objective *for pages 9–11*

■ To find the solution of an equation in one variable whose replacement set is given.

Teaching Suggestions

The structure of mathematical expression has some notable parallels in language and grammar. For example, the expression $x + 5$ can be considered a phrase. Add a verb, and it can become a sentence: $x + 5 = 16$. This is an open sentence, because it contains the variable x. Point out that variables have a role similar to that of pronouns. That is, a sentence with a pronoun, such as "She was awarded the Nobel Prize," is open; it is neither true nor false. When a noun is "substituted" for the pronoun, the sentence is then true or false. This is also true for mathematical open sentences.

It may be worthwhile to show that a sentence may have different solutions for different replacement sets.

1b

For example, if the replacement set is {1, 2, 3, 4}, then the sentence "$3x$ is divisible by 6" has solutions 2 and 4. For the same sentence, if the replacement set is {1, 3, 5, 7, 9}, then there are no solutions at all. If the replacement set is the whole numbers, then the solution is the set of even numbers, {2, 4, 6, ...}.

Resource Book: Page 8 (Use After Page 11)

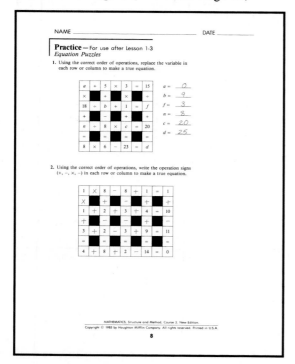

Related Activities

To provide a challenge, ask students to solve the sentence, "$(n \times n) + (n + 11)$ is a prime number," using the replacement set {0, 1, 2, ..., 10}. The solution set is {0, 1, 2, 3, 4, 5, 6, 7, 8, 9}.

To enhance understanding of open sentences and solutions, have students write open sentences having the following solutions.

1. George Washington
2. Clara Barton
3. Florida, Alabama, Mississippi, Louisiana, and Texas
4. protein, carbohydrates, and vitamins

1-4 Inequalities

Objective *for pages 12–15*

■ To find the solutions of an inequality in one variable whose replacement set is given.

Teaching Suggestions

For any two real numbers a and b one and only one of the following must be true:

$$a < b \qquad a = b \qquad a > b$$

The statement $a < b$ can be interpreted as meaning that b is to the right of a on the number line. Point out that $a < b$ and $b > a$ are equivalent statements. This gives us a way to convert any "greater than" statement to a "less than" statement and vice versa. For example, we can replace the statement $5 < x$ with $x > 5$, which students find much easier to understand and graph.

Some students may enjoy learning of two more inequality symbols, formed by negating the $>$ and $<$ symbols. Point out that $a \not> 2$ is equivalent to $a \le 2$, and $c \not< 9$ is equivalent to $c \ge 9$.

Note that the Written Exercises contain, in Exercises 37–44, several inequalities with infinite solution sets. Remind students of the difference between finite and infinite sets.

Related Activities

To extend students' understanding of infinite sets, ask which segment in the diagram below has more points. Then show how to set up a one-to-one correspondence, proving that $\overline{AB}$ and $\overline{CD}$ have the same number of points.

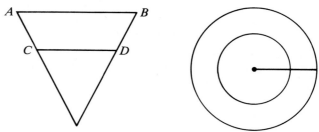

Use a similar line of reasoning with the two circles. In each case, students will want to say one is "longer" than the other, but will be forced, perhaps contrary to common sense, to conclude that both are "equal," in that they have the same number of points. Students might like to read Chapter 1 of *One, Two Three . . . Infinity* by George Gamow.

To extend the idea of inequalities, show students how to write compound inequalities in BASIC. For example,

$x >= 2$ means $x \geq 2$, and $A <= 5$ means $A \leq 5$.

Show the statement

$$P <> Q,$$

and ask what this means. (Mathematically, it would be written $P \neq Q$.)

Resource Book: Page 9 (Use After Page 15)

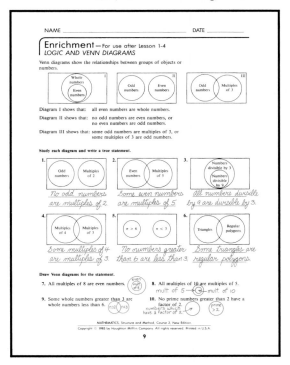

1-5 Inverse Operations

Objective *for pages 16–19*

■ To use the relationships between addition and subtraction and between multiplication and division to solve equations and inequalities.

Teaching Suggestions

Students saw in Section 1-3 what it means to solve an equation. The objective is to isolate the variable on one side of the equation, with a number on the other side. We then have the "world's easiest" equation, which can be solved by inspection.

For example, instead of

$$x + 13 = 41,$$

we write

$$x = 28;$$

the solution of the latter equation is obviously 28, so this is the solution of the original equation, too.

The approach taken here is almost an intuitive one, based on the inverse relationship between addition and subtraction and the inverse relationship between multiplication and division. A more technical approach will be presented in Chapter 5. Remind students to check solutions in the original open sentence.

In solving sentences containing two operations, be sure that students eliminate the added or subtracted term first, then use the inverse of multiplication or division. For example, to solve $3x - 5 > 7$, we write

$$3x > 7 + 5$$
$$3x > 12$$
$$x > 12 \div 3$$
$$x > 4.$$

Students who try to begin by writing

$$3x - 5 > 7$$
$$x - 5 > 7 \div 3$$

will not obtain the correct solution.

Notice that we do not mention that there are times when inequalities must be reversed in the solving process. This problem occurs only when dealing with negative numbers, which are introduced in Chapter 3.

Related Activities

To enhance understanding of solving an open sentence, ask students to write open sentences that are true

(a) for no real number;

(b) for all real numbers.

There should be great variety in their answers.

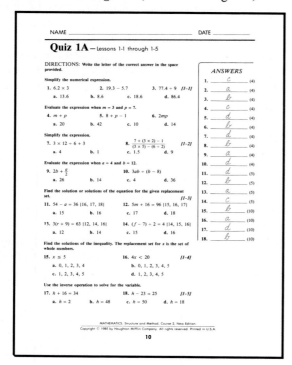

WORDS INTO SYMBOLS

1-6 Writing Expressions for Word Phrases

Objective *for pages 20–23*

- To translate word phrases describing numerical operations into variable expressions.

Teaching Suggestions

A major reason for studying mathematics is to be able to use mathematical models to represent situations in the real world. The real world does not usually present a problem tidily wrapped up as an equation or inequality. Thus, it is essential that we be able to translate from ordinary language into mathematical terms. Once this is done, we can use all our knowledge of mathematics to solve the problem. In this and the next two sections students gradually progress to the point of being able to express simple problems mathematically and to solve them. In the present section, students should have little difficulty; the expressions used require only a very direct translation.

Related Activities

To broaden understanding of the relationship between word phrases and the corresponding mathematical expression, show how seemingly very different situations can be described by the same variable expression. Ask students to write a variable expression for each word phrase.

1. Mary's age, if she is 25 years older than Harry, who is *x* years old.
2. The amount of money, if there were *x* cents before and a quarter was deposited.
3. The length of a board that is 25 cm longer than a board *x* cm long.
4. Your speed, if you were going *x* miles per hour over the speed limit in a 25-miles-per-hour zone.
5. Gary's weight, if he weighed *x* pounds last year and has since gained 25 pounds.

Each of these situations can be represented by the expression *x* + 25.

1-7 Equations and Inequalities for Word Sentences

Objective *for pages 24–26*

- To translate word sentences involving numerical operations into equations or inequalities.

Teaching Suggestions

A difficulty in teaching students to solve "story," or word, problems is that students seem to expect to see the solution virtually instantly, with little real grappling with the problem. In most cases they cannot, so they need to be cautioned frequently to slow down and to move ahead a step at a time.

As an example of writing an open sentence a step at a time, consider writing an equation for the sentence

"The sum of two consecutive whole numbers is

five more than the smaller of the numbers."

Smaller number: x

Larger number (1 more than smaller number): $x + 1$

Sum of the two numbers: $x + (x + 1)$

A number five more than the smaller number: $x + 5$

The whole sentence becomes: $x + (x + 1) = x + 5$

Students will see that this lesson simply carries the previous lesson one step further. The earlier comments about algebra as a language, in which sentences must have verbs, is germane here, too.

Related Activities

To provide a challenge, ask students to write an equation for the famous algebra problem concerning the life of the ancient Greek mathematician Diophantus:

Diophantus's youth was $\frac{1}{6}$ of his life. After $\frac{1}{12}$ more of his life he grew a beard. After $\frac{1}{7}$ more he married. Five years later he had a son. The son lived half as long as Diophantus, who died four years after his son.

Students may need hints, one being that all the parts must add up to Diophantus's age when he died.

$$x = \frac{x}{6} + \frac{x}{12} + \frac{x}{7} + 5 + \frac{x}{2} + 4$$

1-8 A Plan for Solving Problems

Objective *for pages 27–31*

■ To use a five-step plan to solve word problems involving one or more operations.

Teaching Suggestions

Here we outline a very broad framework that can be applied to a variety of problem settings. To the dismay of many a student, there is no single "formula" that can be followed to solve any given problem. The five-step plan should at least help students to focus their thinking and to keep the elements of a problem organized.

As you present Example 1, have the students read the problem several times to make sure that they understand it. You may want to list the facts on the chalkboard, ask whether enough facts are given (yes), and cross out the unnecessary fact (the time). Draw a dia-

gram like the one on page 28 and show how to use it to solve the problem. Emphasize the importance of checking the calculations and making sure you have answered the question.

To show how important it is to read a problem carefully, you may want to have students suggest other questions that could have been asked about the facts in Example 1. One possibility is,

"Where did the Nizels stop for lunch?"

For this question students could use the diagram to show that the stop was between Harbor Bluffs and Newton. Another possible question is,

"What was the average speed on the

trip from Topsfield to Harbor Bluffs?"

In this case the trip time would be a necessary fact. Students would need to supply the fact that there are 60 minutes in an hour in order to calculate the average speed, 47.4 mi/h.

Some students may become impatient with the five-step plan. Point out that even with a problem so simple that they can solve it almost intuitively, they are using these steps in a quick and informal way. They should learn to apply the plan consciously so that they can use it to solve the difficult problems that they will encounter later on.

The Enrichment on pages 32–33 discusses the development of computers. If your students will do programming or computer graphics, you might want to use the programming paper and computer screen paper on pages 159–160 of the Resource Book.

Related Activities

To emphasize the connection between algebra and problem solving, provide equations and have each student choose one. Have them write a story containing a problem situation that can be described by that equation. Encourage stories with missing facts or unnecessary facts. Have students exchange stories, write the equation, and try to solve the problem. For example, for the equation $185 - 3x = 170$, a student might write this story: "Marty weighs 185 lb. Two years ago he weighed 160 lb. He would like to weigh 170 lb. He plans to lose the same amount each week for three weeks. How much should he lose each week?" (Answer: 5 lb)

Resource Book: Pages 11–14 (Use After Page 31)

Page 11

NAME _____ DATE _____

Problem Solving — For use after lesson 1-8
Using a Table or Chart

Sometimes the facts needed to solve a problem are in a table or chart. At the right is a chart giving the price list for school photos. Select the information you need to solve each problem.

Package Contents	Traditional (matte finish)	Reflection (glossy finish)
Selection 1 1 10 x 13 2 8 x 10 2 5 x 7 2 3 x 5 4 gift size 8 wallets 1 class picture	$23.30	$26.85
Selection 2 1 8 x 10 2 5 x 7 2 3 x 5 10 gift size 8 wallets 1 class picture	$15.40	$18.95
Selection 3 with 10 x 13	$21.90	$25.45
Selection 4 1 8 x 10 1 5 x 7 2 3 x 5 2 gift size 8 wallets 1 class picture	$11.00	$14.55
Selection 5 with 10 x 13	$17.50	$21.05
Selection 6 1 5 x 7 1 3 x 5 2 gift size 4 wallets 1 class picture	$7.65	$11.20
Selection 7 with 10 x 13	$14.15	$17.70

1. The Nortons have two boys in the same class so they want only one class picture. Is there a selection they can make without a class picture?
   _no_

2. Which selection would be the least costly for the Nortons if they want a 10 x 13 portrait but do not care about the number of other pictures?
   Selection 7

3. How much more does any selection including a 10 x 13 portrait cost than the same selection without the 10 x 13 portrait?
   _$6.50_

4. Which selection gives you the most individual pictures regardless of size?
   Selection 3

5. Melissa wants as many wallet-size photos as she can get in order to exchange them with her friends. Since her family does not give out too many gift photos, the best choice would be
   Selection 4

6. Roberto likes the Reflection Photos. He does not need a 10 x 13 portrait but would like the maximum number of gift-size photos. How much will the package cost?
   _$18.95_

11

Page 12

NAME _____ DATE _____

Problem Solving — For use after lesson 1-8
Conditions that Affect Solutions

When solving a problem, you need to be aware of the conditions that could affect the solution.

In the schedule of bus fares at the right, how much could you save by buying a monthly bus pass?

The problem cannot be solved unless you know these conditions:

(1) To which zone are you traveling?

(2) Are you disabled, a student, a senior citizen, and so on?

(3) How many trips do you take each month?

Schedule of Fares Effective August 20

	Zone 1	Zone 2	Zone 3	Zone 4	Zone 5
CHILDREN — up to 4 years of age	Free	Free	Free	Free	Free
DISABLED PERSONS Attendant may ride free (one-way fares)	$0.35	$0.50	$0.70	$0.85	$1.05
SENIOR CITIZEN 65 years (one-way fares)	$0.35	$0.50	$0.70	$0.85	$1.05
STUDENT — K through 12 (one-way fare)	$0.50	$0.75	$1.15	$1.50	$1.90
ALL OTHER PASSENGERS (one-way fare)	$0.75	$1.15	$1.50	$1.90	$2.25
TOKENS 10 one-way fares	$7	$11			
MONTHLY BUS PASSES (round-trip fares)	$29	$44	$57	$72	$86

Use the bus-fare schedule to solve the following problems.

1. You are a 35-year-old nondisabled woman who rides to work and back 22 times each month. How much will you save by buying a monthly pass rather than by buying one-way fares?
   Condition I: if you work in Zone 1? _$4.00_ Condition II: if you work in Zone 2? _$6.60_

2. A 29-year-old father is riding with his 5-year-old kindergarten child. How much will it cost to ride
   Condition I: to Zone 5? _$4.15_ Condition II: to Zone 4? _$3.40_

3. A disabled adult is riding to Zone 3 and back. What is the total bus fare?
   Condition I: if she is riding with one attendant? _$1.40_
   Condition II: if she is riding with her 50-year-old non-disabled sister and an attendant? _$4.40_

12

Page 13

NAME _____ DATE _____

Quiz 1B — Lessons 1-6 through 1-8

DIRECTIONS: Write the letter of the correct answer in the space provided.

Write a variable expression for the word phrase.

1. Five increased by a number x.
2. Five less than twice a number. *[1-6]*
   a. $2x - 5$ b. $5 - 2x$ c. $5 - x$ d. $5 + x$

3. The sum of a number r and a number s, multiplied by 6.
4. Six more than the product of a number r and a number s.
   a. $r + 6s$ b. $6(r + s)$ c. $6 + r + s$ d. $6 + rs$

Write an equation or inequality for the word sentence.

5. The sum of a number x and fourteen is less than or equal to twenty. *[1-7]*
   a. $x + 14 < 20$ b. $14 + x \le 20$ c. $14 + x \ge 20$ d. $x + 14 = 20$

6. The quotient when a number m is divided by seven is equal to five more than four times the number.
   a. $\frac{m}{7} = m + 9$ b. $\frac{m}{7} = 5m + 4$ c. $\frac{m}{7} = 4m + 5$ d. $\frac{7}{m} = 4m + 5$

7. The difference when three times a number is subtracted from twenty-four is eight.
   a. $24 - 3x = 8$ b. $3x - 24 = 8$ c. $8 - 3x = 24$ d. $3x = 16$

Solve using the five-step plan.

8. Mark bought 5 lb of flour for $1.29, 3 lb of apples for 49¢ a pound, and a muffin tin for $3.65. How much change did he receive after paying with a ten-dollar bill? *[1-8]*
   a. $6.41 b. $4.57 c. $3.59 d. $5.43

9. Tickets to a baseball game cost $4.00 for adults, $2.00 for children under 12, and $1.50 for senior citizens. If 450 adults, 60 senior citizens, and 125 children attended the ball game, what was the total amount of ticket money collected?
   a. $2107.50 b. $750 c. $635 d. $2140

ANSWERS

1. _d_ (10)
2. _a_ (10)
3. _b_ (10)
4. _d_ (10)
5. _b_ (10)
6. _c_ (10)
7. _a_ (10)
8. _c_ (15)
9. _d_ (15)

13

Page 14

NAME _____ DATE _____

Review — Chapter 1

Simplify the numerical expression.

1. $2.3 + 8.79$ _11.09_   2. $33.6 \div 4$ _8.4_   3. 5.2×3.8 _19.76_ *[1-1]*

Evaluate the expression when $f = 7$ and $g = 5$.

4. $f - 6$ _1_   5. $g + 6 - f$ _4_   6. $6fg$ _210_

Simplify the expression. *[1-2]*

7. $6 + 15 \div 3$ _11_   8. $12 - 10 + 2 + 3$ _10_   9. $(20 \div 4) \times (13 - 7)$ _30_

Evaluate the expression when $a = 3$ and $b = 8$.

10. $(b + 6) \div 14$ _1_   11. $36 - (5a - 3)$ _3_   12. $9 \times \frac{3b}{a}$ _72_

Find the solution or solutions of the equation for the given replacement set. *[1-3]*

13. $47 - m = 19$; {18, 28, 36} _28_   14. $h + 114 = 205$; {91, 121, 319} _91_

15. $3(c + 5) = 48$; {11, 13, 15} _11_   16. $64 \div (m - 7) = 4$; {23, 24, 25} _23_

Replace _?_ with =, >, or < to make a true statement. *[1-4]*

17. 742 _?_ 724 _>_   18. $83 + 17$ _?_ 100 _=_   19. 55 _?_ $250 \div 5$ _>_

Find the solutions of the inequality. The replacement set for x is the set of whole numbers.

20. $x \ge 9$ _9, 10, 11,_   21. $x < 4$ _0, 1, 2, 3_   22. $16 \le x \le 21$ _16, 17, 18, 19, 20, 21_

Use the inverse operation to write a related equation or inequality and solve for the variable. *[1-5]*

23. $w - 26 = 39$ _w = 39 + 26, w = 65_   24. $13 + n = 17$ _n = 17 - 13, n = 4_

25. $4p + 3 = 35$ _4p = 35 - 3, p = 8_   26. $c - 7 < 11$ _c < 11 + 7, c < 18_

Write a variable expression for the word phrase.

27. The product of a number t and 12. _12t_ *[1-6]*

Write an equation or inequality for the word sentence.

28. Three times a number decreased by seven is twenty-nine. _3x - 7 = 29_ *[1-7]*

Solve, using the five-step plan.

29. Jan purchased 5 yards of fabric costing $2.79 a yard, 2 spools of thread priced at 53¢ a spool, and a pattern costing $1.75. What was the total amount of the purchases? _$16.76_

14

1g

Resource Book: Pages 15–18 (Use After Page 31)

NAME _____ DATE _____

Test — Chapter 1

DIRECTIONS: Write the correct answer in the space provided.

Simplify the numerical expression.

1. 76.3×9 2. $34.77 \div 3$ 3. $0.3 + 1.72$ [1-1]

Evaluate the expression when $r = 8$ and $s = 10$.

4. $27 + s$ 5. $r - 8 + 12$ 6. $5rs - 3$

Simplify the expression.

7. $5 + 20 \div 5$ 8. $(8 \times 3) - (12 \div 3)$ [1-2]

Evaluate the expression when $j = 16$ and $k = 20$.

9. $4 + k \div 2$ 10. $(j + k - 10)(k + 2)$

Find the solution of the equation for the given replacement set.

11. $8a = 96$; {10, 12, 14}   12. $3x + 5 = 113$; {32, 34, 36}   [1-3]

Find the solutions of the inequality. The replacement set for m is the set of whole numbers.

13. $13 \le m$ 14. $12 > m > 9$ [1-4]

Use the inverse operation to write a related equation or inequality and solve for the variable.

15. $18p = 252$ 16. $f - 17 \ge 34$ 17. $6r + 5 = 47$ [1-5]

Write a variable expression for the word phrase.

18. The product of 14 and a number n.   [1-6]

19. Sixteen added to the quotient of seven divided by six times a number p.

Write an equation or inequality for the word sentence.

20. The sum of a number t and three is greater than five.   [1-7]

21. The product of a number r and seven is less than or equal to fourteen.

Solve, using the five-step plan.

22. Arthur earns $8.00 for mowing a lawn and $4.50 for edging a lawn. One week, he edged 5 lawns. If he earned a total of $134.50 for mowing and edging, how many lawns did he mow that week?   [1-8]

ANSWERS	
1. 6867	(4)
2. 1159	(4)
3. 2.02	(4)
4. 37	(4)
5. 12	(4)
6. 397	(4)
7. 9	(4)
8. 20	(4)
9. 14	(4)
10. 260	(4)
11. 12	(5)
12. 36	(5)
13. $13,14,15$	(5)
14. $10,11$	(5)
15. $p = 252 \div 18$	
16. $f \ge 34 + 17$	
$f \ge 51$	
17. $6r = 47 - 5$	
$r = 7$	(5)
18. $14n$	(5)
19. $16 + (7 \div 6p)$	(5)
20. $t + 3 > 5$	(5)
21. $7r \le 14$	(5)
22. 14 lawns	(5)

MATHEMATICS, Structure and Method, Course 2, New Edition.
Copyright © 1985 by Houghton Mifflin Company. All rights reserved. Printed in U.S.A.

15

NAME _____ DATE _____

Make-up Test — Chapter 1

DIRECTIONS: Write the correct answer in the space provided.

Simplify the numerical expression.

1. 11×3.3 2. $43.1 + 0.69$ 3. $14.3 - 5.02$ [1-1]

Evaluate the expression when $e = 5$ and $f = 9$.

4. $f - 4$ 5. $13 + e$ 6. $7ef - 2$

Simplify the expression.

7. $12 - 6 \div 2$ 8. $(15 - 7) \times (3 + 5)$ [1-2]

Evaluate the expression when $l = 15$ and $m = 25$.

9. $10 + m \div 5$ 10. $2l + (m - 10)$

Find the solution of the equation for the given replacement set.

11. $b - 19 = 47$; {28, 66, 88}   12. $15r - 2 = 73$; {3, 4, 5}   [1-3]

Find the solutions of the inequality. The replacement set for r is the set of whole numbers.

13. $r \ge 8$ 14. $2 \le r \le 5$ [1-4]

Use the inverse operation to write a related equation or inequality and solve for the variable.

15. $47 + g = 69$ 16. $m - 13 \le 22$ 17. $(p + 5) + 7 = 17$ [1-5]

Write a variable expression for the word phrase.

18. A number m decreased by the sum of six and two.   [1-6]

19. Eighteen added to the product of seven and a number r.

Write an equation or inequality for the word sentence.

20. Four divided by the product of six and a number n is less than eight.   [1-7]

21. Four greater than the product of nine and a number is equal to the sum of the number and twenty-eight.

Solve, using the five-step plan.

22. Barry Baker deposits $15.50 in his bank account each month. If his bank account had a balance of $120 at the beginning of the year, what was the amount in his bank account at the end of 1 year?   [1-8]

ANSWERS	
1. 36.3	(4)
2. 43.79	(4)
3. 9.28	(4)
4. 5	(4)
5. 18	(4)
6. 313	(4)
7. 9	(4)
8. 64	(4)
9. 15	(4)
10. 45	(4)
11. 66	(5)
12. 5	(5)
13. $8,9,10,11$	(5)
14. $2,3,4,5$	(5)
15. $g = 69 - 47$	
$g = 22$	(5)
16. $m \le 22 + 13$	
$m \le 35$	(5)
17. $p - 5 = 17 - 7$	
$p = 50$	(5)
18. $m - (6 + 2)$	(5)
19. $18 + 7r$	(5)
20. $4 \div 6n < 8$	(5)
21. $9x + 4 = x + 28$	(5)
22. 306	(5)

MATHEMATICS, Structure and Method, Course 2, New Edition.
Copyright © 1985 by Houghton Mifflin Company. All rights reserved. Printed in U.S.A.

16

NAME _____ DATE _____

CUMULATIVE REVIEW — Chapter 1
Exercises

Simplify.

1. $69 + 543$ 612 2. $337 - 65.4$ 271.6 3. $47.6 \div 14$ 3.4

4. 3.7×1.82 6.734 5. 0.6×0.035 0.0210 6. $(12 + 4) \div 4$ 4

7. $27 - 3 \times 5 - 2$ 10 8. $(3 + 9) \times (6 - 3)$ 36 9. $(22 + 3) + (39 - 14)$ 1

Evaluate the expression when $a = 6$ and $b = 4$.

10. $2a + 18$ 30 11. $3b - 7$ 5 12. $b + 5 + a$ 15

13. $30 - ab$ 6 14. $(a - b) \div 2$ 1 15. $b(16 - 9)a$ 168

Find the solution or solutions of the equation with the given replacement set.

16. $m + 13 = 21$; {7, 8, 9} $m = 8$ 17. $36 - f = 19$; {15, 16, 17} $f = 17$

18. $5r - 3 = 32$; {5, 7, 9} $r = 7$ 19. $7(w - 1) = 42$; {5, 6, 7} $w = 7$

Find the solution of the inequality. The replacement set for x is the set of whole numbers.

20. $x < 7$ $0,1,2,3,4,5,6$ 21. $3 \le x$ $3,4,5$ and so on   22. $10 \ge x \ge 7$ $7,8,9,10$

Use inverse operations to write a related equation or inequality and solve for the variable.

23. $f - 11 = 43$ $f = 43 + 11, f = 54$ 24. $d + 6 < 12$ $d < 12 \times 6, d < 72$

25. $3m + 7 = 31$ $3m = 31 - 7, m = 8$ 26. $8r - 3 \ge 69$ $8r \ge 69 + 3, r \ge 9$

Write a variable expression for the word phrase.

27. Eighteen less than a number v. $v - 18$

28. Twelve more than the product of a number h and 16. $16h + 12$

29. The quotient when six times a number b is divided by 42. $6b \div 42$

Write an equation or inequality for the word sentence.

30. Six times a number is 84. $6x = 84$

31. The product of a number t and 6 is 3 more than the sum of t and 2. $6t = 3 + t + 2$

32. Nine divided by the sum of four and a number is less than thirty-eight. $9 \div (4 + x) < 38$

MATHEMATICS, Structure and Method, Course 2, New Edition.
Copyright © 1985 by Houghton Mifflin Company. All rights reserved. Printed in U.S.A.

17

NAME _____ DATE _____

CUMULATIVE REVIEW — Chapter 1 (continued)
Problems

Problem Solving Reminders
Here are some reminders that may help you solve some of the problems on this page.
• Determine which facts are necessary to solve the problem.
• Supply additional information if needed.
• Consider whether drawing a sketch will help.

Solve.

1. A microwave oven uses 1.5 kW·h of electricity in 15 min. How much electricity does it use in 2 h? $12 \, kW \cdot h$

2. Lexington High School plans to buy 3 kilns for each of its 5 art rooms. The cost of each kiln is $342. What will the total cost be? 5130

3. Marie bought a blanket for $16.78, 2 pillows for $6.98 each, and 2 sheets costing $8.50 each. How much change did she get from a fifty-dollar bill? $2.26

4. The Net Tennis Club has 12 tennis courts and 6 racquetball courts. Each court can be rented for $16 an hour. One hour, 3 tennis courts and 1 racquetball court were not used. How much money was collected for that hour? $224

5. A movie theater has 24 rows with 20 seats each. The admission charge is $4.00 for adults and $1.50 for children. If 300 adults and their children fill the movie theater one afternoon, what is the total amount paid for admission? $1470

6. Grapefruit usually sell for 39¢ each. This week, they are on sale for 3 for 89¢. How much money is saved by buying 1 dozen grapefruit this week? $1.12

7. Lenny Costa ordered 3 photo packages for $3.99 each by mail. Each photo package would contain 2 8 x 10 photos and 20 wallet-sized photos. He had to add 84¢ for postage and handling. He had 2 credit coupons for 60¢ each, which he could deduct from his order. How much will Lenny pay for his order? $11.61

8. Max bought a head of lettuce for 89¢, 2 lb of tomatoes costing 69¢ a lb, 2 packages of carrots at 33¢ each, and a package of celery at 69¢. What was the cost of his vegetables? $3.62

MATHEMATICS, Structure and Method, Course 2, New Edition.
Copyright © 1985 by Houghton Mifflin Company. All rights reserved. Printed in U.S.A.

18

1h

Reading Mathematics

Students will learn the meaning of the following mathematical terms in this lesson: *numerical expression, simplify an expression, variable, value of a variable, variable expression, evaluate an expression, terms, numerical coefficient.*

Mathematics has its own vocabulary. Some everyday words, such as *common*, have different meanings in mathematics. Encourage students to pinpoint each key term and learn its meaning. Otherwise, they will not use or understand algebra terminology correctly. Important new terms are printed in boldface type to help students spot them easily.

1-1 Mathematical Expressions

A **numerical expression** is simply a name for a number. For example,

$$4 + 6 \text{ is a numerical expression for the number 10.}$$

Since $4 + 6$ and 10 name the same number, we can use the equals sign, $=$, and write

$$4 + 6 = 10.$$

We **simplify the numerical expression** $4 + 6$ when we replace it with its simplest name, 10.

EXAMPLE 1   Simplify each numerical expression.
   a. 400×4 **b.** $37 - 19$ **c.** $5.1 \div 3$

Solution   **a.** $400 \times 4 = 1600$ **b.** $37 - 19 = 18$ **c.** $5.1 \div 3 = 1.7$

If a computer can do 100 million arithmetic computations in one second, the table below shows how many million computations the computer can do in two, three, and four seconds.

Number of Seconds	Millions of Computations
1	100×1
2	100×2
3	100×3
4	100×4

Each of the numerical expressions 100×1, 100×2, 100×3, and 100×4 fits the pattern

$$100 \times n$$

where n stands for 1, 2, 3, or 4. A letter, such as n, that is used to represent one or more numbers is called a **variable.** The numbers are called the **values of the variable.**

An expression, such as $100 \times n$, that contains a variable is called a **variable expression.** When we write a product that contains a variable, we usually omit the multiplication sign.

$$100 \times n \text{ may be written } 100n.$$

$$x \times y \text{ may be written } xy.$$

In a numerical expression for a product, such as 100×4, we must use a multiplication sign to avoid confusion.

2   *Chapter 1*

A raised dot is also a multiplication sign.

$$100 \times 4 \text{ may be written } 100 \cdot 4.$$

When we replace each variable in a variable expression by one of its values and simplify the resulting numerical expression, we say that we are **evaluating the expression** or **finding the value of the expression.**

When the value of n is 4, the value of $100n$ is 400.

EXAMPLE 2   Evaluate each expression when $a = 6$ and $b = 2$.
a. $9 + a$ **b.** $a \div b$ **c.** $3ab$

Solution   **a.** Substitute 6 for a. $9 + a = 9 + 6 = 15$
b. Substitute 6 for a and 2 for b. $a \div b = 6 \div 2 = 3$
c. Substitute 6 for a and 2 for b. $3ab = 3 \times 6 \times 2 = 36$

In the expression $9 + a$, 9 and a are called the **terms** of the expression because they are the parts that are separated by the $+$. In an expression such as $3ab$, the number 3 is called the **numerical coefficient** of ab.

Reading Mathematics: *Vocabulary*

Look back at this first lesson. Notice the words in heavier type throughout the text. They are important new words and ideas, such as the following:

numerical expression   simplify a numerical expression
variable   value of a variable
variable expression   evaluate a variable expression
terms   numerical coefficient

When you see a word in heavier type, look near it for an explanation or example to help you understand the new word. For an unusual new word, look up the definition in the glossary to help you understand and remember it.

Class Exercises

Simplify the numerical expression.

1. $24 + 18 + 32$ 74   **2.** $125 \div 5$ 25   **3.** $3.6 + 5.1$ 8.7   **4.** 0.25×10 2.5

Evaluate the variable expression when $x = 4$.

5. $x + 7$ 11   **6.** $5x$ 20   **7.** $28 \div x$ 7   **8.** $13 - x$ 9

9. What is another way to write $17 \times x$? 17x

10. In the variable expression $12a$, the numerical coefficient is __?__ 12 and the variable is __?__. a

Written Exercises

Simplify the numerical expression.

A **1.** $16 \cdot 3$ **48**   **2.** $37 + 12$ **49**   **3.** $114 - 9$ **105**   **4.** $918 \div 6$ **153**

5. $1.65 + 12.5$ **14.15**   **6.** $1.05 + 9.7$ **10.75**   **7.** 0.5×9 **4.5**   **8.** $2.53 \div 11$ **0.23**

Evaluate the expression when $y = 2$.

9. $y + 23$ **25**   **10.** $6y$ **12**   **11.** $8 \div y$ **4**   **12.** $4 + y + 7$ **13**

Evaluate the expression when $q = 3$.

13. $36 \div q$ **12**   **14.** $q \div 3$ **1**   **15.** $q \times 9$ **27**   **16.** $q - q$ **0**

Evaluate the expression when $a = 5$.

17. $a - 3$ **2**   **18.** $a \times a$ **25**   **19.** $42 + a$ **47**   **20.** $a + a$ **10**

Evaluate the expression when $m = 8$.

21. $6 + 9 + 3 + m$ **26**   **22.** $m \times 3$ **24**   **23.** $m \times m \times m$ **512**   **24.** $m \div m$ **1**

Evaluate the expression when $x = 8$ and $y = 1$.

B **25.** $x + y$ **9**   **26.** $x - y - 2$ **5**   **27.** $3x$ **24**   **28.** $x \div y$ **8**

Evaluate the expression when $c = 7.5$ and $d = 3$.

29. $c \div d$ **2.5**   **30.** $c + d + 20$ **30.5**   **31.** $c \times 15$ **112.5**   **32.** $4cd$ **90**

Evaluate the expression when $s = 12.3$ and $t = 6.15$.

33. $9st$ **680.805**   **34.** $s \div t$ **2**   **35.** $s - t - 3$ **3.15**   **36.** $73.8 \div s$ **6**

C **37.** Find the value of a for which the expressions $2a$ and $2 + a$ have the same value. **2**

38. Find a value of x for which $x \div 7$ and $7 \div x$ are equal. **7**

Review Exercises

Perform the indicated operation.

1. $43.8 + 8.07$ **51.87**   **2.** 51×3.4 **173.4**   **3.** $80.47 - 34.54$ **45.93**   **4.** $6.29 + 0.124$ **6.414**

5. $11.61 \div 43$ **0.27**   **6.** 6.328×0.729 **4.613112**   **7.** $32.004 \div 5.08$ **6.3**   **8.** $2403 - 976.8$ **1426.2**

4 *Chapter 1*

1-2 Order of Operations

The expression

$$2 + (6 \times 3)$$

involves both addition and multiplication. The parentheses indicate that the multiplication is to be done first.

$$2 + (6 \times 3) = 2 + 18 = 20$$

For the expression

$$(2 + 6) \times 3$$

the parentheses indicate that the addition is to be done first.

$$(2 + 6) \times 3 = 8 \times 3 = 24$$

Parentheses used to indicate the order of the arithmetic operations are called **grouping symbols.** Operations within grouping symbols are to be done first.

We usually write a product such as $4 \times (3 + 5)$ without the multiplication symbol as $4(3 + 5)$. We may also use parentheses in any one of the following ways to indicate a product such as 4×8:

$$4(8) \qquad \text{or} \qquad (4)8 \qquad \text{or} \qquad (4)(8).$$

A fraction bar is both a division symbol and a grouping symbol. Recall that $18 \div 2$ may be written as $\frac{18}{2}$. When operation symbols appear above or below the fraction bar, those operations are to be done before the division. For example, to simplify

$$\frac{6 + 15}{3},$$

we add first:

$$\frac{6 + 15}{3} = \frac{21}{3} = 7.$$

EXAMPLE 1 Evaluate each expression when $n = 8$.

    a. $4(n - 3)$ **b.** $\dfrac{45 - 15}{n + 7}$

Solution   Substitute 8 for n in each expression.

    a. $4(n - 3) = 4(8 - 3) = 4(5) = 20$

    b. $\dfrac{45 - 15}{n + 7} = \dfrac{45 - 15}{8 + 7} = \dfrac{30}{15} = 2$

Introduction to Algebra   **5**

Teaching Suggestions p. 1a

Related Activities p. 1b

Reading Mathematics
Students will learn the meaning of the following mathematical terms in this lesson: *grouping symbols, order of operations*.

Many students have never thought of a fraction bar as a grouping symbol. Some may not even realize that a fraction bar indicates division. They may still think of fractions exclusively in terms of parts of a whole. Clarify the uses of the fraction bar, advocating use of a horizontal bar rather than a diagonal slash. This will be important when they write fractions such as $\frac{1}{x + 2}$. Students who use a diagonal slash may write $1/x + 2$, which is not the same expression. Using parentheses, as in $1/(x + 2)$, is not incorrect but $\frac{1}{x + 2}$ is easier to read and to work with.

Chalkboard Examples

Simplify the expression.

1. $(5 + 3) \times (8 - 6)$ **16**

2. $\frac{5 + 3}{8}$ **1**

3. $\frac{16 + 9}{2 + 3}$ **5**

Evaluate the expression when $t = 7$.

4. $38 + 4t$ **66**

5. $t(3 + t)$ **70**

6. $\frac{10 - t}{t - 4}$ **1**

Simplify the expression.

7. $2 + 8 \times 6 - 3$ **47**

8. $5 \times 7 - 2 \times 3$ **29**

9. $12 + 4 \div 2 - 5$ **9**

If there are no grouping symbols in an expression, we agree to perform the operations in the following order.

> ### *Rule for Order of Operations*
> When there are no grouping symbols:
> 1. Perform all multiplications and divisions in order from left to right.
> 2. Perform all additions and subtractions in order from left to right.

EXAMPLE 2 Simplify $392 + 637 \div 49$.

Solution
$$392 + \underbrace{637 \div 49}$$
$$\underbrace{392 + \quad 13}$$
$$405$$

When a product of two numbers or of a number and a variable is written without a multiplication symbol, as in 5(7) or 4n, we perform the multiplication before the other operations.

EXAMPLE 3 Evaluate the expression when $x = 6$.

a. $27 \div 2x$ **b.** $\dfrac{3x - 2}{4}$

Solution Substitute 6 for x in each expression.

a. $27 \div 2x = 27 \div 2(6) = 27 \div 12 = 2.25$

b. $\dfrac{3x - 2}{4} = \dfrac{3(6) - 2}{4} = \dfrac{18 - 2}{4} = \dfrac{16}{4} = 4$

1. Mult.; add   2. Add; mult.   3. Div.; subtr.; add
4. Add; div.; subtr.   5. Div.; subtr.; add   6. Add; add; div.

Class Exercises

Tell in which order the operations should be performed to simplify the expression.

1. $6 + 14 \times 3$ **2.** $(6 + 14)3$ **3.** $18 - 12 \div 3 + 1$

4. $18 - 12 \div (3 + 1)$ **5.** $23 - 9 \div 5 + 2$ **6.** $(9 + 16) \div (4 + 1)$

6   *Chapter 1*

PEMDAS

Evaluate the expression when $m = 4$.

7. $(m + 6)2$ **20**

8. $5m + 8$ **28**

9. $3(m - 1)$ **9**

10. $8 \div m + 7$ **9**

11. $m(2 + m)$ **24**

12. $\dfrac{3m}{18 - 6}$ **1**

Written Exercises

Simplify the expression.

A   1. $35 - 14 \div 2 + 64$ **92**   2. $54 \div 6 + 18 \times 2$ **45**   3. $44 + 17 - 5 \times 2$ **51**

4. $(45 - 19)(8 + 7)$ **390**   5. $(12 + 18) \div (19 - 4)$ **2**   6. $\dfrac{9 + (4 \times 3)}{7}$ **3**

Evaluate the expression when $n = 7$.

7. $(14 + n)6$ **126**

8. $36 \div (n - 3)$ **9**

9. $(n + 28) \div 5$ **7**

10. $(27 - n)3$ **60**

11. $12(n - 4)$ **36**

12. $\dfrac{94 - 38}{n}$ **8**

Evaluate the expression when $t = 10$.

13. $5t \div (14 - 9)$ **10**

14. $\dfrac{25 - t}{10 - 5}$ **3**

15. $(t + 6 - 9)t$ **70**

16. $2(t + 5) - t$ **20**

17. $(t - 4)(t - 4)$ **36**

18. $50 \div (t + 15) + t$ **12**

Evaluate the expression when $s = 16$.

19. $7(s + 12)$ **196**

20. $5(s - 4)$ **60**

21. $(s + 32) \div s$ **3**

22. $(3s - 6) \div 7$ **6**

23. $18(6s - 12)$ **1512**

24. $4s \div (s - 8)$ **8**

Evaluate the expression when $b = 6$ and $c = 7$.

B   25. $(b + c)c$ **91**

26. $3c \div (b - 4)$ **10.5**

27. $2bc \div (c - b)$ **84**

Evaluate the expression when $m = 4$ and $n = 9$.

28. $5n \div (m + 5)$ **5**

29. $(n + m) \div (35 - n)$ **0.5**

30. $m(n - m) \div 8$ **2.5**

Evaluate the expression when $a = 3.6$ and $b = 8.2$.

31. $ab \div 2a$ **4.1**

32. $(b - a)(3a + 6)$ **77.28**

33. $7ab(3b + a)$ **5827.248**

Introduction to Algebra   **7**

Additional A Exercises

Simplify the expression.

1. $18 - 3 \times 4 \div 6$ **16**

2. $(22 - 7)(5 + 3)$ **120**

Evaluate the expression when $c = 11$.

3. $3c - 5$ **28**

4. $(c - 3)(c + 3)$ **112**

5. $(42 - c)c$ **341**

Suggested Assignments

Minimum
   7/1–6; 7–33 odd
   8/Rev. 1–10

Average
   7/1–23 odd; 25–33
   8/34–36
   8/Rev. 1–9 odd
   8/Calculator Key-In

Maximum
   7/1–23 odd; 25–33
   8/34–39
   8/Calculator Key-In

Supplementary Materials

Practice Masters, p. 3

Evaluate the expression when $e = 5$, $f = 8$, and $g = 13$.

34. $(e + f)(g + e)$ 234   **35.** $f \div (g - f) + g$ 14.6   **36.** $f(e + g) - e$ 139

Copy the expression as shown. Add grouping symbols so that the value of the expression is 24 when $x = 3$, $y = 7$, and $z = 21$.

C   **37.** $2x \times (y - 4) + 2x$ **38.** $(y + z) \div 4 \times x + x$ **39.** $x \times (y + z \div 3 + 1) - z$
or $2x \times y - (4 + 2)x$

Review Exercises

Simplify in your head if you can. Write down the answer.

1. 2.4×10 24   **2.** 3.1×5 15.5   **3.** 2.2×6 13.2   **4.** 5.4×20 108   **5.** 6.8×300 2040

6. $8.4 \div 10$ 0.84   **7.** $6.5 \div 5$ 1.3   **8.** $14.21 \div 7$ 2.03   **9.** $18.9 \div 30$ 0.63   **10.** $25.2 \div 400$ 0.063

■■■ **Calculator Key-In**

To use your calculator to simplify an expression with more than one operation, you must keep in mind the order in which you want the operations to be performed. Try to simplify $2(6 + 4)$ by entering the following on your calculator exactly as it is shown.

$$\boxed{2} \; \boxed{\times} \; \boxed{6} \; \boxed{+} \; \boxed{4} \; \boxed{=}$$

Although the correct answer is 20, your calculator will perform the operations in the order in which you entered them and will display 16 for the answer.

To obtain the correct answer, you must enter the expressions in the order in which you want them to be performed. Enter the following exactly as it is shown.

$$\boxed{6} \; \boxed{+} \; \boxed{4} \; \boxed{=} \; \boxed{\times} \; \boxed{2} \; \boxed{=}$$

Now your calculator should display the correct answer, 20. By entering = after entering the expression in parentheses, you complete the operation inside the parentheses before doing the next operation. Some calculators will complete the operation for you even if you do not enter = between operations. Check to see if your calculator will.

Use your calculator to simplify the expression.

1. $12(15 + 9)$ 288   **2.** $57 \div (36 - 17)$ 3   **3.** $(437 + 322) \div 46$ 16.5

4. $(108 + 63) \div (9 - 6)$ 57   **5.** $(55 + 8) \times (2 + 94)$ 6048   **6.** $(56 - 32) \div (4 + 16) \times 5$ 6

1-3 Equations

A **number sentence** indicates a relationship between two mathematical expressions. A sentence, such as the one below, that indicates that two expressions name the same number is called an **equation.**

$$4 \times 3 = 12$$

The expressions to the left and to the right of the equals sign are called the **sides** of the equation. In the example above, 4×3 is the left side of the equation, and 12 is the right side of the equation.

A number sentence may be *true* or *false*. For example, $3 + 9 = 12$ is a true equation, but $3 + 9 = 13$ is a false equation.

A number sentence that contains one or more variables is called an **open number sentence,** or simply an **open sentence.** Frequently a set of intended values, called the **replacement set,** for a variable is specified. An open sentence may be true or false when each variable is replaced by one of the values in its replacement set.

When a value of the variable makes an open sentence a true statement, we say that the value is a **solution** of, or **satisfies,** the sentence. We can **solve** an open sentence in one variable by finding all the solutions of the sentence. An open sentence may have one solution, several solutions, or no solutions.

EXAMPLE 1   The replacement set for x is $\{5, 6, 7\}$. Find all solutions of

$$x + 6 = 13.$$

Solution   Substitute each value in the replacement set for the variable x.

$5 + 6 = 13$	$6 + 6 = 13$	$7 + 6 = 13$
$11 = 13$	$12 = 13$	$13 = 13$
false	false	true

The solution of the equation is 7.

EXAMPLE 2   The replacement set for q is the set of whole numbers. Find all solutions of

$$2q = 9.$$

Solution   The replacement set for q is $\{0, 1, 2, 3, \ldots\}$, so $2q$ must be one of the numbers $2 \times 0, 2 \times 1, 2 \times 2, 2 \times 3, \ldots$, or $0, 2, 4, 6, \ldots$. Because 9 is not one of these numbers, the equation $2q = 9$ has no solution in the given replacement set.

Notice that in the solution to Example 2, we used three dots, read *and so on,* to indicate that the list of numbers continues without end.

Introduction to Algebra   **9**

Teaching Suggestions p. 1b

Related Activities p. 1c

Reading Mathematics

Students will learn the meaning of the following mathematical terms in this lesson: *number sentence, equation, sides, open sentence, replacement set, solution, satisfy, solve.*

Notice the statement, "A number sentence may be true or false." Here we have *or* used in the exclusive sense, meaning "true or false but not both." Most mathematical usage uses an inclusive *or,* meaning the first, or the second, or both.

Chalkboard Examples

The replacement set for x is $\{8, 9, 10, 11\}$. Find all solutions of the equation.

1. $3x = 33$ 11

2. $x + 5 = 23 - x$ 9

3. $13 - x = 1$ No solution

4. $x(x - 3) = 70$ 10

5. $x + 1 = x + 2$ No solution

6. $2x = x + x$ 8, 9, 10, 11

Class Exercises

Tell whether the equation is true or false for the given value of the variable.

1. $20 - y = 17; y = 3$ True

2. $n \times 7 = 42; n = 8$ False

3. $144 \div r = 46; r = 3$ False

4. $18x = 90; x = 5$ True

5. $156 + q = 179; q = 23$ True

6. $t + 5 = 20; t = 5$ False

State the solution or solutions of the equation for the given replacement set.

7. $x + 7 = 12; \{4, 5, 6\}$ 5

8. $7y = 56; \{8, 9, 10\}$ 8

9. $m + 6 = 72; \{50, 60, 70, 80\}$ No solution

10. $x \div 12 = 7; \{81, 82, 83, 84\}$ 84

11. $r - 23 = 19; \{40, 41, 42, 43\}$ 42

12. $b \times 8 = 64; \{2, 4, 6, 8\}$ 8

Written Exercises

Tell whether the equation is true or false for the given value of the variable.

A

1. $x + 9 = 35; x = 26$ True

2. $r - 15 = 40; r = 55$ True

3. $10m = 130; m = 10$ False

4. $9 + y = 100; y = 91$ True

5. $44 - q = 11; q = 55$ False

6. $t \times 7 = 84; t = 91$ False

7. $n \div 8 = 104; n = 832$ True

8. $26 \div d = 2; d = 52$ False

9. $p \times 15 = 255; p = 13$ False

10. $32a = 448; a = 14$ True

Find the solution or solutions of the equation for the given replacement set.

11. $r + 8 = 14; \{6, 7, 8\}$ 6

12. $12a = 84; \{5, 6, 7\}$ 7

13. $m - 26 = 59; \{80, 85, 90\}$ 85

14. $g + 113 = 789; \{900, 901, 902\}$ No solution

15. $5d = 145; \{29, 30, 31\}$ 29

16. $t - 53 = 67; \{13, 14, 15\}$ No solution

17. $b \times 14 = 112; \{6, 8, 10\}$ 8

18. $c \div 12 = 228; \{17, 19, 21\}$ No solution

19. $98 - h = 21; \{75, 80, 85\}$ No solution

20. $38f = 912; \{24, 25, 26\}$ 24

21. $e \div 19 = 152; \{8, 18, 28\}$ No solution

22. $46 + n = 99; \{50, 52, 54\}$ No solution

23. $q \div 23 = 66$; $\{1516, 1517, 1518\}$ 1518   **24.** $b \div 41 = 7$; $\{287, 288, 289\}$ 287

25. $106 + a = 123$; $\{16, 17, 18\}$ 17   **26.** $75 - r = 43$; $\{30, 31, 32\}$ 32

B **27.** $4n + 7 = 51$; $\{10, 11, 12\}$ 11   **28.** $58 - 3a = 10$; $\{16, 17, 18\}$ 16

29. $6x - 12 = 294$; $\{50, 51, 52\}$ 51   **30.** $8r + 24 = 208$; $\{21, 22, 23\}$ 23

31. $4(b - 5) = 28$; $\{10, 11, 12\}$ 12   **32.** $17(k + 4) = 170$; $\{4, 6, 8\}$ 6

33. $(t + 18) \div 3 = 9$; $\{9, 10, 11\}$ 9   **34.** $56 \div (d + 8) = 4$; $\{5, 6, 7\}$ 6

35. $5(2c - 4) = 0$; $\{0, 1, 2\}$ 2   **36.** $(3f + 7) \div 4 = 4$; $\{3, 4, 5\}$ 3

Find the solution or solutions of the equation. The replacement set is all even whole numbers.

37. $x + 1 = 10$ No solution   **38.** $5x = 35$ No solution   **39.** $4x = 16$ 4   **40.** $x - 1 = 20$ No solution

Write an equation with the given solution if the replacement set is all whole numbers. 41–44: Answers will vary.

C **41.** 10   **42.** 15   **43.** 100

44. Write an equation with no solution if the replacement set is all whole numbers.

Replace __?__ with $+, -, \times,$ or $\div$ so the equation has the given solution.

45. $x \underline{\ ?\ }^{+} 17 \underline{\ ?\ }^{-} 13 = 24$; $\{20\}$ **46.** $n \underline{\ ?\ }^{\div} 12 \underline{\ ?\ }^{+} 8 = 11$; $\{36\}$

47. $14 \underline{\ ?\ }^{+} r \underline{\ ?\ }^{\div} 9 = 17$; $\{27\}$ **48.** $y \underline{\ ?\ }^{+} 12 \underline{\ ?\ }^{\div} 6 = 10$; $\{8\}$

49. $d \underline{\ ?\ } (16 \underline{\ ?\ } 4) \underline{\ ?\ } 8 = 8$; $\{12\}$ **50.** $27 \underline{\ ?\ }^{\div} (q \underline{\ ?\ }^{-} 9) \underline{\ ?\ }^{\times} 15 = 45$; $\{18\}$

51. $21 \underline{\ ?\ }^{-} (19 \underline{\ ?\ }^{+} 8) \underline{\ ?\ }^{+} b = 12$; $\{3\}$ **52.** $11 \underline{\ ?\ }^{\times} (16 \underline{\ ?\ }^{-} a) \underline{\ ?\ }^{+} 4 = 59$; $\{11\}$
49. $-, -, +$; or $+, \div, -$; or $\div, -, \times$

Review Exercises

Simplify.

1. $14(11 + 31)$ 588   **2.** $(36 - 5)8$ 248

3. $(15 + 17) \div 4$ 8   **4.** $4 \times 11 - 56 \div 8$ 37

5. $116 \times 4 \div 16 + 31$ 60   **6.** $100 - 39 \div 3 \times 4$ 48

7. $(21 + 14 + 8)(22 - 18)$ 172   **8.** $(136 - 82) \div (115 - 106)$ 6

Introduction to Algebra **11**

Suggested Assignments

Minimum
Day 1: 10/1–22
Day 2: 11/23–32
     11/Rev. 1–8

Average
Day 1: 10/1–22
     11/23–26
Day 2: 11/27–41; 45–46
     11/Rev. 2–8

Maximum
     10/6–16 even
     11/28–34 even;
     37–50

Supplementary Materials

Practice Masters, p. 4

Reading Mathematics

Students will learn the meaning of the following mathematical terms in this lesson: *inequality, graph, coordinate, origin.*

Chalkboard Examples

True or False?

1. $8 < 5$ False

2. $23 - 8 \neq 168 \div 12$ True

3. $5 < 10 < 11$ True

4. If the replacement set for c is $\{1, 2, 3, 4, 5, 6\}$, find the solutions of $3c \geq 12$.

4, 5, 6

5. If the replacement set is all the whole numbers, find the solutions of $x + 16 \leq 20$.

0, 1, 2, 3, 4

1-4 Inequalities

The sentences below are called **inequalities.**

$$8 > 6 \qquad\qquad 6 < 8$$
Eight *is greater than* six. \qquad Six *is less than* eight.

The sentences illustrate how we use the inequality symbols $>$ and $<$ to compare numbers or mathematical expressions. To avoid confusing these symbols, think of them as arrowheads whose small ends point toward the smaller numbers.

A good way to picture numbers is to use a number line. The **graph** of a number is the point paired with the number on the number line. The number paired with a point is called the **coordinate** of the point. The graphs of the whole numbers 0 through 8 are shown on the number line below. The coordinates of the points shown are 0, 1, 2, 3, 4, 5, 6, 7, and 8.

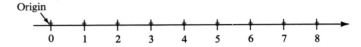

Starting with the graph of 0, which is called the **origin,** the graphs of the whole numbers are equally spaced. The greater a number is, the farther to the right its graph is.

We can indicate that one number is between two others by combining two inequalities. We know that $5 < 6$ and $6 < 8$; thus we can write

$$5 < 6 < 8 \qquad \text{or} \qquad 8 > 6 > 5.$$

Other inequality symbols that we use are shown below with their meanings.

$$\neq \qquad \text{*is not equal to*}$$
$$\geq \qquad \text{*is greater than or equal to*}$$
$$\leq \qquad \text{*is less than or equal to*}$$

We can use inequality symbols to write open sentences. The open sentence $n \leq 6$ means $n < 6$ or $n = 6$.

Sometimes it is helpful to draw a graph to find the solutions of an open sentence with an inequality symbol. Example 1 shows how a graph is used to find the solutions of an inequality.

EXAMPLE 1 Find the solutions of $t \leq 7$. The replacement set is the set of all whole numbers.

12 *Chapter 1*

Solution First, draw a number line showing the replacement set of whole numbers, {0, 1, 2, 3, 4, 5, 6, 7, 8, 9, 10, . . .}. Then graph all the whole numbers that are less than 7 or equal to 7.

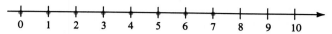

The graph shows that there are only eight numbers in the replacement set that are less than or equal to 7. The solutions are 0, 1, 2, 3, 4, 5, 6, and 7.

EXAMPLE 2 Find the solutions of $r + 8 \geq 15$. The replacement set for r is {5, 7, 9}.

Solution Substitute each value of the replacement set for r.

$5 + 8 \geq 15$	$7 + 8 \geq 15$	$9 + 8 \geq 15$
$13 \geq 15$	$15 \geq 15$	$17 \geq 15$
false	true	true

The solutions are 7 and 9.

Replace __?__ with =, >, or < to make a true statement.

1. 63 __?__ 74   <
2. 2004 ÷ 4 __?__ 25 × 20   >
3. 4 × 5 × 6 __?__ 5 × 5 × 5   <

Graph the solutions on the number line. The replacement set for x is {0, 1, 2, 3, 4, 5, 6, 7, 8}.

4. $x \geq 6$

5. $10 - x > 7$

6. $3 < x < 7$

Class Exercises

Read each sentence.

1. Five is less than seven.
2. n is greater than or equal to nine.
3. Twenty-four is greater than twelve which is greater than eight.
4. y is less than or equal to fifteen.

1. $5 < 7$ **2.** $n \geq 9$ **3.** $24 > 12 > 8$ **4.** $y \leq 15$

True or false?

5. $7 > 7$ False   **6.** $18 \leq 20$ True   **7.** $15 > 5$ True

8. $14 > 6 > 2$ True   **9.** $20 < 18 < 16$ False   **10.** $33 \geq 24 \geq 11$ True

The replacement set for x is {1, 2, 3, 4, 5}. Find the solutions.

11. $x < 9$ 1, 2, 3, 4, 5   **12.** $7 - x > 3$ 1, 2, 3   **13.** $2x \geq 4$ 2, 3, 4, 5

Written Exercises

Check students' graphs.

For each exercise, draw a number line and graph the given numbers.

A **1.** 0, 2, 5, 7, 8   **2.** 0, 1, 3, 4, 6   **3.** 7, 11, 13, 19, 15

4. 12, 2, 7, 5, 14   **5.** 9, 14, 4, 0, 3   **6.** 6, 1, 12, 2, 17

Introduction to Algebra **13**

Replace __?__ with =, >, or < to make a true statement.

7. 21 __?__ 14 >

8. 18 __?__ 35 <

9. 76 __?__ 67 >

10. 104 __?__ 104 =

11. 265 __?__ 256 >

12. 390 __?__ 309 >

13. $17 + 82$ __?__ 93 >

14. $47 - 31$ __?__ 61 <

15. $25 \div 5$ __?__ 10 <

16. 26×4 __?__ 52 >

17. 19×11 __?__ 208 >

18. $84 \div 3$ __?__ 24 >

Use > or < to write a true statement with the given numbers.
Answers may vary. One statement is given.

19. $18, 46, 32$ $18 < 32 < 46$

20. $29, 5, 31$ $5 < 29 < 31$

21. $103, 130, 310$
$103 < 130 < 310$

22. $256, 652, 526$
$256 < 526 < 652$

23. $986, 689, 698$
$689 < 698 < 986$

24. $717, 177, 771$
$177 < 717 < 771$

Graph the solutions of the inequality on the number line. The replacement set for b is $\{1, 2, 3, 4, 5, 6, 7, 8, 9, 10\}$.

25. $b < 11$

26. $b > 6$

27. $b \geq 5$

28. $b \leq 8$

29. $b + 4 < 9$

30. $20 - b > 16$

31. $2b \leq b$

32. $12 + b \geq 15$

33. $19 + b > 24$

34. $5b < 20$

35. $b - 1 \geq 9$

36. $18 - b \leq 13$

Find the solutions of the inequality. The replacement set for x is the set of whole numbers.

EXAMPLE **a.** $7 < x$ **b.** $10 > x > 5$

Solution **a.** The solutions are 8, 9, 10, and so on.
b. The solutions are 6, 7, 8, and 9.

37. $12 > x$

38. $x \geq 15$

39. $6 \leq x$

40. $x < 11$

41. $24 < x$

42. $35 \leq x$

43. $x \geq 66$

44. $x > 14$

B **45.** $10 < x < 19$

46. $16 > x > 6$

47. $28 \geq x \geq 22$

48. $35 \leq x \leq 42$

49. $104 \leq x \leq 117$

50. $200 < x < 209$

Find the solutions of the inequality for the given replacement set.

51. $3x + 5 \leq 35$; $\{5, 10, 15\}$ 5, 10

52. $6r - 9 > 20$; $\{5, 6, 7\}$ 5, 6, 7

53. $12y - 18 > 126$; $\{10, 11, 12\}$ No solution

54. $2t + 2 < 30$; $\{10, 20, 30\}$ 10

55. $6(w + 5) \geq 165$; $\{21, 22, 23\}$ 23

56. $3(14 - q) \leq 6$; $\{12, 13, 14\}$ 12, 13, 14

57. $(m + 14) \div 6 < 5$; $\{4, 10, 16\}$ 4, 10   **58.** $24 \div (b + 2) \geq 4$; $\{2, 4, 6\}$ 2, 4

59. $(a - 7)4 < 32$; $\{14, 15, 16\}$ 14   **60.** $(f - 8) \div 6 \geq 41$; $\{253, 254, 255\}$ 254, 255

61. $(n - 9) \div 5 > 11$; $\{60, 62, 64\}$ No solution   **62.** $5(x + 3) < 25$; $\{0, 1, 2\}$ 0, 1

Find the solutions of the inequality. The replacement set is $\{1, 2, 3, 4, 5, 6, 7, 8, 9, 10\}$.

EXAMPLE $4 < y + 1 < 9$.

Solution   The inequality has two parts:

$$4 < y + 1 \qquad \text{and} \qquad y + 1 < 9$$

Find the solutions of each part.

$$4, 5, 6, 7, 8, 9, 10 \qquad 1, 2, 3, 4, 5, 6, 7$$

Those numbers that occur in the solutions of *both* parts are the solutions of the inequality. The solutions of the inequality $4 < y + 1 < 9$ are 4, 5, 6, and 7.

C **63.** $12 > y + 2 > 6$ 5, 6, 7, 8, 9   **64.** $4 \leq y - 1 \leq 8$ 5, 6, 7, 8, 9   **65.** $20 \geq 2y \geq 10$ 5, 6, 7, 8, 9, 10

66. $9 < 3y < 27$ 4, 5, 6, 7, 8   **67.** $5 < 2y + 1 < 15$ 3, 4, 5, 6   **68.** $15 > 2y - 1 > 5$ 4, 5, 6, 7

Review Exercises

Simplify.

1. $16.5 + 5.4$ 21.9   **2.** $21.9 - 5.4$ 16.5   **3.** $8.07 - 1.9$ 6.17

4. $6.17 + 1.9$ 8.07   **5.** 18.3×5 91.5   **6.** $91.5 \div 18.3$ 5

7. $21.6 \div 24$ 0.9   **8.** 0.9×24 21.6   **9.** 0.07×0.092 0.00644

■■■ Challenge

Each letter in each exercise stands for a digit from 0 through 9. Find the value of each letter to make the computation correct. (There may be more than one correct answer.) **One answer is given for each.**

3.
```
   1032
 -   87
    945
```

1.
```
   H O W      163
 + A R E    + 702
   Y O U      865
```

2.
```
   T I M E      9248
 + S U R E    + 6038
 F L I E S    15,286
```

3.
```
   M A T H
 -     I S
   F U N
```

Introduction to Algebra **15**

Suggested Assignments
Minimum
Day 1: 13/2-6 even
    14/8–36 even
Day 2: 14/25–55 odd
    15/Rev. 1–9
Average
Day 1: 13/2-6 even
    14/8–44 even
Day 2: 14/45–56
    15/57–62
    15/Rev. 1–9 odd
    15/Challenge
Maximum
    13/3, 6
    14/16–52 even
    15/63–68
    15/Challenge

Supplementary Materials
Practice Masters, p. 4

Reading Mathematics

Students will learn the meaning of the following mathematical term in this lesson: *inverse operations*.

The word *inverse* is used in several different ways in mathematics. Reciprocals are called multiplicative inverses; opposites are called additive inverses; certain functions have inverses; there are inverse proportions; and so on. Students encounter the same profusion of meanings in connection with the "−" sign.

Chalkboard Examples

Use inverse operations to write a related equation or inequality, and solve for the variable.

1. $x + 21 = 35$
   $x = 35 - 21; 14$

2. $x + 7 > 12$ $x > 12 - 7;$
   all numbers greater than 5

3. $12a = 60$ $a = 60 \div 12; 5$

4. $t \div 5 \leq 7$ $t \leq 7 \times 5;$
   all numbers less than or equal to 35

Is the solution correct for the given equation or inequality?

5. $a - 9 = 22, a = 13$ **No**

6. $c \div 2 = 8; c = 16$ **Yes**

7. $x + 16 > 31; x > 47$ **No**

Additional A Exercises

Use inverse operations to write a related equation or inequality, and solve for the variable.

1. $x + 3 = 12$
   $x = 12 - 3; 9$

2. $x - 12 = 18$
   $x = 18 + 12; 30$

1-5 Inverse Operations

Addition and subtraction are related operations, as shown by the following facts.

$$5 + 6 = 11$$
$$5 = 11 - 6$$

We say that adding a number and subtracting the same number are **inverse operations.**

The relationship between addition and subtraction holds when we work with variables, as well. Thus we can write the following related equations.

$$n + 6 = 11$$
$$n = 11 - 6$$

We can use this relationship to solve equations that involve addition or subtraction. Throughout the rest of the chapter if no replacement set is given for an open sentence, assume that the solution can be any number.

EXAMPLE 1 Use the inverse operation to write a related equation and solve for the variable.

      a. $x + 9 = 35$ **b.** $y - 12 = 18$

Solution   **a.** $x = 35 - 9$ **b.** $y = 18 + 12$
                    $x = 26$ $y = 30$
           The solution is 26.   The solution is 30.

To check each solution, substitute the value of the variable in the original equation.

    a. $x + 9 = 35$ **b.** $y - 12 = 18$
       $26 + 9 = 35$ ✓ $30 - 12 = 18$ ✓

Multiplying by a number and dividing by the same number are inverse operations.

$$4 \times 6 = 24$$
$$6 = 24 \div 4$$

We can use this relationship to help solve equations that involve multiplication and division.

EXAMPLE 2 Use the inverse operation to write a related equation and solve for the variable.

      a. $6r = 30$ **b.** $x \div 7 = 12$

16   *Chapter 1*

Solution **a.** Recall that $6r$ means $6 \times r$.

$$6 \times r = 30$$
$$r = 30 \div 6$$
$$r = 5$$

The solution is 5.

Check: $6 \times 5 = 30$ $\checkmark$

b. $x \div 7 = 12$
$$x = 12 \times 7$$
$$x = 84$$
The solution is 84.

Check: $84 \div 7 = 12$ $\checkmark$

We can use inverse operations to solve equations that contain two operations.

EXAMPLE 3 Use inverse operations to solve the equation
$$3n + 25 = 61.$$

Solution First write the related subtraction equation that will give the value of $3n$.
$$3n = 61 - 25$$
$$3n = 36$$

Then write the related division equation that will give the value of n.
$$n = 36 \div 3$$
$$n = 12$$

The solution is 12.

Check: $3n + 25 = 61$
$3(12) + 25 = 61$
$36 + 25 = 61$ $\checkmark$

We can also use inverse operations to solve inequalities that involve addition, subtraction, multiplication, or division.

EXAMPLE 4 Use the inverse operation to write a related inequality and solve for the variable.
a. $y + 6 > 10$ **b.** $5t \leq 25$

Solution **a.** $y > 10 - 6$
$y > 4$

The solutions are all numbers greater than 4.

Check: $4 + 6 = 10$, so any number greater than 4 will be a solution. $\checkmark$

b. $t \leq 25 \div 5$
$t \leq 5$

The solutions are all numbers less than or equal to 5.

Check: $5 \times 5 = 25$, so any number less than or equal to 5 will be a solution. $\checkmark$

Introduction to Algebra **17**

3. $5c > 15$ $c > 15 \div 5$; **all numbers greater than 3**

4. $a + 100 \leq 104$
$a \leq 104 - 100$; **all the numbers less than or equal to 4**

5. $17 + n = 22$
$n = 22 - 17$; **5**

6. $x \div 9 = 72$
$x = 72 \times 9$; **648**

7. $y - 14 = 14$
$y = 14 + 14$; **28**

8. $7m = 42$
$m = 42 \div 7$; **6**

Suggested Assignments

Minimum
Day 1: 18/2–40 even
Day 2: 18/17–55 odd
       19/Self-Test A

Average
Day 1: 18/8–56 even
Day 2: 18/27–55 odd
       19/57–61
       19/Self-Test A

Maximum
       18/25–55 odd
       19/60–65
       19/Self-Test A

Supplementary Materials

Practice Masters, p. 4
Test 1A, pp. 3–4

Additional Answers
Class Exercises

5. $t > 18 - 7$; all the numbers greater than 11

6. $t \leq 32 \div 4$; all the numbers less than or equal to 8

10. $t < 79 + 38$; all the numbers less than 117

12. $t < 90 \times 15$; all the numbers greater than or equal to 1350

Class Exercises

Use the inverse operation to state a related equation or inequality and solve for t.

1. $t + 6 = 15$ $t = 15 - 6$; 9

2. $t - 4 = 7$ $t = 7 + 4$; 11

3. $6t = 48$ $t = 48 \div 6$; 8

4. $t \div 8 = 7$ $t = 7 \times 8$; 56

5. $t + 7 > 18$

6. $4t \leq 32$

7. $t + 24 = 60$ $t = 60 - 24$; 36

8. $13t = 78$ $t = 78 \div 13$; 6

9. $t - 26 = 59$ $t = 59 + 26$; 85

10. $t - 38 < 79$

11. $t \div 32 = 8$ $t = 8 \times 32$; 256

12. $t \div 15 \geq 90$

Written Exercises

Use the inverse operation to write a related equation and solve for the variable.

A

1. $x + 8 = 15$ $x = 15 - 8$; 7

2. $a + 6 = 11$ $a = 11 - 6$; 5

3. $f + 38 = 74$ $f = 74 - 38$; 36

4. $t + 46 = 91$ $t = 91 - 46$; 45

5. $y - 9 = 14$ $y = 14 + 9$; 23

6. $n - 7 = 9$ $n = 9 + 7$; 16

7. $b - 25 = 32$ $b = 32 + 25$; 57

8. $r - 55 = 87$ $r = 87 + 55$; 142

9. $3c = 27$ $c = 27 \div 3$; 9

10. $5g = 45$ $g = 45 \div 5$; 9

11. $9m = 108$ $m = 108 \div 9$; 12

12. $4d = 88$ $d = 88 \div 4$; 22

13. $n \div 6 = 9$ $n = 9 \times 6$; 54

14. $s \div 8 = 4$ $s = 4 \times 8$; 32

15. $g \div 16 = 7$ $g = 7 \times 16$; 112

16. $w \div 9 = 14$ $w = 14 \times 9$; 126

17. $a + 17 = 17$ $a = 17 - 17$; 0

18. $j - 54 = 61$ $j = 61 + 54$; 115

19. $14n = 42$ $n = 42 \div 14$; 3

20. $e + 26 = 61$ $e = 61 - 26$; 35

21. $h \div 11 = 297$ $h = 297 \times 11$; 3267

22. $b + 45 = 256$ $b = 256 - 45$; 211

23. $d - 87 = 110$ $d = 110 + 87$; 197

24. $18b = 18$ $b = 18 \div 18$; 1

25. $31q = 465$ $q = 465 \div 31$; 15

26. $k \div 17 = 527$ $k = 527 \times 17$; 8959

27. $p + 208 = 358$ $p = 358 - 208$; 150

28. $f - 11 = 523$ $f = 523 + 11$; 534

29. $c + 511 = 536$ $c = 536 - 511$; 25

30. $18r = 414$ $r = 414 \div 18$; 23

31. $g - 19 = 401$ $g = 401 + 19$; 420

32. $m \div 4 = 216$ $m = 216 \times 4$; 864

Use the inverse operation to write a related inequality and solve for the variable.

33. $r + 8 > 12$

34. $x - 9 < 18$

35. $4p \geq 36$

36. $m \div 11 \leq 99$

37. $q - 24 \leq 59$

38. $13d > 182$

39. $a \div 17 < 340$

40. $x + 21 \geq 50$

41. $c + 113 \leq 177$

42. $f \div 27 < 162$

43. $t - 55 \geq 9$

44. $39n > 273$

45. $y \div 80 < 20$

46. $a - 109 \leq 214$

47. $43x > 86$

Use inverse operations to solve.

B

48. $3q + 9 = 27$ 6

49. $4a + 19 = 39$ 5

50. $7d - 12 = 37$ 7

51. $5b - 16 = 39$ 11

52. $3r + 24 = 63$ 13

53. $2s - 30 = 62$ 46

54. $9x - 84 = 69$ 17

55. $6w + 81 = 486$ 67.5

56. $(z \div 3) + 22 = 30$ 24

57. $(t \div 7) - 4 = 4$ 56   **58.** $(c \div 5) - 13 = 11$ 120   **59.** $(y \div 3) + 15 = 36$
63

C 60. $3n + 10 > 40$ **61.** $5b - 12 \le 42$ **62.** $6m - 17 \ge 49$

63. $4d + 21 \ge 53$ **64.** $(y \div 14) - 32 \le 38$ **65.** $(x \div 8) + 15 < 19$

Self-Test A

Simplify the numerical expression.

7.6

1. 4.3×6 25.8   **2.** $4.15 + 1.6$ 5.75   **3.** $8.16 - 5.7$ 2.46   **4.** $68.4 \div 9$ [1-1]

Evaluate the expression when $k = 4$ and $m = 6$.

5. $184 \div k$ 46   **6.** $8 + m + 1$ 15   **7.** $7km$ 168

Simplify the expression.

8. $8 + 3 \times 14$ 50   **9.** $48 \div (6 \times 2 - 4)$ 6   **10.** $\dfrac{7 + (9 \times 3) - 2^{2}}{(5 \times 4) - (2 \times 2)}$ [1-2]

Evaluate the expression when $s = 12$ and $t = 18$.

11. $\dfrac{s}{4} + 6$ 9   **12.** $(t + 2) \div 5$ 4   **13.** $2s - t$ 6

Find the solution or solutions for the given replacement set.

14. $72 - m = 43$; $\{19, 29, 31\}$ 29   **15.** $6r = 48$; $\{6, 7, 8\}$ 8   [1-3]

16. $t \div 12 = 11$; $\{23, 24, 25\}$ No solution   **17.** $4d + 16 = 28$; $\{3, 4, 5\}$
3

Replace ? with $=$, $>$, or $<$ to make a true statement.

=

18. $430 \underline{\ ?\ } 403$ >   **19.** $52 \div 17 \underline{\ ?\ } 19$ <   **20.** $225 \underline{\ ?\ } 9 \times 25$ [1-4]

Find the solutions of the inequality. The replacement set for x is the set of whole numbers.

19, 20, 21, . . . , 27

21. $x < 5$ **22.** $x \ge 85$ 85, 86, 87, and so on   **23.** $19 \le x \le 27$
0, 1, 2, 3, 4

Use inverse operations to solve. $d < 112 \div 7$; $d < 16$; $5a = 49 - 4$;
$g = 12 + 32$; 44   all the numbers less $a = 45 \div 5$; 9
24. $g - 32 = 12$ **25.** $7d < 112$ than 16   **26.** $5a + 4 = 49$ [1-5]

Self-Test answers and Extra Practice are at the back of the book.

Introduction to Algebra **19**

19

Teaching Suggestions p. 1e

Related Activities p. 1e

Reading Mathematics

There is often some confusion in students' minds over expressions like "three more than x" and "three is more than x." The usual error encountered is a tendency to use $3 > x$ as a translation of the first phrase, instead of the proper $x + 3$. The same is true, of course, about "five less than x" and "five is less than x." Another common error is to use $4 - x$ rather than $x - 4$ for "four less than x."

1-6 Writing Expressions for Word Phrases

In mathematics we often use symbols to translate word phrases into mathematical expressions. The same mathematical expression can be used to translate many different word expressions. Consider the phrases below.

Three more than a number n The sum of three and a number n

Written as a variable expression, each of the phrases becomes

$$3 + n.$$

Notice that both the phrase *more than* and the phrase *the sum of* indicate addition.

    The following are some of the word phrases that we associate with each of the four operations.

+	−	×	÷
add	subtract	multiply	divide
sum	difference	product	quotient
plus	minus	times	
total	remainder		
more than	less than		
increased by	decreased by		

EXAMPLE 1   Write a variable expression for the word phrase.
    a. A number t increased by nine   **b.** Sixteen less than a number q
    c. A number x decreased by twelve, divided by forty
    d. The product of sixteen and the sum of five and a number r

Solution   **a.** In this expression, the phrase *increased by* indicates that the operation is addition. $t + 9$

    b. In this expression, the phrase *less than* indicates that the operation is subtraction. $q - 16$

    c. In this expression, the phrases *decreased by* and *divided by* indicate that two operations, subtraction and division, are involved. $(x - 12) \div 40$

    d. In this expression, the words *product* and *sum* indicate that multiplication and addition are involved.
    $16 \times (5 + r)$,   or $16(5 + r)$

Reading Mathematics: *Attention to Order*

Often a word expression contains more than one phrase that indicates an operation. Notice in Example 1 parts (c) and (d), on page 20, how parentheses were needed to represent the word phrase accurately. When translating from words to symbols, be sure to include grouping symbols if they are needed to make the meaning of an expression clear.

Many words that we use in everyday speech indicate operations or relationships between numbers. *Twice* and *doubled,* for example, indicate multiplication by 2. *Consecutive* whole numbers are whole numbers that differ by 1. The *preceding* whole number is the whole number *before* a particular number, and the *next* whole number is the whole number *after* a particular number.

EXAMPLE 2 If twice n is a whole number, represent (a) the preceding whole number and (b) the next four consecutive whole numbers. Represent the whole number by $2n$.

Solution a. The preceding whole number is 1 less than $2n$, or $2n - 1$.

  b. Each of the next whole numbers is 1 more than the whole number before.
$$2n + 1, \ 2n + 2, \ 2n + 3, \ 2n + 4$$

Class Exercises

Match.

1. A number x multiplied by fourteen   I

2. The quotient of fourteen divided by a number x E

3. Fourteen less than a number x G

4. Seven increased by a number x H

5. A number x subtracted from fourteen   A

6. Fourteen more than a number x J

7. Seven more than the product of fourteen and a number x D

8. Twice the sum of a number x and seven   B

9. The product of seven and the sum of fourteen and a number x F

10. Fourteen divided by the difference when a number x is subtracted from seven   C

A. $14 - x$

B. $2(x + 7)$

C. $14 \div (7 - x)$

D. $7 + 14x$

E. $14 \div x$

F. $7(14 + x)$

G. $x - 14$

H. $7 + x$

I. $14x$

J. $x + 14$

Chalkboard Examples

Write a variable expression for the word phrase.

1. A number eleven more than a number t $t + 11$

2. Twice the sum of a number a and twelve
   $2(a + 12)$

3. Six more than twice a number x $2x + 6$

4. The sum of two consecutive whole numbers if the first is n $n + (n + 1)$, or
   $2n + 1$

5. The difference of twenty and the product of four and a number c $20 - 4c$

Introduction to Algebra   **21**

Written Exercises

Write a variable expression for the word phrase.

A

1. The product of eight and a number b $8b$
2. A number q divided by sixteen $q \div 16$
3. A number d subtracted from fifty-three $53 - d$
4. Four less than a number f $f - 4$
5. Thirty increased by a number t $30 + t$
6. Five times a number c $5c$
7. The sum of a number g and nine $g + 9$
8. A number k minus twenty-seven $k - 27$
9. Seventy-eight decreased by a number m $78 - m$
10. A number y added to ninety $90 + y$
11. Nineteen more than a number n $19 + n$
12. Sixty-two plus a number h $62 + h$
13. The quotient when a number d is divided by eleven $d \div 11$
14. The difference when a number a is subtracted from a number b $b - a$
15. The remainder when a number z is subtracted from twelve $12 - z$
16. The total of a number x, a number y, and thirteen $x + y + 13$
17. Fifteen more than the product of a number t and eleven $15 + 11t$
18. The quotient when a number b is divided by nine, decreased by seven $(b \div 9) - 7$
19. The sum of a number m and a number n, multiplied by ninety-one $(m + n) \times 91$
20. Forty-one times the difference when six is subtracted from a number a $41(a - 6)$
21. A number r divided by the remainder of eighty-three minus ten $r \div (83 - 10)$
22. The total of a number p and twelve, divided by eighteen $(p + 12) \div 18$
23. The product of a number c and three more than the sum of nine and twelve $c(3 + 9 + 12)$
24. The sum of a number y and ten, divided by the difference when a number x is decreased by five $(y + 10) \div (x - 5)$

22   *Chapter 1*

25. The total of sixty, forty, and ten, divided by a number d $(60 + 40 + 10) \div d$

26. The product of eighteen less than a number b and the sum of twenty-two and forty-five $(b - 18)(22 + 45)$

B 27. The greatest of four consecutive whole numbers, the smallest of which is b $b + 3$

28. The smallest of three consecutive whole numbers, the greatest of which is q $q - 2$

29. The greatest of three consecutive even numbers following the even number x $x + 6$

30. The greatest of three consecutive odd numbers following the odd number y $y + 6$

31. The value in cents of q quarters $0.25q$

32. The number of inches in f feet $12f$

33. The number of hours in x minutes $x \div 60$

34. The number of dollars in y cents $y \div 100$

C 35. The difference between two numbers is ten. The greater number is x. Write a variable expression for the smaller number. $x - 10$

36. One number is six times another. The greater number is a. Write a variable expression for the smaller number. $a \div 6$

Review Exercises

Use the inverse operation to solve for the variable.

1. $x + 32 = 59$ **27**   2. $2y = 68$ **34**   3. $a \div 8 = 72$ **576**   4. $q - 14 = 23$ **37**

5. $m - 27 > 45$
All the numbers greater than 72

6. $f \div 6 < 8$
All the numbers less than 48

7. $n + 12 \leq 26$
All the numbers less than or equal to 14

8. $6d \geq 132$
All the numbers greater than or equal to 22

▮▮▮ Challenge

In the set of whole numbers, there are two different values for a for which this equation is true.

$$a + a = a \times a$$

What are they? **0; 2**

Introduction to Algebra **23**

Suggested Assignments
Minimum
Day 1: 22/1–20
Day 2: 22/21–24
       23/25–34
       23/Rev. 1–8
Average
       22/12–24
       23/25–36
       23/Rev. 2–8 even
       23/Challenge
Maximum
       22/12–24
       23/25–36
       23/Challenge

Supplementary Materials
Practice Masters, p. 5

1-7 Equations and Inequalities for Word Sentences

We can use what we know about translating word phrases into variable expressions to translate word sentences into equations and inequalities.

EXAMPLE 1 Write an equation or inequality for the word sentence.
  a. Twice a number *x* is less than or equal to 14.
  b. Thirty-five is sixteen more than a number *t*.
  c. The product of five and the difference when ten is subtracted from a number *r* is greater than forty.

Solution **a.** First, write the word phrase *twice a number x* as the variable expression $2x$. Use the symbol $\leq$ to translate the phrase *is less than or equal to*.

$$2x \leq 14$$

  b. Use the equals sign to translate *is*. Write *sixteen more than a number t* as $t + 16$.

$$35 = t + 16$$

  c. Write *the product of five and the difference when ten is subtracted from a number r* as $5(r - 10)$. Use the symbol $>$ to express *is greater than*.

$$5(r - 10) > 40$$

A word sentence may involve an unknown number without specifying a variable. When translating such a sentence into an equation or inequality, we may use any letter to represent the unknown number.

EXAMPLE 2 Write an equation or inequality for the word sentence.
  a. The sum of a number and seven is less than thirteen.
  b. A number increased by six is equal to three times the number.

Solution **a.** Let *n* stand for the unknown number. $n + 7 < 13$

  b. Let *x* stand for the unknown number. $x + 6 = 3x$

Both sides of an equation or inequality may be variable expressions, as illustrated in Example 2, part (b).

Class Exercises

Tell how you would translate each word sentence into an equation or an inequality.

  1. The sum of six and a number *m* is greater than fifteen.

2. A number p subtracted from forty-eight is seventeen.

3. Fourteen times a number r is less than or equal to two hundred.

4. Twice the sum of eleven and nine is four times a number b.

Write an equation or inequality for the word sentence.

5. Eighty-two is less than three times a number q. $82 < 3q$

6. Eighty-three is fifteen less than a number g. $83 = g - 15$

7. Six times a number z is greater than or equal to z plus two. $6z \geq z + 2$

8. A number divided by eleven is twelve. $n \div 11 = 12$

9. The product of a number and five is less than the number minus three.
$$5n < n - 3$$

Written Exercises

Write an equation or inequality for the word sentence.

A
  1. Five times a number d is greater than twenty. $5d > 20$

  2. A number t increased by thirty-five is sixty. $t + 35 = 60$

  3. Seven less than the product of a number w and three equals eight.
$$3w - 7 = 8$$

  4. The difference when a number z is subtracted from sixteen is two.
$$16 - z = 2$$

  5. Five divided by the product of six and a number r is less than forty-two. $5 \div 6r < 42$

  6. The sum of a number and seven is greater than or equal to nine. $n + 7 \geq 9$

  7. A number decreased by one is less than five. $n - 1 < 5$

  8. Twelve is greater than a number divided by four. $12 > n \div 4$

  9. Twice a number, divided by three, is fifteen. $2n \div 3 = 15$

  10. The product of a number and eight, decreased by three, is less than or equal to nine. $8n - 3 \leq 9$

B 11. The quotient when the sum of four and x is divided by two is thirty-four. $(4 + x) \div 2 = 34$

  12. The sum of n and twenty-two, multiplied by three, is seventy-eight. $(n + 22)3 = 78$

  13. The product of a and the difference of six minus one is equal to a. $a(6 - 1) = a$

  14. The sum of z and seventeen is less than or equal to the difference of twenty-one minus z. $z + 17 \leq 21 - z$

Introduction to Algebra **25**

Suggested Assignments

Minimum
  25/1–14
  26/15–22
  26/Rev. 1–9
Average
  25/2–10 even; 11–14
  26/15–24
  26/Rev. 2–8 even
Maximum
  25/1–14
  26/15–26

Supplementary Materials

Practice Masters, p. 5

Write an equation or inequality for the word sentence.

15. Fifty-nine minus x is greater than the sum of twice x and three. $59 - x > 2x + 3$

16. Two increased by eight times a number is equal to the number divided by five. $2 + 8n = n \div 5$

17. The product when the sum of y and twelve is multiplied by five is one hundred. $(y + 12)5 = 100$

18. The difference when the product of m and nine is subtracted from sixty-six is zero. $66 - 9m = 0$

19. The sum when the quotient of b divided by eight is added to nine is less than thirty. $(b \div 8) + 9 < 30$

20. The quotient when a number is divided by five is greater than the sum of the product of the number and two added to eleven. $n \div 5 > 2n + 11$

21. Twice a number is equal to the product when the sum of the number and four is multiplied by eight. $2n = (n + 4)8$

22. The sum when the quotient of a number divided by three is added to thirteen is greater than or equal to the difference when the product of the number multiplied by five is subtracted from ten. $(n \div 3) + 13 \geq 10 - 5n$

For each exercise, (a) write an equation or inequality for the word sentence and (b) solve the equation or inequality for the given replacement set.

23. Twice a number x is equal to thirty-two. $\{14, 15, 16\}$ $2x = 32; 16$

24. A number z decreased by nine is less than fifteen. $\{23, 24, 25\}$ $z - 9 < 15; 23$

C **25.** The product of y and ten, decreased by six, is greater than or equal to twenty-five. $\{3, 4, 5\}$ $10y - 6 \geq 25; 4, 5$

26. The difference when the product of a number and three is subtracted from thirty is greater than or equal to the number increased by ten. $\{0, 5, 10, 15\}$ $30 - 3n \geq n + 10; 0, 5$

Review Exercises

Simplify the expression.

1. $13 - 9 \div 3 + 12$ 22   **2.** $40 \div 8 + 21 \times 3$ 68   **3.** $16(2 + 5) - 4$ 108

4. $6(94 - 72) + 18$ 150   **5.** $(8 + 11 - 3) \div 8$ 2   **6.** $(19 + 2)(81 - 54)$ 567

7. $(14 + 9) \div (10 - 3)$ **8.** $13.11 - (3.8 + 5.2) \div 3$ **9.** $4(8.15 - 2.11) + 9.50$
$\frac{23}{7}$, or $3\frac{2}{7}$ 10.11   33.66

1-8 A Plan for Solving Problems

What we know about mathematics enables us to solve many problems. Problems, however, are not usually as neatly organized as the information in the expressions with which we have been working. We must sort out and organize the facts of a problem before we begin to solve. A plan such as the one below can be useful in solving many kinds of problems.

> ## Plan for Solving Word Problems
>
> 1. Read the problem carefully. Make sure that you understand what it says. You may need to read it more than once.
>
> 2. Use questions like these in planning the solution:
>   What is asked for?
>   What facts are given?
>   Are enough facts given? If not, what else is needed?
>   Are unnecessary facts given? If so, what are they?
>   Will a sketch or diagram help?
>
> 3. Determine which operation or operations can be used to solve the problem.
>
> 4. Carry out the operations carefully.
>
> 5. Check your results with the facts given in the problem. Give the answer.

EXAMPLE 1 On Saturday, the Nizel family drove 17 mi from Topsfield to Newton and 22.5 mi from Newton to Harbor Bluffs. The trip took 50 min. On the way back, the Nizels took the same route, but they stopped for lunch after driving 9.5 mi. If they continue on the same route after lunch, how much farther will they have to drive to return to Topsfield?

Solution • The problem asks for the number of miles to return to Topsfield.

• The following facts are given in the problem:
  17 mi from Topsfield to Newton
  22.5 mi from Newton to Harbor Bluffs
  drove 9.5 mi back toward Topsfield

(The solution is continued on the next page.)

Introduction to Algebra **27**

Reading Mathematics

Students need to read a problem several times to understand the facts and relationships involved. They should read with pencil and paper at hand, to note the symbolic representation of what they read.

1. Martha walked 4 mi on the Ridge Trail, from the Bluffs to Long View, and then 7 mi farther, from Long View to the Knob. How far must she walk to return to the Bluffs? **11 mi**

2. Frank has $2.00 in nickels. How many nickels does he have? **40**

3. What must three grades total, if the average is 90?

   270

Additional A Exercises

Solve, using the five-step plan.

1. The elevation of Terra Alta is 2521 ft, and that of Cumberland is 1885 ft. How much higher is Terra Alta? **636 ft**

2. Hugh Yoshioko received change for $3: $1 each in nickels, dimes, and quarters. How many coins did he get? **34**

3. Of the eggs The Hennery produced today, 87 dozen were shipped, and 7 eggs were left over. How many eggs did The Hennery produce today? **1051**

4. Maria Martinez ordered seeds for her garden as follows: 2 packages of asters, 89¢ each; 1 package of tomatoes, $1.09; 5 lb of potting mix, $8.25. Find the total cost of the order, including a $2.50 charge for shipping and handling. **$13.62**

- We have enough facts to solve the problem since we know the distance between the cities and the distance driven toward Topsfield.

- We do not need to know that the trip took 50 min.

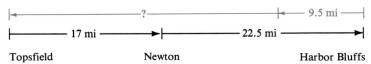

- The sketch shows that we subtract the distance driven back toward Topsfield from the distance between Topsfield and Harbor Bluffs.

$$(17 + 22.5) - 9.5 = 30$$

- Check: If they drive 9.5 mi and 30 mi farther, will the Nizels have driven the distance from Harbor Bluffs to Topsfield?

$$9.5 + 30 = 17 + 22.5 \ \checkmark$$

The Nizels must drive 30 mi to return to Topsfield.

EXAMPLE 2   Records at the Howard City Weather Bureau show that it rained on a total of 17 days during the months of July through September and on twice as many days during the months of October through December. During October through December, how many days did not have rain?

Solution

- The problem asks for the number of days without rain during October, November, and December.

- Given facts: 17 days of rain in July through September
  twice as many days of rain in October through December

- We need to supply these facts:
  31 days in October, 30 days in November, 31 days in December

- To find the number of days without rain, subtract the number of days that did have rain from the total number of days.
  $$(31 + 30 + 31) - (2 \times 17) = 92 - 34 = 58$$

- Check: Are 34 days twice as many as 17? $34 \div 2 = 17 \ \checkmark$
  Do 58 days without rain and 34 days with rain total the number of days in the three months?
  $$58 + 34 = 31 + 30 + 31 \ \checkmark$$

During October through December, 58 days did not have rain.

28   *Chapter 1*

Class Exercises

For each problem, answer the following questions.
a. What number or numbers does the problem ask for?
b. Are enough facts given? If not, what else is needed?
c. Are unneeded facts given? If so, what are they?
d. What operation or operations would you use to find the answer?

1. Kevin completed the bicycle race in 2 h 24 min, Lori completed the race in 2 h 13 min, and Helen completed the race in 2 h 54 min. How much faster than Kevin's time was Lori's time?

2. Steve bought 1 lb of Swiss cheese, 12 oz of mild cheddar cheese, and 6 oz of sharp cheddar cheese. How much cheese did he buy in all?

3. Elise bought a record for $5.69, another record for $4.88, and a record cleaning kit for $12.75. How much more than the cost of the records was the cost of the kit?

4. The eighth-grade classes are holding a hobbies and crafts fair on Saturday. Maurice plans to help out at the stamp-collecting booth from 9 A.M. to 11 A.M. and at the model-airplane booth from 2 P.M. to 5 P.M. How many hours does he plan to spend helping?

Problems

Solve, using the five-step plan.

A 1. Mimi is buying weather-stripping tape for some windows. How much should she buy for a window that needs 4.85 m, a window that needs 4.25 m, and a window that needs 2.55 m? 11.65 m

2. A package of 2 paintbrushes is on sale for $2.40. How much will 3 packages cost? $7.20

3. Irene Lanata pays $235.40 each month to repay her automobile loan. How much will she pay in one year? $2824.80

4. On its fifth orbit, the space shuttle *Freedom* was as close as 110 mi from Earth and as far away as 180 mi from Earth. By how many miles do these distances differ? 70 mi

5. Hill School plans to buy 4 computers for each of 12 classrooms. The cost of each computer is $865. What will the total cost be? $41,520

6. An 8 mm camera shoots 24 frames of film each second. How many frames will it shoot in 5 min? 7200 frames

Introduction to Algebra **29**

Suggested Assignments

Minimum
Day 1: 29/Prob. 1–6
      30/Prob. 7–10
Day 2: 30/Prob. 11–14
      31/Prob. 15
      31/Self-Test B

Average
Day 1: 29/Prob. 1–6
      30/Prob. 7–14
Day 2: 31/Prob. 15–17
      31/Self-Test B

Maximum
Day 1: 29/Prob. 1–6
      30/Prob. 7–14
Day 2: 31/Prob. 15–17
      31/Self-Test B

Supplementary Materials

Practice Masters, p. 6
Test 1B, pp. 5–6
Computer Activity 1
Computer Activity 2

Quick Quiz B

Write a variable expression for the word phrase.

1. Eight more than a number t $t + 8$

2. The quotient of 15 divided by a number c

   $15 \div c$

3. Seven less than three times a number a

   $3a - 7$

4. Eighteen less than the product of nine and a number n $9n - 18$

(Continue on next page.)

30

Solve, using the five-step plan.

7. There are 38 rows with 2 dozen seats each in the Little Theater. An additional 24 people are allowed to stand during a performance. What is the total number of people that can attend a performance? 936 people

8. Yesterday it took Jeff Holland 1 h to get to work. This morning, Jeff drove to the train station in 20 min, waited for the train for 7 min, rode the train for 12 min, and then walked for 15 min to get to work. How long did it take Jeff to get to work this morning? 54 min

9. Roy paid $81.88 for a new jacket and sweater. He then exchanged the sweater, which cost $23.00, for another sweater that cost $19.99. What was the final cost for Roy's jacket and sweater? $78.87

10. The information on a bag of High-Pro dog food states that a dog weighing 50 pounds should eat 3 cups of food each day and a dog weighing 20 pounds should eat 1.5 cups each day. How much food should 3 dogs, each weighing 50 pounds, eat in one day? 9 cups of food

B 11. Tickets for the drama club's performance last weekend cost $2.50 for adults and $2.00 for students. Four hundred twenty adults attended the performance, and 273 students attended. What was the total amount of money collected from tickets for the performance last weekend? $1596

12. On September 1, City Auto had an inventory of 220 Firefly station wagons and 317 Firefly sedans. On October 1, the inventory was 108 Firefly station wagons and 192 Firefly sedans. How many more sedans than station wagons were sold? 13 sedans

13. First-class tickets on flight 107 to Los Angeles cost $482, tourist-class tickets cost $324, and economy-class tickets cost $212. Today 41 economy-class passengers, 237 tourist-class passengers, and 8 first-class passengers were on the flight. What was the total cost of the tickets for passengers on the flight? $89,336

14. Sarah Holness had her car tuned up for $60 and she purchased 4 new tires for $37 each. She gave the cashier 11 twenty-dollar bills. How much change did Sarah receive? $12

30   *Chapter 1*

15. Gregory ordered the following items from the Huntington Gardens catalog: a watering can for $15.80, a trowel for $4.49, and 6 packages of seeds for $.75 each. He must add $2.50 for shipping charges. He has 2 coupons, each allowing him to deduct $2.00 from his order. How much will Gregory pay for the order? $23.29

C **16.** Joy and David Kramer had $30 to spend on dinner, a movie, and parking. Dinner cost $15.50 and parking cost $4. The Kramers had $2 left after paying for everything. What was the cost of one movie ticket? $4.25

17. The museum charges $4.50 per person for a 2 h tour with fewer than 20 people. If 20 or more people take the tour, the charge is $3.75 per person. Of the 23 people in today's tour, 17 had paid $4.50 in advance. How much money will the museum return as a refund? $12.75

Self-Test B

Write a variable expression for the word phrase.

1. Twelve divided by a number y $12 \div y$ [1-6]

2. Five less than a number x $x - 5$

3. The difference when twenty-one is subtracted from the product of nine and a number g $9g - 21$

Write an equation or inequality for the word sentence.

4. Fifteen is the sum of nine and twice a number x. $15 = 9 + 2x$ [1-7]

5. Twenty-five times the sum of a number b and 7 is greater than eleven divided by four. $25(b + 7) > 11 \div 4$

6. When the product of four and a number is subtracted from twenty-four, the result is less than or equal to twelve. $24 - 4n \leq 12$

Solve, using the five-step plan.

7. Laura bought a hammer for $12.95, 5 lb of nails for $5.20, and 8   [1-8] sheets of plywood for $12 each. What was her total bill? $114.15

8. Between the hours of 6 A.M. and 9 P.M., 8 buses that were filled to capacity left the terminal. Since the capacity of each bus is the same and 392 tickets were sold, how many passengers were on each bus?
49 passengers

Self-Test answers and Extra Practice are at the back of the book.

Introduction to Algebra   **31**

Write an equation or inequality for the word sentence.

5. The sum of a number x and seventeen is more than 41. $x + 17 > 41$

6. Nine more than the product of a number and six is thirty-three.

$6n + 9 = 33$

7. The quotient when the product of four and a number t is divided by five is greater than eight.

$4t \div 5 > 8$

8. The sum of twice a number and sixteen is the same as the product of four and the number.

$2n + 16 = 4n$

Solve, using the five-step plan.

9. Lisa bought a shirt for $13.95, a sweater for $17.50, and three pairs of socks for $2.25 each. What was the total cost?

$38.20

10. For the senior trip, the buses cost $850 and other charges totaled $481. All but 5 of the 126 seniors went, and agreed to share costs equally. How much did each senior who went pay? $11

11. In Taxamaxa, real estate is taxed at $1.20 per $100 of assessed value. The assessed value is half the market value. The Millers bought their house in 1973, and it now has a market value of $95,000. How much do they pay in taxes this year? $570

Enrichment Note
The technical developments that made it possible for computers to become smaller, cheaper, and more powerful included the transistor and the integrated circuit. If you have access to these components or vacuum tubes, you might want to show them to the students. A mainframe sounds very large, but some are not much larger than a teacher's desk.

The speeds at which computers operate are, for the most part, inconceivable to humans. These times are measured in

milliseconds $\left(\frac{1}{1000}\text{s}\right)$,

microseconds $\left(\frac{1}{1,000,000}\text{s}\right)$,

nanoseconds $\left(\frac{1}{1,000,000,000}\text{s}\right)$,

and picoseconds

$\left(\frac{1}{1,000,000,000,000}\text{s}\right)$.

The Development of Computers

The development of the modern computer began in 1946 with the completion of the ENIAC computer. It weighed 30 tons, contained 18,000 vacuum tubes and 6000 switches, and filled a room 30 feet by 50 feet. Since that time computers have become steadily more compact, powerful, and inexpensive.

Today's large computer systems, called **mainframes,** can process large amounts of data at very fast speeds. **Minicomputers** are smaller and somewhat slower, meeting the needs of colleges and small businesses at lower cost. The smallest of today's computers, such as the computer shown in the photo above, are the **microcomputers.** These computers are often called personal computers because they are inexpensive enough and small enough to go into classrooms and homes. The processing unit of these small computers is the **microprocessor,** a one-quarter-inch-square integrated circuit chip. This tiny chip is more powerful than the ENIAC with its 18,000 vacuum tubes.

The microprocessor controls the microcomputer and performs arithmetic operations. But other parts are needed to make the computer a useful tool. The computer has two kinds of **memory. ROM** (read only memory) permanently stores information needed for the computer to work properly. It cannot be changed by the user. **RAM** (random access memory) is available to the user and can store the user's programs and data. Memory size is measured in **bytes** or K. One K is about 1000 bytes. Each byte can store one character (letter or digit), so an 8K memory can store about 8000 typed characters.

32 *Chapter 1*

The **keyboard** is used to input programs and data, and the **CRT** screen displays input, results, and graphics. A **disk drive** can be used to read programs and data into the computer from a disk, or to save programs on disk. A **printer** will save output in printed form. A **modem** can connect you to a network of other computers over your telephone line.

As computers have evolved, people have invented programming languages to help users program the computer to solve problems. Some of the more common languages are **BASIC,** which is available on almost all microcomputers, **FORTRAN,** often used for scientific problem solving, and **COBOL,** a business-oriented language. **Pascal** and **Logo** are two languages finding increasing application in education.

The development of computers has opened many new careers. Systems analysts use computers to analyze and solve problems for business and government. Programmers write the programs, or software, that help users apply the computer to their needs. Installation and maintenance of a computer's physical components, or hardware, are done by field engineers.

1. The fastest modern computers can do 100 million arithmetic operations in a second. Estimate how long it would take you to do this many additions. Suppose you are adding two four-digit numbers each time. Answers will vary.

2. Each byte of memory will hold one typed character. About how many K of memory would it take to store these two pages? A disk for a microcomputer holds 160 K. About how many pages of this book could you store on one disk? 3 K; 107 pages

3. Ask your librarian to help you find out about the Mark I, IBM 360, and UNIVAC 1 computers. Find out about the size of each computer, the number of its components, its purpose, its inventors.

4. The computer language ADA was named after Ada Byron Lovelace (1815–1852). See what you can find out about Ada Lovelace and the computer language.

Career Activity

Look in the Help Wanted section of a newspaper and make a list of the job openings for systems analysts and programmers. Include in your list education requirements, what computers or computer languages the candidate should be familiar with, and the salary range.

In Exercise 1 on page 33, the speed mentioned, 100 million arithmetic operations in a second, is the same as 10 nanoseconds per operation. To give some meaning to these time units, give the following comparisons.

1. A millisecond is to a second as a penny is to a $10 bill.

2. A microsecond is to a second as half an hour is to an average human life.

3. A nanosecond is to a second as $1\frac{1}{2}$ inches are to the distance around Earth at the equator.

4. A picosecond is to a second as a $1 bill is to the annual U.S. gross national product.

If students are familiar with binary numbers, you might point out that a byte, typically, is an eight-digit binary number. There are 256 possible combinations of eight 0's and 1's, so 256 distinct bytes are possible. Each of these 256 combinations can represent a letter of the alphabet or other character.

Introduction to Algebra **33**

Chapter Review

Match.

1. 22×8 **B**

2. $52.6 - 9.95$ **D**

A. 32   **B.** 176   [1–1]

3. $9 \times (3 + 1) - 4$ **A**

4. $\dfrac{4 + (6 \times 2 \times 3)}{(14 - 12)5}$ **C**

C. 4   **D.** 42.65   [1–2]

Is the equation or inequality true or false for the given value of the variable?

5. $9y = 108$; $y = 12$ True

6. $k \div 4 = 28$; $k = 7$ False

7. $6g + 2 = 20$; $g = 3$ True   [1–3]

8. $a \geq 18$; $a = 14$ False

9. $5x > 15$; $x = 5$ True

10. $r - 24 \leq 12$; $r = 30$ True   [1–4]

True or false?

11. If $k + 5 = 140$, $k = 140 - 5$. True

12. If $p \div 21 < 14$, $p < 21 - 14$. False   [1–5]

13. If $9b = 162$, $b = 162 \div 9$. True

14. If $t - 87 \leq 87$, $t \leq 87 - 87$. False

Match.

15. Six more than a number x **B**

A. $\dfrac{x}{6} - 9$ [1–6]

16. The difference when nine is subtracted from the quotient of a number x divided by six **A**

B. $x + 6$

17. Nine less than the product of six and a number x is twice the number x. **D**

C. $9(x + 6) < 2 \times 6$

D. $6x - 9 = 2x$ [1–7]

18. The product of nine and the sum of a number x plus six is less than the product of two and six. **C**

Write the letter of the correct answer.

19. Julia Carmona hired 3 people to landscape her yard. They each received the same hourly rate and it took them 5 h to do the job. If her bill was $60, how much did each person earn an hour? **d**   [1–8]

   a. $6   **b.** $12   **c.** $3   **d.** $4

20. The ski resort has 5 beginners' trails. Two of them are 1.1 km long, 2 others are 2.8 km long, and 1 trail is 4.5 km long. How many kilometers of trails are available for beginners? **c**

   a. 12.1 km   **b.** 11.2 km   **c.** 12.3 km   **d.** 9.5 km

Chapter Test

Evaluate the expression when $a = 4$ and $b = 12$.

1. $91 + a$ 95   **2.** $27 - b - a$ 11   **3.** $5b$ 60   **4.** $36 \div a \div b$ 0.75   [1–1]

Evaluate the expression when $m = 14$ and $n = 16$.

5. $n - 4 \times 3$ 4   **6.** $3 \times \frac{m}{7}$ 6   **7.** $2mn - 9$ **8.** $(m + n) \div 3$ 10   [1–2]

                                                                   439

Find the solution or solutions for the given replacement set.

9. $d - 9 = 27$; $\{3, 18, 35\}$ No solution   **10.** $14r = 70$; $\{3, 4, 5\}$ 5   [1–3]

11. $9(x + 4) = 63$; $\{1, 2, 3\}$ 3   **12.** $3k + 1 = 13$; $\{4, 5, 6\}$ 4

Find the solutions of the inequality. The replacement set for t is the set of whole numbers.

13. $t \le 9$ **14.** $7 < t$ **15.** $3 \le t \le 8$ **16.** $12 > t$ [1–4]
0, 1, 2, . . . , 9   8, 9, 10, and so on   3, 4, 5, 6, 7, 8   0, 1, 2, . . . , 11

Use the inverse operation to write a related equation or inequality and solve for the variable.

                                          $b \ge 44 \times 9$;
                                 all the numbers greater

17. $6g = 72$ $g = 72 \div 6$;   **18.** $b \div 9 \ge 44$ **19.** $3f - 1 = 53$ [1–5[
            12   **than or equal to 396** $3f = 53 + 1$;
                                                     $f = 54 \div 3$;

Write a variable expression for the word phrase.   18

20. The quotient of a number divided by seven $n \div 7$ [1–6]

21. Twenty added to the product of a number and ten $20 + 10n$

Write an equation or inequality for the word sentence.

22. The sum of fourteen and a number l is greater than thirty. $14 + l > 30$ [1–7]

23. Two less than the product of a number k and three equals four.

                                            $3k - 2 = 4$

Solve, using the five-step plan.

24. The tickets for the theater cost $7.50 each. Miles bought 4 of them   [1–8]
and gave the cashier a fifty dollar bill. What was the cost of the
tickets? $30

25. There are 120 students in each of the freshman and junior classes.
There are 20 more sophomores than juniors and 15 fewer seniors
than sophomores. What is the total number of students in the four
classes? 505 students

Cumulative Review

Exercises

Simplify.

1. $28 + 781$ 809

2. $630 - 52.1$ 577.9

3. $65.1 \div 21$ 3.1

4. 1.2×3.64 4.368

5. $48 + 303.9$ 351.9

6. 0.042×0.8 0.0336

7. $3(14 - 5)$ 27

8. $(6 + 3) \div 9$ 1

9. $4 \times 5 + 5$ 25

10. $16 - 2 \times 3 - 1$ 9

11. $(8 + 2) \div (12 - 7)$ 2

12. $(14 + 36) \times (54 - 8)$ 2300

Evaluate the expression when $p = 7$ and $q = 8$.

13. $4q + 23$ 55

14. $3q - 6$ 18

15. $p + q \div 5$ 8.6

16. $pq - 6$ 50

17. $28 \div (q - p)$ 28

18. $p(13 - 9)q$ 224

Find the solution or solutions of the equation for the given replacement set.

19. $k + 16 = 23$; $\{5, 6, 7\}$ 7

20. $58 - d = 31$; $\{39, 38, 37\}$ No solution

21. $7x - 1 = 20$; $\{1, 2, 3\}$ 3

22. $8(y - 3) = 32$; $\{7, 8, 9\}$ 7

23. $5a = 2a + 57$; $\{19, 20, 21\}$ 19

24. $(c + 6) \div 6 = 1$; $\{0, 1, 2\}$ 0

Find the solution of the inequality. The replacement set for x is the set of whole numbers.

25. $x > 12$ 13, 14, 15, and so on

26. $2 \geq x$ 0, 1, 2

27. $x < 9$ 0, 1, 2, . . . , 8

28. $3 < x < 5$ 4

29. $12 \geq x \geq 8$ 8, 9, 10, 11, 12

30. $15 \leq x \leq 20$ 15, 16, 17, 18, 19, 20

Use inverse operations to solve.

31. $18 + g = 20$ $g = 20 - 18$; 2

32. $a \div 9 = 18$ $a = 18 \times 9$; 162

33. $5z < 65$ $z < 65 \div 5$; all the numbers less than 13

34. $20d + 8 = 68$ $20d = 68 - 8$; $d = 60 \div 20$; 3

35. $7f - 1 \leq 13$ $7f \leq 13 + 1$; $f \leq 14 \div 7$; all the numbers less than or equal to 2

36. $3h + 2 \geq 26$ $3h \geq 26 - 2$; $h \geq 24 \div 3$; all the numbers greater than or equal to 8

Write a variable expression for the word phrase.

37. A number t decreased by thirty-one $t - 31$

38. The quotient when a number m is divided by eighty-three $m \div 83$

39. Four more than the product of two and a number k $4 + 2k$

40. The product of twelve and the sum of a number b and six $12(b + 6)$

Write an equation or inequality for the word sentence.

41. Fifteen less than a number is twenty-four. $n - 15 = 24$

42. Twenty increased by the product of a number y and eight is sixty.
$20 + 8y = 60$

43. The difference when three is subtracted from the product of a number and two is nine. $2n - 3 = 9$

44. Forty-five more than a number is less than fifty-one. $45 + n < 51$

Problems

Problem Solving Reminders

Here are some reminders that may help you solve some of the problems on this page.

- Determine which facts are necessary to solve the problem.
- Supply additional information if needed.
- Consider whether drawing a sketch will help.

---

1. Jeanne can type 45 words each minute and Brian can type 68 words each minute. What is the combined number of words they can type in 1 h? **6780 words**

2. Martin bought 0.8 kg of bananas at $.55 a kilogram, 1.5 kg of tomatoes at $1.54 a kilogram, and 18 oranges for $1.77. How much did he spend? **$4.52**

3. Nine crew teams will attend the annual regatta. Each team consists of eight members and a coxswain. If each person on a team is to receive a certificate, how many certificates need to be ordered?
81 certificates

4. A car can go 600 km on 1 tank of gas. How many kilometers can it go on 2.5 tanks of gas? **1500 km**

5. In an opinion survey concerning breakfast drinks, 398 people preferred orange juice, 275 people preferred grapefruit juice, and 88 people liked both juices equally. How many of the people interviewed liked at least one kind of juice? **761 people**

6. A chemist has 558 mL of a solution and needs to prepare samples of it. If each sample must contain 23.25 mL, how many samples can be prepared? **24 samples**

7. A swimming pool is 24 m by 18 m. If you swim its length 3 times, how far will you swim? **72 m**

Introduction to Algebra **37**

2

The Decimal System

Astronomers and some other scientists deal with extremely large or small numbers. Their work is greatly simplified by the use of exponents, which you will learn about in this chapter.

Using radio telescopes like the one pictured, astronomers can "see" far beyond the distances possible with optical telescopes. Radio waves can go through interstellar dust clouds that light cannot. Many objects in space give off radio waves. Quasars, for example, look like ordinary stars but are very strong radio sources. They are actually much brighter than stars and very far away. One quasar may be ten billion light years away and ten thousand times as bright as all the stars in our galaxy put together.

Career Note

Astronomers are scientists who study objects in space. To become an astronomer, you need a strong background in advanced mathematics as well as training in the sciences. Astronomy is a difficult but rewarding field of research, in which you often read reports of new discoveries and may sometimes present your own. Some astronomers combine teaching with their careers in research.

Lesson Commentary
Chapter 2 The Decimal System

Overview

This chapter begins with a careful study of exponential numbers and especially the importance of powers of 10 in our number system. Students will learn to round decimal numbers and to use rounding to estimate answers to challenging problems. Basic properties of addition and multiplication are introduced and applied to decimal numbers.

Students will simplify numerical and algebraic expressions that involve exponents, decimals, and correct usage of the order of operations. Applying what they have learned, students will solve problems using the plan for solving word problems learned in Chapter 1.

DECIMALS

2-1 Exponents

Objective *for pages 40–43*

■ To read, write, and simplify exponential expressions.

Teaching Suggestions

Emphasize that 5^3 means 5 used as a factor three times, *not* 5 multiplied by itself three times. Show that 5^3 actually involves just two multiplications. Also, be certain that students do not think

$$5^3 \text{ means } 5 \times 3.$$

The product 5×3 means

$$5 + 5 + 5.$$

Another way to explain 7^0 is to show that if 7^2 means 7 is used as a factor two times, then 7^0 means 7 is used as a factor zero times or not at all. Remind students that one is a factor of every number and thus, $7^0 = 1$.

Remind students that $4n$ means 4 times n, where n is a variable and can represent any number assigned to it. Any letter of the alphabet can be used as a variable, but

o and l are avoided since they could be confused with zero and one. In this section x is not used as a variable because $\times$ is used to indicate multiplication.

Related Activities

To help students in future computations, challenge them to memorize the squares and cubes of the whole numbers 2 through 10 and the squares of the whole numbers 11 through 25.

To provide a preview of the use of exponents in algebraic expressions, ask students to find the missing base or bases in problems such as these:

$$a^2 - (7 \times 3^2) = 1 \qquad b^3 + c^2 = 17$$

Resource Book: Page 19 (Use After Page 43)

NAME _____ DATE _____

CALCULATOR — For use after Lesson 2-1
Estimating Roots

Use your calculator to find each missing root to the nearest whole number.

1. $x^3 = 38$ $x = \underline{3}$
2. $x^3 = 187$ $x = \underline{6}$
3. $x^3 = 514$ $x = \underline{8}$
4. $x^3 = 1479$ $x = \underline{11}$
5. $x^3 = 3456$ $x = \underline{15}$
6. $x^3 = 26{,}015$ $x = \underline{30}$
7. $x^3 = 73{,}420$ $x = \underline{42}$
8. $x^3 = 113{,}902$ $x = \underline{48}$
9. $x^3 = 239{,}017$ $x = \underline{62}$
10. $x^3 = 503{,}466$ $x = \underline{80}$
11. $x^3 = 1{,}000{,}634$ $x = \underline{100}$
12. $x^4 = 7342$ $x = \underline{9}$
13. $x^5 = 183{,}105$ $x = \underline{11}$
14. $x^6 = 341{,}264$ $x = \underline{8}$
15. $x^7 = 811{,}243$ $x = \underline{7}$

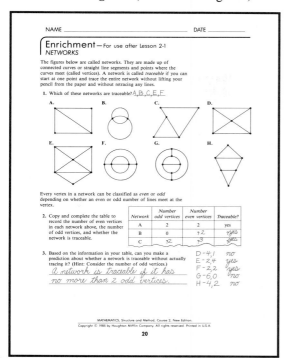

Related Activities

To relate mathematics to another subject, discuss the proper placement of library books using the Dewey decimal system and card catalogs.

To compare different number systems, have students investigate the binary system. It should interest them because of its use with computers.

Resource Book: Page 21 (Use After Page 47)

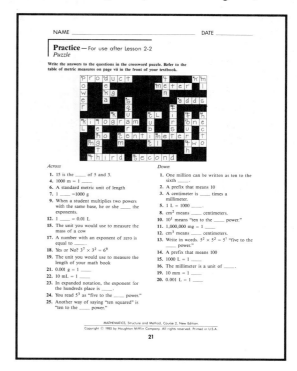

2-2 The Decimal System

Objective for pages 44–47

■ To read, write, and order decimal numbers.

Teaching Suggestions

Explain to students that our numbers are called decimal numbers because they are based on powers of ten and not because they have a decimal point. For example, 342 is a decimal number even though the decimal point is not shown.

Have students read decimal numbers aloud, especially numbers with zeros such as 807.0405. Insist that students say "eight hundred seven *AND* four hundred five ten thousandths." Point out that the word *and* is used only once in the correct reading.

A zero should always be placed in front of the decimal point if the value of the number is less than one.

2-3 Rounding

Objectives for pages 48–50

■ To round decimal numbers.
■ To use rounding to estimate an answer.

Teaching Suggestions

Students have probably learned rounding in an earlier grade. If they have not completely mastered the skill you may want to present more examples.

For example, round 14.862 to the nearest:

ten	tenth	hundredth
14.862	14.862	14.862
^	^	^
10	14.9	14.86
$14.862 \approx 10$	$14.862 \approx 14.9$	$14.862 \approx 14.86$

Be sure that students focus on the digit immediately to the right of the place to which they are rounding. When rounding to the nearest tenth, for example, students often round 0.749 incorrectly to 0.8 instead of 0.7 because they round 0.749 to 0.75 and then to 0.8.

Rounding or approximating numbers is a valuable skill to use when checking computations, particularly when placement of decimal points is a problem for students. For example, will the product of 6.82×4.7 be 3205.4? 320.54? 32.054? Since $6.82 \approx 7$ and $4.7 \approx 5$, 6.82×4.7 must be approximately 7×5 or 35. Thus, 32.054 is the most reasonable answer.

Resource Book: Page 22 (Use After Page 50)

Related Activities

To help students prepare for standardized tests, show how rounding can speed their work. For example:

Multiply: 12.2×6.21
a. 7.5762　　**b.** 75.762　　**c.** 757.62

Approximation would show the correct choice, 75.762, without actual computation.

OPERATIONS WITH DECIMALS

2-4 Basic Properties

Objective *for pages 51–55*

■ To use the properties of addition and multiplication.

Teaching Suggestions

To help students understand the words *commutative, associative,* and *distributive,* ask students what it means to "commute to work or school." What does it mean to belong to an "association" or to "associate with certain people"? Point out that when you ask a student to "distribute worksheets," this means the student is to give a worksheet to *each* student in the room.

Students may ask about $0 \div 0$. Explain that $0 \div 0$ has many possible answers. The sentence

$$0 \times \underline{\ ?\ } = 0$$

has infinitely many solutions. Such problems are said to be not well defined.

Emphasize the use of the basic properties to simplify expressions. This is covered in more detail in Section 2-5.

Related Activities

To relate mathematics to students' lives, show how they can use the distributive property to do calculations in their heads. For example,

if one pen costs 89¢, how much do six cost?

This problem is easier if you think,

$$89 = 90 - 1.$$

2-5 Simplifying Expressions

Objective for pages 56–58

■ To simplify an expression.

Teaching Suggestions

Review the importance of using the order of operations correctly. For example, in Example 1 point out that

$$[1.8 \div 10 + 4] = [0.18 + 4].$$

When students simplify expressions, encourage them to work vertically with one step under another. You may even want them to write the name of the property used in each step. For example,

$3a + 11 + 4a$
$3a + 4a + 11$ Commutative Property of Addition
$(3 + 4)a + 11$ Distributive Property
$7a + 11$

To discuss like terms, you may need to show students that $3a + 4a$ means

$$(a + a + a) + (a + a + a + a)$$

for a total of seven a's.

Prove to students that $3a$ and $5c$ are unlike terms by using substitution in a problem involving $3a + 5c$. Show that if $a = 2$ and $c = 4$, then $3a + 5c$ means

$$3 \times 2 + 5 \times 4 = 6 + 20 = 26.$$

If students think $3a + 5c = 8ac$, then show that $8 \times 2 \times 4 = 64$, not 26. Explain also that when different variables are used, this usually means to choose different values of the variable. Two expressions are equal only if *every* value substituted yields a true statement.

Related Activities

To provide a change of pace, give students a string of digits such as

1 2 3 4 5 6 7 8 9

or   5 5 5 5 5 5 5 5 5 5.

Challenge them to place grouping and operation symbols in as many ways as possible to give the expression different values.

2-6 Solving and Checking Problems

Objective for pages 59–63

■ To solve and check a word problem.

Teaching Suggestions

You may want to review the plan for solving word problems on page 27. As you go through the examples, show how to follow the steps, organize the facts, and plan a solution.

Ask which basic property is used in Example 2, Method 2. (It is the distributive property.) Ask which method students prefer. Emphasize that there may be more than one "right way" to solve a problem.

Related Activities

To relate mathematics to students' lives, have each student write five practical problems that use decimals. Let each student choose one to illustrate, with the solution on the reverse side of the paper. Post these on the bulletin board for other students to see and work.

NAME _____ DATE _____

Problem Solving—For use after Lesson 2-6
Too Much Information—Choosing the Necessary Facts

Some problems supply too much information. Some facts are not necessary in the solution of the problem. It is important to choose only the facts that are necessary to solve the problem.

EXAMPLE	SOLUTION
Ten children attend a day-care center in both the morning and afternoon. Five children come only for the morning session and five only for the afternoon session. Six other children attend after 3 P.M. only. How many children are in the center at 4 P.M.?	The fact that five children attend only in the morning is not needed to answer the question: How many attend at 4 P.M.? The total attendance at 4 P.M. is 10 + 5 + 6 = 21 children.

Cross out the unnecessary fact(s).
Use only the facts needed to solve each problem.

1. The Neils took a 528 mi trip and averaged 32 mi/gal. If the trip took 12 h, what was their average rate of speed?   *44 mph*

2. Attendance at a Single Parents Group meeting for five consecutive months was 28, 32, 35, 26, and 30. The average attendance was 30 members per meeting. If each member uses 2 cups for beverages per meeting, will 300 cups be enough for 5 meetings?   *no, 302 cups*

3. Forty-nine people can be seated on a city bus. Twenty-six passengers got on at the first stop and half as many got on at the second stop, where 12 passengers got off. At the third stop, twice the number of passengers that got on at the second stop, got off, and none got on. How many people got on the bus at the 3 stops?   *39*

4. A van leaving Vancouver for Montreal travels at a rate of 88 km/h. At the same time another van leaves Montreal for Vancouver and travels at a rate of 50 km/h. When the two vans meet, which one will be nearer to Montreal?   *They're both the same distance from Montreal when they met.*

5. On a 4-h 57-min flight from Hartford, Conn. to Phoenix, Ariz., a plane stops for 21 min in St. Louis, Mo. If the plane takes off from Hartford at 9:32 A.M. EST (Eastern Standard Time), at what time (EST) does it land in Phoenix?   *2:29 PM*

6. Stamped postcard invitations to a party cost 13¢ each. A package of 12 party invitations costs $12.50 and postage costs 20¢ each. How much does Damian have to spend to send 30 postcard invitations?   *$3.90*

MATHEMATICS, Structure and Method, Course 2, New Edition.
Copyright © 1985 by Houghton Mifflin Company. All rights reserved. Printed in U.S.A.

23

NAME _____ DATE _____

Problem Solving—For use after Lesson 2-6
Working Backwards

In some problems, you are given the final result of a situation and you must determine the conditions leading up to that result. Working backwards is then the appropriate strategy.

EXAMPLE

Jug A contains more cider than jug B. You perform the following:

(1) Pour from A into B as much cider as B already contains.

(2) Pour from B into A as much cider as A now contains.

(3) Pour from A into B as much cider as B now contains.

Both jugs now have 64 L. How many liters were in each jug at the beginning?

SOLUTION

Begin with the end result. Pour in reverse.

A = 64   B = 64

(3) Pour half of B's cider from B to A.
$\frac{1}{2}$ of 64 = 32
A = 64 + 32 = 96   B = 64 − 32 = 32

(2) Pour from A into B half of A's cider.
$\frac{1}{2}$ of 96 = 48
A = 96 − 48 = 48   B = 32 + 48 = 80

(1) Pour from B into A half of B's cider.
$\frac{1}{2}$ of 80 = 40
A = 48 + 40 = 88   B = 80 − 40 = 40

A had 88 L and B had 40 L at the beginning.

Solve each problem by working backwards.

1. If you were to continue the number pattern as shown at the right, what number would you put in the square with the star? Don't fill in all the numbers to find out!   *75—Figure out where the last number will be and count backwards.*

2. In the year 2013, Claire will go to a 50th-year college reunion. If Claire was 20 when she graduated from college, how old was she in 1983?   *40*

3. Three players play 4 rounds of a game and end up with a tie score of 80. A different player wins each round. When that player wins, he doubles his points. The two losers each subtract the amount the winner adds from their scores. What were the scores at the end of the first round?   *Scores are: 190, 150, 90*

Player	Rounds 1	2	3	*=winner 4
A	190	100	40*	80
B	150	60*	120	80
C	90*	180	120	80

MATHEMATICS, Structure and Method, Course 2, New Edition.
Copyright © 1985 by Houghton Mifflin Company. All rights reserved. Printed in U.S.A.

24

NAME _____ DATE _____

Quiz 2B—Lessons 2-4 through 2-6

DIRECTIONS: Write the letter of the correct answer in the space provided.

Use the properties of addition and multiplication to simplify the expression.

1. 3(11 − 7) + 8 × 5   *[2-4]*
   a. 66   b. 20   c. 52   d. 100

2. (18 × 7) + (6 × 7) − 18
   a. 294   b. 150   c. 49   d. 168

3. (23.4 × 9) − (5.4 × 9) + 2
   a. 198   b. 162   c. 164   d. 261.2

4. (14.7 × 1) + (6.3 × 0) + (18.4 + 0) − 0.53
   a. 32.57   b. 38.87   c. 33.43   d. 39.4

5. 3(84 ÷ 4) − 3(68 ÷ 4)
   a. 63   b. 12   c. 51   d. 114

Simplify the expression.

6. (13.8 − 3²)5   7. $\frac{30 \div 3 + 12}{(42 \div 6) + 4 - 1}$ *[2-5]*
   a. 583.2   b. $\frac{2}{11}$ c. 2   d. 24

8. (3m + 8)3 + 2m   9. (2m + 3)6 + (9 + m)2m
   a. 5m + 24   b. 2m² + 30m + 18   c. 11m + 24   d. 32m + 18

Evaluate the expression when f = 3, g = 2.06, and h = 1.2.

10. 3g + h²   11. [3f − 2(g − h)]f
   a. 7.62   b. 18.06   c. 20.58   d. 21.84

Solve.

12. Phillip earns $8.50 for mowing a lawn. Last week he mowed 9 lawns. This week he earned $\frac{2}{3}$ as much as last week. How much did he earn this week?   *[2-6]*
   a. $76.50   b. $51.00   c. $25.50   d. $153.00

ANSWERS		
1.	*c*	(6)
2.	*b*	(6)
3.	*c*	(6)
4.	*a*	(6)
5.	*b*	(6)
6.	*d*	(10)
7.	*c*	(10)
8.	*c*	(10)
9.	*a*	(10)
10.	*b*	(10)
11.	*d*	(10)
12.	*b*	(10)

MATHEMATICS, Structure and Method, Course 2, New Edition.
Copyright © 1985 by Houghton Mifflin Company. All rights reserved. Printed in U.S.A.

25

NAME _____ DATE _____

Review—Chapter 2

Simplify the expressions.

1. 5⁴   *625*   2. 3² + 4³   *73*   3. (3 × 2)²   *36*   *[2-1]*
4. (4 + 6)⁰   *1*   5. (6 + 4)¹   *10*   6. 3² × 2²   *36*

Evaluate the expression if r = 2, s = 7, and t = 4.

7. 3s²   *147*   8. (5r)³   *1000*   9. 4ᵗ + 4ʳ   *272*

Replace _____ with the symbols =, >, or < to make a true statement.

10. 3⁴   *>*   4³   11. 6 × 2   *<*   6²   *[2-2]*
12. (4 × 5)²   *>*   2 × 4 × 5   13. 58.4   *>*   58.392
14. 0.0629   *<*   0.063   15. 4.3 + 9.8   *=*   14.10

Round to the place specified.

16. hundreds: 746.368   *700*   17. tenths: 37.947   *37.9*   *[2-3]*
18. tens: 35.753   *40*   19. thousandths: 3.45795   *3.458*

Use the properties of addition and multiplication to simplify the expression.

20. (25 × 6) + (25 × 14)   *500*   21. (3 + 7)5 + (6 +9)8   *170*   *[2-4]*
22. 6(64 ÷ 4) + 6(56 ÷ 4)   *180*   23. [(176 ÷ 4) ÷ 2]5   *110*

What value of the variable makes the statement true?

24. 7p = 7   *p = 1*   25. 7.43 × 0 = b   *b = 0*   *[2-2]*
26. 7(12 + 5) = (m × 12) + (m × 5)   *m = 7*   27. (3.2 + 4)6 = (3.2t) + (4t)   *t = 6*

Simplify the expression.

28. 16 + 3² + 4 × 2³   *57*   29. $\frac{(60 + 10) + 12}{(20 + 4) - 8}$ *6*   *[2-5]*
30. (10p²)(3p³) + 5   *30p⁵ + 5*   31. (4 + 6a)3 + a(7 + 2)   *12 + 27a*

Solve.

32. Ellen Chin purchased 5 yards of fabric at $3.98 a yard, 3 spools of thread costing 4 for $1.00, and a pattern costing $1.75. How much change did she receive from $25.00?   *$2.60*   *[2-6]*

33. Matthew Gold enlarges his vegetable garden so that its new dimensions are three times its original dimensions. If the new dimensions are 176.4 cm by 240.6 cm, what were the original dimensions?   *58.8 by 80.2*

MATHEMATICS, Structure and Method, Course 2, New Edition.
Copyright © 1985 by Houghton Mifflin Company. All rights reserved. Printed in U.S.A.

26

Resource Book: Pages 27–30 (Use After Page 63)

Test —Chapter 2

NAME _____ DATE _____

DIRECTIONS: Write the correct answer in the space provided.

Which is greater?

1. 6^2 or 2^6 2. $(3 + 5)^3$ or $(3 \times 5)^2$ [2-1]

Write as a single power of the given base.

3. $5^2 \times 5^6$ 5. $m^1 \times m^4$

Evaluate the expression if $a = 3$, $b = 7$, and $c = 2$.

5. a^3 6. $3b + 2c$ 7. $(2 + a)^c$

Write the number in expanded form.

8. 102   9. 0.378   [2-2]

Use the symbol < to order the numbers from least to greatest.

10. 3.2, 3.32, 3.023   11. 0.063, 0.06, 0.105

Round to the place specified.

12. hundreds: 3742.876   13. tenths: 724.463   [2-3]

What value of the variable makes the statement true?

14. $17p = 17$ [2-4]

15. $6(8 + 3) = (k \times 8) + (k \times 3)$

16. $4(10.2 + 25) = 40.8 + x$

17. $(3.86 + 2.14)1 = r$

Simplify the expression.

18. $[8^2 \div (3 + 1)] \div 2$ 19. $3a(a + 5) + 2(1 + 3a)$ [2-5]

20. $1.3 + 7.2n + 5.3 - 2.8n$

Solve and check your answer.

21. Danny bought 2 shirts for $14.89 each, a belt for $5.50, and 3 sweaters for $19.98 each. What was the total cost of his purchases?   [2-6]

22. Bea opened her piggy bank and found 28 pennies, 35 nickels, 49 dimes, 18 quarters, and 27 one-dollar bills. How much money did she have?

ANSWERS

1. 2^6 (4)
2. $(3 + 5)^3$ (4)
3. 5^8 (4)
4. m^5 (4)
5. 27 (5)
6. 25 (5)
7. 25 (5)
8. $(1 \times 100) + 2$ (4)
9. $(3 \times 0.1) + (7 \times 0.01) + (8 \times 0.001)$ (4)
10. $3.023 < 3.2$ (4)
11. $0.06 < 0.063 < 0.105$ (4)
12. 3700 (4)
13. 724.5 (4)
14. $p = 1$ (4)
15. $k = 6$ (5)
16. $x = 100$ (5)
17. $r = 6$ (5)
18. 8 (5)
19. $3a^2 + 21a + 2$ (5)
20. $6.6 + 4.4n$ (5)
21. $45.22 (5)
22. $38.43 (5)

27

Make-up Test —Chapter 2

NAME _____ DATE _____

DIRECTIONS: Write the correct answer in the space provided.

Which is greater?

1. 5^2 or 2^5 2. $(2 + 6)^3$ or $(2 \times 6)^2$ [2-1]

Write as a single power of the given base.

3. $8^3 \times 8^2$ 4. $f^3 \times f^1$

Evaluate the expression if $r = 8$, $s = 6$, and $t = 2$.

5. $2s - r$ 6. s^t 7. $(r + s)^t$

Write the decimal in expanded form.

8. 307   9. 0.058   [2-2]

Use the symbol < to order the numbers from least to greatest.

10. 0.304, 0.032, 0.037   11. 8.54, 8.06, 8.5

Round to the place specified.

12. tens: 734.872   13. hundredths: 365.283   [2-3]

What value of the variable makes the statement true?

14. $(3.2 + 5) + 9.8 = 13 + d$ 15. $14r = 14$ [2-4]

16. $(2 + 7)3 = (2 \times f) + (7 \times f)$ 17. $(3.87 + 7.43)1 = w$

Simplify the expression.

18. $3[(4.2 - 3.1)g + 4.8]$ 19. $(8.5 + 3^2)9$ [2-5]

20. $4.8 + 3.4m + 2.7 + 1.6m$

Solve and check your answer.

21. Martin Lane bought an art canvas costing $3.85, 4 tubes of oil paints for $1.15 each, an easel for $14.50, and 5 brushes costing 95¢ each. What was the total cost of his art supplies?   [2-6]

22. Marie, Amy, and Kim baby-sit. Last week, Kim earned $7.50 more than Marie, and Amy earned twice as much as Kim. If Marie earned $12.80, how much did Amy and Marie earn?

ANSWERS

1. 2^5 (4)
2. $(2 + 6)^3$ (4)
3. 8^5 (4)
4. f^4 (4)
5. 4 (5)
6. 36 (5)
7. 196 (5)
8. $(3 \times 100) + 7$ (4)
9. $(5 \times 0.01) + (8 \times 0.001)$ (4)
10. $0.032 < 0.037$ (4)
11. $8.06 < 8.5$ (4)
12. < 8.54 (4)
13. 730 (4)
14. 365.28 (4)
15. $d = 5$ (5)
16. $r = 1$ (5)
17. $g = 3$ (5)
18. $w = 113$ (5)
19. $33g + 14.4$ (5)
20. 157.5 (5)
21. $5m + 7.5$ (5)
22. $27.70 (5)
23. Kim = $20.30, Amy = $40.60 (5)

28

CUMULATIVE REVIEW —Chapters 1–2

Exercises

NAME _____ DATE _____

Evaluate the expression using the given values of the variables.

1. $r + s$; $r = 3.8$, $s = 5.8$ 9.6   2. $4a - b$; $a = 7.3$, $b = 8$ 21.2

3. $\frac{c}{d} - 2$; $c = 12$, $d = 0.6$ 18   4. $\frac{f}{3} + g$; $f = 15$, $g = 1.8$ 6.8

5. $3k^2 + 7l$; $k = 4$, $l = 1.3$ 57.1   6. $n - m$; $n = 28.4$, $m = 4$ 7.1

Evaluate the expression when $f = 3.8$, $g = 10$, and $h = 5.4$.

7. $fg - h$ 32.6   8. $gh + f$ 57.8   9. $2h + 5(g - f)$ 41.8

10. $(f + h)(g + h)$ 141.68   11. $3/hg$ 615.6   12. $5f + 6h$ 51.4

13. $(h + f) \div g$ 0.92   14. $6(h + 11.6)$ 102   15. $\frac{24 - h}{f + 2.2}$ 3.1

Use inverse operations to solve the equation.

16. $r + 14 = 108$ $r = 94$ 17. $d - 27 = 85$ $d = 112$ 18. $8m + 5 = 61$ $m = 7$

Use < to order the numbers from least to greatest.

19. 7, 15, 11 $7 < 11 < 15$ 20. 2.3, 1.9, 2.25 $1.9 < 2.25 < 2.3$ 21. 43, 33, 23 $23 < 33 < 43$

22. 3^2, 4^2, 3^3 $3^2 < 4^2 < 3^3$ 23. 3^2, 3^2, 4^0 $4^0 < 3^2 < 3^2$ 24. 5^3, 6^2, 2^5 $2^5 < 6^2 < 5^3$

Select the most reasonable estimated answer.

25. $37.4 - 8.73$ a. 14   b. 33   c. 28   c
26. 76.74×9.6 a. 770   b. 700   c. 680   a
27. $12.3 + 17.8 + 7.93$ a. 45   b. 30   c. 37   c
28. $152.43 - 17.8$ a. 140   b. 134   c. 128   b
29. $278.8 \div 19.8$ a. 140   b. 14   c. 20   b

True or false?

30. $(54 - 45) = (45 - 54)$ F   31. $47.5 \times 1 = 47.5$ T
32. $63.7 \times 0 = 63.7$ F   33. $15(3 + 6) = 15 \times 3 + 15 \times 2$ F
34. $17.4 - (5 + 3) = (17.4 - 5) + 3$ F   35. $18 + (10 \div 2) = (18 + 10) \div 2$ F
36. $(7 + 6)3 = 7 \times 3 + 6 \times 3$ T   37. $(25.3 + 6.25) = (6.25 + 25.3)$ T
38. $30 \div 5 + 1 = 30 \div (5 + 1)$ F

29

CUMULATIVE REVIEW —Chapters 1–2 (continued)

Problems

NAME _____ DATE _____

Problem Solving Reminders

Here are some reminders that may help you solve some of the problems on this page.
- Determine which facts are necessary to solve the problem.
- Supply additional information if needed.
- Check by using rounding to find an estimated answer.
- If more than one method can be used to solve a problem, use one method to solve and the other to check.

Solve.

1. Carlos and Bill delivered newspapers together, earning a total of $18.00 each week. After sharing their earnings for sixteen weeks, Martin joined them, and the earnings were divided three ways. How much did Carlos earn for 50 weeks? $348

2. Pistachio nuts cost $1.80 for 2 oz, $7.00 for $\frac{1}{2}$ lb, and $12.00 for a pound. What is the cost of each ounce if you buy a pound? How much do you save per ounce if you buy a pound?   75¢, 15¢

3. Hearty Chicken Soup is on sale for 3 cans for 99¢. How much is saved by buying a dozen cans of soup at the sale price? $1.54

4. Bart Kahn ordered a crystal fruit bowl as a gift at a cost of $47.50. The additional costs included $2.85 for tax, $1.25 for a gift box, and $3.95 for shipping. What was the total price of the order? $55.55

5. Speedy Cleanser costs 49¢ for an 8-oz can and 89¢ for a 15-oz can. How much change will you receive if you buy 15 larger-size cans of cleanser and pay with a $20 bill? $6.65

6. A membership to the Finley Art Museum costs $42 per year and includes a subscription to a monthly magazine. If the magazine costs $2.50 an issue, what are the annual dues for membership alone? $12.00

7. House numerals that are 3 in. high cost $2.00 each. Numerals that are 5 in. high cost $6.00 each. How much will it cost to buy numerals that are 5 in. high for your house if your address is 2742 Colonial Drive? $24.00

8. The February electric bill was $132.40, which was twice as much as the January bill. The March electric bill was $25.00 higher than the January bill. What was the total cost of electricity for January, February, and March? $289.80

30

Teaching Suggestions p. 39a

Related Activities p. 39a

Reading Mathematics

Students will learn the meaning of the following mathematical terms in this lesson: *factor, base, exponent, power, square, cube.*

Chalkboard Examples

Simplify.

1. 3^3 **27**
2. 2^4 **16**
3. $3^2 \times 2^4$ **144**
4. $3^2 + 2^4$ **25**
5. Write $9^4 \times 9^3$ as a single power of 9. **9^7**
6. Evaluate $3m^2n$ if $m = 2$ and $n = 5$. **60**

2-1 Exponents

When two or more numbers are multiplied, these numbers are called **factors** of the product. For example,

$$\underline{5 \times 8} = 40 \quad \text{and} \quad \underline{3 \times 7} = 21.$$
$$\text{factors} \qquad\qquad \text{factors}$$

When one factor is used a number of times, we may use an *exponent* to simplify the notation, as shown in the following example.

$$125 = \underbrace{5 \times 5 \times 5}_{\text{equal factors}} = 5^3$$

The expression 5^3 is read *5 cubed,* or *5 to the third power,* where 5 is the **base** and 3 is the **exponent.**

Since 125 is the product of three factors of 5, we say that 125 is *the third power of 5.* Examples of other bases and exponents are listed below.

$15 = 15^1$	*15 to the first power*
$36 = 6 \times 6 = 6^2$	*6 squared,* or *6 to the second power*
$64 = 4 \times 4 \times 4 = 4^3$	*4 cubed,* or *4 to the third power*
$16 = 2 \times 2 \times 2 \times 2 = 2^4$	*2 to the fourth power*

EXAMPLE 1 Express 81 as a power of 3.

Solution $81 = 3 \times 3 \times 3 \times 3$
$$= 3^4$$

EXAMPLE 2 Simplify the expression $2^3 \times 5^2$.

Solution $2^3 = 2 \times 2 \times 2 = 8 \qquad 5^2 = 5 \times 5 = 25$
$$2^3 \times 5^2 = 8 \times 25 = 200$$

Can we give an expression such as 7^0 a meaning? When the powers of any base are listed in order, we may recognize a pattern. Study the example at the top of the next page.

40 *Chapter 2*

$$7^4 = 7 \times 7 \times 7 \times 7 = 2401$$
$$7^3 = 7 \times 7 \times 7 = 343$$
$$7^2 = 7 \times 7 = 49$$
$$7^1 = 7$$

Notice that in increasing order each power of 7 is seven times the preceding power. Conversely, in decreasing order, each power of 7 is the quotient of the preceding power divided by a factor of 7. That is, $7^3 = 7^4 \div 7$, $7^2 = 7^3 \div 7$, and so on. This decreasing pattern suggests that 7^0 (read *7 to the zero power*) is $7^1 \div 7$. Study the example below to verify that the expression $7^0 = 1$.

$$7^0 = 7^1 \div 7 = 7 \div 7 = 1$$

In general,

Definition

For every number a ($a \neq 0$), $a^0 = 1$.

If an expression contains powers of the same base, the expression may be written as a single power of that base. For example, $13^2 \times 13^3$ can be written as a single power of 13.

$$13^2 \times 13^3 = (13 \times 13) \times (13 \times 13 \times 13)$$
$$= 13 \times 13 \times 13 \times 13 \times 13$$
$$= 13^5$$

Notice that the exponent in the product is the sum of the exponents in the factors, that is, $2 + 3 = 5$.

In general,

Rule

For every number a ($a \neq 0$) and all whole numbers m and n,

$$a^m \times a^n = a^{m+n}$$

Notice that the bases must be the same.

EXAMPLE 3 Write $15^3 \times 15^4$ as a single power of 15.

Solution $\qquad 15^3 \times 15^4 = 15^{3+4} = 15^7$

EXAMPLE 4 Evaluate the expression if $n = 3$.

$\qquad$ **a.** n^2 $\qquad$ **b.** $4n^2$ $\qquad$ **c.** $(4n)^2$ $\qquad$ **d.** $n^2 \times n^2$

Solution $\qquad$ Replace n with 3 in each expression and simplify.

$\qquad$ **a.** $n^2 = 3^2 = 3 \times 3 = 9$

$\qquad$ **b.** $4n^2 = 4(3^2) = 4 \times 9 = 36$

$\qquad$ **c.** $(4n)^2 = (4 \times 3)^2 = 12^2 = 12 \times 12 = 144$

$\qquad$ **d.** $n^2 \times n^2 = n^{2+2} = n^4 = 3^4 = 3 \times 3 \times 3 \times 3 = 81$

Notice in parts (b) and (c) of Example 4 how grouping symbols change the values of expressions that have the same numbers.

Reading Mathematics: *Study Helps*

Look back at this lesson. Notice that the information in the blue boxes on page 41 summarizes important ideas from the lesson. The first box gives a definition and the second box states a rule. Both are applied in the examples. Throughout the book, boxes are used to help you identify important definitions, rules, properties, facts, and formulas. Use them as reminders when you do the exercises and when you review the lesson.

1. "4 to the fifth power"
2. "9 to the first power, or 9"
3. "15 squared, or 15 to the second power"
4. "3 to the seventh power"
5. "10 cubed, or 10 to the third power"
6. "2 to the eighth power"

Class Exercises

Read each expression.

1. 4^5 $\qquad$ **2.** 9^1 $\qquad$ **3.** 15^2 $\qquad$ **4.** 3^7 $\qquad$ **5.** 10^3 $\qquad$ **6.** 2^8

Write using exponents.

7. 9 to the third power 9^3 $\qquad$ **8.** 15 cubed 15^3 $\qquad$ **9.** 4 squared 4^2

10. 6 to the fifth power 6^5 $\qquad\qquad$ **11.** 216 is the third power of 6. $6^3 = 216$

Express the number as a power of 3.

12. 9 3^2 $\qquad$ **13.** 27 3^3 $\qquad$ **14.** 3 3^1 $\qquad$ **15.** 243 3^5 $\qquad$ **16.** 1 3^0

Simplify the expression.

17. 8^2 64 $\qquad$ **18.** 2^3 8 $\qquad$ **19.** 1^{11} 1 $\qquad$ **20.** 18^0 1 $\qquad$ **21.** 83^1 83

Written Exercises

Simplify the expression.

A **1.** 2^6 **64** **2.** 5^4 **625** **3.** 10^2 **100** **4.** 6^3 **216** **5.** 14^1 **14**

6. $3^2 + 5^2$ **34** **7.** $(3 \times 5)^2$ **225** **8.** $2^4 + 3^2$ **25** **9.** $(5 + 12)^0$ **1** **10.** $(5 + 12)^1$
17

Which is greater?

11. 2^3 or 3^2 **3²** **12.** 5^2 or 2^5 **2⁵** **13.** 9×2 or 9^2 **9²**

14. 3×10 or 10^3 **10³** **15.** $(16 \times 4)^2$ or $2 \times 16 \times 4$ **16.** $(10 + 2)^0$ or $10 + 2$
$(16 \times 4)^2$ **10 + 2**

Write as a single power of the given base.

17. $2^3 \times 2^4$ **2⁷** **18.** $3^2 \times 3^5$ **3⁷** **19.** 10×10^4 **10⁵** **20.** $5^5 \times 5^6$ **5¹¹** **21.** $n^3 \times n^8$
n^{11}

Evaluate the expression if $m = 5$, $n = 3$, and $p = 2$.

22. p^2 **4** **23.** $4m^2$ **100** **24.** $(9n)^2$ **729** **25.** $9n^2$ **81** **26.** n^0 **1**

27. $(8n)^2$ **576** **28.** np^0 **3** **29.** $(mn)^0$ **1** **30.** $m^3 - n^3$ **98** **31.** $5m^3n$ **1875**

B **32.** $(7n)^n$ **9261** **33.** $(3m)^p$ **225** **34.** $6^m \times 6^n$ **35.** $(8 + m)^{n-3}$ **1** **36.** $(15^n)^{p-1}$
1,679,616 **3375**
52
37. $p^n m^n$ **1000** **38.** $(7 + n^m)^n$ **39.** np^m **96** **40.** $(p^m p^n) + 4$ **260** **41.** $m^p + n^n$
15,625,000
42. $(m^p)^n$ **43.** $(m - n)^p$ **4** **44.** $\dfrac{m^n}{m^p}$ **5** **45.** $\dfrac{3p^n}{6p^m}$ **$\frac{1}{8}$** **46.** $\dfrac{(m-1)^{n+1}}{p}$
15,625 **128**

C **47.** Find a value of n such that $(5 + 2)^n = 5^n + 2^n$. **$n = 1$**

48. Is the equation true?
    a. $4^4 \div 4^3 = 4^1$ **yes** **b.** $5^3 \div 5^1 = 5^2$ **yes** **c.** $2^7 \div 2^4 = 2^3$ **yes**
    d. Using your answers from parts (a)–(c), state a general rule to describe what appears to be true for division of powers of the same base. $\dfrac{a^m}{a^n} = a^{m-n}$

Review Exercises

Replace __?__ with $>$ or $<$ to make a true statement.

1. $19 \underline{\ ?\ }^< 24 \underline{\ ?\ }^< 31$ **2.** $84 \underline{\ ?\ }^> 79 \underline{\ ?\ }^> 66$

3. $56 \underline{\ ?\ }^> 49 \underline{\ ?\ }^> 41$ **4.** $20 \underline{\ ?\ }^< 40 \underline{\ ?\ }^< 50$

5. $81 \underline{\ ?\ }^> 46 \underline{\ ?\ }^> 17$ **6.** $37 \underline{\ ?\ }^> 33 \underline{\ ?\ }^> 30$

7. $28 \underline{\ ?\ }^< 67 \underline{\ ?\ }^< 82$ **8.** $44 \underline{\ ?\ }^< 91 \underline{\ ?\ }^< 99$

The Decimal System **43**

Reading Mathematics

Students will learn the meaning of the following mathematical terms in this lesson: *decimal system, value, place value, decimal number, decimal, expanded form.*

2-2 The Decimal System

Our number system uses the powers of 10 to express all numbers. This system is called the **decimal system** (from the Latin word *decem,* meaning *ten*). Using the digits 0, 1, 2, . . . , 9, we can write any number. The **value** of each digit depends on the position of the digit in the number. For example, the 2 in 312 means 2 ones, but the 2 in 298 means 2 hundreds. The decimal system is a system with **place value.**

The chart below shows place values for some of the digits of a **decimal number,** or **decimal.**

Place-value Chart

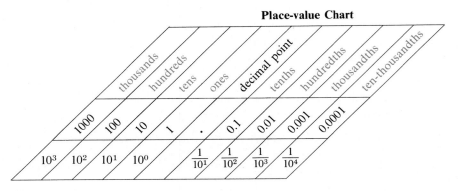

Moving left to right, place values decrease. As illustrated in the examples below, each place value is one tenth, or 0.1, of the place value to its left.

$$1000 \times 0.1 = 100 \qquad 10 \times 0.1 = 1 \qquad 0.01 \times 0.1 = 0.001$$

We can see from the place-value chart that values to the left of the decimal point are greater than or equal to 1, while values to the right are less than 1.

When a decimal number is written, the value of the number is the sum of the values of the digits. To illustrate this, we can write decimal numbers in **expanded form,** that is, as a sum of products of each digit and its place value.

EXAMPLE 1 Write the decimal in expanded form.

a. 3053   **b.** 16.9   **c.** 0.074

Solution

a. $3053 = (3 \times 1000) + (5 \times 10) + 3$

b. $16.9 = (1 \times 10) + 6 + (9 \times 0.1)$

c. $0.074 = (7 \times 0.01) + (4 \times 0.001)$

44   *Chapter 2*

Recall that zeros can be added at the right of a decimal in the following manner without changing the value of the number.

$$1.039 = 1.0390 = 1.03900$$

We will need to use this fact when we compare decimals.

When comparing two decimals, we compare their place values. For example, 382 is greater than 97.5 because its first digit is in the hundreds' place and the first digit of 97.5 is in the tens' place.

When we compare 6.5142 and 6.5187, the first place from the left in which the numbers differ is the thousandths' place. Because the value of 4 thousandths is less than the value of 8 thousandths, 6.5142 is less than 6.5187.

382
97.5
6.5142
6.5187

EXAMPLE 2 Replace __?__ with $>$ or $<$ to make a true statement.

a. 97,486 __?__ 305,472   b. 130 __?__ 7.42   c. 0.59 __?__ 0.592

Solution

a. Reading from left to right, the first digit in 305,472 is in the hundred-thousands' place, while the first digit in 97,486 is in the ten-thousands' place. Thus 97,486 $<$ 305,472.

b. The first digit in 130 is in the hundreds' place, while the first digit in 7.42 is in the ones' place. Thus 130 $>$ 7.42.

c. We write 0.59 as 0.590 and see that the first place in which the digits differ is the thousandths' place. Zero is less than 2, so 0.59 $<$ 0.592.

EXAMPLE 3 Use the symbol $<$ to order the numbers from least to greatest.

1.038, 1.036, 1.0045

Solution Using place value to order the numbers from least to greatest, we have the following.

$$1.0045 < 1.036 < 1.038$$

Class Exercises

1. "five thousand, four hundred, ninety-six"
2. "fifty-one hundredths"
3. "twenty-eight and seven tenths"
4. "three hundred, seventeen ten-thousandths"
5. "Eight and twenty-six thousandths"

Read the number.

1. 5496   2. 0.51   3. 28.7   4. 0.0317   5. 8.026

Name the value of the digit 6 in the number.

6. 657.3 600   7. 0.062 0.06   8. 8.1416 0.0006   9. 6.023 6   10. 408.6 0.6

The Decimal System **45**

Chalkboard Examples

Read.

1. 472.34
2. 0.0452

Write as a decimal.

3. Eighty-three and fourteen hundredths **83.14**
4. Nine hundred thirty-four thousandths **0.934**

Write in expanded form.

5. 490 (4 × 100) + (9 × 10)
6. 5.623 5 + (6 × 0.1) + (2 × 0.01) + (3 × 0.001)

Replace __?__ with $>$ or $<$ to make a true statement.

7. 0.098 __?__ 0.01 **<**
8. 41.6 __?__ 40.9 **>**

Use the symbol $<$ to order the numbers from least to greatest.

9. 1.374, 1.089, 1.098 **1.089 < 1.098 < 1.374**
10. 0.153, 0.072, 0.058 **0.058 < 0.072 < 0.153**

Write as a decimal.

11. 255 thousandths
0.255

12. 4 and 11 hundredths
4.11

13. 307 ten-thousandths
0.0307

Replace __?__ with > or < to make a true statement.

14. 0.255 __?<__ 0.619

15. 4.11 __?>__ 0.0307

16. 194,763 __?>__ 78,241

Additional A Exercises

Write in expanded form.

1. 32.5 (3 × 10) +
2 + (5 × 0.1)

Write as a decimal.

2. (6 × 100) + (9 × 10) + 4
694

3. 22 and 3 hundredths
22.03

Replace __?__ with =, <, or > to make a true statement.

4. 33.3 __?__ 33.33
<

5. 0.02 __?__ 0.20
<

6. 4.16 × 7 __?__ 28
>

Written Exercises

Write the decimal in expanded form.

A **1.** 38 (3 × 10) + 8   **2.** 256 (2 × 100) + (5 × 10) + 6   **3.** 8091 (8 × 1000) + (9 × 10) + 1   **4.** 5 5   **5.** 0.47 (4 × 0.1) + (7 × 0.01)

6. 28.4 (2 × 10) + 8 + (4 × 0.1)   **7.** 0.063 (6 × 0.01) + (3 × 0.001)   **8.** 9.070 9 + (7 × 0.01)   **9.** 0.187 (1 × 0.1) + (8 × 0.01) + (7 × 0.001)   **10.** 5.5 5 + (5 × 0.1)

Write as a decimal.

11. (5 × 10) + 4 + (5 × 0.1) + (7 × 0.01) 54.57

12. (4 × 100) + (7 × 0.01) + (3 × 0.001) + (2 × 0.0001) 400.0732

13. (9 × 1000) + 2 + (1 × 0.1) + (4 × 0.01) + (6 × 0.001) 9002.146

14. (1 × 100) + (9 × 10) + 3 + (2 × 0.01) + (3 × 0.001) 193.023

Write as a decimal.

15. 7 and 43 hundredths 7.43

16. 11 and 4 tenths 11.4

17. 19 and 5 thousandths 19.005

18. 37 ten-thousandths 0.0037

19. 48 ten-thousandths 0.0048

20. 5 and 6 hundredths 5.06

21. 6 and 25 thousandths 6.025

22. 94 and 7 ten-thousandths 94.0007

Replace __?__ with =, >, or < to make a true statement.

23. 32.41 __?<__ 324.1

24. 65.7 __?>__ 6.57

25. 0.086 __?>__ 0.0798

26. 6.308 __?<__ 6.312

27. 87.06 __?>__ 87.009

28. 0.0208 __?<__ 0.208

29. 92.077 __?>__ 92.07

30. 0.002 __?<__ 0.01

31. 0.135 __?<__ 1.035

32. 43 __?<__ 17 + 28

33. 0.06 __?<__ 0.038 + 0.052

34. 3.62 − 2.91 __?=__ 0.71

35. 59.81 − 42.65 __?>__ 16.16

36. 2.14 × 0.8 __?<__ 2

37. 43.472 __?=__ 8.36 × 5.2

38. 81.9 ÷ 9 __?>__ 9

39. 2.68 __?=__ 13.4 ÷ 5

B **40.** $57.4 + 32.8$ _?_ $=108.64 - 18.44$ **41.** $94.76 - 51.36$ _?_ $>83.97 - 65.14$

42. $176 \div 5$ _?_ $>85.49 - 63.24$ **43.** 6.13×0.2 _?_ $=6.13 \div 5$

Use $<$ to order the numbers from least to greatest.

44. 1.28, 1.09, 1.42 $1.09 < 1.28 < 1.42$ **45.** 3.97, 3.16, 3.08 $3.08 < 3.16 < 3.97$

46. 62.08, 62.1, 62.9 $62.08 < 62.1 < 62.9$ **47.** 0.07, 0.2, 0.08 $0.07 < 0.08 < 0.2$

48. 0.188, 0.029, 0.04 $0.029 < 0.04 < 0.188$ **49.** 7.028, 7.11, 7.0862
$7.028 < 7.0862 < 7.11$

50. 3×1.65, 3×2.1, 3×1.2806 $3 \times 1.2806 < 3 \times 1.65 < 3 \times 2.1$

51. $0.27 + 0.81$, $0.406 + 0.215$, $1.62 + 0.09$ $0.406 + 0.215 < 0.27 + 0.81 < 1.62 + 0.09$

52. 2×0.86, 5×1.24, 10×0.09 $10 \times 0.09 < 2 \times 0.86 < 5 \times 1.24$

53. $(5 \times 10^3) + (2 \times 10^2) + (8 \times 10^1) + (0 \times 10^0)$ **54.** $(6 \times 10^1) + (4 \times 10^0) + \left(7 \times \dfrac{1}{10^1}\right)$

Write in expanded form using exponents by writing each number as a sum of multiples of powers of 10.

55. $(1 \times 10^2) + (8 \times 10^1) + (3 \times 10^0) + \left(0 \times \dfrac{1}{10^1}\right) + \left(8 \times \dfrac{1}{10^2}\right)$

1000	100	10	1	.	0.1	0.01	0.001
10^3	10^2	10^1	10^0	and	$\dfrac{1}{10} = \dfrac{1}{10^1}$	$\dfrac{1}{100} = \dfrac{1}{10^2}$	$\dfrac{1}{1000} = \dfrac{1}{10^3}$

56. $\left(0 \times \dfrac{1}{10^1}\right) + \left(4 \times \dfrac{1}{10^2}\right) + \left(3 \times \dfrac{1}{10^3}\right)$ **57.** $\left(0 \times \dfrac{1}{10^1}\right) + \left(9 \times \dfrac{1}{10^2}\right) + \left(1 \times \dfrac{1}{10^3}\right)$

EXAMPLE   367.04

Solution $(3 \times 10^2) + (6 \times 10^1) + (7 \times 10^0) + \left(0 \times \dfrac{1}{10^1}\right) + \left(4 \times \dfrac{1}{10^2}\right)$

58. $(1 \times 10^1) + (2 \times 10^0) + \left(9 \times \dfrac{1}{10^1}\right) + \left(3 \times \dfrac{1}{10^2}\right) + \left(1 \times \dfrac{1}{10^3}\right)$

53. 5280   **54.** 64.7   **55.** 183.08   **56.** 0.043

57. 0.091   **58.** 12.931   **59.** 7.482   **60.** 0.806

61. 204.5   **62.** 0.306   **63.** 38.003   **64.** 10.009

59. $(7 \times 10^0) + \left(4 \times \dfrac{1}{10^1}\right) + \left(8 \times \dfrac{1}{10^2}\right) + \left(2 \times \dfrac{1}{10^3}\right)$ **60.** $\left(8 \times \dfrac{1}{10^1}\right) + \left(0 \times \dfrac{1}{10^2}\right) + \left(6 \times \dfrac{1}{10^3}\right)$

61. $(2 \times 10^2) + (0 \times 10^1) + (4 \times 10^0) + \left(5 \times \dfrac{1}{10^1}\right)$ **62.** $\left(3 \times \dfrac{1}{10^1}\right) + \left(0 \times \dfrac{1}{10^2}\right) + \left(6 \times \dfrac{1}{10^3}\right)$

Review Exercises   **63.** $(3 \times 10^1) + (8 \times 10^0) + \left(0 \times \dfrac{1}{10^1}\right) + \left(0 \times \dfrac{1}{10^2}\right) + \left(3 \times \dfrac{1}{10^3}\right)$

Simplify in your head. Write down the answer.

1. $30 + 20 + 40$ 90   **2.** 80×30 2400   **3.** $150 \div 30$ 5

4. $70 - 10 - 30$ 30   **5.** $110 + 30 + 70 + 40$ 250   **6.** $15 \times 10 \div 30$ 5

7. $420 \div 60 + 20$ 27   **8.** $40 \times 8 + 50$ 370   **9.** $100 \div 50 \div 10$ 0.2

64. $(1 \times 10^1) + (0 \times 10^0) + \left(0 \times \dfrac{1}{10^1}\right) + \left(0 \times \dfrac{1}{10^2}\right) + \left(9 \times \dfrac{1}{10^3}\right)$

The Decimal System   **47**

Suggested Assignments

Minimum
Day 1: 46/2–38 even
    47/44–49
Day 2: 46/1–39 odd
    47/53–57
    47/Rev. 1–9

Average
Day 1: 46/2–38 even
    47/40–49
Day 2: 46/1–39 odd
    47/50–59
    47/Rev. 2–8 even

Maximum
    46/2–38 even
    47/40–64 even

Supplementary Materials

Practice Masters, p. 8

2-3 Rounding

When we use an *approximation* for a number, we say that we are **rounding** the number. For example, suppose that a distance is 6.7 km. We know that 6.7 is between 6 and 7. If we round 6.7 to the nearest whole number, we say that the distance is about 7 km.

We can see that 6.7 is closer to 7 than to 6 by graphing 6.7 on the number line. First we divide the portion of the number line between 6 and 7 into ten equal parts. Then we graph 6.7 on the number line as shown.

Since 6.7 rounded to the nearest whole number is 7, we can write $6.7 \approx 7$. The symbol $\approx$ means *is approximately equal to*.

The rule for rounding decimal numbers can be stated as follows:

> **1.** Find the decimal place to which you wish to round, and mark it with a caret ($_\wedge$). Look at the digit to the right.
>
> **2.** If the digit to the right is 5 or greater, add 1 to the marked digit. If the digit to the right is less than 5, leave the marked digit unchanged.
>
> **3.** If the marked digit is to the left of the decimal point, replace each digit to the right of the marked place with "0," and drop all digits to the right of the decimal point.
> If the marked digit is to the right of the decimal point, drop all digits to the right of the marked place.

EXAMPLE 1   Round 16.0973 to the nearest

 a. ten   **b.** tenth   **c.** hundredth

Solution   **a.** 16.0973   **b.** 16.0973   **c.** 16.0973
                     $^\wedge$ $^\wedge$ $^\wedge$
              20   16.1   16.10

          $16.0973 \approx 20$ $16.0973 \approx 16.1$ $16.0973 \approx 16.10$

Rounding is often used as a quick check on calculations. In general, we **estimate** by rounding to the highest place value of the smaller number for all operations. As a result, our estimated answer should be reasonably close to the exact answer.

48   *Chapter 2*

EXAMPLE 2 Find an estimated answer for each operation.

	a. 386 $+\ 54$	**b.** 2.849 $-\ 0.154$	**c.** 32.9 $\times\ 8.7$	**d.** $12\overline{)253}$

Solution

a. $\begin{array}{r}386\\+\ 54\end{array} \longrightarrow \begin{array}{r}390\\+\ 50\\\hline 440\end{array}$

b. $\begin{array}{r}2.849\\-\ 0.154\end{array} \longrightarrow \begin{array}{r}2.8\\-\ 0.2\\\hline 2.6\end{array}$

c. $\begin{array}{r}32.9\\\times\ 8.7\end{array} \longrightarrow \begin{array}{r}33\\\times\ 9\\\hline 297\end{array}$

d. $12\overline{)253} \longrightarrow 10\overline{)250}^{\,25}$

Class Exercises

Round to the place underlined.

1. 8.0<u>3</u>9 8.04
2. 2<u>9</u>4.65 290
3. 7<u>5</u>,452 75,000
4. 1<u>0</u>.988 11
5. 0.9<u>9</u>6 1.00
6. 1.35<u>4</u>7 1.355
7. <u>3</u>19.84 300
8. 0.<u>3</u>828 0.4

Round to the highest place value.

9. 43 40
10. 127.14 100
11. 0.036 0.04
12. 0.8981 0.9
13. 1986 2000
14. 532.3 500
15. 0.073 0.07
16. 0.0249 0.02

Written Exercises

Round to the nearest ten.

A
1. 27.5149 30
2. 82.604 80
3. 293.4 290
4. 70.76 70
5. 648.01 650
6. 108.3 110
7. 159.62344 160
8. 97.23 100

Round to the nearest hundredth.

9. 72.459 72.46
10. 26.804 26.80
11. 0.0643 0.06
12. 12.395 12.40
13. 0.0103 0.01
14. 8.142 8.14
15. 18.1657 18.17
16. 0.70605 0.71

Round to the nearest thousandth.

17. 0.0006 0.001
18. 12.3568 12.357
19. 401.0904 401.090
20. 30.0317 30.032
21. 250.3407 250.341
22. 7.0063 7.006
23. 8.0995 8.100
24. 0.9996 1.000

The Decimal System **49**

Select the most reasonable estimated answer.

B **25.** 89.6 + 13.5 b   **a.** 90   **b.** 100   **c.** 70

26. 35 + 12 + 26 + 11 c   **a.** 70   **b.** 110   **c.** 90

27. 65.43 − 8.92 a   **a.** 56   **b.** 60   **c.** 90

28. 2196 − 924 a   **a.** 1300   **b.** 1000   **c.** 3100

29. 6.82 × 4.7 b   **a.** 24   **b.** 35   **c.** 28

30. 54 ÷ 2.5 c   **a.** 30   **b.** 20   **c.** 18

31. 36)$\overline{283}$ c   **a.** 10   **b.** 3   **c.** 7

32. 4.7 × 1.8 + 3.7 b   **a.** 7   **b.** 14   **c.** 32

Self-Test A

Simplify the expression.

1. 2^4 16   **2.** 8^3 512   **3.** 9^1 9   **4.** $5^2 \times 5^3$ 3125   **5.** $a^6 \times a^5$ a^{11} [2–1]

Replace __?__ with > or < to make a true statement.

6. 30.694 __?>__ 27.35   **7.** 0.024 __?>__ 0.017   **8.** 0.87 __?<__ 1.22   [2–2]

Round to the place specified.

9. tens: 84.307 80   **10.** hundredths: 3.176 3.18   **11.** hundreds: 293.84 300   [2–3]

Self-Test answers and Extra Practice are at the back of the book.

▮▮▮ | Calculator Key-In

Use a calculator to simplify the expressions.

1. $15^2 - 13^2$ and (15 + 13)(15 − 13) 56, 56

2. $47^2 - 21^2$ and (47 + 21)(47 − 21) 1768, 1768

3. $82^2 - 59^2$ and (82 + 59)(82 − 59) 3243, 3243

4. $104^2 - 76^2$ and (104 + 76)(104 − 76) 5040, 5040

Do you recognize a pattern? yes

Write two expressions that will result in the same pattern. Anything of the form $a^2 - b^2$, $(a + b)(a - b)$

50   *Chapter 2*

2-4 Basic Properties

Reading Mathematics

Students will learn the meaning of the following mathematical terms in this lesson: *commutative property, associative property, identity element, distributive property.*

When we work with decimals, we see that the properties of whole numbers apply to decimals as well.

Changing the order of the addends in a sum or the factors in a product does not change the sum or product. For example,

$$9.2 + 4.7 = 4.7 + 9.2 \qquad 3.5 \times 8.4 = 8.4 \times 3.5$$

Commutative Property

For all numbers a and b,

$$a + b = b + a \qquad \text{and} \qquad a \times b = b \times a$$

Changing the grouping of addends in a sum or of factors in a product does not change the sum or product. For example,

$5.6 + 0.8 + 11.2$	$4.1 \times 2.3 \times 7.2$
$(5.6 + 0.8) + 11.2 = 17.6$	$(4.1 \times 2.3) \times 7.2 = 67.896$
$5.6 + (0.8 + 11.2) = 17.6$	$4.1 \times (2.3 \times 7.2) = 67.896$

Associative Property

For all numbers a, b, and c,

$$(a + b) + c = a + (b + c)$$

$$\text{and} \qquad (a \times b) \times c = a \times (b \times c)$$

We can use these properties to find the easiest way to add or multiply a long list of numbers.

EXAMPLE 1 Use the properties to simplify the expression.
  a. $4.8 + 1.1 + 0.2 + 3.9 + 7$ **b.** $2 \times 6 \times 5 \times 3$

Solution One possible way to rearrange the numbers is shown.

  a. $\quad 4.8 + 1.1 + 0.2 + 3.9 + 7$ **b.** $\quad 2 \times 6 \times 5 \times 3$
      $(4.8 + 0.2) + (1.1 + 3.9) + 7$ $(2 \times 5) \times (6 \times 3)$
              $5 + 5 + 7$ 10×18
                  $10 + 7$ 180
                    17

Name the property illustrated.

1. $3.2 + 6.5 = 6.5 + 3.2$
   Commutative

2. $(4 + 7.3) + 2.1 = 4 + (7.3 + 2.1)$
   Associative

3. $6.4 \times 4.5 = 4.5 \times 6.4$
   Commutative

4. $2.6 + 0 = 2.6$ **Addition Property of Zero**

5. $(12.7 + 4) \times 3 = (12.7 \times 3) + (4 \times 3)$
   Distributive

6. $(7.8 \times 2) + (4.2 \times 2) = (7.8 + 4.2) \times 2$
   Distributive

Use the properties to simplify the expression. Name the property or properties used.

7. $12.8 \times 2 \times 50$ **1280; Associative Property**

8. $5.1 + 6.3 + 4.9$ **16.3; Commutative Property**

9. $37.5 \times 84.2 \times 0$ **0; Multiplication Property of Zero**

10. $(4.3 \times 3.7) + (4.3 \times 6.3)$ **43; Distributive Property**

What value of the variable makes the statement true?

11. $8 + 4 = r + 8$ **4**

12. $2.9 \times 5 = 5g$ **2.9**

13. $9(3 + 7) = 27 + t$ **63**

The numbers 0 and 1 are called the **identity elements** for addition and multiplication respectively. The word *identity* comes from the Latin word *idem,* which means *the same.* The result of adding 0 to a number or subtracting 0 from a number is the same as the original number. The result of multiplying a number by 1 or dividing a number by 1 is the same as the original number. Study the following examples.

$$4.53 + 0 = 4.53 \qquad 29.7 \times 1 = 29.7$$
$$4.53 - 0 = 4.53 \qquad 29.7 \div 1 = 29.7$$

Addition and Subtraction Properties of Zero

For every number a, $\qquad a + 0 = a \qquad a - 0 = a$

$\qquad\qquad\qquad\qquad\qquad 0 + a = a \qquad a - a = 0$

Multiplication and Division Properties of One

For every number a, $\qquad a \times 1 = a \qquad a \div 1 = a$

$\qquad\qquad\qquad\qquad\qquad 1 \times a = a \qquad a \div a = 1$

The product of any number and 0 is 0. Similarly, 0 divided by any number is 0.

$$3.784 \times 0 = 0 \qquad\qquad 0 \div 3.784 = 0$$

Can we divide by 0? Recall that multiplication and division are inverse operations. Thus, if we were to divide 3.784 by 0, we would have the following.

$$3.784 \div 0 = x \qquad\qquad 3.784 = x \times 0$$

We cannot accept the equation at the right because any number times 0 is 0. So it makes no sense to divide by 0.

Multiplication and Division Properties of Zero

For every number a,

$$a \times 0 = 0 \qquad \text{and} \qquad 0 \times a = 0$$

For every number a, $a \neq 0$,

$$0 \div a = 0$$

The distributive property is different from the other properties because it involves two operations. The example below illustrates how we
may distribute a multiplier over each term in an addition expression.

$$7 \times (8.2 + 1.8) \qquad (7 \times 8.2) + (7 \times 1.8)$$
$$7 \times 10 \qquad\qquad\qquad 57.4 + 12.6$$
$$70 \qquad\qquad\qquad\qquad 70$$

Therefore $7 \times (8.2 + 1.8) = (7 \times 8.2) + (7 \times 1.8)$.

We may also distribute a multiplier over each term in a subtraction
expression.

Distributive Property

For all numbers a, b, and c,

$$a \times (b + c) = (a \times b) + (a \times c)$$

$$a \times (b - c) = (a \times b) - (a \times c)$$

EXAMPLE 2 Use the distributive property to simplify the expression.
   a. $(4 + 6.2)5$ **b.** $(13 \times 2.7) - (13 \times 1.3)$

Solution **a.** $(4 + 6.2)5 = (4 \times 5) + (6.2 \times 5) = 20 + 31 = 51$

   b. $(13 \times 2.7) - (13 \times 1.3) = 13(2.7 - 1.3) = 13(1.4) = 18.2$

EXAMPLE 3 What value of the variable makes the statement true?
   a. $6 + 5 = 5 + m$ **b.** $3.7 \times 4 = 4t$ **c.** $3(14 + 20) = 42 + b$

Solution **a.** $6 + 5 = 5 + m$ **b.** $3.7 \times 4 = 4t$
   $6 + 5 = 5 + 6$, so $m = 6$ $3.7 \times 4 = 4 \times 3.7$, so $t = 3.7$

   c. $3(14 + 20) = 42 + b$
   $3(14 + 20) = (3 \times 14) + (3 \times 20) = 42 + 60$, so $b = 60$

Class Exercises

Name the property illustrated.

1. $7.6 + 0 = 0 + 7.6$ Commutative Prop.

2. $(19 \times 3)6.2 = 19(3 \times 6.2)$ Associative Prop.

3. $11.9 \times 1 = 11.9$ Multiplication Prop. of 1

4. $5(9 + 8.2) = (5 \times 9) + (5 \times 8.2)$ Distributive Prop.

5. $138.6 \times 7.4 = 7.4 \times 138.6$ Commutative Prop.

6. $6(1.2 + 0.8) = (1.2 + 0.8)6$ Commutative Prop.

Use the properties of addition and multiplication to simplify the expression. Name the property or properties used.

7. 0.4×0 0; Multiplication Prop. of 0   **8.** $3.02 \times 5 \times 2$ 30.2; Associative   **9.** 1×12.87 12.87; Multiplication Prop. of 1

10. $2.4 + 13 + 2.6$ 18; Commutative and Associative   **11.** $(8 \times 13) + (8 \times 7)$ 160; Distributive   **12.** 5.93×0 0; Multiplication Prop. of 0

What value of the variable makes the statement true?

13. $25 + 37 = m + 25$ 37   **14.** $(7 \times 6) + (5 \times 6) = (7 + 5)q$ 6

15. $(17 + 12) + 8 = b + (12 + 8)$ 17   **16.** $9(w - 20) = (9 \times 35) - (9 \times 20)$ 35

Additional A Exercises

Use the properties to simplify the expression. Name the property or properties used.

1. $25 \times 5 \times 4 \times 2$ 1000; Commutative Property

2. $7.3 \times 3.5 \times 9.4 \times 0$ 0; Multiplication Property of Zero

3. $(4 \times 17) + (4 \times 13)$ 120; Distributive Property

4. $3.8 + 4.6 + 5.4$ 13.8; Associative Property

True or false?

5. $13.736 \times 0 = 0$ True

6. $5 + (3 \times 7) = (5 + 3) \times (5 + 7)$ False

7. $6 + 7 + 4 + 3 = 10 + 10$ True

What value of the variable makes the statement true?

8. $3k = k$ 0

9. $4.8 \times 3.9 = 3.9g$ 4.8

10. $9(8 - 5) = 72 - m$ 45

Written Exercises

Use the properties to simplify the expression. Name the property or properties used.

A

1. $2.6 + 11.5 + 0.5$ 14.6; Associative   **2.** 0×23.15 0; Multiplication Prop. of 0

3. $4(2.5 + 1.06)$ 14.24; Distributive   **4.** $8(40 - 12)$ 224; Distributive

5. $7.24 + 8.97 + 2.76$ 18.97; Commutative and Associative   **6.** $(22 \times 8) + (22 \times 2)$ 220; Distributive

7. $0.5 \times 2.1 \times 0.2$ 0.21; Commutative and Associative   **8.** $4 \times 32 \times 5.25$ 672; Commutative and Associative

9. $15.3 \times 317 \times 0$ 0; Associative and Multiplication Prop. of 0   **10.** $11.5 + 2.6 + 0.5 + 0.4$ 15; Commutative and Associative

11. $(15.7 \times 6) - (3.7 \times 6)$ 72; Distributive   **12.** $(6 \times 1.3) + (6 \times 1.7)$ 18; Distributive

True or false?

13. $7.386 + 0 = 0$ False   **14.** $(3 + 12)6 = (3 \times 6) + (12 \times 6)$ True

15. $(19.7 + 36 + 41.5)0 = 0$ True   **16.** $15(2 + 7.4) = (15 + 2) \times (15 + 7.4)$ False

17. $3.84 + 6.73 + 3.77 + 2.1 = 3.84 + 10.5 + 21$ False

18. $9(15.1 - 6.3) = (9 \times 15.1) + (9 \times 6.3)$ False

What value of the variable makes the statement true?

19. $6 + n = 6$ $n = 0$ **20.** $7.02 \times 23 = t \times 7.02$ $t = 23$

21. $6.4 + t = 3.2 + 6.4$ $t = 3.2$ **22.** $3r = 3$ $r = 1$

23. $5w = w$ $w = 0$ **24.** $(6 + 4.03) + 0.97 = 6 + (x + 0.97)$ $x = 4.03$

25. $9(8 + 5) = (c \times 8) + (c \times 5)$ $c = 9$ **26.** $2.43 \times 0 = f$ $f = 0$

27. $(15.9 \times 3)4.2 = g(3 \times 4.2)$ $g = 15.9$ **28.** $(13 - 11.7)8 = (13 \times 8) - (r \times 8)$ $r = 11.7$

54   *Chapter 2*

29. $(2 + 4.8)3 = (2n) + (4.8n)$ $n = 3$ **30.** $(3.02 + 4.9)1 = b$ $b = 7.92$

31. $5(11.7 + 313) = 58.5 + d$ $d = 1565$ **32.** $(7 \times 1.2) + (7 \times 3.8) = 7m$ $m = 5$

33. $(8.31 + 2.73)t = t$ $t = 0$ **34.** $2.59 + 7.03 + 18.61 + 3.97 = a + 11$
$a = 21.2$

Use the properties to simplify the expression.

B **35.** $116 \times 3.7 \times 0 \times 4.93 \times 1.47 + 3.88$ 3.88

36. $(78 \times 1) + (1.36 \times 0) + (92 + 0)$ 170

37. $(18 + 46) + (12 + 4) + (8 \times 17) + (23 \times 8)$ 400

38. $(12 \times 7) + (56 \div 8) + (13 \times 12)$ 247

39. $5(81 \div 3) + 5(63 \div 1) + 450$ 900

40. $(18 + 9)4 + (12 + 11)4$ 200

Find values for *a*, *b*, and *c* that show that the equation is not true for all numbers. Answers will vary. Examples are given.

C **41.** $(a \times b) + (b \times c) = b(a \times c)$ $a = 1, b = 2, c = 3; (1 \times 2) + (2 \times 3) \neq 2(1 \times 3)$

42. $(a + b)(b + c) = b(a + c)$ $a = 2, b = 5, c = 1; (2 + 5)(5 + 1) \neq 5(2 + 1)$

43. $(b + c)(a + c) = c(b \times a)$ $a = 4, b = 6, c = 10; (6 + 10)(4 + 10) \neq 10(6 \times 4)$

Review Exercises

Evaluate the expression when $a = 7$ and $m = 9$.

1. $3 + a + 12 + m$ 31

2. $(63 \div a) + m$ 18

3. $(27 - a) + 6m$ 74

4. $95 - (am) + 12 - a$ 37

5. $(11m + 12a - 14) \div 13$ 13

6. $(am + 4m) \div 11m$ 1

7. $35 + (6a \div 21) + (m \div 3)$ 40

8. $m(a + 2a + 3a)$ 378

▮▮▮ **Challenge**

If k = age, the steps yield $[(4k + 2) \div 2] - k$, or (by distrib.
Start with your age in years. prop.) $2k + 1 - k$. This simplifies to $k + 1$, your age in 1
year.

1. Multiply by 4.

2. Add 2.

3. Divide by 2.

4. Subtract your age.

Your answer is your age one year from now! Can you explain?

The Decimal System **55**

Suggested Assignments

Minimum
Day 1: 54 / 1–18
Day 2: 54 / 19–28
55 / 29–40
55 / Rev. 1–8

Average
Day 1: 54 / 1–28
Day 2: 55 / 29–40
55 / Rev. 1–7 odd
55 / Challenge

Maximum
54 / 1–27 odd
55 / 29–33 odd; 35–43
55 / Challenge

Supplementary Materials

Practice Masters, p. 9

Reading Mathematics

Students will learn the meaning of the following mathematical terms in this lesson: *brackets, like terms, unlike terms.*

Chalkboard Examples

Simplify the expression.

1. $7 + 2^2$ **11**
2. $(7 + 2)^2$ **81**
3. $7 + 2 \times 7$ **21**
4. $3a + 6 + 2a$ **5a + 6**
5. $4(p + 3) + 2p$ **6p + 12**
6. $6(4p - 5)$ **24p - 30**

2-5 Simplifying Expressions

We have already seen how parentheses are used as grouping symbols in a mathematical expression. We may also use brackets, [ ], as grouping symbols. When more than one pair of grouping symbols are used, we perform the operation in the innermost pair of grouping symbols first. Then we work outward until the whole expression is simplified.

When an expression contains exponents, we simplify the terms containing the exponents before proceeding with the other operations.

EXAMPLE 1 Simplify the expression.

a. $[(5 - 3.2) \div (7.3 + 2.7) + 4]7$ **b.** $\dfrac{(4^2 - 15)3^2}{3^3 - (2 \times 12)}$

Solution **a.** $[(5 - 3.2) \div (7.3 + 2.7) + 4]7 = [1.8 \div 10 + 4]7$
$$= [0.18 + 4]7$$
$$= [4.18]7 = 29.26$$

b. $\dfrac{(4^2 - 15)3^2}{3^3 - (2 \times 12)} = \dfrac{(16 - 15)9}{27 - 24} = \dfrac{(1)9}{3} = \dfrac{9}{3} = 3$

In a variable expression such as

$$3a + 11 + 4a,$$

the terms $3a$ and $4a$ are called **like terms** because they differ only in their numerical coefficients. We can use the properties of addition and multiplication to simplify expressions with like terms. To simplify $3a + 11 + 4a$, we use the commutative and distributive properties.

$$3a + 11 + 4a = (3a + 4a) + 11$$
$$= (3 + 4)a + 11$$
$$= 7a + 11$$

The terms $7a$ and 11 cannot be combined because they are *unlike terms.* When an expression is in simplest form, it contains no like terms.

EXAMPLE 2 Simplify the expression.
a. $[(37 + 51)a + 5 + 7a]3$ **b.** $7m + 6(2 + 4m)$

Solution **a.** $[(37 + 51)a + 5 + 7a]3 = [88a + 5 + 7a]3$
$$= [(88a + 7a) + 5]3$$
$$= [(88 + 7)a + 5]3$$
$$= [95a + 5]3$$
$$= (95a \times 3) + (5 \times 3)$$
$$= 285a + 15$$

b. $7m + 6(2 + 4m) = 7m + (6 \times 2) + (6 \times 4m)$
$= 7m + 12 + 24m$
$= (7m + 24m) + 12$
$= (7 + 24)m + 12 = 31m + 12$

Additional A Exercises
Simplify the expression.
1. $6 \times 3^2 + 4 \times 2^2$ **70**
2. $2a + 3a$ **5a**
3. $(2a^3)(3a^3)$ **6a⁶**
4. $6.7 + 1.5 \div 3$ **7.2**
5. $(2 + 3p)5$ **10 + 15p**
6. $(abc)^0$ **1**

Class Exercises

Name the order of the operations to use in simplifying the expression.

1. $(2.8 + 0.36)0.2 - 4$ Add., Mult., Sub.

2. $310 \div 5 + 7$ Div., Add.

3. $[(0.42 \div 7) + 0.94]8$ Div., Add., Mult.

4. $6 \times 7 - 4 + 8 \div 2$ Mult., Div., Sub., Add.

5. $260 + 8^2 \times 6$ Simplify exponent; Mult., Add.

6. $15 + (6 \div 2) + 4$ Div., Add.

Has the expression on the left side of the equation been simplified correctly? If not, give the correct answer.

7. $14.7 + 0.8 \times 2.1 = 16.38$ Yes

8. $14 + 8 + 26 \div 2 = 24$ No; 35

9. $8 + 12 \div 4 + 4 = 24$ No; 15

10. $5.4 \div 9 + 3.8 \div 8 = 1$ No; 1.075

Written Exercises

Simplify the expression.

A 1. $5 + 7^2$ **54**

2. $(9^2 \div 3)6$ **162**

3. $2^2 \times 5 \times 2^3 + 17$ **177**

4. $(3.8 + 2)5$ **29**

5. $9 \times 2^3 + 7 \times 5^2$ **247**

6. $8.7 + 1.5 \div 3$ **9.2**

7. $(1.3 + 0.9) \div 4$ **0.55**

8. $(6.4 \div 2^3)7$ **5.6**

9. $5^2 + 6(72 \div 3^2)$ **73**

10. $(56x^2)(0.4x^2)$ **22.4x⁴**

11. $(18m^2)(3m^4) + 7$ **54m⁶ + 7**

12. $(a^2)(a^3)(a^4)7$ **7a⁹**

13. $\left[\dfrac{7.6 + 16.4 \times 0.5}{(24.7 - 16.7) \div 4}\right] + (2 \times 11)$ **29.9**

14. $\dfrac{(2.4 - 1.8)3 + 6.2}{[0.5(11.7 - 4.9)] + 4.6}$ **1**

15. $14x + 8y + 3x + 6y$ **17x + 14y**

16. $0.56 + 8.3n + 1.6 + 2.1n$ **2.16 + 10.4n**

17. $6[(4.5 - 3.6)d + 5.1d]$ **36d**

18. $[7(p + 5) + p] + 6p$ **14p + 35**

19. $[(2 + 3)m + 5(4 + 6m)]8$ **280m + 160**

20. $5a^2(a + 3) + (4 + 8a)6$ **5a³ + 15a² + 48a + 24**

Evaluate the expression when $a = 3.04$, $b = 0.8$, and $c = 4$.

21. $6a + b^3$ **18.752**

22. $3b^2c^3$ **122.88**

23. $(abc)^0$ **1**

24. $(a + b)^2$ **14.7456**

25. $a + 5(c^2 \div b)$ **103.04**

26. $a(2c + 3) - 5b$ **29.44**

27. $8c + (10b + c^2)4$ **128**

28. $(3c - 5)(3c)^2$ **1008**

29. $[9a - 2(c - a)]c$ **101.76**

The Decimal System **57**

Suggested Assignments
Minimum
Day 1: 57/1–20
Day 2: 57/21–29
58/30–33
58/Rev. 1–8
Average
Day 1: 57/1–25
Day 2: 57/26–29
58/30–35
58/Rev. 2–8 even
58/Computer Byte
Maximum
Day 1: 57/1–25
Day 2: 57/26–29
58/30–35
58/Computer Byte

Supplementary Materials
Practice Masters, p. 9

Place grouping symbols so that the expression will have the given value.

EXAMPLE $10 \times 6^2 \div 2 - 3 \div 3 = 50$

Solution $10 \times 6^2 \div 2 - 3 \div 3 = 10[(6^2 \div 2 - 3) \div 3]$
$= 10[(36 \div 2 - 3) \div 3]$
$= 10[(18 - 3) \div 3]$
$= 10[15 \div 3] = 10 \times 5 = 50$

B **30.** $4^2 - (3 \times 5 - 2) = 3$ **31.** $(4^2 - 3) \times 5 - 2 = 63$

32. $6 \times (7 - 2^3 \div 2^2) = 30$ **33.** $12 - 10 \div 2 + 3 \times 8 = 31$

34. $4.9 - 0.7 \times 2.5 + 11 = 14.15$ **35.** $4.2 + 3 \times (3.6 \div 0.4 + 9.6) = 60$

Review Exercises

Round to the highest place value.

1. 0.00614 0.006   **2.** 18.59 20   **3.** 240.003 200   **4.** 0.9817 1.0

5. 5.53002 6   **6.** 7481.99 7000   **7.** 34.956 30   **8.** 0.08024 0.08

  Computer Byte

This program will round a decimal to any desired place value.

```
10   PRINT "INPUT NUMBER TO BE ROUNDED";
20   INPUT N
30   PRINT "ROUND TO THE NEAREST ";
40   INPUT T
50   LET A = T * INT (N / T + .5)
60   PRINT A
70   END
```

Use the program to round each number to the place value specified.

1. 785 to the nearest 100 800   **2.** 785 to the nearest 10 790

3. 6898 to the nearest 1000 7000   **4.** 6898 to the nearest 10 6900

5. 17.49 to the nearest 1 17   **6.** 15.057 to the nearest 0.01 15.06

7. 0.004 to the nearest 0.1 0.0   **8.** 3.999731 to the nearest 0.001 4.000

Now try these.

9. Round 76 to the nearest 5. 75   **10.** Round $37,487.15 to the nearest $500. $37,500

58   *Chapter 2*

2-6 Solving and Checking Problems

You can now apply what you have learned about decimal numbers to solving problems. Recall the steps in the plan for solving word problems that you learned in Chapter 1. Remember that some problems may require more than one operation to reach their answers. When you have reached an answer, it is important not only to check your result with the facts given in the problem, but also to reread the question to be sure that you have answered with the information requested.

EXAMPLE 1 Alice Grego is recruiting volunteers for the Blood Drive. On Monday morning 15 people signed up. That afternoon an additional 17 people volunteered. The next day twice as many people signed up as on Monday. How many people were recruited each day?

Solution
- The problem asks for the number of people recruited on each day.

- Given facts: 15 volunteers on Monday morning
  17 volunteers on Monday afternoon
  twice as many people on Tuesday as on Monday

- First we add to find the total number of people recruited on Monday.

$$15 + 17 = 32$$

The total number of volunteers recruited on Monday is 32.

The problem asks for the number of people recruited on *each* day, so we must also find the number of volunteers recruited on Tuesday. Multiply the first answer, the total number recruited on Monday, by 2.

$$2 \times 32 = 64$$

- Alice recruited 32 volunteers on Monday and 64 on Tuesday.

Check: Are 32 people 17 more than 15 people? $32 - 17 = 15$ ✓
Are 64 people twice as many as 32 people?
$64 \div 2 = 32$ ✓

Was the question answered? Yes, the answer includes the number recruited on each day.

When planning your solution to a problem, you may find that there is more than one way to proceed. When there is more than one method for solving a problem, you may find it helpful to use one method to obtain an answer and to use the other method to check your results. Study the example on the following page.

The Decimal System **59**

Teaching Suggestions p. 39d

Related Activities p. 39d

Reading Mathematics

As you explain the examples, review and list key mathematical words to look for in solving problems. In Example 1 note *additional, twice,* and *each.* In Example 2, relate *money received* to total income. In Example 3, *distance traveled* also means total distance. Other key words in these applications are *deposits, deduct, base price, charge, collected, more, commission, difference,* and *sum.*

Chalkboard Examples

Solve.

1. Mrs. Weeks wrote five checks in May: $225.50, $14.63, $35, $7.59, and $82.90. She made one deposit of $600. What was the balance in her account at the end of May if the beginning balance was $681.70? $916.08

2. Tickets to the school dance cost $1.75 each. If 215 tickets were sold, how much money remained as profit after expenses of $250 were paid? $126.25

EXAMPLE 2 The Treble Clef celebrated Heritage Day with a two-week sale on the Flexwood turntables. Twelve turntables were sold during the first week of the sale and 17 were sold during the second week of the sale. The sale price for each turntable was $74.90. How much money did the Treble Clef receive for the turntables sold during the sale?

Solution

• The problem asks for the amount of money received from the sale of the turntables.

• Given facts: 12 turntables sold the first week
      17 more sold the second week
      $74.90 received for each turntable

• There are two ways to solve this problem.

Method 1
First multiply the sale price by the number sold each week to find the amount of money received each week.

$$12 \times 74.90 = 898.80 \qquad 17 \times 74.90 = 1273.30$$

Then add the amounts of money received to find the total amount of money received from the sale of the turntables.

$$898.80 + 1273.30 = 2172.10$$

Method 2
First add to find the total number of turntables sold during the sale.

$$12 + 17 = 29$$

Then multiply the sale price by the total number sold to find the amount of money received from the sale of the turntables.

$$29 \times 74.90 = 2172.10$$

• By either method, the Treble Clef received $2172.10 from the sale of the turntables.

Another way to check an answer is to use rounding to find an estimated answer. If the answer and the estimate are close, then the estimate leads us to accept our answer.

EXAMPLE 3 Last summer Elka and David drove from Los Angeles to Boston. Along the way they stopped in Albuquerque, Kansas City, Atlanta, and Washington, D.C. They recorded the distance they traveled, as shown on the next page.

Los Angeles–Albuquerque	806 mi
Albuquerque–Kansas City	790 mi
Kansas City–Atlanta	810 mi
Atlanta–Washington, D.C.	630 mi
Washington, D.C.–Boston	437 mi

How many miles did Elka and David travel?

Solution

- The problem asks for the total distance traveled.

- Given facts: traveled 806 mi, 790 mi, 810 mi, 630 mi, 437 mi

- To find the total distance traveled, we add.

$$806 + 790 + 810 + 630 + 437 = 3473$$

- Elka and David traveled 3473 miles on their trip.

To check the answer, we round the distances and add. In this case, round to the nearest hundred miles.

$$800 + 800 + 800 + 600 + 400 = 3400$$

The estimate, 3400 mi, and the answer, 3473 mi, are quite close, so the actual answer seems reasonable.

Class Exercises

State the operations you would use to solve the problem and the order in which you would use them.

1. The Dreyer Trucking Company moved 453 cartons one day, and then 485 the next day. On the third day they moved twice as many as on the first two days. What is the total number of cartons moved during those three days? Addition, Multiplication, Addition

State two methods that you could use to solve the problem.

2. Three friends went out to dinner. The bill was $41.10, and they left a $6.15 tip. If they divided the total three ways, how much did each person pay? Add $41.10 and $6.15, divide total by 3.
   Or: Divide $41.10 by 3, divide $6.15 by 3, add the results.

Estimate the answer to the problem.

3. Frank is in the check-out line at the grocery store. He has a gallon of milk ($1.83), a bag of flour ($2.15), a box of oatmeal ($1.15), a package of cheese ($1.57), and a dozen eggs ($1.05). How much is the bill? $8

Solve.

1. Dana has two 90-minute tape cassettes, one 60-minute cassette, and two 45-minute cassettes. How many hours would it take to play them all? $5\frac{1}{2}$

2. The telephone rate between two cities is $.75 for the first 3 minutes and $.05 for each additional minute. How much does an 18-minute call cost?

   $1.50

Problems

Solve. Check to be sure you have answered the question.

A 1. The August electric bill for $75.80 was twice as much as the July bill. What was the total cost of electricity for July and August? $113.70

2. Alvin has $1863.50 in his savings account. His sister Alvis has $756 more in her account. Geoffrey borrowed $257 from each person. How much money do Alvin and Alvis have left in each of their accounts after making the loans?
   Alvin has $1606.50, Alvis has $2362.50.

Solve. Check by using an alternate method.

3. Each member of the Best Buy Book Club receives 2 bonus points for every book ordered through the club. So far Chris has ordered 3 books in March, 2 in April, and 6 in May. How many bonus points has Chris accumulated so far? 22 bonus points

4. The admission ticket to Tyler Amusement Park is $1.25 per person. A total of 815 tickets were sold on Saturday. The attendance decreased by 96 on Sunday. How much money did the park receive from ticket sales in all? $1917.50

Solve. Check by estimating the answer to the problem.

41 points

5. During one game at a bowling tournament the five-member Bright Team scored the following points: 169, 152, 187, 174, and 193. What is the difference between the highest and the lowest scores?

6. Jackie is taking an inventory of the furniture going on sale next week.

   sofas, 128   platform beds, 250
   love seats, 105   stereo cabinets, 83
   lamps, 216   bookcases, 45

   How many items are going on sale? 827 items

Solve.

B 7. The Hillview School Band held a car wash on Friday and Saturday. The charge was $2.25 per car on Friday and $2.50 per car on Saturday. On Friday, 87 cars were washed. On Saturday, 117 cars were washed. What was the total amount of money collected? $488.75

62 *Chapter 2*

8. A photograph is enlarged so that its new dimensions are four times its original dimensions. If the new dimensions are 19.2 cm by 25.6 cm, what were the original dimensions? **4.8 cm by 6.4 cm**

9. Today the firm of Beckman and Beckman bought three types of stocks: 4780 shares of utility stocks, 1389 shares of commodity stocks, and 3542 shares of energy-related stocks. This is exactly three times the number of shares the firm bought yesterday. How many shares of stock did the firm buy in the past two days? **12,948 shares**

10. Yukio bought traveler's checks in the following denominations: five $50 checks, thirty $20 checks, five $10 checks, and twenty $5 checks. What is the total value of the checks bought? **$1000**

11. Katelyn had 3 twenty-dollar bills to buy school clothes. She picked out a pair of jeans for $15.90, two pairs of socks at $2.35 each, and three blouses at $12.50 each. How much change did she receive? **$1.90**

12. A direct dial call from Boston to Australia costs $3.17 for the first minute and $1.19 for each additional minute. A station-to-station operator-assisted call costs $9.45 for the first 3 minutes and $1.19 for each additional minute. How much money would you save by dialing direct for a 5-minute call? **$3.90**

Self-Test B

Use the properties of addition and multiplication to simplify.

1. $12(15 - 8) + 6 \times 3$ **102**

2. $(31 \times 4) + (15 \times 4) - 91$ **93** [2-4]

3. $7(56 \div 8) - 7(24 \div 6)$ **21**

4. $9(0.36 \times 4) + 55$ **67.96**

5. $[(128 \div 4) \div 8)]9$ **36**

6. $(12 + 9)5 + (17 - 3)6$ **189**

Simplify the expression.

7. $(6a + 7)2 + 4a$ **16a + 14**

8. $(1.26 + 3.74)^2 \div 4$ **6.25** [2-5]

9. $[(12 + 6) \div 6] + [(25 + 5) \div 3]$ **13**

10. $(7b + 3)5 + (11 + 4b)2$ **43b + 37**

Solve.

11. Jeremy and his roommate share the monthly utility bills evenly. For November the cost of electricity was $87.90, gas was $24.35, heating fuel was $215.80, and water was $36.43. How much did each person pay that month? **$182.24** [2-6]

Self-Test answers and Extra Practice are at the back of the book.

The Decimal System **63**

Suggested Assignments

Minimum
Day 1: 62/1–7
Day 2: 63/8–12
  63/Self-Test B
Average
Day 1: 62/1–7
Day 2: 63/8–12
  63/Self-Test B
Maximum
Day 1: 62/1–7
Day 2: 63/8–12
  63/Self-Test B

Supplementary Materials

Practice Masters, p. 10
Test 2B, pp. 11–12
Computer Activity 3
Computer Activity 4

Quick Quiz B

Use the properties of addition and multiplication to simplify the expression.

1. $7(6 + 2) - 48 \div 12$ **52**
2. $3 \times 4 - 5 \times 1 - 4$ **3**
3. $(3 \times 2 \div 6) + (2 \times 3 \div 6)$ **2**
4. $10(5.3 \times 2) - 25$ **81**
5. $(18 - 9 \times 2)3$ **0**
6. $(15 + 5)5 + (15 - 5)2$ **120**
7. $3(a + 2) + 2$ **3a + 8**
8. $(1.4 - 0.2)^2 \div 10$ **0.144**
9. $(4^3 - 2^4) + 5$ **53**
10. $4(3 + 2x) + (3x + 5)2$ **14x + 22**

Solve.

11. Susan and Shannon ordered three tape cassettes from a record club. Each cassette cost $6.98. If the girls each paid half the total cost, how much did each girl pay? **$10.47**

BASIC, A Computer Language

Computers are very powerful tools, but issuing an order such as "Do problem 12 on page 46 of my math book" will produce no results at all. There are many things computers can do more quickly and efficiently than people, but we need to communicate with computers in a special way to get them to work for us.

To tell a computer what to do, we write a set of instructions, called a *program,* using a *programming language.* Since most microcomputers use some version of BASIC (with slight differences), that is the language that we will use in this book. A BASIC program is made up of a set of *numbered lines* that provide step-by-step instructions for the computer. We can use any numbers from 1 to 99999 for line numbers, but we often use numbers in intervals of 10 so that we can insert other lines later if we need to.

A *statement* that tells the computer what to do follows each line number in a program. In the BASIC language, we use the symbols shown below to tell the computer to perform arithmetic operations.

+	addition	−	subtraction
*	multiplication	/	division

The symbol ↑ (or some similar symbol) is used to indicate exponentiation. Thus 3 ↑ 6 means 3^6. When a statement contains more than one operation, the computer will perform all operations in parentheses first and will follow the order of operations that you learned in Chapters 1 and 2.

We use a **PRINT** statement to tell the computer to perform the operations listed in a statement and to print the result. We use an **END**

64   *Chapter 2*

statement to tell the computer that the program is over. The program shown below tells the computer to simplify the numerical expression and print the answer.

```
10  PRINT 5↑3 * (16 - 8 / 2)
20  END
```

After you have typed in this program (press RETURN or ENTER after each line), you type the *command* **RUN** to tell the computer to run (or *execute*) the program. The result, or *output*, is 1500.

A computer handles variables much as we do. We can ask it, for example, to give us the value of a variable expression when we give it a value of the variable in it. One way of doing this is to use an **INPUT** statement. This causes the computer to print a question mark and wait for the value to be typed in. Here is a simple program with a RUN shown at the right below.

```
10  INPUT X                          RUN
20  PRINT X↑2 + 2 * X + 4            ?10
30  END                               124
```

As you can see, we need some statement to tell the person using this program what is expected after the question mark. We do this by enclosing a descriptive expression in quotation marks in a PRINT statement, as in line 5 below. The semicolon at the end of line 5 will cause the question mark from line 10 to be printed right after the quoted expression. We have also inserted lines 12 and 15. After typing lines 5, 12, and 15, we can type the command **LIST** to see the revised program. A RUN is shown at the right below.

```
5  PRINT "WHAT IS YOUR VALUE OF X";
10  INPUT X                          RUN
12  PRINT "FOR X = ";X               WHAT IS YOUR VALUE OF X?10
15  PRINT "X↑2 + 2X + 4 = ";         FOR X = 10
20  PRINT X↑2 + 2 * X + 4            X↑2 + 2X + 4 = 124
30  END                              124
```

1. Change lines 15 and 20 in the program above to evaluate another variable expression, with *x* as the variable, that involves the operation or operations listed.

a. subtraction
b. multiplication
c. division
d. multiplication and addition
e. division and subtraction

2. Change the program above to evaluate a variable expression using *m* as the variable.

Additional Answers

Answers will vary. An example of each is given.

1. a. 15 PRINT "X − 5 = ";
20 PRINT X − 5
b. 15 PRINT "3 * X = ";
20 PRINT 3 * X
c. 15 PRINT "X/7 = ";
20 PRINT X/7
d. 15 PRINT "2 * X + 1 = ";
20 PRINT 2 * X + 1
e. 15 PRINT "X/4 − 1 = ";
20 PRINT X/4 − 1

2. 5 PRINT "WHAT IS YOUR VALUE OF M";
10 INPUT M
12 PRINT "FOR M = "; M
15 PRINT "M ↑ 2 − *M* = ";
20 PRINT M ↑ 2 − *M*
30 END

Chapter Review

Complete. Use =, >, or < to make a true statement.

1. 2^3 __?=__ 2×4 **2.** $14 \div 7$ __?>__ 19^0 **3.** $(4 + 3)^1$ __?<__ 4×3 [2–1]

4. 7.1 __?>__ $7 + 0.01$ **5.** $4.2 \div 2$ __?=__ 0.7×3 [2–2]

6. $7.23 \div 5$ __?>__ 1.44 **7.** $82.03 - 5.4$ __?<__ 87.43

True or false?

8. 21.09 to the nearest whole number is 20. False   [2–3]

9. 124.4 to the nearest hundred is 100. True

10. 83.415 to the nearest hundredth is 83.42. True

11. 0.959 to the nearest tenth is 1.0. True

12. $(17.2 + 1.8)4 = (1.8 + 17.2)4$ illustrates the commutative property. True   [2–4]

13. $(8 + 7.9)2.3 = (8 \times 2.3) + (7.9 \times 2.3)$ illustrates the distributive property of multiplication with respect to subtraction. False

14. $1.3(7 + 4) = (7 + 4)1.3$ illustrates the associative property. False

Match.

15. $5 + (4^2 \div 2)^2$ B   **16.** $4 \times 5 + 6^2 \div 9$ F   **A.** 0.512   **B.** 69   [2–5]

17. $6 + 5a + 3a + 4^2$ C   **18.** $[0.2 \times (3 + 1)]^3$ A   **C.** $8a + 22$ **D.** 17

19. $4 + 2a(5 + 6) + 4$ E   **20.** $\dfrac{1.5 + 3.5 \times 2}{3.6 \div 18 + 0.3}$ D   **E.** $22a + 8$ **F.** 24

Write the letter of the correct answer.

21. There were 27,240 books at the library at the start of the day on   [2–6]
Friday. During the day the following transactions occurred: 21 people borrowed 2 books each, 12 people borrowed 3 books each, 8
people borrowed a single book each, and 46 books were returned.
How many books were in the library at the close of the day? b
a. 27,154   **b.** 27,200   **c.** 27,280   **d.** 27,240

22. To raise money for a local charity, the 26 students of the eighth-
grade class participated in a bike-a-thon. Each of the sponsors
agreed to pay the students $.35 for each mile they rode their bicy-
cles. If 20 students ride 20 mi each and the rest of the students ride
30 mi each, for how many miles will the students be paid? d
a. $203   **b.** 50 mi   **c.** $17.50   **d.** 580 mi

66 *Chapter 2*

Chapter Test

Supplementary Materials
Chapter 2 Test, pp. 13–14

Which is greater?

1. 3^3 or 2^4 $_{3^3}$ **2.** $(2 + 3)^2$ or 4^3 $_{4^3}$ **3.** 10^3 or $(4 \times 6)^2$ $_{10^3}$ [2–1]

Write as a single power of the given base.

4. $3^4 \times 3^2$ $_{3^6}$ **5.** $6^5 \times 6^7$ $_{6^{12}}$ **6.** $a \times a^3$ $_{a^4}$

Evaluate the expression if $m = 6$, $n = 4$, and $p = 8$.

100,000,000

7. p^2 $_{64}$ **8.** $5m - p$ $_{22}$ **9.** $(2n)^3$ $_{512}$ **10.** $(m + n)^p$

Write the decimal in expanded form.

$(1 \times 100) + (2 \times 10) + 1$ $1 + (4 \times 0.1) + (1 \times 0.001)$

11. 121   **12.** 80.08   **13.** 1.401   **14.** 5.2   [2–2]

$(8 \times 10) + (8 \times 0.01)$ $5 + (2 \times 0.1)$

Use the symbol $<$ to order the numbers from least to greatest.

15. 4.003, 4.01, 4.023   **16.** 0.297, 0.035, 0.03

$4.003 < 4.01 < 4.023$ $0.03 < 0.035 < 0.297$

Round to the place specified.

17. tenths: 7.49 $_{7.5}$ **18.** tens: 423.6 $_{420}$ **19.** hundredths: 4.283   [2–3]

$_{4.28}$

What value of the variable makes the statement true?

$r = 7.8$

20. $2.4 + (r + 9.5) = 2.4 + (9.5 + 7.8)$ **21.** $19.2k = k$ $_{k = 0}$ [2–4]

22. $62d - 19d = (62 - 19)4$ $_{d = 4}$ **23.** $1(3.4 + 1.3) = a$ $_{a = 4.7}$

Simplify the expression.

24. $114.5 - (6.3 + 2.7)^2$ $_{33.5}$ **25.** $[6^2 \div (8 + 1)] + 5$ $_9$ [2–5]

26. $12x + 14 + 2x + 8 + 3y$ **27.** $5p(p + 4) + 3p$ $_{5p^2 + 23p}$

$_{14x + 3y + 22}$

Solve and check your answer.

28. For the trip, Kari bought 3 stocking caps for $6.75 each and 3 scarfs   [2–6]
for $8.50 each. How much money did she spend? $45.75

29. Dean commutes 17 km to work and Bob commutes 8 km more than
Dean. If Becky commutes 3 times as far as Bob, how far does she
commute? 75 km

30. Mickey Dayton purchased 5 cases of packages of flour. If each
package was 2.2 kg and each case contained 20 packages, how many
kilograms of flour were purchased? 220 kg

The Decimal System   **67**

Simplify.

1. $42 + 83.5 - 1.27$
   124.23
2. $63 \div 14 + 3.2$ **7.7**
3. $8.6 - 99 \div 44$ **6.35**
4. $4 \times 12.75 \div 3$ **17**
5. $3 + 5 \times 7 + 2$ **40**
6. $12 \div 4 - 2 + 1$ **2**
7. $(6.4 - 3.7)(2.1 + 4.9)$
   18.9
8. $(10 - 1.4)(0.6 + 5)$
   48.16
9. $15 - 2 + 3 \times 4$ **25**
10. $10 + 6 \div 3$ **12**
11. $10 - 8 + 5$ **7**
12. $(2.8 + 3)(6 - 0.4)$
    32.48

Evaluate the expression
when $a = 5$ and $b = 2$.

13. $8a - 24$ **16**
14. $6ab$ **60**
15. $a + 3b$ **11**
16. $(a - b)(3b - a)$ **3**
17. $4(2a - 3b)$ **16**
18. $a(5b - 5)$ **25**

Find the solution or solutions
of the equation or inequality
for the given replacement
set.

19. $6f = 84$; $\{12, 13, 14\}$ **14**
20. $2y + 3 = 15$; $\{5, 6, 7\}$ **6**
21. $m - 12 = 36$;
    $\{48, 49, 50\}$ **48**
22. $20 - 3a = 5$; $\{4, 5, 6\}$ **5**
23. $60 \div 5k = 2$; $\{4, 5, 6\}$ **6**
24. $4(g + 1) \geq 12$; $\{1, 2, 3\}$
    2, 3
25. $2t + 5 < 10$; $\{1, 2, 3\}$
    1, 2
26. $6c - 3 \geq 33$; $\{2, 4, 6\}$ **6**
27. $12 - 3j > 3$; $\{2, 3, 4\}$ **2**

(Continued on p. 69)

Cumulative Review (Chapters 1 and 2)

Exercises

Evaluate the expression using the given values of the variables.

1. xy; **7.5**
   $x = 3, y = 2.5$

2. $3a - b$; **6.6**
   $a = 4.2, b = 6$

3. $\frac{m}{n} + 3$; **23**
   $m = 8, n = 0.4$

4. $f + \frac{g}{6}$; **13**
   $f = 10, g = 18$

5. $x^2 + 3xy$; **124**
   $x = 8, y = 2.5$

6. $a \div b$; **4.1**
   $a = 12.3, b = 3$

7. $4d + 7c^3$; **57.2**
   $d = 0.3, c = 2$

8. $6m - 8n$; **59**
   $m = 10.5, n = 0.5$

9. $\frac{p}{q} - 2p$; **0**
   $p = 15, q = 0.5$

Evaluate the expression when $a = 4.2$, $b = 9.5$, and $c = 3.2$.

10. $2a + 3(a - c)$ **11.4**
11. $ab - c$ **36.7**
12. $bc + a$ **34.6**
13. $(a + c)(a + b)$ **101.38**
14. $4ab(b + c)$ **2026.92**
15. $6c + (b - a)$ **24.5**
16. $a \div (c - 2.8)$ **10.5**
17. $(b + 0.5) \div (5.2 - c)$ **5**
18. $(30 - a) \div (a + 3.8)$
    3.225

Use $>$ or $<$ to write a true statement with the given numbers. Answers may vary.

19. 15, 48, 26 $15 < 26 < 48$
20. 83, 93, 43, 53 $43 < 53 < 83 < 93$
21. 125, 115, 225 $115 < 125 < 225$
22. $4^2, 2^3, 3^2$ $2^3 < 3^2 < 4^2$
23. $3^5, 5^3, 2^2$ $2^2 < 5^3 < 3^5$
24. $6^2, 2^6, 3^2$ $3^2 < 6^2 < 2^6$

Select the most reasonable estimated answer.

25. $43.6 - 2.79$ **a.**   **a.** 41   **b.** 20   **c.** 45
26. 9.6×53.66 **c.**   **a.** 500   **b.** 450   **c.** 540
27. $22.7 + 18.9 + 7.38$ **a.**   **a.** 49   **b.** 37   **c.** 110
28. $165.7 + 38.21 + 6.44$ **b.**   **a.** 1300   **b.** 210   **c.** 246

True or false?

29. $46.7 \times 1.0 = 46.7$ **True**
30. $87.91 \times 0 = 87.91$ **False**
31. $4(8 + 2) = 4 \times 8 + 4 \times 2$ **True**
32. $16 \div 8 + 2 = 16 \div (8 + 2)$ **False**
33. $99.5 - (6 + 7) = (99.5 - 6) + 7$ **False**
34. $(43 \times 0) + (43 \times 1) = 0$ **False**
35. $11.89 + (426 \div 2) = (11.89 + 426) \div 2$ **False**
36. $(68 - 7) = (7 - 68)$ **False**
37. $(658 + 15)7 = (7 \times 658) + (7 \times 15)$ **True**

Problems

> **Problem Solving Reminders**
>
> Here are some reminders that may help you solve some of the problems on this page.
> * Determine which facts are necessary to solve the problem.
> * Supply additional information if needed.
> * Check by using rounding to find an estimated answer.
> * If more than one method can be used to solve a problem, use one method to solve and the other to check.

Solve.

1. Merry and Sandy rented an apartment for $645 each month and shared the rent equally. After 4 months, Tess moved in and the rent was divided three ways. How much was Merry's rent for the year? $3010

2. Hungarian paprika costs $1.30 for 2 oz, $4.00 for $\frac{1}{2}$ lb, and $6.00 for a pound. What is the cost of each ounce if you buy a pound? How much do you save per ounce if you buy a pound? $.375/oz; $.275/oz

3. Mal ordered a set of 6 steak knives for $35.00. Additional costs included $4.95 for shipping, $1.25 for a gift box, and $1.75 for tax. What was the total cost of the order? $42.95

4. "I can save $19.50 if I buy a half dozen glasses on sale," said Ellis. How much is saved on each glass? If Ellis pays $30.00 for 6 glasses on sale, what was the original price of each glass? $3.25/glass; $8.25

5. House numerals that are 4 in. high cost $4.00 each. Numerals that are 7 in. high cost $10.00 each. How much will it cost to buy numerals that are 4 in. high for your house if your address is 16332 Long Meadow Road? $20

6. In 1918, a sheet of 100 airmail stamps was mistakenly printed with an airplane upside down. A stamp collector bought the sheet for $.24 per stamp and later sold the sheet for $15,000. How much did the collector make on his lucky buy? $14,976

7. A membership to the Science Center costs $53 per year and includes a subscription to a monthly magazine. If the magazine costs $3 per issue, what are the annual dues for membership alone? $17

8. Dale took advantage of the gas company's offer to make average monthly payments. The payments were based on the average of the two highest and the two lowest bills for the past 12 months. If these bills were $135.50, $142.71, $68.29, and $56.30, what is Dale's average monthly payment? $100.70

The Decimal System **69**

28. $4(9 - b) \leq 8$; {6, 7, 8}
    7, 8

Use inverse operations to solve.

29. $2n \div 3 = 8$ **12**

30. $2h + 3 = 25$ **11**

31. $5g - 1 = 19$ **4**

32. $d + 7 = 8d - 7$ **2**

33. $2q - 4 = 28$ **16**

34. $6s + 1 = 5s + 10$ **9**

Write a variable expression for the word phrase.

35. A number k added to 12
    $12 + k$

36. Seven times a number j
    $7j$

37. The product of a number m and eight **8m**

Write an equation or inequality for the word sentence.

38. A number y decreased by ten is greater than fourteen. $y - 10 > 14$

39. Twice a number t, divided by five, is twenty.
    $2t \div 5 = 20$

40. Four times a number g is less than or equal to g plus two. $4g \leq g + 2$

3
Positive and Negative Numbers

Geysers are underground springs that spout extremely hot water and steam. They occur in regions where volcanic forces heat the underground terrain. Geysers may spout a few meters or a few hundred meters and at short or long intervals. Old Faithful, a geyser at Yellowstone National Park, earned its name by spouting regularly at intervals of approximately 65 min.

Cloud formations, such as those in the photograph, are produced by the extreme differences in the temperatures of the hot steam and the cold winter air. As air temperatures drop, steam from the geyser condenses on plants and flowers, forming a frosty coating. When air temperatures fall below 0°C, the ice crystals begin to form beautiful patterns. In this chapter, you will learn to work with the numbers that we use to represent values that are below 0.

Career Note

State and national parks provide facilities for many forms of outdoor recreation. Park rangers help maintain park areas by enforcing rules and regulations, providing information for visitors, and protecting the area's wildlife and natural resources. A college degree with courses in earth science and animal care is essential for park ranger candidates. Courses in behavioral sciences that stress skills needed for dealing with people are also desirable.

Lesson Commentary
Chapter 3 Positive and Negative Numbers

Overview

This chapter begins with definitions important to the integers and expands these definitions to include positive and negative decimal numbers. The basic concepts in this chapter include an understanding of positive and negative, opposites, absolute value, order, and rules governing the four basic operations of addition, subtraction, multiplication, and division. Chapter 4, which covers the rational numbers, is dependent on these basic concepts.

SUMS AND DIFFERENCES

3-1 The Integers

Objectives *for pages 72–74*

- To represent positive and negative integers on a number line.
- To compare positive and negative integers.

Teaching Suggestions

Discuss ways positive and negative numbers are used. Use examples such as those in the first two paragraphs on page 72. The scale of a thermometer can be thought of as a vertical number line.

Emphasize that zero is neither positive nor negative. On a number line, positive numbers are to the *right* of zero. Negative numbers are to the *left* of zero.

Insist that students space the markings on their number lines equally. Then the number lines can more accurately show opposites, absolute value, and order.

Related Activities

To enhance students' understanding of the integers, ask them to solve these equations:

$$
\begin{array}{ccc}
x = 5 & x = {}^-4 & x = 0 \\
{}^-x = 5 & {}^-x = {}^-4 & {}^-x = 0 \\
|x| = 5 & |x| = {}^-4 & |x| = 0
\end{array}
$$

Explain that most of these equations have only one solution. But the equation

$$|x| = 5 \text{ has two solutions, 5 and } {}^-5,$$

and the equation

$$|x| = {}^-4 \text{ has no solution.}$$

An inequality such as $|x| > 0$ has infinitely many solutions: 1, 2, 3, 4, . . . and $^-1, {}^-2, {}^-3, {}^-4,$ . . . . Only the number 0 will not satisfy this inequality.

In solving equations students must be cautioned that there may be more than one correct solution. Ask them to think of other examples with more than one correct solution. (Possible answers might include $x \times 0 = 0$ or $x \times 1 = x$.)

Resource Book: Page 31 (Use After Page 74)

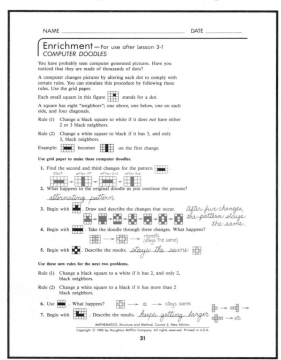

3-2 Decimals on the Number Line

Objectives *for pages 75–78*

- To represent positive and negative decimals on a number line.
- To compare positive and negative decimals.

Teaching Suggestions

Spend ample time in this lesson placing decimal numbers correctly on the number line, especially the negative decimal numbers. Stress that ⁻2.5 is between ⁻3 and ⁻2 and *not* to the right of ⁻2. You might also show students that between ⁻2.5 and ⁻2 are other decimals such as ⁻2.25, ⁻2.13, and ⁻2.064.

Just as the integers include all whole numbers, decimal numbers include integers and whole numbers. This may be easier for students to remember by showing them examples such as 2 = 2.0 and ⁻3 = ⁻3.0.

Related Activities

To relate this work to a familiar topic, ask students to compare the number line to a football field where 0 represents the line of scrimmage and 10 or more would represent a first down. If in a series of three plays, a team gains 3 yd, loses 5 yd, and gains 7 yd, would the team have a first down? Graph the action:

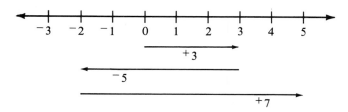

No, the team is 5 yd short of a first down.

3-3 Adding Positive and Negative Numbers

Objective *for pages 79–83*

- To find the sum of two or more positive or negative numbers.

Teaching Suggestions

Integer addition can be shown concretely by using manipulatives. Give each student several squares of paper. Ask them to mark a sheet of paper in half and label one side positive and one side negative.

For ⁺2 + ⁺3, ask students to place 2 squares on the positive side and add 3 squares on the positive side. Ask, "What do you have now?" Answer: 5 squares on the positive side. Thus ⁺2 + ⁺3 = ⁺5.

For ⁻2 + ⁻3 place 2 squares on the negative side. Add 3 squares on the negative side and the result is 5 squares on the negative side. Thus ⁻2 + ⁻3 = ⁻5.

For ⁺2 + ⁻3 place 2 squares on the positive side and 3 on the negative side. Explain that any pair consisting of a positive square and a negative square can be canceled out. In this case, one square on the negative side cannot be canceled out. Thus ⁺2 + ⁻3 = ⁻1.

For ⁻2 + ⁺3 place 2 squares on the negative side and 3 squares on the positive side. Cancel out two negatives with two positives. All that is left is 1 square on the positive side. Thus, ⁻2 + ⁺3 = ⁺1.

Do several examples for integers and develop the rules carefully before using decimals.

Related Activities

To provide practice in a different way, give every student several copies of the triangle below. Fill in integers along the bottom row and have students add upward two at a time to reach the top. Do this as a class activity to encourage speed as well as accuracy.

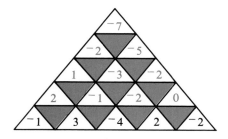

For the integers shown in this triangle, the addition examples include:

$$⁻1 + 3 = 2 \qquad 3 + ⁻4 = ⁻1$$
$$⁻4 + 2 = ⁻2 \qquad 2 + ⁻2 = 0$$

3-4 Subtracting Positive and Negative Numbers

Objective for pages 84–87

■ To find the difference of two positive or negative numbers.

Teaching Suggestions

Emphasize that the rule for subtraction requires that we add the opposite of the *second* number to the first. The first number remains unchanged. Compare this procedure to division of fractions, in which we multiply by the reciprocal of the *second* number and once again the first number remains unchanged.

Point out that when unraised minus signs are used, parentheses must often be used to make the meaning clear. For example,

$$12.4 - (-8) \text{ is clearer than } 12.4 - -8.$$

Resource Book: Page 32 (Use After Page 87)

NAME _____ DATE _____

Quiz 3A —Lessons 3-1 through 3-4

DIRECTIONS: Write the letter of the correct answer in the space provided.

Write the integers in order from least to greatest.

1. 0, 7, ⁻5, ⁻6, 1   2. ⁻3, 8, ⁻7, 2   [3-1]
   a. ⁻7, ⁻3, 2, 8   b. ⁻5, ⁻6, 0, 1, 7
   c. 2, ⁻3, ⁻7, 8   d. ⁻6, ⁻5, 0, 1, 7

List the integers that can replace x to make the statement true.

3. |x| = 3   4. |x| < 4
   a. 3, ⁻3   b. 3
   c. 0, 1, 2, 3   d. ⁻3, ⁻2, ⁻1, 0, 1, 2, 3

Write the numbers in order from least to greatest.

5. ⁻5.11, 1.692, 1.7, ⁻5   6. 3.03, ⁻0.3, 30, ⁻1.3   [3-2]
   a. 1.692, 1.7, ⁻5, ⁻5.11   b. ⁻0.3, ⁻1.3, 3.03, 30
   c. ⁻1.3, ⁻0.3, 3.03, 30   d. ⁻5.11, ⁻5, 1.692, 1.7

List the decimal numbers that can replace x to make the statement true.

7. |x| = 0.043   8. |x| = |⁻4.3|
   a. 0.043   b. ⁻4.3
   c. 0.043, ⁻0.043   d. 4.3, ⁻4.3

Find the sum or difference.

9. ⁻4.68 + 13.79   10. ⁻13.79 + ⁻4.68   [3-3]
   a. 18.47   b. ⁻18.47   c. 9.11   d. ⁻9.11

11. ⁻4.1 + 2.6 + ⁻3.5   12. 0.9 + ⁻3.2 + 7.3
    a. ⁻10.2   b. 5.0   c. ⁻5.0   d. ⁻11.4

13. 9 − (−24)   14. −24 − (−9)   [3-4]
    a. ⁻33   b. 33   c. 15   d. ⁻15

Evaluate the expression when s = ⁻3.2 and t = ⁻4.5.

15. s − t   16. s + t   17. t − (−s)   18. s − |t|
    a. ⁻7.7   b. 7.7   c. 1.3   d. ⁻1.3

	ANSWERS	
1.	d	(4)
2.	a	(4)
3.	a	(4)
4.	d	(4)
5.	d	(4)
6.	c	(4)
7.	c	(4)
8.	d	(4)
9.	c	(4)
10.	b	(4)
11.	c	(5)
12.	b	(5)
13.	b	(5)
14.	d	(5)
15.	c	(10)
16.	a	(10)
17.	a	(10)
18.	a	(10)

MATHEMATICS, Structure and Method, Course 2, New Edition.
Copyright © 1985 by Houghton Mifflin Company. All rights reserved. Printed in U.S.A.
32

Resource Book: Page 33 (Use After Page 87)

NAME _____ DATE _____

Problem Solving —For use after Lesson 3-4
Estimates as Answers

Sometimes it is not practical to use the exact answer to a problem. Often an estimate or a number rounded to the nearest whole number makes more sense.

EXAMPLES

I Marta Stoehr has to feed 3 people. The casserole she is making serves 2 and uses 1 egg. How many times the recipe should she make?

II How many tablecloths can be made from 14 yd of material if 2.5 yd are needed for each?

SOLUTIONS

Although 3 ÷ 2 is 1½ times the recipe, it is difficult to use 1½ eggs. Marta should make twice the recipe.

14 ÷ 2.5 = 5.6
Part of a tablecloth doesn't make sense. Drop the remainder. Five tablecloths can be made.

Solve. Use estimated or rounded answers that make sense.

1. Ned Wright has a five-dollar bill and five singles in his pocket. If he buys 2 dozen large eggs at $1.08 a dozen, 3 lb of ground beef at $1.69 a pound, and 2 boxes of frozen mixed vegetables at 59¢ each, will he have two single bills left to change for 8 quarters at the laundromat? _____ *no*

2. The average rainfall for the town of Lipton in the fall months is 2.2 in. If it rained a total of 3.5 in. in September, 0.2 in. in October, and 1.3 in. in November, is the fall rainfall above or below the average? _____ *below*

3. How many 10-ft boards will Cindy Leftkowitz need in order to make 15 book shelves if each shelf must be 37 in. long? _____ *5*

4. Jennifer's checking account has a balance of $52.18 on Tuesday. She withdraws $17.62 on Wednesday and deposits $81.00 on Thursday. Can she write a check for $102.71 on Friday? _____ *yes*

5. Janet Pearle is making a brick border around her patio and garden. The bricks come in lots of 24. She uses 2 lots to complete 32 ft of the border. How many lots will she need in order to complete the job if she estimates the border to be 72 ft? _____ *3 lots*

6. A lake increases in depth 2.3 m for every 1.5 m you go directly out from shore. How far from shore should Steve fish if he wants to fish in water at least 9 m deep? _____ *6 m*

MATHEMATICS, Structure and Method, Course 2, New Edition.
Copyright © 1985 by Houghton Mifflin Company. All rights reserved. Printed in U.S.A.
33

Related Activities

To provide mixed practice following this lesson, give students problems that involve a mixture of addition and subtraction. Explain that when students use the rule for subtraction and add the opposite, numbers may be added in any order desired.

1. $-2 + (-3.1) - 6 =$ **⁻11.1**
2. $4.6 - 2.15 + (-8) =$ **⁻5.55**
3. $-25 - (-6.3) - 7 =$ **⁻25.7**
4. $4.9 + (-3.8) - 5.1 =$ **⁻4**

PRODUCTS AND QUOTIENTS

3-5 Multiplying Positive and Negative Numbers

Objective for pages 88–91

■ To find the product of two or more positive and negative numbers.

Teaching Suggestions

Give each student a multiplication table like the one below:

×	3	2	1	0	−1	−2	−3
3	9	6	3	0	−3	−6	−9
2	6	4	2	0	−2	−4	−6
1	3	2	1	0	−1	−2	−3
0	0	0	0	0	0	0	0
−1	−3	−2	−1	0	1	2	3
−2	−6	−4	−2	0	2	4	6
−3	−9	−6	−3	0	3	6	9

Help students to complete the table by beginning in the upper left corner with 3×3, 3×2, 3×1, and 3×0. When students ask about 3×-1, ask them to look for patterns in the products they have already found. In this row products decrease by 3. Continue the pattern for 3×-2 and 3×-3. Use this same approach for multiplying by 2. Complete the next two rows emphasizing rules for multiplying by 1 and 0.

To multiply $(-3) \times (3)$ students may use the commutative property for $(3) \times (-3)$ or they may notice decreasing patterns in the column headed by positive 3. Complete the entire chart using properties and patterns. Examine the completed chart and notice positive products in the upper left and lower right hand sections. The lower left and upper right sections are negative products.

In a later algebra course students will learn that simplifying an expression as in Example 3 is referred to as combining coefficients. The expression $15 - 8a - 6 + 4a$ is usually regarded as a shorthand version of $15 + (-8a) + (-6) + 4a$. The coefficient of the second term is -8.

Related Activities

To re-emphasize the Distributive Property, ask students to work these problems using the correct order of operations.

1. a. $-6(8) + -6(2)$ **−60**
b. $-6(8 + 2)$ **−60**

2. a. $3(4.1) - 2(4.1)$ **4.1**
b. $(3 - 2)(4.1)$ **4.1**

3. a. $-18.3(10) + -4.5(10)$ **−228**
b. $(-18.3 + -4.5)(10)$ **−228**
4. a. $17.9(6.2) - 13.8(6.2)$ **25.42**
b. $(17.9 - 13.8)(6.2)$ **25.42**

3-6 Dividing Positive and Negative Numbers

Objective for pages 92–94

■ To find the quotient of two positive or negative numbers.

Teaching Suggestions

Remind students that we cannot divide by 0 (page 52). If necessary, review the reason, using the fact that $a \div b = c$ if and only if $b \times c = a$. Thus $0 \div 4 = 0$ since $4 \times 0 = 0$. Explain that $4 \div 0$ is meaningless since there is no number c such that $0 \times c = 4$. Some students have a better understanding of this when asked to answer $0\overline{)4}$. There is no possible quotient which will multiply times the divisor to give 4. When students ask about $0 \div 0$, show that infinitely many numbers can be found rather than a unique result.

Related Activities

To provide mixed practice following the lesson, give students problems that involve all four operations.

1. $-42 \div 6 \times (-3)$ **21**
2. $-42 \times 6 \div (-3)$ **84**
3. $-42 + 6 \div (-3)$ **−44**
4. $-42 + 6 - (-3)$ **−33**
5. $-42 - 6 \times (-3)$ **−24**
6. $-42 \div 6 - (-3)$ **−4**

3-7 Negative Integers as Exponents

Objective for pages 95–97

■ To simplify expressions involving negative exponents.

Teaching Suggestions

Recall from page 47 the expanded form for 367.04:

$$(3 \times 10^2) + (6 \times 10^1) + (7 \times 10^0)$$
$$+ \left(0 \times \frac{1}{10^1}\right) + \left(4 \times \frac{1}{10^2}\right)$$

Point out that the powers of 10 decrease by 1, so 367.04 may be expanded as:

$$(3 \times 10^2) + (6 \times 10^1) + (7 \times 10^0)$$
$$+ (0 \times 10^{-1}) + (4 \times 10^{-2})$$

Thus $\frac{1}{10^1} = 10^{-1}$, $\frac{1}{10^2} = 10^{-2}$, and $\frac{1}{10^n} = 10^{-n}$.

It is also helpful to include the relationship between negative exponents and reciprocals. Since $10 \times 0.1 = 1$, 10 and 0.1 are reciprocals. Since $100 \times 0.01 = 1$, 100 and 0.01 are reciprocals. To find 10^{-3} ask for the reciprocal of 10^3. Since $1000 \times 0.001 = 1$, the reciprocal of 10^3 is 0.001.

Related Activities

To relate this material to another subject, have students find examples of the use of negative exponents to represent very small numbers. For instance, the diameter of an atom of silver is 2.5×10^{-8} cm. The diameter of a red blood cell is 7.7×10^{-4} cm, or 0.00077 cm. The speed mentioned in Exercise 1 on page 33, 100 million arithmetic operations in a second, is the same as 10 nanoseconds per operation. A nanosecond is 10^{-9} second, so each operation takes 10^{-8} second.

Resource Book: Pages 35–36 (Use After Page 97)

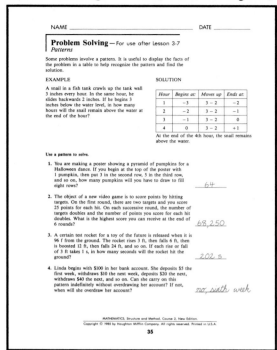

Resource Book: Page 34 (Use After Page 97)

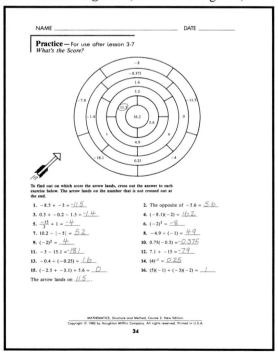

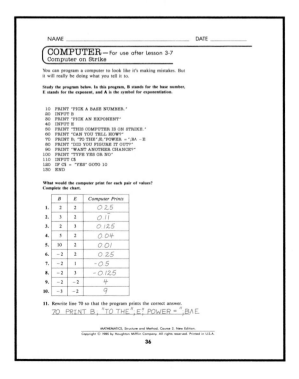

Resource Book: Pages 37–40 (Use After Page 97)

Quiz 3B — Lessons 3-5 through 3-7

DIRECTIONS: Write the letter of the correct answer in the space provided.

Find the product.

1. $-3.2(15.4)$ 2. $4.3(-2.6)(-3)$ *[3-5]*
   a. -33.54 b. 49.28 c. -49.28 d. 33.54

3. $(-4)(3)(-6)(0)(-1)$ 4. $(-2)(-3)(6)(4)(-1)$
   a. -72 b. 0 c. 144 d. -144

Use the properties of addition and multiplication to simplify the expression.

5. $14 + 3 - 2(-6 + 4)$
   a. 21 b. -30 c. 13 d. 17

6. $(-3.2 + 6.8)(-3.8 - 6.2)$
   a. -36 b. 8.64 c. 36 d. -8.64

Find the quotient.

7. $-225 \div (-5)$ 8. $270 \div (-0.6)$ *[3-6]*
   a. -450 b. 450 c. -45 d. 45

9. $0 \div (-1.2)$ 10. $-0.36 \div (-0.3)$
   a. -1.2 b. 1.2 c. 0 d. 12

Use inverse operations to solve for the variable.

11. $-8b = 40$ 12. $b \div (-8) = -40$
   a. $b = 320$ b. $b = -320$ c. $b = 5$ d. $b = -5$

Write the expression without exponents.

13. 3^{-2} 14. 2^{-3} *[3-7]*
   a. -6 b. $-\frac{1}{9}$ c. $\frac{1}{8}$ d. $\frac{1}{9}$

15. $6^3 \times 6^0 \times 6^{-1}$ 16. $(-6)^{-3} \times 6^1 \times (-6)^5$
   a. 216 b. 0 c. 36 d. -36

ANSWERS

1. _c_ (4)
2. _d_ (4)
3. _b_ (4)
4. _d_ (4)
5. _a_ (4)
6. _a_ (4)
7. _d_ (5)
8. _d_ (5)
9. _c_ (5)
10. _b_ (5)
11. _a_ (8)
12. _a_ (8)
13. _d_ (10)
14. _c_ (10)
15. _c_ (10)
16. _a_ (10)

37

Review — Chapter 3

Replace ? with > or < to make a true statement.   *[3-1]*

1. $-7 \underline{?} -8$ 2. $-2 \underline{?} 0$ $<$ 3. $|-8| \underline{?} -8$ $>$

List the integers that can replace x to make the statement true.

4. $|x| = 9$ $9, -9$ 5. $|x| < 3$ $-2, -1, 0, 1, 2$

Write the numbers in order from least to greatest.   *[3-2]*

6. $-5.2, 3.8, -7.3, 0$ $-7.3, -5.2, 0, 3.8$ 7. $0.4, -0.43, 0.34, -0.2$ $-0.43, -0.2, 0.34, 0.4$

List the decimal numbers that can replace x to make the statement true.

8. $|x| = 18.7$ $18.7, -18.7$ 9. $|x| = 0$ 0 10. $|x| = -3.4$ $-3.4, 3.4$

Find the sum.

11. $-3.2 + 4.9$ 1.7 12. $-14.4 + -0.78$ -15.18 *[3-3]*

13. $-7 + 3 + -8 + 0$ -12 14. $-12.6 + 17.2 + -1.8$ 2.8

Solve.

15. One month, the price of a stock went up $4, then down $5, then up $2.50. What was the net change in the price of the stock that month? *up $1.50 (or +$1.50)*

Find the difference.

16. $10 - 19$ -9 17. $3.6 - (-5.4)$ 9.0 *[3-4]*

18. $42 - (-42)$ 84 19. $0 - [3.9 - (-5.6)]$ -9.5

Solve.

20. On a winter day, the temperature dropped from 2°C to -9°C. Find the change in temperature. *down 11°C (or -11°C)*

Find the product.

21. $-6(-3)(4)$ 72 22. $(-1.7)(-4)(-0.5)$ -3.4 *[3-5]*

Find the quotient.

23. $-14.6 \div -2$ 7.3 24. $24.8 \div 0.01$ 2480 *[3-6]*

Write the expression without exponents.

25. 3^{-3} $\frac{1}{27}$ 26. $(-1)^{-5}$ -1 *[3-7]*

27. $6^9 \times 6^{-9}$ 1 28. $(-2)^3 \times (2)^0 \times (-2)^1$ 16

38

Test — Chapter 3

DIRECTIONS: Write the correct answer in the space provided.

Replace ? with =, >, or < to make a true statement.   *[3-1]*

1. $-12 \underline{?} 14$ 2. $-23 \underline{?} -25$

Express as an integer.

3. $|5|$ 4. $|-13|$

Write the numbers in order from least to greatest.   *[3-2]*

5. $-4.5, 45, -1.45, 4.54$

6. $-0.78, -7.8, 7.8, -0.87$

Find the sum.   *[3-3]*

7. $-3 + 22$ 8. $-4.3 + 7.1$

9. $-7.29 + -3.8$ 10. $0 + -3.85$

Find the difference.   *[3-4]*

11. $13 - 27$ 12. $-5 - (-18)$

13. $28.7 - (-3.5)$ 14. $-0.7 - 3.5$

Evaluate the expression when $r = -6$ and $t = -2.7$.

15. $r - t$ 16. $-r - (-t)$

17. $-|t|$ 18. $|r| + |t|$

Find the product.   *[3-5]*

19. $-7(-9)$ 20. $-2.4(-5.5)$ 21. $-1(23.86)$ 22. $(1.3)(-4)(-3.1)$

Find the integer n that will make the statement true.

23. $5(n) = 8(-5)$ 24. $-n(-6) = -12(0)$

Find the quotient.   *[3-6]*

25. $36 \div (-3)$ 26. $-0.6 \div 2.4$ 27. $-0.08 \div (-0.2)$ 28. $0 \div (-0.3)$

Evaluate the expression when $c = -10$ and $d = 2.5$.

29. $c \div d$ 30. $2d \div (-c)$ 31. $-3c \div cd$ 32. $-2c \div d$

ANSWERS

1. $<$ (2)
2. $>$ (2)
3. 5 (2)
4. 13 (2)
5. $-4.5, -1.45, 4.54, 45$ (2)
6. $-7.8, -0.87, -0.78, 7.8$ (2)
7. 19 (3)
8. 2.8 (3)
9. -11.09 (3)
10. -3.85 (3)
11. -14 (3)
12. 13 (3)
13. 32.2 (3)
14. -4.2 (3)
15. -3.3 (3)
16. 3.3 (3)
17. -2.7 (3)
18. 8.7 (3)
19. 63 (3)
20. 13.2 (3)
21. -23.86 (2)
22. 16.12 (2)
23. -8 (3)
24. 0 (3)
25. -12 (3)
26. -0.25 (5)
27. 0.4 (4)
28. 0 (5)
29. -4 (5)
30. 0.5 (5)
31. -1.2 (5)
32. 8 (5)

39

Make-up Test — Chapter 3

DIRECTIONS: Write the correct answer in the space provided.

Replace ? with =, >, or < to make a true statement.   *[3-1]*

1. $16 \underline{?} -15$ 2. $-5 \underline{?} -8$

Express as an integer.

3. $|-9|$ 4. $|6|$

Write the numbers in order from least to greatest.   *[3-2]*

5. $8.9, -1.98, 9.8, -1.89$

6. $0.23, -2.3, -2.23, 2$

Find the sum.   *[3-3]*

7. $-17 + 8$ 8. $-7.4 + -3.9$

9. $-11.5 + 4.8$ 10. $0 + -4.76$

Find the difference.   *[3-4]*

11. $-3.6 - (-4.2)$ 12. $32.1 - (-32.1)$

Evaluate the expression when $e = -7$ and $f = -2.8$.

13. $-|f|$ 14. $|e + f|$

Find the product.   *[3-5]*

15. $-8(-7)$ 16. $-3.8(-6.5)$ 17. $-1(72.93)$ 18. $3.2(-5)(-6.1)$

Find the integer n that will make the statement true.

19. $-4(n) = 9(-4)$ 20. $-n(-8) = -15(0)$

Find the quotient.   *[3-6]*

21. $64 \div (-4)$ 22. $-0.8 \div 3.2$ 23. $-0.006 \div (-0.3)$ 24. $0 \div (-1.4)$

Evaluate the expression when $l = 7.5$ and $m = -30$.

25. $m \div l$ 26. $4l \div m$ 27. $-3m \div lm$ 28. $2l \div m$

ANSWERS

1. $>$ (2)
2. $>$ (2)
3. 9 (2)
4. 6 (2)
5. $-1.98, -1.89, 8.9, 9.8$ (2)
6. $-2.3, -2.23, 0.23, 2$ (2)
7. -9 (3)
8. -11.3 (3)
9. -7.7 (3)
10. -4.76 (3)
11. 0.6 (3)
12. 64.2 (3)
13. -2.8 (3)
14. 9.8 (3)
15. 56 (3)
16. 24.7 (3)
17. -72.93 (4)
18. 97.6 (4)
19. 9 (4)
20. 0 (4)
21. -16 (4)
22. -0.25 (4)
23. 0.02 (3)
24. 0 (4)
25. -4 (4)
26. -1 (4)
27. -0.4 (4)
28. -0.5 (4)

40

71f

NAME _____ DATE _____

CUMULATIVE REVIEW—Chapters 1-3
Exercises

Use the inverse operation to write a related equation or inequality and solve
for the variable.

1. $13 + p = 21$ $p = 21-13, p = 8$
2. $6r > 72$ $r > 72-6, r > 12$
3. $b + 4 < 28$ $b < 28 \times 4, b < 112$
4. $27 - d = 4$ $d = 27-4, d = 23$
5. $s - 18 \geq 30$ $s \geq 30+18, s \geq 48$
6. $w + 83 \leq 95$ $w \leq 95-83, w \leq 12$

Write a variable expression for the word phrase.

7. The sum of thirteen and a number n squared. $13 + n^2$
8. The difference of a number r and fifty-three. $r - 53$
9. The quotient when a number d is divided by seventeen. $d - 17$
10. The product of thirty-two and a number a cubed. $32a^3$

Write an equation or inequality for the word sentence.

11. Forty-one is greater than the sum of m and four. $41 > m + 4$
12. The product when twelve is multiplied by five more than d is fifty. $12(5+d)=50$
13. The sum of w and negative seven and two fifths is fourteen. $w + (-7\frac{2}{5})=14$
14. The difference when x is subtracted from sixty-four is less than or equal to the sum when x is added to eight. $64 - x \leq x + 8$

Round to the place specified.

15. tens: 276.43 280
16. thousandths: 39.00783 39.008
17. hundredths: 43.3609 43.36
18. tenths: 342.96 343.0

Simplify the expression.

19. $(4.7 + 5.3)^2 + 33.2$ 133.2
20. $(3^2 - 2^2) \times (62 - 4^2)$ 230
21. $6x - 32 - 2x + y$ $4x - 32 + y$
22. $3r + 12s - r - 3$ $2r + 12s - 3$
23. $3r^2 \times 3t^3 \times w^2$ $9t^5w^2$
24. $5(3 - d) + 7(d + 2)$ $2d + 29$

Express as an integer.

25. $|23|$ 23
26. $|-10|$ 10
27. $|0|$ 0

Write the integers in order from least to greatest.

28. 14, -3, 16, -5, 0, 2 $-5, -3, 0, 2, 14, 16$
29. -4, -8, 8, 4, 0, -1, 2 $-8, -4, -1, 0, 2, 4, 8$

MATHEMATICS, Structure and Method, Course 2, New Edition.

41

NAME _____ DATE _____

CUMULATIVE REVIEW—Chapters 1-3 *(continued)*
Problems

Problem Solving Reminders
Here are some problem solving reminders that may help you solve some of the problems on this page.
- Determine which facts are necessary to solve the problem.
- Determine which operations are needed to solve the problem.
- Supply additional information if necessary.

Solve.

1. At Marsh Sporting Goods, an aluminum tennis racquet costs $49.95. At Walter's Sport Discount, a similar racquet can be purchased for $8.70 less. What is the price at Walter's Sport Discount? $41.25

2. The Oakhurst Ice Skating Arena sells an admission discount card for $5.00 and rents ice skates for $1.00 a session. The card entitles you to pay an admission fee of $1.25 instead of the regular admission fee of $1.50 each time you skate. What is the minimum number of times you would have to go ice skating to make it worthwhile to purchase a discount card? 21 times

3. Approximately 5.2 calories are burned per hour per kilogram of body mass by bicycle riding. If a student with mass 62 kg takes a 15 min ride to school, how many calories are burned? 80.6 calories

4. Mrs. West's Cheese Blintzes are being promoted by supermarket taste demonstration. An average of 175 samples are distributed between 9:00 A.M. and 4:00 P.M. each day. Find the average number of samples given out each hour. If the daily cost of samples averages $70, what is the average cost per sample? 25 samples 40¢ per sample

5. At the beginning of the summer, when peaches were not in season, the price was 89¢ a lb. As the summer progressed, the price first decreased by 20¢ a lb, then by 12¢ a lb, and then by 15¢ a lb. At the end of the summer season, the price increased by 18¢ a lb and then by 5¢ a lb. What was the final price? 65¢ a lb

6. The Video Den has a special offer that allows customers to rent one movie at the regular price of $7.95 and receive another rental free. The Groovy Movie gives out coupons that let customers deduct $2.50 from the regular price of $6.25 for each movie rental. Is it more expensive to rent two movies at the Video Den or the Groovy Movie? How much more expensive? Video Den more expensive by 45¢

MATHEMATICS, Structure and Method, Course 2, New Edition.

42

NAME _____ DATE _____

CUMULATIVE TEST—Chapters 1-3

DIRECTIONS: Write the answer in the space provided.

Chapter 1

Evaluate the expression when $e = 6$ and $f = 14$.

1. $e + f$
2. $f - e \times 2$
3. $42 + \frac{f}{2}$
4. $2f - e$

Replace $\underline{?}$ with =, >, or < to make a true statement.

5. $20 + 4 \underline{?} 12$
6. $102 \underline{?} 4 \times 28$
7. $2468 \underline{?} 2648$
8. $36,720 \underline{?} 36,072$

Use the inverse operation to write a related equation or inequality and solve for the variable.

9. $9r = 126$
10. $m \div 3 \leq 12$
11. $2b + 6 = 28$
12. $s + 9 > 15$

Write an equation or inequality for the word sentence.

13. The product of thirteen and a number d is ninety-one.
14. The sum of twenty-two and two less than a number n is fifty-four.

Solve, using the five-step plan.

15. Adam purchased a fishing rod for $19.98, a package of six hooks for $2.00, a roll of 200 ft of fishing line costing $3.75, three lures costing 92¢ each, and a tackle box costing $5.83. How much change did he get after paying with a $50 bill?

Chapter 2

Which is greater?

16. 2^3 or 3^2
17. $3^2 \times 3^5$ or $4^3 \times 4^4$
18. $(3 + 2)^3$ or 10^2
19. 10^2 or $5^2 \times 2$

Round to the place specified.

20. hundredths: 132.3998
21. tens: 385.045

Simplify the expression.

22. $432.8 - (12.5 + 7.4)^2$
23. $2x + 3 + 4y + x + 2 + 5y$

ANSWERS
1. 20 (2)
2. 2 (2)
3. 6 (2)
4. 22 (2)
5. $>$ (2)
6. $<$ (2)
7. $<$ (2)
8. $r = 126 \div 9$ $r = 14$ (2)
9. $m \leq 12 \times 3$ $m \leq 36$ (2)
10. $b = (28-6) \div 2$ $b = 11$ (2)
11. $s > 15 - 9$ $s > 6$ (2)
12. $13d = 91$ (2)
13. $22 + n - 2 = 54$ (2)
14. 15.68 (2)
15. 3^2 (2)
16. $4^3 + 4^4$ (2)
17. $(3+2)^3$ (2)
18. 10^2 (2)
19. 132.40 (2)
20. 390 (2)
21. 36.79 (2)
22. $3x + 9y + 5$ (2)

(Continue on next page.)

MATHEMATICS, Structure and Method, Course 2, New Edition.

43

NAME _____ DATE _____

CUMULATIVE TEST—Chapters 1-3 *(continued)*

Solve and check your answer.

24. Jane worked as a gas-station attendant for 18 h this week and 15 h last week. If she earns $3.25 an hour, how much did she earn for two weeks?

25. Thomas is 3 y younger than Chris. Kim is twice as old as Thomas. If Chris is 17, how old is Kim?

Chapter 3

Replace $\underline{?}$ with =, >, or < to make a true statement.

26. $-3 \underline{?} -5$
27. $|6| \underline{?} |-7|$
28. $12 \underline{?} -13$
29. $-8 \underline{?} 3$

Find the sum or difference.

30. $-16.3 + 24.1$
31. $-8.2 + -0.36$
32. $-7 + 5 + -11$
33. $46.9 - (-12.3)$
34. $-8.3 - (-8.3)$
35. $0 - 54.7$

Find the product or quotient.

36. $-5.2 (-14.3)$
37. $-3(-2)(-5)(-10)$
38. $-0.06 \div 0.2$
39. $-8(3.06)$

Evaluate the expression when $r = -2.4$ and $s = -5.6$.

40. $r + s$
41. $10rs$
42. $-|s|$
43. $|r| + |s|$

Write the expression without exponents.

44. 4^{-2}
45. $5^{-7} \times 5^6$
46. $(-2)^3 \times (-2)^{-2}$
47. 3×10^{-4}

ANSWERS
24. $\$107.25$ (2)
25. 28 (2)
26. $>$ (2)
27. $<$ (2)
28. $>$ (2)
29. $<$ (2)
30. 7.8 (2)
31. -8.56 (2)
32. -13 (2)
33. 59.2 (2)
34. 0 (2)
35. -54.7 (2)
36. 74.36 (2)
37. 300 (2)
38. -0.3 (2)
39. -24.48 (2)
40. -8 (2)
41. 134.4 (2)
42. -5.6 (2)
43. 8 (2)
44. $\frac{1}{16}$ (2)
45. $\frac{1}{5}$ (2)
46. $\frac{-2}{1}$ (2)
47. $\frac{3}{10,000}$ (2)

MATHEMATICS, Structure and Method, Course 2, New Edition.

44

LOGIC PROBLEMS

To challenge students to use their powers of logical reasoning, you can use the problems that follow. These problems do not require the use of any specific mathematical skills; they are, therefore, suitable for use at any time throughout the year.

1. A man standing in front of a portrait says the following verse about the portrait: "Brothers and sisters I have none, but this man's father is my father's son." Who is the man in the portrait?

   The speaker's father's son must be himself. Therefore the man in the portrait is the speaker's son.

2. Linda, Dawn, and Ken have formed a rock band. One person plays lead guitar, one plays the drums, and one plays bass guitar. Only one of the following statements is true. Who plays what instrument?
   (a) Linda plays the bass guitar.
   (b) Linda does not play the drums.
   (c) Ken does not play lead guitar.
   (d) Ken does not play the drums.

   If (a) was the only true statement, that would mean that Ken would play the drums as well as lead guitar. Since each person plays one instrument, this must be false. Similarly, (b) must be false. If (c) was true, then Linda and Ken would both play the drums. Statement (d) must be the true statement. This means Linda plays the drums, Ken plays lead guitar, and Dawn plays bass guitar.

3. There are five teams in a local baseball league. From the following clues, can you tell the order that the teams finished in last year's season?
   (a) Cairo finished ahead of Acton.
   (b) Belmont finished ahead of Elmwood and Dennis.
   (c) Acton finished between Dennis and Belmont.

   Since Acton finished between Dennis and Belmont, Cairo finished ahead of Acton, and Elmwood finished after Acton, Acton had to finish third. It follows that Cairo finished first, Belmont finished second, Dennis finished fourth, and Elmwood fifth.

4. Four neighbors have painted their houses, each a different color from the following choices: red, blue, white, and yellow. Determine from the clues the color selected by each neighbor.
   (a) Mickey didn't paint his house blue or white.
   (b) Mickey and Steve live across the street from Nancy and Miles.

   (c) All four neighbors started painting at the same time and the yellow house was the first one completed.
   (d) Steve bought all the paint for his house as well as a can of blue paint for one of his neighbors.
   (e) Steve's house took the longest to paint. The house next to Miles took the least time to paint.

   The person living next to Miles is Nancy. Since she was the first one done, her house must be yellow. Because Mickey didn't use blue or white, his house is red. Steve bought a can of blue paint for his neighbor, so his house must be white. Miles painted his house blue.

5. Two pairs of twins work in the same office. They live in four separate communities. From the information below, can you determine the names of each pair of twins?
   (a) Janet drives to work with Diane. Terry and Kim each commute alone.
   (b) Diane is the only person who can open the office.
   (c) Kim is always the last person to arrive at the office.
   (d) Janet's sister walks to work. Each morning she is waiting at the office to be let in.

   Because Kim is the last to arrive at work and since Diane commutes with Janet, Terry must be Janet's twin. Diane and Kim are twins.

6. Four trains, each from a different side of a city, are heading for the central terminal. From the following clues, determine which side of the city each train is from and the name of the town where each train started.
   (a) The train from the east was the first to arrive at the terminal. The train from Dover was the next to arrive.
   (b) The train from Harwich is not from the east or west side of town.
   (c) The train from Lakeville was the last to arrive, just after the train from the north.
   (d) Dover and Littleton are on opposite sides of the city.

   The train from the east, which arrived first, is not from Dover, Harwich, or Lakeville, so it is from Littleton. Therefore the train from Dover is from the opposite direction, west. The train from the north, which arrived third, was not from Dover, Littleton, or Lakeville, so it is from Harwich. Therefore the train from the south is from Lakeville.

3-1 The Integers

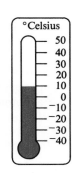

°Celsius

When we measure temperature, we use a scale that has 0 as a reference point. We use *positive numbers* to indicate temperatures above 0°, and we use *negative numbers* to indicate temperatures below 0°.

We often have occasion to measure quantities on different sides of a zero reference point, such as distances above and below sea level, time before and after a rocket launch, increases and decreases in stock prices, and deposits and withdrawals in a bank account. Positive and negative numbers help us to measure these quantities.

We may graph both positive and negative numbers on a horizontal number line by extending the number line to the *left* of the origin as shown below. Like the positive whole numbers, the negative whole numbers are equally spaced, but they are positioned to the left of 0.

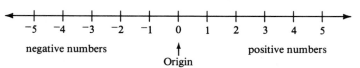

We read ⁻1 as *negative one*. We may read 1 as *positive one,* or simply *one*. For emphasis, we may use the symbol ⁺1 for positive one.

Any pair of numbers, such as 3 and ⁻3, that are the same distance from the origin but in opposite directions are called **opposites.** The opposite of 3 is ⁻3 and the opposite of ⁻3 is 3. The opposite of 0 is 0.

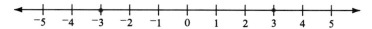

We use the symbol $|^-3|$, read *the absolute value of ⁻3,* to represent the distance between ⁻3 and 0. Because ⁻3 is 3 units from the origin, $|^-3| = 3$. In general, $|n|$ (read *the absolute value of n*) represents the distance between the number n and the origin.

The whole numbers, 0, 1, 2, 3, . . . , together with their opposites, 0, ⁻1, ⁻2, ⁻3, . . . , form the set of numbers called the **integers:**

$$. . . , ^-3, ^-2, ^-1, 0, 1, 2, 3, ...$$

The **positive integers** are the numbers 1, 2, 3, . . . , and the **negative integers** are the numbers ⁻1, ⁻2, ⁻3, ... Although 0 is an integer, it is neither positive nor negative.

EXAMPLE 1   Express as an integer.

  a. $|^-5|$ **b.** $|0|$

72   *Chapter 3*

Solution **a.** $|^-5|$ represents the distance between 0 and the number $^-5$. Thus $|^-5| = 5$.

   b. $|0|$ represents the distance between 0 and 0. Thus $|0| = 0$.

EXAMPLE 2 Arrange $^-3$, 1, $^-4$, 0, $^-1$ in order from least to greatest.

Solution   We can graph the numbers on a number line, with 1 at the right of 0.

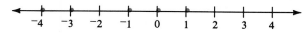

Reading the coordinates of the points from left to right will order the numbers from least to greatest. $^-4$, $^-3$, $^-1$, 0, 1

Class Exercises

Name an integer that represents each of the following.

1. 15 s before blastoff of a rocket $^-$15

2. A gain of 6 yd in a football play 6

3. A withdrawal of 90 dollars from a bank account $^-$90

4. An elevation of 350 ft below sea level $^-$350

5. The opposite of 80 $^-$80   **6.** The opposite of $^-2$ 2

7. The absolute value of $^-14$ 14   **8.** The absolute value of 27 27

9. Name two integers, each of which is 12 units from 0. 12, $^-$12

10. If $|n| = 15$, then $n = \underline{\ ?\ }$ or $n = \underline{\ ?\ }$.
$\qquad\qquad\qquad\qquad\qquad$15$\qquad\qquad$$^-$15

Replace $\underline{\ ?\ }$ with > or < to make a true statement.

11. a. $^-6 \underline{\ ?\ } ^-2$ **b.** $|^-6| \underline{\ ?\ } |^-2|$ **12. a.** $4 \underline{\ ?\ } ^-5$ **b.** $|4| \underline{\ ?\ } |^-5|$
$\qquad\quad$<$\qquad\qquad\qquad\quad$>$\qquad\qquad\qquad\qquad$>$\qquad\qquad\qquad$<

Written Exercises

Graph the integers in each exercise on the same number line. Check students' graphs.

A **1.** 0, 1, $^-1$, 3, $^-3$ **2.** 0, 2, $^-2$, 5, $^-5$ **3.** 6, 0, $^-4$, $^-9$, 7   **4.** $^-1$, 3, $^-8$, 4, $^-6$

Graph the number and its opposite on the same number line. Check students' graphs.

5. 3   **6.** 10   **7.** $^-7$ **8.** $^-2$ **9.** 0   **10.** $^-4$

Positive and Negative Numbers   **73**

Suggested Assignments

Minimum
   73/1–10
   74/11–30; 32–38 even
   74/Rev. 1–9

Average
   73/2–10 even
   74/12–30 even; 31–44
   74/Rev. 2–8 even

Maximum
   73/2–10 even
   74/12–30 even; 31–45

Supplementary Materials

Practice Masters, p. 11

Replace __?__ with > or < to make a true statement.

11. $^-3$ __?__ $^-4$ >   **12.** $^-2$ __?__ 1 <   > **13.** 7 __?__ $^-8$

14. 0 __?__ $^-2$ >   **15.** $^-11$ __?__ 0 <   < **16.** $^-7$ __?__ 10

Express as an integer.

17. $|^-3|$ 3 **18.** $|^-6|$ 6 **19.** $|0|$ 0 **20.** $|12|$ 12 **21.** $|9|$ 9 **22.** $|^-7|$ 7 **23.** $|^-8|$ 8 **24.** $|^-1|$ 1

Write the integers in order from least to greatest.

25. 6, $^-15$, 0, $^-2$ $^-15$, $^-2$, 0, 6   **26.** $^-3$, 1, 0, $^-7$ $^-7$, $^-3$, 0, 1

27. $^-12$, 7, $^-8$, 1, $^-1$ $^-12$, $^-8$, $^-1$, 1, 7   **28.** 0, 2, $^-5$, $^-9$, 10 $^-9$, $^-5$, 0, 2, 10

29. $^-10$, 4, 14, $^-14$, 8 $^-14$, $^-10$, 4, 8, 14   **30.** 3, 9, $^-13$, 11, $^-15$ $^-15$, $^-13$, 3, 9, 11

For Exercises 31-42, (a) list the integers that can replace n to make the statement true, and (b) graph the integers on the number line. (b) Check students' graphs.

B **31.** $|n| = 6$ 6, $^-6$ **32.** $|n| = 3$ 3, $^-3$ **33.** $|n| = 4$
                                                                                      4, $^-4$

34. $|n| = 5$ 5, $^-5$ **35.** $|n| = 0$ 0   **36.** $|n| = 14$
                                                                                     14, $^-14$

37. $|n| < 2$ $^-1$, 0, 1   **38.** $|n| < 5$ $^-4$, $^-3$, $^-2$, . . . 2, 3, 4   **39.** $|n| \leq 4$
                                                                                            $^-4$, $^-3$, $^-2$, . . . 2, 3, 4

40. $|n| \leq 7$ **41.** $2 < |n| < 8$ $^-7$, $^-6$, $^-5$, $^-4$, $^-3$,   **42.** $0 < |n| < 3$
    $^-7$, $^-6$, $^-5$, . . . 5, 6, 7   3, 4, 5, 6, 7 $^-2$, $^-1$, 1, 2

Complete with the word *positive* or *negative*.

C **43.** If an integer is equal to its absolute value, then the integer must be
      a __?__ integer or 0. Positive

44. If an integer is equal to the opposite of its absolute value, then the
    integer must be a __?__ integer or 0. Negative

45. Explain why there is no number that can replace n to make the
    equation $|n| = {}^-3$ true. $|n|$ represents the distance n from the origin.

Review Exercises

Replace __?__ with the symbols < or > to make a true statement.

1. 43.8 __?__ 4.38 >   **2.** 27.35 __?__ 273.5 <   > **3.** 0.064 __?__ 0.0597

4. 0.003 __?__ 0.02 <   **5.** 0.182 __?__ 1.082 <   < **6.** 5.407 __?__ 5.413

7. 98.04 __?__ 09.007 >   **8.** 48.066 __?__ 46.06 >   < **9.** 0.0705 __?__ 0.705

3-2 Decimals on the Number Line

The graphs of the *positive decimal* 2.5 and its opposite, the *negative decimal* ⁻2.5, are shown on the number line below. We graph 2.5 by locating the point that is 2.5 units to the *right* of 0, and we graph ⁻2.5 by locating the point that is 2.5 units to the *left* of 0.

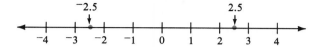

The positive decimals together with the negative decimals and 0 form the set of *decimal numbers*. The set of decimal numbers includes all of the whole numbers and all of the integers.

EXAMPLE 1   Write the following numbers in order from least to greatest.

$$^-2, 4.1, 0.2, {}^-2.6, {}^-1.34$$

Solution   We can graph the given numbers on a number line.

Reading the coordinates from left to right will give the numbers in order from least to greatest.

$$^-2.6, {}^-2, {}^-1.34, 0.2, 4.1$$

We have been representing decimals by their graphs, that is, by dots on a number line. We can also use directed line segments or arrows to illustrate decimals. Arrows that point to the *left* (the negative direction) represent negative numbers. Arrows that point to the *right* (the positive direction) represent positive numbers.

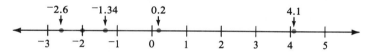

Notice in the diagram above that both the arrow representing ⁻2.5 and the arrow representing 2.5 have length 2.5.

Positive and Negative Numbers   **75**

Teaching Suggestions p. 71b

Related Activities p. 71b

Reading Mathematics

Students will learn the meaning of the following mathematical terms in this lesson: *positive decimal, negative decimal*.

Chalkboard Examples

Graph these numbers.

1. 2.7

2. ⁻1.01

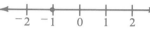

3. 0.6

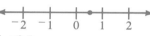

4. ⁻2.7

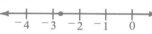

5. ⁻3.5

6. 1.2

An arrow representing a number may have any point on the number line as its starting point, as long as it has length and direction indicated by that number. The length of the arrow is the absolute value of the number that the arrow represents. The direction of the arrow is determined by the sign of the number.

On the number line above, each arrow represents the decimal number ⁻4, for each has length 4 and points to the left.

EXAMPLE 2   What number is represented by the arrow above the number line below?

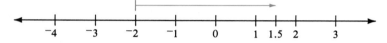

Solution   The starting point of the arrow is ⁻2 and the endpoint is 1.5. The arrow points to the right and is 3.5 units long. Thus, the arrow represents the positive decimal number 3.5.

EXAMPLE 3   An arrow representing the number ⁻7 has starting point 3. What is its endpoint?

Solution   Draw a number line. Starting at 3, draw an arrow 7 units long in the negative direction (left). The endpoint of the arrow is ⁻4.

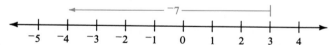

Class Exercises

Name a decimal number that represents each of the following.

1. The opposite of 8.71 ⁻8.71

2. The opposite of ⁻10.16 10.16

3. A discount of fifty-nine cents ⁻0.59

4. A rise in body temperature of 0.6°C 0.6

5. The absolute value of ⁻67.5 67.5

6. The absolute value of 9.07 9.07

7. Name the letter written above the graph of the given number.

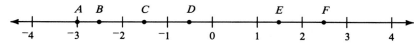

a. ⁻0.5 _D_   **b.** ⁻1.5 _C_   **c.** 1.5 _E_   **d.** ⁻2.5 _B_

8. State the numbers in Exercise 7 in order from least to greatest.

⁻2.5, ⁻1.5, ⁻0.5, 1.5

Name the number represented by each arrow described below.

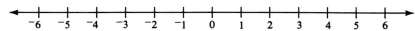

9. Starting point at 0, endpoint at ⁻2.5   **10.** Starting point at ⁻1, endpoint at 3

⁻2.5   4

11. Starting point at 2, endpoint at ⁻4   **12.** Starting point at ⁻0.5, endpoint at 5

⁻6   5.5

Written Exercises

Graph the numbers in each exercise on the same number line. Check students' graphs.

A   **1.** ⁻2, ⁻3.5, 0   **2.** 3.2, ⁻4, ⁻3.2   **3.** ⁻1.5, ⁻7, ⁻3.25   **4.** ⁻0.9, ⁻1, ⁻4.1

Graph the number and its opposite on the same number line. Check students' graphs.

5. 2.25   **6.** 1.9   **7.** ⁻0.5   **8.** ⁻3.1

9. ⁻4.2   **10.** 0.75   **11.** 0.3   **12.** 5.5

Write the decimal number that is equal to each of the following.

13. |⁻2.36| **14.** |1.921| **15.** |⁻16| **16.** |⁻100| **17.** |3.03| **18.** |⁻0.2|
2.36   1.921   16   100   3.03   0.2

Replace _?_ **with** < **or** > **to make a true statement.**

19. ⁻2.93 _?_ 1.1 <   **20.** 4 _?_ ⁻0.5 >   < **21.** ⁻8.1 _?_ 2.3

22. ⁻1.95 _?_ ⁻1.96 >   **23.** ⁻5.01 _?_ ⁻4.99 <   < **24.** ⁻2.99 _?_ ⁻2.98

25. 0.1 _?_ ⁻18.25 >   **26.** 12.2 _?_ ⁻13.3 >   < **27.** ⁻3.7 _?_ 3.07

Write the numbers in order from least to greatest.

28. ⁻2.72, ⁻3, 0.03, ⁻3.5, 0.2   **29.** 6.3, ⁻8, ⁻7.6, ⁻1.75, 6.03
⁻3.5, ⁻3, ⁻2.72, 0.03, 0.2   ⁻8, ⁻7.6, ⁻1.75, 6.03, 6.3
30. 0, 2.99, ⁻10, ⁻0.1, ⁻0.01   **31.** ⁻100.5, ⁻2, 3.11, ⁻2.1, ⁻46.8
⁻10, ⁻0.1, ⁻0.01, 0, 2.99   ⁻100.5, ⁻46.8, ⁻2.1, ⁻2, 3.11
32. ⁻0.5, ⁻0.05, ⁻5, ⁻50, 500   **33.** ⁻0.3, 30.3, ⁻0.33, ⁻3.3, 33
⁻50, ⁻5, ⁻0.5, ⁻0.05, 500   ⁻3.3, ⁻0.33, ⁻0.3, 30.3, 33

Positive and Negative Numbers   **77**

Additional A Exercises

Replace _?_ with < or > to make true statements.

1. ⁻0.3 _>?_ ⁻0.33

2. ⁻8 _<?_ ⁻7.3

3. 2.1 _>?_ 2.01

4. ⁻4 _>?_ ⁻40

Write in order from least to greatest.

5. ⁻3.4, ⁻2.1, ⁻5
⁻5, ⁻3.4, ⁻2.1
6. 0, 0.3, ⁻0.4
⁻0.4, 0, 0.3

Suggested Assignments

Minimum
Day 1: 77/1–33 odd
    78/34–40
Day 2: 77/2–32 even
    78/41–50
    78/Rev. 1–9

Average
Day 1: 77/1–33 odd
    78/34–43
Day 2: 77/2–32 even
    78/44–54
    78/Rev. 1–9 odd

Maximum
    77/1–33 odd
    78/35–39 odd; 41–54

Supplementary Materials

Practice Masters, p. 11

Draw an arrow to represent each decimal number described below.
Check students' graphs.
34. The number 3, with starting point ⁻1

35. The number 2.5, with starting point ⁻0.5

36. The number ⁻5, with starting point 1.5

37. The number ⁻3, with starting point ⁻0.5

38. The number 5.5, with starting point ⁻3

39. The number ⁻4, with endpoint ⁻2

40. The number ⁻2, with endpoint 5

List the decimal numbers that can replace *x* to make the statement true.

B **41.** $|x| = 4.1$ 4.1, ⁻4.1   **42.** $|x| = 0.001$ 0.001, ⁻0.001   **43.** $|x| = 26.3$
26.3, ⁻26.3
44. $|x| = 0$ 0   **45.** $|x| = |⁻1.19|$ 1.19, ⁻1.19   **46.** $|x| = |⁻2.2|$
2.2, ⁻2.2

Copy and complete the chart so that the two arrows represent the same decimal number.

	Arrow 1		Arrow 2	
	Starting Point	**Endpoint**	**Starting Point**	**Endpoint**
47.	⁻2.5	⁻7	0	? ⁻4.5
48.	? 7	4	1.5	⁻1.5
49.	⁻0.5	8.5	? ⁻12	⁻3
50.	4	⁻6.25	? 8.25	⁻2

For Exercises 51–54, (a) list the *integers* that can replace *n* to make the statement true, and (b) show their graphs on a number line. (b) Check students' graphs.

51. $|n| < 4.3$ **52.** $|n| < 2.99$ **53.** $|n| \leq 5.001$ **54.** $|n| \leq 0.08$
⁻4, ⁻3, ⁻2, . . . 2, 3, 4   ⁻2, ⁻1, 0, 1, 2   ⁻5, ⁻4, ⁻3, . . . 3, 4, 5   0

Review Exercises
4. 15.78; Commutative and Associative
Use the properties to simplify the expression. Name the property or properties used.

1. $2(4.5 + 1.07)$
11.14; Distributive
2. $3.7 + 12.5 + 0.5$
16.7; Associative
3. 1×27.18 27.18;
Multiplication Prop. of One
4. $8.69 + 4.78 + 2.31$
5. $7(30 - 11.1)$
132.3; Distributive
6. $(44 \times 0.3) + (44 \times 0.7)$
44; Distributive
7. $6.25 \times 43 \times 4$
1075; Commutative
8. $0.2 \times 3.7 \times 0.5$
0.37; Commutative
9. $17.6 \times 283 \times 0$
0; Associative and

78 *Chapter 3* and Associative   and Associative   Multiplication Prop.
of Zero

3-3 Adding Positive and Negative Numbers

Teaching Suggestions p. 71b

Related Activities p. 71b

Reading Mathematics

Students will learn the meaning of the following mathematical terms in this lesson: *addend, sum.*

Chalkboard Examples

Find the sum.

1. ⁻19 + 42 **23**
2. ⁻33 + ⁻12 **⁻45**
3. 50 + ⁻6 **44**
4. ⁻14.3 + ⁻9.7 **⁻24**
5. 6 + ⁻3.2 **2.8**
6. 2.8 + ⁻1.6 + ⁻5 **⁻3.8**

We can use arrows on the number line, as shown below, to add two positive numbers or to add two negative numbers. We draw a solid arrow with starting point 0 to represent the first addend. We draw another solid arrow with *starting point at the endpoint of the first arrow* to represent the second addend. To represent the sum, we draw a dashed arrow from the starting point of the first arrow to the endpoint of the second arrow.

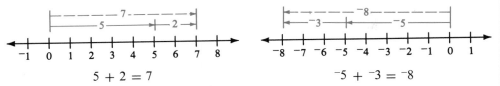

$$5 + 2 = 7 \qquad\qquad ^-5 + ^-3 = ^-8$$

In each case, if we add the absolute values of the addends, we obtain the absolute value of the sum. The sum has the same sign as the addends.

> ### *Rules*
>
> The sum of two positive numbers is positive.
>
> The sum of two negative numbers is negative.

EXAMPLE 1   Find the sum.   **a.** 2.5 + 4.3   **b.** ⁻7 + ⁻1.5

Solution   **a.** Since the addends are positive, the sum is positive.
$$2.5 + 4.3 = 6.8$$

b. Since the addends are negative, the sum is negative.
$$^-7 + ^-1.5 = ^-8.5$$

We can also use arrows on the number line to add a positive and a negative number. The sum of a positive and a negative number may be positive, negative, or zero, as shown in the following illustrations.

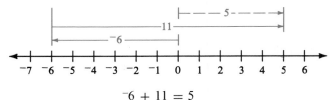

The positive number 11 has greater absolute value than the negative number ⁻6. Thus the sum is positive.

$$^-6 + 11 = 5$$

Positive and Negative Numbers   **79**

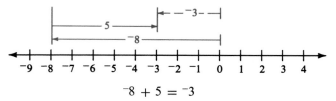

$$-8 + 5 = -3$$

The negative number -8 has greater absolute value than the positive number 5. Thus the sum is negative.

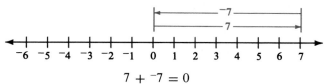

$$7 + -7 = 0$$

The positive number 7 and the negative number -7 are opposites and thus have the same absolute value. The sum is zero.

Notice that, in each case, the absolute value of the sum is the *difference* of the absolute values of the addends. The sum has the same sign as the addend with the greater absolute value.

> ## Rules
>
> The sum of a positive number and a negative number is
>
> **1.** positive if the positive number has the greater absolute value.
> **2.** negative if the negative number has the greater absolute value.
> **3.** zero if the numbers have the same absolute value.

EXAMPLE 2 Find the sum.
  a. $3.5 + -10.5$ **b.** $-7.6 + 12.2$ **c.** $-4.8 + 0$

Solution   **a.** The negative addend has the greater absolute value, so the sum is negative. $3.5 + -10.5 = -7$

  b. The positive addend has the greater absolute value, so the sum is positive. $-7.6 + 12.2 = 4.6$

  c. Think of adding 0 as *moving no units* on the number line. Thus, $-4.8 + 0 = -4.8$.

As shown in Example 2, part (c), the addition property of zero holds for the positive and negative decimals. All of the properties for positive decimals hold for negative decimals as well.

EXAMPLE 3 Sally Wright bought some stock in ABC Computer Company. The stock went down $2.50 per share in the first week, went up $3.00 in the second week, and went down $1.25 in the third week. If Sally paid $30.50 per share for the stock, did she gain or lose money?

Solution
- The question asks if Sally gained or lost money.

- Given information: Sally paid $30.50 per share
  price went down $2.50, went up $3.00, went
  down $1.25

- First, find the new price per share. Express the given information
  as a sum of positive and negative decimals.
  $$30.50 + {}^-2.50 + 3 + {}^-1.25 = (30.50 + 3) + ({}^-2.50 + {}^-1.25)$$
  $$= 33.50 + {}^-3.75$$
  $$= 29.75$$
  To find whether Sally gained or lost money, compare the new
  price per share to the price paid per share.
  $$29.75 < 30.50$$

- Because the new price per share is less than the price paid per
  share, Sally lost money.

Problem Solving Reminder
Many problems involve *more than one step*, but the steps may not always
involve operations. In Example 3, we used addition in the first step, but in
the second step we compared the answer to the first step with an amount
given in the problem.

Class Exercises

State the addition fact illustrated by the diagram.

1.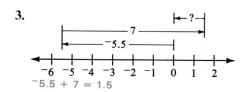
$^-2 + {}^-3 = {}^-5$

2.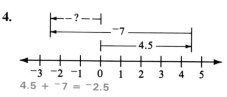
$2.8 + {}^-2.8 = 0$

3.

$^-5.5 + 7 = 1.5$

4.

$4.5 + {}^-7 = {}^-2.5$

Without computing the exact sum, state whether the sum is positive, negative, or 0.

5. $^-3.4 + {}^-2.6$ negative

6. $25.7 + {}^-8.6 + {}^-25.7$ negative

7. $2.37 + {}^-9.99$
   negative

8. $^-6.8 + 11.5$ positive

9. $36.3 + 0.14 + {}^-36.3$ positive

10. $^-15.4 + 0 + {}^-3.2$
    negative

Positive and Negative Numbers **81**

Written Exercises

Find the sum by using arrows on a number line. Check students' graphs.

A **1.** ⁻3 + ⁻8 **2.** 10.7 + ⁻10.7 **3.** ⁻12.5 + 22 **4.** 2.9 + ⁻6.9

Find the sum.

5. ⁻2 + ⁻17 **⁻19** **6.** ⁻8 + ⁻9 **⁻17** **7.** 8.3 + ⁻21.3 **⁻13** **8.** ⁻4.6 + 38.6 **34**

9. ⁻0.1 + ⁻0.2 **⁻0.3** **10.** ⁻1.82 + ⁻3.68 **⁻5.5** **11.** 16.5 + ⁻16.5 **0** **12.** ⁻8.7 + 3.4 **⁻5.3**

13. 16.9 + ⁻0.7 **16.2** **14.** ⁻51.3 + 51.3 **0** **15.** 12.37 + ⁻8.2 **4.17** **16.** ⁻85 + ⁻41 **⁻126**

17. ⁻16 + ⁻68 **⁻84** **18.** 4.1 + ⁻13 **⁻8.9** **19.** 26.4 + ⁻15.9 **10.5** **20.** 9.65 + ⁻10.1 **⁻0.45**

21. ⁻13.12 + ⁻5.6 **⁻18.72** **22.** ⁻26.01 + 26.0 **⁻0.01** **23.** 2.9 + ⁻29 **⁻26.1** **24.** 7 + ⁻13.2 **⁻6.2**

25. 81.9 + ⁻81.9 **0** **26.** 32.8 + ⁻36 **⁻3.2** **27.** 0 + ⁻0.12 **⁻0.12** **28.** ⁻7.9 + 0 **⁻7.9**

29. ⁻4.2 + ⁻6.5 + 17 **6.3** **30.** 7.1 + ⁻9 + 2.3 **0.4** **31.** 5 + ⁻16.9 + 1.1 **⁻10.8**

32. ⁻8.6 + ⁻17.1 + ⁻4.3 **⁻30** **33.** ⁻3.3 + ⁻7.25 + 3.3 **⁻7.25** **34.** 0.98 + ⁻13.4 + ⁻0.98 **⁻13.4**

What value of the variable makes the statement true?

35. ⁻8 + x = 4 **12** **36.** x + 4 = ⁻9 **⁻13** **37.** ⁻41 + x = ⁻53 **⁻12**

38. ⁻19 + x = 0 **19** **39.** 18.5 + x = 0 **⁻18.5** **40.** ⁻6 + x = ⁻1 **5**

B **41.** ⁻4.3 + x = ⁻6.7 **⁻2.4** **42.** x + ⁻5.6 = ⁻37 **⁻31.4** **43.** x + 18.6 = ⁻1.2 **⁻19.8**

44. ⁻0.66 + x = 0.10 **0.76** **45.** 12.9 + x = ⁻13 **⁻25.9** **46.** x + 20.2 = ⁻5.1 **⁻25.3**

47. a. 9 + 6.7 + x = 9 **⁻6.7** **48. a.** ⁻6.3 + ⁻8.1 + x = ⁻6.3 **8.1**

    b. 9 + 6.7 + x = 6.7 **⁻9**   **b.** ⁻6.3 + ⁻8.1 + x = ⁻8.1 **6.3**

Replace __?__ with =, >, or < to make a true statement.

49. (⁻25.3 + ⁻8.8) __?__ (⁻12.4 + ⁻19.7) **<** **50.** (6.24 + ⁻15.9) __?__ (⁻6.24 + 15.9) **<**

51. (⁻34.9 + 27.5) __?__ (9.7 + ⁻18.4) **>** **52.** (14.4 + ⁻18.6) __?__ (⁻3.2 + ⁻0.98) **<**

C **53. a.** |⁻3 + ⁻19| __?__ |⁻3| + |⁻19| **=** **b.** |⁻4.6 + 4.6| __?__ |⁻4.6| + |4.6| **<**

    c. |⁻8.7 + 12.6| __?__ |⁻8.7| + |12.6| **<** **d.** |⁻18.6 + 4.9| __?__ |⁻18.6| + |4.9| **<**

    e. |53.5 + 3.7| __?__ |53.5| + |3.7| **=** **f.** |⁻4 + 13.75| __?__ |⁻4| + |13.75| **<**

    g. On the basis of your answers to parts (a)–(f), write a general rule for $|x + y|$ __?__ $|x| + |y|$ that holds for all numbers x and y. Explain why this rule is true.

82 *Chapter 3*

Problems

Solve each problem by first expressing
the given data as a sum of positive and
negative numbers. Then, compute the
sum of the numbers and answer the questions.

A 1. The temperature in Lynn at 7:00 A.M.
was ⁻7°C. By 12:00 noon, the temperature had increased by 13°C, but
it then decreased by 3°C between
noon and 5:00 P.M. What was the
temperature reading at 5:00 P.M.?
⁻7 + 13 + ⁻3; 3°C

2. From the Andersons' farm, Bonnie
drove 20.4 km due east to Fairvale.
From Fairvale, she drove 33.7 km
due west to Ward City. How far was
she then from the farm and in what
direction? 20.4 + ⁻33.7; 13.3 km west

3. The Tigers football team gains 3.5 yd on a first down, loses 11 yd on
the second down, and gains 2 yd on the third down. Do the Tigers
gain or lose total yardage in these three plays? What is the total
number of yards gained or lost? 3.5 + ⁻11 + 2; lost; 5.5 lost

B 4. For a summer job, Tom plans to clean the Wilsons' house. He
estimates that each week he will spend $1.25 and $3.80 on cleaning
supplies. How much should he charge the Wilsons if he wishes to
make a profit of $6.50 each week? 1.25 + 3.80 + 6.50; $11.55

5. Carl purchased stock in the Dependable Equipment Company.
The price per share of the stock fell by $4.30 in the first month, rose
by $2.50 in the second month, and rose by $2.60 in the third month.
Carl sold the stock for $22.00 per share at the end of the third
month. Did he gain or lose money? ⁻4.30 + 2.50 + 2.60; gain

Review Exercises

Evaluate the expression when s = 2.7 and t = 8.4.

1. $(25 - s)7$ 156.1

2. $102 \div (t + 12)$ 5

3. $11(7s - 13)$ 64.9

4. $(t + 6 - 4.4)t$ 84

5. $(s + 4)(s + 4)$ 44.89

6. $10st \div (t - 4.2)$
54

7. $st \div 2s$ 4.2

8. $(s + t) \div (t + 13.8)$ 0.5

9. $(t - s)(5t + 8)$
285

Positive and Negative Numbers **83**

Suggested Assignments

Minimum
Day 1: 82/1–40
Day 2: 82/41–46
          83/Prob. 1–5
          83/Rev. 1–9

Average
Day 1: 82/1–48
Day 2: 82/49–52
          83/Prob. 1–5
          83/Rev. 2–8 even

Maximum
Day 1: 82/1–48
Day 2: 82/49–53
          83/Prob. 1–5

Supplementary Materials

Practice Masters, p. 12

83

Teaching Suggestions p. 71c

Related Activities p. 71c

Reading Mathematics

Students will learn the meaning of the following mathematical terms in this lesson: *opposite, difference.*

Chalkboard Examples

Find the difference.

1. 5 − (−2) **7**

2. −5 − 2 **−7**

3. −5 − (−2) **−3**

4. 7.8 − 9.3 **−1.5**

5. −12 − (4.7) **−16.7**

6. 0 − 9.1 **−9.1**

3-4 Subtracting Positive and Negative Numbers

You know that $7.5 - 3 = 4.5$. In the preceding lesson, you learned that $7.5 + {}^-3 = 4.5$. Thus, $7.5 - 3 = 7.5 + {}^-3$. This example suggests the following general rule.

Rule

For any numbers a and b,

$$a - b = a + (\text{the opposite of } b)$$

or

$$a - b = a + (-b)$$

Note the lowered position of the minus sign in the expression $(-b)$, above. We use an *unraised* minus sign to mean *the opposite of.* For example,

$$-3 = {}^-3, \text{ read } \textit{the opposite of three equals negative three}$$

$$-({}^-5) = 5, \text{ read } \textit{the opposite of negative five equals five}$$

Because the numerals -3 and ${}^-3$ name the same number, one may be used in place of the other. From now on, we will use an unraised minus sign to denote subtraction, a negative number, and the opposite of a number.

EXAMPLE 1   Find the difference.
  a. $5 - 13$ **b.** $12.4 - (-8)$
  c. $-4.6 - 1.5$ **d.** $-10.9 - (-3.4)$

Solution   **a.** $5 - 13 = 5 + (-13) = -8$

  b. $12.4 - (-8) = 12.4 + 8 = 20.4$

  c. $-4.6 - 1.5 = -4.6 + (-1.5) = -6.1$

  d. $-10.9 - (-3.4) = -10.9 + 3.4 = -7.5$

It is important to read a variable expression such as $-n$ as *the opposite of n* because n may denote a negative number, a positive number, or 0.

EXAMPLE 2   Evaluate the expression when $m = -5.2$.
  a. $m - 14$ **b.** $-m - 14$

84   *Chapter 3*

Solution   **a.** $m - 14 = -5.2 - 14 = -5.2 + (-14) = -19.2$

b. $-m - 14 = -(-5.2) - 14 = 5.2 - 14 = 5.2 + (-14) = -8.8$

Reading Mathematics: *Using Examples*
The worked-out examples in each lesson show you how the general statements in the lesson can be applied to specific situations. If you need help as
you work on the exercises, look back at the examples for models to follow or
for ideas on how to begin your solutions.

Class Exercises

Complete.

1. $6 - 12 = 6 + \underline{\ ?\ } -12$

2. $-10 - 8 = -10 + \underline{\ ?\ } -8$

3. $6.7 - (-1.5) = 6.7 + \underline{\ ?\ } \; 1.5$

4. $-26.01 - (-8.2) = -26.01 + \underline{\ ?\ }$
8.2

**Without computing the exact difference, state whether the difference is
positive, negative, or 0.**

5. $-4.2 - 4.2$ neg. **6.** $4.2 - (-4.2)$ pos. **7.** $4.2 - 4.2$ 0   **8.** $-4.2 - (-4.2)$
0

Find the difference.

9. $3 - (-6)$ 9   **10.** $-2 - (-3.5)$ 1.5 **11.** $-1.8 - 5.8$ −7.6 **12.** $2.25 - 4$ −1.75

Written Exercises

Write the difference as a sum.

A **1.** $7 - 19$
$7 + (-19)$

2. $-21 - 42$
$-21 + (-42)$

3. $6.2 - (-8.3)$
$6.2 + 8.3$

4. $-2.9 - (-11.6)$
$-2.9 + 11.6$

5-8. Find each difference in Exercises 1-4 above.
5. −12   **6.** −63   **7.** 14.5   **8.** 8.7

Find the difference.

9. $4 - 10$ −6   **10.** $25 - 34$ −9   **11.** $-3 - 24$ −27   **12.** $-12 - 5$ −17

13. $9 - (-33)$ 42   **14.** $14 - (-46)$ 60   **15.** $-2 - (-17)$ 15   **16.** $-6 - (-5)$ −1

17. $0 - 43$ −43   **18.** $0 - 101$ −101   **19.** $0 - (-20)$ 20   **20.** $0 - (-14)$ 14

21. $44 - 0$ 44   **22.** $-16 - 0$ −16   **23.** $6.9 - 8$ −1.1   **24.** $12 - 20.5$ −8.5

25. $4.3 - 2.1$ 2.2   **26.** $23.4 - 6.8$ 16.6   **27.** $-16.1 - 8.5$
−24.6

28. $-0.4 - 8.9$ −9.3

29. $-19 - 5.6$
−24.6

30. $-41.1 - 2.9$
−44

31. $0 - (-3.37)$
3.37

32. $0 - 12.8$ −12.8

Positive and Negative Numbers **85**

Additional A Exercises
Find the difference.
1. $-1.7 - 38$ −39.7
2. $-42 - (-10.6)$ −31.4
3. $59.4 - 107.5$ −48.1
4. $2.35 - (-9.8)$ 12.15

Suggested Assignments

Minimum
Day 1: 85/1–32
86/33–57 odd
Day 2: 86/34–58 even
86/Prob. 1–4
87/Prob. 5–6
87/Self-Test A

Average
Day 1: 85/1–31 odd
86/33–53 odd; 54–58
Day 2: 86/59–65
86/Prob. 1–4
87/Prob. 5–8
87/Self-Test A

Maximum
Day 1: 85/1–31 odd
86/33–53 odd; 54–58
Day 2: 86/59–66
86/Prob. 1–4
87/Prob. 5–8
87/Self-Test A

Supplementary Materials

Practice Masters, p. 12
Test 3A, pp. 15–16

Find the difference.

33. $12.4 - (-12.4)$ 24.8   **34.** $-18.1 - (-25)$ 6.9   **35.** $-52.9 - (-11.6)$
-41.3

36. $(6 - 9.7) - 8.8$ -12.5 **37.** $(-2.5 - 8.1) - (-12.4)$ 1.8   **38.** $(0 - 8.3) - (-24.1)$
15.8

39. $[0 - (-0.2)] - 6.1$ **40.** $0 - [3.6 - (-2.1)]$ -5.7 **41.** $5.3 - (8 - 10.7)$
-5.9 8

Evaluate the expression when $a = -4.5$ **and** $b = -6.2$.

42. $-a$ 4.5   **43.** $-b$ 6.2   **44.** $-|b|$ -6.2 **45.** $-|a|$ -4.5

46. $a - b$ 1.7   **47.** $b - a$ -1.7 **48.** $-a - b$ 10.7   **49.** $-b - a$
10.7

50. $a - (-b)$ -10.7 **51.** $b - (-a)$ -10.7 **52.** $-b - (-a)$ 1.7   **53.** $-a - (-b)$
-1.7

What value of the variable makes the statement true?

B **54.** $2 - d = -6$ 8   **55.** $d - 5 = -13$ -8 **56.** $-3 - d = -11$
8

57. $8 - d = 13$ -5 **58.** $-7 - d = 12$ -19 **59.** $d - (-6) = -7$
-13

60. $-d - 4 = 14$ -18 **61.** $-d - 5 = -9$ 4   **62.** $7 - (-d) = 14$
7

63. $d - (-8) = 17$ 9   **64.** $-8 - (-d) = -16$ -8 **65.** $-4 - (-d) = 10$
14

C **66.** Replace __?__ with $=$, $>$, or $<$ to make a true statement.   >
$=$ **a.** $|13.6 - 8.9|$ __?__ $|13.6| - |8.9|$ **b.** $|-8.9 - (-13.6)|$ __?__ $|-8.9| - |-13.6|$
$>$ **c.** $|8.9 - 13.6|$ __?__ $|8.9| - |13.6|$ **d.** $|-8.9 - 13.6|$ __?__ $|-8.9| - |13.6|$ >
e. Based on your answers to parts (a)–(d), write a general rule for
$|x - y|$ __?__ $|x| - |y|$, where x and y are any decimal numbers.
$|x - y| \geq |x| - |y|$, where x and y are any decimal numbers

---

Problems

Solve Problems 1–6 by first expressing the given data as a difference of positive and negative numbers. Then, compute the difference of the numbers and answer the question.

A **1.** On a winter day, the temperature dropped from $-3°C$ to $-11°C$. Find the change in temperature. $-3 - (-11)$; $8°C$

2. Find the difference in the ages of two people if one was born in 27 B.C. and the other was born in 16 A.D. $16 - (-27)$; 43 yrs

3. The elevation of the highest point in a region is 1226 m above sea level. If the difference between the highest point and lowest point in the region is 1455 m, find the elevation of the lowest point.
$1226 - 1455$; -229 m

4. Two stages of a rocket burn for a total of 114.5 s. If the first stage burns for 86.8 s, how long does the second stage burn?
$114.5 - 86.8$; 27.7 s

86   *Chapter 3*

5. A parachutist jumped from an air-plane flying at an altitude of 1100 m, dropped 200 m in the first 25 s, and then dropped 350 m in the next 35 s. What was the altitude of the para-chutist 60 s after jumping?
(1100 − 200) − 350; 550 m

6. In Summit City, 78 cm of snow fell on Sunday. The snow melted ap-proximately 5.8 cm on Monday, ap-proximately 7.5 cm on Tuesday, and approximately 12 cm on Wednes-day. Approximately how much snow remained? [(78 − 5.8) − 7.5] − 12; 52.7 cm

B 7. Donna receives an allowance every 2 weeks that includes $20 for school lunches. During the past 4 weeks, she spent $7.50, $8.25, $5.25, and $8.75 on lunches. How much did Donna have left from the money allowed for lunches for the 4 weeks? $10.25

8. Eric Chung had $65.10 in his checking account on June 1. He wrote two checks in June, one for $42.99. Eric forgot to write down the amount of the other check. At the end of the month, he received a notice that his account was overdrawn by $22.11. What was the amount of Eric's second check? $44.22

Self-Test A

Replace __?__ with =, >, or < to make a true statement.

1. $^-4$ __?__ $^-5$ 2. 0 __?__ $^-3$ 3. $^-8$ __?__ 9 4. $|^-7|$ __?__ 7 5. $|0|$ __?__ 0 [3-1]
    >   >   <   =   =

Write the numbers in order from least to greatest.

6. $0, 5.4, ^-4.52, ^-0.25, ^-54$ 7. $^-3.79, 37, ^-7.3, ^-0.37, ^-0.09$ [3-2]
   $^-54, ^-4.52, ^-0.25, 0, 5.4$ $^-7.3, ^-3.79, ^-0.37, ^-0.09, 37$

Find the sum or difference.

8. $^-9.3 + 42.3$ 33   9. $17.8 + ^-17.8$ 0   10. $8.76 + ^-10.2$ [3-3]
                                              −1.44

11. $8 − (−27)$ 35   12. $−5.1 − (−5.1)$ 0   13. $0 − 36$ [3-4]
                                               −36

Evaluate the expression when $a = −6.4$ and $b = −5.2$.

14. $−b − a$ 11.6   15. $a − (−b)$ −11.6   16. $b − |a|$ −11.6

Self-Test answers and Extra Practice are at the back of the book.

Positive and Negative Numbers   **87**

3-5 Multiplying Positive and Negative Numbers

To find a product such as $5(-2)$, we can think of the product as the sum of five identical addends.

$$5(-2) = -2 + (-2) + (-2) + (-2) + (-2)$$

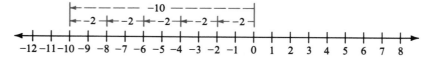

The diagram shows that $-2 + (-2) + (-2) + (-2) + (-2) = -10$. Thus $5(-2) = -10$.

To find the product $-7(2)$, we may use the commutative property of multiplication to write

$$-7(2) = 2(-7).$$

We know that $2(-7) = -7 + (-7) = -14$, so $-7(2) = -14$.

Notice that in the two examples above, the product is the opposite of the product of the absolute values of the numbers. The examples suggest the following rule.

> ### *Rule*
>
> The product of a positive number and a negative number is a negative number.

We may use other properties that we have learned for addition and multiplication of positive decimals to determine what a product of negative numbers, such as $-5(-3)$, must be. The multiplication property of zero states that the product of any number and 0 is 0. Thus,

$$-5(0) = 0.$$

Since we know that $3 + (-3) = 0$, we may write

$$-5[3 + (-3)] = 0.$$

By the distributive property, we may write the following.

$$-5(3) + (-5)(-3) = 0$$

$$-15 + (-5)(-3) = 0$$

But we know that $-15 + 15 = 0$, so $-5(-3)$ must equal 15.

88   *Chapter 3*

Notice that the product of $-5(-3)$ is the product of the absolute values of the factors. The example suggests the following rule.

> ## Rule
> The product of two negative numbers is a positive number.

EXAMPLE 1 Find the product.
    a. $-4.5(8.6)$ **b.** $5.32(-1)$ **c.** $-1(-14.7)$ **d.** $-9.2(-3.1)$

Solution   **a.** One number is negative and one number is positive, so the product is negative.
$$-4.5(8.6) = -38.7$$

b. One number is positive and one number is negative, so the product is negative.
$$5.32(-1) = -5.32$$

c. Both numbers are negative, so the product is positive.
$$-1(-14.7) = 14.7$$

d. Both numbers are negative, so the product is positive.
$$-9.2(-3.1) = 28.52$$

Notice in Example 1, parts (b) and (c), that when one of the factors is -1, the product is the opposite of the other factor.

> ## Rule
> The product of -1 and any number equals the opposite of that number.

We may use the rules for products of positive and negative numbers to multiply any number of positive and negative numbers.

EXAMPLE 2 Find the product.
    a. $-3.7(2.5)(-4.8)$ **b.** $-11.1(-7)(6.5)(-3.2)$

Solution   **a.** $-3.7(2.5)(-4.8) = [-3.7(2.5)](-4.8) = (-9.25)(-4.8) = 44.4$

b. $-11.1(-7)(6.5)(-3.2) = [-11.1(-7)][(6.5)(-3.2)]$
$$= 77.7(-20.8) = -1616.16$$

Positive and Negative Numbers   **89**

Example 2, on the preceding page, illustrates the following rules.

> ## *Rules*
> For a product with no zero factors:
> **1.** if the number of negative factors is odd, the product is negative.
> **2.** if the number of negative factors is even, the product is positive.

We can use the properties of addition and multiplication to simplify variable expressions that involve positive and negative numbers.

EXAMPLE 3 Simplify.
   a. $15 - 8a - 6 + 4a$ **b.** $8x - 2(x - 1)$

Solution   **a.** $15 - 8a - 6 + 4a = 15 + (-8a) + (-6) + 4a$
$$= 15 + (-6) + (-8a) + 4a$$
$$= 9 + (-4a) = 9 - 4a$$

   b. $8x - 2(x - 1) = 8x + (-2)(x - 1) = 8x + (-2x + 2)$
$$= 8x + (-2x) + 2 = 6x + 2$$

Class Exercises

Without computing the exact product, state whether the product is positive, negative, or 0.

1. $-3(-4.2)$
positive

2. $2.1(-0.8)$
negative

3. $-5(1.6)(-7)$
positive

4. $-4.5(3.7)(0)$ 0

Find the product.

5. $3(-16)$
-48

6. $-7(-12)$
84

7. $13(-1)(-5)$
65

8. $-2(-8)(-5)(0)$
0

Written Exercises

Find the product.

A   **1.** $-3(-9)$ 27   **2.** $4(-6)$ -24 **3.** $-8(7)$ -56 **4.** $-7(-11)$ 77

5. $2(-8)(-6)$ 96   **6.** $-3(5)(-6)$ 90   **7.** $-2(0)(-12)$ 0   **8.** $14(-1)(0)$ 0

9. $-1.5(8)$ -12 **10.** $0.6(-9)$ -5.4 **11.** $-3.4(-1.5)$ 5.1   **12.** $-0.4(-0.7)$ 0.28

90   *Chapter 3*

13. $2.9(-1)$ _-2.9_   **14.** $-1(7.84)$ _-7.84_   **15.** $-8.8(-1.75)$ _15.4_ **16.** $-1.11(70)$ _-77.7_

17. $-20(0.25)$ _-5_   **18.** $12(-1.2)$ _-14.4_   **19.** $-15(-30.6)$ _459_   **20.** $0.24(-100)$ _-24_

21. $3.9(-17.1)$ **22.** $-5.6(80.1)$ **23.** $-13.7(0)$ _0_   **24.** $16.7(0)$ _0_
    _-66.69_   _-448.56_
25. $-1.8(-1.9)$ **26.** $-0.125(-8.1)$ **27.** $-5.4(20.6)$ **28.** $-8.9(30.9)$
    _3.42_   _1.0125_   _-111.24_   _-275.01_
29. $10.1(3.75)$ **30.** $4.25(20.4)$ **31.** $-3.72(-16.5)$ **32.** $0.78(-42)$
    _37.875_   _86.7_   _61.38_   _-32.76_
33. $-1.7(-0.2)(-3.1)$ **34.** $-9(-2.7)(-80)$ **35.** $3.25(-17)(0)$
    _-1.054_   _-1944_   _0_
36. $-1.21(0)(-1.1)$ **37.** $9.4(-3.5)(-11)$ **38.** $18(-5.75)(6.2)$
    _0_   _361.9_   _-641.7_

Simplify the expression.

B **39.** $(-1.2 - 6.5)(-1.2 + 6.5)$ _-40.81_   **40.** $18 + 3 - (-12 - 7)$ _40_

41. $(-7)(2.4)(0)(-9.3)(-1) + (-8.2)$ _-8.2_ **42.** $(14.4 - 200)(14.4 + 200)$ _-39,792.64_

43. $(-8.1 - 0.02)(-8.1 - 0.03)$ _66.0156_ **44.** $[6.2 - (-9.7)][6.2 - (-9.7)]$ _252.81_

45. $-4[27 - (-9)] + (-4)(-2 - 9)$ _-100_ **46.** $(-20 + 12)7 + (-2 + 20)7$ _70_

47. $6m - 11 + 3m$ _9m - 11_   **48.** $-19 + 5r - 12$ _5r - 31_

49. $2q - 9 - 2q + 11$ _2_   **50.** $-3n + 7 + 2n - 8$ _-n - 1_

51. $-a[9 + (-3)] + a$ _-5a_   **52.** $3x + 12 - x(2 + 5)$ _12 - 4x_

53. $[4 + (-3)]b - b(-6 + 2)$ _5b_   **54.** $y(-8 + 11) + y(-9 - 5)$ _-11y_

Find the integer _n_ that will make the statement true.

55. $-3(n) = 6$ _-2_   **56.** $4(n) = -28$ _-7_   **57.** $-9(-n) = -18$
                                                                        _-2_
58. $3(n) = 6(-3)$ _-6_   **59.** $-n(-7) = -14(0)$ _0_   **60.** $-5(n) = 25(2)$
                                                                          _-10_

C **61.** $-3(-1.5)(-n) = -18(-1)(-0.5)$ _2_ **62.** $-1.2(30)(-n) = -9(-0.4)(-100)$
                                                                              _-10_
63. $-1.5(n)(-0.8) = -12(-1.5)(-2)$ _-30_ **64.** $-0.6(-n)(-1.9) = -18(-1.3)(0)$
                                                                              _0_
65. $n(-3.7 + 61.4) = 0$ _0_   **66.** $-n(-1.1 - 30.6) = 0$ _0_

Review Exercises

Use the inverse operation to solve for the variable.

1. $f + 27 = 83$ _56_ **2.** $n - 13 = 54$ _67_ **3.** $g + 364 = 518$ _154_ **4.** $w - 216 = 435$
                                                                                        _651_
5. $6c = 78$ _13_   **6.** $x \div 17 = 6$ _102_ **7.** $14j = 364$ _26_   **8.** $y \div 37 = 142$
                                                                                        _5254_

Positive and Negative Numbers   **91**

Suggested Assignments

Minimum
    90/1-12
    91/13-42
    91/Rev. 1-8

Average
    90/2-12 even
    91/14-38 even; 39-57
    91/Rev. 2-8 even

Maximum
    91/14-54 even; 55-66

Supplementary Materials

Practice Masters, p. 13

Reading Mathematics

Students will learn the meaning of the following mathematical term in this lesson: *quotient*.

Chalkboard Examples

Find the quotient.

1. $7 \div (7)$ **1**

2. $24 \div (-12)$ **—2**

3. $-132 \div 3$ **—44**

4. $-13.32 \div 0.9$ **—14.8**

5. $-4.42 \div (-0.26)$ **17**

6. $1108.89 \div (-33.3)$ **—33.3**

3-6 Dividing Positive and Negative Numbers

Recall that multiplication and division are inverse operations for positive numbers. For example, because we know that $4 \times 8 = 32$, we also know that $8 = 32 \div 4$. We can use the relationship between multiplication and division to find quotients of positive and negative numbers. Consider the following examples.

$$4 \times (-8) = -32 \qquad -8 = -32 \div 4$$
$$-4 \times 8 = -32 \qquad 8 = -32 \div -4$$
$$-4 \times (-8) = 32 \qquad -8 = 32 \div -4$$

Notice that in the examples above, the quotient of two numbers with differing signs is the opposite of the quotient of the absolute values of the numbers. The quotient of two numbers with the same sign is the quotient of the absolute values of the numbers.

The examples suggest the following rules for dividing positive and negative numbers.

Rules

The quotient of two positive or two negative numbers is positive.

The quotient of a positive number and a negative number is negative.

By the multiplication property of zero, we know that $-4 \times 0 = 0$ and thus $0 = 0 \div (-4)$. Remember that we cannot divide by 0.

EXAMPLE Find the quotient.
  a. $-3.06 \div 0.9$ **b.** $36.8 \div (-2.3)$ **c.** $-4.046 \div (-1.7)$

Solution **a.** Since -3.06 is negative and 0.9 is positive, the quotient will be negative.
$$-3.06 \div 0.9 = -3.4$$

  b. Since 36.8 is positive and -2.3 is negative, the quotient will be negative.
$$36.8 \div -2.3 = -16$$

  c. Since -4.046 and -1.7 are both negative, the quotient will be positive.
$$-4.046 \div (-1.7) = 2.38$$

92 *Chapter 3*

Class Exercises

Without computing the exact quotient, state whether the quotient is positive, negative, or 0.

1. $-3.6 \div (-40)$
positive

2. $-0.216 \div 400$
negative

3. $0 \div (-17.5)$
0

4. $850 \div (-0.05)$
negative

Find the quotient.

5. $-28 \div 7$ -4

6. $33 \div (-1)$ -33

7. $0 \div -50$ 0

8. $-51 \div (-3)$ 17

9. $-22 \div 4$ -5.5

10. $-75 \div 15$ -5

Written Exercises

Find the quotient.

A

1. $-18 \div 3$ -6

2. $25 \div (-5)$ -5

3. $-21 \div (-7)$ 3

4. $-54 \div (-18)$ 3

5. $0 \div (-7)$ 0

6. $0 \div (-24)$ 0

7. $144 \div (-12)$ -12

8. $-100 \div 25$ -4

9. $22.5 \div (-3)$ -7.5

10. $-42 \div 4$ -10.5

11. $-3.6 \div (-1)$ 3.6

12. $-1.01 \div (-1)$ 1.01

13. $-1.75 \div 0.05$ -35

14. $-69.3 \div 3.3$ -21

15. $-32.86 \div 6.2$ -5.3

16. $-17.05 \div (-1.1)$ 15.5

17. $-0.48 \div (-0.06)$ 8

18. $0.06 \div (-0.3)$ -0.2

19. $0 \div (-14.7)$ 0

20. $0 \div (-0.25)$ 0

21. $-0.9 \div 1.8$ -0.5

22. $-0.042 \div (-0.6)$ 0.07

23. $-38 \div 4$ -9.5

24. $-45 \div (-6)$ 7.5

25. $9.9 \div (-4.5)$ -2.2

26. $46.2 \div (-6)$ -7.7

27. $-13.8 \div (-1)$ 13.8

28. $0.003 \div (-1)$ -0.003

29. $-9.27 \div (-60)$ 0.1545

30. $0.25 \div (-40)$ -0.00625

31. $13.23 \div (-2.1)$ -6.3

32. $-2.6 \div 0.52$ -5

33. $-14.57 \div (-3.1)$ 4.7

34. $-0.53 \div (-0.1)$ 5.3

35. $-18.5 \div 10$ -1.85

36. $3.84 \div (-9.6)$ -0.4

Evaluate the expression when $a = -8$ and $b = 2.5$.

37. $a \div b$ -3.2

38. $b \div a$ -0.3125

39. $2b \div (-a)$ 0.625

40. $-3a \div b$ 9.6

41. $(a - b) \div b$ -4.2

42. $2ab \div a$ 5

43. $-9a \div 3ab$ -1.2

44. $-5b \div (-2a)$ -0.78125

Use inverse operations to solve for the variable.

B

45. $-3n = 6$ -2

46. $d \div 5 = -7$ -35

47. $b \div (-8) = 9$ -72

48. $-15x = -30$ 2

49. $-2y - 8 = 8$ -8

50. $4c + 12 = -36$ -12

Positive and Negative Numbers **93**

Additional A Exercises

Find the quotient.

1. $0 \div 32$ 0

2. $0.92 \div (-0.368)$ -2.5

3. $-22.4 \div (-5.6)$ 4

4. $-7.54 \div 5.8$ -1.3

5. $2.3 \div (-100)$ -0.023

6. $-10 \div (2.5)$ -4

Suggested Assignments

Minimum
Day 1: 93/1–49 odd
Day 2: 93/2–50 even
    94/Rev. 1–10

Average
Day 1: 93/1–49 odd
    94/51–52
Day 2: 93/2–50 even
    94/Rev. 2–10 even
    94/Calculator Key-In

Maximum
Day 1: 93/1–49 odd
    94/51–52
Day 2: 93/2–50 even
    94/Calculator Key-In

Supplementary Materials

Practice Masters, p. 14

C **51.** Explain why $\left|\frac{x}{y}\right| = \frac{|x|}{|y|}$ for all decimal numbers for which it is possible to find the quotient $\frac{x}{y}$.

52. Replace ___?___ with $=$, $>$, or $<$ to make a true statement.

a. 0.10 __?__ 2.5 $<$

$\frac{0.10}{0.5}$ __?__ $\frac{2.5}{0.5}$ $<$

$\frac{0.10}{-0.5}$ __?__ $\frac{2.5}{-0.5}$ $>$

b. -0.21 __?__ 0 $<$

$\frac{-0.21}{70}$ __?__ $\frac{0}{70}$ $<$

$\frac{-0.21}{-70}$ __?__ $\frac{0}{-70}$ $>$

c. -3.6 __?__ -1.5 $<$

$\frac{-3.6}{3}$ __?__ $\frac{-1.5}{3}$ $<$

$\frac{-3.6}{-3}$ __?__ $\frac{-1.5}{-3}$ $>$

Use your answers to parts (a)–(c) to answer parts (d) and (e).

d. If $x < y$ and if k is a positive number, then $\frac{x}{k}$ __?__ $\frac{y}{k}$. $<$

e. If $x < y$ and if j is a negative number, then $\frac{x}{j}$ __?__ $\frac{y}{j}$. $>$

Write examples similar to those in parts (a)–(c) to answer parts (f) and (g). **Check students' examples.**

f. If $x > y$ and if k is a positive number, then $\frac{x}{k}$ __?__ $\frac{y}{k}$. $>$

g. If $x > y$ and if j is a negative number, then $\frac{x}{j}$ __?__ $\frac{y}{j}$. $<$

Review Exercises

Evaluate the expression if $x = 3$, $y = 7$, and $z = 4$.

1. y^2 49 **2.** $5x^2$ 45 **3.** $(7z)^2$ 784 **4.** z^0 1 **5.** $7z^2$ 112

6. $(6x)^2$ 324 **7.** $(yz)^0$ 1 **8.** xy^0 3 **9.** $z^3 - x^3$ 37 **10.** $8x^3y$ 1512

▮▮▮▮ **Calculator Key-In**

Does your calculator have a change-sign key? The key may look like this: $\boxed{+/-}$. If you press this key after entering a number or doing a calculation, the sign of the number displayed on your calculator will change. For example, if you enter 116 $\boxed{+/-}$, your calculator will change 116 to -116.

Solve with a calculator that has a change-sign key, if possible.

1. $20.7 + (-19.6)$ 1.1 **2.** $-55.59 + 438.2$ 382.61 **3.** $-0.86 + (-27.341)$ -28.201

4. $-426.38 - (-25.004)$ -401.376 **5.** $-83.5(-61.09)$ 5101.015 **6.** $6.8(-4.17)(-1.61)$ 45.65316

94 *Chapter 3*

3-7 Negative Integers as Exponents

You know by the rule of exponents that you learned for multiplying powers of the same base that

$$10^1 \times 10^2 = 10^{1+2} = 10^3.$$

Since we want to apply the same rule to negative exponents, we must have

$$10^1 \times 10^{-1} = 10^{1+(-1)} = 10^0 = 1$$
$$10^2 \times 10^{-2} = 10^{2+(-2)} = 10^0 = 1$$

and so on. We know that

$$10^1 \times \frac{1}{10} = 10 \times 0.1 = 1 \text{ and } 10^2 \times \frac{1}{10^2} = 100 \times 0.01 = 1,$$

so 10^{-1} should equal $\frac{1}{10}$ and 10^{-2} should equal $\frac{1}{10^2}$. This example suggests the following general rule.

> ### Rule
> For all numbers $a(a \neq 0)$, m, and n,
> $$a^{-m} = \frac{1}{a^m}$$

EXAMPLE   Write the expression without exponents.
   a. 5^{-2} **b.** $(-3)^{-2}$ **c.** $(-4)^{-1}(-4)^{-2}$

Solution   **a.** $5^{-2} = \frac{1}{5^2} = \frac{1}{5 \times 5} = \frac{1}{25}$

   b. $(-3)^{-2} = \frac{1}{(-3)^2} = \frac{1}{(-3)(-3)} = \frac{1}{9}$

   c. $(-4)^{-1} \times (-4)^{-2} = (-4)^{-1+(-2)} = (-4)^{-3}$
   $$= \frac{1}{(-4)^3} = \frac{1}{(-4)(-4)(-4)} = \frac{1}{-64}$$

Class Exercises

Use the rules for exponents to state the expression without exponents.

   1. 3^{-4} $\frac{1}{81}$ **2.** $(-6)^{-2}$ $\frac{1}{36}$ **3.** $10^4 \times 10^{-4}$ 1   **4.** $3^5 \times 3^{-7}$ $\frac{1}{9}$ **5.** $(-2)^3(-2)^{-1}_{4}$

Teaching Suggestions p. 71d

Related Activities p. 71e

Reading Mathematics

Students will learn the meaning of the following mathematical term in this lesson: *negative exponent.*

Chalkboard Examples

Write the expression without exponents.

   1. 2^{-4} $\frac{1}{16}$

   2. 3^{-1} $\frac{1}{3}$

   3. 17^0 1
   4. $(-2)^{-2}$ $\frac{1}{4}$

   5. $(-3)^{-2}$ $\frac{1}{9}$

   6. $(-4)^{-3}$ $-\frac{1}{64}$

Additional A Exercises

Write the expression without exponents.

1. $(-5)^{-2}$ $\frac{1}{25}$

2. 4^{-3} $\frac{1}{64}$

3. $2^{-1} \times 2^{-1}$ $\frac{1}{4}$

4. $12^{-2} \times 12^2$ 1

5. $32^{-1} \times 32^0$ $\frac{1}{32}$

6. $8^{-3} \times 8^{-1} \times 8^5$ 8

Use exponents to state as a power of 2.

6. 8 2^3 7. $\frac{1}{8}$ 2^{-3} 8. 64 2^6 9. $\frac{1}{64}$ 2^{-6} 10. $\frac{1}{512}$ 2^{-9}

Written Exercises

Write the expression without exponents.

A   1. $(-2)^{-5}$ $-\frac{1}{32}$ 2. 3^{-3} $\frac{1}{27}$ 3. 10^{-3} $\frac{1}{1000}$ 4. $(-3)^{-5}$ $-\frac{1}{243}$ 5. 1^{-4} 1

6. $(-1)^{-6}$ 1   7. $(-5)^{-2}$ $\frac{1}{25}$ 8. 4^{-5} $\frac{1}{1024}$ 9. 2^{-6} $\frac{1}{64}$ 10. $(-4)^{-2}$ $\frac{1}{16}$

11. $7^4 \times 7^{-6}$ $\frac{1}{49}$ 12. $10^3 \times 10^{-2}$ 10   13. $5^{10} \times 5^{-10}$ 1

14. $6^{-23} \times 6^{23}$ 1   15. $3^{-3} \times 3^0$ $\frac{1}{27}$ 16. $2^{-3} \times 2^{-4}$ $\frac{1}{128}$

17. $(-4)^{-2} \times (-4)^{-2}$ $\frac{1}{256}$ 18. $(-7)^{-1} \times (-7)^{-1}$ $\frac{1}{49}$ $-\frac{1}{8}$ 19. $(-2)^{-6} \times (-2)^3$

20. $(-8)^{-2} \times (-8)^0$ $\frac{1}{64}$ 21. $6^{-1} \times 6^3 \times 6^{-2}$ 1   22. $9^{-5} \times 9^{-1} \times 9^7$
                                                                        9

What value of the variable makes the statement true?

23. $5^n = \frac{1}{125}$ -3 24. $4^{-n} = \frac{1}{256}$ 4   25. $3^{-n} = \frac{1}{243}$ 5

26. $4^2 \times 4^{-2} = 4^n$ 0   27. $7^3 \times 7^{-5} = 7^n$ -2 28. $9^{-4} \times 9^3 = \frac{1}{9^n}$ 1

B   29. $3^7 \times 3^n = 3^5$ -2 30. $2^{-3} \times 2^n = 2^{-11}$ -8

31. $(-2)^{-5} \times (-2)^n = -8$ 8   32. $(-10)^3 \times (-10)^{-n} = -10$ 2

33. $144 \times 12^{-2} = 12^n$ 0   34. $5^{-3} \times 25 = 5^{-n}$ 1

35. $4^n \times 4^{-3} = \frac{1}{16}$ 1   36. $6^{-n} \times 6^3 = \frac{1}{216}$ 6

37. $9^{-7} \times 9^{-n} = \frac{1}{729}$ -4 38. $8^{-4} \times 8^{-n} = \frac{1}{64}$ -2

39. $(-5)^{-n} \times (-5)^{-3} = 1$ -3 40. $(-3)^{-n} \times (-3)^{-8} = \frac{1}{-243}$ -3

Simplify. Write the expression with non-negative exponents.

41. x^{-5} $\frac{1}{x^5}$ 42. n^{-9} $\frac{1}{n^9}$ 43. $a^{-3} \times a^{-2}$ $\frac{1}{a^5}$

44. $b^7 \times b^{-7}$ b^0 45. $w^{-10} \times w^3 \times w^{-1}$ $\frac{1}{w^8}$ 46. $v^4 \times v^{-12} \times v^3$
                                                                                                        $\frac{1}{v^5}$

C   47. Explain why $a^m = (-a)^m$ if m is any even integer.
              If the number of neg. factors is even, the product is pos.

48. Explain why $(-a)^n = -1(a)^n$ if n is any odd integer.
              If the number of neg. factors is odd, the product is neg.

96   *Chapter 3*

Self-Test B

Find the product.

1. $4.2(-11.3)$ -47.46 **2.** $-6.7(20.4)$ -136.68 **3.** $7.5(-4.2)(-12)$ 378 [3-5]

Find the quotient.

4. $121 \div (-11)$ -11 **5.** $-68.2 \div 2.2$ -31 **6.** $-0.56 \div (-0.07)$ 8 [3-6]

Write the expression without exponents.

7. 4^{-2} $\frac{1}{16}$ **8.** $(-6)^{-3}$ $-\frac{1}{216}$ **9.** $7^5 \times 7^{-8}$ $\frac{1}{343}$ **10.** $(-9)^{-2} \times (-9)^0$ $\frac{1}{81}$ [3-7]

Self-Test answers and Extra Practice are at the back of the book.

■■■ **Challenge**

We use the symbol $[x]$ (read *the greatest integer in x*) to represent the greatest integer less than or equal to x.

EXAMPLE **a.** $[5.4]$ **b.** $[-3.2]$

Solution **a.** There is no integer equal to 5.4, so we must find the greatest integer that is less than 5.4.

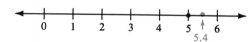

As shown on the number line, the greatest integer that is less than 5.4 is 5. Thus *the greatest integer in 5.4 is 5.*

b. There is no integer equal to -3.2, so we must find the greatest integer that is less than -3.2.

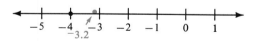

As shown on the number line, the greatest integer that is less than $^-3.2$ is $^-4$. Thus the *greatest integer in $^-3.2$ is $^-4$.*

Find the value of each of the following.

1. $[6.2]$ 6 **2.** $[1.23]$ 1 **3.** $[3]$ 3 **4.** $[45]$ 45

5. $[-12]$ -12 **6.** $[-1]$ -1 **7.** $[-4.89]$ -5 **8.** $[-0.36]$ -1

Positive and Negative Numbers **97**

Suggested Assignments

Minimum
Day 1: 96/1–28
Day 2: 96/29–43
97/Self-Test B

Average
Day 1: 96/1–35
Day 2: 96/36–48
97/Self-Test B
97/Challenge

Maximum
Day 1: 96/1–35
Day 2: 96/36–48
97/Self-Test B
97/Challenge

Supplementary Materials

Practice Masters, p. 14
Test 3B, pp. 17–18
Computer Activity 5
Computer Activity 6

Quick Quiz B

Solve.

1. $-3.9(-12.2)$ 47.58

2. $-4.5(42.6)$ -191.7

3. $2.6(3.4)(-5.1)$ -45.084

4. $225 \div (-15)$ -15

5. $-4.4 \div (0.25)$ -17.6

6. $0.166 \div (-0.2)$ -0.83

Write the expression without exponents.

7. 3^{-2} $\frac{1}{9}$

8. $(-2)^{-3}$ $\frac{1}{-8}$

9. $8^5 \times 8^{-7}$ $\frac{1}{64}$

10. $(-3)^{-2} \times (-3)^0$ $\frac{1}{9}$

Scientific Notation

Scientists frequently deal with data that range from very small to very large magnitudes. For example, when Saturn is closest to Earth, it is about 1,630,000,000 km away. The diameter of a hydrogen atom is approximately $\frac{1}{100,000,000}$ cm. To cope with numbers such as these, a method for writing numbers, called **scientific notation,** has been adopted.

Scientific notation makes use of positive exponents to write large numbers and negative exponents to write small numbers. For example,

$$4800 = 4.8 \times 1000 = 4.8 \times 10^3$$

$$0.000507 = 5.07 \times \frac{1}{10,000} = 5.07 \times 10^{-4}$$

Rule

To express any positive number in scientific notation, write it as the product of a power of ten and a number between 1 and 10.

In addition to being a convenient method for expressing very large or very small numbers, scientific notation provides an exact gauge of the precision of a measurement, based on the smallest unit of calibration on the measuring instrument. Each digit in a number that specifies the degree of precision of measurement is called a **significant digit.**

98   *Chapter 3*

Zeros that appear to the right of nonzero digits, and to the right of the decimal point, are significant. For example,

0.50 has two significant digits,

40,521 has five significant digits.

The zeros in a measurement such as 41,500 km, however, may be misleading since it is unclear whether the number is rounded to the nearest hundred or is an exact measurement. Scientific notation provides a means of avoiding this confusion. For example, when we write 40,500 as 4.05×10^4, it means that the measurement is precise to three significant digits. When we write 40,500 as 4.050×10^4, it means that the measurement is precise to four significant digits.

In general, to write a number in scientific notation, shift the decimal point to just after the first nonzero digit. Then multiply by 10^n, when n is the number of places the decimal point was shifted. As an example,

$$3\underline{165} = 3.165 \times 10^3.$$

Note that 7.46 is written as 7.46 since $10^0 = 1$. Also, 1,000,000 is usually written simply as 10^6 rather than 1×10^6.

Write the number in scientific notation.

1. 5798
   5.798×10^3
2. 30,090
   3.009×10^4
3. 8,915,673
   8.915673×10^6
4. 2,175,000,000
   2.175×10^9
5. 1.75
   1.75
6. 0.003
   3×10^{-3}
7. 0.0501
   5.01×10^{-2}
8. 0.0333
   3.33×10^{-2}

Write the number in decimal form.

9. 3.79×10^3
   3790
10. 4.86×10^4
    $48,600$
11. 3.01×10^5
    $301,000$
12. 6×10^9
    $6,000,000,000$
13. 5.6×10^{-2}
    0.056
14. 7.09×10^{-3}
    0.00709
15. 3.99×10^{-8}
    0.0000000399
16. 2.0111×10^{-6}
    0.0000020111

17. The diameter of a red blood cell is about 0.00074 cm. Write this number in scientific notation with two significant digits. 7.4×10^{-4}

18. An atom of gold is about 0.0000000025 m in diameter. Write this number in scientific notation with two significant digits. 2.5×10^{-9}

19. The radius of Earth's orbit is 150,000,000,000 m. Write this number in scientific notation with two significant digits. 1.5×10^{11}

20. A communications satellite was orbited at an altitude of 625,000 m. Write this number in scientific notation with three significant digits. 6.25×10^5

Chapter Review

Complete. Use $=$, $>$, or $<$ to make a true statement.

1. $^-2 \underline{\ ?\ } 3$ $<$
2. $^-6 \underline{\ ?\ } {}^-7$ $>$
3. $3 \underline{\ ?\ } {}^-4$ $>$ [3–1]

4. $0 \underline{\ ?\ } {}^-1$ $>$
5. $|^-9| \underline{\ ?\ } 9$ $=$
6. $|2| \underline{\ ?\ } {}^-2$ $>$

7. $^-8.7 \underline{\ ?\ } {}^-0.87$ $<$
8. $^-42 \underline{\ ?\ } 2.4$ $<$
9. $3.05 \underline{\ ?\ } -3.55$ $>$ [3–2]

10. $0.4 \underline{\ ?\ } {}^-4.3$ $>$
11. $|^-5.6| \underline{\ ?\ } {}^-5.6$ $>$
12. $|4.93| \underline{\ ?\ } |^-4.93|$ $=$

True or false?

13. $0 + {}^-14.2 = 0$ F
14. $16.8 + {}^-16.8 = 33.6$ F [3–3]

15. $^-13.2 + {}^-7.8 = {}^-21$ T
16. $7.6 + {}^-10.5 = 2.9$ F

17. $^-33 + 20.2 = {}^-12.8$ T
18. $19.5 + {}^-14.3 = {}^-5.2$ F

19. $37.2 - (-9.6) = 25.6$ F
20. $-5.8 - (-5.8) = 11.6$ F [3–4]

21. $-12.2 - 13.1 = -25.3$ T
22. $0 - (-0.5) = -0.05$ F

23. If $a = -7$, $-a = -7$. F
24. If $b = -2.4$, $-|b| = -2.4$. T

25. $-40(0.33) = -1.42$ F
26. $1.2(-6.2) = -7.4$ F [3–5]

27. $-17(-24.2) = 411.4$ T
28. $7(-8.3)0 = -58.1$ F

29. $-5(2.8)(-20) = 280$ T
30. $-12(-1)(-8.6) = 103.2$ F

31. $75.5 \div (-5) = -15.1$ T
32. $-0.006 \div (-1) = 0.006$ T [3–6]

33. $-115.2 \div (-2.4) = 48$ T
34. $-5.04 \div 3.6 = 1.4$ F

35. $0 \div (-19.8) = 0$ T
36. $-6.21 \div (-0.23) = -27$ F

What value of the variable makes the statement true? Write the letter of the correct answer.

37. $3^n = \dfrac{1}{81}$ **c.**
a. 4
b. 81
c. -4
d. 9
[3–7]

38. $4^{-n} = \dfrac{1}{64}$ **d.**
a. 16
b. -16
c. 4
d. 3

39. $7^{-6} \times 7^6 = 7^n$ **b.**
a. -36
b. 0
c. 12
d. -12

40. $(-2)^{-3} \times (-2)^n = \dfrac{1}{-32}$ **c.**
a. 2
b. -5
c. -2
d. -7

Chapter Test

Supplementary Materials
Chapter 3 Test, pp. 19–20

Replace __?__ with =, >, or < to make a true statement.

1. $^-7$ __?__ 8   **2.** 4 __?__ $^-5$ **3.** 0 __?__ $^-6$ **4.** $^-2$ __?__ $^-3$ [3–1]

    <   >   >   >

Express as an integer.

5. $|^-3|$ 3   **6.** $|7|$ 7   **7.** $|^-12|$ 12   **8.** $|0|$ 0

Write the numbers in order from least to greatest.

9. $^-6.5$, $^-56$, 6.05, $^-556$, $^-0.6$ **10.** 3.02, $^-3.2$, $^-23$, 0.32, $^-333$ [3–2]
   $^-556$, $^-56$, $^-6.5$, $^-0.6$, 6.05 $^-333$, $^-23$, $^-3.2$, 0.32, 3.02

Find the sum.

11. $^-8.4 + 36.8$ 28.4   **12.** $^-6.3 + ^-0.12$ $^-6.42$ **13.** $13.2 + ^-13.2$ 0   [3–3]

14. $14.6 + 23.1$ 37.7   **15.** $0 + ^-11.5$ $^-11.5$ **16.** $0.89 + ^-16.1 + ^-0.94$ $^-16.15$

Find the difference.

17. $26.5 - 8.3$ 18.2   **18.** $-4.3 - 20.6$ $^-24.9$ **19.** $0 - 13.6$ $^-13.6$ [3–4]

20. $-14.2 - (-9.5)$ **21.** $41 - (-11.67)$ **22.** $-6.4 - (-6.4)$ 0
       $^-4.7$ 52.67

Evaluate the expression when $a = -5$ and $b = -3.6$.

23. $-a - b$ 8.6   **24.** $-a - (-b)$ 1.4   **25.** $-|b|$ $^-3.6$

Find the product.

26. $12(-6.37)$ $^-76.44$ **27.** $-30(0.45)$ $^-13.5$ **28.** $-0.37(-20.8)$ 7.696   [3–5]

29. $-1(-14.27)$ 14.27   **30.** $5.4(-8.2)(-3)$ **31.** $-6.11(-9)(-5.5)$ $^-302.445$
                             132.84

Find the quotient.

32. $69.3 \div (-3)$ $^-23.1$ **33.** $-18 \div (-2.5)$ 7.2   **34.** $-19.2 \div 10$ $^-1.92$ [3–6]

35. $-0.004 \div (-1)$ **36.** $0 \div (-15)$ 0   **37.** $-0.08 \div (-0.2)$ 0.4
       0.004

Write the expression without exponents.

38. 6^{-2} $\frac{1}{36}$ **39.** $(-5)^{-3}$ $-\frac{1}{125}$ **40.** $8^{-9} \times 8^7$ $\frac{1}{64}$ **41.** $(-3) \times (-3)^{-2}$ $-\frac{1}{3}$ [3–7]

Positive and Negative Numbers   **101**

Review for Retention

Complete. Use $=$, $>$, or $<$ to make a true statement.

1. $3^4 \underline{\ \overset{>}{?}\ } 4^3$

2. $86^0 \underline{\ \overset{>}{?}\ } 0 \times 86$

3. $1.75 \div 14 \underline{\ \overset{=}{?}\ } 1 \div 8$

4. $4 \div 0.01 \underline{\ \overset{<}{?}\ } 10^3$

5. $5^4 \times 5^8 \underline{\ \overset{=}{?}\ } 5^{12}$

6. $6^6 \div 6^3 \underline{\ \overset{>}{?}\ } 6^2$

7. $2^4 \underline{\ \overset{<}{?}\ } 4.774 \div 0.154$

8. $4^3 \underline{\ \overset{<}{?}\ } 42.51 \div 0.63$

Evaluate the expression if $f = 3$, $g = 4$, and $h = 6$.

9. g^2 **16**

10. fh **18**

11. $gh \div f$ **8**

12. $g(3f - h)$ **12**

13. $2fg + h$ **30**

14. g^f **64**

15. $h \div g$ **1.5**

16. $f(g + 2h)$ **48**

Round to the place specified.

17. tens: 26 **30**

18. hundredths: 152.430 **152.43**

19. thousands: 37,874 **38,000**

20. thousandths: 0.1791 **0.179**

21. hundreds: 749 **700**

22. tenths: 180.673 **180.7**

(Continue on next page.)

Cumulative Review (Chapters 1–3)

Exercises

2. All the numbers greater than 3
3. All the numbers less than 180
6. All the numbers less than 1152
8. All the numbers greater than or equal to 24

Use inverse operations to solve.

1. $9x = 54$ **6**
2. $17 + a > 20$
3. $a \div 6 < 30$
4. $35 - b = 7$ **28**
5. $15z = 45$ **3**
6. $w \div 12 < 96$
7. $18 + p = 35$ **17**
8. $n - 5 \geq 19$

Write a variable expression for the word phrase.

9. The sum of a number p and forty-two **$p + 42$**

10. The quotient when a number x is divided by three tenths **$x \div 0.3$**

11. A number w raised to the third power plus seventeen **$w^3 + 17$**

12. The difference of sixty-eight and a number q **$68 - q$**

13. The product of a number y cubed and fifty-nine **$59y^3$**

Write an equation or inequality for the word sentence.

14. Twenty-nine is greater than twice the sum of x and nine. **$29 > 2(x + 9)$**

15. Three times a number m is thirty-three. **$3m = 33$**

16. The sum of x and negative four and three tenths is eleven. **$x + (-4.3) = 11$**

17. The difference when seventy-seven is subtracted from x is less than or equal to the sum when x is added to five. **$x - 77 \leq x + 5$**

18. The quotient when a number is divided by twelve is equal to the number multiplied by five. **$x \div 12 = x \times 5$**

Round to the place specified.

19. tenths: 68.461 **68.5**

20. thousandths: 4.00891 **4.009**

21. tens: 188.72 **190**

22. hundreds: 7740.68 **7700**

23. hundredths: 37.5505 **37.55**

24. tenths: 909.09 **909.1**

Simplify the expression.

25. $75.8 + (6.7 + 3.3)^2$ **175.8**

26. $100.6 + (3^3 \div 9)$ **103.6**

27. $(4^3 - 6) \times (81 - 5^2)$ **3248**

28. $3x + 4 - 2x + y$ **$x + y + 4$**

29. $5n - 5m + 12n$ **$17n - 5m$**

30. $3(a^2)(a^3)$ **$3a^5$**

31. $2a^2 \times 4a^3 \times b^2$ **$8a^5b^2$**

32. $[6(4 - r) + r] - 12r$ **$24 - 17r$**

33. $4w^5 + (w^2 \times 3w)$ **$4w^5 + 3w^3$**

Express as an integer.

34. $|-2|$ **2**

35. $|6|$ **6**

36. $|0|$ **0**

37. $|-100|$ **100**

38. $|-15|$ **15**

102 *Chapter 3*

Write the integers in order from least to greatest.

39. 12, 15, 0, −7, 6, −20
−20, −7, 0, 6, 12, 15

40. 0, −5, 6, −6, 5
−6, −5, 0, 5, 6

41. 7, 9, −3, −5, 0, 1
−5, −3, 0, 1, 7, 9

Problems

Problem Solving Reminders

Here are some reminders that may help you solve some of the problems on this page.
- Determine which facts are necessary to solve the problem.
- Determine which operations are needed to solve the problem.
- Supply additional information if necessary.

Solve.

1. At Angler's Supply Company, deluxe waders cost $69.95 a pair. A similar product can be purchased for $10.49 less at Go Fish Discount. What is the price at Go Fish Discount? **$59.46**

2. Alice's Mountain Goat Cheese is currently being promoted through supermarket taste demonstrations. An average of 200 samples are distributed between 11:00 A.M. and 5:00 P.M. each day. To the nearest whole number, find the average number of samples given out each hour. If the daily cost of samples averages $50, what is the average cost per sample? **33 samples; 25¢**

3. Cabin Fever Ski Area runs a mountain slide ride during the summer months. A single ride costs $3.75 and a day's pass costs $14.00. How many times would you have to ride the slide to make it less expensive to buy a day's pass? **4 times**

4. Approximately 3.3 Calories are burned per hour per kilogram of body mass by walking. If a student with mass 58 kg takes 20 min to walk to school, how many Calories are burned? **63.8 Cal**

5. The Gourmet Luncheonette is giving out coupons that let customers buy one large roast beef sandwich at the regular price of $2.45 and receive one free. Deli Delights is giving out coupons that let customers deduct $.75 from the regular price of $1.95 for every large roast beef sandwich. Is it less expensive to buy two large roast beef sandwiches at The Gourmet Luncheonette or at Deli Delights? **Deli Delights**

6. Because of a grain shortage, the price of a loaf of bread increased by 2 cents. When grain again became plentiful, the price decreased by 4 cents, but later it again rose by 5 cents because of inflation. If the original price was 86 cents per loaf, what was the final price? **89 cents**

Positive and Negative Numbers **103**

---

23. thousands: 49,266
49,000

24. hundredths: 0.5974
0.60

What value of the variable makes the statement true?

25. $4.7j = j$ **0**

26. $4 + t = 16 - t$ **6**

27. $6.3a = 9.45$ **1.5**

28. $2h + 5 = 13$ **4**

29. $24 \div 3w = 4$ **2**

30. $15b - 4b = 33$ **3**

31. $48 - 7g = 6$ **6**

32. $k \div 12 = 24$ **288**

Simplify.

33. $86.5 - (48 \div 1.5)$
54.5

34. $7^2 + (9.2 - 4.2)^2$
74

35. $2d + 5 + 3d - 2$
$5d + 3$

36. $4m(3 - 2m)$
$12m - 8m^2$

37. $12g - 6(2 - 3g)$
$30g - 12$

38. $a^3 \times a^5 \div a^4$
a^4

39. $43.7 - 3t + 6.2(2 + 5t)$
$56.1 + 28t$

40. $y^4 \div y^2 \times y^5$
y^7

4

Rational Numbers

Hummingbirds, like the Violet-Capped Woodnymph Hummingbird shown at the right, can fly forward, vertically, and even backward. Perhaps their most unusual feat is their ability to hover apparently motionless in the air while sipping nectar from a flower. This ability comes from their specialized wing structure and its unique movement. The hummingbird pictured lives in the forests of Brazil. It is only $4\frac{1}{2}$ in. long and has a wing beat of 33 beats per second. To photograph the hummingbird so that its wings appear motionless, an electronic flash time of about $\frac{1}{1000}$ of a second was used. Exposure times of $\frac{1}{100,000}$ of a second have been used to study the precise motion of some hummingbirds' wings and to learn exactly how the wings enable hummingbirds to remain at a fixed point with great ease. In this chapter on rational numbers, you will learn about fractions and decimals and their relationship to each other.

Career Note

Understanding the relationship between animals and their environments is the job of the ecologist. Ecologists study the influence that factors such as temperature, humidity, rainfall, and altitude have on the environment. They monitor levels of pollutants and predict their long term effects on the life cycles of plants and animals.

Lesson Commentary
Chapter 4   Rational Numbers

Overview

In this chapter students will study the properties of rational numbers and review operations with fractions. A rational number is a number that can be expressed as a fraction $\frac{a}{b}$, where a and b are integers and b is not 0.

Thus, the rational numbers include all fractional numbers and their opposites. All the properties and rules of computation for integers and fractional numbers are also true for rational numbers. Students continuing in mathematics must have a firm grasp of rational numbers and a thorough understanding of addition, subtraction, multiplication, and division. Extensive use of rational numbers is necessary in working with ratio, proportion, percent, measurement, and probability, and in finding solutions for equations and inequalities.

SUMS AND DIFFERENCES

4-1 Positive and Negative Fractions

Objective *for pages 106–109*

■ To use terms and properties concerning positive and negative fractions.

Teaching Suggestions

Emphasize the relationship between fractions and division. Since $\frac{3}{5}$ means $3 \div 5$, we will be able to find decimal and percent equivalents for fractions. This also explains why decimals and percents are themselves rational numbers.

Stress that $\frac{3}{5}$ means $\frac{1}{5} + \frac{1}{5} + \frac{1}{5}$ as well as $3 \times \frac{1}{5}$. Then $-\frac{3}{5}$, written as $\frac{-3}{5}$, becomes $3 \times (-\frac{1}{5})$ or $(-\frac{1}{5}) + (-\frac{1}{5}) + (-\frac{1}{5})$.

It is necessary that students understand that $-\frac{3}{5} = \frac{-3}{5} = \frac{3}{-5}$ but not $\frac{-3}{-5}$, which equals $+\frac{3}{5}$. Remind students that a negative number divided by a negative number equals a positive number.

Related Activities

To relate this topic to students' lives, ask them to watch and listen for frequently used fractions. List these on a poster and discuss which numbers are most frequently used in denominators.

To develop an awareness of the history and uses of mathematics, have students investigate when, where, and why fractions were first used.

Resource Book: Page 45 (Use After Page 109)

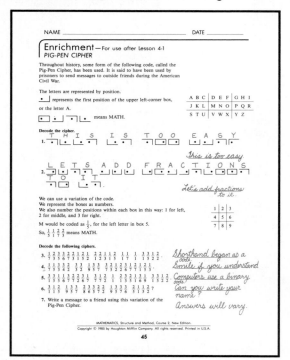

4-2 Equivalent Fractions

Objective *for pages 110–114*

■ To write proper and improper fractions as equivalent fractions or mixed numbers in lowest terms.

Teaching Suggestions

The number line using halves and fourths presents an opportunity to review markings on a ruler. Show that most inch rulers are divided into sixteenths of an inch. Two sixteenths, $\frac{2}{16}$, is usually read *one eighth*, $\frac{1}{8}$. Four sixteenths, $\frac{4}{16}$, is usually read *one fourth*, $\frac{1}{4}$, and so on. Use a different number line to show fifths and tenths or thirds and sixths.

When you present the Rule on page 110, you could point out that multiplying both the numerator and the denominator of a fraction by c is equivalent to multiplying the fraction by $\frac{c}{c}$, or 1.

Students should be familiar with common factors and the Greatest Common Factor (GCF) from earlier courses, but a brief review may be useful. For example, ask for the GCF of 16 and 12. The factors of 16 are 1, 2, 4, 8, and 16. The factors of 12 are 1, 2, 3, 4, 6, and 12. The common factors of 16 and 12 are 1, 2, and 4. The GCF is 4.

Review the most basic divisibility tests so that students can use them in finding prime factorization and GCF.

Divisor	Divisibility Test
2	The last digit is 0, 2, 4, 6, or 8.
3	The sum of the digits is divisible by 3.
5	The last digit is 0 or 5.
9	The sum of the digits is divisible by 9.
10	The last digit is 0.

Students may also need to be reminded of factor trees and repeated division. For example:

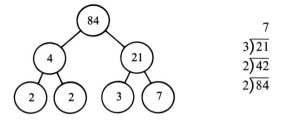

Both methods show that the prime factors of 84 are 2, 2, 3, and 7.

Related Activities

To help develop an awareness of patterns:

1. See if students know or can find the divisibility tests for 4, 6, 7, 8, and 11.
2. Have students consider these possibilities and test each one with several numbers: (a) If a number is divisible by 2 and 3, is it divisible by 6? **Yes** (b) If a number is divisible by 2 and 5, is it divisible by 10? **Yes**

4-3 Least Common Denominator

Objective *for pages 115–117*

■ To write two or more fractions as equivalent fractions with the least common denominator.

Teaching Suggestions

If students are concerned about finding the least common denominator, assure them that any common denominator will do. A common denominator can always be found by multiplying the denominators of the two fractions. For example:

$$\frac{3}{20} + \frac{4}{25} = \frac{75}{500} + \frac{80}{500} = \frac{155}{500} = \frac{31}{100}$$

However, it is more efficient to use the LCD:

$$\frac{3}{20} + \frac{4}{25} = \frac{15}{100} + \frac{16}{100} = \frac{31}{100}$$

Listing all multiples is a valid way to find the LCM, but time-consuming. For Example 1, this would mean listing

Multiples of 24 =
24, 48, 72, 96, 120, 144, 168, 192, 216, 240, . . .
Multiples of 48 = 48, 96, 144, 192, 240, . . .
Multiples of 120 = 120, 240, . . .

before the LCM, 240, is found.

Prime factorization is helpful in finding the equivalent fraction. You may want to use this method with your students.

$$\frac{1}{24} = \frac{1}{2^3 \times 3} = \frac{1 \times 2 \times 5}{2^3 \times 3 \times 2 \times 5} = \frac{10}{240}$$

$$\frac{5}{48} = \frac{5}{2^4 \times 3} = \frac{5 \times 5}{2^4 \times 3 \times 5} = \frac{25}{240}$$

$$\frac{11}{120} = \frac{11}{2^3 \times 3 \times 5} = \frac{11 \times 2}{2^3 \times 3 \times 5 \times 2} = \frac{22}{240}$$

Example 3 presents an important algebra readiness exercise. Written Exercises 29–32 are based on it. You might ask students whether, in the example, ab is the least common denominator of the fractions for all values of a and b. The answer is no. For example, when $a = 6$ and $b = 4$, the LCD is 12, not 24.

Related Activities

To develop a greater understanding of factorization, have students look for generalizations and clues for finding the LCD. One is that if the denominators have no common factors, the LCD is their product. For example, the denominators may both be prime numbers: The LCD of $\frac{1}{3}$ and $\frac{1}{7}$ is $3 \times 7 = 21$. The denominators may be consecutive numbers: the LCD of $\frac{1}{8}$ and $\frac{1}{9}$ is $8 \times 9 = 72$. Challenge students to look for other clues.

4-4 Adding and Subtracting Fractions

Objective *for pages 118–121*

■ To add and subtract fractions and mixed numbers.

Teaching Suggestions

Before calculating sums and differences of fractions, review sums and differences of integers. Remind students that we subtract by adding the opposite.

Some students may wish to add and subtract mixed numbers by first converting them to improper fractions. In addition and most subtraction problems this should be discouraged as time-consuming and unnecessary. When it becomes necessary to regroup or "borrow" in subtraction, however, conversion to improper fractions is an acceptable alternative, especially for students who have difficulty with regrouping. Example 2 of the lesson could be done as follows:

$$5\frac{1}{4} = 5\frac{3}{12} = \frac{63}{12}$$
$$-2\frac{1}{3} = -2\frac{4}{12} = -\frac{28}{12}$$
$$\frac{35}{12} = 2\frac{11}{12}$$

Some students have difficulty with negative mixed numbers. Show them that, for example, $-2\frac{1}{3} = -2 - \frac{1}{3}$, not $-2 + \frac{1}{3}$.

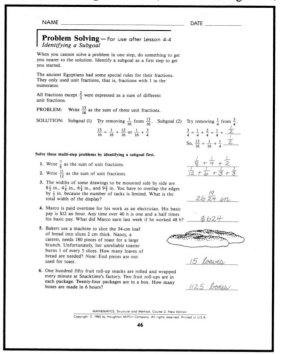

Related Activities

To provide practice in a different way, have students complete addition tables such as the one at the right.

$+$	$\frac{1}{4}$	$-\frac{2}{3}$	$-2\frac{1}{8}$
$-\frac{5}{12}$	$-\frac{1}{6}$	$-1\frac{1}{12}$	$-2\frac{13}{24}$
$\frac{1}{3}$	$\frac{7}{12}$	$-\frac{1}{3}$	$-1\frac{19}{24}$
$1\frac{1}{5}$	$1\frac{9}{20}$	$\frac{8}{15}$	$-\frac{37}{40}$

PRODUCTS AND QUOTIENTS

4-5 Multiplying Fractions

Objective *for pages 122–125*

■ To multiply fractions and mixed numbers.

Teaching Suggestions

The rule for multiplying any two fractions, given in the middle of page 123, suggests that you do not need a common denominator to multiply fractions. Emphasize this fact to your students. If students ask what happens in a multiplication when you use common denominators, demonstrate that you get the correct answer but do a great deal more work. Example 1 on page 123 would be done as follows:

$$-\frac{4}{12} \times \frac{3}{12} = -\frac{4 \times 3}{12 \times 12} = -\frac{12}{144} = -\frac{1}{12}$$

Also show students "short cuts" involving GCF and cancellation. Students should look for the GCF of any numerator and denominator:

$$\frac{\overset{3}{\cancel{21}}}{\underset{2}{\cancel{4}}} \times \frac{\overset{5}{\cancel{10}}}{\underset{1}{\cancel{7}}} = \frac{3}{2} \times \frac{5}{1}$$

Here we use the facts that 21 and 7 are both divisible by 7, and 4 and 10 are both divisible by 2. This method can be very helpful and efficient.

Related Activities

To relate this lesson to earlier work, you may wish to show students how to use the distributive property (page 53) to multiply a whole number and a mixed number:

$$4 \times 3\frac{1}{3} = 4 \times \left(3 + \frac{1}{3}\right)$$
$$= 4 \times 3 + 4 \times \frac{1}{3}$$
$$= 12 + 1\frac{1}{3}$$
$$= 13\frac{1}{3}$$

4-6 Dividing Fractions

Objective *for pages 126–130*

■ To divide fractions and mixed numbers.

Teaching Suggestions

In this lesson students will learn that to divide by a fraction means to multiply by the reciprocal of the divisor, the second fraction. Compare this to subtraction of negative numbers, in which we add the opposite of the second number.

Help students to develop general rules about the signs of reciprocals by reminding them that the product of any number and its reciprocal must be +1. Therefore, the reciprocal of a positive fraction is a positive fraction, and the reciprocal of a negative fraction is a negative fraction.

Related Activities

To provide a challenge, introduce students to complex fractions by showing that

$$\frac{3}{5} \div \frac{1}{4} = \frac{\frac{3}{5}}{\frac{1}{4}}$$

Ask students to simplify such problems as:

$$\frac{\frac{2}{3}}{\frac{4}{5}} = \frac{5}{6} \qquad \frac{7 + 3\frac{1}{3}}{\frac{1}{4}} = 41\frac{1}{3}$$

$$\frac{\frac{3}{8} + \frac{1}{3}}{4\frac{1}{5} + 2\frac{1}{2}} = \frac{85}{804}$$

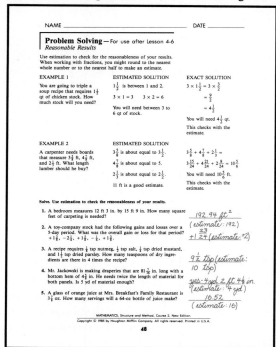

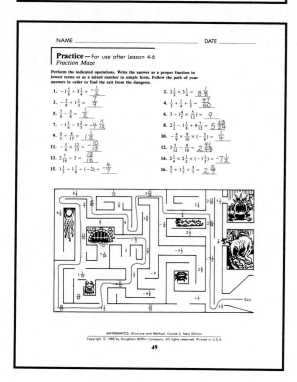

4-7 Fractions and Decimals

Objectives *for pages 131–135*

- To write fractions and mixed numbers as equivalent terminating or repeating decimals.
- To write terminating or repeating decimals as equivalent fractions or mixed numbers.

Teaching Suggestions

Review the meaning of $\frac{a}{b}$, emphasized on page 106 as $a \div b$. For students who think that $\frac{3}{5}$ means $3\overline{)5}$ instead of $5\overline{)3.0}$, remind them that $\frac{3}{5}$ is less than $\frac{5}{5}$ or 1, so $3 \div 5$ must also be less than 1.

Explain that every rational number can be written as a terminating or repeating decimal. Demonstrate this on the chalkboard by using a fraction that can be written as a repeating decimal, such as

$$\frac{5}{7} = 0.\overline{714285}.$$

As you do the division, $7\overline{)5}$, ask students if they see a relationship between the remainder and the divisor. Ask questions such as:

1. What are the possible remainders?
   0, 1, 2, 3, 4, 5, 6
2. How many digits are in the repeating block? **6**
3. What is the maximum number of digits possible in a repeating block? **A number one less than the divisor (denominator)**
4. How can we tell that this is a repeating decimal? **We get a remainder that we have had before: 5.**
5. How would we know if this were a terminating decimal? **At some point we would get a remainder of 0.**

Have students read decimal numbers orally before they write the fractional equivalent. For example, 0.37 is read thirty-seven hundredths, so $0.37 = \frac{37}{100}$. This helps students use the correct denominator.

Give some examples of irrational numbers. For example, the ratio of the circumference of a circle to its diameter is π. The length of the diagonal of a square with sides of length 1 is $\sqrt{2}$. These numbers can be shown to be irrational using advanced methods. Students might like to try to find a fraction whose square is 2.

Related Activities

To help students memorize fractional equivalents, have them complete a chart similar to the one below:

$\frac{1}{2} = 0.5$	$\frac{1}{3} = 0.\overline{3}$	$\frac{1}{4} = 0.25$	$\frac{1}{5} = 0.2$	$\frac{1}{6} = 0.1\overline{6}$	$\frac{1}{8} = 0.125$

	$\frac{2}{3} = 0.\overline{6}$	$\frac{2}{4} = 0.5$	$\frac{2}{5} = 0.4$	$\frac{2}{6} = 0.\overline{3}$	$\frac{2}{8} = 0.25$

		$\frac{3}{4} = 0.75$	$\frac{3}{5} = 0.6$	$\frac{3}{6} = 0.5$	$\frac{3}{8} = 0.375$

			$\frac{4}{5} = 0.8$	$\frac{4}{6} = 0.\overline{6}$	$\frac{4}{8} = 0.5$

				$\frac{5}{6} = 0.8\overline{3}$	$\frac{5}{8} = 0.625$

$\frac{6}{8} = 0.75$

$\frac{7}{8} = 0.875$

Some students will ask why the sevenths and ninths were left out. Explain that these are less-used fractional equivalents but nevertheless very interesting. Encourage students to investigate them. The elevenths also produce an interesting pattern.

To emphasize that many problems can be solved in more than one way, provide students with problems involving fractions and decimals. Allow them to work each problem in the most convenient way. Examples:

1. $3\frac{1}{8} + 4.75$ **7.875**

2. $5\frac{1}{3} - 2.5$ **2.8$\overline{3}$ or $2\frac{5}{6}$**

3. $-2\frac{1}{7} \times (-5.6)$ **12**

4. $-4\frac{1}{5} \times 2.75$ **−11.55**

Resource Book: Page 50 (Use After Page 135)

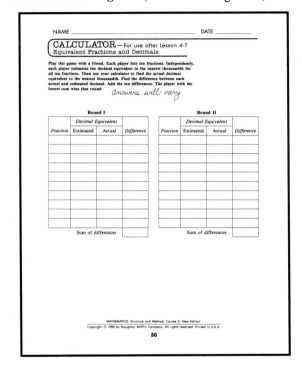

Resource Book: Pages 51–54 (Use After Page 135)

Quiz 4B — Lessons 4-5 through 4-7

DIRECTIONS: Write the letter of the correct answer in the space provided.

Multiply. Show the answer as a proper fraction in lowest terms or as a mixed number in simple form.

1. $-\frac{3}{5} \times -\frac{20}{27}$ [4-5]
   a. $\frac{10}{36}$ b. $-\frac{10}{36}$ c. $\frac{5}{18}$ d. $3\frac{3}{5}$

2. $5\frac{5}{8} \times \frac{2}{9}$
   a. $\frac{5}{18}$ b. $-\frac{5}{4}$ c. $1\frac{18}{72}$ d. $1\frac{1}{4}$

Divide. Show the answer as a proper fraction in lowest terms or as a mixed number in simple form.

3. $\frac{2}{7} \div -\frac{16}{21}$ [4-6]
   a. $2\frac{2}{3}$ b. $-\frac{3}{8}$ c. $-2\frac{2}{3}$ d. $\frac{3}{8}$

4. $-4 \div (1\frac{15}{2} \times \frac{2}{3})$
   a. 6   b. -6 c. $-2\frac{2}{3}$ d. $\frac{8}{3}$

Show as a terminating or repeating decimal. Use a bar to show the repetend.

5. $\frac{3}{8}$ [4-7]
   a. 0.38   b. 0.375   c. 0.385   d. $0.\overline{3}$

6. $1\frac{3}{11}$
   a. $0.\overline{27}$ b. $1.\overline{27}$ c. 0.14   d. 1.311

Show as a proper fraction in lowest terms or as a mixed number in simple form.

7. -10.125
   a. $10\frac{125}{1000}$ b. $10\frac{1}{8}$ c. $-9\frac{7}{8}$ d. $-10\frac{1}{8}$

8. $0.\overline{36}$
   a. $\frac{36}{100}$ b. $\frac{9}{25}$ c. $-\frac{12}{33}$ d. $\frac{4}{11}$

ANSWERS
1. ___c___ (10)
2. ___d___ (10)
3. ___b___ (10)
4. ___c___ (10)
5. ___b___ (15)
6. ___b___ (15)
7. ___d___ (15)
8. ___d___ (15)

51

Review — Chapter 4

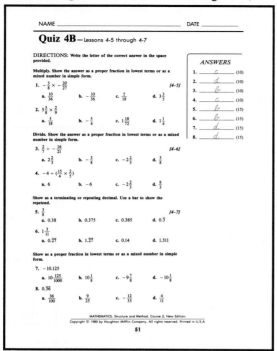

Complete.
1. $\frac{7}{?} \times 6 = \frac{6}{7}$ 2. $9 \times \frac{?}{9} = -1$ 3. $-\frac{5}{8} \times \frac{8}{5} = -1$ [4-1]

Write as a proper fraction in lowest terms or as a mixed number in simple form.
4. $\frac{16}{36}$ $\frac{4}{9}$ 5. $-\frac{92}{7}$ $-13\frac{1}{7}$ 6. $-\frac{116}{348}$ $-\frac{1}{3}$ [4-2]

Write as an improper fraction.
7. $3\frac{3}{8}$ $\frac{27}{8}$ 8. $-7\frac{4}{9}$ $\frac{67}{9}$ 9. $1\frac{7}{15}$ $\frac{22}{15}$

Solve. Write fractional answers in lowest terms.
10. Of the 48 orchestra members appearing in tonight's performance, 18 are violinists. What fraction of the orchestra are violinists? $\frac{3}{8}$

Write each pair of fractions as equivalent fractions with the least common denominator.
11. $\frac{2}{5}, \frac{7}{15}$ $\frac{6}{15}$ $\frac{7}{15}$ 12. $\frac{5}{8}, \frac{13}{20}$ $\frac{25}{40}$ $\frac{26}{40}$ 13. $\frac{5}{x}, \frac{8}{y}$ $\frac{5y}{xy}$ $\frac{8x}{xy}$ [4-3]

Add or subtract. Write the answer as a proper fraction in lowest terms or as a mixed number in simple form.
14. $-\frac{5}{12} + \frac{14}{18}$ $\frac{13}{36}$ 15. $7\frac{1}{4} - \frac{7}{8}$ $6\frac{3}{8}$ 16. $\frac{5}{6} + 3\frac{1}{3}$ $-9\frac{3}{5}$ $-5\frac{1}{12}$ [4-4]

Multiply. Write the answer as a proper fraction in lowest terms or as a mixed number in simple form.
17. $\frac{3}{5} \times -\frac{20}{30}$ $-\frac{2}{5}$ 18. $-4\frac{1}{2} \times 2\frac{2}{9}$ -10 19. $-6\frac{2}{3} \times -7 \times 1\frac{1}{5}$ 56 [4-5]

Divide. Write the answer as a proper fraction in lowest terms or as a mixed number in simple form.
20. $2\frac{9}{10} \div 1\frac{3}{5}$ $\frac{13}{16}$ 21. $2\frac{4}{7} \div \frac{9}{4}$ $-1\frac{1}{7}$ 22. $2 \div (-\frac{3}{4})$ $-2\frac{2}{3}$ [4-6]

Solve.
23. How much wire will be needed to fence in a rectangular vegetable garden measuring $14\frac{1}{3}$ ft by $16\frac{1}{4}$ ft? $61\frac{5}{6}$ ft

Write as a terminating or repeating decimal. Use a bar to show a repetend.
24. $\frac{8}{25}$ 0.32 25. $3\frac{7}{8}$ 3.875 26. $\frac{8}{15}$ $0.5\overline{3}$ [4-7]

52

Test — Chapter 4

DIRECTIONS: Write the correct answer in the space provided.

Complete.
1. $9 \times \frac{?}{?} = \frac{9}{14}$ 2. $\frac{1}{5} \times 5 = \underline{?}$ [4-1]
3. $-\frac{2}{3} \div -\frac{2}{3} = \underline{?}$ 4. $-8 \div 11 = \underline{?}$

Show as a proper fraction in lowest terms or as a mixed number in simple form.
5. $\frac{42}{48}$ 6. $\frac{18}{8}$ 7. $-\frac{68}{5}$ [4-2]

Show as an improper fraction.
8. $6\frac{5}{6}$ 9. $-7\frac{1}{7}$ 10. $16\frac{2}{3}$

Show each pair of fractions as equivalent fractions with the least common denominator.
11. $\frac{2}{3}, \frac{5}{12}$ 12. $\frac{7}{12}, \frac{11}{30}$ 13. $\frac{x}{3}, \frac{y}{5}$ [4-3]

Add or subtract. Show the answer as a proper fraction in lowest terms or as a mixed number in simple form.
14. $3\frac{5}{6} + 2\frac{1}{3}$ 15. $\frac{7}{8} - (-\frac{3}{4})$ [4-4]
16. $4\frac{7}{20} + (-6\frac{1}{4})$ 17. $\frac{5}{a} - \frac{3}{a}$

Multiply. Show the answer as a proper fraction in lowest terms or as a mixed number in simple form.
18. $\frac{5}{9} \times (-\frac{18}{80})$ 19. $10\frac{1}{3} \times 4\frac{2}{3}$ [4-5]

Divide. Show the answer as a proper fraction in lowest terms or as a mixed number in simple form.
20. $\frac{9}{10} \div 1\frac{3}{5}$ 21. $\frac{3}{5} \div -\frac{6}{20}$ [4-6]

Write as a terminating or repeating decimal. Use a bar to show a repetend.
22. $-4\frac{5}{8}$ 23. $\frac{4}{33}$ 24. $\frac{5}{12}$ [4-7]

Write as a proper fraction in lowest terms or as a mixed number in simple form.
25. -12.04 26. $4.\overline{6}$ 27. $0.2\overline{6}$

ANSWERS
1. $\frac{7}{14}$ (2)
2. 1 (2)
3. 1 (2)
4. $-\frac{8}{11}$ (3)
5. $\frac{7}{8}$ (3)
6. $2\frac{1}{4}$ (4)
7. $-13\frac{3}{5}$ (4)
8. $\frac{41}{6}$ (4)
9. $-\frac{50}{7}$ (4)
10. $\frac{50}{3}$ (4)
11. $\frac{8}{12}, \frac{5}{12}$ (4)
12. $\frac{35}{60}, \frac{22}{60}$ (4)
13. $\frac{5x}{15}, \frac{3y}{15}$ (4)
14. $6\frac{1}{6}$ (4)
15. $1\frac{5}{8}$ (4)
16. $-2\frac{9}{10}$ (4)
17. $\frac{2}{a}$ (4)
18. $-\frac{1}{8}$ (4)
19. $47\frac{4}{9}$ (4)
20. $\frac{9}{16}$ (4)
21. -2 (4)
22. -4.625 (4)
23. $0.\overline{12}$ (4)
24. $0.41\overline{6}$ (4)
25. $-12\frac{1}{25}$ (4)
26. $4\frac{2}{3}$ (4)
27. $\frac{4}{15}$ (4)

53

Make-up Test — Chapter 4

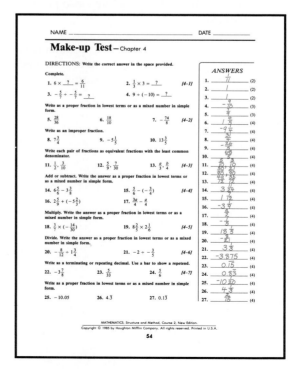

DIRECTIONS: Write the correct answer in the space provided.

Complete.
1. $6 \times \frac{?}{?} = \frac{6}{11}$ 2. $\frac{1}{3} \times 3 = \underline{?}$ [4-1]
3. $-\frac{5}{7} \div -\frac{5}{7} = \underline{?}$ 4. $9 \div (-10) = \underline{?}$

Write as a proper fraction in lowest terms or as a mixed number in simple form.
5. $\frac{28}{36}$ 6. $\frac{18}{10}$ 7. $-\frac{74}{8}$ [4-2]

Write as an improper fraction.
8. $7\frac{3}{4}$ 9. $-5\frac{1}{5}$ 10. $13\frac{3}{8}$

Write each pair of fractions as equivalent fractions with the least common denominator.
11. $\frac{1}{2}, \frac{3}{10}$ 12. $\frac{5}{12}, \frac{7}{30}$ 13. $\frac{a}{3}, \frac{b}{4}$ [4-3]

Add or subtract. Write the answer as a proper fraction in lowest terms or as a mixed number in simple form.
14. $6\frac{5}{8} - 3\frac{1}{3}$ 15. $\frac{5}{6} - (-\frac{3}{4})$ [4-4]
16. $2\frac{5}{12} + (-5\frac{5}{6})$ 17. $\frac{3a}{4} - \frac{a}{4}$

Multiply. Write the answer as a proper fraction in lowest terms or as a mixed number in simple form.
18. $\frac{3}{5} \times (-\frac{14}{30})$ 19. $8\frac{2}{3} \times 2\frac{1}{6}$ [4-5]

Divide. Write the answer as a proper fraction in lowest terms or as a mixed number in simple form.
20. $-\frac{8}{12} \div 1\frac{1}{4}$ 21. $-2 \div -\frac{3}{5}$ [4-6]

Write as a terminating or repeating decimal. Use a bar to show a repetend.
22. $-3\frac{7}{8}$ 23. $\frac{5}{33}$ 24. $\frac{5}{6}$ [4-7]

Write as a proper fraction in lowest terms or as a mixed number in simple form.
25. -10.05 26. $4.\overline{3}$ 27. $0.1\overline{3}$

ANSWERS
1. $\frac{7}{11}$ (2)
2. 1 (2)
3. 1 (2)
4. $-\frac{9}{10}$ (3)
5. $\frac{7}{9}$ (3)
6. $1\frac{4}{5}$ (4)
7. $-9\frac{1}{4}$ (4)
8. $\frac{31}{4}$ (4)
9. $-\frac{26}{5}$ (4)
10. $\frac{107}{8}$ (4)
11. $\frac{5}{10}, \frac{3}{10}$ (4)
12. $\frac{25}{60}, \frac{14}{60}$ (4)
13. $\frac{4a}{12}, \frac{3b}{12}$ (4)
14. $3\frac{7}{24}$ (4)
15. $1\frac{7}{12}$ (4)
16. $-3\frac{5}{12}$ (4)
17. $\frac{a}{2}$ (4)
18. $-\frac{7}{25}$ (4)
19. $18\frac{7}{9}$ (4)
20. $-\frac{8}{15}$ (4)
21. $3\frac{1}{3}$ (4)
22. -3.875 (4)
23. $0.\overline{15}$ (4)
24. $0.8\overline{3}$ (4)
25. $-10\frac{1}{20}$ (4)
26. $4\frac{1}{3}$ (4)
27. $\frac{2}{15}$ (4)

54

105g

Resource Book: Pages 55–56 (Use After Page 135)

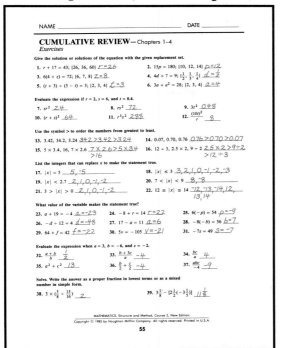

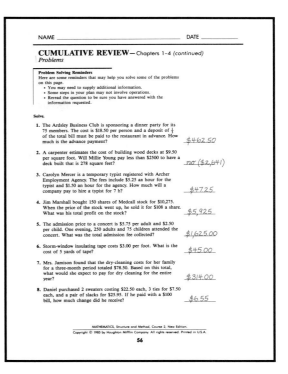

NAME _____ DATE _____

CUMULATIVE REVIEW—Chapters 1–4
Exercises

Give the solution or solutions of the equation with the given replacement set.

1. $r + 17 = 43$; {26, 36, 60} $r = 26$
2. $15p = 180$; {10, 12, 14} $p = 12$
3. $6(4 + z) = 72$; {6, 7, 8} $z = 8$
4. $4d + 7 = 9$; {$\frac{1}{2}$, $\frac{1}{3}$, $\frac{1}{4}$} $d = \frac{1}{2}$
5. $(t + 3) \div (5 - t) = 3$; {2, 3, 4} $t = 3$
6. $3a + a^2 = 28$; {2, 3, 4} $a = 4$

Evaluate the expression if $r = 2$, $s = 6$, and $t = 0.4$.

7. sr^2 24
8. rs^2 72
9. $3t^2$ 0.48
10. $(r + s)^2$ 64
11. r^3s^2 288
12. $\frac{(10n)^2}{r}$ 8

Use the symbol > to order the numbers from greatest to least.

13. 3.42, 34.2, 3.24 $34.2 > 3.42 > 3.24$
14. 0.07, 0.70, 0.76 $0.76 > 0.70 > 0.07$
15. 5×3.4, 16, 7×2.6 $7 \times 2.6 > 5 \times 3.4$ > 16
16. $12 \div 3$, 2.5×2, $9 \div 2$ $2.5 \times 2 > 9 \div 2$ $> 12 \div 3$

List the integers that can replace x to make the statement true.

17. $|x| = 5$ $5, -5$
18. $|x| \le 3$ $3, 2, 1, 0, -1, -2, -3$
19. $|x| < 2.7$ $2, 1, 0, -1, -2$
20. $7 < |x| < 9$ $8, -8$
21. $3 > |x| > 0$ $2, 1, 0, -1, -2$
22. $12 \le |x| \le 14$ $-12, -13, -14, 12,$ $13, 14$

What value of the variable makes the statement true?

23. $a + 19 = -4$ $a = -23$
24. $-8 + r = 14$ $r = 22$
25. $6(-p) = 54$ $p = -9$
26. $-d + 12 = 4$ $d = -48$
27. $17 - a = 11$ $a = 6$
28. $-8(-b) = 56$ $b = 7$
29. $64 + f = 42$ $f = -22$
30. $5v = -105$ $v = -21$
31. $-7s = 49$ $s = -7$

Evaluate the expression when $a = 3$, $b = -6$, and $c = -2$.

32. $\frac{a + b}{b}$ $\frac{1}{2}$
33. $\frac{b + 3c}{a}$ -4
34. $\frac{bc}{a}$ 4
35. $a^2 + c^2$ 13
36. $\frac{b}{2} + \frac{c}{2}$ -4
37. $\frac{abc}{-4}$ -9

Solve. Write the answer as a proper fraction in lowest terms or as a mixed number in simple form.

38. $3 \times (\frac{5}{8} + \frac{15}{16})$ 2
39. $3\frac{1}{8} - [2\frac{1}{2}(-3\frac{1}{3})]$ $11\frac{1}{2}$

NAME _____ DATE _____

CUMULATIVE REVIEW—Chapters 1–4 *(continued)*
Problems

Problem Solving Reminders
Here are some reminders that may help you solve some of the problems on this page.
- You may need to supply additional information.
- Some steps in your plan may not involve operations.
- Reread the question to be sure you have answered with the information requested.

Solve.

1. The Ardsley Business Club is sponsoring a dinner party for its 75 members. The cost is $18.50 per person and a deposit of $\frac{1}{3}$ of the total bill must be paid to the restaurant in advance. How much is the advance payment? $\$462.50$

2. A carpenter estimates the cost of building wood decks at $9.50 per square foot. Will Millie Young pay less than $2500 to have a deck built that is 278 square feet? $no (\$2,641)$

3. Carolyn Mercer is a temporary typist registered with Archer Employment Agency. The fees include $5.25 an hour for the typist and $1.50 an hour pay to the agency. How much will a company pay to hire a typist for 7 h? $\$47.25$

4. Jim Marshall bought 150 shares of Medcall stock for $10,275. When the price of the stock went up, he sold it for $108 a share. What was his total profit on the stock? $\$5,925$

5. The admission price to a concert is $5.75 per adult and $2.50 per child. One evening, 250 adults and 75 children attended the concert. What was the total admission fee collected? $\$1,625.00$

6. Storm-window insulating tape costs $3.00 per foot. What is the cost of 5 yards of tape? $\$45.00$

7. Mrs. Jamison found that the dry-cleaning costs for her family for a three-month period totaled $78.50. Based on this total, what would she expect to pay for dry cleaning for the entire year? $\$314.00$

8. Daniel purchased 2 sweaters costing $22.50 each, 3 ties for $7.50 each, and a pair of slacks for $25.95. If he paid with a $100 bill, how much change did he receive? $\$6.55$

Teaching Suggestions
p. 105a

Related Activities p. 105a

Reading Mathematics

Students will learn the meaning of the following mathematical terms in this lesson: *numerator, denominator, opposite, rational number.*

4-1 Positive and Negative Fractions

In any fraction the number above the fraction bar is called the **numerator** and the number below the bar is called the **denominator**. Since the fraction bar indicates division,

$$\frac{3}{5} \text{ means } 3 \div 5.$$

A study of fractions on a number line shows some important properties of fractions.

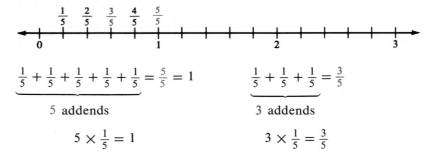

$$\underbrace{\frac{1}{5} + \frac{1}{5} + \frac{1}{5} + \frac{1}{5} + \frac{1}{5}}_{5 \text{ addends}} = \frac{5}{5} = 1 \qquad \underbrace{\frac{1}{5} + \frac{1}{5} + \frac{1}{5}}_{3 \text{ addends}} = \frac{3}{5}$$

$$5 \times \frac{1}{5} = 1 \qquad\qquad 3 \times \frac{1}{5} = \frac{3}{5}$$

We can state these properties in general terms that apply to all positive fractions.

Properties

For all whole numbers a and b ($a > 0, b > 0$),

$$\underbrace{\frac{1}{b} + \frac{1}{b} + \cdots + \frac{1}{b}}_{b \text{ addends}} = \frac{b}{b} = 1 \qquad \underbrace{\frac{1}{b} + \frac{1}{b} + \cdots + \frac{1}{b}}_{a \text{ addends}} = \frac{a}{b}$$

$$b \times \frac{1}{b} = 1 \qquad\qquad a \times \frac{1}{b} = \frac{a}{b}$$

$$1 \div b = \frac{1}{b} \qquad\qquad a \div b = \frac{a}{b}$$

Just as the negative integers are the opposites of the positive integers, the negative fractions are the opposites of the positive fractions. For every fraction $\frac{a}{b}$ there is a fraction denoted by $-\frac{a}{b}$ that is said to be the **opposite** of $\frac{a}{b}$. On the number line the graphs of $\frac{a}{b}$ and $-\frac{a}{b}$ are on opposite sides of 0 and at equal distances from 0. For example, $\frac{3}{5}$ and $-\frac{3}{5}$ are opposites. They are shown on the number line below.

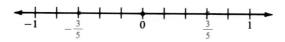

Properties similar to those for positive fractions apply to negative fractions.

$$-\frac{1}{5} + \left(-\frac{1}{5}\right) + \left(-\frac{1}{5}\right) + \left(-\frac{1}{5}\right) + \left(-\frac{1}{5}\right) = -1 \qquad -\frac{1}{5} + \left(-\frac{1}{5}\right) + \left(-\frac{1}{5}\right) = -\frac{3}{5}$$

$$\underbrace{\phantom{-\frac{1}{5} + \left(-\frac{1}{5}\right) + \left(-\frac{1}{5}\right) + \left(-\frac{1}{5}\right) + \left(-\frac{1}{5}\right)}}_{\text{5 addends}} \qquad \underbrace{\phantom{-\frac{1}{5} + \left(-\frac{1}{5}\right) + \left(-\frac{1}{5}\right)}}_{\text{3 addends}}$$

$$5 \times \left(-\frac{1}{5}\right) = -1 \qquad 3 \times \left(-\frac{1}{5}\right) = -\frac{3}{5}$$

In an earlier section you learned that the quotient of two numbers of opposite sign is negative. Using this rule we can write the following:

$$1 \div (-4) = \frac{1}{-4} = -\frac{1}{4} \qquad (-1) \div 4 = \frac{-1}{4} = -\frac{1}{4}$$

Therefore, we can write the opposite of $\frac{1}{4}$ as $-\frac{1}{4}$, or as $\frac{-1}{4}$, or as $\frac{1}{-4}$. In general, for $b \neq 0$, $-\frac{a}{b} = \frac{-a}{b} = \frac{a}{-b}$.

EXAMPLE 1 Express $-\frac{3}{8}$ in two other ways.

Solution $-\frac{3}{8} = \frac{-3}{8} = \frac{3}{-8}$

EXAMPLE 2 Complete.

    a. $\left(-\frac{1}{3}\right) + \left(-\frac{1}{3}\right) + \left(-\frac{1}{3}\right) = \underline{}$ **b.** $3 \times \underline{} = -1$

    c. $2 \times \left(-\frac{1}{5}\right) = \underline{}$ **d.** $-\frac{2}{5} = \underline{} \div 5$

Solution   **a.** $\left(-\frac{1}{3}\right) + \left(-\frac{1}{3}\right) + \left(-\frac{1}{3}\right) = -1$ **b.** $3 \times \left(-\frac{1}{3}\right) = -1$

    c. $2 \times \left(-\frac{1}{5}\right) = -\frac{2}{5}$ **d.** $-\frac{2}{5} = \frac{-2}{5} = -2 \div 5$

Rational Numbers **107**

Express in two other ways.

1. $-\frac{1}{5}$ $\frac{-1}{5}$, $\frac{1}{-5}$

2. $\frac{-12}{7}$ $\frac{12}{-7}$, $-\frac{12}{7}$

3. $\frac{4}{-9}$ $\frac{-4}{9}$, $-\frac{4}{9}$

Complete.

4. $\underline{\quad?\quad} \times \left(-\frac{4}{3}\right) = -4$ 3

5. $1 \div 2 = \underline{\quad?\quad}$ $\frac{1}{2}$

6. $5 \times \underline{\quad?\quad} = \frac{5}{7}$ $\frac{1}{7}$

Suggested Assignments

Minimum
   108/1–16
   109/17–30
   109/Rev. 1–6

Average
   108/1–16
   109/17–37
   109/Rev. 1–6

Maximum
   108/1–15 odd
   109/17–43

Supplementary Materials

Practice Masters, p. 17

When we work with fractions having numerators and denominators that are integers, we are working with a new set of numbers called *rational numbers.* Any number that can be represented by a fraction $\frac{a}{b}$, where a and b are integers and b is not 0, is a **rational number.** Notice that the integers themselves are rational numbers. For example, -9 can be written as $\frac{-9}{1}$, 0 as $\frac{0}{1}$, and 26 as $\frac{26}{1}$.

Class Exercises

Name the rational numbers whose graphs are shown.

1.

2.

3.

4.

Complete.

5. $\frac{1}{7} + \frac{1}{7} = \underline{\quad?\quad}$ $\frac{2}{7}$

6. $2 \times \frac{1}{7} = \underline{\quad?\quad}$ $\frac{2}{7}$

7. $2 \div 7 = \underline{\quad?\quad}$ $\frac{2}{7}$

8. $\left(-\frac{1}{8}\right) + \left(-\frac{1}{8}\right) + \left(-\frac{1}{8}\right) = \underline{\quad?\quad}$ $-\frac{3}{8}$

9. $3 \times \left(-\frac{1}{8}\right) = \underline{\quad?\quad}$ $-\frac{3}{8}$

10. $3 \div (-8) = \underline{\quad?\quad}$ $-\frac{3}{8}$

11. $4 \times \underline{\quad?\quad} = -1$ $-\frac{1}{4}$

12. $5 \times \underline{\quad?\quad} = -\frac{5}{8}$ $-\frac{1}{8}$

13. $\frac{2}{9} = 2 \div \underline{\quad?\quad}$ 9

Written Exercises

Graph each set of rational numbers on a number line.

A

1. $-1, -\frac{1}{3}, 0, \frac{1}{3}, 1$

2. $-1, -\frac{1}{4}, 0, \frac{1}{4}, 1$

3. $0, \frac{1}{5}, \frac{5}{5}, \frac{6}{5}$

4. $-\frac{4}{3}, -\frac{3}{3}, -\frac{2}{3}, 0$

5. $-\frac{5}{4}, -\frac{3}{4}, \frac{3}{4}, \frac{5}{4}$

6. $-\frac{5}{3}, -\frac{4}{3}, \frac{4}{3}, \frac{5}{3}$

Express in two other ways.

7. $-\frac{1}{2}$ $\frac{-1}{2}, \frac{1}{-2}$

8. $\frac{-1}{3}$ $-\frac{1}{3}, \frac{1}{-3}$

9. $\frac{-1}{11}$ $-\frac{1}{11}, \frac{1}{-11}$

10. $\frac{-1}{6}$ $-\frac{1}{6}, \frac{1}{-6}$

11. $\frac{2}{-9}$ $-\frac{2}{9}, \frac{-2}{9}$

12. $\frac{-9}{10}$ $-\frac{9}{10}, \frac{9}{-10}$

13. $-\frac{13}{6}$ $\frac{-13}{6}, \frac{13}{-6}$

14. $\frac{5}{-8}$ $-\frac{5}{8}, \frac{-5}{8}$

15. $-\frac{3}{4}$ $\frac{-3}{4}, \frac{3}{-4}$

16. $\frac{5}{-9}$ $-\frac{5}{9}, \frac{-5}{9}$

Complete.

17. $\underline{\quad?\quad} \times \left(-\frac{1}{6}\right) = -1$ $_6$

18. $4 \times \underline{\quad?\quad} = \frac{4}{7}$ $\frac{1}{7}$

19. $3 \times \underline{\quad?\quad} = \frac{3}{4}$ $\frac{1}{4}$

20. $5 \div 6 = \underline{\quad?\quad}$ $\frac{5}{6}$

21. $2 \div \underline{\quad?\quad} = \frac{2}{3}$ 3

22. $4 \times \underline{\quad?\quad} = -\frac{4}{9}$ $-\frac{1}{9}$

Evaluate the expression when $a = 4$, $b = -3$, and $c = 5$.

B **23.** $\frac{a + c}{b}$ -3

24. $\frac{a - c}{a}$ $-\frac{1}{4}$

25. $\frac{2b - 1}{8}$ $-\frac{7}{8}$

26. $\frac{2c - b}{a}$ $\frac{13}{4}$

27. $\frac{a^2 - c^2}{a + c}$ -1

What value of the variable makes the statement true?

28. $x \times \frac{1}{5} = 1$ 5

29. $3y = -1$ $-\frac{1}{3}$

30. $\frac{1}{b} = -\frac{1}{8}$ -8

31. $-\frac{3}{4} = \frac{c}{4}$ -3

32. $-\frac{3}{5} = d \div 5$ -3

33. $\frac{-5}{9} = \frac{5}{m}$ -9

Write the expression as a positive or a negative fraction.

EXAMPLE **a.** $3(7)^{-1}$ **b.** $(-5)^{-1}$

Solution **a.** $3(7)^{-1} = 3 \times \frac{1}{7} = \frac{3}{7}$ **b.** $(-5)^{-1} = \frac{1}{-5} = -\frac{1}{5}$

C **34.** $2(3)^{-1}$ $\frac{2}{3}$

35. $7(6)^{-1}$ $\frac{7}{6}$

36. $5^{-1} + 5^{-1}$ $\frac{2}{5}$

37. $7^{-1} + 7^{-1} + 7^{-1}$ $\frac{3}{7}$

38. $(-2)^{-1}$ $-\frac{1}{2}$

39. $(-9)^{-1}$ $-\frac{1}{9}$

40. $3(-5)^{-1}$ $-\frac{3}{5}$

41. $2(-7)^{-1}$ $-\frac{2}{7}$

42. $(-3)^{-1} + (-3)^{-1}$ $-\frac{2}{3}$

43. $(-8)^{-1} + (-8)^{-1} + (-8)^{-1}$ $-\frac{3}{8}$

Review Exercises

Complete.

1. Factors of 72: 1, 2, $\underline{\quad?\quad}$ 3, $\underline{\quad?\quad}$ 4, 6, $\underline{\quad?\quad}$ 8, 9, 12, $\underline{\quad?\quad}$ 18, 24, $\underline{\quad?\quad}$ 36, 72

2. What is the prime factorization of 72? $2 \times 2 \times 2 \times 3 \times 3$

3. Factors of 90: $\underline{\quad?\quad}$ 1, 2, 3, $\underline{\quad?\quad}$ 5, $\underline{\quad?\quad}$ 6, 9, $\underline{\quad?\quad}$ 10, $\underline{\quad?\quad}$ 15, 18, $\underline{\quad?\quad}$ 30, $\underline{\quad?\quad}$ 45, 90

4. What is the prime factorization of 90? $2 \times 3 \times 3 \times 5$

5. $18x^2y = 3 \times \underline{\quad?\quad}$ 6 $\times x \times \underline{\quad?\quad}$ x $\times y$

6. $24ab^3 = 4 \times \underline{\quad?\quad}$ 6 $\times \underline{\quad?\quad}$ a $\times \underline{\quad?\quad}$ b $\times b \times b$

Reading Mathematics

Students will learn the meaning of the following mathematical terms in this lesson: *equivalent fractions, lowest terms, prime factorization, prime number, relatively prime, proper fraction, improper fraction, mixed number, simple form.*

Chalkboard Examples

State an equivalent fraction in lowest terms.

1. $\frac{12}{36}$ $\frac{1}{3}$

2. $\frac{60}{132}$ $\frac{5}{11}$

3. $-\frac{30}{45}$ $-\frac{2}{3}$

4. $\frac{14}{63}$ $\frac{2}{9}$

Write as a mixed number in simple form.

5. $\frac{24}{5}$ $4\frac{4}{5}$

6. $\frac{16}{3}$ $5\frac{1}{3}$

7. $-\frac{49}{14}$ $-3\frac{1}{2}$

8. $-\frac{402}{20}$ $-20\frac{1}{10}$

Write as an improper fraction.

9. $3\frac{2}{3}$ $\frac{11}{3}$

10. $1\frac{5}{9}$ $\frac{14}{9}$

11. $-4\frac{1}{5}$ $-\frac{21}{5}$

12. $-1\frac{7}{10}$ $-\frac{17}{10}$

4-2 Equivalent Fractions

The number line shows the graphs of several fractions.

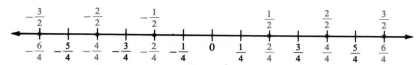

Since $-\frac{1}{2}$ and $-\frac{2}{4}$ have the same graph, they are two names for the same number. Fractions that represent the same number are called **equivalent** fractions. Thus,

$$-\frac{3}{2} \text{ is equivalent to } -\frac{6}{4};$$

$$\frac{3}{2} \text{ is equivalent to } \frac{6}{4}.$$

Notice that $\frac{3}{2} = \frac{3 \times 2}{2 \times 2} = \frac{6}{4}$ and $\frac{6}{4} = \frac{6 \div 2}{4 \div 2} = \frac{3}{2}$.

We may state the following general rule.

> ## *Rule*
> For all numbers a, b, and c ($b \neq 0$, $c \neq 0$),
> $$\frac{a}{b} = \frac{a \times c}{b \times c} \qquad \text{and} \qquad \frac{a}{b} = \frac{a \div c}{b \div c}$$

EXAMPLE 1 Write as an equivalent fraction with a denominator of 12.

   a. $\frac{5}{6}$ **b.** $-\frac{32}{48}$

Solution **a.** Since $6 \times 2 = 12$, we write $\frac{5}{6} = \frac{5 \times 2}{6 \times 2} = \frac{10}{12}$.

b. *Method 1*
Since $48 \div 4 = 12$, we write

$$-\frac{32}{48} = \frac{-32}{48} = \frac{-32 \div 4}{48 \div 4} = \frac{-8}{12}, \text{ or } -\frac{8}{12}.$$

Method 2
$$-\frac{32}{48} = -\frac{32 \div 4}{48 \div 4} = -\frac{8}{12}$$

110 *Chapter 4*

Sometimes we simply show the results of dividing a numerator and denominator by the same number. In Example 1, we can think of dividing by 4 as we write

$$-\frac{\overset{8}{\cancel{32}}}{\underset{12}{\cancel{48}}} = -\frac{8}{12}.$$

A fraction is in **lowest terms** when the numerator and denominator have no common factor other than 1. To write a fraction in lowest terms, we can divide numerator and denominator by a common factor as many times as needed until they have no common factor other than 1.

$$\frac{45}{75} = \frac{45 \div 5}{75 \div 5} = \frac{9 \div 3}{15 \div 3} = \frac{3}{5}$$

Sometimes it is easier to use the *prime factorization method* shown below. Recall that a **prime number** is a whole number greater than 1 whose only factors are the number itself and 1. Every whole number can be written as a product of prime factors in exactly one way except for the order of the factors.

EXAMPLE 2   Write $\frac{84}{120}$ as an equivalent fraction in lowest terms.

Solution   Prime factorization of 84: $2 \times 2 \times 3 \times 7$
Prime factorization of 120: $2 \times 2 \times 2 \times 3 \times 5$

$$\frac{84}{120} = \frac{\overset{1}{\cancel{2}} \times \overset{1}{\cancel{2}} \times \overset{1}{\cancel{3}} \times 7}{2 \times \underset{1}{\cancel{2}} \times \underset{1}{\cancel{2}} \times \underset{1}{\cancel{3}} \times 5} = \frac{7}{2 \times 5} = \frac{7}{10}$$

When two whole numbers have no common factor other than 1, they are called **relatively prime.** For example, 7 and 10, as just discovered, are relatively prime. A fraction is in lowest terms when its numerator and denominator are relatively prime.

A **proper fraction** is a positive fraction whose numerator is less than its denominator, or the opposite of such a fraction, for example $\frac{3}{8}$ or $-\frac{7}{9}$. A fraction that is not a proper fraction, such as $\frac{9}{4}$ or $-\frac{9}{4}$, is called an **improper fraction.** A number, such as $1\frac{1}{4}$, consisting of a whole number plus a fraction is called a **mixed number.** Mixed numbers may be written as improper fractions, and improper fractions may be written as mixed numbers. A mixed number is in **simple form** if the fractional part is in lowest terms.

$$7\frac{15}{27} \text{ in simple form is } 7\frac{5}{9}.$$

EXAMPLE 3 Write as a mixed number in simple form.

> **a.** $\frac{12}{8}$ **b.** $-\frac{12}{8}$

Solution   **a.** $\frac{12}{8} = 12 \div 8$, which gives 1 R4.

> Therefore $\frac{12}{8} = 1\frac{4}{8} = 1\frac{1}{2}$.

> **b.** $-\frac{12}{8}$ is *the opposite of* $\frac{12}{8}$, so $-\frac{12}{8} = -1\frac{1}{2}$.

EXAMPLE 4 Write $7\frac{2}{5}$ as an improper fraction.

Solution $7\frac{2}{5} = \frac{7}{1} + \frac{2}{5} = \frac{7 \times 5}{1 \times 5} + \frac{2}{5} = \frac{(7 \times 5) + 2}{5} = \frac{37}{5}$

Class Exercises

Complete.

1. $\frac{4}{7} = \frac{?}{21}$ 12   **2.** $-\frac{4}{18} = -\frac{?}{9}$ 2   **3.** $\frac{3}{5} = \frac{?}{15}$ 9   **4.** $\frac{-6}{8} = \frac{?}{4}$ -3 **5.** $\frac{16}{28} = \frac{?}{7}$ 4

For each fraction, state the GCF of the numerator and denominator. Then state an equivalent fraction in lowest terms.

6. $\frac{4}{24}$ 4, $\frac{1}{6}$ **7.** $\frac{5}{20}$ 5, $\frac{1}{4}$ **8.** $\frac{-12}{16}$ 4, $\frac{-3}{4}$ **9.** $-\frac{8}{12}$ 4, $-\frac{2}{3}$ **10.** $\frac{-9}{12}$ 3, $\frac{-3}{4}$

State an equivalent improper fraction.

11. $3\frac{2}{5}$ $\frac{17}{5}$ **12.** $-4\frac{1}{8}$ $-\frac{33}{8}$ **13.** $-7\frac{2}{3}$ $-\frac{23}{3}$ **14.** $9\frac{3}{4}$ $\frac{39}{4}$ **15.** $-5\frac{1}{6}$ $-\frac{31}{6}$

State an equivalent mixed number in simple form.

16. $\frac{13}{5}$ $2\frac{3}{5}$ **17.** $-\frac{14}{4}$ $-3\frac{1}{2}$ **18.** $\frac{-24}{5}$ $-4\frac{4}{5}$ **19.** $\frac{19}{3}$ $6\frac{1}{3}$ **20.** $\frac{-32}{10}$ $-3\frac{1}{5}$

Written Exercises

Complete.

A   **1.** $\frac{2}{3} = \frac{?}{6}$ 4   **2.** $\frac{5}{7} = \frac{?}{21}$ 15   **3.** $1 = \frac{5}{?}$ 5   **4.** $4 = \frac{?}{2}$ 8   **5.** $-\frac{14}{32} = -\frac{7}{?}$ 16

    6. $\frac{42}{-54} = \frac{?}{-9}$ 7   **7.** $\frac{18}{27} = \frac{2}{?}$ 3   **8.** $-7 = -\frac{?}{3}$ 21   **9.** $\frac{-7}{25} = \frac{-35}{?}$ 125   **10.** $-\frac{3}{4} = -\frac{12}{?}$ 16

Write as a proper fraction in lowest terms or as a mixed number in simple form.

11. $\frac{21}{35}$ $\frac{3}{5}$ **12.** $\frac{24}{40}$ $\frac{3}{5}$ **13.** $\frac{11}{4}$ $2\frac{3}{4}$ **14.** $\frac{25}{7}$ $3\frac{4}{7}$ **15.** $-\frac{9}{81}$ $-\frac{1}{9}$

16. $\frac{54}{81}$ $\frac{2}{3}$ **17.** $-\frac{17}{3}$ $-5\frac{2}{3}$ **18.** $-\frac{56}{72}$ $-\frac{7}{9}$ **19.** $\frac{-34}{85}$ $\frac{-2}{5}$ **20.** $-\frac{29}{5}$ $-5\frac{4}{5}$

21. $\frac{125}{12}$ $10\frac{5}{12}$ **22.** $\frac{49}{63}$ $\frac{7}{9}$ **23.** $-\frac{79}{13}$ $-6\frac{1}{13}$ **24.** $\frac{32}{10}$ $3\frac{1}{5}$ **25.** $\frac{-300}{7}$ $-42\frac{6}{7}$

26. $\frac{560}{490}$ $1\frac{1}{7}$ **27.** $\frac{1440}{960}$ $1\frac{1}{2}$ **28.** $-\frac{84}{144}$ $-\frac{7}{12}$ **29.** $\frac{461}{15}$ $30\frac{11}{15}$ **30.** $\frac{-462}{12}$ $-38\frac{1}{2}$

Write as an improper fraction.

31. $3\frac{1}{4}$ $\frac{13}{4}$ **32.** $2\frac{1}{8}$ $\frac{17}{8}$ **33.** $5\frac{3}{7}$ $\frac{38}{7}$ **34.** $6\frac{3}{16}$ $\frac{99}{16}$ **35.** $5\frac{3}{8}$ $\frac{43}{8}$

36. $-4\frac{3}{8}$ $-\frac{35}{8}$ **37.** $-3\frac{7}{8}$ $-\frac{31}{8}$ **38.** $-16\frac{1}{3}$ $-\frac{49}{3}$ **39.** $-7\frac{2}{9}$ $-\frac{65}{9}$ **40.** $-8\frac{3}{10}$ $-\frac{83}{10}$

What value of the variable makes the statement true?

B **41.** $\frac{b}{4}=\frac{6}{12}$ 2 **42.** $\frac{x}{16}=\frac{9}{48}$ 3 **43.** $\frac{a}{6}=\frac{10}{60}$ 1 **44.** $\frac{d}{5}=\frac{-3}{15}$ -1

45. $\frac{1}{x}=\frac{4}{16}$ 4 **46.** $\frac{0}{6}=\frac{n}{12}$ 0 **47.** $\frac{5}{-1}=\frac{20}{n}$ -4 **48.** $\frac{1}{3}=\frac{8}{n}$ 24

Simplify by writing an equivalent fraction in which the numerator and denominator have no common factors.

EXAMPLE $\dfrac{15x^2y}{20xy^2} = \dfrac{3 \times \overset{1}{\cancel{5}} \times \overset{1}{\cancel{x}} \times x \times \overset{1}{\cancel{y}}}{4 \times \underset{1}{\cancel{5}} \times \underset{1}{\cancel{x}} \times \underset{1}{\cancel{y}} \times y} = \dfrac{3x}{4y}$

49. $\frac{2a}{6a}$ $\frac{1}{3}$ **50.** $\frac{4b}{20}$ $\frac{b}{5}$ **51.** $\frac{c}{c^2}$ $\frac{1}{c}$ **52.** $\frac{d^2e}{de^2}$ $\frac{d}{e}$

53. $\frac{3x}{15y}$ $\frac{x}{5y}$ **54.** $\frac{6n^2}{18n}$ $\frac{n}{3}$ **55.** $\frac{4h}{6hk}$ $\frac{2}{3k}$ **56.** $\frac{uv^2}{3u^2v}$ $\frac{v}{3u}$

Problems

Solve. Write fractional answers in lowest terms.

A **1.** Of the 24 apartments in the building, 16 have been newly painted. What fraction of the apartments have not been newly painted? $\frac{1}{3}$

2. John has one half dollar, one quarter, and two dimes. Express the total value as a fraction of a dollar. $\frac{19}{20}$

3. Gene Cornell pays five cents of every dollar he earns to the government for taxes. Jim Watanabe pays $\frac{1}{20}$ of his earnings for taxes. Do they pay equivalent fractions of their earnings for taxes? Yes

Rational Numbers **113**

Suggested Assignments

Minimum
Day 1: 112/1–10
        113/11–30; 31–47
        odd
Day 2: 113/Prob. 1–3
        114/Prob. 4–7
        114/Rev. 1–10
Average
Day 1: 112/2–10 even
        113/12–40 even;
        41–56
Day 2: 113/Prob. 1–3
        114/Prob. 4–8
        114/Rev. 2–10 even
Maximum
Day 1: 112/2–10 even
        113/12–40 even;
        41–56
Day 2: 113/Prob. 1–3
        114/Prob. 4–9

Supplementary Materials

Practice Masters, p. 17

4. One day Bob worked 8 h. Janet said she worked a third of the day. Did they spend equivalent portions of the day working? Yes

B **5.** In an eighth-grade class of 30 students, there are 15 students who can speak both Spanish and English. There are 12 others who can speak both French and English. The rest speak only English.
 a. What fraction of the class can speak Spanish? $\frac{1}{2}$
 b. What fraction of the class can speak French? $\frac{2}{5}$
 c. What fraction of the class can speak English? $\frac{30}{30}$, or $\frac{1}{1}$
 d. What fraction of the class can speak a second language? $\frac{9}{10}$

6. Lisa Washington, a radio reporter, is allowed exactly 90 s to relate a story. What part of a broadcast that is 30 min long is this? $\frac{1}{20}$

7. A bulb importer advertised six varieties of tulips in a collection of 72 bulbs, with an equal number of each variety. Colors of the varieties were red, pink, maroon, yellow, white, and blue. Pearl Wang bought the collection.
 a. What part of the bulbs were yellow? $\frac{1}{6}$
 b. Pearl planted the red, white, and blue bulbs in one flower bed. What fraction of the total collection is planted in that flower bed? $\frac{1}{2}$

8. In a flock of 75 sheep, there are 3 sets of twins. What fraction of the sheep in the flock do not have a twin? $\frac{23}{25}$

C **9.** The results of a survey of 100 families showed that 75 families used the town swimming pool, 20 families used the town tennis courts, and 15 families used both the pool and the courts. What fraction of the families surveyed used neither the pool nor the courts? $\frac{1}{5}$

Review Exercises

Simplify.

1. 7^2 49 **2.** 11^3 1331 **3.** 6^4 1296 **4.** 2^8 256 **5.** 1^5 1

6. $5^2 \times 3^2$ 225 **7.** $4^3 \times 9^2$ 5184 **8.** $2^7 \times 6^2$ 4608 **9.** $3^3 \times 3^2$ 243 **10.** $8^2 \times 2^4$ 1024

4-3 Least Common Denominator

In calculations and comparisons, we work with more than one fraction. It is sometimes necessary to replace fractions with equivalent fractions so that all have the same denominator, called a *common denominator*. For example, in the addition $\frac{1}{6} + \frac{3}{4}$ we may write $\frac{1}{6}$ as $\frac{2}{12}$ and $\frac{3}{4}$ as $\frac{9}{12}$, using 12 as a common denominator. We may also use 24, 36, 48, or any other multiple of both denominators as a common denominator.

The **least common denominator** (LCD) of two or more fractions is the *least common multiple* (LCM) of their denominators. The LCD of $\frac{1}{6}$ and $\frac{3}{4}$ is 12, since 12 is the LCM of 6 and 4.

EXAMPLE 1 Write equivalent fractions with the LCD: $\frac{1}{24}$, $\frac{5}{48}$, $\frac{11}{120}$.

Solution The LCD is the least common multiple of 24, 48, and 120. Use prime factorization to find the LCM.

Prime factorization of 24: $2 \times 2 \times 2 \times 3$, or $2^3 \times 3$
Prime factorization of 48: $2 \times 2 \times 2 \times 2 \times 3$, or $2^4 \times 3$
Prime factorization of 120: $2 \times 2 \times 2 \times 3 \times 5$, or $2^3 \times 3 \times 5$

The LCM is the product of the highest powers of each factor. The LCM $= 2^4 \times 3 \times 5 = 240$, so the LCD $= 240$.

$$\frac{1}{24} = \frac{1 \times 10}{24 \times 10} = \frac{10}{240} \qquad \frac{5}{48} = \frac{5 \times 5}{48 \times 5} = \frac{25}{240} \qquad \frac{11}{120} = \frac{11 \times 2}{120 \times 2} = \frac{22}{240}$$

EXAMPLE 2 Replace __?__ with $<$, $>$, or $=$ to make a true statement.

a. $\frac{5}{6}$ __?__ $\frac{6}{7}$ **b.** $-\frac{5}{8}$ __?__ $-\frac{9}{14}$

Solution First rewrite each pair of fractions as equivalent fractions with the LCD. Then compare the fractions.

a. The LCD is the LCM of 6 and 7, or 42.

$$\frac{5}{6} = \frac{5 \times 7}{6 \times 7} = \frac{35}{42} \qquad \frac{6}{7} = \frac{6 \times 6}{7 \times 6} = \frac{36}{42}$$

$$\frac{35}{42} < \frac{36}{42}, \text{ so } \frac{5}{6} < \frac{6}{7}.$$

b. The LCD is the LCM of 8 and 14, or 56.

$$-\frac{5}{8} = -\frac{5 \times 7}{8 \times 7} = -\frac{35}{56} \qquad -\frac{9}{14} = -\frac{9 \times 4}{14 \times 4} = -\frac{36}{56}$$

$$-\frac{35}{56} > -\frac{36}{56}, \text{ so } -\frac{5}{8} > -\frac{9}{14}.$$

Rational Numbers **115**

Teaching Suggestions
p. 105b

Related Activities p. 105c

Reading Mathematics

Students will learn the meaning of the following mathematical terms in this lesson: *common denominator, least common denominator, least common multiple.*

Chalkboard Examples

State the LCD of the pair of fractions.

1. $\frac{2}{3}, \frac{1}{9}$ **9**

2. $-\frac{3}{10}, \frac{3}{4}$ **20**

3. $-\frac{1}{6}, \frac{1}{8}$ **24**

4. $-\frac{1}{12}, -\frac{3}{8}$ **24**

5. $\frac{13}{20}, \frac{13}{16}$ **80**

6. $\frac{2}{5}, -\frac{3}{20}$ **20**

When fractions have variables in their denominators, we may obtain a common denominator by finding a common multiple of the denominators.

EXAMPLE 3   Write equivalent fractions with a common denominator: $\frac{2}{a}, \frac{3}{b}$.

Solution $\frac{2}{a} = \frac{2 \times b}{a \times b} = \frac{2b}{ab}$ $\frac{3}{b} = \frac{3 \times a}{b \times a} = \frac{3a}{ab}$

Class Exercises

State the LCM of the pair of numbers.

1. 6, 18   18   2. 11, 4   44   3. 10, 8   40   4. 15, 12   60   5. 32, 48
    96

State the LCD of the pair of fractions.

6. $\frac{1}{2}, \frac{3}{4}$ 4   7. $\frac{5}{6}, \frac{1}{2}$ 6   8. $\frac{3}{4}, -\frac{1}{3}$ 12   9. $-\frac{2}{9}, \frac{1}{6}$ 18   10. $\frac{1}{16}, \frac{5}{12}$
    48

Written Exercises

Write the fractions as equivalent fractions with the least common denominator (LCD).

A

1. $\frac{1}{3}, \frac{1}{12}$ $\frac{4}{12}, \frac{1}{12}$ 2. $\frac{1}{4}, \frac{1}{12}$ $\frac{3}{12}, \frac{1}{12}$ 3. $\frac{3}{4}, \frac{5}{8}$ $\frac{6}{8}, \frac{5}{8}$ 4. $\frac{3}{8}, \frac{3}{16}$ $\frac{6}{16}, \frac{3}{16}$

5. $\frac{2}{9}, -\frac{1}{27}$ $\frac{6}{27}, -\frac{1}{27}$ 6. $-\frac{1}{7}, \frac{1}{49}$ $-\frac{7}{49}, \frac{1}{49}$ 7. $\frac{10}{21}, \frac{2}{49}$ $\frac{70}{147}, \frac{6}{147}$ 8. $\frac{7}{18}, \frac{5}{36}$ $\frac{14}{36}, \frac{5}{36}$

9. $-\frac{2}{3}, \frac{7}{30}$ 10. $\frac{5}{12}, -\frac{6}{11}$ 11. $\frac{4}{75}, \frac{7}{100}$ $\frac{16}{300}, \frac{21}{300}$ 12. $\frac{9}{56}, \frac{4}{63}$

13. $-\frac{3}{7}, -\frac{7}{112}$ 14. $-\frac{4}{17}, -\frac{9}{16}$ 15. $\frac{5}{42}, \frac{5}{49}$ $\frac{35}{294}, \frac{30}{294}$ 16. $\frac{5}{84}, \frac{7}{12}$ $\frac{5}{84}, \frac{49}{84}$

B

17. $\frac{7}{8}, \frac{5}{16}, \frac{21}{40}$ $\frac{70}{80}, \frac{25}{80}, \frac{42}{80}$ 18. $\frac{1}{4}, \frac{1}{9}, \frac{1}{5}$ $\frac{45}{180}, \frac{20}{180}, \frac{36}{180}$ 19. $\frac{3}{7}, \frac{7}{4}, \frac{4}{9}$ $\frac{108}{252}, \frac{441}{252}, \frac{112}{252}$ 20. $\frac{5}{18}, \frac{1}{54}, \frac{2}{27}$ $\frac{33}{54}, \frac{1}{54}, \frac{4}{54}$

21. $\frac{1}{65}, \frac{3}{5}, \frac{9}{26}$ 22. $-\frac{7}{8}, \frac{9}{28}, \frac{2}{49}$ 23. $-\frac{5}{6}, \frac{2}{9}, -\frac{7}{8}$ 24. $\frac{11}{12}, \frac{1}{72}, -\frac{7}{8}$

25. $\frac{a}{3}, \frac{b}{6}$ $\frac{2a}{6}, \frac{b}{6}$ 26. $\frac{m}{25}, \frac{n}{15}$ $\frac{3m}{75}, \frac{5n}{75}$ 27. $\frac{h}{25}, \frac{h}{100}, \frac{h}{125}$ 28. $\frac{a}{2}, \frac{b}{3}, \frac{c}{4}$

Write the fractions as equivalent fractions with a common denominator.

29. $\frac{1}{c}, \frac{2}{3c}$ $\frac{3}{3c}, \frac{2}{3c}$ 30. $\frac{1}{x}, \frac{1}{y}$ $\frac{y}{xy}, \frac{x}{xy}$ 31. $\frac{3}{x}, \frac{1}{y}, \frac{5}{z}$ $\frac{3yz}{xyz}, \frac{xz}{xyz}$,   32. $\frac{-1}{r}, \frac{2}{rs}, \frac{r}{s}$
                                                      $\frac{5xy}{xyz}$ $-\frac{s}{rs}, \frac{2}{rs}, \frac{r^2}{rs}$

116   *Chapter 4*

Replace __?__ with <, >, or = to make a true statement.

33. $\frac{1}{3}$ _?<_ $\frac{3}{6}$

34. $\frac{3}{4}$ _?>_ $\frac{5}{8}$

35. $-\frac{2}{3}$ _?<_ $-\frac{7}{12}$

36. $-\frac{5}{8}$ _?<_ $-\frac{5}{16}$

37. $-\frac{3}{5}$ _?>_ $-\frac{5}{7}$

38. $-\frac{2}{4}$ _?>_ $-\frac{3}{5}$

39. $\frac{7}{21}$ _?=_ $\frac{9}{27}$

40. $\frac{7}{15}$ _?<_ $\frac{11}{20}$

41. $\frac{8}{45}$ _?>_ $\frac{13}{75}$

42. $\frac{5}{24}$ _?<_ $\frac{8}{21}$

43. $-\frac{3}{34}$ _?>_ $-\frac{5}{39}$

44. $\frac{27}{36}$ _?=_ $\frac{6}{8}$

C **45.** Let $\frac{a}{b}$ and $\frac{c}{d}$ be fractions with $b > 0$ and $d > 0$. Write $\frac{a}{b}$ and $\frac{c}{d}$ as equivalent fractions with a common denominator. How do $\frac{a}{b}$ and $\frac{c}{d}$ compare when $ad < bc$? when $ad = bc$? when $ad > bc$? Give two examples to illustrate each of your conclusions.

Review Exercises

4.87

1. $17.06 + 8.7$ **25.76**

2. $8.73 + (-11.2)$ **−2.47**

3. $-4.16 + 9.03$

4. $-5.8 + (-3.24)$ **−9.04**

5. $-9.2 - 2.6$ **−11.8**

6. $6.4 - 11.2$ **−4.8**

7. $23 - (-0.4)$ **23.4**

8. $-5.4 - (-1.82)$ **−3.58**

9. $-16.5 - (-31)$
14.5

▮▮ ▮ **Calculator Key-In**

You can use your calculator to compare fractions. Simply carry out the division of each fraction to express each as a decimal. Then compare the decimals.

EXAMPLE Which is greater, $\frac{11}{40}$ or $\frac{5}{8}$?

Solution $\frac{11}{40} = 11 \div 40 = 0.275$ $\qquad$ $\frac{5}{8} = 5 \div 8 = 0.625$

$$0.275 < 0.625$$

$\frac{5}{8}$ is greater.

Use your calculator to compare these fractions. Replace the __?__ with >, <, or = to make a true statement.

1. $\frac{3}{16}$ _?<_ $\frac{1}{5}$

2. $\frac{6}{25}$ _?<_ $\frac{3}{8}$

3. $\frac{5}{32}$ _?>_ $\frac{3}{20}$

4. $\frac{25}{64}$ _?<_ $\frac{37}{80}$

Suggested Assignments

Minimum
  116/1–16; 18–32 even
  117/34–44 even
  117/Rev. 1–9

Average
  116/1–15 odd; 17–32
  117/33–44
  117/Rev. 1–9 odd
  117/Calculator Key-In

Maximum
  116/1–15 odd; 17–32
  117/33–45
  117/Calculator Key-In

Supplementary Materials

Practice Masters, p. 18

**Additional Answers
Written Exercises**

45. $\frac{a}{b} = \frac{ad}{bd}$, $\frac{c}{d} = \frac{bc}{bd}$. If $ad < bc$,

$\frac{a}{b} < \frac{c}{d}$: $3 \times 4 < 2 \times 7$

so $\frac{3}{2} < \frac{7}{4}$; $5 \times 7 < 6 \times 8$

so $\frac{5}{6} < \frac{8}{7}$. If $ad = bc$,

$\frac{a}{b} = \frac{c}{d}$: $2 \times 6 = 3 \times 4$

so $\frac{2}{3} = \frac{4}{6}$; $4 \times 9 = 6 \times 6$

so $\frac{4}{6} = \frac{6}{9}$. If $ad > bc$,

$\frac{a}{b} > \frac{c}{d}$: $4 \times 5 > 6 \times 3$

so $\frac{4}{6} > \frac{3}{5}$; $7 \times 8 > 9 \times 6$

so $\frac{7}{9} > \frac{6}{8}$.

Teaching Suggestions
p. 105c

Related Activities p. 105d

Chalkboard Examples

Add or subtract. Write the answer as a proper fraction in lowest terms or as a mixed number in simple form.

1. $\frac{3}{11} + \frac{9}{11}$ $1\frac{1}{11}$

2. $-\frac{2}{3} + \frac{3}{7}$ $-\frac{5}{21}$

3. $-5 + 2\frac{1}{10}$ $-2\frac{9}{10}$

4. $8\frac{1}{4} - 2\frac{3}{4}$ $5\frac{1}{2}$

5. $-\frac{5}{6} - \frac{2}{9}$ $-1\frac{1}{18}$

6. $13\frac{7}{12} - \left(-3\frac{5}{16}\right)$ $16\frac{43}{48}$

4-4 Adding and Subtracting Fractions

You have added fractions having a common denominator by adding the numerators and writing the result over the denominator. We can illustrate the reasoning for this rule by looking at the sum $\frac{2}{13} + \frac{5}{13}$. The reason for each statement in the column on the left below is given on the same line in the column on the right. For example, the second statement means that $(2 \times \frac{1}{13}) + (5 \times \frac{1}{13}) = (2 + 5) \times \frac{1}{13}$ because of the distributive property. All the properties that you have learned for addition, subtraction, multiplication, and division of positive and negative decimals hold true for the rational numbers.

$$\frac{2}{13} + \frac{5}{13} = \left(2 \times \frac{1}{13}\right) + \left(5 \times \frac{1}{13}\right) \qquad \text{By the rule: } \frac{a}{b} = a \times \frac{1}{b}$$

$$= (2 + 5) \times \frac{1}{13} \qquad \text{By the distributive property}$$

$$= (7) \times \frac{1}{13} \qquad \text{Substitution of 7 for } 2 + 5$$

$$= \frac{7}{13} \qquad \text{By the rule: } a \times \frac{1}{b} = \frac{a}{b}$$

The methods you learned for adding and subtracting positive fractions apply as well to adding and subtracting negative fractions.

Rules

For all numbers a, b, and c ($c \neq 0$),

$$\frac{a}{c} + \frac{b}{c} = \frac{a + b}{c} \qquad \text{and} \qquad \frac{a}{c} - \frac{b}{c} = \frac{a - b}{c}$$

EXAMPLE 1   Add or subtract. Write the answer to part (a) in lowest terms.

  a. $-\frac{3}{8} + \frac{1}{8}$ **b.** $\frac{1}{a} - \frac{2}{a}$

Solution   **a.** $-\frac{3}{8} + \frac{1}{8} = \frac{-3}{8} + \frac{1}{8}$ **b.** $\frac{1}{a} - \frac{2}{a} = \frac{1 - 2}{a}$

$$= \frac{-3 + 1}{8} \qquad\qquad\qquad = \frac{-1}{a}, \text{ or } -\frac{1}{a}$$

$$= \frac{-2}{8} = \frac{-1}{4}, \text{ or } -\frac{1}{4}$$

When two fractions have different denominators, we may need to write the fractions as equivalent fractions with a common denominator before adding or subtracting.

118   *Chapter 4*

The rules for adding and subtracting fractions also apply to mixed numbers.

EXAMPLE 2 Subtract. Write the answer in lowest terms.

a. $5\frac{1}{4} - 2\frac{1}{3}$ 　　　　　　　　　　**b.** $2\frac{3}{8} - \left(-1\frac{1}{6}\right)$

Solution　**a.**　$\begin{aligned} 5\frac{1}{4} &= 5\frac{3}{12} = 4\frac{15}{12} \\ -\,2\frac{1}{3} &= -\,2\frac{4}{12} = -\,2\frac{4}{12} \\ \hline &\phantom{= -2\frac{4}{12} =\ } 2\frac{11}{12} \end{aligned}$ 　　**b.**　$\begin{aligned} 2\frac{3}{8} &= 2\frac{9}{24} \\ -\left(-1\frac{5}{6}\right) &= +\,1\frac{20}{24} \\ \hline & 3\frac{29}{24} = 4\frac{5}{24} \end{aligned}$

Class Exercises

Add or subtract. Write the answer as a proper fraction in lowest terms or as a mixed number in simple form.

1. $\frac{3}{16} + \frac{8}{16}$ 　$\frac{11}{16}$ 　　**2.** $\frac{3}{10} + \frac{6}{10}$ 　$\frac{9}{10}$ 　　　**3.** $\frac{5}{8} - \frac{2}{8}$ 　$\frac{3}{8}$ 　　　　**4.** $\frac{17}{6} - \frac{4}{6}$ 　$2\frac{1}{6}$

5. $-\frac{3}{4} + \frac{1}{4}$ 　$-\frac{1}{2}$ 　　**6.** $-\frac{5}{6} - \frac{5}{6}$ 　$-1\frac{2}{3}$ 　　**7.** $2\frac{7}{8} - 1\frac{5}{8}$ 　$1\frac{1}{4}$ 　　**8.** $7\frac{3}{4} - 6\frac{1}{4}$ 　$1\frac{1}{2}$

9. $1\frac{4}{8} - \frac{1}{8}$ 　$1\frac{3}{8}$ 　　**10.** $-1\frac{3}{7} - \left(-\frac{3}{7}\right)$ 　-1 　　**11.** $-3\frac{4}{8} - \left(-2\frac{1}{8}\right)$ 　$-1\frac{3}{8}$ 　　**12.** $-\frac{6}{n} - \frac{2}{n}$ 　$-\frac{8}{n}$

Written Exercises
11. $-\frac{41}{72}$ 　　**12.** $-\frac{44}{105}$ 　　**16.** $-\frac{7}{30}$

Add or subtract. Write the answer as a proper fraction in lowest terms or as a mixed number in simple form.

A 　**1.** $\frac{3}{4} + \frac{3}{4}$ 　$1\frac{1}{2}$ 　　　**2.** $\frac{9}{4} - \frac{8}{4}$ 　$\frac{1}{4}$ 　　　**3.** $\frac{2}{3} - \frac{2}{3}$ 　0 　　　**4.** $\frac{2}{3} + \frac{4}{3}$ 　2

5. $\frac{3}{4} - \frac{3}{8}$ 　$\frac{3}{8}$ 　　　**6.** $-\frac{3}{4} + \frac{5}{16} - \frac{7}{16}$ 　　**7.** $-\frac{2}{3} - \frac{1}{4} - \frac{11}{12}$ 　　**8.** $\frac{1}{6} - \frac{1}{3} - \frac{1}{6}$

9. $\frac{11}{12} + \frac{13}{13}$ 　$1\frac{11}{12}$ 　**10.** $\frac{5}{6} + \frac{3}{20}$ 　$\frac{59}{60}$ 　　**11.** $-\frac{5}{8} + \frac{1}{18}$ 　　**12.** $-\frac{2}{15} - \frac{6}{21}$

13. $3\frac{1}{4} + \frac{1}{8}$ 　$3\frac{3}{8}$ 　**14.** $5 - \frac{3}{4}$ 　$4\frac{1}{4}$ 　　**15.** $1\frac{1}{12} - \frac{5}{6}$ 　$\frac{1}{4}$ 　　**16.** $-2\frac{5}{6} + 2\frac{3}{5}$

17. $-1\frac{5}{6} + 2\frac{3}{8}$ 　$\frac{13}{24}$ 　**18.** $-\frac{3}{4} + \left(-\frac{5}{12}\right) - 1\frac{1}{6}$ **19.** $\frac{3}{4} - \left(-\frac{5}{12}\right)$ 　$1\frac{1}{6}$ 　**20.** $8\frac{1}{8} - \left(-2\frac{1}{2}\right)$

21. $-3\frac{1}{4} - \left(-1\frac{1}{6}\right)$ 　$-2\frac{1}{12}$ **22.** $7 + \left(-3\frac{1}{5}\right)$ 　$3\frac{4}{5}$ 　**23.** $-16\frac{1}{2} - \frac{1}{21}$ 　$16\frac{23}{42}$ **24.** $13\frac{1}{3} - 5\frac{5}{6}$ 　$10\frac{5}{8}$ 　$8\frac{1}{6}$

B 　**25.** $\frac{1}{4} + \frac{1}{5} + \frac{1}{2}$ 　$\frac{19}{20}$ 　　**26.** $\frac{1}{6} + \frac{1}{8} + \frac{1}{12}$ 　$\frac{3}{8}$ 　　　**27.** $\frac{3}{2} + \frac{7}{4} + \left(-\frac{5}{3}\right)$ 　$1\frac{7}{12}$

Additional A Exercises

Add or subtract. Write the answer as a proper fraction in lowest terms or as a mixed number in simple form.

1. $\frac{3}{8} + \frac{5}{6}$ 　$1\frac{5}{24}$

2. $5\frac{3}{5} + 2\frac{1}{3}$ 　$7\frac{14}{15}$

3. $-\frac{5}{9} + \frac{1}{6}$ 　$-\frac{7}{18}$

4. $\frac{5}{12} - \frac{3}{16}$ 　$\frac{11}{48}$

5. $2\frac{3}{8} - \frac{7}{12}$ 　$1\frac{19}{24}$

6. $-3\frac{5}{7} - 1\frac{5}{6}$ 　$-5\frac{23}{42}$

Add or subtract. Simplify the answer.

28. $2\frac{7}{12} + 1\frac{3}{7} - \frac{1}{8}$ $3\frac{149}{168}$

29. $-2\frac{1}{3} + \frac{2}{3} - 5$ $-6\frac{2}{3}$

30. $7 - 1\frac{1}{4} - \frac{1}{2}$ $5\frac{1}{4}$

31. $38\frac{7}{8} + 22\frac{1}{4} - 13\frac{2}{3}$ $47\frac{11}{24}$

32. $101\frac{1}{4} - 98\frac{3}{40} - 10\frac{1}{8}$ $-6\frac{19}{20}$

33. $11\frac{1}{6} - 19\frac{3}{4} + 1\frac{1}{10}$ $-7\frac{29}{60}$

34. $\dfrac{13}{a} - \dfrac{8}{a}$ $\dfrac{5}{a}$

35. $\dfrac{b}{6} + \dfrac{5}{6}$ $\dfrac{b+5}{6}$

36. $\dfrac{2}{c} + \dfrac{3}{d}$ $\dfrac{2d+3c}{cd}$

37. $\dfrac{5}{g} - \dfrac{3}{g}$ $\dfrac{2}{g}$

38. $8 - \dfrac{1}{a}$ $\dfrac{8a-1}{a}$

39. $3b + \dfrac{1}{2}$ $\dfrac{6b+1}{2}$

40. $\dfrac{2c}{3} - 1$ $\dfrac{2c-3}{3}$

41. $-5 - \dfrac{3}{a}$ $\dfrac{-5a-3}{a}$

C

42. $\dfrac{a}{6} + \dfrac{5a}{6}$ a

43. $\dfrac{7t}{4} - \dfrac{t}{4}$ $\dfrac{3t}{2}$

44. $\dfrac{7e}{b} - \dfrac{3e}{b}$ $\dfrac{4e}{b}$

45. $\dfrac{n}{2r} - \dfrac{5n}{2n}$ $\dfrac{5n}{2r}$

46. $\dfrac{7d}{5} + \dfrac{d}{10}$ $\dfrac{3d}{2}$

47. $\dfrac{5y}{2} - \dfrac{3y}{4}$ $\dfrac{7y}{4}$

48. $\dfrac{c}{2} + 4c$ $\dfrac{9c}{2}$

49. $\dfrac{2x}{3} + x$ $\dfrac{5x}{3}$

50. Show that $\dfrac{a}{c} + \dfrac{b}{c} = \dfrac{a+b}{c}$ $(c \neq 0)$ by supplying the rule or property that justifies each statement.

$\dfrac{a}{c} + \dfrac{b}{c} = \left(a \times \dfrac{1}{c}\right) + \left(b \times \dfrac{1}{c}\right)$ Why? **By the rule:** $\dfrac{a}{b} = a \times \dfrac{1}{b}$

$= (a + b) \times \dfrac{1}{c}$ Why? **By the Distributive Property**

$= \dfrac{a + b}{c}$ Why? **By the rule:** $a \times \dfrac{1}{b} = \dfrac{a}{b}$

51. As in Exercise 50, show that $\dfrac{a}{c} - \dfrac{b}{c} = \dfrac{a-b}{c}$ $(c \neq 0)$.

Problems

Solve. Write the answer as a proper fraction in lowest terms or as a mixed number in simple form.

A

1. Jess is using three recipes. One requires $\frac{2}{3}$ cup of flour, another requires $\frac{7}{8}$ cup of flour, and the third requires $\frac{3}{4}$ cup of flour. How much flour will Jess use? $2\frac{7}{24}$ **cups**

2. The Meyers family drove $1\frac{1}{2}$ h to a ball game. The trip home by another route took $1\frac{2}{3}$ h. What was the total travel time? $3\frac{1}{6}$ **h**

3. Joan Kent bought $15\frac{3}{4}$ yd of drapery material for $63 at a sale. If she used all except $1\frac{1}{16}$ yd, how much material did she actually use? $14\frac{11}{16}$ **yd**

120   *Chapter 4*

4. Carl is 4 ft tall. If he grew $1\frac{1}{8}$ in. during the past year, and $\frac{3}{4}$ in. the year before, how tall was he one year ago? $\quad$ 3 ft $10\frac{7}{8}$ in.

5. On Monday, Kim jogged $1\frac{1}{2}$ mi in $\frac{1}{4}$ h. On Wednesday she jogged $2\frac{1}{3}$ mi in $\frac{1}{3}$ h. How much farther did Kim jog on Wednesday than on Monday? $\quad \frac{5}{6}$ mi

B **6.** Last year, total rainfall for April and May was $7\frac{1}{4}$ in. This year 3 in. of rain fell in April and $2\frac{5}{8}$ in. fell in May. How much less rain fell this year than last year during April and May? $\quad 1\frac{5}{8}$ in.

C **7.** A 512-page book has pages 7 in. wide by 9 in. high. The printed area measures $5\frac{3}{8}$ in. by $7\frac{3}{4}$ in. The left margin is $\frac{5}{16}$ in. and the top margin is $\frac{9}{16}$ in. How wide are the margins at the right and the bottom of each page? $\quad$ Right: $1\frac{5}{16}$ in.; bottom: $\frac{11}{16}$ in.

Self-Test A

Complete.

1. $5 \times \underline{\quad?\quad} = \frac{5}{8}$ $\frac{1}{8}$ **2.** $3 \times \underline{\quad?\quad} = -1$ $-\frac{1}{3}$ [4-1]

3. $7 \div 9 = \underline{\quad?\quad}$ $\frac{7}{9}$ **4.** $-\frac{2}{3} = \frac{-2}{3} = \underline{\quad?\quad}$ $\frac{2}{-3}$

Write as a proper fraction in lowest terms or as a mixed number in simple form.

5. $\frac{16}{64}$ $\frac{1}{4}$ **6.** $-\frac{72}{30}$ $-2\frac{2}{5}$ **7.** $\frac{32}{42}$ $\frac{16}{21}$ **8.** $\frac{-71}{48}$ $-1\frac{23}{48}$ **9.** $\frac{68}{16}$ $4\frac{1}{4}$ [4-2]

Write as an improper fraction.

10. $2\frac{1}{5}$ $\frac{11}{5}$ **11.** $-3\frac{2}{3}$ $-\frac{11}{3}$ **12.** $6\frac{4}{15}$ $\frac{94}{15}$ **13.** $1\frac{7}{12}$ $\frac{19}{12}$ **14.** $-8\frac{5}{8}$ $-\frac{69}{8}$

Write as equivalent fractions with the least common denominator.

15. $\frac{7}{9}, \frac{7}{8}$ $\frac{56}{72}, \frac{63}{72}$ **16.** $-\frac{10}{49}, \frac{2}{21}$ $\frac{-30}{147}, \frac{14}{147}$ **17.** $\frac{3}{50}, \frac{6}{225}$ $\frac{27}{450}, \frac{12}{450}$ **18.** $-\frac{8}{15}, -\frac{1}{30}$ $\frac{-16}{30}, \frac{-1}{30}$ [4-3]

Add or subtract. Write the answer as a proper fraction in lowest terms or as a mixed number in simple form.

19. $\frac{1}{3} + \frac{1}{4}$ $\frac{7}{12}$ **20.** $\frac{1}{5} - \frac{1}{3}$ $-\frac{2}{15}$ **21.** $\frac{2}{15} + \left(-\frac{5}{6}\right)$ $-\frac{7}{10}$ [4-4]

22. $16\frac{5}{8} - \frac{3}{4}$ $15\frac{7}{8}$ **23.** $17\frac{1}{3} + 5\frac{1}{9}$ $22\frac{4}{9}$ **24.** $-6\frac{3}{8} + 2\frac{1}{6}$ $-4\frac{5}{24}$

Self-Test answers and Extra Practice are at the back of the book.

Rational Numbers   **121**

Write as a proper fraction in lowest terms or as a mixed number in simple form.

5. $\frac{12}{36}$ $\frac{1}{3}$

6. $-\frac{90}{100}$ $-\frac{9}{10}$

7. $-\frac{48}{36}$ $-1\frac{1}{3}$

8. $\frac{22}{55}$ $\frac{2}{5}$

9. $\frac{58}{14}$ $4\frac{1}{7}$

Write as an improper fraction.

10. $4\frac{1}{8}$ $\frac{33}{8}$

11. $-3\frac{1}{3}$ $-\frac{10}{3}$

12. $1\frac{11}{12}$ $\frac{23}{12}$

13. $-7\frac{2}{5}$ $-\frac{37}{5}$

14. $2\frac{2}{9}$ $\frac{20}{9}$

Write as equivalent fractions with the least common denominator.

15. $\frac{3}{5}, \frac{7}{20}$ $\frac{12}{20}, \frac{7}{20}$

16. $-\frac{2}{3}, \frac{6}{7}$ $-\frac{14}{21}, \frac{18}{21}$

17. $\frac{3}{16}, \frac{1}{24}$ $\frac{9}{48}, \frac{2}{48}$

18. $\frac{11}{16}, \frac{5}{14}$ $\frac{77}{112}, \frac{40}{112}$

Add or subtract. Write the answer as a proper fraction in lowest terms or as a mixed number in simple form.

19. $\frac{3}{4} + \frac{5}{6}$ $1\frac{7}{12}$

20. $\frac{7}{8} - \frac{2}{5}$ $\frac{19}{40}$

21. $5\frac{1}{4} + 6\frac{9}{13}$ $11\frac{49}{52}$

22. $7\frac{2}{3} - \frac{3}{4}$ $6\frac{11}{12}$

23. $5\frac{1}{5} + 12\frac{3}{4}$ $17\frac{19}{20}$

24. $-6\frac{3}{8} - 4\frac{1}{2}$ $-10\frac{7}{8}$

121

Teaching Suggestions
p. 105d

Related Activities p. 105d

Reading Mathematics

The Reading Mathematics feature on page 124 is intended to call students' attention to the importance of directionality in mathematical symbols. This will become even more important as students deal with more complex algebraic expressions. Remind them of the use of directionality in distinguishing between:

$$57 \quad \text{and} \quad 75$$
$$x^3 \quad \text{and} \quad 3x$$
$$2\overline{)4} \quad \text{and} \quad 4\overline{)2}$$

If students have difficulty reading fractions or other expressions, try writing an expression on the chalkboard and reading it aloud, pointing to each symbol in order. Note any possible alternative readings.

4-5 Multiplying Fractions

To develop a method for multiplying fractions, we begin by showing that $\frac{7}{3} \times 3 = 7$.

$$\frac{7}{3} \times 3 = \left(7 \times \frac{1}{3}\right) \times 3 \qquad \text{By the rule: } \frac{a}{b} = a \times \frac{1}{b}$$

$$= 7 \times \left(\frac{1}{3} \times 3\right) \qquad \text{By the associative property}$$

$$= 7 \times \left(3 \times \frac{1}{3}\right) \qquad \text{By the commutative property}$$

$$= 7 \times 1 \qquad \text{By the rule: } b \times \frac{1}{b} = 1$$

$$= 7 \qquad \text{By the multiplication property of one}$$

In a similar way, it can be shown that $-\frac{7}{3} \times 3 = -7$. It is possible to prove the following general rule for all fractions.

Rule

For all numbers a and b ($b \neq 0$),

$$\frac{a}{b} \times b = a$$

The rule tells us how to find the product of a fraction and a whole number. Using the rule on page 106, we can arrive at another rule for finding the product of two fractions such as $\frac{1}{5} \times \frac{1}{2}$. We begin by showing that $10 \times \left(\frac{1}{5} \times \frac{1}{2}\right) = 1$.

$$10 \times \left(\frac{1}{5} \times \frac{1}{2}\right) = (2 \times 5) \times \left(\frac{1}{5} \times \frac{1}{2}\right) \qquad \text{Substitution of } 2 \times 5 \text{ for } 10$$

$$= \left(2 \times \frac{1}{2}\right) \times \left(5 \times \frac{1}{5}\right) \qquad \text{By the associative and commutative properties}$$

$$= 1 \times 1 \qquad \text{By the rule: } b \times \frac{1}{b} = 1$$

$$= 1 \qquad \text{By the multiplication property of one}$$

We have shown that $10 \times \left(\frac{1}{5} \times \frac{1}{2}\right) = 1$ and we know that $10 \times \frac{1}{10} = 1$, so we conclude that $\frac{1}{5} \times \frac{1}{2} = \frac{1}{10}$. Similarly, we may prove the following general rule.

122 *Chapter 4*

Rule

For all numbers a and b ($a \neq 0$, $b \neq 0$),

$$\frac{1}{a} \times \frac{1}{b} = \frac{1}{ab}$$

EXAMPLE 1 Multiply $\frac{1}{-3} \times \frac{1}{4}$.

Solution $\frac{1}{-3} \times \frac{1}{4} = \frac{1}{-3 \times 4} = \frac{1}{-12}$, or $-\frac{1}{12}$

In Exercise 44 you will have an opportunity to prove the following rule for multiplying any two fractions.

Rule

For all numbers a, b, c, and d ($b \neq 0$, $d \neq 0$),

$$\frac{a}{b} \times \frac{c}{d} = \frac{ac}{bd}$$

EXAMPLE 2 Multiply. Write the answers to parts (a) and (b) as proper fractions in lowest terms or as mixed numbers in simple form.

a. $\frac{5}{6} \times \frac{7}{3}$ **b.** $\frac{3}{2} \times \left(-\frac{5}{7}\right)$ **c.** $-\frac{7}{a} \times \left(-\frac{4}{b}\right)$

Solution **a.** $\frac{5}{6} \times \frac{7}{3} = \frac{5 \times 7}{6 \times 3} = \frac{35}{18}$, or $1\frac{17}{18}$

b. $\frac{3}{2} \times \left(-\frac{5}{7}\right) = \frac{3}{2} \times \frac{-5}{7} = \frac{3 \times (-5)}{2 \times 7} = \frac{-15}{14}$, or $-1\frac{1}{14}$

c. $-\frac{7}{a} \times \left(-\frac{4}{b}\right) = \frac{-7}{a} \times \frac{-4}{b} = \frac{-7 \times (-4)}{a \times b} = \frac{28}{ab}$

Sometimes it is easier to divide by common factors of the numerator and denominator before multiplying.

EXAMPLE 3 Multiply $\frac{-3}{5} \times \frac{15}{16} \times \frac{-2}{3}$.

Solution $\frac{-3}{5} \times \frac{15}{16} \times \frac{-2}{3} = \frac{\overset{-1}{\cancel{-3}}}{\underset{1}{\cancel{5}}} \times \frac{\overset{3}{\cancel{15}}}{\underset{8}{16}} \times \frac{\overset{-1}{\cancel{-2}}}{\underset{1}{\cancel{3}}} = \frac{-1 \times 3 \times (-1)}{1 \times 8 \times 1} = \frac{3}{8}$

Rational Numbers **123**

Chalkboard Examples

Multiply. Write the answer as a proper fraction in lowest terms or as a mixed number in simple form.

1. $-\frac{3}{4} \times \frac{4}{5}$ $-\frac{3}{5}$

2. $-\frac{9}{14} \times \frac{18}{45}$ $-\frac{9}{35}$

3. $-2\frac{5}{8} \times \left(-\frac{16}{19}\right)$ $2\frac{4}{19}$

4. $8 \times \left(-\frac{3}{4}\right) \times \left(-3\frac{1}{4}\right)$ $19\frac{1}{2}$

5. $6\frac{3}{4} \times (-10) \times \left(-1\frac{1}{3}\right)$ 90

6. $-4\frac{1}{3} \times \frac{3}{13}$ -1

Usually you read across a line from left to right, and you read a page from top to bottom. You have learned many special ways to read things in mathematics. For example, you read a fraction from top to bottom. You read first the numerator and then the denominator of each fraction before continuing to the next word or symbol.

To multiply mixed numbers, first write each mixed number as an improper fraction.

EXAMPLE 4 Multiply. Write the answer as a proper fraction in lowest terms or as a mixed number in simple form.

$$\textbf{a. } 3\frac{1}{2} \times \left(-\frac{1}{4}\right) \qquad \textbf{b. } 5\frac{1}{4} \times 1\frac{3}{7}$$

Solution $\textbf{a. } 3\frac{1}{2} \times \left(-\frac{1}{4}\right) = \frac{7}{2} \times \frac{-1}{4} = \frac{-7}{8}, \text{ or } -\frac{7}{8}$

$\textbf{b. } 5\frac{1}{4} \times 1\frac{3}{7} = \overset{3}{\underset{2}{\cancel{\frac{21}{4}}}} \times \overset{5}{\underset{1}{\cancel{\frac{10}{7}}}} = \frac{15}{2}, \text{ or } 7\frac{1}{2}$

Class Exercises

Multiply.

1. $\frac{5}{6} \times 6$ 5
2. $-\frac{3}{5} \times (-5)$ 3
3. $-4 \times \frac{7}{4}$ −7
4. $9 \times \left(-\frac{8}{9}\right)$ −8

5. $\frac{1}{8} \times \frac{1}{3}$ $\frac{1}{24}$
6. $-\frac{1}{4} \times \frac{1}{5}$ $-\frac{1}{20}$
7. $\frac{1}{15} \times \left(-\frac{1}{2}\right)$ $-\frac{1}{30}$
8. $-\frac{1}{10} \times \left(-\frac{1}{10}\right)$ $\frac{1}{100}$

9. $\frac{5}{8} \times \frac{3}{11}$ $\frac{15}{88}$
10. $\frac{2}{5} \times \left(-\frac{3}{7}\right)$ $-\frac{6}{35}$
11. $1\frac{1}{2} \times 2$ 3
12. $-3 \times 1\frac{1}{5}$ $-3\frac{3}{5}$

Written Exercises

Multiply. Write the answer as a proper fraction in lowest terms or as a mixed number in simple form.

A
1. $\frac{7}{12} \times 12$ 7
2. $-6 \times \frac{3}{6}$ −3
3. $3 \times \left(-\frac{2}{3}\right)$ −2
4. $-14 \times \left(-\frac{5}{14}\right)$ 5

5. $-\frac{1}{4} \times \left(-\frac{1}{7}\right)$ $\frac{1}{28}$
6. $\frac{1}{8} \times \left(-\frac{1}{20}\right)$ $-\frac{1}{160}$
7. $-\frac{1}{10} \times \frac{1}{6}$ $-\frac{1}{60}$
8. $-\frac{1}{15} \times \frac{1}{2}$ $-\frac{1}{30}$

9. $\frac{2}{3} \times \frac{5}{9}$ $\frac{10}{27}$
10. $\frac{6}{7} \times \frac{2}{5}$ $\frac{12}{35}$
11. $\frac{3}{8} \times \left(-\frac{2}{3}\right)$ $-\frac{1}{4}$
12. $\frac{5}{6} \times \left(-\frac{2}{5}\right)$ $-\frac{1}{3}$

13. $-\frac{1}{3} \times \frac{2}{9}$ $-\frac{2}{27}$
14. $-\frac{3}{8} \times \frac{2}{9}$ $-\frac{1}{12}$
15. $\frac{-5}{8} \times (-1)$ $\frac{5}{8}$
16. $\frac{-2}{5} \times \left(-\frac{15}{16}\right)$ $\frac{3}{8}$

124 *Chapter 4*

Additional A Exercises

Multiply. Write the answer as a proper fraction in lowest terms or as a mixed number in simple form.

1. $-3\frac{5}{8} \times (-4)$ $14\frac{1}{2}$

2. $-13\frac{1}{3} \times 2\frac{2}{5}$ −32

3. $\frac{24}{25} \times \left(-\frac{35}{16}\right)$ $-2\frac{1}{10}$

4. $-\frac{3}{8} \times \frac{4}{9}$ $-\frac{1}{6}$

5. $1\frac{1}{6} \times 4\frac{4}{5}$ $5\frac{3}{5}$

6. $-2\frac{2}{3} \times \frac{3}{7}$ $-1\frac{1}{7}$

7. $-2\frac{7}{12} \times \left(1\frac{1}{6}\right)$ $-3\frac{1}{72}$

8. $3\frac{4}{5} \times \frac{5}{19}$ 1

17. $-\frac{1}{4} \times 0$ 0   **18.** $-\frac{3}{4} \times 0$ 0   **19.** $\frac{5}{16} \times \frac{30}{40}$ $\frac{15}{64}$ **20.** $\frac{9}{8} \times \frac{24}{27}$ 1

B 21. $3\frac{1}{4} \times \frac{4}{13}$ 1   **22.** $5\frac{2}{5} \times \frac{5}{9}$ 3   **23.** $4\frac{1}{4} \times 10\frac{1}{3}$ $43\frac{11}{12}$ **24.** $10\frac{1}{2} \times 2\frac{3}{4}$ $28\frac{7}{8}$

25. $-4\frac{2}{7} \times 5\frac{1}{6}$ $-22\frac{1}{7}$ **26.** $3\frac{1}{8} \times \left(-4\frac{1}{5}\right)$ $-13\frac{1}{8}$ **27.** $-2\frac{1}{3} \times \left(-1\frac{4}{9}\right)$ $3\frac{10}{27}$ **28.** $-6\frac{1}{4} \times \left(-5\frac{2}{5}\right)$ $33\frac{3}{4}$

29. $\frac{1}{4} \times \frac{1}{3} \times \frac{1}{2}$ $\frac{1}{24}$ **30.** $\frac{5}{16} \times \frac{1}{2} \times \frac{1}{5}$ $\frac{1}{32}$ **31.** $\frac{3}{4} \times \frac{1}{6} \times \frac{1}{9}$ $\frac{1}{72}$

32. $-\frac{5}{8} \times \left(-\frac{3}{25}\right) \times \left(-\frac{1}{9}\right)$ $-\frac{1}{120}$ **33.** $-2\frac{1}{4} \times 6\frac{1}{2} \times \frac{12}{39}$ $-4\frac{1}{2}$ **34.** $-5\frac{1}{8} \times \frac{24}{25} \times 10\frac{1}{2}$ $-51\frac{33}{50}$

Multiply. Simplify the answer.

EXAMPLE $\dfrac{3}{5} \times 15a = \dfrac{3}{\underset{1}{\cancel{5}}} \times \dfrac{\overset{3a}{\cancel{15a}}}{1} = \dfrac{3 \times 3a}{1 \times 1} = 9a$

35. $\frac{2}{3} \times 9n$ $6n$ **36.** $5 \times \frac{3x}{10}$ $\frac{3x}{2}$ **37.** $-3 \times \frac{y}{6}$ $-\frac{y}{2}$ **38.** $-5 \times \left(\frac{-7a}{10}\right)$ $\frac{7a}{2}$

39. $\frac{2r}{5} \times \frac{1}{r}$ $\frac{2}{5}$ **40.** $\frac{-6}{s} \times \frac{s}{2}$ -3 **41.** $\frac{3c}{5} \times \frac{5}{c}$ 3   **42.** $\frac{2m}{7} \times \frac{14}{m}$ 4

C 43. Let $\frac{a}{b}$ be any fraction ($b \neq 0$). Show that $\frac{a}{b} \times b = a$ by supplying
the rule or property that justifies each statement.

$\frac{a}{b} \times b = \left(a \times \frac{1}{b}\right) \times b$ Why? By the rule: $\frac{a}{b} = a \times \frac{1}{b}$

$= a \times \left(\frac{1}{b} \times b\right)$ Why? By the Associative Property

$= a \times \left(b \times \frac{1}{b}\right)$ Why? By the Commutative Property

$= a \times 1$ Why? By the rule: $b \times \frac{1}{b} = 1$

$= a$ Why? By the Multiplication Property of 1

44. Let $\frac{a}{b}$ and $\frac{c}{d}$ represent any two fractions ($b \neq 0$, $d \neq 0$). Show as in

Exercise 43 that $\frac{a}{b} \times \frac{c}{d} = \frac{ac}{bd}$.

Review Exercises

Evaluate the expression when $x = -8$ and $y = 12$.

1. $5 \times y$ 60   **2.** $7x \div 4$ -14 **3.** $3x - y$ -36 **4.** $x + 8y$ 88

5. $2(x + y)$ 8   **6.** $x \div (y - 6)$ $-1\frac{1}{3}$ **7.** $(2y + 4) \div (x - 1)$ $-3\frac{1}{9}$ **8.** $(x \div 4) \times (y \div 3)$ -8

Rational Numbers   **125**

Suggested Assignments

Minimum
  124/1–16
  125/17–20; 21–37 odd
  125/Rev. 1–8

Average
  124/1–15 odd
  125/17, 19; 21–42
  125/Rev. 1–7 odd

Maximum
  124/1–15 odd
  125/17, 19, 21–44

Supplementary Materials

Practice Masters, p. 19

**Additional Answers
Written Exercises**

44. $\frac{a}{b} \times \frac{c}{d}$

$= \left(a \times \frac{1}{b}\right) \times \left(c \times \frac{1}{d}\right)$

By the rule:
$\frac{a}{b} = a \times \frac{1}{b}$

$= (a \times c) \times \left(\frac{1}{b} \times \frac{1}{d}\right)$

By the commutative and associative properties

$= ac \times \frac{1}{bd}$

By substitution and the rule:
$\frac{1}{a} \times \frac{1}{b} = \frac{1}{ab}$

$= \frac{ac}{bd}$

By the rule:
$a \times \frac{1}{b} = \frac{a}{b}$

Teaching Suggestions p. 105d

Related Activities p. 105d

Reading Mathematics

Students will learn the meaning of the following mathematical term in this lesson:
reciprocal.

Chalkboard Examples

State the reciprocal of:

1. $-4 \quad -\dfrac{1}{4}$

2. $\dfrac{4}{9} \quad \dfrac{9}{4}$

3. $\dfrac{1}{2} \quad 2$

Divide. Write the answer as a
proper fraction in lowest
terms or as a mixed number
in simple form.

4. $\dfrac{7}{12} \div \left(-\dfrac{5}{6}\right) \quad -\dfrac{7}{10}$

5. $-3\dfrac{1}{6} \div \dfrac{1}{4} \quad -12\dfrac{2}{3}$

6. $-5\dfrac{1}{4} \div \left(-3\dfrac{3}{8}\right) \quad 1\dfrac{5}{9}$

4-6 Dividing Fractions

To develop a method for dividing fractions, recall that multiplication
and division are inverse operations. If $2 \times n = 10$, then $n = 10 \div 2$.
Similarly, if $\frac{7}{5} \times x = \frac{2}{3}$, then $x = \frac{2}{3} \div \frac{7}{5}$. We can show by substitution
that the multiplication equation is true when the value of x is $(\frac{2}{3} \times \frac{5}{7})$.

$$\frac{7}{5} \times \left(\frac{2}{3} \times \frac{5}{7}\right) = \frac{\cancel{7} \times 2 \times \cancel{5}}{\cancel{5} \times 3 \times \cancel{7}} = \frac{2}{3}$$

Therefore, the related division equation must also be true when the
value of x is $(\frac{2}{3} \times \frac{5}{7})$. That is,

$$\frac{2}{3} \times \frac{5}{7} = \frac{2}{3} \div \frac{7}{5}.$$

Two numbers, like $\frac{5}{7}$ and $\frac{7}{5}$, whose product is 1 are called **recipro-
cals.** The reciprocal of $\frac{c}{d}$ is $\frac{d}{c}$ because $\frac{c}{d} \times \frac{d}{c} = 1$. Every nonzero rational number has exactly one reciprocal.

We may state the following general rule.

Rule

For all numbers a, b, c, and d ($b \neq 0$, $c \neq 0$, $d \neq 0$),

$$\frac{a}{b} \div \frac{c}{d} = \frac{a}{b} \times \frac{d}{c}$$

To divide by a fraction, multiply by its reciprocal.

EXAMPLE 1 Name the reciprocal, if any.

  a. $\dfrac{2}{3}$ **b.** $-\dfrac{5}{8}$ **c.** 2   **d.** 0

Solution **a.** The reciprocal of $\frac{2}{3}$ is $\frac{3}{2}$ since $\frac{2}{3} \times \frac{3}{2} = 1$.

  b. The reciprocal of $-\frac{5}{8}$ is $-\frac{8}{5}$ since $-\frac{5}{8} \times \left(-\frac{8}{5}\right) = 1$.

  c. The reciprocal of 2 is $\frac{1}{2}$ since $2 \times \frac{1}{2} = 1$.

  d. The equation $0 \times n = 1$ has no solution since 0 times any number is 0. Therefore, 0 has no reciprocal.

126 *Chapter 4*

EXAMPLE 2 Divide. Write the answer as a proper fraction in lowest terms or as a mixed number in simple form.

     a. $\dfrac{5}{6} \div \dfrac{3}{2}$ **b.** $-\dfrac{4}{3} \div \dfrac{5}{8}$ **c.** $2\dfrac{1}{3} \div 1\dfrac{3}{8}$ **d.** $\dfrac{\frac{2}{5}}{\frac{1}{4}}$

Solution   **a.** $\dfrac{5}{6} \div \dfrac{3}{2} = \dfrac{5}{\underset{3}{6}} \times \dfrac{\overset{1}{2}}{3} = \dfrac{5}{9}$

           b. $-\dfrac{4}{3} \div \dfrac{5}{8} = -\dfrac{4}{3} \times \dfrac{8}{5} = -\dfrac{32}{15}$, or $-2\dfrac{2}{15}$

           c. $2\dfrac{1}{3} \div 1\dfrac{3}{8} = \dfrac{7}{3} \div \dfrac{11}{8} = \dfrac{7}{3} \times \dfrac{8}{11} = \dfrac{56}{33}$, or $1\dfrac{23}{33}$

           d. $\dfrac{\frac{2}{5}}{\frac{1}{4}} = \dfrac{2}{5} \div \dfrac{1}{4} = \dfrac{2}{5} \times \dfrac{4}{1} = \dfrac{8}{5}$, or $1\dfrac{3}{5}$

EXAMPLE 3 Ann bought 2 packages of ground beef. One package was $2\frac{1}{2}$ lb, and the other package was $3\frac{1}{8}$ lb. Ann divided the total amount of beef into 5 equal packages for the freezer. How many pounds were in each package?

Solution   • The problem asks for the number of pounds in each of the 5 packages.

          • Given facts: $2\frac{1}{2}$ lb and $3\frac{1}{8}$ lb of beef

                  total divided into 5 equal packages

          • To solve, first add to find the total amount of beef, and then divide to find the amount in each package.

$$2\dfrac{1}{2} + 3\dfrac{1}{8} = 2\dfrac{4}{8} + 3\dfrac{1}{8} = 5\dfrac{5}{8}$$

$$5\dfrac{5}{8} \div 5 = \dfrac{\overset{9}{45}}{8} \times \dfrac{1}{\underset{1}{5}} = \dfrac{9 \times 1}{8 \times 1} = \dfrac{9}{8}, \text{ or } 1\dfrac{1}{8}$$

          Each package contained $1\frac{1}{8}$ lb of beef.

Problem Solving Reminder

When solving a problem, *review the problem solving strategies and tips that you have learned.* As you work through the problems in the lesson, remember that you may need to supply additional information, eliminate extra information, or plan more than one step. Remember to reread the problem to be sure your answer is complete.

Class Exercises

State the reciprocal.

1. $4\frac{1}{4}$ **2.** -5 $-\frac{1}{5}$ **3.** $\frac{3}{4}$ $\frac{4}{3}$ **4.** $-\frac{5}{8}$ $-\frac{8}{5}$ **5.** $\frac{2}{7}$ $\frac{7}{2}$ $\frac{3}{11}$ **6.** $\frac{11}{3}$

7. $-\frac{2}{3}$ $-\frac{3}{2}$ **8.** $-\frac{6}{5}$ $-\frac{5}{6}$ **9.** $\frac{11}{12}$ $\frac{12}{11}$ **10.** $\frac{3}{16}$ $\frac{16}{3}$ **11.** $-\frac{4}{7}$ $-\frac{7}{4}$ **12.** $\frac{14}{5}$

$\frac{5}{14}$

Complete.

13. $\frac{2}{3} \div 5 = \frac{2}{3} \times \underline{\ ?\ }$ $\frac{1}{5}$ **14.** $\frac{2}{3} \div \frac{1}{5} = \frac{2}{3} \times \underline{\ ?\ }$ 5 **15.** $\frac{6}{5} \div (-10) = \underline{\ ?\ }$ $\frac{6}{5}$ $\times \left(-\frac{1}{10}\right)$

16. $-\frac{3}{8} \div 7 = \underline{\ ?\ } \times \frac{1}{7}$ $-\frac{3}{8}$ **17.** $\frac{5}{16} \div \frac{1}{8} = \underline{\ ?\ } \times \underline{\ ?\ }$ $\frac{5}{16}$ 8 **18.** $-\frac{3}{4} \div \frac{3}{10} = \underline{\ ?\ } \times \underline{\ ?\ }$ $-\frac{3}{4}$ $\frac{10}{3}$

Written Exercises

Divide. Write the answer as a proper fraction in lowest terms or as a mixed number in simple form.

A

1. $\frac{2}{5} \div \frac{3}{5}$ $\frac{2}{3}$ **2.** $\frac{7}{8} \div \frac{3}{8}$ $2\frac{1}{3}$ **3.** $5 \div \frac{1}{5}$ 25 **4.** $10 \div \frac{1}{2}$ 20

5. $\frac{5}{8} \div \frac{9}{5}$ $\frac{25}{72}$ **6.** $\frac{3}{4} \div \frac{7}{8}$ $\frac{6}{7}$ **7.** $\frac{\frac{5}{9}}{\frac{1}{7}}$ $3\frac{8}{9}$ **8.** $\frac{\frac{2}{3}}{\frac{3}{8}}$ $1\frac{7}{9}$

9. $-\frac{21}{4} \div \left(-\frac{7}{8}\right)$ 6 **10.** $-\frac{4}{5} \div \left(-\frac{36}{25}\right)$ $\frac{5}{9}$ **11.** $3\frac{1}{4} \div \frac{5}{8}$ $5\frac{1}{5}$ **12.** $10\frac{1}{2} \div \frac{8}{9}$ $11\frac{13}{16}$

13. $-5\frac{5}{8} \div 10$ $-\frac{9}{16}$ **14.** $11\frac{1}{9} \div 100$ $\frac{1}{9}$ **15.** $-6\frac{1}{3} \div \left(-\frac{19}{21}\right)$ 7 **16.** $-10\frac{1}{3} \div \left(-\frac{31}{33}\right)$

11

B

17. $6\frac{1}{8} \div \left(\frac{8}{3} \times \frac{3}{7}\right)$ $5\frac{23}{64}$ **18.** $-7 \div \left(\frac{21}{4} \times \frac{3}{7}\right)$ $-3\frac{1}{9}$ **19.** $\left(-1\frac{2}{3} \times \frac{18}{5}\right) \div 3$

-2

20. $-\left(\frac{35}{4} \times \frac{2}{7}\right) \div \left(-\frac{4}{3}\right)$ $1\frac{7}{8}$ **21.** $-\left(3\frac{1}{5} \times \frac{5}{2}\right) \div \frac{8}{9}$ -9 **22.** $\left(-2\frac{1}{6} \div \frac{1}{9}\right) \times \frac{1}{13}$

$-1\frac{1}{2}$

23. $-\left(4\frac{1}{6} \div 5\right) \times \left(-\frac{2}{5}\right)$ $\frac{1}{3}$ **24.** $-3\frac{1}{8} \div 4 \div \left(-\frac{5}{4}\right)$ $\frac{5}{8}$ **25.** $5\frac{1}{3} \div 2\frac{2}{3} \div (-4)$

$-\frac{1}{2}$

Divide. Simplify the answer.

EXAMPLE   **a.** $\frac{5a}{3} \div \frac{2a}{3}$ **b.** $\frac{x}{2} \div \frac{y}{4}$

Solution   **a.** $\frac{5a}{3} \div \frac{2a}{3} = \frac{5\overset{5}{\cancel{a}}}{\cancel{3}} \times \frac{\overset{1}{\cancel{3}}}{2\cancel{a}} = \frac{5 \times 1}{1 \times 2} = \frac{5}{2}$, or $2\frac{1}{2}$

          b. $\frac{x}{2} \div \frac{y}{4} = \frac{x}{\cancel{2}_1} \times \frac{\overset{2}{\cancel{4}}}{y} = \frac{x \times 2}{1 \times y} = \frac{2x}{y}$

128   *Chapter 4*

26. $\frac{6x}{5} \div 2\frac{3x}{5}$ **27.** $-4 \div \frac{1}{2y}$ $-8y$ **28.** $42r \div \frac{3r}{4}$ 56   **29.** $\left(-\frac{6a}{7}\right) \div \left(-\frac{3d}{4}\right)$ $1\frac{1}{7}$

C   **30.** $-8b \div \frac{5}{3b}$ $-\frac{24b^2}{5}$ **31.** $\frac{-5}{7c} \div \frac{5c}{14}$ $\frac{-2}{c^2}$ **32.** $\frac{-8c^2}{9} \div \frac{4c}{5}$ $\frac{-10c}{9}$ **33.** $\frac{5de^2}{6} \div \frac{10d^2e}{9}$ $\frac{3e}{4d}$

Evaluate the expression when $x = \frac{1}{2}$, $y = \frac{2}{3}$, and $z = \frac{5}{6}$.

EXAMPLE $\frac{1-z}{y}$

Solution $\dfrac{1-z}{y} = \dfrac{1-\frac{5}{6}}{\frac{2}{3}} = \left(1 - \frac{5}{6}\right) \div \frac{2}{3} = \frac{1}{6} \times \frac{3}{2} = \frac{1}{4}$

34. $\frac{x}{y}$ $\frac{3}{4}$ **35.** $\frac{y}{z}$ $\frac{4}{5}$ **36.** $\frac{2x}{z}$ $1\frac{1}{5}$ **37.** $\frac{z}{3y}$ $\frac{5}{12}$ **38.** $\frac{x+1}{z}$ $1\frac{4}{5}$ **39.** $\frac{y\frac{2}{5}}{y+1}$

Problems

Solve. Write the answer as a whole number, as a proper fraction in lowest terms, or as a mixed number in simple form.

A   **1.** How many packages will $5\frac{1}{2}$ lb of raisins fill if each package holds 9 oz? $9\frac{7}{9}$ **packages**

2. Karen Northrup worked $12\frac{1}{2}$ h last week and earned $50. What was her hourly rate of pay? **$4 per hour**

3. A television station released 300 balloons at an outdoor celebration. Of these, $\frac{3}{4}$ were orange. How many were orange? **225 balloons**

4. Leo Delray earns $2 an hour for babysitting. If he works $3\frac{1}{4}$ h one evening, how much does he earn? **$6.50**

5. To the nearest million, the number of households in the United States having television sets was 4 million in 1950 and 76 million in 1980. Express the first number as a fraction of the second. $\frac{1}{19}$

6. A gasoline tank with a capacity of 15 gal is $\frac{3}{4}$ full. How many gallons will it take to fill the tank? $3\frac{3}{4}$ **gal**

7. A town has raised $\frac{3}{8}$ of the $12,000 it needs to furnish its new library. How much more is it hoping to raise? **$7500**

Rational Numbers   **129**

Suggested Assignments

Minimum
Day 1: 128/1–16; 18–24
         even
       129/26, 28
Day 2: 129/Prob. 1–7
       130/Prob. 8–10
       130/Rev. 1–8

Average
Day 1: 128/2–16 even;
       17–25
       129/26–29; 30–36
       even
Day 2: 129/Prob. 1–7
       130/Prob. 8–12
       130/Rev. 2–8 even
       130/Challenge

Maximum
Day 1: 128/2–24 even
       129/26, 28; 30–39
Day 2: 129/Prob. 1–7
       130/Prob. 8–14
       130/Challenge

Supplementary Materials

Practice Masters, p. 19

Solve. Simplify the answer.

8. In a recent year there were 32,000 persons in the United States who had celebrated their 100th birthday. Of these, $\frac{3}{4}$ were women. How many were men? **8000 men**

B 9. How much fringe will be needed for all four edges of a rectangular rug measuring $11\frac{3}{4}$ ft by $8\frac{1}{3}$ ft? If the fringe is 3 in. wide, what are the dimensions of the rug after the fringe is added? **$40\frac{1}{6}$ ft; $12\frac{1}{4}$ ft by $8\frac{5}{6}$ ft**

10. An advertising sign is to have six lines of printing. The letters are to be $1\frac{1}{2}$ in. high with $\frac{1}{4}$ in. between the lines.
   a. How much vertical space is required for the printing? **$10\frac{1}{4}$ in.**
   b. If there is a top margin of 3 in. and a lower margin of $3\frac{1}{2}$ in., what will be the total height of the sign? **$16\frac{3}{4}$ in.**

11. One half of the class voted to have a picnic. One third of the class voted to hold a dinner instead. What fraction of the class wanted neither a picnic nor a dinner? **$\frac{1}{6}$**

12. A picture measures $8\frac{3}{4}$ in. by 8 in. When framed it measures $10\frac{3}{4}$ in. by 10 in. How wide is each side of the frame? **1 in.**

C 13. Only $\frac{1}{5}$ of the downtown workers drive to work. Of those who do not drive, $\frac{3}{16}$ ride bicycles to work. What fraction of the workers ride bicycles to work? **$\frac{3}{20}$**

14. Kevin's regular rate of pay is $4 per hour. When he works overtime, he earns $1\frac{1}{2}$ times as much per hour. How much will Kevin earn for $5\frac{1}{2}$ h of overtime work? **$33**

Review Exercises

1. $n = 240 - 135$; 105   2. $x = 52 + 45$; 97
3. $y = 156 \div 4$; 39   4. $t = 504 \div 9$; 56

Use the inverse operation to write a related equation. Solve for the variable.

1. $n + 135 = 240$ 2. $x - 45 = 52$ 3. $4y = 156$ 4. $9t = 504$

5. $12x = 432$ 6. $r \div 17 = 27$ 7. $38m = 418$ 8. $a \div 22 = 33$
5. $x = 432 \div 12$; 36   6. $r = 27 \times 17$; 459
7. $m = 418 \div 38$; 11   8. $a = 33 \times 22$; 726

Challenge

Answers may vary.

Write a fraction whose value is between the given fractions.

1. $\frac{2}{5} < \underline{\ \ ?\ \frac{1}{2}\ \ } < \frac{3}{5}$ 2. $-\frac{2}{3} < \underline{\ \ ?\ \frac{-\,?}{5}\ \ } < -\frac{1}{3}$ 3. $\frac{1}{8} < \underline{\ \ ?\ \frac{3}{16}\ \ } < \frac{1}{4}$

4. $-\frac{2}{7} < \underline{\ \ ?\ \frac{-5}{14}\ \ } < -\frac{3}{14}$ 5. $\frac{1}{6} < \underline{\ \ ?\ \frac{?}{24}\ \ } < \frac{1}{4}$ 6. $-\frac{5}{6} < \underline{\ \ ?\ \frac{-29}{36}\ \ } < -\frac{7}{9}$

4-7 Fractions and Decimals

Any fraction can be represented as a decimal. You may recall that a fraction such as $\frac{3}{4}$ can be easily written as an equivalent fraction whose denominator is a power of 10, and then as a decimal. To represent $\frac{3}{4}$ as a decimal, we first write it as an equivalent fraction with denominator 100.

$$\frac{3}{4} = \frac{3 \times 25}{4 \times 25} = \frac{75}{100} = 0.75$$

For most fractions, however, we use the fact that $\frac{a}{b} = a \div b$ and divide numerator by denominator.

EXAMPLE 1 Write as a decimal: **a.** $-\frac{5}{16}$ **b.** $\frac{24}{55}$

Solution   **a.** First find $5 \div 16$.

```
       0.3125
   16)5.0000
      4 8
        20
        16
        40
        32
         80
         80
          0
```

Therefore, $-\frac{5}{16} = -0.3125$.

The decimal -0.3125 is called a **terminating decimal** because the final remainder is 0 and the division ends.

b. Find $24 \div 55$.

```
       0.43636
   55)24.00000
      22 0
       2 00
       1 65
         350
         330
         200
         165
         350
         330
          20
```

Therefore, $\frac{24}{55} = 0.43636\ldots$.

The digits 36 continue to repeat without end. The decimal $0.43636\ldots$ is called a **repeating decimal.** We often write $0.43636\ldots$ as $0.4\overline{36}$, with a bar over the block of digits that repeats.

Rational Numbers **131**

Reading Mathematics

Students will learn the meaning of the following mathematical terms in this lesson: *terminating decimal, repeating decimal, irrational number, real number.*

Chalkboard Examples

Express as a fraction in lowest terms or as a mixed number in simple form.

1. 2.8 $2\frac{4}{5}$

2. -5.25 $-5\frac{1}{4}$

3. $21.\overline{33}$ $21\frac{1}{3}$

4. $4.\overline{72}$ $4\frac{8}{11}$

Express as a terminating or repeating decimal.

5. $-\frac{7}{6}$ $-1.1\overline{6}$

6. $\frac{1}{5}$ 0.2

7. $3\frac{1}{8}$ 3.125

8. $2\frac{5}{12}$ $2.41\overline{6}$

To say that $\frac{24}{55} = 0.43636\ldots$ means that the successive decimals 0.436, 0.4363, 0.43636, and so on, will come closer and closer to the value $\frac{24}{55}$.

We can predict when a fraction will result in a terminating decimal because the fraction in lowest terms has a denominator with no prime factors other than 2 and 5. Thus, the fraction $\frac{24}{55}$ does not result in a terminating decimal because its denominator has 11 as a prime factor.

When working with a mixed number, such as $-1\frac{5}{16}$ or $1\frac{24}{25}$, we may consider the mixed number as a sum of a whole number and a fraction, or we may rewrite the mixed number as an improper fraction and then divide.

If a and b are integers and $b \neq 0$, the quotient $a \div b$ is either a terminating decimal or a repeating decimal. The reason for this is that, for any divisor, the number of possible remainders at each step of the division is limited to the whole numbers less than the divisor. Sooner or later, either the remainder is 0 and the division ends, as in part (a) of Example 1, or one of the remainders reappears in the division as in part (b) of Example 1. Then the same block of digits will reappear in the quotient.

Property

Every rational number can be represented by either a terminating decimal or a repeating decimal.

You already know how to write a terminating decimal as a fraction. Rewrite the decimal as a fraction whose denominator is a power of 10.

EXAMPLE 2 Write -0.625 as a fraction in lowest terms.

Solution $-0.625 = -\dfrac{625}{1000} = -\dfrac{625 \div 125}{1000 \div 125} = -\dfrac{5}{8}$

The next example shows a method for writing a repeating decimal as a fraction.

EXAMPLE 3 Write $-1.\overline{21}$ as a fraction in lowest terms.

Solution   Let $n = 1.\overline{21}$.

Multiply both sides of the equation by a power of 10 determined by the number of digits in the block of repeating digits. Since there are

2 digits that repeat in the number $1.\overline{21}$, we multiply by 10^2, or 100.

$$100n = 121.\overline{21}$$

Subtract:
$$n = 1.\overline{21}$$
$$\overline{99n = 120}$$

$$n = \frac{120}{99} = \frac{40}{33}$$

Thus, $-1.\overline{21} = -\frac{40}{33}$, or $-1\frac{7}{33}$.

Property

Every terminating or repeating decimal represents a rational number.

Some decimals, such as those below, neither terminate nor repeat.

$$0.01001000100001\ldots \qquad 1.234567891011121314\ldots$$

The two decimals shown follow patterns, but they are not repeating patterns. The decimal on the right is made up of consecutive whole numbers beginning with 1.

Decimals that neither terminate nor repeat represent **irrational numbers.** Together, the rational numbers and the irrational numbers make up the set of **real numbers.** The number line that you have studied is sometimes called the **real number line.** For every point on the line, there is exactly one real number and for every real number there is exactly one point on the number line.

Class Exercises

Tell whether the decimal for the fraction is terminating or repeating. If the decimal is terminating, state the decimal.

1. $\frac{1}{4}$ Term., 0.25   **2.** $\frac{5}{6}$ Repeating   **3.** $2\frac{2}{5}$ Term., 2.4   **4.** $-\frac{9}{10}$ Term., -0.9 **5.** $-1\frac{1}{2}$ Term., -1.5 **6.** $\frac{13}{30}$ Repeating

State as a fraction in which the numerator is an integer and the denominator is a power of 10.

7. 0.13 $\frac{13}{100}$ **8.** -0.9 $-\frac{9}{10}$ **9.** 1.4 $\frac{14}{10}$ **10.** -0.007 $-\frac{7}{1000}$ **11.** 3.03 $\frac{303}{100}$ **12.** -5.001 $-\frac{5001}{1000}$

State the repeating digit(s) for each decimal.

13. 6.666 . . . ₆ **14.** 0.0444 . . . ₄ **15.** 6.050505 . . . ₀₅ **16.** 0.1666 . . . ₆

17. 5.1$\overline{5}$ 5 **18.** 0.$\overline{422}$ 422 **19.** 1.0$\overline{6}$ 6 **20.** 0.3$\overline{64}$ 64

Written Exercises 12. 0.4$\overline{6}$ 34. $-10\frac{1}{1000}$ 39. $-1\frac{413}{500}$ 49. $-1\frac{4}{33}$

Write as a terminating or repeating decimal. Use a bar to show repeating digits.

A **1.** $\frac{1}{4}$ 0.25 **2.** $\frac{1}{5}$ 0.2 **3.** $\frac{2}{9}$ 0.$\overline{2}$ **4.** $\frac{3}{16}$ 0.1875 **5.** $\frac{9}{10}$ 0.9 **6.** $-\frac{1}{18}$ $^{-0.0\overline{5}}$

7. $-\frac{2}{3}$ $-0.\overline{6}$ **8.** $\frac{4}{9}$ 0.$\overline{4}$ **9.** $-\frac{3}{8}$ $^{-0.375}$ **10.** $\frac{3}{5}$ 0.6 **11.** $-\frac{3}{25}$ -0.12 **12.** $\frac{7}{15}$

13. $1\frac{1}{10}$ 1.1 **14.** $5\frac{2}{5}$ 5.4 **15.** $\frac{7}{12}$ 0.58$\overline{3}$ **16.** $-\frac{3}{11}$ $-0.\overline{27}$ **17.** $\frac{4}{15}$ 0.2$\overline{6}$ **18.** $-4\frac{7}{8}$ $^{-4.875}$

19. $-1\frac{7}{18}$ $-1.3\overline{8}$ **20.** $2\frac{1}{9}$ 2.$\overline{1}$ **21.** $\frac{3}{20}$ 0.15 **22.** $\frac{17}{36}$ 0.47$\overline{2}$ **23.** $3\frac{2}{7}$ **24.** $\frac{5}{13}$

3.$\overline{285714}$ 0.$\overline{384615}$

Write as a proper fraction in lowest terms or as a mixed number in simple form.

25. 0.05 $\frac{1}{20}$ **26.** 0.005 $\frac{1}{200}$ **27.** -0.6 $-\frac{3}{5}$ **28.** -2.1 $-2\frac{1}{10}$ **29.** 2.07 $2\frac{7}{100}$

30. -0.62 $-\frac{31}{50}$ **31.** 5.125 $5\frac{1}{8}$ **32.** 4.3 $4\frac{3}{10}$ **33.** -1.375 $-1\frac{3}{8}$ **34.** -10.001

35. 12.625 $12\frac{5}{8}$ **36.** 10.3 $10\frac{3}{10}$ **37.** 0.225 $\frac{9}{40}$ **38.** 0.8375 $\frac{67}{80}$ **39.** -1.826

B **40.** 0.444 . . . $\frac{4}{9}$ **41.** -0.555 . . . $-\frac{5}{9}$ **42.** 0.0$\overline{3}$ $\frac{1}{30}$ **43.** $-1.0\overline{1}$ $-1\frac{1}{90}$ **44.** 5.$\overline{9}$ 6

45. 0.1515 . . . $\frac{5}{33}$ **46.** $-1.\overline{20}$ $-1\frac{20}{99}$ **47.** 0.$\overline{35}$ $\frac{35}{99}$ **48.** 0.$\overline{72}$ $\frac{8}{11}$ **49.** $-1.\overline{12}$

50. 1.3$\overline{62}$ $1\frac{359}{990}$ **51.** 2.13$\overline{4}$ $2\frac{121}{900}$ **52.** $-8.0\overline{16}$ $-8\frac{8}{495}$ **53.** 0.$\overline{123}$ $\frac{41}{333}$ **54.** $-5.\overline{862}$ $-5\frac{862}{999}$

Tell whether the number is rational or irrational.

55. $\frac{-13}{17}$ Rational **56.** 1.515151 . . . Rational **57.** -3.72 Rational **58.** 2.121121112 . . . Irrational

Arrange the numbers in order from least to greatest.

59. 3.0, 3.0$\overline{9}$, 3.00$\overline{9}$, 3.1 3.0, 3.00$\overline{9}$, 3.0$\overline{9}$, 3.1 **60.** 0.182, 0.182$\overline{5}$, 0.18$\overline{2}$, 0.1$\overline{8}$ 0.182, 0.18$\overline{2}$, 0.182$\overline{5}$, 0.1$\overline{8}$

a. Express the first number as a fraction or mixed number.
b. Compare the first number with the second.

C **61.** 0.$\overline{9}$; 1 1, = **62.** 0.4$\overline{9}$; $\frac{1}{2}$ $\frac{1}{2}$, = **63.** $-1.24\overline{9}$; $-\frac{5}{4}$ $-\frac{5}{4}$, = **64.** 2.3$\overline{9}$; $2\frac{2}{5}$ $2\frac{2}{5}$, =

134 *Chapter 4*

Self-Test B

Multiply or divide. Write the answer as a proper fraction in lowest terms or as a mixed number in simple form.

1. $\frac{3}{4} \times 5$ $3\frac{3}{4}$

2. $\frac{1}{8} \times \left(-\frac{1}{3}\right)$ $-\frac{1}{24}$

3. $\frac{28}{35} \times \frac{21}{14}$ $1\frac{1}{5}$ [4-5]

4. $8\frac{3}{4} \times \frac{3}{16}$ $1\frac{41}{64}$

5. $-3\frac{1}{8} \times \left(-4\frac{4}{5}\right)$ 15

6. $-2\frac{4}{7} \times 3\frac{1}{6}$ $-8\frac{1}{7}$

7. $\frac{5}{8} \div \frac{10}{24}$ $1\frac{1}{2}$

8. $-\frac{11}{16} \div \frac{44}{8}$ $-\frac{1}{8}$

9. $-\frac{18}{5} \div \left(-\frac{9}{35}\right)$ 14 [4-6]

10. $1\frac{1}{4} \div 25$ $\frac{1}{20}$

11. $4\frac{1}{3} \div \left(-\frac{26}{27}\right)$ $-4\frac{1}{2}$

12. $-4\frac{2}{7} \div \left(-2\frac{1}{14}\right)$ $2\frac{2}{29}$

Write as a decimal. Use a bar to show repeating digits.

13. $\frac{5}{8}$ 0.625

14. $\frac{2}{11}$ $0.\overline{18}$

15. $-\frac{1}{80}$ -0.0125

16. $\frac{7}{6}$ $1.1\overline{6}$ [4-7]

Write as a proper fraction in lowest terms or as a mixed number in simple form.

17. 0.875 $\frac{7}{8}$

18. $1.\overline{6}$ $1\frac{2}{3}$

19. -2.213 $-2\frac{213}{1000}$

20. $0.2\overline{3}$ $\frac{7}{30}$

Self-Test answers and Extra Practice are at the back of the book.

▮▮▮ Computer Byte

The following program will print a decimal approximation for any positive proper fraction. The first approximation is rounded to the number of digits that the computer usually displays. The computer will then print an approximation to any desired number of digits.

```
10   PRINT "INPUT NUMERATOR, THEN DENOMINATOR"
20   INPUT N,D
30   IF N > D THEN 10
40   PRINT N;"/";D;" = ";N / D
50   PRINT "HOW MANY DIGITS DO YOU WANT ?";
60   INPUT K
70   PRINT "OR .";
80   FOR I = 1 TO K
90   LET P = 10 * N / D
100    PRINT  INT (P);
110    LET N = 10 * N - D *  INT (P)
120    NEXT I
130    END
```

1. $0.\overline{142857}$
2. $0.\overline{285714}$
3. $0.\overline{90}$
4. $0.\overline{384615}$
5. $0.\overline{76}$
6. $0.\overline{324}$
7. $0.\overline{51}$
8. $0.\overline{402}$

Use the program to discover the repeating pattern for these fractions.

1. $\frac{1}{7}$ **2.** $\frac{2}{7}$ **3.** $\frac{10}{11}$ **4.** $\frac{5}{13}$ **5.** $\frac{76}{99}$ **6.** $\frac{12}{37}$ **7.** $\frac{17}{33}$ **8.** $\frac{134}{333}$

Rational Numbers **135**

Enrichment Note

To do a simple calculation such as finding the area of one rectangle, there is little point in using a computer. However, using a FOR-NEXT loop, you could have the computer calculate the areas of hundreds of rectangles, and it would never complain of being tired or bored.

Have students think of monotonous and repetitive tasks in industry for which computers are being used.

For solving more complex equations, the use of computers can be valuable and efficient. The volume and surface area formulas in Chapter 9—particularly for the cylinder, cone, and sphere—are sufficiently complex to provide a challenge to a programmer.

Programming in BASIC

On pages 64–65, you learned about programs that use PRINT, INPUT, and END statements. We can also give a value to a variable by using a **LET** statement, for example, LET A = 215. A LET statement can also be used to evaluate a formula, as shown in this program.

```
10   PRINT "INPUT LENGTH AND WIDTH";
20   PRINT "OF RECTANGLE";
30   INPUT L, W  ◄───────────────── For example, type 18, 10
40   LET A = L * W
50   PRINT "AREA = ";A
60   END
```

The programs on pages 58 and 135 use the "greatest integer" function. That is, **INT(X)** represents the greatest integer less than or equal to X:

$$INT(4) = 4 \qquad\qquad INT(4.9) = 4$$

The program on page 135 uses two more kinds of statements. Line 30 has an **IF-THEN** statement. It means that if $N > D$, the computer is to go back to line 10. Otherwise (if $N \leq D$), it is to go on to line 40. In the BASIC language, we use the symbols $>$ and $<$ as we do when we write inequalities. To indicate $\leq$, however, we type in $< =$. To indicate $\geq$, we type in $> =$.

Lines 80–120 in the program on page 135 contain a **FOR-NEXT** *loop*. It tells the computer to perform a computation over and over

136 *Chapter 4*

136

again for a specific number of times. Here, the variable I does not appear in the computation, although in some cases the loop variable may. In this case, the variable I is just a counter that allows the computer to repeat the computation K times. The variable N is given a new value in line 110 each time through.

1. Copy and RUN the program on page 136 for several sets of values of L and W.

2. Verify on your computer that INT(4) = 4 and INT(4.9) = 4.

3. Use INT to print out quotients and remainders as follows:

```
10   PRINT "TO DIVIDE N BY D, N > D"
20   PRINT "INPUT N, D";
30   INPUT N, D
40   LET Q = N / D
50   LET Q1 = INT(Q)
60   LET R = N - D * Q1
70   PRINT N;"/";D;" = ";Q1;
80   PRINT ", REMAINDER ";R
90   END
```

RUN this for: 60, 14; 100, 9; and 80, 16.   **4 R4; 11 R1; 5 R0**

Research Activities

1. Computers can also handle various forms of graphics. Programs can be written to produce drawings that can be made to appear in various or changing forms. The photo on page 136 shows a computer generated picture that is used in biological research to study the make-up of certain fibers. Find out about some other fields in which computer graphics are important.

2. If you were to diagram the programs shown on this page and on page 136, you might use a diagram like the one shown at the right. More elaborate versions of such diagrams are called flow charts. Longer programs would have more sections. When you write longer, more complicated programs, you will want to separate the sections of the programs with REM (remark) statements. Find out about REM statements and how they can help you keep track of what is being done in a program.

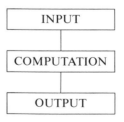

Rational Numbers   **137**

Chapter Review

True or false?

1. $8 \times \frac{1}{9} = \frac{9}{8}$ F   2. $4 \times \left(-\frac{1}{5}\right) = -\frac{4}{5}$ T   3. $\frac{-7}{11} = -\frac{7}{11}$ T   [4-1]

4. $\frac{15}{18}$ in lowest terms is $\frac{3}{5}$. F   [4-2]

5. $-\frac{24}{148}$ in lowest terms is $-\frac{12}{74}$. F

6. $\frac{46}{8}$ written as a mixed number in simple form is $5\frac{6}{8}$. F

7. $-12\frac{2}{7} = \frac{86}{7}$ F   8. $7\frac{3}{8} = \frac{29}{8}$ F

9. The LCD of $\frac{2}{3}$ and $\frac{5}{11}$ is 33. T   [4-3]

10. The LCD of $\frac{4}{7}$ and $\frac{5}{42}$ is 6. F

11. The LCD of $\frac{7}{30}$ and $-\frac{3}{35}$ is 150. F

12. The LCD of $\frac{2}{9}$ and $\frac{4}{5}$ is 36. F

Match.

13. $-\frac{5}{12} + \frac{11}{18}$ C   14. $4\frac{2}{5} + 2\frac{3}{10}$ G   **A.** $-2\frac{11}{18}$ **B.** $-8\frac{17}{18}$ [4-4]

15. $1\frac{3}{7} - \frac{5}{8}$ K   16. $-2\frac{1}{6} + \left(-\frac{4}{9}\right)$ A   **C.** $\frac{7}{36}$ **D.** $\frac{3}{16}$

17. $-\frac{9}{16} - \left(-\frac{3}{4}\right)$ D   18. $\frac{1}{8} - \frac{3}{8}$ F   **E.** $\frac{27}{28}$ **F.** $-\frac{1}{4}$ [4-5]

19. $\frac{1}{4} \times \frac{1}{9}$ H   20. $\frac{4}{5} \times \frac{3}{8}$ L   **G.** $6\frac{7}{10}$ **H.** $\frac{1}{36}$

21. $-7\frac{2}{3} \times 1\frac{1}{6}$ B   22. $\frac{2}{5} \times 5$ I   **I.** 2   **J.** $-1\frac{19}{30}$ [4-6]

23. $\frac{3}{14} \div \frac{2}{9}$ E   24. $1\frac{2}{5} \div \left(-\frac{6}{7}\right)$ J   **K.** $\frac{45}{56}$ **L.** $\frac{3}{10}$

Complete. Use a bar to show repeating digits.

25. $\frac{5}{16}$ written as a decimal is ___?___. 0.3125   [4-7]

26. $\frac{4}{3}$ written as a decimal is ___?___. $1.\overline{3}$

27. -0.125 written as a fraction in lowest terms is ___?___. $-\frac{1}{8}$

28. $2.\overline{42}$ written as a mixed number in simple form is ___?___. $2\frac{14}{33}$

Chapter Test

Supplementary Materials
Chapter 4 Test, pp. 27–28

Complete.

1. $5 \times \underline{\ ?\frac{1}{7}\ } = \frac{5}{7}$ **2.** $6 \times \frac{1}{6} = \underline{\ ?1\ }$ [4-1]

3. $12 \div (-13) = \underline{\ ?\ } -\frac{12}{13}$ **4.** $\frac{-1}{4} = \frac{1}{-4} = \underline{\ ?\ } -\frac{1}{4}$

Write as a proper fraction in lowest terms or as a mixed number in simple form.

5. $\frac{14}{40}\ \frac{7}{20}$ **6.** $-\frac{26}{52}\ -\frac{1}{2}$ **7.** $-\frac{136}{160}\ -\frac{17}{20}$ **8.** $\frac{15}{4}\ 3\frac{3}{4}$ **9.** $\frac{-83}{9}\ -9\frac{2}{9}$ [4-2]

Write as an improper fraction.

10. $4\frac{4}{7}\ \frac{32}{7}$ **11.** $-5\frac{3}{5}\ -\frac{28}{5}$ **12.** $7\frac{8}{9}\ \frac{71}{9}$ **13.** $-21\frac{3}{10}\ -\frac{213}{10}$

Write each pair of fractions as equivalent fractions with the least common denominator.

14. $\frac{3}{7},\frac{5}{14}\ \frac{6}{14},\frac{5}{14}$ **15.** $\frac{1}{9},\frac{6}{11}\ \frac{11}{99},\frac{54}{99}$ **16.** $\frac{5}{8},\frac{13}{36}\ \frac{45}{72},\frac{26}{72}$ **17.** $\frac{7}{12},\frac{5}{24}\ \frac{14}{24},\frac{5}{24}$ [4-3]

Add or subtract. Write the answer as a proper fraction in lowest terms or as a mixed number in simple form.

18. $\frac{3}{8}-\frac{1}{7}\ \frac{13}{56}$ **19.** $\frac{3}{10}-\left(-\frac{1}{4}\right)\ \frac{11}{20}$ **20.** $-\frac{1}{6}+\frac{3}{14}\ \frac{1}{21}$ [4-4]

21. $1\frac{3}{4}+\left(-2\frac{1}{2}\right)\ -\frac{3}{4}$ **22.** $5\frac{5}{6}-3\frac{1}{3}\ 2\frac{1}{2}$ **23.** $-\frac{7}{9}-\frac{5}{6}\ -1\frac{11}{18}$

Multiply. Write the answer as a proper fraction in lowest terms or as a mixed number in simple form.

24. $\frac{4}{7}\times\left(-\frac{4}{11}\right)\ -\frac{16}{77}$ **25.** $3\frac{1}{8}\times2\frac{3}{5}\ 8\frac{1}{8}$ **26.** $-\frac{1}{4}\times\left(-\frac{1}{6}\right)\ \frac{1}{24}$ [4-5]

Divide. Write the answer as a proper fraction in lowest terms or as a mixed number in simple form.

27. $\frac{2}{3}\div\frac{7}{9}\ \frac{6}{7}$ **28.** $-\frac{6}{19}\div\frac{9}{38}\ -1\frac{1}{3}$ **29.** $-1\frac{1}{6}\div\left(-4\frac{2}{3}\right)\ \frac{1}{4}$ [4-6]

Write as a terminating or repeating decimal. Use a bar to show repeating digits.

30. $\frac{6}{25}\ 0.24$ **31.** $\frac{5}{33}\ 0.\overline{15}$ **32.** $\frac{9}{16}\ 0.5625$ **33.** $\frac{4}{9}\ 0.\overline{4}$ [4-7]

Write as a proper fraction in lowest terms or as a mixed number in simple form.

34. $0.04\ \frac{1}{25}$ **35.** $-0.375\ \frac{-3}{8}$ **36.** $6.125\ 6\frac{1}{8}$ **37.** $0.\overline{7}\ \frac{7}{9}$

Rational Numbers   **139**

Review for Retention

True or false?

1. If $8y = 72$, $y = 9$
   True

2. If $b \div 4 = 24$, $b = 6$
   False

3. If $3m + 6 = 12$, $m = 6$
   False

4. If $5t - 10 = 25$, $t = 7$
   True

5. If $s = 2$, $22 - 8s \leq 10$
   True

6. If $j = 4$, $3j + 5 > 17$
   False

7. If $k = 12$, $5k < 60$
   False

8. If $c = 7$, $4c - 9 \geq 20$
   False

9. $8.35 + 0 = 8.35$
   True

10. $12.7 \times 1 = 1$
    False

11. $-3 \times -5 = 15$
    True

12. $-24 \div 6 = -4$
    True

13. $0.05 \times 0.01 = 5$
    False

14. $6 \times 0 \times 5 = 30$
    False

15. $-32 \div -8 = 4$
    True

16. $0.102 \div 0.01 = 10.2$
    True

17. $1 \div 17 = 1$
    False

18. $64 \div -8 = -8$
    True

19. If $q = -5$, $-q = -5$
    False

20. If $b = -2$, $-|b| = -2$
    True

Replace __?__ with $=$, $>$, or $<$ to make a true statement.

21. 0 __?__ -3 $>$

22. $|6|$ __?__ 6 $=$

23. -3.2 __?__ -3.1 $<$

24. $|-4|$ __?__ -4 $>$

(Continued on p. 141)

Cumulative Review (Chapters 1–4)

Exercises

Give the solution of the equation for the given replacement set.

1. $x - 12 = 46$; $\{58, 59, 60\}$ 58

2. $8d = 2$; $\left\{\frac{1}{3}, \frac{1}{4}, \frac{1}{5}\right\}$ $\frac{1}{4}$

3. $3(6 + y) = 39$; $\{7, 14, 21\}$ 7

4. $(5 - a) \div (a + 7) = \frac{1}{5}$; $\{1, 2, 3\}$ 3

5. $16r - 11 = 69$; $\{0, 5, 10\}$ 5

6. $m^2(7 + m) = 176$; $\{3, 4, 5\}$ 4

Evaluate the expression if $a = 3$, $b = 0.2$, and $c = 5$.

7. ab^2 0.12

8. $a^2 + b^2$ 9.04

9. a^2c^2 225

10. bc^2 5.0

11. $2b^2$ 0.08

12. a^2b^3 0.072

13. $(a + b)^2$ 10.24

14. $c(a^2 + b)$ 46

15. $2ac^2 \div b$ 750

16. $\frac{10b^2}{c^2}$ 0.016

Use the symbol $>$ to order the numbers from greatest to least.

17. 75.70, 75.40, 75.06
    $75.70 > 75.40 > 75.06$

18. 19.05, 19.18, 19.50
    $19.50 > 19.18 > 19.05$

19. 0.03, 0.30, 0.33
    $0.33 > 0.30 > 0.03$

20. 105.07, 10.507, 1050.7
    $1050.7 > 105.07 > 10.507$

List the integers that can replace x to make the statement true.

21. $|x| = 7$ $7, -7$

22. $|x| = 18$ $18, -18$

23. $|x| \geq 5$ $5, 6, 7, \ldots$,

24. $|x| < 7.3$ $-7, -6, -5, \ldots, 0, \ldots, 5, 6, 7$

25. $4 < |x| < 6$ $5, -5$

26. $6 > |x| > 0$ $5, 4, 3, 2, 1, -5, -4, -3, -2, -1$

27. $31 < |x| < 40$ $32, 33, 34, \ldots, 39, -32, -33, \ldots, -39$

28. $17 \leq |x| \leq 25$ $17, 18, \ldots, 25, -17, -18, \ldots, -25$

What value of the variable makes the statement true?

29. $-7 + y = 11$ $y = 18$

30. $-3n = 51$ $n = -17$

31. $-6(-b) = 72$ $b = 12$

32. $17 - x = -5$ $x = 22$

33. $8(-n) = 32$ $n = -4$

34. $-a \div 15 = 3$ $a = -45$

Evaluate the expression when $x = 5$, $y = -7$, and $z = -5$.

35. $\frac{y + 3}{x} - \frac{4}{5}$

36. $\frac{xy}{z}$ 7

37. $\frac{x + y}{z}$ $\frac{2}{5}$

38. $\frac{yz}{x}$ 7

39. $\frac{x - z}{y}$ $-1\frac{3}{7}$

40. $\frac{x^2 + y^2}{z^2}$ $2\frac{24}{25}$

41. $\frac{x}{7} + \frac{y}{7} - \frac{2}{7}$

42. $\frac{2x}{15} + \frac{z}{3} - 1$

43. $\frac{-y + z}{x}$ $\frac{2}{5}$

44. $\frac{-z - x}{-y}$ 0

Solve. Write the answer as a proper fraction in lowest terms or as a mixed number in simple form.

45. $-5 \times \left(\frac{3}{8} \div \frac{1}{3}\right)$ $-5\frac{5}{8}$

46. $2\frac{1}{2} \div \left(\frac{5}{8} \times 1\frac{3}{4}\right)$ $2\frac{2}{7}$

47. $7\frac{3}{8} + \left[-4\frac{1}{2} \div \left(-5\frac{2}{3}\right)\right]$ $8\frac{23}{136}$

140   Chapter 4

Problems

Problem Solving Reminders

Here are some reminders that may help you solve some of the problems on this page.
- You may need to supply additional information.
- Some steps in your plan may not involve operations.
- Reread the question to be sure you have answered with the information requested.

Solve.

1. The Maxwell children have hired a caterer to provide food for an anniversary party for their parents. The caterer has quoted a price of $15.75 per person and is asking for an advance payment of $\frac{1}{4}$ of the total bill. If the estimated number of guests is 50, how much is the advance payment? **$196.88**

2. The Clean-as-a-Whistle Company provides a matching service for people looking for home cleaners and people wishing to clean homes. The fees include $6.50 per hour for the cleaner, plus $1.50 per hour for the agency. If you hire a cleaner from the company for 5 h, how much will you pay? **$40**

3. As a general rule for brick work, masons estimate 6.5 bricks per square foot. Based on this estimate, will 2500 bricks be enough for a patio that is 396 ft²? **No**

4. The controller of a hospital found that laundry fees for a four-month period totaled $8755. Based on this total, what would be the estimated fee for an entire year? **$26,265**

5. Store owners at the Wagon Wheel Mall pay a monthly rental fee plus a maintenance fee. The maintenance fee is determined by the number of square feet occupied by the shop. The entire mall is 200,000 ft² and the annual fee for the entire mall is $63,000. What is the annual share of the maintenance fee for a store that occupies 2500 ft²? **$787.50**

6. An investor bought 12 acres of land for $70,000. She later subdivided the land into 22 lots that she sold for $4500 apiece. What was her profit on the sale? **$29,000**

7. Douglas bought 75 shares of Health Care Company (HCC) stock and 150 shares of Bowwow Brands (BWB) stock. Last year HCC paid a dividend of $1.85 per share and BWB paid a dividend of $2.04 per share. What was the total of the dividends that Douglas received? **$444.75**

Rational Numbers **141**

Write an equation or inequality for the word phrase.

25. The sum of ten and a number q is less than twenty.
$10 + q < 20$

26. The product of six and the sum of a number w plus two is equal to twelve.
$6(w + 2) = 12$

27. Five less than the product of a number j and eight equals nine.
$8j - 5 = 9$

28. Six less than the product of three and a number k is more than twice the number k.
$3k - 6 > 2k$

Solve for the variable.

29. $d + 13 = 20$ **7**
30. $8n = 32$ **4**
31. $12 - g = 5$ **7**
32. $w \div 3 = 6$ **18**
33. $2h + 5 = 17$ **6**
34. $5j - 3 = j + 1$ **1**
35. $6a + 2 = 26$ **4**
36. $3k + 9 = 3$ **−2**
37. $4y + 10 = 0$ **−2.5**

Write without exponents.

38. 8^{-2} $\frac{1}{64}$
39. $(-2)^{-3}$ $-\frac{1}{8}$
40. $(-3)^5 \times (-3)^{-3}$ **9**

5

Equations and Inequalities

The trains pictured at the right were introduced in France. They can travel at speeds of up to 160 km/h on conventional tracks and nearly triple that on their own continuously welded tracks. The speed of a train on an actual trip depends, of course, on the number of curves and the type of track. A trip of 425 km from Paris to Lyon that takes about 4 h in a conventional train, for instance, can be completed in about 2.5 h in one of these trains.

The time it takes a train to complete a trip depends on the speed of the train and the distance traveled. Some relationships, such as the relationship between time, rate, and distance, can be expressed as equations. Other relationships can be expressed as inequalities. You will learn more about equations and inequalities and methods to solve both in this chapter. You will also learn how to use equations to help solve problems.

Career Note

Reporters representing newspapers, magazines, and radio and television stations often attend newsworthy events such as the introduction of new trains. Reporters need a wide educational background. They must report facts, not their own opinions. They must be willing to meet deadlines and often to work at irregular hours.

Lesson Commentary
Chapter 5   Equations and Inequalities

Overview

A somewhat informal introduction to solving equations and inequalities was given in Chapter 1. There the approach was almost an intuitive one, based on the use of inverse operations to derive simpler equivalent equations. Since Chapter 1 there has been extensive treatment of negative numbers, fractions, and decimals. Now it is possible to study the solution of equations and inequalities more formally and generally, since we can use opposites and reciprocals. The approach here is more sophisticated, based on the standard transformations used to derive equivalent but simpler open sentences.

Word problems are presented again, at a higher level of sophistication. Now we have a more powerful mathematical tool to use in solving problems: translating from the given problem into an equation or inequality.

SOLVING EQUATIONS

5-1 Properties of Equality

Objective *for pages 144–145*

■ To use the addition and multiplication properties of equality.

Teaching Suggestions

The addition and multiplication properties of equality are as important, in terms of skill development, as any topic in the course, so a thorough grounding is necessary.

To illustrate the properties, use some concrete materials. For example, show students two collections of coins: one is a quarter, a dime, and a nickel; the other is 2 dimes and four nickels. Then add a quarter to each grouping. Ask students to state conclusions about the values of the resulting coin groups. They will readily see that adding the same coin (the quarter) to coins having equal values results in equal values.

Next, make one collection of a dime and a nickel and another of three nickels. Then triple the coins in each set by adding to each group two more groups identical to the original coins. Again, ask for conclusions and generalize the result. We have three times two equal amounts, and the final results are also equal.

Similar illustrations can be made using the heights or lengths of building blocks or amounts of water in graduated cylinders. In each case the point to be made is that we start and finish with equal quantities.

You may want to point out that these properties do not exist for the sole purpose of solving equations. Indeed, we can add any number, or multiply any nonzero number, on both sides of an equation. It is in no way mandatory that the properties be used to produce "simpler" equations.

Resource Book: Page 57 (Use After Page 145)

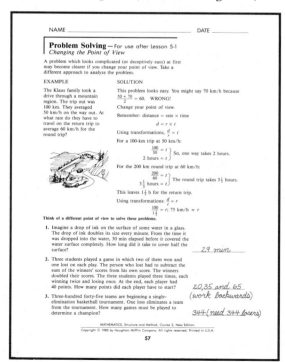

Related Activities

To give the addition property of equality a simple geometric interpretation, have students use graph paper to make rectangles with dimensions 3×10 and 5×6. Add two 2×5 rectangles to each of these, making two 5×10 rectangles. Thus, by adding equal areas to equal areas we get equal areas.

5-2 Equivalent Equations

Objective for pages 146–148

■ To simplify the expressions in an equation to obtain an equivalent equation.

Teaching Suggestions

Students have no difficulty in seeing the sense behind simplifying the expressions in an equation. It seems perfectly natural that this can, and should, be done.

Caution students against making two very common errors. The distributive property is often misapplied in removing parentheses. Students will incorrectly write, for example,

$$3(a - 2) = 3a - 2$$

rather than correctly distributing the 3:

$$3(a - 2) = 3a - 6$$

When combining like terms, students sometimes omit the variable, particularly in subtraction expressions. They may incorrectly write $9x - 5x$ as 4, rather than correctly writing $4x$. A word of warning may steer them away from these errors. It would also help to draw attention to the fact that a fraction bar is, besides a division sign, also a grouping symbol. Thus,

$$\frac{12 + 8}{4} = \frac{20}{4} = 5 \qquad \text{is correct, while}$$

$$\frac{12 + 8}{4} = 3 + 8 = 11 \quad \text{is incorrect.}$$

Related Activities

To reinforce the proper use of the distributive property, have students cut graph paper into rectangles with dimensions such as 5×8, 5×4, and 4×3. These can be assembled into larger rectangles by joining them along sides of the same length. For example, 5×8 and 5×4 pieces can be combined into a 5×12 rectangle. By considering areas, lead students to make statements such as:

$$5 \times 8 + 5 \times 4 = 5(8 + 4)$$
$$= 5 \times 12$$

By starting with the combined 5×12 rectangle and removing one of the smaller pieces, students can even derive statements illustrating the fact that multiplication is distributive over subtraction.

$$5 \times 12 - 5 \times 4 = 5 \times 8$$
$$5(12 - 4) = 5 \times 8$$

5-3 Solving Equations with Addition and Subtraction

Objective for pages 149–151

■ To solve an equation in one variable that involves addition or subtraction.

Teaching Suggestions

You can designate an equation of the form $x = c$ as "the world's easiest equation." Students will see that c itself is the solution of $x = c$. This means that the task of solving an equation really boils down to finding the equivalent "world's easiest equation."

If your students are ready for a small note of rigor, start them off on the right foot by insisting that they state the solution of an equation as a number, rather than as another equation. For example, the solution of $x - 6 = 4$ is, strictly speaking, the number 10, not the equation $x = 10$.

Inverse operations were studied in Chapter 1, and the addition and subtraction properties of equality were presented earlier in this chapter. In this section the two concepts are combined to develop a technique for solving any equation of the form $x + a = b$ or $x - a = b$. In lesson 5-1, we found that any number could be added or subtracted on both sides of an equation. Now we see that, although this is true, the number selected does make a difference. By careful selection, we choose the number so that we are doing inverse operations. The reason, of course, is that this reduces our equation to one of the form $x = c$.

Related Activities

To enhance understanding of the use of inverse operations and the addition and subtraction properties of equality, introduce students to "zero sandwiches." You will need a collection of three different colors of small disks or chips. Suppose we use red chips for x, blue for positive units, and green for negative units. We can now represent the equation $x - 3 = 2$ by forming one group of a red chip and three green chips, and another group of two blue chips.

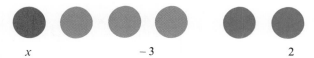

x -3 2

A zero sandwich consists of one blue and one green chip. Every time a zero sandwich can be made, it can be removed from consideration, since its value is zero. Returning to the equation above, we now ask how many chips, of what color, must be placed on the left to get the x chip by itself. To make zero sandwiches we place three blue chips on each side of the equation.

x 5

After eliminating all zero sandwiches on either side, we have chips remaining that represent the equation $x = 5$, and the solution is 5. Have students solve the following equations using the chips.

1. $x + 4 = 2$ -2
2. $x - 2 = -3$ -1
3. $x - 5 = -3$ 2

5-4 Solving Equations with Multiplication and Division

Objective *for pages 152–154*

■ To solve an equation in one variable that involves multiplication or division.

Teaching Suggestions

The parallels between this section and the preceding one will be fairly obvious to students. Multiplication and division have the same inverse relationship that addition and subtraction do. Also, by choosing carefully we apply the multiplication and division properties of equality to produce an equation of the form $x = c$ ("the world's easiest equation") to solve, as we did before by applying the addition and subtraction properties.

Before solving equations, it would probably be helpful to remind students that

$$\frac{ab}{a} = b \quad \text{and} \quad \frac{b}{a} \times a = b \quad (a \neq 0).$$

Practice using these identities to simplify expressions.

Related Activities

To clarify the reason why we must have $c \neq 0$ in order for $a = b$ to be equivalent to $ac = bc$, ask what is wrong with this argument:

$$5 \times (4 - 3 - 1) = (5 \times 4) - (5 \times 3) - (5 \times 1)$$
$$= 20 - 15 - 5 = 0$$
$$6 \times (4 - 3 - 1) = (6 \times 4) - (6 \times 3) - (6 \times 1)$$
$$= 24 - 18 - 6 = 0.$$

Therefore,

$$5 \times (4 - 3 - 1) = 6 \times (4 - 3 - 1),$$

and accordingly, $5 = 6$.

5-5 Using Several Transformations

Objective *for pages 155–158*

■ To use several transformations to solve an equation in one variable.

Teaching Suggestions

Equations that require more than one transformation do not require any new theoretical tools for their solution, but students must use transformations carefully. Remind them to choose the transformation properly, so that they are not adding when they should be multiplying, for example. Also remind them to perform any given operation on both sides, using the same operation. Students sometimes get so indoctrinated by our left-to-right bias that they feel they must always get the variable on the left side. Advise them that this is not necessary; $a = x$ is just as acceptable as $x = a$.

Many students wonder which transformation must be done first in an equation such as $3x - 12 = 6$. It is possible to divide by 3 first and then add. However, the division by 3 must be distributed over all terms, and students often forget to do this. Students tend to do better if they add 12 first. Both methods work, and both are mathematically correct, but for most students the latter approach is safer.

Related Activities

To illustrate the necessity of doing the operations in the proper order when solving equations, ask what operations (ordinary actions), in what order, are needed to solve each of the following problems.
1. A person wearing shoes and socks wants to go barefoot.
2. A package of frozen fish is to be broiled for dinner.
3. A table is set with dishes and a tablecloth. You wish to clear the table completely.

Resource Book: Page 58 (Use After Page 158)

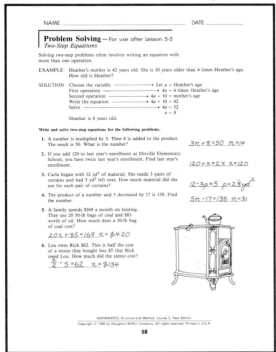

Resource Book: Pages 59–60 (Use After Page 158)

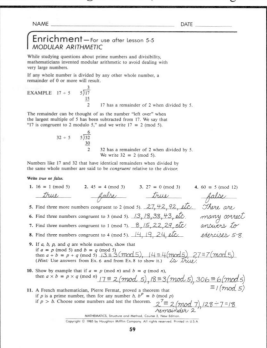

INEQUALITIES, PROBLEM SOLVING

5-6 Equivalent Inequalities

Objective *for pages 159–162*

■ To solve an inequality in one variable that involves addition, subtraction, multiplication, or division.

Teaching Suggestions

Many students are relieved to find that there is no more difference between techniques for solving equations and inequalities than there is. They are prepared to have to learn a whole new set of skills, but find that the only significant difference is the need to reverse inequality signs when multiplying or dividing by a negative number.

Remind students that solving an open sentence means finding all numbers that satisfy the sentence. They may also need to be reminded of the existence of nonintegral numbers. Otherwise, when considering an inequality such as $x > 2\frac{1}{2}$, they may want to say that the solution is $\{3, 4, 5, \ldots\}$, which is not correct. The solution is actually all numbers greater than $2\frac{1}{2}$. Note that the solution of an inequality is typically an infinite set; this is another major difference compared to equations.

Trying to proceed by rote, students may have difficulty with inequalities like $2 > x$. They can become so determined that this is a "greater than" inequality that they give the solution as all numbers greater than 2. Suggest that they rewrite such inequalities, using $x > a$ for $a < x$ and $x < a$ for $a > x$. Most people are more comfortable with inequalities in which the variable is on the left and the constant is on the right.

Related Activities

To emphasize the reversal involved when multiplying by a negative number, have students draw nomographs as follows. To make a "×3" nomograph, draw two number lines, with arrows from numbers on one line to the products by 3 on the other.

Now draw a "×(−2)" nomograph. This time draw arrows from numbers to their products by −2. The difference will be apparent. In a "multiplication by a negative number" nomograph, the reversal is given a visual interpretation.

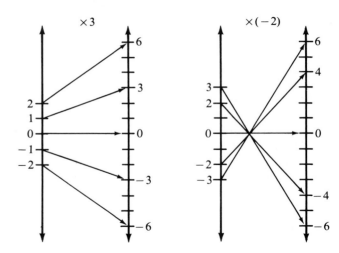

Have students construct nomographs for:

1. ×1   **2.** ×(−1)   **3.** ×$\frac{1}{2}$

4. ×(−3)   **5.** ×0   **6.** ×$\left(-\frac{1}{2}\right)$

5-7 Solving Inequalities by Several Transformations

Objective *for pages 163–166*

■ To use several transformations to solve an inequality in one variable.

Teaching Suggestions

An earlier warning can be repeated here. Just because an inequality contains a "greater than" symbol does not guarantee that the graph is an arrow pointing to the right. For example, the graph of $-3 > x$ is

Students may have great difficulty when an inequality simplifies to one like $-x > 2$. Frequently they proceed as if this says $x > 2$ and graph it incorrectly. Remind them that the procedure we use requires us to have the variable only, alone on one side. Thus $-x > 2$ must be transformed:

$$-x > 2$$
$$-1(-x) < -1(2)$$
$$x < -2$$

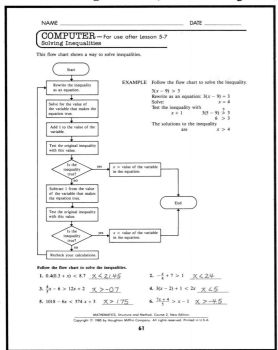

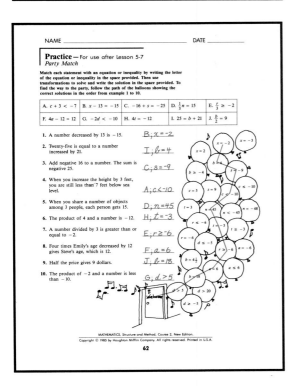

Related Activities

To reverse the usual process, give students the graph, and ask them to give an inequality for that graph.

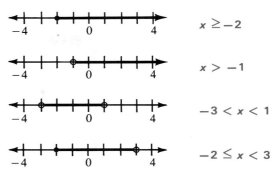

$x \geq -2$

$x > -1$

$-3 < x < 1$

$-2 \leq x < 3$

To review absolute values and strengthen skill in graphing inequalities, have students give an inequality of the form $|x| > a$, $|x| \geq a$, $|x| < a$, or $|x| \leq a$.

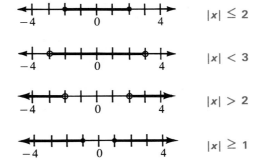

$|x| \leq 2$

$|x| < 3$

$|x| > 2$

$|x| \geq 1$

5-8 Equations into Word Problems

Objective *for pages 167–168*

■ To interpret an equation as a word problem.

Teaching Suggestions

This section should be a welcome change of pace. There are no tedious calculations, rules to learn, or long lists of equations to solve. Rather, students are asked to deal with a much more creative activity, imagining a real situation that could be described by a given equation. Some students may require some encouragement, not being used to this kind of problem in a math class. They may need to be reassured that there is no set answer; any answer that fits is correct. In fact, it should be possible to have as many answers for a single equation as there are people answering. Notice in the Class Exercises that a context has been provided in which to frame a problem. This should help those who initially have trouble in using their imagination. Emphasize to your students that they are not required to solve any problems or equations.

Related Activities

To provide a challenge, ask students to write word problems for more complicated equations and inequalities such as those they studied earlier in this chapter. Problems involving inequalities may contain phrases such as "at least enough" or "not more than." Students may want to write their best problems and the related equations or inequalities on separate pieces of paper and set up a large matching exercise on the bulletin board.

5-9 Word Problems into Equations

Objective *for pages 169–173*

■ To use an equation to solve a word problem.

Teaching Suggestions

This will be a challenging section for many students. Encourage them to build up equations a bit at a time as they read and understand the parts of a problem. Also encourage them to use the plan and to write equations. Unfortunately, students tend to view word problems as arithmetic. Urge them to write and solve equations in the easy problems so they will be prepared for the later problems for which a strictly arithmetic approach is too limiting.

Related Activities

To reinforce the importance of rereading a problem and checking the answer, point out that a mathematical model cannot represent every aspect of a problem. For example, in Examples 2 and 3 the solutions of the equations ($2\frac{1}{3}$ h and 3.3 buses) are not the complete answers to the problems. Ask students to find or write other problems for which this is true.

143g

NAME _____ DATE _____

Quiz 5B— Lessons 5-6 through 5-9

DIRECTIONS: Write the letter of the correct answer in the space provided.

Use transformations to solve the inequality.

	ANSWERS
	1. *b* (8)
	2. *c* (8)
	3. *a* (8)
	4. *c* (8)
	5. *d* (10)
	6. *d* (10)
	7. *c* (12)
	8. *d* (12)
	9. *b* (12)
	10. *b* (12)

1. $3 + t > -8$ [5-6]
   a. $t > -5$ b. $t > -11$ c. $t \geq -5$ d. $t \geq 5$

2. $3t \geq -15$
   a. $t > -5$ b. $t > -11$ c. $t \geq -5$ d. $t \geq 5$

3. $4 > \frac{r}{-2}$
   a. $-8 < r$ b. $26 < r$ c. $-8 > r$ d. $8 > r$

4. $7 - 5p + 3 + 8p - 1 > -9$ [5-7]
   a. $p > 9$ b. $p > 0$ c. $p > -6$ d. $p > 6$

5. $17 + 11p - 2 > 3p + 63$
   a. $p > 9$ b. $p > 0$ c. $p > -6$ d. $p > 6$

6. $-13 + 49 > 6(h - 17)$
   a. $-23 > h$ b. $-24 < h$ c. $-24 > h$ d. $23 > h$

Which equation represents the problem?

7. After counting 139 ballots, the school committee has 87 ballots left to count. How many ballots were there in all? [5-8]
   a. $87 + x = 139$ b. $87x = 139$ c. $x - 87 = 139$ d. $\frac{x}{87} = 139$

8. Janet Mark earns $2.35 per hour. How much will she earn the week that she works 15 hours?
   a. $15 + x = 2.35$ b. $x - 15 = 2.35$ c. $15x = 2.35$ d. $\frac{x}{15} = 2.35$

Use an equation to solve.

9. Barry spent four times as long on his homework as on his trumpet practicing. If he spent 80 min on his homework, how long did he spend practicing the trumpet? [5-9]
   a. 16 min   b. 20 min   c. $\frac{3}{4}$ h   d. $\frac{1}{4}$ h

10. Juan is 2 years older than David. Marni is twice as old as David. If the sum of their ages is 34, how old is Marni?
   a. 8 years old   b. 16 years old   c. 10 years old   d. 21 years old

MATHEMATICS, Structure and Method, Course 2, New Edition.
Copyright © 1985 by Houghton Mifflin Company. All rights reserved. Printed in U.S.A.

63

NAME _____ DATE _____

Review— Chapter 5

Use one of the properties of equality to form a true sentence.

1. If $13 = r + 2$, then $11 = r$
2. If $-2 + p = -16$, then $p = -14$ [5-1]
3. If $-7 = \frac{1}{35}m$, then $-245 = m$
4. If $5t = -7.05$, then $t = -1.41$

Simplify the expressions on each side of the equation to obtain an equivalent equation.

5. $5x + 12 + 4x - 16 = 100 \div 2$ $9x - 4 = 50$ [5-2]
6. $6 = 3(4n + 7 - n - 17)$ $6 = 9n - 30$

Use transformations to solve the equation.

7. $-24 = -3 + w + 11$ $w = -32$
8. $6\frac{2}{3} + r = 5\frac{1}{6}$ $r = -4\frac{1}{2}$ [5-3]
9. $3.8 = 0.02x$ $x = 190$
10. $\frac{1}{5}p = 20$ $p = 100$ [5-4]
11. $7(d + 3) = -18 + 4$ $d = -5$
12. $\frac{1}{3}t + 2 = -13$ $t = -45$ [5-5]
13. $2.5(6 + k) = 3k$ $k = 30$
14. $f + 4 = 3f - 14$ $f = 9$

Use transformations to solve the inequality.

15. $n - 9 \geq 20$ $n \geq 29$
16. $3p < -39$ $p < -13$ [5-6]
17. $28 < -7f$ $-4 > f$
18. $\frac{w}{6} > 6.6$ $w > 39.6$
19. $19 - 3m + 5 + 7m \leq 0$ $m \leq -6$
20. $-15 > -5(s - 8)$ $11 < s$ [5-7]
21. $-2g + 3 > 4g - 15$ $3 > g$
22. $\frac{3}{8}d + 5 < -10$ $d < -40$

Write a problem that each equation can represent.

23. $x + 7 = 40$ *Bob has 7 more tapes than Josh. If Bob has 40 tapes, how many does Josh have? (other answers possible)* [5-8]
24. $8x = 192$ *Tara makes 8 equal deposits into her bank account. If she saves a total of $192, what is the amount of each deposit? (other answers possible)*

Use an equation to solve.

25. Dianne took $1\frac{1}{2}$ times as long as Amy to complete an art project. If Dianne needed 9 h to complete her project, how long did Amy need? *6 h* [5-9]
26. Admission to an Automobile Show is $3.00 per adult and $2.00 per student. A total of $742.00 in admission fees was collected. If 200 adults attended the show, how many students attended? *71 students*

MATHEMATICS, Structure and Method, Course 2, New Edition.
Copyright © 1985 by Houghton Mifflin Company. All rights reserved. Printed in U.S.A.

64

Resource Book: Pages 65-68 (Use After Page 173)

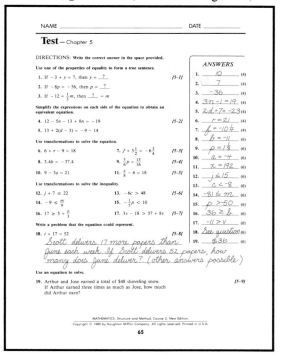

NAME ______________________ DATE ____________

Test — Chapter 5

DIRECTIONS: **Write the correct answer in the space provided.**

Use one of the properties of equality to form a true sentence.

1. If $-3 + y = 7$, then $y =$ __?__ [5-1]
2. If $-8p = -56$, then $p =$ __?__
3. If $-12 = \frac{1}{3}m$, then __?__ $= m$

Simplify the expressions on each side of the equation to obtain an equivalent equation.

4. $12 - 5n - 13 + 8n = -19$ [5-2]
5. $13 + 2(d - 3) = -9 - 14$

Use transformations to solve the equation.

6. $6 + r - 9 = 18$ 7. $f + 3\frac{1}{2} = -6\frac{3}{4}$ [5-3]
8. $3.4b = -37.4$ 9. $\frac{5}{6}p = \frac{15}{16}$ [5-4]
10. $9 - 3a = 21$ 11. $\frac{x}{8} - 6 = 18$ [5-5]

Use transformations to solve the inequality.

12. $j + 7 \le 22$ 13. $-6c > 48$ [5-6]
14. $-9 \le \frac{m}{9}$ 15. $-\frac{1}{5}p < 10$
16. $17 \ge 5 + \frac{b}{3}$ 17. $3v - 18 > 37 + 8v$ [5-7]

Write a problem that the equation could represent.

18. $t + 17 = 52$ [5-8]

Scott delivers 17 more papers than June each week. If Scott delivers 52 papers, how many does June deliver? (other answers possible)

Use an equation to solve.

19. Arthur and Jose earned a total of $48 shoveling snow. If Arthur earned three times as much as Jose, how much did Arthur earn? [5-9]

ANSWERS

1.	10	(4)
2.	7	(4)
3.	-36	(4)
4.	$3n - 1 = 19$	(4)
5.	$2d + 7 = -23$	(4)
6.	$r = 21$	(4)
7.	$f = -10\frac{1}{4}$	(4)
8.	$b = -11$	(6)
9.	$p = 1\frac{1}{8}$	(6)
10.	$a = -4$	(6)
11.	$x = 192$	(6)
12.	$j \le 15$	(6)
13.	$c < -8$	(6)
14.	$-81 \le m$	(6)
15.	$p > -50$	(6)
16.	$36 \ge b$	(6)
17.	$-11 > v$	(6)
18.	See question	(6)
19.	$36	(6)

MATHEMATICS, Structure and Method, Course 2, New Edition.

65

NAME ______________________ DATE ____________

Make-up Test — Chapter 5

DIRECTIONS: **Write the correct answer in the space provided.**

Use one of the properties of equality to form a true sentence.

1. If $8 + d = 6$, then $d =$ __?__ [5-1]
2. If $-6 = \frac{1}{2}b$, then __?__ $= b$
3. If $-4n = -56$, then $n =$ __?__

Simplify the expressions on each side of the equation to obtain an equivalent equation.

4. $-2r - 19 + 7r + 11 = -38$ [5-2]
5. $14 + 3(c - 2) = -9 - 10$

Use transformations to solve the equation.

6. $-6 + d + 11 = -3$ 7. $g + 2\frac{1}{3} = -7\frac{5}{6}$ [5-3]
8. $7.6r - -91.2$ 9. $\frac{3}{8}s = \frac{9}{10}$ [5-4]
10. $6n - 7 = -49$ 11. $13 = 4 - \frac{x}{3}$ [5-5]
12. $12 - 3w = w + 28$ 13. $3(2t - 5) = 57$

Use transformations to solve the inequality.

14. $k - 9 \le 28$ 15. $-4t < 24$ [5-6]
16. $-7 \le \frac{x}{7}$ 17. $-\frac{1}{6}r > 12$
18. $\frac{1}{12}r - 2 > 2$ 19. $-20 < -4(c + 2)$ [5-7]

Write a problem that the equation could represent.

20. $6r = 78$ [5-8]

Peggy's grandfather is six times as old as Peggy. If her grandfather is 78 years old, how old is Peggy? (other answers possible)

Use an equation to solve.

21. Joan and Gayle sold 89 magazines. If Joan sold one more than three times the number Gayle sold, find the number sold by Joan. [5-9]

ANSWERS

1.	-2	(4)
2.	-12	(4)
3.	14	(4)
4.	$5r - 8 = -38$	(4)
5.	$3c + 8 = -19$	(4)
6.	$d = -8$	(4)
7.	$g = -10\frac{1}{6}$	(4)
8.	$r = -12$	(4)
9.	$s = 2\frac{2}{5}$	(4)
10.	$n = -7$	(4)
11.	$x = -27$	(4)
12.	$w = -4$	(4)
13.	$t = 12$	(4)
14.	$k \le 37$	(6)
15.	$t > -6$	(6)
16.	$-49 \le x$	(6)
17.	$r < -72$	(6)
18.	$n > 48$	(6)
19.	$3 > c$	(6)
20.	See question	(6)
21.	67 magazines	(6)

MATHEMATICS, Structure and Method, Course 2, New Edition.

66

NAME ______________________ DATE ____________

CUMULATIVE REVIEW — Chapters 1-5

Exercises

Replace the variable with the given value and tell whether the resulting statement is true or false.

1. $r - 7 \ge 12$; 18 __F__ 2. $2d + 3 = 37$; 17 __T__
3. $3s - 1 < 8$; $2\frac{1}{2}$ __T__ 4. $t + 9 < 4 - t$; -3 __T__
5. $5a + 7 = 2a - 5$; -4 __T__ 6. $\frac{a}{9} - 4 \ge 5$; 1 __F__

Use the symbol < to order the numbers from least to greatest.

7. 5, 3.4, −1.0, −2.8, 1.0 __$-2.8 < -1.0 < 1.0 < 3.4 < 5$__ 8. 3.2, −2.3, 0.32, −1.02 __$-2.3 < -1.02 < 0.32 < 3.2$__
9. 5, 9, −3, 2, −8, −7 __$-8 < -7 < -3 < 2 < 5 < 9$__ 10. −5.1, 3.8, 2.1, −5.19, −2 __$-5.19 < -5.1 < -2 < 2.1 < 3.8$__

Write the fractions as equal fractions having the least common denominator (LCD).

11. $\frac{1}{3}, \frac{2}{9}$ __$\frac{3}{9}, \frac{2}{9}$__ 12. $\frac{5}{6}, \frac{1}{2}$ __$\frac{5}{6}, \frac{3}{6}$__ 13. $\frac{2}{3}, \frac{3}{5}$ __$\frac{10}{15}, \frac{9}{15}$__
14. $\frac{1}{4}, -\frac{2}{7}$ __$\frac{7}{28}, \frac{-8}{28}$__ 15. $-\frac{3}{10}, \frac{4}{15}$ __$\frac{-9}{30}, \frac{8}{30}$__ 16. $-\frac{3}{4}, -\frac{1}{10}$ __$\frac{-15}{20}, \frac{-2}{20}$__

Perform the indicated operation.

17. $17.43 + (-38.29)$ __−20.86__ 18. $-24.2 \div 0.16$ __−151.25__
19. $-3\frac{5}{6} \div 1\frac{2}{3}$ __$-2\frac{3}{10}$__ 20. $-12.864 - 0.907$ __−13.771__

Express as a fraction or mixed number in lowest terms.

21. 0.6 __$\frac{3}{5}$__ 22. 2.25 __$2\frac{1}{4}$__ 23. 18.45 __$18\frac{9}{20}$__ 24. 9.64 __$9\frac{16}{25}$__
25. 0.08 __$\frac{2}{25}$__ 26. 6.002 __$6\frac{1}{500}$__ 27. 0.475 __$\frac{19}{40}$__ 28. 98.05 __$98\frac{1}{20}$__

Round to the place specified.

29. tenths: 67.345 __67.3__ 30. hundreds: 6,249.036 __6,200__
31. thousandths: 3.0749 __3.075__ 32. hundredths: 29.4073 __29.41__

Solve.

33. $v - 29 = 108$ __$v = 137$__ 34. $7n + 11 \ge 88$ __$n \ge 11$__
35. $9p - 6 = -42$ __$p = -4$__ 36. $20d + 2 = 80$ __$d = 8$__
37. $16 - 4x < 24$ __$x > -2$__ 38. $19r + 11 = 27r + 3$ __$r = 1$__
39. $5a + 3(a + 2) = 102$ __$a = 12$__ 40. $3 - 7f > -39$ __$f < 6$__
41. $-6m + 3 = 9m - 27$ __$m = 2$__

MATHEMATICS, Structure and Method, Course 2, New Edition.

67

NAME ______________________ DATE ____________

CUMULATIVE REVIEW — Chapters 1-5 *(continued)*

Problems

Problem Solving Reminders
Here are some problem solving reminders that may help you solve some of the problems on this page.
- Determine which facts are necessary to solve the problem.
- Check your answer by using rounding to find an estimated answer.
- Supply additional information if necessary.

Solve.

1. Bread is on sale for 2 loaves for $1.19. How much will one dozen loaves cost? __$7.14__
2. Jason earned twice as much as Larry did shoveling snow. Together they earned $85.50. How much did Jason earn? __$57.00__
3. An election survey showed that 2.3 million people voted in the state election. Approximately $\frac{1}{4}$ of them were under 25 years old. About how many voters were under 25? __575,000__
4. ABC Sportswear is having a sale where $\frac{1}{3}$ of the original price is deducted from the cost. What is the sale price of a suit that originally sold for $188.70? __$125.80__
5. The Ross family planned to spend $2000 on their vacation. They spent the following amounts:

   Food: $436.75 Admission Fees: $185.50
   Room: $425.00 Souvenirs: $43.60
   Transportation: $785.85

   Did they stay within their budget? __yes ($1,876.70)__
6. Gwen is 3 years older than Sara and Janet is twice as old as Sara. If the sum of their ages is 51, how old is Janet? __24 years old__
7. Martin Downs earns $498.60 per week. Pat O'Connor earns $75 more per week than Martin. If Bob Rebern earns $\frac{7}{8}$ as much as Pat does, how much does Bob earn? __$501.90__
8. The school soccer team won $\frac{3}{4}$ of its games. The school football team won $\frac{5}{8}$ of its games. The two teams played the same number of games and together won a total of 55 games. How many games did the football team win? __25 games__
9. William's recipe for carrot pudding calls for $3\frac{1}{4}$ cups of flour and $2\frac{1}{2}$ cups of sugar. He plans to make $\frac{2}{3}$ of the amount of the recipe. How much sugar should he use? __$1\frac{2}{3}$ cups__

MATHEMATICS, Structure and Method, Course 2, New Edition.

68

Teaching Suggestions
p. 143a

Related Activities p. 143b

Reading Mathematics

Students will learn the meaning of the following mathematical terms in this lesson:
Addition Property of Equality,
Multiplication Property of
Equality.

Chalkboard Examples

Complete the statement so that it is true.

1. If $5 + 9 = 14$, then $(5 + 9) + 3 = 14 + $? . **3**

2. If $6 + 7 = 13$, then $2(6 + 7) = $? (13). **2**

3. If $a + 6 = 10$, then $a + 6 = $? $+ 6$. **4**

4. If $5c = 35$, then $5c = 5($? $)$. **7**

5. If $x + 4 = 11$, then $x + 4 = 7 + 4$ and $x = $? . **7**

6. If $7m = 42$, then $7m = 7(6)$ and $m = $? . **6**

5-1 Properties of Equality

Consider the following examples.

$$8 + 7 = 15 \qquad (8 + 7) + 10 = 15 + 10$$

These examples illustrate that we may add the same number to two equal expressions and the sums that result will be equal.

In general,

Addition Property of Equality

For all numbers a, b, and c:

If $a = b$, then $a + c = b + c$.

If $a + c = b + c$, then $a = b$.

We may also multiply two equal expressions by the same number and the resulting products will be equal.

$$14 - 6 = 8 \qquad (14 - 6)3 = (8)3$$

Multiplication Property of Equality

For all numbers a, b, and c:

If $a = b$, then $ac = bc$.

If $ac = bc$ and $c \neq 0$, then $a = b$.

Notice that if $c = 0$, then $a \times 0 = b \times 0$, but we can still have $a \neq b$. For example, $8 \times 0 = 3 \times 0$ but $8 \neq 3$.

EXAMPLE Use the properties of equality to form a true sentence.
  a. If $a + 2 = 12$, then $a = $? .   **b.** If $3r = 15$, then $r = $? .

Solution   **a.** $a + 2 = 12$ and $12 = 10 + 2$
        $a + 2 = 10 + 2$
    So by the addition property of equality, $a = 10$.

    b. $3r = 15$ and $15 = 3 \times 5$
        $3r = 3 \times 5$
    By the multiplication property of equality, $r = 5$.

144   *Chapter 5*

Class Exercises

Use one of the properties of equality to form a true sentence.

1. If $c + 8 = 15$, then $c = \underline{\ ?\ }$. 7

2. If $20 = b + 6$, then $\underline{\ ?\ } = b$. 14

3. If $m + (-11) = -23$, then $m = \underline{\ ?\ }$. -12

4. If $-30 = b + 10$, then $\underline{\ ?\ } = b$. -40

5. If $4p = 28$, then $p = \underline{\ ?\ }$. 7

6. If $15 = -5f$, then $\underline{\ ?\ } = f$. -3

Written Exercises

Name the property of equality illustrated.

A

1. If $z + 7 = 11$, then $z = 4$. Add.

2. If $m = 9$, then $4m = 36$. Mult.

3. If $8x = 56$, then $x = 7$. Mult.

4. If $r + 23 = 51$, then $r = 28$. Add.

5. If $y = 13$, then $y + 8 = 21$. Add.

6. If $72 = 12q$, then $6 = q$. Mult.

7. If $90 = 5a$, then $18 = a$. Mult.

8. If $46 = 4 + d$, then $42 = d$. Add.

Use one of the properties of equality to form a true sentence.

9. If $x + 4 = 15$, then $x = \underline{\ ?\ }$. 11

10. If $d + 18 = 14$, then $d = \underline{\ ?\ }$. -4

11. If $11 = b + 16$, then $\underline{\ ?\ } = b$. -5

12. If $12 = g + 7$, then $\underline{\ ?\ } = g$. 5

13. If $13 = -8 + n$, then $\underline{\ ?\ } = n$. 21

14. If $-14 + j = 6$, then $j = \underline{\ ?\ }$. 20

15. If $4x = 12$, then $x = \underline{\ ?\ }$. 3

16. If $5g = 35$, then $g = \underline{\ ?\ }$. 7

17. If $-6m = 18$, then $m = \underline{\ ?\ }$. -3

18. If $21 = -3n$, then $\underline{\ ?\ } = n$. -7

19. If $-56 = -8r$, then $\underline{\ ?\ } = r$. 7

20. If $7a = 63$, then $a = \underline{\ ?\ }$. 9

B

21. If $3x = 3.6$, then $x = \underline{\ ?\ }$. 1.2

22. If $4.5 = 4y$, then $\underline{\ ?\ } = y$. 1.125

23. If $0.3z = -2.7$, then $z = \underline{\ ?\ }$. -9

24. If $-2r = 42.6$, then $r = \underline{\ ?\ }$. -21.3

25. If $4 = \frac{1}{3}p$, then $\underline{\ ?\ } = p$. 12

26. If $-4 = \frac{1}{6}m$, then $\underline{\ ?\ } = m$. -24

C

27. If $5n = -2$, then $10n + 4 = \underline{\ ?\ }$. 0

28. If $3s = 5$, then $9s + 6 = \underline{\ ?\ }$. 21

Review Exercises

Throughout this chapter, answers in the form of decimals, fractions, or mixed numbers are acceptable.

Simplify.

1. $46 + 19 \times 3$ 103

2. $57 \div 12 + 5$ 9.75

3. $33 + 18 \div 9$ 35

4. $2(17 + 5) \div 3$
$\frac{44}{3}$, or $14\frac{2}{3}$

5. $(54 + 27) \div (6 \times 9)$ 1.5

6. $[63.7 \div (13.6 - 4.5)]4$ 28

Equations and Inequalities **145**

Additional A Exercises

Use a property of equality to form a true statement.

1. If $n + 9 = 12$, then $n = \underline{\ ?\ }$. 3

2. If $y + 6 = 18$, then $y = \underline{\ ?\ }$. 12

3. If $3 + t = 12$, then $t = \underline{\ ?\ }$. 9

4. If $-8 + c = 11$, then $c = \underline{\ ?\ }$. 19

5. If $4x = 28$, then $x = \underline{\ ?\ }$. 7

6. If $-3r = 15$, then $r = \underline{\ ?\ }$. -5

7. If $-48 = -3h$, then $\underline{\ ?\ } = h$. 16

Suggested Assignments

Minimum
145/1–20
145/Rev. 1–6

Average
145/1–26
145/Rev. 1–6

Maximum
145/1–28

Supplementary Materials

Practice Masters, p. 21

5-2 Equivalent Equations

On page 9, you learned that a *solution* of an equation involving a variable is a value of the variable that makes the equation true. Because the equation

$$x + 5 = 18$$

is true when $x = 13$, 13 is a solution of the equation. An equation may have no solution, one solution, or more than one solution.

The set of numbers that a variable may represent is called the *replacement set.* When the replacement set is small, we may substitute the values for the variable to solve the equation. When the replacement set is larger, for example the rational numbers, substitution may not be practical. In such cases, we use the properties that we have learned to change, or **transform,** the equation into a simpler equation that has the same solution. Two equations that have the same solution are called **equivalent equations.**

One transformation that we may use to obtain an equivalent equation is the following.

> Simplify numerical expressions and variable expressions.

The example that follows shows how to use this transformation to obtain equivalent equations. You will learn how to solve equations in the lessons that follow.

EXAMPLE   Simplify the expressions on both sides of the equation to obtain an equivalent equation.

    a. $y - 8 + 3 = 24 \div 6$ **b.** $38 = 2n + 6 + 3n$ **c.** $2(a + 3) = 18$

Solution   **a.** Perform the operations on each side of the equation to simplify the numerical expressions.

$$y - 8 + 3 = 24 \div 6$$
$$y - 5 = 4$$

    b. Combine like terms to simplify the variable expressions.

$$38 = 2n + 6 + 3n$$
$$38 = 2n + 3n + 6$$
$$38 = 5n + 6$$

    c. Use the distributive property to simplify the left side.

$$2(a + 3) = 18$$
$$2a + 2(3) = 18$$
$$2a + 6 = 18$$

Throughout the rest of the chapter, if no replacement set is given for an equation, assume that the solution can be any number.

Reading Mathematics: *Study Skills*
When you find a reference in the text to material that you studied earlier, reread the material in the earlier section to help you understand the new lesson. For example, page 146 includes a reference to the definition of *solution* that you learned earlier. Turn back to page 9 to review the definition.

Class Exercises

Simplify the expressions on both sides of the equation to obtain an equivalent equation.

1. $m - 9 + 5 = 32 \div 8$ $\quad m - 4 = 4$

2. $4 \times 12 = 3 + h - 10$ $\quad 48 = h - 7$

3. $13 + 8 + k = 11 \times 5$ $\quad 21 + k = 55$

4. $45 \div 9 = t - 7 - 8$ $\quad 5 = t - 15$

5. $42 = 3n + 2 + 5n$ $\quad 42 = 8n + 2$

6. $8v - 10 + 2v = 30$ $\quad 10v - 10 = 30$

7. $7q + 15 - 2q = 25$ $\quad 5q + 15 = 25$

8. $35 = y - 7 + 5y$ $\quad 35 = 6y - 7$

9. $3(x + 2) = 18$ $\quad 3x + 6 = 18$

10. $20 = 5(a - 3)$ $\quad 20 = 5a - 15$

Written Exercises

15. $10x + 7 = -13$ $\qquad$ **8.** $16 = t + 9$

Simplify the expressions on both sides of the equation to obtain an equivalent equation.

A

1. $b + 10 - 3 = 44 \div 2$ $\quad b + 7 = 22$

2. $5 \times 23 = 8 + k + 7$ $\quad 115 = k + 15$

3. $24 \times 3 = 8 + 12 + u$ $\quad 72 = 20 + u$

4. $c - 11 + 4 = 54 \div 9$ $\quad c - 7 = 6$

5. $26 \div 13 = -7 - 5 + v$ $\quad 2 = -12 + v$

6. $8 \times 12 = e + 14 - 2$ $\quad 96 = e + 12$

7. $4 + 9 + f - 3 = 24 \div 2 \times 3$ $\quad 10 + f = 36$

8. $6 \times 8 \div 3 = t + 12 - 9 + 6$

9. $33 = 4n - 7 + 6n$ $\quad 33 = 10n - 7$

10. $12a + 8 - 3a = 35$ $\quad 9a + 8 = 35$

11. $13q - 2q - 2 = 20$ $\quad 11q - 2 = 20$

12. $14 = 7d - 2 + d$ $\quad 14 = 8d - 2$

13. $15 = 3z + 5 + 2z$ $\quad 15 = 5z + 5$

14. $-8v + 2v + 3 = 21$ $\quad -6v + 3 = 21$

15. $4x + 8x - 2x + 7 = -13$

16. $18 = 2f - 5f + 9 + 6f$ $\quad 18 = 3f + 9$

17. $4(j + 2) = 36$ $\quad 4j + 8 = 36$

18. $42 = (g + 3)7$ $\quad 42 = 7g + 21$

19. $20 = (e - 5)2$ $\quad 20 = 2e - 10$

20. $-8(m - 1) = 24$ $\quad -8m + 8 = 24$

Equations and Inequalities **147**

Additional A Exercises

Simplify the expression to obtain an equivalent equation.

1. $a - 12 + 20 = 6$
  $a + 8 = 6$

2. $39 \div 3 = 6 + t + 7$
  $13 = t + 13$

3. $16 = 3n - 8 + 4n$
  $16 = 7n - 8$

4. $5h + 4 - 3h = 2 \times 5$
  $2h + 4 = 10$

5. $-2(v - 3) = 9$
  $-2v + 6 = 9$

6. $11 - 5 = 3x + 4(3 - 2x)$
  $6 = -5x + 12$

Suggested Assignments

Minimum
  147/1–20
  148/21–30
  148/Rev. 1–9

Average
  147/1–19 odd
  148/21–25 odd; 27–38
  148/Rev. 1–9 odd
  148/Challenge

Maximum
  147/1–19 odd
  148/21–25 odd; 27–44
  148/Challenge

Supplementary Materials

Practice Masters, p. 21

Simplify the expressions on both sides of the equation to obtain an equivalent equation.

21. $-6(3 + w) = 48$ $-18 - 6w = 48$ **22.** $27 = (5 - u)3$ $27 = 15 - 3u$

23. $14 = 2(13 + b - 5)$ $14 = 16 + 2b$ **24.** $(6 + 4 + p)3 = 21$ $30 + 3p = 21$

25. $(2n + 6 + n)5 = 45$ $15n + 30 = 45$ **26.** $12 = 4(7 + 8n - 3n)$ $12 = 28 + 20n$

B   **27.** $0.4 \times 8 = -2.2 + 17.8 + c$ $3.2 = 15.6 + c$ **28.** $3 \times 10.1 = 17.8 + h - 5.6$ $30.3 = 12.2 + h$

29. $36 \div \frac{3}{2} = \frac{4}{3} + k + \frac{2}{3}$ $24 = k + 2$ **30.** $\frac{1}{2}u + \frac{3}{7} - \frac{4}{7} = 9 \times \frac{1}{3}$ $\frac{1}{2}u - \frac{1}{7} = 3$

31. $0.6g + 4.3 + 19.4g = 24.3$ $20g + 4.3 = 24.3$ **32.** $19.8 = 17.5y - 3.5y + 8.2$ $19.8 = 14y + 8.2$

33. $\frac{-8}{7} = \frac{6}{7} + \frac{5}{4}v - \frac{9}{4}v$ $-\frac{8}{7} = \frac{6}{7} - v$ **34.** $\frac{4}{5}m + \frac{1}{2} + \frac{11}{5}m = \frac{3}{2}$ $3m + \frac{1}{2} = \frac{3}{2}$

35. $6.6 = (11 - 10x)0.3$ $6.6 = 3.3 - 3x$ **36.** $28 = (10v - 20)0.2$ $28 = 2v - 4$

37. $\frac{1}{2}(4h - 10) = 17$ $2h - 5 = 17$ **38.** $15 = (6y + 9)\frac{1}{3}$ $15 = 2y + 3$

C   **39.** $8m + 5(-3 - 6m) = \frac{27 - 9}{3}$ $-22m - 15 = 6$ **40.** $6q(3.5 + 2.7) - 12q = (3.5 - 2.7)$ $25.2q = 0.8$

41. $\frac{1}{2}(36.8n + 13.2n + 12.6) = 52.6 \div 2$ $25n + 6.3 = 26.3$ **42.** $81 \times \frac{1}{3} = \left(\frac{-9}{4} + 7e - 8e\right)\frac{4}{3}$ $27 = -3 - \frac{4}{3}e$

43. $\left(8d + \frac{3}{4}\right) \div 6 + \frac{1}{4} + 2d = 99 \div 3$ $\frac{10}{3}d + \frac{3}{8} = 33$

44. $\frac{2}{5} \times 140 = \left[\left(\frac{5}{8}w - 32\right) \div 4\right] + \frac{3}{8}w - 6$ $56 = \frac{17}{32}w - 14$

Review Exercises

What value of the variable makes the statement true?

1. $-x + 9 = 15$ -6 **2.** $-7 + x = 8$ 15 **3.** $x - (-8) = -9$ -17

4. $6 - (-x) = 15$ 9 **5.** $x + (-3) = -11$ -8 **6.** $6 + x = -13$ -19

7. $-4 - x = -12$ 8 **8.** $x - 5 = -15$ -10 **9.** $8 + (-x) = -12$ 20

■■■■   **Challenge**

A snail is climbing up the side of a slippery well that is 2.45 m deep. Each hour the snail climbs 45 cm, but falls back 5 cm. How long will it take the snail to climb to the top of the well?   6.125 h

5-3 Solving Equations with Addition and Subtraction

The usual way to solve an equation is to transform it into the form

$$x = c \qquad \text{or} \qquad c = x,$$

where x is the variable alone on one side, and c is a number. Then the solution is simply c.

We know that addition and subtraction are inverse operations. In the example below, the addition of 9 *undoes* the subtraction of 9.

$$17 - 9 = 8 \qquad\qquad 8 + 9 = 17$$

We can use this idea and the addition property of equality to transform an equation that involves subtraction into an equivalent equation with the variable alone on one side. If

$$n - 8 = 24$$

then

$$n - 8 + 8 = 24 + 8.$$

When we simplify the numerical expressions on both sides of the equation, we obtain

$$n = 32.$$

Because subtraction of a number is the same as adding the opposite of the number, we may use similar transformations for an equation involving addition, as in the following example.

$$n + 6 = 32$$
$$n + 6 + (-6) = 32 + (-6)$$
$$n + 6 - 6 = 32 - 6$$
$$n = 26$$

In general, we may use the following transformation to solve equations involving addition or subtraction.

> *Transformation by addition or subtraction:* Add the same number to, or subtract the same number from, both sides of an equation.

When you have solved an equation, it is a good idea to check your solution to be sure that you have not made any errors in transforming the equation. To check, simply substitute your answer in the original equation.

Equations and Inequalities **149**

Teaching Suggestions p. 143b

Related Activities p. 143c

Reading Mathematics

The word *inverse* in mathematics is used in a number of different ways. We have seen it used to designate the additive inverse (opposite) or multiplicative inverse (reciprocal) of a number. Here we use it to refer to an operation, namely the one that "undoes" another operation. Students who continue to higher math will see the same word used to refer to a particular function relationship.

Complete the equivalent equation.

1. $c + 8 = 22$
$c + 8 - 8 = 22 \underline{\quad ? \quad}$ **−8**

2. $t - 9 = 11$
$t - 9 + 9 = 11 \underline{\quad ? \quad}$ **+9**

3. $3 + x = 36$
$3 + x \underline{\quad ? \quad} = 36 - 3$ **−3**

4. $12 = h - 11$
$12 \underline{\quad ? \quad} = h - 11 + 11$
+11

5. $3 + m - 8 = 1$
$m - 5 = 1$
$m - 5 + 5 = 1 \underline{\quad ? \quad}$ **+5**

6. $3(c + 8) - 2c = 10$
$3c + 24 - 2c = 10$
$c + 24 = 10$
$c + 24 \underline{\quad ? \quad} = 10 - 24$
−24

Are the two equations equivalent?

7. $y - 9 = 16$
$y = 7$ **No**

8. $2r + 8 - r = 10$
$r = 2$ **Yes**

Operations are performed on both sides unless otherwise specified. Accept equivalent answers.

1. Subtracted 18

2. Added 9

3. Added 10

4. Subtracted 2

5. Simplified the left side; subtracted 5

6. Simplified the right side; added 3

150

EXAMPLE 1   Solve $y - 14.5 = 35$.

Solution   Add 14.5 to both sides of the equation to obtain y alone on the left side.

$$y - 14.5 = 35$$
$$y - 14.5 + 14.5 = 35 + 14.5$$
$$y = 49.5$$

The solution is 49.5.

Check: $y - 14.5 = 35$
$49.5 - 14.5 \stackrel{?}{=} 35$
$35 = 35 \ \checkmark$

We may need to use more than one transformation to solve some equations involving addition or subtraction.

EXAMPLE 2   Solve $18 = -4 + x + 6$.

Solution   Simplify the right side of the equation.
$$18 = -4 + x + 6$$
$$18 = x + 2$$

Subtract 2 from both sides of the equation.
$$18 - 2 = x + 2 - 2$$
$$16 = x$$

The solution is 16.

Check: $18 = -4 + x + 6$
$18 \stackrel{?}{=} -4 + 16 + 6$
$18 = 18 \ \checkmark$

When a solution to an equation involves several steps, be sure that you can identify which transformation you are using in each step.

Class Exercises

Identify the transformation used in each step.

1. $y + 18 = 7$
$y + 18 - 18 = 7 - 18$

2. $m - 9 = 13$
$m - 9 + 9 = 13 + 9$

3. $5 = w - 10$
$5 + 10 = w - 10 + 10$

4. $12 = k + 2$
$12 - 2 = k + 2 - 2$

5. $-3 + d + 8 = 14$
$d + 5 = 14$
$d + 5 - 5 = 14 - 5$

6. $16 = -9 + h + 6$
$16 = h - 3$
$16 + 3 = h - 3 + 3$

150   *Chapter 5*

Complete in order to solve and identify the transformation used.

7. $21 = r - 19$
$21 \underline{\ ?\ } 19 = r - 19 \underline{\ ?\ } 19 \ +, +$

8. $u + 15 = 27$
$u + 15 \underline{\ ?\ } 15 = 27 \underline{\ ?\ } 15 \ -, -$

Written Exercises

**Use transformations to solve the equation. Write down all the steps.
Check your solution.**

A

1. $f + 8 = 23$ **15**
2. $p + 4 = 13$ **9**
3. $x + 10 = -16$ **−26**

4. $n - 7 = -12$ **−5**
5. $w - 5 = 18$ **23**
6. $a - 11 = 14$ **25**

7. $-15 = v + 9$ **−24**
8. $-26 = d + 8$ **−34**
9. $17 = e + 10$ **7**

10. $22 = g - 6$ **28**
11. $-19 = r - 3$ **−16**
12. $-28 = q - 11$ **−17**

13. $9 + y + 6 = 14$ **−1**
14. $-5 + 8 + l = 26$ **23**
15. $13 + u - 7 = -32$ **−38**

16. $10 - 6 + k = -17$ **−21**
17. $-5 + m - 12 = 23$ **40**
18. $14 - 10 + n = 21$ **17**

19. $-18 = 8 + w + 12$ **−38**
20. $-34 = 9 + h - 4$ **−39**
21. $24 = a + 17 - 6$ **13**

22. $42 = -7 + b + 3$ **46**
23. $-25 = j + 5 - 8$ **−22**
24. $-18 = -10 + w - 9$ **1**

B

25. $j + 4\frac{3}{8} = 8$ **$3\frac{5}{8}$**
26. $-5 = t + 6\frac{1}{3}$ **$-11\frac{1}{3}$**
27. $-7\frac{1}{4} + m = 2$ **$9\frac{1}{4}$**

28. $7 = k - 4.3$ **11.3**
29. $10 = 3.6 + u$ **6.4**
30. $f - 8.5 = -2$ **6.5**

31. $3 = -8\frac{2}{7} + d + 1\frac{1}{7}$ **$10\frac{1}{7}$**
32. $5\frac{1}{3} + g - 2\frac{1}{6} = -9$ **$-12\frac{1}{6}$**
33. $6 = 3\frac{4}{9} + y + 8\frac{5}{9}$ **−6**

34. $8.4 + h + 1.6 = 11$ **1**
35. $2.1 + n - 8.3 = 10$ **16.2**
36. $4 = 6.7 + 3.5 + v$ **−6.2**

EXAMPLE $|q| + 8 = 14$

Solution $|q| + 8 - 8 = 14 - 8$, so $|q| = 6$.

By the definition of absolute value, q is 6 or q is -6.

C

37. $|x| + 5 = 7$ **−2 or 2**
38. $5 = |g| - 2$ **−7 or 7**
39. $-3 + |w| = 8$ **−11 or 11**
40. $8 + |d| = 9$ **−1 or 1**

Review Exercises

Evaluate the expression when $a = \frac{1}{2}$ and $b = \frac{2}{3}$.

1. ab **$\frac{1}{3}$**
2. $6ab$ **2**
3. $\frac{3}{8}ab$ **$\frac{1}{8}$**
4. $a \div 6$ **$\frac{1}{12}$**
5. $ab \div 4$ **$\frac{1}{12}$**
6. $a \div \frac{3}{5}$ **$\frac{5}{6}$**

Equations and Inequalities   **151**

Additional A Exercises

Use transformations to solve
the equation.

1. $b + 11 = 18$ **7**
2. $c - 16 = 41$ **57**
3. $6 = 2 + w - 9$ **13**
4. $-19 + t - 4 = -10$ **13**
5. $-11 = -5 + w - 6$ **0**
6. $a - 6 = -9 - 7$ **−10**

Suggested Assignments

Minimum
151/1–30
151/Rev. 1–6
Average
151/2–24 even; 25–36
151/Rev. 1–6
Maximum
151/2–24 even; 25–40

Supplementary Materials

Practice Masters, p. 22

Reading Mathematics

Many mathematical words are formed by using prefixes and suffixes. Clear understanding of words that use the prefix *non-* requires some logic. Generally, *non-* means "not." Thus *nonzero number* means any number except zero. *Nonpositive* means zero or negative; *nonnegative* means zero or positive. Observe that *nonpositive* is not the same as *negative*, nor is *nonnegative* the same as *positive*.

Chalkboard Examples

State the transformation you would use to solve the equation.

1. $6x = -18$ **Divide by 6**

2. $-\frac{3}{8}n = 12$

Divide by $-\frac{3}{8}$

3. $\frac{a}{7} = -6$ **Multiply by 7**

Are the equations equivalent?

4. $-3x = 48$
$\quad x = 16$ **No**

5. $\frac{c}{4} = -20$
$\quad c = -5$ **No**

6. $\frac{2}{3}y = 18$
$\quad y = 12$ **No**

5-4 Solving Equations with Multiplication and Division

We can use the multiplication property of equality and the fact that multiplication and division are inverse operations to transform an equation that involves division into an equivalent equation with the variable on one side. For example, if

$$x \div 8 = 12$$

we can multiply both sides by 8 to obtain x alone on the left side.

$$x \div 8 \times 8 = 12 \times 8$$
$$x = 96$$

We can use similar transformations to solve an equation involving multiplication.

$$13y = 195$$
$$13y \times \frac{1}{13} = 195 \times \frac{1}{13}$$

Because the result of multiplying a number by its reciprocal is 1, we obtain the following.

$$y = \frac{195}{13}$$
$$y = 15$$

Because multiplying by $\frac{1}{13}$ is the same as dividing by 13, we could have written the first step above as $\frac{13y}{13} = \frac{195}{13}$.

In general, we can use the following transformation to solve equations involving multiplication or division.

> *Transformation by multiplication or division:* Multiply or divide both sides of an equation by the same nonzero number.

EXAMPLE 1 Solve $-15n = 75$.

Solution Divide both sides of the equation by -15.
$$-15n = 75$$
$$\frac{-15n}{-15} = \frac{75}{-15}$$
$$n = -5$$

The solution is -5.

152 *Chapter 5*

EXAMPLE 2 Solve $22 = \frac{r}{3.6}$.

Solution Multiply both sides of the equation by 3.6.

$$22 = \frac{r}{3.6}$$
$$22 \times 3.6 = \frac{r}{3.6} \times 3.6$$
$$79.2 = r$$

The solution is 79.2.

When the variable expression in an equation involves a fraction, as in the equation $\frac{1}{5}n = 14$, we can divide both sides of the equation by the fraction. Because dividing by a fraction is the same as multiplying by its reciprocal, we can transform the equation by multiplying both sides of the equation by the reciprocal. To solve $\frac{1}{5}n = 14$, we multiply both sides of the equation by 5, the reciprocal of $\frac{1}{5}$. In general, we can solve equations involving fractions in the following way.

If an equation has the following form (where a, b, and c are numbers, $a \neq 0$, $b \neq 0$, and x is a variable),

$$\frac{a}{b}x = c,$$

multiply both sides by the reciprocal of $\frac{a}{b}$, namely $\frac{b}{a}$.

EXAMPLE 3 Solve $18 = -\frac{4}{9}m$.

Solution Multiply both sides of the equation by $-\frac{9}{4}$, the reciprocal of $-\frac{4}{9}$.

$$18 = -\frac{4}{9}m$$
$$-\frac{9}{4} \times 18 = -\frac{9}{4} \times \left(-\frac{4}{9}m\right)$$
$$-\frac{9}{4} \times \overset{9}{\underset{2}{18}} = m$$
$$m = -\frac{81}{2}, \text{ or } -40\frac{1}{2}$$

The solution is $-\frac{81}{2}$, or $-40\frac{1}{2}$.

As shown in Example 3, we may exchange the sides of an equation and still have an equivalent equation.

Equations and Inequalities **153**

154

Class Exercises

a. Identify the transformation you would use to solve the equation.
b. Solve the equation.

1. $5x = 35$ 7
2. $\frac{x}{8} = 42$ 336
3. $56 = 7x$ 8
4. $108 = \frac{x}{12}$ 1296

5. $84 = -3x$ −28
6. $\frac{x}{9} = -8$ −72
7. $\frac{x}{-6} = 30$ −180
8. $\frac{x}{1.5} = 10$ 15

9. $2.4x = 12$ 5
10. $\frac{1}{5}x = 45$ 225
11. $\frac{5}{7}x = 15$ 21
12. $-\frac{3}{4}x = 9$ −12

Written Exercises
14. $\frac{85}{2}$, or $42\frac{1}{2}$ **16.** −55.8, or $-55\frac{4}{5}$ **20.** −2160

Use transformations to solve the equation. Write down all the steps.
Check your solution.

A
1. $6x = 36$ 6
2. $49 = -7z$ −7
3. $-114 = 3y$ −38
4. $-9a = -153$ 17

5. $-\frac{5}{7}n = 35$ −49
6. $\frac{1}{2}r = 18$ 36
7. $-27 = -\frac{3}{11}b$ 99
8. $\frac{2}{3}q = -46$ −69

9. $16 = \frac{w}{8}$ 128
10. $-7 = \frac{r}{13}$ −91
11. $\frac{a}{-24} = 22$ −528
12. $\frac{n}{-7} = -12$ 84

13. $-12g = 204$ −17
14. $\frac{2}{5}d = 17$
15. $-\frac{1}{9}a = 459$ −4131
16. $837 = -15p$

17. $\frac{m}{18} = 54$ 972
18. $62 = \frac{b}{31}$ 1922
19. $8 = \frac{c}{-612}$ −4896
20. $\frac{t}{240} = -9$

21. $0.5a = 42$ 84
22. $81 = 2.7b$ 30
23. $5 = \frac{m}{31.7}$ 158.5
24. $\frac{b}{0.6} = 18$ 10.8

25. $\frac{t}{0.8} = 19$ 15.2
26. $12 = \frac{a}{2.53}$ 30.36
27. $3604 = -9.01x$ −400
28. $-7.3d = -146$ 20

B
29. $\frac{2}{7}b = \frac{5}{8}$ $\frac{35}{16}$, or $2\frac{3}{16}$
30. $\frac{1}{5}x = -\frac{9}{10}$ $-\frac{9}{2}$, or $-4\frac{1}{2}$
31. $-\frac{1}{8} = \frac{3}{4}q$ $-\frac{1}{6}$
32. $\frac{5}{9} = -\frac{2}{3}n$ $-\frac{5}{6}$

33. $2.8 = 0.01x$ 280
34. $7.9r = -19.75$ −2.5
35. $-3.72y = 5.208$ −1.4
36. $5.01m = 85.671$ 17.1

C
37. $-\frac{3}{8}a = 46.5$ −124
38. $\frac{x}{3.2} = -\frac{1}{4}$ −0.8
39. $\frac{7}{12} = \frac{d}{5.4}$ 3.15
40. $\frac{5}{9}n = -1.004$ −1.8072

Review Exercises
1. 6, 5, 4, 3, 2, 1, 0   **2.** 19, 20, 21, and so on
3. 22, 23, 24, and so on   **4.** 11, 12, 13, and so on

Find the solutions of the inequality. The replacement set for x is the set
of whole numbers.

1. $x < 7$
2. $x \geq 19$
3. $21 < x$
4. $x > 10$

5. $9 \geq x$ 9, 8, 7, 6, 5, 4, 3, 2, 1, 0
6. $x \leq 5$ 5, 4, 3, 2, 1, 0
7. $4 \leq x \leq 11$ 4, 5, 6, . . . , 11
8. $6 > x > 1$ 2, 3, 4, 5

154   *Chapter 5*

5-5 Using Several Transformations

When we simplify the numerical and variable expressions in an equation, we may obtain an equation in one of the following forms, where a, b, and c are numbers and x is a variable.

$$ax + b = c \qquad ax - b = c \qquad b - ax = c$$

For equations such as these, we must use more than one operation to transform the equation into the form $x = c$.

EXAMPLE 1   Solve $9 - 5n = 36 - 12$.

Solution   Simplify the numerical expression on the right side of the equation.

$$9 - 5n = 36 - 12$$
$$9 - 5n = 24$$

Subtract 9 from both sides of the equation.

$$9 - 5n - 9 = 24 - 9$$
$$-5n = 15$$

Divide both sides of the equation by -5.

$$\frac{-5n}{-5} = \frac{15}{-5}$$
$$n = -3$$

The solution is -3.

The transformations that we used in Example 1 suggest the following steps for solving equations in which all the variables are on the same side.

1. Simplify each side of the equation.

2. If there are still indicated additions or subtractions, use the inverse operations to undo them.

3. If there are indicated multiplications or divisions involving the variable, use the inverse operations to undo them.

In steps 2 and 3, always remember to *perform the same operation on both sides of the equation.*

Equations and Inequalities   **155**

Teaching Suggestions
p. 143c

Related Activities p. 143d

Chalkboard Examples

An equation is given. What transformation will produce each of the following equations?

1. $3x + 1 = 25$
$3x = 24$ **Subtract 1**
$x = 8$ **Divide by 3**

2. $-9 + 4a = 12$
$4a = 21$ **Subtract -9**
$a = 5.25$ **Divide by 4**

3. $11 + \frac{m}{3} = 5$
$\frac{m}{3} = -6$ **Subtract 11**
$m = -18$ **Multiply by 3**

4. $1.8 = 16 - x$
$x + 1.8 = 16$ **Add x**
$x = 14.2$
  Subtract 1.8

Additional A Exercises

Use transformations to solve the equation.

1. $-3w - 5 = 4$ **−3**

2. $-22 = -8 - 4c + 2$ **4**

3. $-20 = \frac{a}{6} - 8$ **−72**

4. $-3(4 - 2x) = 24$ **6**

5. $4 - 8t = 34 + 2t$ **−3**

6. $4 - \frac{2}{5}m = 16$ **−30**

EXAMPLE 2   Solve $35 = \frac{5}{8}(r - 24)$.

Solution   Simplify the right side.

$$35 = \frac{5}{8}(r - 24)$$

$$35 = \frac{5}{8}r - \frac{5}{8}(24)$$

$$35 = \frac{5}{8}r - 15$$

Add 15 to both sides.

$$35 + 15 = \frac{5}{8}r - 15 + 15$$

$$50 = \frac{5}{8}r$$

Multiply both sides by $\frac{8}{5}$.

$$\frac{8}{5} \times 50 = \frac{8}{5} \times \frac{5}{8}r$$

$$\frac{8}{\cancel{5}} \times \overset{10}{\cancel{50}} = r$$

$$80 = r$$

The solution is 80.

Some equations have variables on both sides. To transform equations in this form, we may add a variable expression to both sides or subtract a variable expression from both sides.

EXAMPLE 3   Solve $8x = x + 14$.

Solution   Subtract x from both sides.

$$8x = x + 14$$
$$8x - x = x + 14 - x$$
$$7x = 14$$

Divide both sides by 7.

$$\frac{7x}{7} = \frac{14}{7}$$
$$x = 2$$

The solution is 2.

156   *Chapter 5*

156

Class Exercises

State which transformations you would use to solve the equation. State them in the order in which you would use them.

1. $8x + 18 = 42$

2. $6t - 2 = 28$

3. $\frac{b}{5} - 3 = 33$

4. $12 + \frac{d}{7} = 18$

5. $9 = \frac{1}{2}r - 10$

6. $\frac{2}{3}n + 6 = 8$

7. $13 + 11 = 5a + 6$

8. $\frac{m}{5} + 8 = 3(2 + 7)$

9. $-4(y + 8) = 16$

10. $5n = 2n - 9$

11. $3b + 6 = \frac{1}{2}b$

12. $11 - 4x = 7x + 8$

Written Exercises

Identify the transformation used in each step.

A

1. $8x - 2x = 54 \times 3$
$6x = 162$
$x = \frac{162}{6}$

2. $2x + 3 = 17$
$2x = 14$
$x = \frac{14}{2}$

3. $31 = 4 - 3x$
$27 = -3x$
$\frac{27}{-3} = x$

4. $5(18 + x) = 45$
$90 + 5x = 45$
$5x = -45$
$x = \frac{-45}{5}$

5. $52 = 4(x - 3)$
$52 = 4x - 12$
$64 = 4x$
$\frac{64}{4} = x$

6. $3x + 13 - 7x = 37$
$-4x + 13 = 37$
$-4x = 24$
$x = \frac{24}{-4}$

Solve. **25.** $\frac{10}{9}$, or $1\frac{1}{9}$ **30.** $-\frac{11}{2}$, or $-5\frac{1}{2}$

7. $2w + 1 = 5$ 2

8. $8 + 4q = 16$ 2

9. $11x - 17 = 49$ 6

10. $8d - 31 = 33$ 8

11. $2y - 2 = -3 + 7$ 3

12. $-14 + 5 = 7x - 30$ 3

13. $\frac{a}{2} + 3 = 6$ 6

14. $14 + \frac{t}{11} = 17$ 33

15. $\frac{z}{4} - 5 = 9$ 56

16. $39 = \frac{n}{5} - 21$ 300

17. $\frac{1}{3}x + 4 = -6$ −30

18. $\frac{3}{8}m + 9 = 18$ 24

19. $42 = 6 - \frac{1}{5}q$ −180

20. $\frac{1}{9}e - 8 = 30$ 342

21. $-2(x - 3) = -3(-8)$ −9

22. $\frac{105}{5} = 3(4 - 2b)$ $-\frac{3}{2}$, or $-1\frac{1}{2}$

23. $-5a - 9 + a = \frac{45}{3}$ −6

24. $13 + f - 8f = 25 \times 5$ −16

25. $7m = -2m + 10$

26. $3x = -x + 2$ $\frac{1}{2}$

27. $y - 5 = 2y + 10$ −15

28. $3x + 4 = 2x - 6$ −10

29. $5b - 2 = b + 10$ 3

30. $-7r - 8 = -5r + 3$

B

31. $5(y - 1) + 8 = -9$ $-\frac{12}{5}$, or $-2\frac{2}{5}$

32. $34 = 3(t + 6) - 8$ 8

33. $9 - 4(x - 3) = 17$ 1

Equations and Inequalities   **157**

Operations are performed on both sides unless otherwise specified.

Answers may vary.

1. Subtract 18; divide by 8.
2. Add 2; divide by 6.
3. Add 3; multiply by 5.
4. Subtract 12; multiply by 7.
5. Add 10; multiply by 2.
6. Subtract 6; multiply by $\frac{3}{2}$.
7. Simplify the left side; subtract 6; divide by 5.
8. Simplify the right side; subtract 8; multiply by 5.
9. Simplify the left side; add 32; divide by −4.
10. Subtract 2n; divide by 3.
11. Subtract $\frac{1}{2}b$; subtract 6; multiply by $\frac{2}{5}$.
12. Add 4x; subtract 8; divide by 11.

**Additional Answers
Written Exercises**

Operations are performed on both sides unless otherwise specified. Answers may vary in Exercises 1–6.

1. Simplified both sides; divided by 6.
2. Subtracted 3; divided by 2.
3. Subtracted 4; divided by −3.
4. Simplified the left side; subtracted 90; divided by 5.
5. Simplified the right side; added 12; divided by 4.
6. Simplified the left side; subtracted 13; divided by −4.

157

Solve.

34. $15 - 6(x + 2) = 1 \frac{1}{3}$　**35.** $50 = 2(5r + 2) - 1$ ^4.7　**36.** $26 = -5(4 + 8y) - 6$ ^−1.3

37. $3a = 2.5(8 + a)$ **40**　**38.** $0.3(p + 4) = 2.7p$ **0.5**　**39.** $x(4.8 - 2) = 4.8x - 2$ ^1

40. $4q + 19 = \frac{5}{6}q$ **−6**　**41.** $\frac{3}{5}c = 2c - 7$ **5**　**42.** $\frac{2}{3}a = -15 - a$ **−9**

C **43.** $\frac{1}{2}b + \frac{3}{5} = 2b - \frac{9}{10}$ **1**

44. $\frac{3}{4}f - \frac{1}{2} = 2f + \frac{1}{2}$ $-\frac{4}{5}$

45. $-\frac{1}{6}\left(t - \frac{1}{3}t\right) = -t + 36$ $\frac{81}{2}$, or $40\frac{1}{2}$　**46.** $-z - 9 = \frac{3}{4}\left(2z + \frac{4}{3}\right)$ **−4**

47. $\frac{2}{3}\left(m - \frac{1}{2}\right) + 3 = \frac{m}{3} - 7$ **−29**　**48.** $\frac{1}{2}(-4x - 5) = 7x - \frac{1}{2}$ $-\frac{2}{9}$

Write an equation for the word sentence and solve for y.

49. Nine divided by six is four times the difference of a number y subtracted from four. $\frac{9}{6} = 4(4 - y)$; $\frac{29}{8}$, or $3\frac{5}{8}$

50. Five times the sum of a number y and 11 is seventeen minus three. $5(y + 11) = 17 - 3$; $-\frac{41}{5}$, or $-8\frac{1}{5}$

51. Five eighteenths subtracted from one third of a number y is twice the number y. $\frac{1}{3}y - \frac{5}{18} = 2y$; $-\frac{1}{6}$

52. One half the sum of five and a number y is one quarter y. $\frac{1}{2}(5 + y) = \frac{1}{4}y$; **−10**

Self-Test A

Use one of the properties of equality to form a true sentence.

1. If $35 + p = 47$, then $p = \underline{\ ?\ }$. **12**　　**2.** If $-6a = 48$, then $a = \underline{\ ?\ }$. ^−8　[5-1]

Simplify the expressions on both sides of the equation to obtain an equivalent equation. $17 = 8x - 17$ ... $8 = 5m - 45$

3. $17 = 3x - 9 + 5x - 8$　　**4.** $24 \div 3 = 5(m - 9)$　[5-2]

Use transformations to solve the equation.

5. $x + 19 = 24$ **5**　**6.** $36 = y - 11$ **47**　**7.** $a + 14 = -9 - 3$ **−26**　[5-3]

8. $-8q = 56$ **−7**　**9.** $\frac{m}{18} = 9$ **162** $-\frac{33}{2}$, or $-16\frac{1}{2}$　**10.** $\frac{1}{4}d = 8$ **32**　[5-4]

11. $27 = 2y - 13$ **20**　**12.** $-2(7 + 2b) = 52$　**13.** $6n - 9 - 3n = n - 17$ **−4**　[5-5]

Self-Test answers and Extra Practice are at the back of the book.

158　*Chapter 5*

5-6 Equivalent Inequalities

To solve an inequality, we transform the inequality into an **equivalent inequality.** The transformations that we use are similar to those we use to solve equations.

> Simplify numerical expressions and variable expressions.
>
> Add the same number to, or subtract the same number from, both sides of the inequality.
>
> Multiply or divide both sides of the inequality by the same *positive* number.
>
> Multiply or divide both sides of the inequality by the same *negative number and reverse the direction of the inequality.*

Notice that we do not multiply the sides of an inequality by 0.

The following shows why we must change the inequality when multiplying or dividing by a negative number.

$$-6 < 5 \qquad\qquad\qquad -6 < 5$$
$$2(-6) \ ? \ 2(5) \qquad\qquad -2(-6) \ ? \ -2(5)$$
$$-12 < 10 \qquad\qquad\qquad 12 > -10$$

EXAMPLE 1   Solve each inequality.
   a. $x + 7 \leq -18$ **b.** $y - 4.5 > 32$

Solution   **a.** Subtract 7 from both sides of the inequality.

$$x + 7 \leq -18$$
$$x + 7 - 7 \leq -18 - 7$$
$$x \leq -25$$

The solutions are all the numbers less than or equal to -25.

b. Add 4.5 to both sides of the inequality.

$$y - 4.5 > 32$$
$$y - 4.5 + 4.5 > 32 + 4.5$$
$$y > 36.5$$

The solutions are all the numbers greater than 36.5.

Equations and Inequalities   **159**

Teaching Suggestions
p. 143e

Related Activities p. 143e

Reading Mathematics

Students will learn the meaning of the following mathematical term in this lesson: *equivalent inequality*.

Chalkboard Examples

Complete the inequality to form a true statement.

1. If $a > 2$, then
   $a + 6$ __?__ 8. $>$

2. If $c < 5$, then
   $c - 4$ __?__ 1. $<$

3. If $x \leq -2$, then
   $4x$ __?__ -8. $<$

4. If $y > -4$, then
   $-3y$ __?__ 12. $<$

5. If $-5 < t$, then
   t __?__ -5. $>$

6. If $\frac{x}{6} > 4$, then
   x __?__ 24. $>$

Use transformations to solve the inequality.

1. $h + 4 > 18$ **All the numbers greater than 14**

2. $x - 7 \leq -10$ **All the numbers less than or equal to -3**

3. $3c > -42$ **All the numbers greater than -14**

4. $6 < w - 16$ **All the numbers greater than 22**

5. $\frac{v}{-6} \geq 4$ **All the numbers less than or equal to -24**

6. $-7m < -98$ **All the numbers greater than 14**

Suggested Assignments

Minimum
Day 1: 161/1–18
       162/19–24
Day 2: 162/25–47 odd
       162/Rev. 1–8

Average
       161/1–17 odd
       162/19–47 odd
       162/Rev. 1–7 odd

Maximum
       161/1–17 odd
       162/19–47 odd; 49–52

Supplementary Materials

Practice Masters, p. 23

EXAMPLE 2   Solve $2\frac{1}{4} - \frac{1}{2} \geq n$.

Solution   We may exchange the sides of the inequality and *reverse the inequality sign* before we simplify the numerical expression.

$$2\frac{1}{4} - \frac{1}{2} \geq n$$

$$n \leq 2\frac{1}{4} - \frac{1}{2}$$

$$n \leq \frac{7}{4}, \text{ or } 1\frac{3}{4}$$

The solutions are all the numbers less than or equal to $\frac{7}{4}$.

EXAMPLE 3   Solve each inequality.

     a. $7a < 91$ **b.** $-3x \geq 18$ **c.** $26 \leq \frac{y}{4}$ **d.** $\frac{d}{-9} > -108$

Solution   **a.** Divide both sides by 7.

$$7a < 91$$
$$\frac{7a}{7} < \frac{91}{7}$$
$$a < 13$$

The solutions are all the numbers less than 13.

b. Divide both sides by -3 and *reverse the inequality sign.*

$$-3x \geq 18$$
$$\frac{-3x}{-3} \leq \frac{18}{-3}$$
$$x \leq -6$$

The solutions are all the numbers less than or equal to -6.

c. Multiply both sides by 4.

$$26 \leq \frac{y}{4}$$
$$4 \times 26 \leq 4 \times \frac{y}{4}$$
$$104 \leq y$$

The solutions are all the numbers greater than or equal to 104.

d. Multiply both sides by -9 and *reverse the inequality sign.*

$$\frac{d}{-9} > -108$$
$$-9 \times \frac{d}{-9} < -9 \times (-108)$$
$$d < 972$$

The solutions are all the numbers less than 972.

160   *Chapter 5*

Class Exercises

Identify the transformation used to transform the first inequality into the second.

1. $e + 5 > 8$ Subtracted 5

$e + 5 - 5 > 8 - 5$

2. $q - 3 < 7$ Added 3

$q - 3 + 3 < 7 + 3$

3. $\frac{1}{2}k < 4$ Multiplied by 2

$2 \times \frac{1}{2}k < 2 \times 4$

4. $6a > 12$ Divided by 6

$\frac{6a}{6} > \frac{12}{6}$

5. $-\frac{1}{4}u > 3$ Multiplied by −4 and reversed the inequality sign

$-4 \times -\frac{1}{4}u < -4 \times 3$

6. $-9m < 27$ Divided by −9 and reversed the inequality sign

$\frac{-9m}{-9} > \frac{27}{-9}$

Identify each transformation and complete the equivalent inequality.

7. $n - 6 > 9$ Added 6

$n - 6 + 6 \underline{\;?\;} 9 + 6$ $>$

8. $d + 4 < -3$ Subtracted 4

$d + 4 - 4 \underline{\;?\;} -3 - 4$ $<$

9. $3r < 15$ Divided by 3

$\frac{3r}{3} \underline{\;?\;} \frac{15}{3}$ $<$

10. $\frac{1}{5}v > 6$ Multiplied by 5

$5 \times \frac{1}{5}v \underline{\;?\;} 5 \times 6$ $>$

11. $-4z > 32.8$ Divided by −4

$\frac{-4z}{-4} \underline{\;?\;} \frac{32.8}{-4}$ $<$

12. $-\frac{1}{3}s < 2\frac{1}{3}$ Multiplied by −3

$-3 \times -\frac{1}{3}s \underline{\;?\;} -3 \times \frac{7}{3}$ $>$

Written Exercises

Use transformations to solve the inequality. Write down all the steps.

A

1. $-4 + 16 > k$

2. $g < -18 - 9$

3. $(17 + 4)2 < j$

4. $f \geq 7(23 - 9)$

5. $a + 7 < 10$

6. $c + 8 > 13$

7. $e - 11 \geq 9$

8. $m - 5 \leq 15$

9. $-16 > n + 2$

10. $-13 < q - 6$

11. $8w < 56$

12. $7y > 42$

13. $-5t > 35$

14. $-6a < 18$

15. $-48 \leq -4b$

16. $-49 \geq -7m$

17. $\frac{u}{3} \leq 5$

18. $\frac{w}{4} \geq 9$

Equations and Inequalities   **161**

Use transformations to solve the inequality. Write down all the steps.

19. $\frac{f}{-2} > 13$

20. $\frac{n}{-5} < 12$

21. $-10 \le \frac{y}{-6}$

22. $-9 \ge \frac{d}{4}$

23. $\frac{4h - 2h}{2} \le -6 - 5$

24. $\frac{16}{4} > \frac{7n - 2n}{5}$

B **25.** $-8(13.4 + 7.6) > a$

26. $12 \le p - 4.27$

27. $3r > 63.9$

28. $10\left(3\frac{1}{2} + 4\frac{2}{5}\right) \ge g$

29. $j + 3\frac{4}{7} < 9$

30. $d + 5\frac{1}{4} > -8$

31. $-10 \ge n - 6.13$

32. $c < (18.7 - 7.6)4$

33. $e \le \left(5\frac{1}{3} + 2\frac{1}{2}\right)6$

34. $42.4 < 4t$

35. $\frac{d}{0.6} \le -18$

36. $\frac{1}{5}w \ge \frac{2}{5}$

37. $\frac{3}{4} \le \frac{1}{4}n$

38. $\frac{m}{3.1} \ge 12$

39. $-7 > -\frac{1}{3}d$

40. $-\frac{1}{2}f \le -13$

41. $-6y < 24.6$

42. $42.5 > -5b$

43. $\frac{a}{-13.2} \ge 7$

44. $\frac{x}{-0.3} < -9$

45. $h - 10\frac{2}{3} > 12\frac{1}{5}$

46. $-8.27 \le k + 17.41$

47. $22.5 \ge -2.5m$

48. $3.2u \ge 25.6$

C **49.** $\frac{3}{4}n + \frac{1}{2}n > \frac{2}{3} \times \frac{3}{8}$

50. $\frac{-5}{8}p - \frac{1}{8}p > \frac{1}{4} \div 7$

51. $3.4(21.2 - 18.9) < 4.6(-3b + 2b)$

52. $\frac{5(-1.6t)}{2.5} < -14.3 - 9.6$

Review Exercises

Write the numbers in order from least to greatest.

1. $-1.4, 1.2, -2.6, 3.2$
$-2.6, -1.4, 1.2, 3.2$

2. $3.7, 4.02, -3.07, -4.1, 3$
$-4.1, -3.07, 3, 3.7, 4.02$

3. $12, -12.2, -12.09, 112, -11.2$

4. $9.8, -8.09, 0.89, -0.98, -9$

5. $-5.03, 3.05, -30.05, 0.35, -5.3$

6. $-0.2, -0.02, -2, -20, 200$

7. $2.89, 2.089, -2.8, 28.9, -2.89$
$-2.89, -2.8, 2.089, 2.89, 28.9$

8. $-7.6, -0.76, -7.06, -0.076, -76.0$
$-76.0, -7.6, -7.06, -0.76, -0.076$

5-7 Solving Inequalities by Several Transformations

We may need to use more than one transformation to solve some inequalities. It is helpful to follow the same steps that we use for solving equations.

> 1. Simplify each side of the inequality.
>
> 2. Use the inverse operations to undo any indicated additions or subtractions.
>
> 3. Use the inverse operations to undo any indicated multiplications or divisions.

EXAMPLE 1   Solve $-4r + 6 + 2r - 18 < -8$.

Solution   Simplify the left side.
$$-4r + 6 + 2r - 18 < -8$$
$$-2r - 12 < -8$$

Add 12 to both sides.
$$-2r - 12 + 12 < -8 + 12$$
$$-2r < 4$$

Divide both sides by -2 and reverse the inequality sign.
$$\frac{-2r}{-2} > \frac{4}{-2}$$
$$r > -2$$

The solutions are all the numbers greater than -2.

The solutions to the inequality in Example 1 include all numbers greater than -2. We show the graph of the solutions on the number line in the following way.

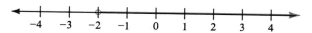

The open dot at -2 indicates that -2 is not on the graph of the solutions of the inequality.

We use a solid dot to show that a number is on the graph of the solutions. We graph the solutions of $r \geq -2$ in the following way.

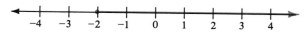

Equations and Inequalities   **163**

Teaching Suggestions
p. 143e

Related Activities p. 143f

Reading Mathematics

Some students use the terms *empty* and *filled* for *open* and *solid*, respectively, when referring to dots on a number line. Reassure students that using the correct terms is not as important as distinguishing between points whose coordinates do satisfy the condition (solid dots) and those that do not (open dots).

Chalkboard Examples

Match the correct inequality with the graph.

A. $a \leq -2$ **B.** $b \leq 1$
C. $c > -2$ **D.** $d < 1$

1.   **D**
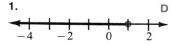

2.   **C**
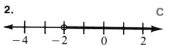

3.   **A**
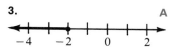

4.   **B**
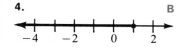

Complete each inequality so that it is equivalent to the preceding one.

5. $8 - 3x < -4$
$-3x < \underline{\ ?\ } -12$
$x > \underline{\ ?\ } 4$

6. $6 - 2x \geq 11 + 3x$
$6 \geq 11 + \underline{\ ?\ } 5x$
$-5 \underline{\ ?\ } 5x \geq$
$5x \underline{\ ?\ } -5 \leq$
$x \leq \underline{\ ?\ } -1$

Additional A Exercises

Solve.

1. $2a - 8 > -10$ **All the numbers greater than −1**

2. $10 - 3m < 1$ **All the numbers greater than 3**

3. $-2 \geq \frac{w}{2} - 5$ **All the numbers less than or equal to 6**

4. $5a - 4 \leq 7a + 10$ **All the numbers greater than or equal to −7**

5. $-7(m - 2) < 42$ **All the numbers greater than −4**

Suggested Assignments

Minimum
Day 1: 165/1–20
Day 2: 165/21–26
      166/27–30
      166/Rev. 1–8

Average
Day 1: 165/1–24
Day 2: 165/25–26
      166/27–38
      166/Rev. 1–8
      166/Calculator Key-In

Maximum
Day 1: 165/2–26 even
      166/27–33
Day 2: 166/34–40
      166/Calculator Key-In

Supplementary Materials

Practice Masters, p. 23

Additional Answers
Class Exercises

Operations are performed on both sides unless otherwise specified.

Answers may vary.

1. Simplify the left side; subtract 9; divide by 3.

2. Simplify the right side; add 5; divide by −6, and reverse $>$.

3. Simplify the right side; subtract 2; multiply by −5, and reverse $\geq$.

EXAMPLE 2   Solve $3(5 + x) \leq -3$ and graph the solutions.

Solution   Simplify the left side.

$$3(5 + x) \leq -3$$
$$3(5) + 3x \leq -3$$
$$15 + 3x \leq -3$$

Subtract 15 from both sides.

$$15 + 3x - 15 \leq -3 - 15$$
$$3x \leq -18$$

Divide both sides by 3.

$$\frac{3x}{3} \leq \frac{-18}{3}$$
$$x \leq -6$$

The solutions are all the numbers less than or equal to −6.

Because −6 is on the graph, we used a solid dot to graph the solutions of the inequality.

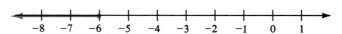

Like equations, inequalities may have variables on both sides. We may add a variable expression to both sides or subtract a variable expression from both sides to obtain an equivalent inequality.

EXAMPLE 3   Solve $-z + 7 \leq 3z - 18$.

Solution   Add z to both sides.

$$-z + 7 \leq 3z - 18$$
$$z + (-z) + 7 \leq z + 3z - 18$$
$$7 \leq 4z - 18$$

Add 18 to both sides.

$$7 + 18 \leq 4z - 18 + 18$$
$$25 \leq 4z$$

Divide both sides by 4.

$$\frac{25}{4} \leq \frac{4z}{4}$$
$$6.25 \leq z$$

The solutions are all the numbers greater than or equal to 6.25.

Class Exercises

State which transformations you would use to solve the inequality. State them in the order in which you would use them.

1. $8x + 7 - 5x + 2 \leq 30$

2. $-29 > 5 - 2y - 10 - 4y$

3. $7 \geq \frac{-4}{5}m + 6 + \frac{3}{5}m - 4$

4. $\frac{6}{7}k - 8 - \frac{5}{7}k + 3 < -3$

5. $4(h - 3) > 16$

6. $-4 \geq \frac{1}{2}(w + 12)$

7. $2 < (k + 45)\frac{-1}{5}$

8. $(3 - s)7 \leq 42$

9. $-u + 8 \geq 4u - 10$

10. $a - 6 < -5a - 18$

Written Exercises

Solve and graph the solutions. Check students' graphs.

A

1. $3q + 5 < -13$

2. $-7 + 5m > 28$

3. $30 \geq -4b - 6$

4. $-57 \leq -8z - 9$

5. $-\frac{w}{2} + 8 > 23$

6. $-\frac{c}{3} + 7 < -18$

7. $-12 \leq -5 + \frac{r}{6}$

8. $13 \geq 6 + \frac{e}{4}$

Solve.

9. $3v + 11 - 8v - 5 < -21$

10. $9 - 12u + 4 + 6u > -5$

11. $12 \geq \frac{3}{5}f + 6 - \frac{4}{5}f + 4$

12. $19 \leq 7 + \frac{1}{3}k + 2 - \frac{2}{3}k$

13. $h > -5h + 18 - 6$

14. $t < 17 - 4t - 2$

15. $38 - 8 - 7n \leq 3n$

16. $-9q + 18 - 3 \geq 6q$

17. $\frac{1}{4}(20 - x) < 6$

18. $\frac{1}{6}(42 - p) > 12$

19. $21 \geq 7(m - 2)$

20. $-25 \leq 5(w + 3)$

21. $j + 8 > 4j - 16$

22. $-6f + 7 < 2f - 9$

23. $10 + \frac{3}{4}a \leq \frac{-7}{8}a + 5$

24. $\frac{5}{6}g - 4 \geq \frac{2}{3}g + 6$

B **25.** $-12.8c + 8 + 7.8c - 6 \geq 17$

26. $4 + 7.5y - 9 + 2.5y > 25$

Equations and Inequalities **165**

Calculator Key-In

Repeating the 3 digits in Step 2 gives the same result as if you had multiplied the number in Step 1 by 1001. Dividing by 7, then by 11, and then by 13 gives the same result as dividing by $7 \times 11 \times 13$, or 1001, which gives you your original number. Multiplying by 1001 again gives you the result you obtained in Step 2 again.

Solve.

27. $1\frac{4}{5} < 8m + 4\frac{1}{5} - 3m - 7\frac{2}{5}$

28. $-2\frac{2}{3} \le 5\frac{2}{3} - 9u + 4\frac{2}{3} + 3u$

29. $0.2(40k + 62.5) \le -3.5$

30. $-0.5(12v - 18.6) < 21.3$

31. $-2\frac{7}{8} > \left(\frac{5}{8} - t\right)\frac{1}{5}$

32. $5\frac{3}{4} \le \frac{1}{3}\left(x - \frac{3}{4}\right)$

33. $2.7e + 8.2 < -9.3e + 32.2$

34. $5.4 - 10.9w \ge 9.1w - 14.6$

35. $\frac{5}{6}f - 2\frac{4}{5} > 1\frac{1}{5} + \frac{2}{3}f$

36. $-2\frac{1}{9}d + \frac{3}{5} \le -3\frac{2}{9}d - 4\frac{2}{5}$

C **37.** $0.11(360 + 25n) < (1.86n \div 6) - 3.06n$

38. $\frac{1}{5}\left(w - 5\frac{5}{9}\right) + \frac{2}{9} + \frac{3}{4}w \ge \frac{1}{8}w - 1 + \frac{5}{8}w$

39. $[(250.25x - 10.5) \div -5] - 14.6 \le -0.05x + 502.5$

40. $9\frac{4}{5} + \frac{2}{7}k - 7\frac{3}{5} > -\frac{11}{12} + \left[\left(\frac{4}{7}k + 2\frac{1}{3}\right) \div \frac{4}{5}\right]$

Review Exercises

Use *n* to write a variable expression for the word phrase.

1. A number increased by nine $n + 9$

2. Twice a number $2n$

3. Sixteen less than a number $n - 16$

4. Half of a number $\frac{1}{2}n$, or $\frac{n}{2}$

5. The sum of a number and three $n + 3$

6. Six more than a number $n + 6$

7. A number divided by five $\frac{n}{5}$, or $n \div 5$

8. Eight times a number $8n$

■■■ ### Calculator Key-In

Do the following on your calculator.

1. Press any 3 digits.	852
2. Repeat the digits.	852,852
3. Divide by 7.	?
4. Divide by 11.	?
5. Divide by 13.	?

852

What is your answer? Now multiply your answer by 1001. Try again using three different digits. Explain your results.

5-8 Equations into Word Problems

An equation such as

$$12x = 132$$

can be used to represent many real-life problems. For example:

> To pay back $132 that his father lent him, Carlton will make 12 equal payments. How much will each be?
>
> 12 payments × x dollars = $132

> One hundred thirty-two people have signed up for a tour of the planetarium. If 12 people are in each group, how many tour groups will there be?
>
> 12 people × x groups = 132 people

In each of the problems, the variable x was used to represent an unknown number. In each case, the product of 12 and the unknown number equals 132. Notice that the equation $12x = 132$ does not answer the question in each problem. We must solve the equation for x to find the answer to the question.

EXAMPLE 1   State two word problems that can be represented by the equation $42 - x = 19$.

Solution   The following are two possibilities.

a. This morning Phyllis must deliver 42 copies of the *Herald News*. After delivering the papers on River Road, she has 19 papers left to deliver. How many copies did she deliver on River Road?

b. Forty-two students had planned to audition for the school play this week. On Wednesday 19 students were still waiting to audition. How many students had auditioned so far?

EXAMPLE 2   Which of the following equations represents the problem below?

a. $15 + x = 60$ **b.** $15 - x = 60$ **c.** $15x = 60$ **d.** $\frac{x}{15} = 60$

Jeff must be at his music teacher's studio in 60 min. If it takes 15 min for him to reach the studio, how much extra time does Jeff have?

Solution   The unknown number in the problem is the number of minutes of extra time Jeff has. The variable x represents this number. The problem states that the travel time, 15 min, and the extra time, x min, together must equal 60 min. Answer (a), $15 + x = 60$, represents the problem.

Equations and Inequalities   **167**

Class Exercises

State a problem that the equation could represent. Use the words in parentheses as the subject of the problem. Answers will vary.

1. $x + 18 = 362$ (attendance at a game)

2. $x - 10 = 24$ (a garden)

3. $15x = 75$ (bicycling)

4. $\frac{x}{4} = 28$ (carpentry)

Written Exercises

Write a problem that the equation could represent. Answers will vary.

A

1. $80 + x = 84$
2. $95 + x = 159$
3. $x - 8 = 24$
4. $x - 45 = 47$
5. $50 - x = 37$
6. $243 - x = 96$
7. $52x = 728$
8. $8x = 96$
9. $\frac{x}{36} = 27$
10. $\frac{x}{24} = 378$
11. $\frac{1}{4}x = 7$
12. $\frac{1}{8}x = 5$

B

13. $3x + 5 = 60$
14. $2x - 8 = 26$
15. $x + 2x = 15$
16. $x + \frac{1}{2}x = 48$

Match.

17. Photo Mart received 32 cartons of photo albums. If each carton contains 10 albums, how many albums were received? **E**

18. If Jocelyn earns $10 a week for mowing the lawn, in how many weeks will she have $32? **C**

19. A single row of 32 square tiles of the same size covers a length of 10 ft. How wide is each tile? **D**

20. Bay Village is 32 km from Londonderry. If a car traveling between the two cities is 10 km from Londonderry, how far is the car from Bay Village? **A**

21. After grading 10 tests, a teacher has 32 tests left to grade. How many tests were there in all? **B**

A. $10 + x = 32$

B. $x - 10 = 32$

C. $10x = 32$

D. $32x = 10$

E. $\frac{x}{10} = 32$

Review Exercises

Solve.

1. $-\frac{2}{3}x = -3$ $\frac{9}{2}$, or $4\frac{1}{2}$
2. $3.2 = t + 4.2$ -1
3. $c - 9 = 35$ 44
4. $28 = -4 + \frac{a}{3}$ 96
5. $-3 = \frac{1}{6}a$ -18
6. $-2(n + 8) = 45$ $-\frac{61}{2}$, or $-30\frac{1}{2}$
7. $6 + 3b = 4b$ 6
8. $\frac{a}{-7} = 31 - 22.8$ -57.4

168 Chapter 5

5-9 Word Problems into Equations

Usually a word problem states some numerical relationships and asks a question. We may write an equation to represent the given information and then solve the equation to answer the question. The following five-step plan is helpful in solving word problems using equations.

Solving a Word Problem Using an Equation

Step 1 Read the problem carefully. Make sure that you understand what it says. You may need to read it more than once.

Step 2 Decide what numbers are asked for. Choose a variable and use it with the given conditions of the problem to represent the number(s) asked for.

Step 3 Write an equation based on the given conditions.

Step 4 Solve the equation and find the required numbers.

Step 5 Check your results with the words of the problem. Give the answer.

EXAMPLE 1 Karyn has earned $56.25 at her afternoon job. If she earns $2.50 per hour, how many more hours must she work to earn a total of $225 to buy a cassette player?

Solution
- The problem says Karyn has earned $56.25, she earns $2.50 per hour, and she would like to earn $225.
- The problem asks how many more hours Karyn must work to have $225. Let x = the number of hours. Since Karyn earns $2.50 per hour, the money after x more hours = $56.25 + 2.50x$. We have two expressions for the total amount of money:
$$225 \quad \text{and} \quad 56.25 + 2.50x.$$
- Use the expressions to write an equation: $225 = 56.25 + 2.50x$.
- Solve.
$$225 = 56.25 + 2.50x$$
$$225 - 56.25 = 56.25 + 2.50x - 56.25$$
$$168.75 = 2.50x$$
$$67.5 = x$$
- Check: If Karyn earns $2.50 per hour, in 67.5 h she will earn $67.5 \times \$2.50$, or $168.75. She now has $56.25, and $56.25 + 168.75 = 225$. ✓

Karyn must work 67.5 h, or $67\frac{1}{2}$ h, more.

Equations and Inequalities **169**

Teaching Suggestions p. 143g

Related Activities p. 143g

Chalkboard Examples

Pat is 200 mi east of Gotham at noon, driving west at 40 mi/h. Write an equation to answer the question.

1. How far is Pat from Gotham at 2:00 P.M.?
$d = 200 - (40 \times 2)$

2. How far is Pat from Gotham at 1:30 P.M.?
$d = 200 - (40 \times 1.5)$

3. How far is Pat from Gotham at a time x hours after noon?
$d = 200 - 40x$

4. At a time x hours after noon, Pat is 83 mi from Gotham. Write an equation to express this.
$83 = 200 - 40x$

EXAMPLE 2   Mark estimates that it will take 7 h to sand and paint the porch floor. He estimates that it will take twice as long to sand the floor as to paint the floor. How long does he expect to spend on each part of the job?

Solution
- The problem says that sanding and painting take 7 h, and sanding takes twice as long as painting.

- The problem asks for the length of time to do each part.
  Let x = the time it takes to paint.
  Use a chart to help organize the information.

paint	sand	total time
x	$2x$	7

The time for sanding and the time for painting make up the total time. We are given 7 as the numerical expression for the total time. From the chart we see that $x + 2x$ is a variable expression for the total time.

- Using the two expressions for the total time, write an equation:
  $x + 2x = 7$.

- Solve. $x + 2x = 7$
  $$3x = 7$$
  $$x = \frac{7}{3}, \text{ or } 2\frac{1}{3}$$

  Therefore, $2x = 2 \times 2\frac{1}{3} = 4\frac{2}{3}$.

- Check: Is the total time 7 h? $2\frac{1}{3} + 4\frac{2}{3} = 7$

  Is $4\frac{2}{3}$ twice as much as $2\frac{1}{3}$? $4\frac{2}{3} \div 2 = 2\frac{1}{3}$ $\checkmark$

  Mark expects to spend $4\frac{2}{3}$ h sanding and $2\frac{1}{3}$ h painting.

We may need to round the answers to some problems. When rounding an answer that is the result of division, we must consider whether it is reasonable to round the answer up or down.

EXAMPLE 3   The eighth-grade classes are taking a bus trip to the art museum. There is room for 60 people on each bus. If 175 students and 23 adults go on the trip, how many buses are needed?

Solution
- The problem says that 175 and 23 people will take the bus trip, and 60 people can fit on each bus.

- The problem asks how many buses are needed. If we let x = the number of buses, then the number of people on the buses is $60x$. We know that there are $175 + 23$ people.

- Using the two expressions for the number of people, write an equation: $60x = 175 + 23$.

- Solve. $60x = 175 + 23$
$$60x = 198$$
$$x = 3.3$$
   To have enough buses for all of the people on the trip, round the answer *up* to the nearest whole number, 4.

- Check: Four buses with 60 people each will carry 4×60, or 240, people; and $240 \geq 175 + 23$. ✓

   Four buses are needed.

Class Exercises

Write an equation for each problem. Do not solve.   Answers may vary.

1. Electricity usage is measured in kilowatt hours (kW·h). A water heater uses an estimated 4219 kW·h of electricity each year. About how many kilowatt hours is this per day? $365x = 4219$

2. Television advertising costs $200,000 per minute. How many minutes can be purchased for $350,000? $200{,}000x = 350{,}000$

3. A delivery truck is carrying an 8713 lb load of pet food. At a weighing station the loaded truck weighs 17,200 lb. What is the weight of the empty truck? $x + 8713 = 17{,}200$

4. On a recent trip to Paris, Janet spent $75 on gifts. If a franc was then worth $.1236, how many francs did she spend? $0.1236x = 75$

5. Harry spent his birthday money on a flying lesson. Mel spent $75 more than Harry. Together they spent $143. How much did Harry get for his birthday? $x + x + 75 = 143$

6. Condominiums in a new building cost $95 per square foot. Sam is looking at a unit that costs $83,125. How large is the unit? $95x = 83{,}125$

7. Gerry bought some plants at $2.49 each. Her total bill before deducting a $10 coupon was $24.90. How many plants did she buy? $2.49x = 24.90$

8. The Spanish Club raised $131.25 by having a garage sale and car wash. The amount raised at the car wash was half the amount raised at the garage sale. How much was raised at each event? $x + \frac{1}{2}x = 131.25$

Equations and Inequalities   **171**

Additional A Problems

Use an equation to solve the problem.

1. To form an investment club, each member deposited $250. How many members are there, if there was a total deposit of $2750?
   $250x = 2750$; 11 members

2. A piece 15 in. long and another piece 22 in. long were cut from a five-foot board. How long was the remaining length of board?
   $x + 15 + 22 = 60$; 23 in.

3. Frank weighs 183 lb and intends to lose enough weight to reach a goal of 168 lb. How much weight must Frank lose?
   $183 - x = 168$; 15 lb

4. Kim earns $2.25 an hour in wages and averages $8.50 an hour in tips. How many hours must Kim work to earn $215?
   $10.75x = 215$; 20 h

Suggested Assignments

Minimum
Day 1: 172/Prob. 1–8
Day 2: 173/Prob. 9–12
        173/Self-Test B

Average
Day 1: 172/Prob. 1–8
Day 2: 173/Prob. 9–13
        173/Self-Test B

Maximum
        172/Prob. 1–8
        173/Prob. 9–13
        173/Self-Test B

Supplementary Materials

Practice Masters, p. 24
Test 5B, pp. 31–32
Computer Activity 9
Computer Activity 10

Additional Answers
Self-Test B

The solutions are all the numbers:

1. greater than 46.
2. greater than or equal to −98.
3. greater than 71.
4. greater than or equal to 5.
5. less than or equal to −25$\frac{1}{2}$.
6. less than −68.
7. less than −1.
8. less than or equal to 6.

172

Problems

A periodic table displays the elements in order of increasing atomic number. Also shown, below the symbol for the element, is its atomic weight. Use the selected entries below, from the periodic table, for Problems 1–6.

10	36	53	76	79
Neon	Krypton	Iodine	Osmium	Gold
Ne	Kr	I	Os	Au
20.183	83.80	126.9044	190.2	196.967

Follow the five-step plan for using an equation to solve.

A 1. Three times the atomic weight of an element is 60.549. What is the element? Neon

2. The atomic weight of an element divided by 8 is 15.86305. What is the element? Iodine

3. The total atomic weight of three elements is 407.35. If two of the elements are neon and gold, what is the third? Osmium

4. The atomic weight of an element is the sum of the protons and neutrons in the element. The atomic number indicates the number of protons. How many neutrons are in an atom of iodine? 73.9044 or about 74

5. The quotient of one element's atomic number divided by another's is 2.$\overline{1}$. If the second element is krypton, what is the first? Osmium

6. The total atomic weight of two elements is 274. The atomic weight of the first is 106.4 less than that of the second. What are the two elements? Osmium and krypton

7. The Plantery delivered a shipment of 300 plants to the Pine Grove Mall. If the shipment is to be divided equally among 27 planters, how many plants will be in each planter? 11 plants

8. The eighth-grade teachers allow three quality points for each book report. How many reports must be written to earn 25 quality points? 9 reports

172   *Chapter 5*

B **9.** Dan has saved 235 trading stamps. He needs a total of 685 stamps to get a pair of skis. If he gets 10 stamps for every dollar he spends at the supermarket, how much must he spend to earn enough stamps for the skis? **$45**

10. Darla made 512 g of energy snack. She used twice as many grams of sunflower seeds as of peanuts and 12 more grams of pumpkin seeds than of peanuts. How much of each ingredient did she use? **125 g peanuts, 137 g pumpkin seeds, and 250 g sunflower seeds**

11. Byrne, Chang, and Weinstein pooled their funds to purchase a car wash franchise. They spent a total of $677,000. Byrne spent five times as much as Chang but $17,000 less than Weinstein. How much did each spend? **Byrne $300,000, Chang $60,000, Weinstein $317,000**

12. Steven tutors 3 students for a total of 8 hours each week. He charges the second student $4 more per week than the first. He charges the third student $1\frac{1}{2}$ times the amount he charges the second student per week. He earns a total of $52 each week. How much does each student pay? **First student $12, second student $16, third student $24**

C **13.** Lianne has some dimes and nickels with a total value of $4.60. The number of dimes she has is 4 more than 3 times the number of nickels. How many nickels does she have? **12**

Self-Test B

Use transformations to solve the inequality.

1. $y - 19 > 27$ **2.** $\frac{b}{7} \geq -14$ **3.** $107 < 36 + t$ **4.** $-9a \leq -45$ [5-6]

5. $\frac{2}{3}p + 6 \leq -11$ **6.** $\frac{n}{-2} - 10 > 24$ [5-7]

7. $16 < 4(3 - x)$ **8.** $-3d + 18 \geq 2d - 12$

Write a problem that the equation could represent. Answers will vary.

9. $x - 15 = 85$ **10.** $3x = 54$ [5-8]

Use an equation to solve.

11. Fran spent 3 times as long on her homework for English class as on her science homework. If she spent 60 min on her homework for both classes, how long did she spend on her science homework? **15 min** [5-9]

Self-Test answers and Extra Practice are at the back of the book.

Equations and Inequalities **173**

Use transformations to solve the inequality.

1. $x + 12 > -5$ All the numbers greater than -17

2. $-3x \geq 9$ All the numbers less than or equal to -3

3. $15 > 28 + t$ All the numbers less than -13

4. $\frac{c}{-3} \leq -3$ All the numbers greater than or equal to 9

5. $\frac{t}{5} < -3$ All the numbers less than -15

6. $16 > 33 + n$ All the numbers less than -17

7. $16 - 4x \leq 52$ All the numbers greater than or equal to -9

8. $42 > \frac{r}{-5} - 3$ All the numbers greater than -225

9. $-12 > 3(5 - c)$ All the numbers greater than 9

10. $21 - 3x < 3x - 15$ All the numbers greater than 6

Write a problem that the equation could represent. Answers will vary.

11. $32 = 19 + a$

12. $16c = 112$

Use an equation to solve.

13. Besides her regular wages of $14.50 an hour, Ada also received $550 in profit-sharing this week. How many hours did she work, if her total pay was $1072? **36 h**

14. The high school used 2000 gal more of heating oil than the elementary school. Together the schools used 76,000 gal of oil. How much oil did the high school use? **39,000 gal**

Credit Balances

Before stores or banks issue credit cards, they do a complete credit check of the prospective charge customer. Why? Because issuing credit is actually lending money. When customers use credit cards they are getting instant loans. For credit loans, interest, in the form of a *finance charge*, is paid for the favor of the loan.

To keep track of charge account activity, monthly statements are prepared. The sample statement below is a typical summary of activity.

Customer's Statement Account Number 35–0119–4G				Billing Cycle Closing Date 9/22 Payment Due Date 10/17		
Date	Dept. No.	Description		Purchases & Charges	Payments & Credits	
9/3 9/14 9/17	753 212	TOYS HOUSEWARES PAYMENT		30.00 12.50	 20.00	
Previous Balance	Payments & Credits	Unpaid Balance	Finance Charge	Purchases & Charges	New Balance	Minimum Payment
40.99	20.00	20.99	.61	42.50	64.10	20.00

Statements usually show any finance charges and a complete list of transactions completed during the billing cycle. Finance charges are determined in a variety of ways. One common method is to compute the amount of the unpaid balance and make a charge based on that amount. Then new purchases are added to compute the new balance on which a minimum payment is due.

To manage the masses of data generated by a credit system, many merchants use computerized cash registers. The cash registers work in the following way. When a customer asks to have a purchase charged, the salesperson enters the amount of the purchase and the customer's credit card number into the computer. The computer then retrieves the

174 *Chapter 5*

account balance from memory, adds in the new purchase, and compares the total to the limit allowed for the account. If the account limit has not been reached, the transaction is completed and the amount of the new purchase is stored in memory. At the end of the billing cycle, the computer totals the costs of the new purchases, deducts payments or credits, adds any applicable finance charges, and prints out a detailed statement.

Copy and complete. Use the chart below to find the minimum payment.

	Previous Balance	Payments and Credits	Unpaid Balance	Finance Charge	Purchases and Charges	New Balance	Minimum Payment
1.	175.86	50.00	?	1.89	35.00	?	?
2.	20.00	20.00	?	0	30.00	?	?
3.	289.75	40.00	?	5.25	68.80	?	?
4.	580.00	52.00	?	8.00	189.65	?	?
5.	775.61	110.00	?	10.48	0	?	?

Solve.

6. Debra Dinardo is comparing her sales receipts to her charge account statement for the month. The billing cycle closing date for the statement is 4/18. Debra has sales receipts for the following dates and amounts.

3/30 $17.60   4/8 $21.54
4/16 $33.12   4/26 $9.75

On April 14, Debra paid the balance on her last statement with a check for $139.80. Her statement shows the information below. Is the statement correct? Explain.

New Balance	Minimum Payment
Up to $20.00	New Balance
$ 20.01 to $200.00	$20.00
$200.01 to $250.00	$25.00
$250.01 to $300.00	$30.00
$300.01 to $350.00	$35.00
$350.01 to $400.00	$40.00
$400.01 to $450.00	$45.00
$450.01 to $500.00	$50.00
Over $500.00	$50.00 plus $10.00 for each $50.00 (or fraction thereof) of New Balance over $500

Yes. Since the billing cycle closing date is 4/18, the

Previous Balance	Payments & Credits	Unpaid Balance	Finance Charge	Purchases & Charges	New Balance	Minimum Payment
139.80	139.80	0	0	72.26	72.26	20.00

$9.75 charged on 4/26 will appear on Debra's next statement.

Research Activity Find out why stores and banks are willing to extend credit. How are the expenses of running the credit department paid for? Why do some stores offer discounts to customers who pay cash?

Equations and Inequalities **175**

Chapter Review

True or false?

1. If $m = -3$, then $6 + m = 9$. False

2. If $t + 9 = 24$, then $t = $ True 15. [5-1]

3. If $3q = -15$, then $q = -5$. True

4. If $a = 12$, then $6a = 2$. False

5. These equations are equivalent: [5-2]
$$2(4n + 8) = 32 \qquad 8n + 16 = 64 \text{ False}$$

6. These equations are equivalent:
$$-4b + 8 - 3 - 2b = 50 \qquad 5 - 6b = 50 \text{ True}$$

7. If $x - 24 = 13$, $x = -11$. False

8. If $46 = m + 18$, $28 = m$. True [5-3]

9. If $13d = 533$, $d = 41$. True

10. If $\frac{x}{-8} = 16$, $x = -2$. False [5-4]

11. If $\frac{f}{9} + 11 = 2$, $f = -1$. False

12. If $4 + 6y = 40$, $y = 6$. True [5-5]

13. If $3a - 12 = 9a + 18$, $-5 = a$. True

14. If $4(6 + x) = 76$, $x = 13$. True

Match the equivalent inequalities.

15. $x + 15 < 25$ D

16. $x - 20 \le 5$ B

A. $x > 10$ B. $x \le 25$ [5-6]

17. $-5x < -50$ A

18. $3x \ge 50 + x$ E

C. $x < 40$ D. $x < 10$ [5-7]

19. $\frac{1}{2}x + 6 < 26$ C

20. $\frac{x}{-5} + 5 \ge 10$ F

E. $x \ge 25$ F. $x \le -25$

Choose the best answer.

21. Which of the equations represents the problem? [5-8]

In a survey for orange juice, one fifth of the people questioned were under 20 years old. If 45 people were under 20, how many people were questioned?

a. $\frac{1}{5}x = 20$ b. $5x = 45$ (c.)$\frac{1}{5}x = 45$ d. $20x = 45$

22. Jess travels twice as far to school as Lee does. If together they travel 6.9 km to school, how far does Jess travel to school? [5-9]

a. 2.3 km   b. 3.45 km   (c.)4.6 km   d. 1.725 km

23. TriCity Taxi Company charges \$1 for the first mile and \$.60 for every mile thereafter. If your trip is measured in tenths of a mile, how far can you ride in a TriCity Taxi for \$12?

a. 6.6 mi   b. 18.3 mi   (c.)19.3 mi   d. 19.4 mi

176   *Chapter 5*

Chapter Test

Supplementary Materials
Chapter 5 Test, pp. 33–34

Additional Answers
Chapter Test

The solutions are all the numbers:
Use one of the properties of equality to form a true sentence.

1. If $-8 + x = 9$, then $x =$ __?__. 17 **2.** If $8 + y = 14$, then $y =$ __?__. 6   [5-1]

3. If $5m = 35$, then $m =$ __?__. 7   **4.** If $-28 = 4d$, then __?__ $= d$. -7

Simplify the expressions on both sides of the equation to obtain an equivalent equation.

5. $-2a - 3 + 4 + 6a = 27$ ↑ $4a + 1 = 27$ **6.** $3(x + 7) = -41 - 8$ ↑ $3x + 21 = -49$ [5-2]

Use transformations to solve the equation.

7. $m - 21 = -16$ 5   **8.** $32 = a + 9$ 23   **9.** $-11 + r = 25$ 36   [5-3]

10. $7p = 49$ 7   **11.** $\frac{1}{2}y = 14$ 28   **12.** $\frac{n}{-3} = 12$ -36 [5-4]

13. $-3b + 4 = -19$ $\frac{23}{3}$, or $7\frac{2}{3}$ **14.** $\frac{x}{6} - 17 = 5$ 132   [5-5]

15. $-8 - 2y = 6y + 4$ $-\frac{3}{2}$ or, $-1\frac{1}{2}$ **16.** $3(5t - 6) = 72$ 6

Use transformations to solve the inequality.

17. $a + 12 < 19$ **18.** $\frac{m}{4} > -8$ **19.** $-3y \le 42$ [5-6]

20. $\frac{w}{-6} \ge 9$ **21.** $75 < 5p$ **22.** $27 \ge n - 16$

Solve and graph the solutions.

23. $\frac{1}{4}d - 2 > 18$ **24.** $-35 \le -5(r + 8)$ [5-7]

25. $\frac{a}{9} + 17 \ge 20$ **26.** $8x - 4 < 5x + 23$

Write a problem that the equation could represent. Answers will vary.

27. $7m = 21$ **28.** $32 + r = 76$ [5-8]

Use an equation to solve.

29. Judith McSweeny plans to interview 18 applicants for a job. If she   [5-9]
spends 3 h interviewing each day and she spends $\frac{3}{4}$ h interviewing
each applicant, how many days will she need for the interviews? 5 days

30. Ross bought 2 books yesterday. The price of one was 3 times as
much as the price of the other. If the sum of the prices was $8.60,
what was the price of each book? $2.15 and $6.45

17. less than 7.
18. greater than -32.
19. greater than or equal to -14.
20. less than or equal to -54.
21. greater than 15.
22. less than or equal to 43.
23. greater than 80.
24. less than or equal to -1.
25. greater than or equal to 27.
26. less than 9.

Equations and Inequalities   **177**

Review for Retention
True or False?

1. 18.63 to the nearest whole number is 18. **False**

2. 4.852 to the nearest tenth is 4.9. **True**

3. 3497 to the nearest thousand is 4000. **False**

4. 0.1294 to the nearest hundredth is 0.13. **True**

5. $4 \times \frac{1}{5} = \frac{4}{5}$ **True**

6. $3 \times \left(-\frac{1}{7}\right) = -\frac{7}{3}$ **False**

7. $-\frac{9}{13} = \frac{9}{-13}$ **True**

8. $\frac{20}{24}$ in lowest terms is $\frac{2}{3}$. **False**

9. $\frac{190}{360}$ in lowest terms is $\frac{19}{36}$. **True**

10. $\frac{79}{11} = 7\frac{2}{11}$ **True**

11. $\frac{53}{6} = -8\frac{5}{6}$ **False**

12. $\frac{52}{9} = 4\frac{7}{9}$ **False**

13. The LCD of $\frac{3}{4}$ and $\frac{3}{8}$ is 12. **False**

14. The LCD of $\frac{11}{24}$ and $\frac{1}{3}$ is 8. **False**

15. The LCD of $\frac{3}{5}$ and $\frac{7}{12}$ is 60. **True**

(Continue on next page.)

Cumulative Review (Chapters 1–5)

Exercises

Replace the variable with the given value and tell whether the resulting statement is true or false.

1. $x + 4 \geq 10$; 7 True　　**2.** $3y - 5 = 12$; $2\frac{1}{3}$ False　　**3.** $6a + 1 < 5$; 1 False

4. $b + 5 < b - 3$; 7 False　　**5.** $2a + 6 = 3a - 1$; 5 False　**6.** $3x \geq x + 5$; 10 True

Graph the numbers on a number line. Check students' graphs.

7. 0, -3.5, 4.0, 1.0, -1.0　　　　　　　**8.** 6, 3, -2, -1.5, 5, 0

9. 4, 8, 3, -2, 0, 1, 5　　　　　　　**10.** -10, -12, -5, -11, -8

Write the fractions as equivalent fractions with the least common denominator (LCD).

11. $\frac{1}{8}$, $\frac{2}{5}$　$\frac{5}{40}$, $\frac{16}{40}$　　**12.** $\frac{4}{9}$, $\frac{6}{7}$　$\frac{28}{63}$, $\frac{54}{63}$　　**13.** $\frac{2}{3}$, $\frac{1}{6}$　$\frac{4}{6}$, $\frac{1}{6}$　　**14.** $\frac{5}{11}$, $\frac{2}{9}$　$\frac{45}{99}$, $\frac{22}{99}$

15. $\frac{-6}{11}$, $\frac{-3}{8}$　$-\frac{48}{88}$, $-\frac{33}{88}$　**16.** $\frac{3}{4}$, $\frac{-2}{7}$　$\frac{21}{28}$, $-\frac{8}{28}$　**17.** $\frac{5}{6}$, $\frac{-7}{8}$　$\frac{20}{24}$, $-\frac{21}{24}$　**18.** $\frac{-3}{4}$, $\frac{-1}{2}$　$-\frac{3}{4}$, $-\frac{2}{4}$

Perform the indicated operation.

19. $-35.7 + (-42.81)$　-78.51　　**20.** $1\frac{1}{3} \times \left(-2\frac{2}{5}\right)$　$-\frac{16}{5}$, or $-3\frac{1}{5}$　　**21.** $-14.4 \div 0.12$　-120

22. $-2\frac{1}{5} - 1\frac{7}{8}$　$-4\frac{3}{40}$　　**23.** $-16.781 - (0.086)$　-16.867　**24.** $-\frac{7}{8} \div 4\frac{1}{5}$　$-\frac{5}{24}$

Express as a fraction or mixed number in lowest terms.

25. 0.75　$\frac{3}{4}$　　**26.** 1.35　$1\frac{7}{20}$　　**27.** 46.55　$46\frac{11}{20}$　　**28.** 0.375　$\frac{3}{8}$　　**29.** 6.88　$6\frac{22}{25}$

30. 17.86　$17\frac{43}{50}$　**31.** 4.08　$4\frac{2}{25}$　**32.** 100.100　$100\frac{1}{10}$　**33.** 99.44　$99\frac{11}{25}$　**34.** 0.885　$\frac{177}{200}$

Round to the place specified.

35. hundredths: 6.0871　6.09　**36.** tens: 116.033　120　　　**37.** thousandths: 5.6568　5.657

38. tenths: 38.555　38.6　　**39.** hundreds: 4010.6　4000　**40.** tenths: 89.659　89.7

Solve.

41. $x + 5 = 17$　12　　　　**42.** $3x - 5 < 8$　　　　　**43.** $4 + 2x > 7$

44. $15x \div 3 = 21$　$\frac{21}{5}$, or $4\frac{1}{5}$　**45.** $12 - 8x \geq 10$　　　　**46.** $42x + 10 = 94$　2

47. $2x + (x - 3) = 18$　7　**48.** $5x = 9x - 14$　$\frac{7}{2}$, or $3\frac{1}{2}$　**49.** $-2x + 16 = 4x - 12$　$\frac{14}{3}$, or $4\frac{2}{3}$

Problems

Problem Solving Reminders

Here are some problem solving reminders that may help you solve some of the problems on this page.
* Determine which facts are necessary to solve the problem.
* Check your answer by using rounding to find an estimated answer.
* Supply additional information if necessary.

Solve.

1. Calculator batteries are being sold at 2 for 99¢. How much will 6 batteries cost? **$2.97**

2. "My new camera cost a fortune," boasted Frank. "Mine cost twice as much as yours," returned Eddie. If together the two cameras cost $545.25, how much did Frank's camera cost? **$181.75**

3. A newspaper with a circulation of 1.1 million readers estimates $\frac{1}{5}$ of its readers have subscriptions. About how many readers have subscriptions? **220,000 readers, or 0.22 million readers**

4. Amos Ellingsworth earns $455 per week. About $\frac{1}{4}$ of his pay is deducted for taxes, insurance, and Social Security. To the nearest dollar, how much does Amos take home each week? **$341**

5. Sally Gray takes home $378.50 per week. She will get a $50 per week raise in her next weekly check. If Sally takes home $\frac{4}{5}$ of her raise, what will be her new take-home pay? **$418.50**

6. The Denver Ducks won $\frac{2}{3}$ of their games. The Minneapolis Moles won half of their games. The two teams played the same number of games and together won a total of 49 games. How many games did each team win? **The Denver Ducks won 28 games; the Minneapolis Moles won 21 games.**

7. The Carpenters make annual mortgage payments of $6430.56 and property tax payments of $1446.00. What are the combined monthly payments for mortgage and taxes? **$656.38**

8. At a recent sales banquet, diners had a choice of beef, chicken, or fish. Four times as many people chose chicken as fish. Five times as many people chose beef as chicken. If 325 people had dinner, how many dinners of each type were served? **13 fish, 52 chicken, and 260 beef dinners**

9. At a recent job fair, there were $\frac{2}{3}$ as many inquiries about jobs in health care as in electronics. A reported 250 inquiries were made about both fields. How many inquiries were made about health care? **100 inquiries**

Equations and Inequalities **179**

16. The LCD of $\frac{3}{8}$ and $\frac{3}{7}$ is 54. **False**

Complete. Use $=$, $>$, or $<$ to make a true statement.

17. $2^2 \times 2^4$ __?__ 2^8 $<$
18. $5^5 \div 5^3$ __?__ 5^2 $=$
19. $3^3 \times 3^2$ __?__ $3^{10} \div 3^2$ $<$
20. 8.04 __?__ 8.0356 $>$
21. 0.001 __?__ 0.0005 $>$
22. $4(8 + 3)$ __?__ $4 \times 8 + 3$ $>$
23. $3t$ __?__ $t \times 3$ $=$
24. $(5 + 2)^0$ __?__ $5 + 2$ $<$

Simplify.

25. $4 + 3j - 2 + 5j$ $2 + 8j$
26. $2k(9 - 2) - 7$ $14k - 7$
27. $837s - 42t - 115s + t$ $722s - 41t$
28. $5(4 + 3g) + g$ $20 + 16g$

Solve.

29. $\frac{2}{5} \times \frac{3}{7}$ $\frac{6}{35}$
30. $\frac{3}{4} \div \frac{1}{6}$ $4\frac{1}{2}$
31. $2\frac{5}{8} + 1\frac{3}{4}$ $4\frac{3}{8}$
32. $3\frac{1}{7} - 2\frac{1}{2}$ $\frac{9}{14}$
33. $-\frac{4}{5} \times \frac{3}{8}$ $-\frac{3}{10}$
34. $4\frac{1}{3} \div 5\frac{1}{5}$ $\frac{5}{6}$

Write as a decimal. Use a bar to show repeating digits.

35. $\frac{5}{6}$ $0.8\overline{3}$
36. $\frac{5}{8}$ 0.625
37. $2\frac{2}{3}$ $2.\overline{6}$
38. $6\frac{1}{4}$ 6.25
39. $\frac{3}{16}$ 0.1875
40. $\frac{3}{7}$ $0.\overline{428571}$

6

Geometry

The photograph at the right shows a part of the interior of the East Building of the National Gallery of Art in Washington, D.C. The building was designed by I. M. Pei and completed in 1978. Although the architecture of the East Building is in sharp contrast to the architecture of the older West Building, the same Tennessee marble was used in the outside construction of both.

The planning and construction of a museum presents some unique problems. Conditions such as temperature, humidity, and adequate space must be carefully considered for the proper care of valuable works of art. The building itself must also reflect a high degree of artistic taste. Notice, for example, how the portion of the National Gallery shown contains triangles, rectangles, and other geometric shapes in repeating patterns.

Career Note

Being an architect involves many years of continuous study in the fields of art, mathematics, and engineering. In designing a building, an architect faces a variety of challenges arising from the purpose and location of the structure. Factors such as the space available and the appearance of adjacent buildings must be taken into account. Architects must also have a current knowledge of the many different types of building materials available.

181

Lesson Commentary
Chapter 6 Geometry

Overview

The first five sections of this chapter review and discuss the basic terms and symbols of geometry. Three terms, *point, line,* and *plane,* are accepted as undefined, but are fundamental to the development of all other terms. Definitions are given to identify angles according to their measure. Students will find measures of angles both by using protractors and by calculating measures using given facts. Students will also draw and construct figures using the compass and straightedge.

The second part of the chapter gives a classification system for triangles, quadrilaterals, and polygons. Using the properties related to each figure, students will determine angle measures and identify congruent polygons and their corresponding parts. Perimeters of polygons and circumferences of circles are also discussed in this chapter.

Throughout the chapter particular attention is given to correct notations and symbols. These notations and symbols must be learned and treated as a part of the understanding of geometry.

BASIC FIGURES

6-1 Points, Lines, and Planes

Objectives *for pages 182–186*

- To name points, segments, rays, lines, and planes.
- To construct segments.

Teaching Suggestions

Vocabulary is such an important part of this chapter that you should have your students plan now to make a list of key words and symbols. Ask them to alert you to any terms which are entirely new to them. Spend additional time explaining these new concepts. With all students a good review is necessary. To help students learn the vocabulary, have them prepare from their lists fill-in-the-blank sentences and True-False questions to use for brief discussions.

Students probably have an intuitive understanding of the terms *point* and *line*. Build on this understanding by drawing representations of points and lines. Explain that although a dot drawn with chalk or pencil must have size in order to be seen, the point it represents has no size. Likewise a line has no thickness. Emphasize that a line in geometry is straight.

The concept of a plane is probably less familiar. (Students may have learned about plains in social studies. Both *plain* and *plane* come from the Latin word *planus,* meaning "flat.") Use the walls, floor, and ceiling of the classroom as examples. Remind students that a plane extends infinitely in all directions and has no thickness.

As is stated in the lesson, *point, line,* and *plane* are undefined terms. The concept of undefined terms, although important, is difficult for many students and need not be emphasized

Emphasize the use of capital letters to name points. Point out that the letter is best placed above or below the dot representing a point and not covering the dot. A dot representing a point on a line should be drawn far enough from the arrow to be clearly distinguished. Explain that even though any two points are used to name a line, segment, or ray, each such figure is composed of infinitely many points yet unnamed or not yet designated in the drawing.

Discuss the compass and straightedge. If your students use rulers as straightedges, you may want to have them put masking tape over the markings to remind them that the straightedge is not used to measure lengths. To minimize the chances of accidentally moving the arm of the compass, it helps to use only the thumb and forefinger of one hand to hold and turn the compass handle. To keep the compass point from sliding, suggest that students put a sheet of cardboard or paper underneath the sheet they are using.

Related Activities

To provide a change of pace, have students illustrate the vocabulary words by drawings, jokes, poems, stories, or mobiles. These will make attractive bulletin boards and displays.

To relate mathematics to history, assign students a famous mathematician of the past to research why these mathematicians are famous and what geometric ideas they contributed to mathematics. Include Thales, Pythagoras, Euclid, Apollonius, Archimedes, Descartes, Pascal, and Lobachevsky.

Resource Book: Page 69 (Use After Page 186)

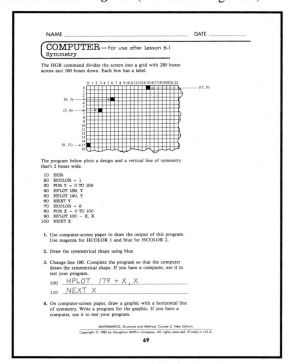

6-2 Circles

Objectives *for pages 187–190*

- To identify parts of a circle.
- To use a circumference formula.

Teaching Suggestions

As a demonstration of the definition of *circle,* draw a point on the chalkboard and ask students to place points 20 cm from the given point. You may want to ask what would happen if we did not specify that the points be in a plane; in that case a sphere would be produced.

To explain the circumference formula, divide the class into groups of three or four students. Give each group one circular object and a piece of string and a ruler, or a measuring tape. Ask each group to measure and record the diameter and circumference of their object, then divide the circumference by the diameter. Prepare a chart to record students' findings:

Group	Circumference, C	Diameter, d	$C \div d$
1			
2			
3			

Each group should get approximately 3.14. Explain that accuracy in measurement will determine the accuracy in the quotient. Some groups may need to measure again.

The ratio $C \div d = \pi$ is usually expressed as $C = \pi d$. Usually students will be told when to use either 3.14 or $3\frac{1}{7}$ for π. Discuss when to use the decimal and when to use the fraction if given a choice.

Related Activities

To provide a variation on the usual procedure, give students examples of drawings made with just a compass, such as those in Exercise 24. Have them write out instructions for the drawings.

To provide a challenge, present the following problem. "If you tied a rope firmly around Earth's equator, lengthened it by 10 ft, and supported it so that it was the same height above the surface all the way around, how high would it be?" Students may be surprised when they calculate that the height would be 3.18 ft. This height is $10 \div \pi$ and is independent of the diameter of the sphere; students may want to prove this algebraically.

6-3 Angles

Objectives *for pages 191–194*

- To identify types of angles.
- To determine measures of angles.
- To construct angles.

Teaching Suggestions

Most students have an idea of what an angle is, but they probably do not know that an angle is formed by two rays. Emphasize that the lengths of the rays drawn do not affect the size of the angle.

Resource Book page 161 has protractors and centimeter rulers. Pages 162 and 163 have grids.

Demonstrate the use of a protractor. Be sure that students locate the vertex of the angle correctly, that one side of the angle is at 0°, and that they use the correct scale. You could do a bit of drill on whether an angle is greater or less than 90°. For example, have students look at the protractor shown on page 191 and ask, "Is the measure of ∠ *QOP* 40 degrees or 140 degrees?"
40 degrees

Students may become confused if the sides of an angle are not long enough to meet the scale of a protractor. Show that the sides can be extended without affecting the size of the angle.

If students need extra practice, you might prepare a worksheet with angles in several different positions and have students measure them.

Related Activities

To develop an awareness of geometry, have students bring in examples of geometric symbols used in advertising.

6-4 Special Angles

Objective *for pages 195–199*

- To recognize and use the properties of perpendicular lines, complementary angles, supplementary angles, and vertical angles.

Teaching Suggestions

Along with the geometric concepts and definitions, this lesson provides ample practice in algebra as students learn to find complementary and supplementary angles. When you present Example 1, be prepared to help students who have trouble because of difficulty in reading the problem. Encourage them to draw diagrams.

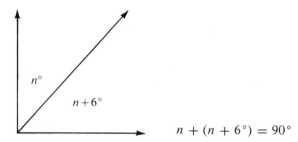

$$n + (n + 6°) = 90°$$

You might also have students complete a table such as this.

Angle	Complement	Supplement
85°	5°	95°
45°	45°	135°
30°	60°	150°
$x°$	$(90 - x)°$	$(180 - x)°$

Example 2 shows how to construct a perpendicular at a point on a line. You could also demonstrate how to construct a perpendicular from a point not on the line. The instructions are the same as those for Example 2.

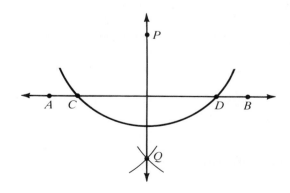

1. Draw an arc with center P, intersecting $\overleftrightarrow{AB}$ at C and D.

2. Draw two intersecting arcs of the same radius with centers C and D. Label the point of intersection of the arcs Q.

3. Draw $\overleftrightarrow{PQ}$.

   Then $\overleftrightarrow{PQ} \perp \overleftrightarrow{AB}$.

You may want to demonstrate the construction of a perpendicular bisector. This is illustrated in Written Exercise 28 on page 199. Once students understand the concept, they need not draw complete circles, only arcs long enough to define A and B.

When you discuss vertical angles, note that when two lines intersect at a point, you need to know the measure of one angle to find the measures of the other three. Draw three lines that intersect at a point, forming six angles. Help students figure out that they need to know the measures of two of these angles to find the measures of the other four. For four intersecting lines, they need to know the measures of three angles.

Related Activities

To demonstrate some applications of geometry, ask students to do creative drawings using the compass and straightedge and use markers or colored pencils to complete an artistic design. (Some students may wish to continue this assignment by studying hex designs and tessellations.)

To show some applications of bisectors (now or in Lesson 6-6, Triangles), have students draw two large scalene triangles and construct the perpendicular bisectors of each side. In one triangle label the point where the bisectors meet point X. Point X is called the **circumcenter** of the triangle. The measure from X to each vertex is the same and would be the radius of the circumscribed circle. In the second triangle connect each vertex with the midpoint of the opposite side. These line segments are called **medians** of the triangle and should meet at a point two-thirds the distance from a vertex to the opposite side along a median. This point of intersection is called the **centroid**, or point of balance, of the triangle. A cardboard triangle should balance at its centroid.

6-5 Parallel Lines

Objectives *for pages 200–203*

■ To identify special angles associated with parallel lines.

■ To determine the measure of angles in diagrams.

Teaching Suggestions

When explaining alternate interior angles, point out that *alternate* means on opposite sides of the transversal and at a different vertex. Interior angles open inside the parallel lines. Corresponding angles have the same position with respect to the different vertices.

Written Exercises 19 and 20 suggest two other important concepts relating to parallel lines. Interior angles on the same side of the transversal are supplementary. Alternate exterior angles are congruent. Students will also notice that exterior angles on the same side of the transversal are supplementary.

Resource Book: Page 70 (Use After Page 203)

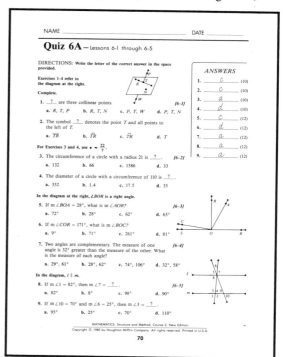

Related Activities

To show an entertaining application of parallel lines, demonstrate optical illusion drawings. Mazes, and drawings using one- and two-point perspective, are also interesting. Encourage students to explore areas of topology such as the Möbius strip for further challenges of the imagination.

FIGURES IN THE PLANE

6-6 Triangles

Objectives *for pages 204–205*

- To classify triangles.
- To determine measures of angles in triangles.

Teaching Suggestions

Any triangle is completely classified by its angles *and* sides: equilateral, acute scalene or acute isosceles, right scalene or right isosceles, obtuse scalene or obtuse isosceles. Because angles opposite congruent sides are congruent, an equilateral triangle is an acute triangle with three 60° angles; it can also be called an equiangular triangle.

Students will better understand triangle classifications when they are asked to measure several triangles and use their measures for classifying. Give students a worksheet with four different triangles and no given measurements. Ask them to measure the angles and sides and give the complete classifications.

To demonstrate that the sum of the angles of a triangle is 180°, have each student cut a large paper triangle. Be sure that all types of triangles are represented in the class. Ask each student to tear off the three corners of the triangle, fit them together, and use a straightedge to confirm that the sum is 180°.

Related Activities

To increase students' awareness of geometry around them, have them look for different kinds of triangles in buildings, bridges, and other structures. Students could mark the triangles on newspaper photographs for a bulletin board display. Ask some students to investigate why the triangle is the best shape for structural work.

6-7 Special Quadrilaterals

Objectives *for pages 209–212*

- To identify quadrilaterals, parallelograms, rhombuses, rectangles, squares, trapezoids, and isosceles trapezoids.
- To find the measures of angles in a parallelogram.
- To construct a parallelogram.

Teaching Suggestions

Be sure students understand that rhombuses, rectangles, and squares are all parallelograms. Every square is a rectangle and a rhombus, but a rectangle or a rhombus may not be a square.

As a review of supplementary angles (page 196) lead students to realize that any two consecutive angles of a parallelogram are supplementary. Therefore, the sum of the measures of the four angles is 360°. (In fact, the sum of the angle measures for any quadrilateral is 360°.)

A table such as the one below may help students relate the properties of parallelograms.

Property	Parallelogram	Rectangle	Rhombus	Square
Opposite sides parallel	√	√	√	√
Opposite sides congruent	√	√	√	√
All sides congruent			√	√
Four right angles		√		√

You can relate trapezoids to triangles by drawing a line parallel to the base of a triangle. Starting with an isosceles triangle, you produce an isosceles trapezoid. From a right triangle, you produce a trapezoid with two right angles like the one in Class Exercise 1.

Trapezoids vary more in shape than parallelograms do. You might have students draw trapezoids from verbal directions such as "Draw a trapezoid with a 60° angle." Have students compare their drawings, noting similarities and differences.

181e

Related Activities

To provide an opportunity for a more thorough investigation of parallelograms, have students draw diagonals and complete a table like this one.

Property	Parallel-ogram	Rec-tangle	Rhombus	Square
Diagonal forms two congruent triangles	✓	✓	✓	✓
Diagonals bisect each other	✓	✓	✓	✓
Diagonals are congruent		✓		✓
Diagonals are perpendicular			✓	✓
Diagonals bisect opposite angles			✓	✓

To help students remember the word *perimeter*, show that

peri-meter means "to measure around."

Write   peRIMeter

to help them associate it with the distance around a rim.

If students need more practice, give them a worksheet with several different polygons. Have them measure the sides and calculate the perimeters.

Related Activities

To provide a challenge, suggest that students develop formulas for the perimeter of a rectangle

$$(P = 2l + 2w)$$

and a square $(P = 4s).$

6-8 Polygons and Their Perimeters

Objectives *for pages 213–216*

- To identify polygons.
- To find the perimeters of polygons.

Teaching Suggestions

Draw on the chalkboard some polygons and some figures that are not polygons.

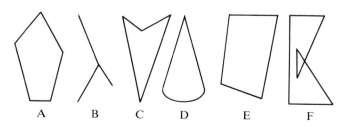

A   B   C   D   E   F

Of the figures above, *B*, *D*, and *F* are not polygons. *C* is a concave polygon.

Resource Book: Page 71 (Use After Page 216)

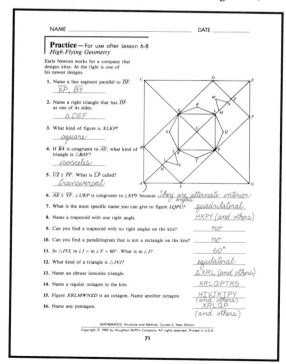

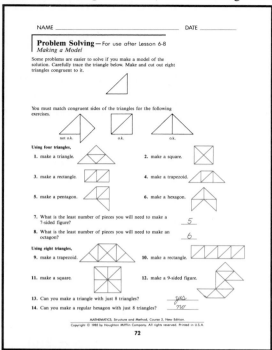

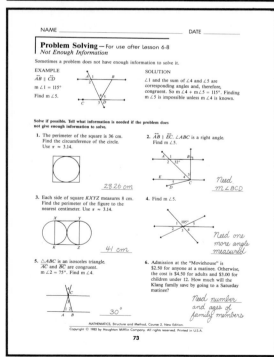

6-9 *Congruent Polygons*

Objective for pages 217–221

- To identify congruent polygons and their corresponding parts.

Teaching Suggestions

Ask students to name congruent polygons in the classroom. For example, the covers of their textbooks are congruent.

An overhead projector can be used to demonstrate the concept of congruence. Draw congruent figures on different transparencies and demonstrate how to use the rigid motions to match the vertices of the figures. Emphasize that the geometric figure changes only in position, not in size or shape. A translation is sometimes called a slide, a rotation is called a turn, and a reflection is called a flip.

Explain that similar markings on drawings indicate congruent parts. As the students begin the problems in this section, they should first sketch the figure and then mark the sketch for congruent parts according to the given information. This will help them in identifying congruent parts.

When you present the tests for congruence, you could have the students experiment with possible tests. To demonstrate the side-angle-side test, for example, have one student draw a triangle with $AB = 5$ cm, $m \angle B = 30°$, and $BC = 7$ cm. Another student, before looking at $\triangle ABC$, can draw $\triangle XYZ$ with $XY = 7$ cm, $m \angle Y = 30°$, and $YZ = 5$ cm.

Compare the triangles and show that

$$\triangle ABC \cong \triangle ZYX.$$

When you demonstrate the side-side-side test, be sure that the lengths you assign will form a triangle.

Not every set of congruent parts will establish that two triangles are congruent. If the three angles of one triangle are congruent to the three angles of another triangle, the triangles may still be of different sizes. For another example, see Exercise 18 of the Chapter Test on page 225. These triangles are not necessarily congruent because angles E and B may be either equal or supplementary.

Related Activities

To provide a change of pace, have students create designs using translations, rotations, and reflections. Each student will need a rectangular grid and a pattern the size of one block on the grid.

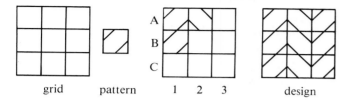

grid   pattern   1   2   3   design

Each student should make up a set of rules to create a design. In the example shown, the pattern is reflected from column 1 to column 2, and translated from row A to row B.

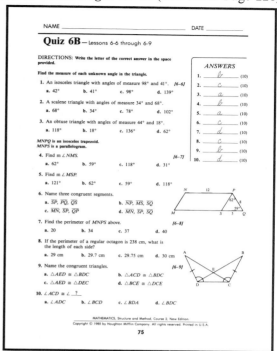

Resource Book: Page 74 (Use After Page 221)

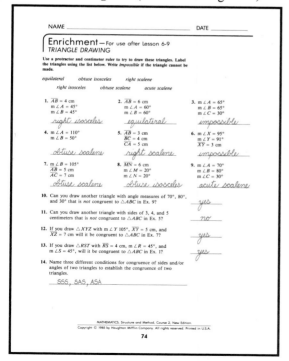

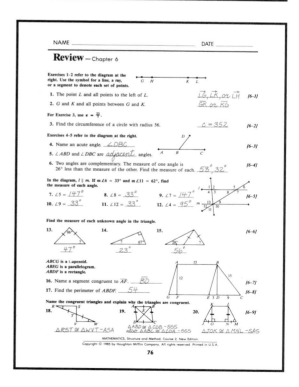

Resource Book: Pages 77-80 (Use After Page 221)

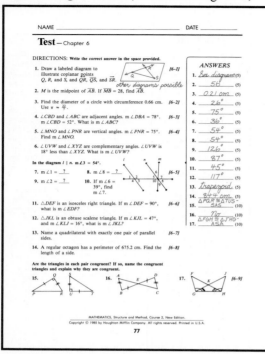

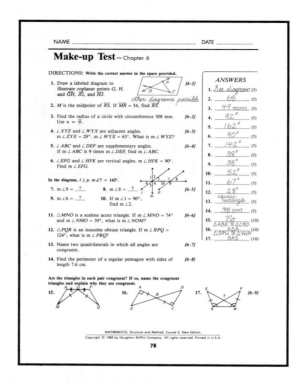

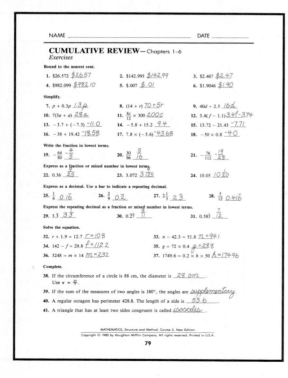

NAME _____ DATE _____

CUMULATIVE REVIEW — Chapters 1-6
Exercises

Round to the nearest cent.

1. $26.572 _$26.57_   2. $142.993 _$142.99_   3. $2.467 _$2.47_
4. $982.099 _$982.10_   5. $.007 _$.01_   6. $1.9046 _$1.90_

Simplify.

7. $p + 0.3p$ _1.3p_   8. $(14 + r)5$ _70 + 5r_   9. $40d ÷ 2.5$ _16d_
10. $7(3a + a)$ _28a_   11. $\frac{8c}{12} \times 300$ _200c_   12. $3.4(f - 1.1)$ _3.4f - 3.74_
13. $-3.7 + (-7.3)$ _-11.0_   14. $-5.8 + 15.2$ _9.4_   15. $13.72 - 21.43$ _-7.71_
16. $-38 + 19.42$ _-18.58_   17. $7.8 \times (-5.6)$ _-43.68_   18. -50×0.8 _-40_

Write the fraction in lowest terms.

19. $-\frac{64}{80}$ _-$\frac{4}{5}$_   20. $\frac{30}{96}$ _$\frac{5}{16}$_   21. $-\frac{76}{112}$ _-$\frac{19}{28}$_

Express as a fraction or mixed number in lowest terms.

22. 0.36 _$\frac{9}{25}$_   23. 3.072 _$3\frac{9}{125}$_   24. 10.05 _$10\frac{1}{20}$_

Express as a decimal. Use a bar to indicate a repeating decimal.

25. $\frac{1}{6}$ _$0.1\overline{6}$_   26. $\frac{2}{9}$ _$0.\overline{2}$_   27. $2\frac{1}{3}$ _$2.\overline{3}$_   28. $\frac{5}{12}$ _$0.41\overline{6}$_

Express the repeating decimal as a fraction or mixed number in lowest terms.

29. $3.\overline{3}$ _$3\frac{1}{3}$_   30. $0.\overline{27}$ _$\frac{3}{11}$_   31. $0.58\overline{3}$ _$\frac{7}{12}$_

Solve the equation.

32. $r + 1.9 = 12.7$ _r = 10.8_   33. $n - 42.3 = 51.8$ _n = 94.1_
34. $142 - f = 29.8$ _f = 112.2_   35. $g = 72 \times 0.4$ _g = 28.8_
36. $3248 = m \times 14$ _m = 232_   37. $1749.6 = 0.2 \times h \times 50$ _h = 174.96_

Complete.

38. If the circumference of a circle is 88 cm, the diameter is _28 cm_. Use $\pi \approx \frac{22}{7}$.

39. If the sum of the measures of two angles is 180°, the angles are _supplementary_.

40. A regular octagon has perimeter 428.8. The length of a side is _53.6_.

41. A triangle that has at least two sides congruent is called _isosceles_.

MATHEMATICS, Structure and Method, Course 2, New Edition.
Copyright © 1985 by Houghton Mifflin Company. All rights reserved. Printed in U.S.A.

79

NAME _____ DATE _____

CUMULATIVE REVIEW — Chapters 1-6 *(continued)*
Problems

Problem Solving Reminders
Here are some reminders that may help you solve some of the problems on this page.
- Consider whether drawing a sketch will help.
- Check by using rounding to find an estimated answer.
- Reread the question to be sure that you have answered with the information requested.

Solve.

1. The perimeter of a rectangle is 82 cm. The length of the rectangle is 34 cm. What is the width of the rectangle? _7 cm_

2. A wood board 29 m long is cut into 2 pieces so that one piece is 5 m longer than the other. Find the length of each piece. _12 m, 17 m_

3. One morning, the temperature at 4:00 A.M. was 3° below zero. By 5:00 A.M., the temperature had fallen 4°. By 7:00 A.M., the temperature rose 5°. What was the temperature then? _2° below zero_

4. The Potters make annual mortgage payments of $9460.38 and property tax payments of $1856.82. What are the combined monthly payments for mortgage and taxes? _$943.10_

5. Two angles are complementary. The measure of one angle is 3° greater than twice the measure of the other angle. Find the measure of the greater angle. _61°_

6. The perimeter of a rhombus is the same as the perimeter of an equilateral triangle with a side of 12 cm. Find the side of the rhombus. _9 cm_

7. Michael purchased 3 shirts and 2 sweaters. Each sweater cost twice as much as each shirt. He spent a total of $64.40. What was the cost of 1 sweater? _$18.40_

MATHEMATICS, Structure and Method, Course 2, New Edition.
Copyright © 1985 by Houghton Mifflin Company. All rights reserved. Printed in U.S.A.

80

181i

NAME _____ DATE _____

CUMULATIVE TEST—Chapters 4-6

DIRECTIONS: Write the answer in the space provided.

Chapter 4

Write as a proper fraction in lowest terms or as a mixed number in simple form.

1. $\frac{16}{56}$　　2. $-\frac{135}{180}$　　3. $\frac{-72}{20}$

Add or subtract. Write the answer as a proper fraction in lowest terms or as a mixed number in simple form.

4. $\frac{3}{4} + \frac{7}{10}$　　　　　5. $-\frac{5}{8} + \frac{11}{12}$

6. $1\frac{2}{3} - (-3\frac{5}{6})$　　　7. $-1\frac{1}{2} - \frac{1}{2}$

Multiply or divide. Write the answer as a proper fraction in lowest terms or as a mixed number in simple form.

8. $\frac{3}{8} \times -\frac{24}{27}$　　　　9. $-6\frac{2}{7} \times -1\frac{3}{11}$

10. $5\frac{1}{9} \div 1\frac{1}{3}$　　　　11. $3\frac{1}{3} \div -2\frac{1}{2}$

Write as a terminating or repeating decimal. Use a bar to show a repetend.

12. $\frac{8}{25}$　　　13. $\frac{7}{8}$　　　14. $\frac{5}{12}$

Solve.

15. Mark Hansen worked $15\frac{1}{2}$ hours last week and earned $62. What was his hourly rate of pay?

Chapter 5

Use one of the properties of equality to form a true sentence.

16. If $3 + f = 14$, then $f = $? .

17. If $53.4 = 3g$, then ? $= g$.

ANSWERS

1. $\frac{2}{7}$ (2)
2. $-\frac{3}{4}$ (2)
3. $-3\frac{3}{5}$ (2)
4. $1\frac{9}{20}$ (2)
5. $\frac{7}{24}$ (2)
6. $5\frac{1}{2}$ (2)
7. -2 (2)
8. $-\frac{1}{3}$ (2)
9. 8 (2)
10. $3\frac{5}{6}$ (2)
11. $-1\frac{1}{3}$ (2)
12. 0.32 (3)
13. 0.875 (3)
14. $0.41\overline{6}$ (3)
15. $\$4$ (3)
16. 11 (3)
17. 17.8 (3)

(Continue on next page.)

MATHEMATICS, Structure and Method, Course 2, New Edition.
Copyright © 1985 by Houghton Mifflin Company. All rights reserved. Printed in U.S.A.

81

NAME _____ DATE _____

CUMULATIVE TEST—Chapters 4-6 *(continued)*

Use transformations to solve the equation or inequality.

18. $-4\frac{1}{5} + t = 5$　　　19. $3.2 + d + 2.8 = -9$
20. $-8a = 13.6$　　　　21. $-\frac{5}{8} = -\frac{1}{4}r$
22. $-4p + 3 = 6p + 13$　　23. $-9a < 72$
24. $-18 \geq 3(2x + 2)$　　25. $-\frac{2}{3}b + 2 < 6$

Write an equation for the problem. Do not solve.

26. Janet is 4 years less than twice William's age. If the sum of their ages is 39, how old is Janet?

Use an equation to solve.

27. Baxter, Romero, and Hirsch pooled their funds to purchase a computer software store. They spent a total of $580,000. Baxter spent three times as much as Hirsch but $13,000 less than Romero. How much did each spend?

Chapter 6

Complete. Use the appropriate symbols for segments, lines, and rays.

28. ? is a segment with endpoints R and S.

29. ? is a ray through point A that begins at point O.

30. If the diameter of a circle is 9, the circumference is ? . Use $\pi \approx 3.14$.

31. The measure of an acute angle is between ? ° and ? °.

Solve.

32. Two angles are supplementary. The measure of one angle is 58° greater than the measure of the other angle. Find the measures of the angles.

33. One of the acute angles of a right triangle has a measure four times as great as the other. What are the measures of the three angles of the triangle?

34. Name two quadrilaterals in which all sides are congruent.

35. The perimeter of a regular octagon is 365.6 cm. Find the length of one side of the octagon.

ANSWERS

18. $t = 9\frac{1}{5}$ (3)
19. $d = -15$ (3)
20. $a = -1.7$ (3)
21. $r = 2\frac{1}{2}$ (3)
22. $p = -1$ (3)
23. $a > -8$ (3)
24. $-4 \geq x$ (3)
25. $b > -6$ (3)
26. $3x - 4 = 39$ (4)
27. $H = \$81,000$ (4)
　　$B = \$243,000$
　　$R = \$256,000$
28. $\overline{RS}$ (3)
29. $\overrightarrow{OA}$ (3)
30. 28.26 (3)
31. $0°, 90°$ (3)
32. $61°, 119°$ (4)
33. $18°, 72°, 90°$ (4)
34. *rhombus,* (4)
　　square
35. 45.7 cm (4)

MATHEMATICS, Structure and Method, Course 2, New Edition.
Copyright © 1985 by Houghton Mifflin Company. All rights reserved. Printed in U.S.A.

82

181j

Teaching Suggestions
p. 181a

Related Activities p. 181b

Reading Mathematics

Students will learn the meaning of the following mathematical terms in this lesson: *point, line, plane, collinear, line segment, endpoints, congruent, midpoint, ray, coplanar, noncollinear, geometric construction.*

The symbols for segments and lines can be read in either direction: $\overline{AB}$ is the same segment as $\overline{BA}$, and $\overleftrightarrow{AB}$ is the same line as $\overleftrightarrow{BA}$. When naming rays, directionality is important: $\overrightarrow{AB}$ is not the same ray as $\overrightarrow{BA}$.

Chalkboard Examples

Draw a labeled diagram for each description.
1. line $\overleftrightarrow{PQ}$

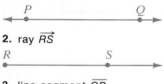

2. ray $\overrightarrow{RS}$

3. line segment $\overline{CD}$

Write a symbol that denotes each drawing.
4.

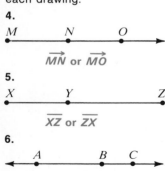

$\overrightarrow{MN}$ or $\overrightarrow{MO}$

5.

$\overleftrightarrow{XZ}$ or $\overleftrightarrow{ZX}$

6.

$\overleftrightarrow{AB}, \overleftrightarrow{AC}, \overleftrightarrow{BC},$
$\overleftrightarrow{BA}, \overleftrightarrow{CA},$ or $\overleftrightarrow{CB}$

6-1 Points, Lines, and Planes

In geometry, we start with three undefined terms: **point, line,** and **plane.** We indicate an exact location by a point. In a drawing, we represent a point by a dot. You probably know the following important fact about lines.

> Through any two distinct points there is exactly one line. That is, two points *determine* a line.

We think of the line AB, below, as passing through points A and B and extending without end in both directions.

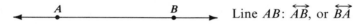

Line AB: $\overleftrightarrow{AB}$, or $\overleftrightarrow{BA}$

Points, such as X, Y, and Z below, through which one line can be drawn are said to be **collinear.**

The drawing below shows a **line segment,** or simply a **segment,** which we denote as $\overline{AB}$ (or $\overline{BA}$). The segment is made up of the points A and B and the part of the line $\overleftrightarrow{AB}$ lying between A and B. The points A and B are called the **endpoints** of the segment.

Segment AB: $\overline{AB}$, or $\overline{BA}$

The length of $\overline{AB}$ is denoted by AB (no bar over the letters). Two segments that have the same length are said to be **congruent.** When $AB = CD$, we write $\overline{AB} \cong \overline{CD}$ to mean $\overline{AB}$ *is congruent to* $\overline{CD}$.

On any segment, such as $\overline{AB}$ below, there is exactly one point M such that $AM = MB$. The point M is called the **midpoint** of $\overline{AB}$.

If we imagine $\overline{AB}$ extended without end in only one direction from endpoint A through point B, we have a **ray,** denoted by $\overrightarrow{AB}$.

Ray AB: $\overrightarrow{AB}$

182 *Chapter 6*

A **plane** can be thought of as a flat surface extending infinitely in all directions. We often draw a portion of a plane to suggest the whole plane, as in the diagram. Points that all lie on one plane are said to be **coplanar.**

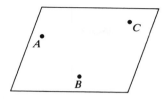

Plane *ABC*

Through any three noncollinear points there is exactly one plane. That is, three noncollinear points determine a plane.

EXAMPLE 1   Write a symbol that denotes each figure.

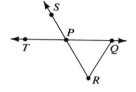

    a. The points of $\overrightarrow{RP}$ between and including *P* and *R*

    b. The line containing *T* and *Q*

    c. The point *Q* and all the points to the left of *Q* on the line that contains *P* and *Q*

Solution   **a.** $\overline{PR}$ (or $\overline{RP}$)

    b. $\overleftrightarrow{TQ}$ (or any of these: $\overleftrightarrow{QT}$, $\overleftrightarrow{PQ}$, $\overleftrightarrow{QP}$, $\overleftrightarrow{PT}$, $\overleftrightarrow{TP}$)

    c. $\overrightarrow{QT}$ (or $\overrightarrow{QP}$)

Reading Mathematics: *Symbols*

Some mathematical symbols, such as those for segments, rays, and lines, look very much alike. When you read such symbols, be sure to give them their complete meanings.

        $\overline{AB}$ is read as *segment AB*.
        $\overrightarrow{AB}$ is read as *ray AB*.
        $\overleftrightarrow{AB}$ is read as *line AB*.

A **geometric construction** is a special kind of drawing for which we use only a compass and a straightedge. For a construction, we may use a ruler as a straightedge to help draw segments but we may not use the ruler to measure length.

EXAMPLE 2   Construct a segment that is congruent to $\overline{AB}$.

Solution   **1.** Use your straightedge to draw a ray with endpoint O.

2. Open your compass until the point is on A and the pencil tip is on B. Then, without changing the setting of the compass, place the point of the compass at O and move the pencil end so that the pencil makes a mark crossing the ray. Call the point of intersection P. Then $\overline{OP} \cong \overline{AB}$.

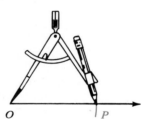

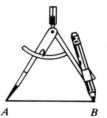

Class Exercises

Write a symbol that denotes each drawing.

1. $\overline{GE}$ or $\overline{EG}$ **2.** $\overrightarrow{HF}$ **3.** $\overleftrightarrow{TP}$ or $\overleftrightarrow{PT}$

Write two symbols that could be used to denote each drawing.

4. $\overrightarrow{TX},\ \overrightarrow{TV}$ **5.** $\overrightarrow{JL},\ \overrightarrow{JK}$ **6.** $\overleftrightarrow{AC},\ \overleftrightarrow{CA}$

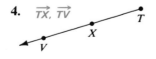

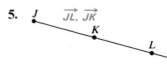

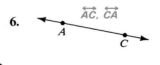

184   *Chapter 6*

Exercises 7–10 refer to the diagram at the right.

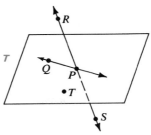

7. Name three collinear points. *R, P, S*

8. Name three coplanar points that are not collinear. *Q, P, T*

9. How many lines can be drawn through both *Q* and *T*? *1*

10. True or false? Points *P*, *Q*, and *R* are coplanar. *True*

Written Exercises

Exercises 1–4 refer to the diagram at the right. Use the symbol for a line, a ray, or a segment to denote each set of points.

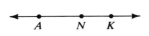

A 1. The point *A* and all points to the right of *A* $\overrightarrow{AN}$ or $\overrightarrow{AK}$

2. *N* and *A* and all points between *N* and *A* $\overline{NA}$ or $\overline{AN}$

3. The point *N* and all points to the left and right of *N* $\overleftrightarrow{AN}$, $\overleftrightarrow{NK}$, $\overleftrightarrow{AK}$, $\overleftrightarrow{NA}$, $\overleftrightarrow{KN}$, $\overleftrightarrow{KA}$

4. The point *K* and all points to the left of *K* $\overrightarrow{KN}$ or $\overrightarrow{KA}$

Draw a labeled diagram to illustrate each description.

5. $\overleftrightarrow{MX}$ and point *P* on $\overleftrightarrow{MX}$ but not on $\overrightarrow{MX}$

6. $\overrightarrow{QR}$ and point *S* on $\overleftrightarrow{QR}$ but not on $\overrightarrow{QR}$

7. $\overleftrightarrow{SP}$ and point *R* not on $\overleftrightarrow{SP}$

8. $\overleftrightarrow{AB}$ and $\overleftrightarrow{BC}$ intersecting at *B*

9. Noncollinear points *P*, *Q*, and *R*, $\overline{PQ}$, $\overline{QR}$, $\overline{PR}$, and point *X* on $\overline{PR}$

10. Noncollinear points *D*, *E*, and *F*, $\overline{DE}$, and $\overrightarrow{EF}$

11. Noncollinear points *C*, *A*, *T*, and *O*, $\overrightarrow{CT}$, and $\overleftrightarrow{OT}$

12. Noncollinear points *D*, *E*, *F*, and *G*, $\overline{DE}$, and $\overrightarrow{EF}$

Exercises 13–16 refer to the diagram at the right.

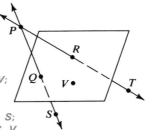

13. Name three collinear points. *P, R, T; P, Q, S*

14. Name three coplanar points that are not collinear. *Q, R, V; Q, R, P; Q, R, T; Q, R, S; and so on.*

15. Do the points *P*, *Q*, and *R* determine a plane? *Yes*

16. Name four coplanar points. *P, R, T, V; P, R, T, Q; P, R, T, S; P, Q, S, R; P, Q, S, T; P, Q, S, V*

Geometry **185**

Referring to $\overline{AB}$ below, use a straightedge and a compass to construct each figure.

A •————————————• B

17. $\overline{CD}$ congruent to $\overline{AB}$ **18.** $\overline{EF}$ such that $EF = 2(AB)$

Exercises 19–22 refer to the diagram at the right. Name each figure, using the symbol for a line, a ray, or a segment.

B   **19.** All the points that are on both $\overrightarrow{FD}$ and $\overrightarrow{EG}$ $\overline{EF}$ or $\overline{FE}$

20. All the points that are on either $\overline{EF}$ or $\overline{FG}$ $\overline{EG}$ or $\overline{GE}$

21. All the points that are on either $\overline{DE}$ or $\overrightarrow{EG}$ $\overrightarrow{DG}$ or $\overrightarrow{DE}$ or $\overrightarrow{DF}$

22. All the points that are on both $\overrightarrow{EG}$ and $\overrightarrow{FG}$ $\overrightarrow{FG}$

Use a straightedge and a compass to construct each figure.

23. Points A, B, and C and $\overline{AB}$, $\overline{BC}$, and $\overline{AC}$ such that B is the midpoint of $\overline{AC}$

24. Points P, Q, and R and $\overline{PQ}$, $\overline{QR}$, and $\overline{PR}$ such that $PQ = QR = PR$

In Exercises 25–32, M is the midpoint of $\overline{CD}$. Find the missing length.

25. $CM = 12$, $CD = \underline{\ ?\ }$ 24   **26.** $CD = 37$, $MD = \underline{\ ?\ }$ 18.5

27. $CD = 3x$, $CM = 15$, $x = \underline{\ ?\ }$ 10   **28.** $CD = 48$, $MD = 8x + 4$, $x = \underline{\ ?\ }$ 2.5

C   **29.** $CM = x$, $MD = 3x - 8$, $x = \underline{\ ?\ }$ 4   **30.** $CM = 2x$, $MD = x + 6$, $x = \underline{\ ?\ }$ 6

31. $MD = x + 4$, $CD = 5x - 13$, $x = \underline{\ ?\ }$ 7   **32.** $CM = 3x$, $CD = 8x - 14$, $x = \underline{\ ?\ }$ 7

Review Exercises

Round each number to the place indicated.

1. 56.0425 to the nearest tenth 56.0   **2.** 2.072 to the nearest hundredth 2.07

3. 1.2012 to the nearest thousandth 1.201   **4.** 7435.807 to the nearest tenth 7435.8

5. 2842.349 to the nearest hundredth 2842.35   **6.** 269.196 to the nearest tenth 269.2

7. 0.8625 to the nearest thousandth 0.863   **8.** 83.025 to the nearest tenth 83.0

9. 7.4553 to the nearest thousandth 7.455   **10.** 14.297 to the nearest hundredth 14.30

6-2 Circles

A **circle** is the set of all points in a plane that are a given distance from a given point in that plane. The given point is called the **center** of the circle, and the given distance is called **the radius** of the circle. A segment joining the center of a circle and a point on the circle is called **a radius** (plural: *radii*) of the circle. In the circle at the right, P is the center and $\overline{PQ}$ is a radius.

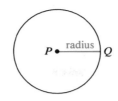

A segment joining two points on a circle is called a **chord.** A chord that passes through the center of the circle is called **a diameter.** We refer to the length of such a chord as **the diameter** of the circle. Thus, the diameter of any circle is twice the radius of the circle. Two points on a circle and the part of the circle between them form an **arc.** If the points are at the ends of a diameter, the arc is a **semicircle.**

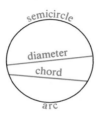

EXAMPLE 1   Construct a circle and a chord that has the same length as the radius of the circle.

Solution

1. With your compass, draw a circle with center O.

2. Without changing the setting of the compass, place the point of the compass at a point X on the circle. Draw an arc that intersects the circle, say at point P.

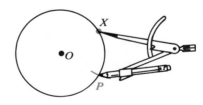

3. With a straightedge, draw $\overline{PX}$. Then $PX = OP$.

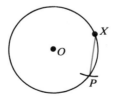

Geometry   **187**

Teaching Suggestions
p. 181b

Related Activities p. 181b

Reading Mathematics

Students will learn the meaning of the following mathematical terms in this lesson: *circle, center, radius, chord, diameter, arc, semicircle, circumference, π, pi.*

Chalkboard Examples

Use the drawing to name the following:

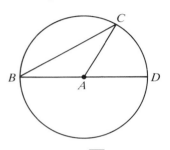

1. a diameter $\overline{BD}$
2. a chord $\overline{BC}, \overline{BD}$
3. two radii
    $\overline{AB}, \overline{AC}, \overline{AD}$

Find the circumference of each circle. Use $\pi \approx 3.14$.

4. $r = 22.4$ in.   **141 in.**
5. $d = 12.6$ cm   **39.6 cm**

Find the circumference of each circle. Use $\pi \approx \frac{22}{7}$.

6. $r = 7$ m   **44 m**
7. $d = 42$ ft   **132 ft**

Suggested Assignments

Minimum
189/1–18
190/19–20
190/Rev. 1–8

Average
189/1–18
190/19–22
190/Rev. 1–7 odd
190/Calculator Key-In

Maximum
189/1–18
190/19–24
190/Calculator Key-In

Supplementary Materials

Practice Masters, p. 25

The distance around a circle is called the **circumference** of the circle. For any circle the circumference, C, divided by the diameter, d, is a fixed number called π (a Greek letter, pronounced "pie"). That is, for any circle

$$\frac{C}{d} = \pi.$$

This relationship can be expressed in several forms.

Formulas for Circles

$$C = \pi \times d = \pi d \qquad \text{or} \qquad C = \pi \times 2r = 2\pi r$$

The number π cannot be expressed exactly as a fraction because π is irrational. Two common approximations of π are 3.14 and $\frac{22}{7}$. Because the approximation of 3.14 is good to only three digits, answers should be given to only three digits when 3.14 is used for π.

EXAMPLE 2   Find the circumference of a circle with radius 4 cm. Use $\pi \approx 3.14$.

Solution   Use the formula $C = 2\pi r$.

$$C \approx 2 \times 3.14 \times 4$$
$$C \approx 25.12$$

The circumference is approximately 25.1 cm.

EXAMPLE 3   Find the diameter of a circle with a circumference of 66 cm. Use $\pi \approx \frac{22}{7}$.

Solution   Use the formula $C = \pi d$.

$$66 \approx \frac{22}{7} \times d$$

Multiply both sides by $\frac{7}{22}$.

$$\frac{7}{22} \times 66 \approx \frac{7}{22} \times \frac{22}{7} \times d$$
$$21 \approx d$$

The diameter of the circle is approximately 21 cm.

Note that when we use an approximation for π, we use the symbol $\approx$.

188   *Chapter 6*

Class Exercises

Tell whether each segment is a chord, a radius, a diameter, or none of these, in relation to the circle with center _O_ shown in the diagram.

1. $\overline{BC}$ **2.** $\overline{OB}$ **3.** $\overline{OD}$ **4.** $\overline{AC}$ **5.** $\overline{AB}$ **6.** $\overline{OA}$
   chord   radius   none   diam.   chord   radius

7. <u>Name two</u> segments of the same length in the diagram.
   OA, OB, OC

8. What is the relationship between _AC_ and _OC_ in the diagram? $AC = 2 \cdot OC$, or $OC = \frac{1}{2}AC$

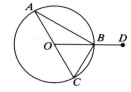

Written Exercises

Draw a labeled diagram to illustrate each description.

A **1.** A circle with center _O_ and a radius $\overline{OP}$

2. A circle with center _T_ and two diameters, $\overline{XY}$ and $\overline{UV}$

3. A circle with center _D_ and chords $\overline{AB}$ and $\overline{BC}$

4. A circle with center _P_, radii $\overline{PM}$ and $\overline{PQ}$, and chord $\overline{MQ}$ not a diameter

Referring to $\overline{AB}$ below, use a straightedge and a compass to construct each figure.

A •————————————————• B

5. Two circles, each with radius _AB_, that intersect at two points

6. A semicircle with radius _AB_

Find the circumference of a circle with the given radius _r_ or the given diameter _d_.

For Exercises 7–10, use $\pi \approx 3.14$. Throughout this chapter when the approximation of 3.14 is used for π, answers are rounded to 3 digits.

7. $d = 750$ m   **8.** $d = 500$ km   **9.** $r = 25$ cm   **10.** $r = 6.5$ m
   2360 m   1570 km   157 cm   40.8 m

For Exercises 11–14, use $\pi \approx \frac{22}{7}$.

11. $d = \frac{14}{11}$ 4   **12.** $d = \frac{7}{33}$ $\frac{2}{3}$ **13.** $r = 21$ 132   **14.** $r = 17.5$
                                                                                    110

Find the radius of a circle with the given circumference. Use $\pi \approx \frac{22}{7}$.

B **15.** $C = 110$ 17.5   **16.** $C = 242$ 38.5   **17.** $C = 0.44$ 0.07   **18.** $C = 4840$
                                                                                         770

Additional A Exercises

Draw a labeled diagram of a circle with the following parts.

1. a <u>center _O_</u> and a radius $\overline{OR}$

2. a diameter $\overline{AB}$

3. a chord $\overline{CD}$

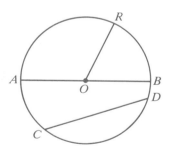

Find the circumference of each circle. Use $\pi \approx 3.14$.

4. $r = 1.3$ cm **8.16 cm**

5. $d = 16$ m **50.2 m**

Find the circumference of each circle. Use $\pi \approx \frac{22}{7}$.

6. $d = 42$ cm **132 cm**

7. $r = 154$ cm **968 cm**

The equator of Mars is approximately a circle with diameter 6787 km. The equator of Earth is approximately a circle with radius 6378 km. Use $\pi \approx 3.14$ to answer the following.

19. What is the approximate difference, in kilometers, between the circumference of Earth and the circumference of Mars? 18,800 km

20. If the circumference of Jupiter's equator is approximately 448,800 km, about how much greater (in kilometers) is the diameter of Jupiter than the diameter of Earth?

130,000 km (to 3 digits)

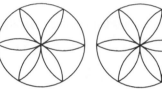

Use a straightedge and a compass to construct each figure.

21. A circle and two congruent chords

22. Two circles of equal radius intersecting in two points, and four radii of these circles forming a four-sided closed figure

C **23.** A circle and 6 chords of the circle such that each chord has the same length as a radius and each chord shares an endpoint with another chord

24. See if you can figure out how to construct the figures shown using only a compass. (*Hint:* See Exercise 23.)

Review Exercises

Replace each __?__ with >, <, or = to make a true sentence.

1. 46 __?__ 90 <   **2.** 118 __?__ 180 <   **3.** 107 __?__ 170 <   **4.** 875 __?__ 857 >

5. 40 + 30 __?__ 80 <   **6.** 75 __?__ 66 + 33 <   **7.** 95 − 27 __?__ 56 >   **8.** 114 − 24 __?__ 90 =

██ ██ ██ | **Calculator Key-In**

Over two thousand years ago, Archimedes found that the number π is between the fractions $3\frac{10}{71}$ and $3\frac{1}{7}$. Use your calculator to find decimal approximations of these numbers to complete the following statement:

3.14084507 __?__ < π < __?__ 3.14285714

6-3 Angles

An **angle** is formed by two rays with a common endpoint, called the **vertex** of the angle. The rays are called the **sides** of the angle. We use the angle symbol ($\angle$) with letters or with numbers, as shown below, to denote angles. By general agreement, when an angle is named with three letters, the middle letter always indicates the vertex of the angle.

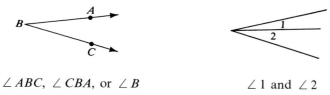

$\angle ABC$, $\angle CBA$, or $\angle B$ $\angle 1$ and $\angle 2$

Although angles are formed by rays, we sometimes show only segments of these rays as the sides of an angle, as in the diagram at the right above.

We measure angles with a **protractor,** as shown below. The measure of angle QOP is 40 degrees. We write this fact as m$\angle QOP = 40°$.

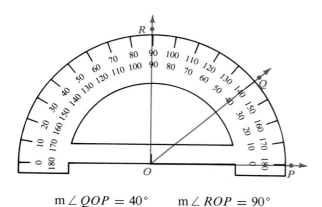

m$\angle QOP = 40°$ m$\angle ROP = 90°$

We classify angles according to their measures as shown in the table below. Angles that have the same measure are called **congruent angles.**

Name	Measure
Acute	Between 0° and 90°
Right	90°
Obtuse	Between 90° and 180°

Geometry   **191**

Teaching Suggestions
p. 181c

Related Activities p. 181c

Reading Mathematics

Students will learn the meaning of the following mathematical terms in this lesson: *angle, vertex, sides, protractor, congruent angles, adjacent angles, bisect, angle bisector.*

1. Name three angles in this drawing.

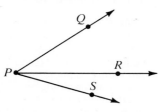

∠QPS, ∠QPR, and ∠RPS

2. Name the common vertex of the three angles above. **P**

3. Name the common ray of ∠QPR and ∠RPS. **PR→**

4. ∠QPR and ∠RPS are ___?___ angles. **adjacent**

5. If m∠QPR = 40° and m∠QPS = 63°, find m∠RPS. **23°**

6. Because of their measures, the three angles above are called ___?___ angles. **acute**

EXAMPLE 1 Construct an angle that is congruent to ∠A.

Solution

1. Draw a ray with endpoint O.

2. Draw two arcs of the same radius, with centers A and O. Label the points of intersection of the arc and ∠A as X and Y. Label the intersection of the arc and *O→* as C.

3. Put the compass point at Y and open the compass so that you can draw an arc through X. Using this radius, draw an arc with center C. Label the point where the two arcs intersect as B.

4. Draw *OB→*. Now ∠BOC is congruent to ∠A.

Original Angle   New Angle

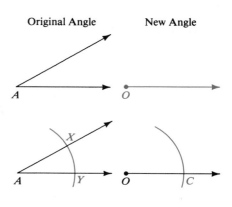

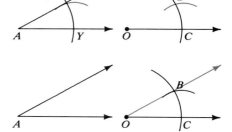

We may write *∠BOC is congruent to ∠A* as ∠BOC ≅ ∠A.

Two angles, like ∠1 and ∠2 in the diagram at the right, that have a common side and a common vertex but do not "overlap" are called **adjacent angles.** If you know the measures of ∠1 and ∠2 in the diagram, you can find the measure of ∠AOC. For example,

if m∠1 = 60° and m∠2 = 20°, then m∠AOC = 60° + 20° = 80°.

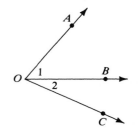

A ray that divides an angle into two congruent angles is said to **bisect** the angle. The ray is called the **angle bisector.** In the diagram at the right, *OP→* is the angle bisector of ∠ROQ. Angles 1 and 2 are marked in the same way to show that they are congruent.

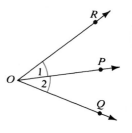

192   *Chapter 6*

EXAMPLE 2 Construct the bisector of ∠ O.

Solution

1. With a compass, draw an arc with center *O*, intersecting the sides of the angle. Label the points of intersection *X* and *Y*.

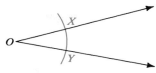

2. Draw an arc inside the angle with center *X*. With center *Y* and the *same* radius, draw another arc intersecting the arc inside the angle. Label the point of intersection *C*.

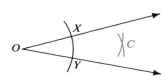

3. Draw $\overrightarrow{OC}$.
   Now ∠ *XOC* ≅ ∠ *YOC*, and $\overrightarrow{OC}$ bisects ∠ *XOY*.

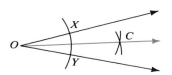

Class Exercises

Exercises 1-7 refer to the diagram at the right.

1. Name two acute angles. ∠*AXE*, ∠*BXC*, ∠*CXD*

2. Name two obtuse angles. ∠*BXE*, ∠*AXC*, ∠*EXD*

3. Name two angles that appear to be right angles. ∠*AXB*, ∠*BXD*

4. Name a pair of adjacent angles. ∠*AXE* and ∠*AXB*; ∠*AXB* and ∠*BXC*; ∠*BXC* and ∠*CXD*; ∠*CXD* and ∠*EXD*; ∠*EXD* and ∠*AXE*; ∠*AXC* and ∠*CXD*, and so on.

5. Name a pair of nonadjacent angles. ∠*AXE* and ∠*BXC* or ∠*CXD*; ∠*AXB* and ∠*CXD* or ∠*EXD*; ∠*BXC* and ∠*EXD*, and so on.

6. Name two angles that appear to be congruent but are not right angles. ∠*AXE* and ∠*CXD*

7. Do ∠*AXC* and ∠*AXB* have a common side and a common vertex? Are they adjacent? Yes; no

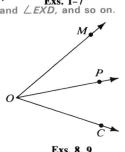

Exs. 1-7

Exercises 8 and 9 refer to the diagram at the right.

8. m∠*MOP* + m∠*COP* = m∠ ? MOC

9. If ∠*MOP* ≅ ∠*COP*, then ? bisects ∠ ? . $\overrightarrow{OP}$; MOC

Exs. 8, 9

Geometry **193**

Suggested Assignments

Minimum
    194/1–12
    194/Rev. 1–12
Average
    194/1–14
    194/Rev. 2–12 even
Maximum
    194/1–15

Supplementary Materials

Practice Masters, p. 26

193

The measures of two angles in the diagram are given. Find the measure of the third angle.

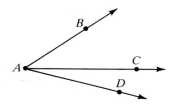

1. m∠ *BAC* = 48°,
   m∠ *CAD* = 22°,
   m∠ *BAD* = __?__° 70

2. m∠ *BAC* = 39°,
   m∠ *BAD* = 63°,
   m∠ *CAD* = __?__° 24

3. m∠ *BAD* = 81°,
   m∠ *CAD* = 35°,
   m∠ *BAC* = __?__° 46

Written Exercises

The measures of two angles in the diagram are given. Find the measure of the third angle.

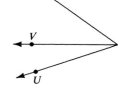

A   1. m∠ *TXV* = 33°; m∠ *VXU* = 17°; m∠ *TXU* = __?__° 50

   2. m∠ *TXU* = 57°; m∠ *VXU* = 21°; m∠ *TXV* = __?__° 36

   3. m∠ *TXU* = 62°; m∠ *TXV* = 28°; m∠ *VXU* = __?__° 34

   4. m∠ *VXU* = 19°; m∠ *TXV* = 35°; m∠ *UXT* = __?__° 54

   5. Draw an acute angle, ∠ *P*. Construct an angle congruent to ∠ *P*.

   6. Draw an obtuse angle, ∠ *Q*. Construct an angle congruent to ∠ *Q*.

   7. Draw an obtuse angle and construct its bisector.

   8. Draw an acute angle and construct its bisector.

In the diagram at the right, ∠ *COB* is a right angle and m∠ *EOD* = 82°. Find the measure of each angle.

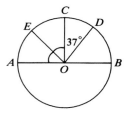

B   9. ∠ *EOC* 45°   10. ∠ *DOB* 53°

   11. ∠ *AOC* 90°   12. ∠ *EOB* 135°

   13. Draw two acute angles, ∠ *A* and ∠ *B*. Construct ∠ *C* such that m∠ *C* = m∠ *A* + m∠ *B*.

   14. Draw any obtuse ∠ *A* and any acute ∠ *B*. Then construct ∠ *D* such that m∠ *D* = m∠ *A* − m∠ *B*.

C   15. Draw a line. Mark points *A*, *X*, and *B* (in that order) on the line. Choose any point *C* not on the line. Draw $\overrightarrow{XC}$. Bisect ∠ *AXC* and ∠ *BXC*. What appears to be true of the two bisectors? They form a right angle.

Review Exercises

Evaluate the expression for the given value of the variable.

1. $n + 60$; $n = 54$ 114   2. $r - 40$; $r = 90$ 50   3. $8s$; $s = 14$ 112

4. $\frac{1}{4}y$; $y = 56$ 14   5. $2m + 36$; $m = 24$ 84   6. $5x - 25$; $x = 36$ 155

7. $\frac{1}{2}t + 45$; $t = 30$ 60   8. $3(z + 20)$; $z = 12$ 96   9. $6(x - 30)$; $x = 42$ 72

10. $(d + 15)7$; $d = 8$ 161   11. $18 + 12w$; $w = 10$ 138   12. $29 - 5c$; $c = 3$ 14

194   *Chapter 6*

6-4 Special Angles

If two lines intersect to form four congruent angles, the lines are **perpendicular.** (Rays or segments are said to be perpendicular if the lines containing them are perpendicular.) Each of the congruent angles is a right angle. In the diagram at the right, $\overleftrightarrow{AB}$ is perpendicular to $\overleftrightarrow{CD}$. We can write $\overleftrightarrow{AB} \perp \overleftrightarrow{CD}$ (or $\overleftrightarrow{CD} \perp \overleftrightarrow{AB}$). The mark (⌐) in the diagram indicates that the lines are perpendicular.

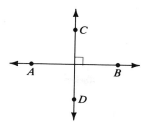

Two angles whose measures have a sum of 90° are called **complementary** angles. Complementary angles may or may not be adjacent.

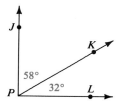

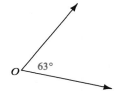

$\angle JPK$ and $\angle KPL$ are complementary. $\angle R$ and $\angle O$ are complementary.

EXAMPLE 1   One of two complementary angles has measure 6° greater than the other. What are the measures of the two angles?

Solution   Let n be the measure of the smaller angle.
Then $n + 6°$ is the measure of the larger.
Because the two angles are complementary, we have

$$n + (n + 6°) = 90°$$
$$2n + 6° = 90°$$
$$2n + 6° - 6° = 90° - 6°$$
$$2n = 84°$$
$$n = \frac{84°}{2} = 42°$$

The smaller angle has measure 42°.
The larger angle has measure 42° + 6°, or 48°.

Problem Solving Reminder

When checking your answer to a problem, reread the problem to be sure to *answer the question asked.* Notice that in Example 1, the solution of the first equation was the measure of one angle. The question asks for two angle measures, however, so a second value was needed to complete the solution.

Geometry   **195**

You can construct perpendicular lines with a straightedge and compass by thinking of the construction as bisecting a "180° angle."

EXAMPLE 2 Construct a line perpendicular to $\overleftrightarrow{AB}$ at point P.

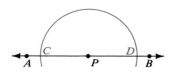

Solution
1. Draw any arc with center P, intersecting $\overleftrightarrow{AB}$ at C and D.

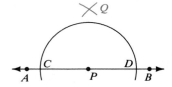

2. Open the compass more. Then draw two intersecting arcs of the same radius with centers C and D. Label the point of intersection of the arcs Q.

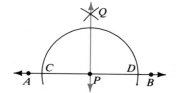

3. Draw $\overleftrightarrow{PQ}$.
   Then $\overleftrightarrow{PQ} \perp \overleftrightarrow{AB}$.

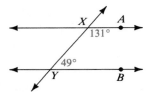

If the sum of the measures of two angles is 180°, the angles are called **supplementary** angles. Like complementary angles, supplementary angles need not be adjacent.

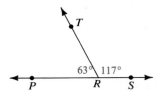

$\angle PRT$ and $\angle SRT$
are supplementary.

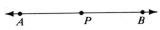

$\angle AXY$ and $\angle BYX$
are supplementary.

Notice that if two supplementary angles are adjacent, as $\angle PRT$ and $\angle SRT$ at the left above, their noncommon sides ($\overrightarrow{RP}$ and $\overrightarrow{RS}$) lie on one line.

196 *Chapter 6*

Whenever two lines intersect to form four angles, the nonadjacent angles are called **vertical** angles. In the diagram, $\angle 1$ and $\angle 2$ are vertical angles. $\angle 3$ and $\angle 4$ are also vertical angles.

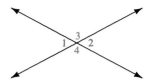

When two lines intersect, the vertical angles formed are congruent.

To see why vertical angles are congruent, note that in the diagram,

$$m\angle 1 + m\angle 3 = 180° \qquad \text{and} \qquad m\angle 2 + m\angle 3 = 180°.$$

If we subtract $m\angle 3$ from both sides of each equation,

$$m\angle 1 = 180° - m\angle 3 \qquad \text{and} \qquad m\angle 2 = 180° - m\angle 3.$$

Therefore, $m\angle 1 = m\angle 2$.

Class Exercises

Tell which of the following describe the given pair of angles (more than one may be correct).

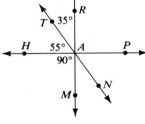

a. complementary   b. supplementary

c. adjacent   d. vertical

1. $\angle TAR$ and $\angle RAP$ c   **2.** $\angle TAR$ and $\angle HAT$ a, c

3. $\angle RAH$ and $\angle HAM$ b, c   **4.** $\angle TAR$ and $\angle MAN$ d

5. $\angle HAT$ and $\angle MAN$ a   **6.** $\angle HAT$ and $\angle TAP$ b, c

True or false?

7. Complementary angles are always adjacent. False

8. Vertical angles are always complementary. False

9. Two right angles are complementary. False

10. Two right angles are supplementary. True

11. Two supplementary angles with equal measure are right angles. True

12. Vertical angles may be adjacent. False

Use the drawing to find the measure of each angle.

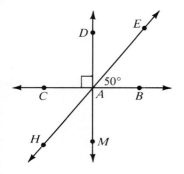

1. ∠CAD **90°**
2. ∠BAM **90°**
3. ∠DAE **40°**
4. ∠CAH **50°**
5. ∠HAM **40°**
6. ∠HAB **130°**
7. ∠CAE **130°**
8. ∠HAD **140°**

Written Exercises

Find the measure of each angle labeled ∠1.

A 1. **38°**

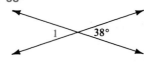

2. **90°**

3. **67°**

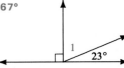

4. **54°**

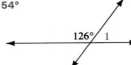

5. **73°**

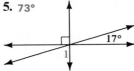

6. **25°**

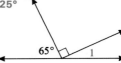

Find the measure of each angle in the diagram at the right.

7. ∠RWS **52°**   8. ∠TWU **100°**

9. ∠TWS **28°**   10. ∠PWQ **28°**

11. ∠QWS **152°**   12. ∠PWT **152°**

13. ∠QWU **80°**   14. ∠PWR **128°**

15. ∠SWU **128°**   16. ∠RWT **80°**

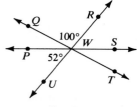

Exs. 7–16

In Exercises 17–20, find the measures of two *complementary* angles satisfying the given conditions.

17. The measure of one angle is 24° greater than the measure of the other. **33° and 57°**

18. The measure of one angle is 8° less than the measure of the other. **49° and 41°**

19. The measure of one angle is 30° greater than the measure of the other. **60° and 30°**

20. The measure of one angle is 70° less than the measure of the other. **10° and 80°**

In Exercises 21–23, find the measures of two *supplementary* angles satisfying the given conditions.

B 21. The measure of one angle is 5 times the measure of the other. **30° and 150°**

22. The measure of one angle is 8 times the measure of the other. **20° and 160°**

23. The measure of one angle is $\frac{2}{3}$ the measure of the other. **72° and 108°**

198 *Chapter 6*

Suggested Assignments

Minimum
   198/1–23
   199/24–25
   199/Rev. 1–9

Average
   198/1–23
   199/24–28
   199/Rev. 1–9 odd

Maximum
   198/1–23
   199/24–30

Supplementary Materials

Practice Masters, p. 26

198

24. If two vertical angles are complementary, what is the measure of each angle? 45°

25. If two vertical angles are supplementary, what is the measure of each angle? 90°

26. a. Draw any $\overleftrightarrow{LM}$ and a point P on $\overleftrightarrow{LM}$. Construct a line perpendicular to $\overleftrightarrow{LM}$ at P.

b. Use the right angle constructed in part (a) to construct a 45° angle.

27. Construct a 135° angle.

28. As illustrated in the diagram at the right, the common chord of two circles of the same radius is perpendicular to the segment joining the centers of the circles and divides this segment exactly in half. That is, in the diagram, $\overline{AB} \perp \overline{PQ}$ and $\overline{PX} \cong \overline{QX}$. $\overline{AB}$ is called the **perpendicular bisector** of $\overline{PQ}$.

Draw any $\overline{RS}$. Use the fact stated above to construct the perpendicular bisector of $\overline{RS}$.

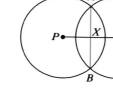

Ex. 28

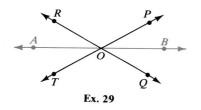

Ex. 29

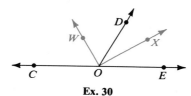

Ex. 30

C **29.** In the diagram, $\overrightarrow{OB}$ bisects $\angle POQ$. Explain how you know that $\overrightarrow{OA}$ bisects $\angle ROT$. m∠POB = m∠BOQ (bisector); m∠POB = m∠AOT and m∠BOQ = m∠ROA (vertical angles); so m∠AOT = m∠ROA

30. In the diagram, $\overrightarrow{OW}$ bisects $\angle COD$ and $\overrightarrow{OX}$ bisects $\angle DOE$. Explain how you know that m∠WOX = 90°.
m∠COD + m∠DOE = 180°; $\frac{1}{2}$mCOD + $\frac{1}{2}$mDOE = 90°; so m∠WOX = 90°

Review Exercises

Solve.

1. $\frac{y}{7} = 49$ 343

2. $2t + 24 = 73$ 24.5

3. $5x - 2x = 18$ 6

4. $130 - 45 = 2n - 20$ 52.5

5. $180 - 4x = 95$ 21.25

6. $z(4 - 2) = 40$ 20

7. $5(3 + s) = 65$ 10

8. $t = 2t - 80$ 80

9. $5r - 25 = r + 17$
10.5

Geometry **199**

Reading Mathematics

Students will learn the meaning of the following mathematical terms in this lesson: *transversal, alternate interior angles, corresponding angles, parallel lines.*

Chalkboard Examples

Use the drawing below to find the measures of these angles. Assume $l \parallel m$.
$m \angle 2 = 135°$

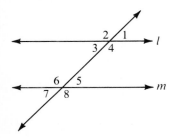

1. $m \angle 1$ **45°**
2. $m \angle 4$ **135°**
3. $m \angle 3$ **45°**
4. $m \angle 5$ **45°**
5. $m \angle 6$ **135°**
6. $m \angle 7$ **45°**
7. $m \angle 8$ **135°**

6-5 Parallel Lines

Sometimes a line is denoted by a single lower-case letter, as line n at the right. A line, such as line n, that intersects two other coplanar lines is called a **transversal.** The following pairs of angles formed by two lines and a transversal are called **alternate interior angles:**

$$\angle 3 \text{ and } \angle 6 \qquad \angle 4 \text{ and } \angle 5$$

The following pairs of angles are called **corresponding angles:**

$$\angle 1 \text{ and } \angle 5 \qquad \angle 2 \text{ and } \angle 6$$
$$\angle 3 \text{ and } \angle 7 \qquad \angle 4 \text{ and } \angle 8$$

If two lines lie in one plane and do not meet, they are called **parallel lines.** We abbreviate the statement r *is parallel to s* by writing $r \parallel s$. If a transversal intersects two parallel lines, then each pair of angles listed above is a pair of congruent angles. In the diagram at the right,

$$\angle 3 \cong \angle 6 \qquad \angle 1 \cong \angle 5 \qquad \angle 2 \cong \angle 6$$
$$\angle 4 \cong \angle 5 \qquad \angle 3 \cong \angle 7 \qquad \angle 4 \cong \angle 8$$

EXAMPLE 1 Lines l and m are parallel and $m \angle 1 = 117°$. Find the measures of the other angles.

Solution Since $m \angle 1 = 117°$,

$m \angle 3 = m \angle 1 = 117°$ (corresponding angles)

$m \angle 6 = m \angle 3 = 117°$ (alternate interior angles)

$m \angle 8 = m \angle 6 = 117°$ (corresponding angles)

Since $m \angle 2 + m \angle 1 = 180°$,

$m \angle 2 = 63°$ (63 + 117 = 180)

$m \angle 5 = m \angle 2 = 63°$ (vertical angles)

$m \angle 7 = m \angle 5 = 63°$ (corresponding angles)

$m \angle 4 = m \angle 7 = 63°$ (vertical angles)

If two lines are cut by a transversal and any two alternate interior angles (or any two corresponding angles) are congruent, then the other pairs are also congruent and the two given lines are parallel. This fact enables us to construct parallel lines by copying one angle.

EXAMPLE 2 Construct a line through point P and parallel to line m.

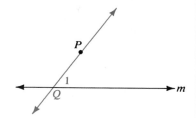

Solution 1. Draw any line through P intersecting m at Q.

2. At P, construct an angle congruent to $\angle 1$ (by the method already learned). Label the line you have just drawn as n. Then, since lines m and n form congruent corresponding angles with transversal $\overleftrightarrow{PQ}$, $n \parallel m$.

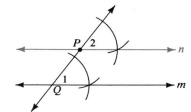

Suggested Assignments

Minimum
Day 1: 202/1–22
Day 2: 202/23
       203/24–25
       203/Self-Test A

Average
Day 1: 202/1–23
Day 2: 203/24–26
       203/Self-Test A

Maximum
Day 1: 202/1–23
Day 2: 203/24–27
       203/Self-Test A

Supplementary Materials

Practice Masters, p. 26
Test 6A, pp. 35–36

Additional A Exercises

In the drawing below $m\angle 1 = 118°$, $l \parallel m$, and $\angle 5 \cong \angle 8$. Find the measures of the other numbered angles.

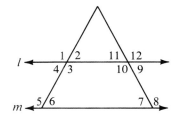

1. $m\angle 2$ 62°
2. $m\angle 3$ 118°
3. $m\angle 4$ 62°
4. $m\angle 5$ 118°
5. $m\angle 6$ 62°
6. $m\angle 7$ 62°
7. $m\angle 8$ 118°
8. $m\angle 9$ 62°
9. $m\angle 10$ 118°
10. $m\angle 11$ 62°
11. $m\angle 12$ 118°

Class Exercises

Exercises 1–8 refer to the diagram at the right.

1. Name two pairs of alternate interior angles. $\angle 7, \angle 3$; $\angle 8, \angle 4$

2. Name four pairs of corresponding angles. $\angle 5, \angle 3$; $\angle 8, \angle 1$; $\angle 6, \angle 4$; $\angle 7, \angle 2$

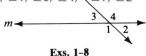

Assume that $l \parallel m$ in Exercises 3–8. If $m\angle 3 = 42°$, find the measure of each angle.

3. $\angle 6$ 138°	**4.** $\angle 7$ 42°	**5.** $\angle 4$ 138°
6. $\angle 5$ 42°	**7.** $\angle 2$ 42°	**8.** $\angle 8$ 138°

Exs. 1–8

Geometry **201**

Written Exercises

Exercises 1–16 refer to the diagram at the right. Name a pair of alternate interior angles, one of which is the given angle.

A 1. ∠5   2. ∠3   3. ∠DBC   4. ∠6
   ∠5, ∠7   ∠3, ∠8   ∠DBC, ∠9   ∠6, ∠ABE

Name a pair of corresponding angles, one of which is the given angle.

5. ∠2   6. ∠5   7. ∠DBC   8. ∠FBE
   ∠2, ∠7   ∠5, ∠10   ∠DBC, ∠11   ∠FBE, ∠9

In the diagram, suppose that $\overleftrightarrow{DE} \parallel \overleftrightarrow{AC}$ and $\overleftrightarrow{BC} \perp \overleftrightarrow{DE}$. If m∠1 = 32°, find the measure of each angle.

9. ∠2 58°   10. ∠3 90°   11. ∠4 32°   12. ∠5 58°

13. ∠6 122° 14. ∠7 58°   15. ∠8 90°   16. ∠ABE 122°

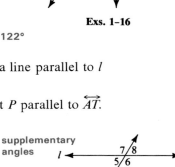

Exs. 1–16

17. Draw a line *l* and a point *B* not on *l*. Construct a line parallel to *l* through *B*.

18. Draw any ∠*TAP*. Construct a line through point *P* parallel to $\overleftrightarrow{AT}$.

B 19. In the diagram, *l* ∥ *m*. What relationship is there between ∠6 and ∠4? (*Hint:* Consider ∠5.)   supplementary angles

20. If *l* ∥ *m* in the diagram, what is the relationship between ∠8 and ∠1? Explain. ∠8 ≅ ∠5 ≅ ∠1

21. Suppose ∠3 ≅ ∠8. Make a sketch of how the diagram would look. Explain how you know that ∠2 ≅ ∠8 also. ∠2 ≅ ∠3

22. Suppose ∠1 ≅ ∠7. Make a sketch of how the diagram would look. Explain how you know that ∠4 ≅ ∠7 also. ∠4 ≅ ∠1

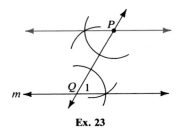

Exs. 19–22

23. a. Construct an angle ≅ ∠1 with vertex P.
    b. ∠1 and the constructed ∠ are ≅ alt. int. ∠s.

23. Use the idea suggested by the diagram.
    a. Describe an alternative method of constructing a line through point *P* parallel to line *m*.
    b. Explain how you know that the method you described produces parallel lines.

Ex. 23

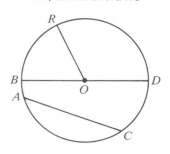
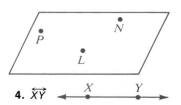

24. In the diagram, *ABCD* is a figure in which *both* pairs of opposite sides are parallel. Explain why ∠1 ≅ ∠2. ∠1 ≅ ∠3 (Corr. ∠s); ∠2 ≅ ∠3 (Alt. int. ∠s)

25. In the diagram, suppose ∠1 ≅ ∠2 and $\overline{AD} \parallel \overline{BC}$. Explain how you know also that $\overline{AB} \parallel \overline{DC}$. ∠2 ≅ ∠3 (Alt. int. ∠s); ∠1 ≅ ∠3 so AB ∥ DC. (Corr. ∠s are ≅.)

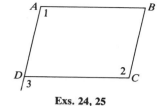

Exs. 24, 25

C 26. Construct two parallel lines and a transversal and construct the bisectors of two interior angles on the *same side* of the transversal (like ∠1 and ∠2 in the diagram). What appears to be true of these bisectors? Explain why.

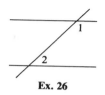

Ex. 26

27. If all sides of a four-sided figure are congruent, then the opposite sides of the figure are parallel. Use this fact to construct two parallel lines.

Self-Test A

Draw a labeled diagram to illustrate each description in Exercises 1–5.

1. $\overline{RS}$ 2. $\overrightarrow{AB}$ 3. Plane *XYZ*   4. $\overleftrightarrow{ST}$ [6-1]

5. A circle with center *P*, a radius $\overline{QP}$, a diameter $\overline{TW}$, and a chord $\overline{XY}$ [6-2]

6. Find the circumference of a circle with diameter 49. Use $\pi \approx \frac{22}{7}$. **154**

7. Draw an acute angle and construct its bisector. [6-3]

8. In the diagram, if m∠*BAD* = 137° and m∠*CAD* = 55°, what is m∠*BAC*? **82°**

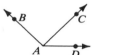

9. ∠*ARQ* and ∠*QRT* are complementary. If m∠*ARQ* is 18° greater than m∠*QRT*, what is the measure of each angle? m∠ARQ = 54°, m∠QRT = 36° [6-4]

10. ∠*XYZ* and ∠*ABC* are supplementary. If m∠*ABC* is 54° less than m∠*XYZ*, what is the measure of each angle? m∠ABC = 63°, m∠XYZ = 117°

In the diagram, $\overleftrightarrow{WX} \parallel \overleftrightarrow{TS}$.

11. ∠*WYQ* and ∠ _?_ are alternate interior angles. **YQS** [6-5]

12. ∠*YXQ* and ∠ _?_ are corresponding angles. **TQR**

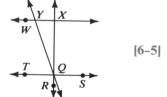

Self-Test answers and Extra Practice are at the back of the book.

Geometry **203**

For Exercises 6 and 7, use $\pi \approx 3.14$.

6. Find the circumference of a circle with diameter 4.8 cm. **15.1 cm**

7. Find the radius of a circle with circumference 154 m. **24.5 m**

8. Draw an obtuse angle and construct its bisector.

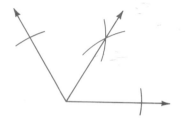

9. ∠*ABC* and ∠*XYZ* are complementary. If m∠*ABC* is 9° more than m∠*XYZ*, what is the measure of each angle? $49\frac{1}{2}°$, $40\frac{1}{2}°$

10. ∠*BPR* and ∠*MNO* are supplementary. If m∠*BPR* is 42° greater than m∠*MNO*, what is the measure of each angle? **111°, 69°**

In the diagram, $\overleftrightarrow{AB} \parallel \overleftrightarrow{CD}$.

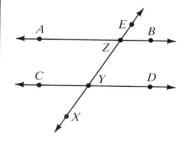

11. ∠*AZY* and ∠ _?_ are alternate interior angles. **DYZ, or DYE**

12. ∠*EZB* and ∠ _?_ are corresponding angles. **ZYD, or EYD**

Teaching Suggestions
p. 181e

Related Activities p. 181e

Reading Mathematics

Students will learn the meaning of the following mathematical terms in this lesson: *vertex, acute triangle, isosceles triangle, equilateral triangle, obtuse triangle, scalene triangle, right triangle.*

Ask other questions for which making a sketch is helpful, such as, "What are the measures of the acute angles of an isosceles right triangle?" **45°, 45°**

Chalkboard Examples

Without using a protractor, find the measure of each unknown angle. Identify each triangle as acute, right, or obtuse; and scalene, isosceles, or equilateral.

1.

26°; scalene acute

2.

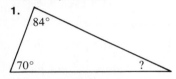

25°, 25°; isosceles obtuse

3.

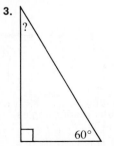

30°; scalene right

6-6 Triangles

If we join three points that are noncollinear, we obtain a **triangle.** Each of the three points is a **vertex** (plural: *vertices*) of the triangle. The triangle with vertices A, B, and C can be denoted as $\triangle ABC$.

Sides of $\triangle ABC$: $\overline{AB}$, $\overline{BC}$, $\overline{AC}$
Angles of $\triangle ABC$: $\angle A$, $\angle B$, $\angle C$

To find the sum of the angle measures of a $\triangle ABC$, draw a line l through one vertex, parallel to the opposite side. Since l is a line, we know that $m\angle 4 + m\angle 2 + m\angle 5 = 180°$. But since $\angle 1$ and $\angle 4$ are alternate interior angles, as are $\angle 3$ and $\angle 5$,

$$m\angle 1 = m\angle 4 \qquad \text{and} \qquad m\angle 3 = m\angle 5.$$

Therefore, $m\angle 1 + m\angle 2 + m\angle 3 = m\angle 4 + m\angle 2 + m\angle 5 = 180°$.

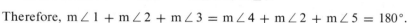

> The sum of the angle measures of any triangle is $180°$.

EXAMPLE 1   Two angles of a triangle are congruent, and the third angle has measure $38°$. Find the measure of one of the congruent angles.

Solution   Let x represent the measure of one of the congruent angles. Then the sum of the three angle measures is $x + x + 38°$.

$$x + x + 38° = 180°$$
$$2x + 38° = 180°$$
$$2x = 142°$$
$$x = 71°$$

Each of the congruent angles has measure $71°$.

We can classify triangles by their angles as follows:

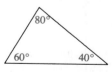   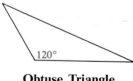

Acute Triangle   **Right Triangle**   **Obtuse Triangle**
Three acute angles   One right angle   One obtuse angle

204   *Chapter 6*

We can also classify triangles by their sides (marks indicate congruent sides):

Scalene Triangle
No two sides
congruent

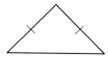

Isosceles Triangle
At least two sides
congruent

Equilateral Triangle
All sides congruent

In an isosceles triangle, the angles opposite congruent sides are congruent.

EXAMPLE 2 Find the measure of one angle of an equilateral triangle.

Solution Sketch a triangle to help you plan your solution. In your sketch, mark congruent sides alike.

Since all sides of the triangle are congruent, all angles of the triangle are congruent, according to the fact above. Let x represent the measure of one of the three congruent angles. Then each angle has measure x, so

$$x + x + x = 180°$$
$$3x = 180°$$
$$x = 60°$$

Each angle of an equilateral triangle has measure 60°.

Problem Solving Reminder

You may want to *make a sketch* to help plan your solutions for some problems. In Example 2 above, sketching the equilateral triangle helped to identify the relationships among the sides and the angles, making it easier to write an equation.

Class Exercises

Refer to the triangles shown. State the letter of each triangle that appears to be

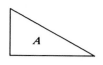

1. acute *B, C*

2. obtuse *E, F*

3. right *A, D, G, H*

4. isosceles *B, D, E, G, C*

5. scalene *A, F, H*

6. equilateral *C*

7. isosceles right *D, G*

8. scalene obtuse *F*

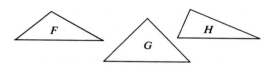

Without using a protractor, find the measure of the unknown angle.

9.
10.
11.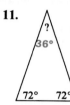
12.

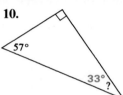
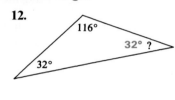

Written Exercises

Without using a protractor, find the measure of each unknown angle.

A 1.
2.
3.

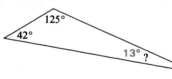
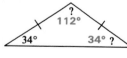

4.
5.
6.

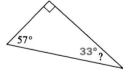

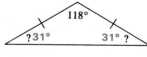

Additional A Exercises

Without using a protractor, find the measure of each unknown angle. Identify each triangle as acute, right, or obtuse; and scalene, isosceles, or equilateral.

1.
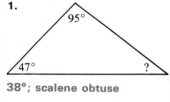

38°; scalene obtuse

2.

68°; scalene right

3.
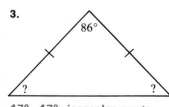

47°, 47°; isosceles acute

Construct each figure.

7. an isosceles right triangle

8. an isosceles obtuse triangle

9. an isosceles acute triangle

10. an equilateral triangle

11. Construct an isosceles triangle and construct the bisector of the angle formed by the congruent sides. Does the bisector appear to divide the opposite side into two congruent segments? Yes

12. Construct a scalene triangle in which one side is much longer than another. Construct the bisector of the angle formed by these two sides. Does the bisector appear to divide the opposite side into two congruent segments? No

13. Find the measure of each angle of an isosceles right triangle. 90°, 45°, 45°

14. One of the acute angles of a right triangle has measure twice as great as the other. What are the measures of the three angles of the triangle? 90°, 60°, 30°

Find the values of _x_ and _y_ in each diagram.

B 15.

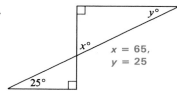

x = 65,
y = 25

16.

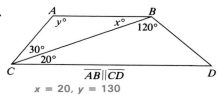

$\overline{AB} \| \overline{CD}$

x = 20, y = 130

17.

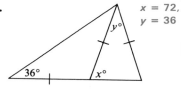

x = 72,
y = 36

18.

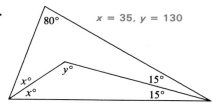

x = 35, y = 130

19.

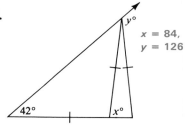

x = 84,
y = 126

20.

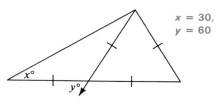

x = 30,
y = 60

Geometry **207**

Suggested Assignments

Minimum
206/1–6
207/7–20
208/Rev. 1–8

Average
206/1–6
207/7–20
208/21–24
208/Rev. 2–8 even

Maximum
206/1–6
207/7–20
208/21–28

Supplementary Materials

Practice Masters, p. 27

21. a. Draw an acute triangle *DEF*.

    b. Construct a new triangle *PRO* such that $\angle P \cong \angle D$ and $\angle R \cong \angle E$ but with $\overline{PR}$ twice as long as $\overline{DE}$.

    c. Repeat part (b) but make $\overline{PR}$ three times as long as $\overline{DE}$.

    d. What appears to be true of the other sides of the new triangle relative to $\triangle DEF$? Each side appears to be three times as long as the corresponding side of $\triangle DEF$.

22. a. Draw a large acute triangle. Bisect each angle.

    b. Repeat part (a) with a large obtuse triangle.

    c. What do you notice about the angle bisectors? They intersect at one point.

23. Construct a circle and a diameter $\overline{AB}$. Choose any point *C* on the circle and draw triangle *ABC*. What special kind of triangle does it appear to be? A right triangle

24. Construct a circle and a diameter $\overline{DE}$. Construct a chord $\overline{FG}$ that is perpendicular to $\overline{DE}$ but is *not* a diameter. Draw triangles *DFG* and *EFG*. What special kind of triangle do these appear to be? Isosceles triangles

C **25.** In $\triangle ABC$, $\mathrm{m}\angle C = 70°$. The bisectors of $\angle A$ and $\angle B$ meet at point *X*. Find $\mathrm{m}\angle AXB$. 125°

  26. In $\triangle DEF$, there is a point *M* of $\overline{EF}$ such that $ME = MF = MD$. Find $\mathrm{m}\angle EDF$. 90°

  27. In equilateral triangle *JKL*, there is a point *Y* of $\overline{JK}$ such that $\overline{LY} \perp \overline{JK}$. Find $\mathrm{m}\angle KLY$. 30°

  28. In isosceles triangle *RST*, $\overline{RT} \perp \overline{ST}$. The bisector of $\angle T$ meets side $\overline{RS}$ at point *Z*. Find $\mathrm{m}\angle RZT$. 90°

Review Exercises

Write an equation or an inequality for the sentence.

1. The difference when nine is subtracted from *d* is five. $d - 9 = 5$

2. A number *n* is the product of three and eleven. $n = 3 \times 11$

3. Negative four is the sum of a number *x* and twenty. $-4 = x + 20$

4. Three times a number *y* is the sum of sixty-four and nineteen. $3y = 64 + 19$

5. The product of fourteen and *z* is greater than ninety-eight. $14z > 98$

6. The quotient when *a* is divided by eight is less then twelve. $\frac{a}{8} < 12$

7. The difference when ten is subtracted from twice *m* is two. $2m - 10 = 2$

8. The product of six and the sum of *t* and three is thirty-six. $6(t + 3) = 36$

208 *Chapter 6*

6-7 Special Quadrilaterals

Any four-sided closed figure is called a **quadrilateral.** A special kind of quadrilateral in which both pairs of opposite sides are parallel is called a **parallelogram.**

Parallelogram $ABCD$

$$\overline{AB} \parallel \overline{CD}$$
$$\overline{AD} \parallel \overline{BC}$$

In any parallelogram, opposite sides are congruent. In the diagram,

$$\overline{AB} \cong \overline{CD} \qquad \text{and} \qquad \overline{AD} \cong \overline{BC}.$$

Also, opposite angles of a parallelogram are congruent. In the diagram,

$$\angle A \cong \angle C \qquad \text{and} \qquad \angle B \cong \angle D.$$

EXAMPLE 1 Find each angle measure.

    a. m $\angle BCD$

    b. m $\angle 1$

    c. m $\angle D$

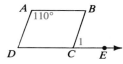

Solution
    a. $\angle BCD \cong \angle A$, so m $\angle BCD = 110°$

    b. m $\angle BCD$ + m $\angle 1 = 180°$
           $110°$ + m $\angle 1 = 180°$
                 m $\angle 1 = 70°$

    c. $\overline{AB} \parallel \overline{DE}$
       m $\angle B$ = m $\angle 1 = 70°$ (alternate interior angles)
       $\angle D \cong \angle B$, so m $\angle D = 70°$

You may be familiar with the names of the following special parallelograms.

Rhombus	**Rectangle**	**Square**
Opposite sides parallel	Opposite sides parallel	Opposite sides parallel
All sides congruent	Opposite sides congruent	All sides congruent
Opposite angles congruent	Four right angles	Four right angles

Geometry **209**

Teaching Suggestions p. 181e

Related Activities p. 181f

Reading Mathematics

Students will learn the meaning of the following mathematical terms in this lesson: *quadrilateral, parallelogram, rhombus, rectangle, square, trapezoid, isosceles trapezoid, diagonal.*

Chalkboard Examples

KLMN is a rhombus. Find each angle measure or each length.

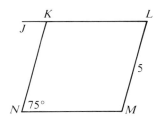

1. m$\angle L$ 75°
2. m$\angle M$ 105°
3. m$\angle JKN$ 75°
4. *KN* 5
5. *KL* 5

RSTU is an isosceles trapezoid. Find each angle measure or each length.

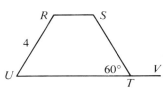

6. m$\angle U$ 60°
7. m$\angle R$ 120°
8. *ST* 4

EXAMPLE 2   Construct a parallelogram.

Solution

1. Draw a line and a point not on the line. Construct a pair of parallel lines and a transversal (by the method already learned). Label the points where the lines intersect as *P* and *Q*.

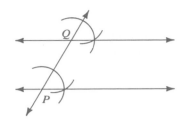

2. Choose any point *S* on one of the parallel lines. Construct a line parallel to $\overleftrightarrow{PQ}$ through *S*, using the same method. Label the point where this line intersects the line through *Q* as *R*.

   Then *PQRS* is a parallelogram.

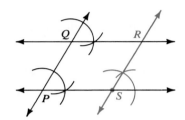

A rhombus, a rectangle, and a square are parallelograms because they each have *two* pairs of parallel sides. A quadrilateral that has exactly *one* pair of parallel sides is called a **trapezoid.** If the nonparallel sides of a trapezoid are congruent, then the trapezoid is called an **isosceles trapezoid.** An isosceles trapezoid also has two pairs of congruent angles.

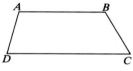

Trapezoid *ABCD*
$\overline{AB} \parallel \overline{CD}$

Isosceles trapezoid *PQRS*
$\overline{PQ} \parallel \overline{RS}$
$\overline{PS} \cong \overline{QR}$
$\angle P \cong \angle Q$
$\angle S \cong \angle R$

A segment that joins opposite vertices of a quadrilateral is called a **diagonal.** In the diagram, $\overline{TR}$ and $\overline{QS}$ are the diagonals of quadrilateral *QRST*.

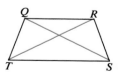

210   *Chapter 6*

Class Exercises

Choose each name that describes the figure.

quadrilateral   rectangle   parallelogram   rhombus
square   trapezoid   isosceles trapezoid

1.
quadrilateral
trapezoid

2.
quadrilateral
rectangle
parallelogram

3.
quadrilateral

4.
quadrilateral
parallelogram

5.
quadrilateral
trapezoid
isosceles trapezoid

6.
quadrilateral
rectangle
parallelogram
rhombus
square

7.
quadrilateral
parallelogram
rhombus

Written Exercises

In the diagram, *PQRS* is a parallelogram. Find each angle measure or each length.

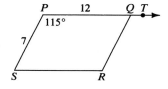

Exs. 1–6

A **1.** m∠*RQT* 115° **2.** m∠*PQR* 65° **3.** m∠*R* 115°

4. m∠*S* 65° **5.** *RS* 12 **6.** *QR* 7

In the diagram, *ABCD* is an isosceles trapezoid and *ABCE* is a parallelogram.

7. Name three congruent segments. $\overline{AB}$, $\overline{EC}$, $\overline{DC}$

8. Give a reason why ∠*CED* ≅ ∠*A*. Corr. ∠s

9. Name two other angles congruent to ∠*A*. ∠*BCE*, ∠*D*, ∠*CED*

10. Name an angle congruent to ∠*B*. ∠*AEC*

Exs. 7–10

True or false?

11. All squares are rhombuses. True   **12.** All rectangles are squares. False

13. A rhombus with at least one right angle must be a square. True

14. A trapezoid can have two right angles. True

15. A parallelogram with at least one right angle must be a rectangle. True

16. If two sides of a quadrilateral are parallel and the other two sides are congruent, the quadrilateral must be a parallelogram. False

Geometry **211**

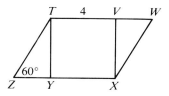

17. Draw a line *l* and a point *P* not on *l*. Construct a parallelogram with one side on *l* and with *P* as one vertex.

18. If two sides of a quadrilateral are congruent *and* parallel, then the quadrilateral is a parallelogram. Use this fact to construct a parallelogram.

B 19. If the opposite sides of a quadrilateral are congruent, then the quadrilateral is a parallelogram. Use this fact to construct a parallelogram (without copying any angles).

20. Construct a rhombus. Draw the diagonals of the rhombus. What appears to be true of the diagonals? They are perpendicular and bisect each other.

21. Construct an isosceles trapezoid.

22. Construct a rectangle. Draw the diagonals of the rectangle and let *O* be their intersection point. Draw a circle with center *O* that passes through one vertex of the rectangle. Does it also pass through the other vertices? Yes

Find the value of *x* in each diagram.

23.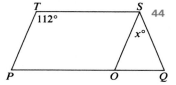

POST is a parallelogram.
$SO = SQ$

24.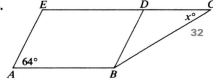

ABDE is a parallelogram.
$DB = DC$

C 25. A line segment that joins the midpoints of the nonparallel sides of a trapezoid is called the **median** of the trapezoid.
   a. Construct a trapezoid and the median of the trapezoid.
   b. What relationship between the median and the parallel sides of the trapezoid appears to be true? The median is parallel to the parallel sides.

Review Exercises

Simplify.

1. $2.5(-3.67)$ −9.175
2. $5.32 \div (-1.4)$ −3.8
3. $-12.4(-7.9)$ 97.96
4. $-5.616 \div 3.9$ −1.44
5. $-8.5(4.16)$ −35.36
6. $-62.5(-2.8)$ 175
7. $-14.4 \div (-1.6)$ 9
8. $17.5(-6.4)$ −112
9. $46.8 \div (-7.5)$ −6.24

6-8 Polygons and Their Perimeters

A **polygon** is a closed figure consisting of segments joined at their endpoints. The points are the **vertices** and the segments are the **sides** of the polygon. You know that a triangle is a three-sided polygon and a quadrilateral is a four-sided polygon. Some other special polygons also have names depending on the number of their sides.

Pentagon
5 sides

Hexagon
6 sides

Octagon
8 sides

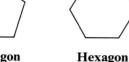
Decagon
10 sides

The **perimeter** of a polygon is the sum of the lengths of the sides.

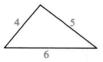

Perimeter = 4 + 5 + 6 = 15

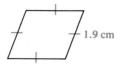

Perimeter = 4 × 1.9 = 7.6 (cm)

If all the sides and all the angles of a polygon are congruent, the polygon is called **regular.**

EXAMPLE   The perimeter of a regular hexagon is 256.2 cm. Find the length of one side of the hexagon.

Solution   Recall that a regular hexagon has 6 sides of the same length. Let s be the length of one side. Then the perimeter is $6 \times s$.

$$256.2 = 6 \times s$$
$$6s = 256.2$$
$$s = \frac{256.2}{6} = 42.7$$

The length of one side is 42.7 cm.

Problem Solving Reminder

To solve some problems, you may have to *supply additional information* such as a mathematics fact that you have learned. In the Example, it was necessary to recall that a regular hexagon has 6 congruent sides in order to find the length of one side.

Geometry **213**

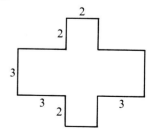
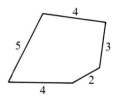
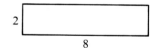
213

Class Exercises

Find the perimeter of each polygon.

1.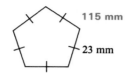
15 m 12 m 47 m
20 m

2.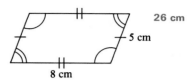
26 cm
5 cm
8 cm

3.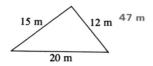
115 mm
23 mm

4.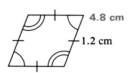
4.8 cm
1.2 cm

In Exercises 5–8, all the angles in the figures are right angles. Find the perimeter of each figure.

5.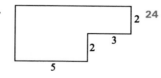
2 24
3
2
5

6.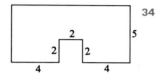
34
2
2 2
5
4 4

7.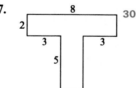
8
2 30
3 3
5

8.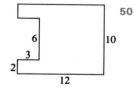
50
6
10
3
2
12

Give another name for each.

9. a regular triangle equilateral

10. a regular quadrilateral square

Written Exercises

Find the perimeter of each.

A 1. A regular pentagon with sides of length 3.2 cm 16 cm

2. A regular octagon with sides of length 12.5 m 100 m

3. An isosceles triangle with two sides of length 18.5 m and the third side of length 13 m 50 m

214 *Chapter 6*

Additional A Exercises

Find the perimeter of each.

1. A square with side 3.2 m. **12.8 m**

2. A rectangle with length 17 cm and width 3.9 cm. **41.8 cm**

3. A polygon with sides 1.6 m, 3.2 m, 4.7 m, 12.6 m, and 4.7 m. **26.8 m**

Find the length of each side of the figure described.

4. An equilateral triangle with perimeter 42 cm. **14 cm**

5. A parallelogram with perimeter 124 ft and base 12 ft. **50 ft**

6. A regular decagon with perimeter 300 cm. **30 cm**

214

Find the perimeter of each.

4. A parallelogram with sides of length 23.6 cm and 52.9 cm 153 cm

5. A regular decagon with sides of length 4.25 mm 42.5 mm

6. A pentagon with three sides of length 26 cm and two sides of length 14.5 cm 107 cm

Find the length of each side of the figure described.

7. A regular hexagon with perimeter 427.2 mm 71.2 mm

8. A regular octagon with perimeter 392.8 cm 49.1 cm

9. A square with perimeter 25 in. 6.25 in.

10. An equilateral triangle with perimeter 572.4 m 190.8 m

11. A rectangle with perimeter 148.6 m and width 29.2 m 45.1 m

12. An isosceles trapezoid with parallel sides of lengths $26\frac{1}{4}$ ft and $38\frac{1}{4}$ ft and perimeter 86 ft $10\frac{3}{4}$ ft

A polygon is *inscribed* in a circle if all of its vertices lie on the circle. Draw a circle for each exercise and construct each figure so that it is inscribed in the circle.

B 13. A regular hexagon (*Hint:* The length of each side of a regular hexagon equals the radius of the circle on which the vertices lie.)

14. A square (*Hint:* The diagonals of a square are perpendicular.)

15. An equilateral triangle (*Hint:* Construct a regular hexagon first.)

16. A regular octagon (*Hint:* Construct two perpendicular diameters and bisect two of the right angles formed.)

If the vertex of an angle is the center of a circle, the angle is called a *central angle*. Use each figure to calculate the measure of one angle formed by two adjacent sides of the given polygon.

17. 135°

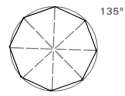

A regular octagon
Each central angle is 45°.

18. 140°

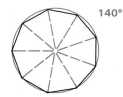

A regular 9-sided polygon
Each central angle is 40°.

Suggested Assignments

Minimum
  214/1–3
  215/4–18
  216/Rev. 1–8
Average
  214/1–3
  215/4–18
  216/19–20
  216/Rev. 2–8 even
  216/Challenge
Maximum
  214/1–3
  215/4–18
  216/19–22
  216/Challenge

Supplementary Materials

Practice Masters, p. 28

Use a method such as the one used for Exercises 17 and 18 to find the measure of one angle formed by two adjacent sides of the given polygon.

19. a regular decagon ₁₄₄°

20. a regular 12-sided polygon ₁₅₀°

C **21. a.** Draw any quadrilateral $ABCD$ and draw the diagonal $\overline{AC}$. What is the sum of the measures of the angles of $ABCD$? ₃₆₀°

b. Draw a pentagon $PQRST$ and diagonals $\overline{RP}$ and $\overline{RT}$. What is the sum of the measures of the angles of $PQRST$? ₅₄₀°

c. In a polygon with n sides, how many triangles can be made by drawing diagonals from one vertex of the polygon? ₙ ₋ ₂

d. Use your answer to part (c) to write a formula for finding the sum of the angles of a polygon with n sides. ₍ₙ ₋ ₂₎₁₈₀°

22. In the diagram below, $ABCDE$ is a regular pentagon. Find the value of y. (*Hint:* See Exercise 21.) ₃₆

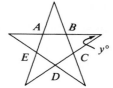

Review Exercises

Simplify.

1. $1.45 + 2.36$ **2.** $-7.82 + 52.4$ **3.** $-3.75 + (-4.2)$ **4.** $-95 + 14.9$

5. $3.82 - (-46)$ **6.** $-18 - 33$ **7.** $-64.5 - (-27.3)$ **8.** $0.75 - 26.15$

1. 3.81   2. 44.58   3. −7.95   4. −80.1
5. 49.82   6. −51   7. −37.2   8. −25.4

| **Challenge**

1–3 can each be done in more than one way. Check students' drawings.

1. Can you remove 8 squares from the figure at the right without changing the perimeter? Yes

2. Can you remove 8 squares to increase the perimeter by 16? Yes

3. Can you rearrange the squares to obtain a perimeter of 36? Yes

4. Rearrange the squares to obtain the greatest possible perimeter.

5. Can you rearrange the squares to obtain a perimeter less than the perimeter shown? No

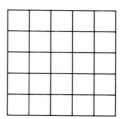

6-9 Congruent Polygons

Two polygons are **congruent** if there is a way to match the vertices of one with the vertices of the other so that the *corresponding sides are congruent and the corresponding angles are congruent.* In the diagram at the right,

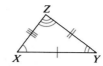

$$\angle R \cong \angle X \qquad \angle S \cong \angle Y \qquad \angle T \cong \angle Z$$

and

$$\overline{RS} \cong \overline{XY} \qquad \overline{ST} \cong \overline{YZ} \qquad \overline{RT} \cong \overline{XZ}$$

Notice that since vertices R and S are matched with vertices X and Y, side $\overline{RS}$ must be matched with side $\overline{XY}$. Notice also that the order in which the vertices are named in the statement tells how the vertices are matched:

$$\triangle RST \cong \triangle XYZ.$$

If two figures are congruent, we can match their vertices by using one or more of the basic **rigid motions.**

Translation

Rotation

Reflection

We can use translation to match triangles RST and XYZ above.

EXAMPLE 1 In the diagram, $ABCD \cong HGFE$.

a. $\angle B \cong \angle$?

b. $\overline{AD} \cong$?

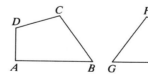

Solution The statement $ABCD \cong HGFE$ indicates that B corresponds to G and $\overline{AD}$ corresponds to $\overline{HE}$. (Note that the polygons can be matched by using reflection.) Therefore,

a. $\angle B \cong \angle G$

b. $\overline{AD} \cong \overline{HE}$

Geometry **217**

Teaching Suggestions p. 181g

Related Activities p. 181h

Reading Mathematics

Students will learn the meaning of the following mathematical terms in this lesson: *congruent, rigid motions, translation, rotation, reflection, side-angle-side test, SAS, angle-side-angle test, ASA, side-side-side test, SSS.*

Chalkboard Examples

In the diagram, $BLAST \cong XYZCD$.

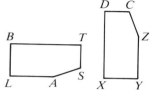

1. $\overline{XY} \cong$? $\overline{BL}$
2. $\overline{LA} \cong$? $\overline{YZ}$
3. $\overline{BT} \cong$? $\overline{XD}$
4. $\angle A \cong \angle$? Z
5. $\angle B \cong \angle$? X
6. $\angle C \cong \angle$? S

When working with triangles, we do not need to check all sides and all angles to establish congruence. Suppose that in the two triangles below, the sides and the angles marked alike are congruent.

If we were to match the congruent parts by using translation, we would find that all other corresponding sides and angles are congruent also. Thus we can use the following method to establish congruence in two triangles.

The side-angle-side (SAS) test for congruence
If two sides of one triangle and the angle they form (the *included angle*) are congruent to two sides and the included angle of another triangle, then the two triangles are congruent.

Two other methods that we can use to establish congruence in triangles are:

The angle-side-angle (ASA) test for congruence
If two angles and the side between them (the *included side*) are congruent to two angles and the included side of another triangle, then the two triangles are congruent.

The side-side-side (SSS) test for congruence
If three sides of one triangle are congruent to the three sides of another triangle, then the two triangles are congruent.

EXAMPLE 2   In the diagram, triangle ABC is isosceles, with $\overline{AB} \cong \overline{CD}$. $\overline{BD}$ bisects $\angle ABC$. Explain why $\triangle ABD \cong \triangle CBD$.

Solution   We know that $\overline{AB} \cong \overline{CB}$.
Since $\overline{BD}$ bisects $\angle ABC$, $\angle 1 \cong \angle 2$.
Also, $\overline{BD}$ is a side of both triangles.
Therefore, by the SAS test,
$\triangle ABD \cong \triangle CBD$.

Class Exercises

In the diagram, △ *HJK* ≅ △ *DOT*.

1. ∠ *J* ≅ ∠ _?_ o   2. ∠ *T* ≅ ∠ _?_ κ
3. $\overline{KJ}$ ≅ _?_ $\overline{TO}$ 4. $\overline{DO}$ ≅ _?_ $\overline{HJ}$

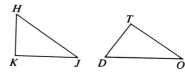

In the diagram, *QRST* ≅ *BAKE*.

5. ∠ *A* ≅ ∠ _?_ R   6. In *BAKE*, m∠ _?_ *E* = 115°
7. *QT* = _?_ 7.8   8. $\overline{TS}$ ≅ _?_ $\overline{EK}$

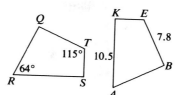

State which of the rigid motions is needed to match the vertices of the triangles in each pair and give a reason why the triangles are congruent.

9.

Translation, SAS

10.
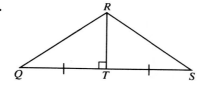
Reflection, or reflection and translation; ASA

11.
Rotation, or rotation and translation; SSS

Written Exercises

Explain why the triangles in each pair are congruent.

A 1.
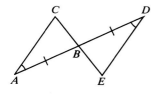
△ *ABC* ≅ △ *DBE* ASA

2.
△ *QRT* ≅ △ *SRT* SAS

3.
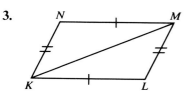
△ *KLM* ≅ △ *MNK* SSS

4.
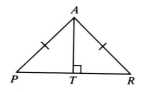
△ *PAT* ≅ △ *RAT* SAS, or ASA

Geometry **219**

Explain why the triangles in each pair are congruent.

1.

ASA or SAS

2.

SSS

3.

SAS

Complete the statements for these congruent polygons.

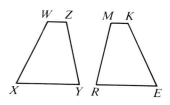

4. $\overline{WZ}$ ≅ _?_ $\overline{KM}$
5. $\overline{ZY}$ ≅ _?_ $\overline{MR}$
6. ∠ *WXY* ≅ _?_ ∠ *KER*

219

5. Draw an acute triangle *ABC*. Use the SAS test to construct a triangle *DEF* such that △*ABC* ≅ △*DEF*. With a compass, check the third sides of the triangles for congruence.

6. Draw an acute triangle *RST*. Use the ASA test to construct a triangle *XYZ* such that △*RST* ≅ △*XYZ*. Use your compass to check the two remaining sides of the triangles to see if the corresponding sides are congruent.

7. $\overline{AM} \perp \overline{PT}$; *PM = MT*. Explain why △*PAM* ≅ △*TAM*.

SAS

8. *LMNO* is a rhombus. Explain why △*LMN* ≅ △*NOL*.

SSS, or SAS, or ASA

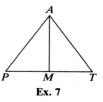
Ex. 7

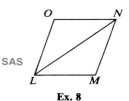
Ex. 8

For Exercises 9–12, name the congruent triangles, state which of the rigid motions (you may use more than one) are needed to match the vertices of the triangles, and explain why the triangles are congruent.

B **9.**
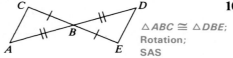
△*ABC* ≅ △*DBE*;
Rotation;
SAS

10.

△*FGH* ≅ △*JIH*;
Reflection; SSS

11.
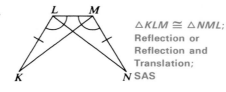
△*KLM* ≅ △*NML*;
Reflection or
Reflection and
Translation;
SAS

12.
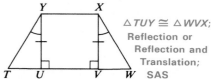
△*TUY* ≅ △*WVX*;
Reflection or
Reflection and
Translation;
SAS

Name a pair of congruent triangles and explain why they are congruent.

13.
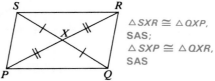
△*SXR* ≅ △*QXP*,
SAS;
△*SXP* ≅ △*QXR*,
SAS

14.
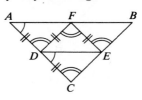

15.
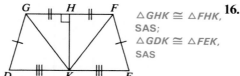
△*GHK* ≅ △*FHK*,
SAS;
△*GDK* ≅ △*FEK*,
SAS

16.
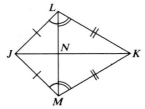

220   *Chapter 6*

17. FDCA is a parallelogram and $\overline{AB} \cong \overline{ED}$. Explain why $\triangle ABC \cong \triangle DEF$. $\angle A \cong \angle D$, $\overline{AC} \cong \overline{FD}$; SAS

18. FDCA is a parallelogram and $\angle ACB \cong \angle EFD$. Explain why $\triangle ABC \cong \triangle DEF$. $\angle A \cong \angle D$, $\overline{AC} \cong \overline{FD}$; ASA

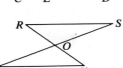

19. $\overline{RS} \parallel \overline{XY}$ and $\overline{XO} \cong \overline{SO}$. Explain why $\triangle XOY \cong \triangle SOR$. $\angle X \cong \angle S$, $\angle ROS \cong \angle YOX$; ASA

20. $\overline{RS} \parallel \overline{XY}$ and $\overline{RS} \cong \overline{XY}$. Explain why $\triangle XOY \cong \triangle SOR$. $\angle R \cong \angle Y$, $\angle S \cong \angle X$; ASA

Self-Test B

Find the measure of each unknown angle in the triangle and tell whether the triangle is acute, right, or obtuse.

1. A scalene triangle with angles of measure 38° and 52° 90°; right [6-6]

2. An equilateral triangle 60°, 60°, 60°; acute

3. An isosceles triangle with angles of measure 110° and 35° 35°; obtuse

QTWX is an isosceles trapezoid. RSWX is a rectangle.

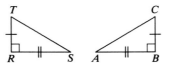

4. Find m∠XRS. 90° [6-7]

5. Find m∠XQR. 54°

6. Name a segment congruent to $\overline{XQ}$. $\overline{WT}$

7. Name a segment congruent to $\overline{WS}$. $\overline{XR}$

8. Find the perimeter of QTWX. 30 [6-8]

9. Find the perimeter of RSWX. 22

10. If a regular pentagon has perimeter 321 cm, what is the length of each side? 64.2 cm

True or false?

11. $\overline{RS} \cong \overline{BA}$ True **12.** $\angle T \cong \angle C$ True [6-9]

13. This statement indicates the corresponding parts correctly:

$$\triangle RTS \cong \triangle CBA. \text{ False}$$

Self-Test answers and Extra Practice are at the back of the book.

Geometry **221**

---

2. An isosceles triangle with angles of measure 45° and 45°. **90°, right**

3. A scalene triangle with angles of measure 88° and 64°. **28°, acute**

In the drawing below, ABCD is a square, and ABFE and DCFE are isosceles trapezoids.

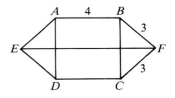

4. Find m∠ADC. **90°**

5. Name three segments congruent to $\overline{AE}$. **$\overline{BF}$, $\overline{CF}$, $\overline{DE}$**

6. Name three segments congruent to $\overline{AB}$. **$\overline{BC}$, $\overline{DC}$, $\overline{AD}$**

7. Find the perimeter of polygon ABFCDE. **20**

8. Find the perimeter of triangle AED. **10**

9. Find the perimeter of polygon ABCD. **16**

10. If a regular hexagon has a perimeter of 750 cm, what is the length of each side? **125 cm**

True or False?

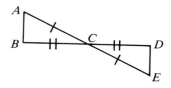

11. $\overline{AC} \cong \overline{CE}$ **True**

12. $\angle ACB \cong \angle DCE$ **True**

13. $\triangle ACB \cong \triangle ECD$ **True**

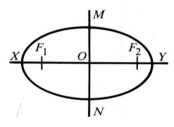
Ellipses

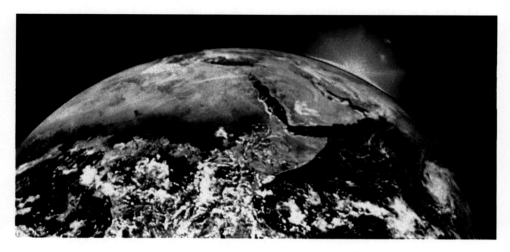

An **ellipse** is a curve that is important in astronomy. The orbit of every planet in our solar system, including Earth, is an ellipse.

You can draw an ellipse with the aid of a piece of string, a pencil, and two nails driven into a piece of wood. Make a loop of string that fits loosely around the nails and put the pencil point inside the loop. Keeping the loop taut with the pencil, draw the largest closed curve you can. The resulting curve is an ellipse. Notice that for every point on the curve that you have drawn, the sum of its distances from the two nails ($p + q$ in the drawing below) is always the same. This is true because the loop has a fixed length. Every ellipse has two points corresponding to the nails above. Each of these points is called a **focus** (plural: *foci*) of the ellipse.

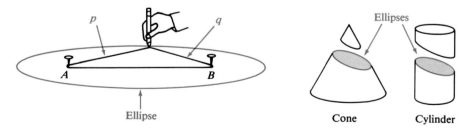

Ellipses occur as cross sections of common geometric solids as shown at the right above.

To illustrate an ellipse, shine a flashlight at a piece of paper. If you hold the paper at a slant through the "cone" of light, you will see an ellipse.

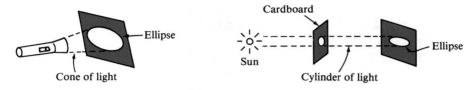

If you let the sun's rays shine through a circular hole in a piece of cardboard and hold a piece of paper at a slant through the "cylinder" of light, you will also see an ellipse.

1. Using an old piece of wood, draw an ellipse using the string method described. Start with a fairly large loop of string. Then shorten the loop by tying a small knot in it and draw another ellipse using the same nails as foci.

2. Make an ellipse by either the flashlight method or the sunlight method described above. Vary the dimensions of the ellipse by changing the slant of the sheet of paper.

3. You can also make an ellipse by folding paper. First cut out a circle of paper. Mark the center of the circle and any other point P inside the circle. Then fold the circle so that the edge just touches the point P and make a crease. Unfold the circle and then repeat the folding process several times, folding from a different direction each time. Do you see an ellipse after making several folds? What appear to be its foci? *P and the center of the circle.*

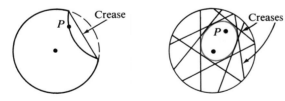

Career Activity

Astronomical instruments have changed greatly since the first telescope was invented in the 1600's. If you were an astronomer today, what are some of the instruments that you might be using?

Geometry **223**

The orbit of a planet is a nearly circular ellipse with the sun at one focus. A planet moves faster when it is close to the sun than when it is farther away. Johannes Kepler discovered a law that describes this variation in speed, making it possible to predict the positions of the planets. The orbits of most comets are very eccentric ellipses. A comet may be close to the sun at one end of its orbit, and farther away than Pluto at the other end.

Chapter Review

Complete. Use the appropriate symbols for segments, lines, and rays.

1. ___?___ is a ray through point E that begins at point O. $\overrightarrow{OE}$ [6–1]

2. ___?___ is a segment with endpoints A and E. $\overline{AE}$ or $\overline{EA}$

3. ___?___ is a line through points A and C. $\overleftrightarrow{AC}$ or $\overleftrightarrow{CA}$

4. If the radius of a circle is 17, the circumference is ___?___. Use $\pi \approx 3.14$. **107**   [6–2]

5. If the circumference of a circle is 37, the diameter is ___?___. Use $\pi \approx 3.14$. **11.8**

6. The measure of an obtuse angle is between ___?___° and ___?___°. **90; 180**   [6–3]

7. The measure of an acute angle is between ___?___° and ___?___°. **0, 90**

8. Two angles that have a common side and a common vertex but do not overlap are called ___?___ angles. **adjacent**

True or false?

9. Complementary angles have a sum of 90°. **True**   [6–4]

10. Supplementary angles are always congruent. **False**

11. Vertical angles always have a sum of 90°. **False**

12. Parallel lines meet in a single point. **False**   [6–5]

13. Alternate interior angles are always congruent. **False**

14. $\triangle NOQ$ is an isosceles obtuse triangle. **True**   [6–6]

15. $\triangle QOP$ is a scalene acute triangle. **True**

16. $m\angle QPO$ is 55°. **False**

Exs. 14–16

17. Opposite angles of a trapezoid are always congruent. **False**   [6–7]

18. All sides and all angles of a rhombus are congruent. **False**

19. A parallelogram with width 53 and length 84 has perimeter 272. **False**   [6–8]

20. A regular octagon with perimeter 564 has sides of length 70.5. **True**

21. Two triangles are always congruent if three sides of one triangle are congruent to three sides of the other. **True**   [6–9]

22. Two triangles are always congruent if three angles of one triangle are congruent to three angles of the other. **False**

Chapter Test

Supplementary Materials

Chapter 6 Test, pp. 39–40

1. Draw a labeled diagram to illustrate points A, B, and C, $\overrightarrow{AB}$, $\overleftrightarrow{BC}$, and $\overline{AC}$.   [6-1]

2. Draw any $\overline{LM}$ and construct $\overline{XY}$ congruent to $\overline{LM}$.

3. Draw a circle with radius $\overline{OM}$, a diameter $\overline{KL}$, and a chord $\overline{NP}$.   [6-2]
   Label an arc and a semicircle.

4. Find the circumference of a circle with radius 42 cm. Use $\pi \approx \frac{22}{7}$. **264**

5. Draw an obtuse angle and construct a congruent angle.   [6-3]

6. $\angle GFH$ and $\angle EFG$ are adjacent angles. $m\angle GFH = 52°$.
   $m\angle EFG = 76°$. What is $m\angle EFH$? **128°**

7. $\angle XYZ$ and $\angle RST$ are supplementary angles. If $m\angle XYZ$ is 9°   [6-4]
   less than $m\angle RST$, what is the measure of each angle? **$m\angle XYZ = 85.5°$**
   $m\angle RST = 94.5°$

8. $\angle ABC$ and $\angle DBE$ are vertical angles. $m\angle DBE = 62°$. Find
   $m\angle ABC$. **62°**

In the diagram, lines l and m are parallel.

9. $\angle 3$ and $\angle\underline{\ ?\ }$ are alternate interior angles. **6**   [6-5]

10. $\angle 6$ and $\angle\underline{\ ?\ }$ are corresponding angles. **8**

11. $m\angle 4 = 138°$. Find the other angle measures.
    $m\angle 1 = m\angle 6 = m\angle 3 = m\angle 8 = 42°$ **$m\angle 2 = m\angle 4 = m\angle 7 = m\angle 5 = 138°$**

12. $\triangle OPQ$ is an isosceles obtuse triangle. If $m\angle QOP$ is 28°, what are   [6-6]
    the measures of the other angles? **28°, 124°**

13. $\triangle RST$ is a scalene acute triangle. If $m\angle SRT$ is 64° and $m\angle STR$
    is 77°, what is $m\angle RST$? **39°**

14. Name two quadrilaterals in which all sides are congruent. **rhombus,**   [6-7]
    square

15. Name two quadrilaterals that have two pairs of congruent angles.
    parallelogram, rhombus, square, rectangle, isosceles trapezoid

16. A regular decagon has perimeter 377.5. Find the length of a side. **37.75**   [6-8]

17. A rectangle has length 18 and width 12. Find the perimeter. **60**

**Are the triangles in each pair congruent? If so, name the triangles that
are congruent and explain why they are congruent.**

18. 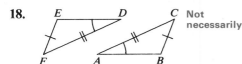 **Not necessarily**

19. 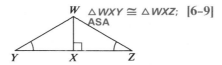 $\triangle WXY \cong \triangle WXZ$;   [6-9]
    ASA

Geometry **225**

Review for Retention

Complete. Use $=$, $>$, or $<$ to make a true statement.

1. -5 __?__ 4 $<$

2. -3.8 __?__ -3 $<$

3. $|-1|$ __?__ 1 $=$

4. $|6|$ __?__ 6 $=$

5. -3.26 __?__ -3.44 $>$

6. $|12.5|$ __?__ 12.5 $=$

True or False?

7. $0 + -8 = 0$ **False**

8. $11.3 + -11.3 = 1$ **False**

9. $1(43.5) = 43.5$ **True**

10. $-3(0)(4.6) = 0$ **True**

11. $-2.6 - (-2.6) = -5.2$ **False**

12. $25 \div (-5) = -5$ **True**

13. $18.4 + (-23.4) = -5$ **True**

14. $-4.6 + 1 = -4.6$ **False**

15. $-0.03 \div (-1) = 0.03$ **True**

16. $64 \div (-4) = 16$ **False**

17. $0 \div 13.7 = 0$ **True**

18. $-3(12)(-0.17) = 6.12$ **True**

19. If $t = 4$, then $3 + t = 7$. **True**

20. If $6g = 12$, then $g = 72$. **False**

21. If $5 - f = 7$, then $f = -12$. **False**

22. If $s \div 3 = 4$, then $s = 1\frac{1}{3}$. **False**

23. If $j = 15$, then $j \div 5 = 3$. **True**

24. If $2k - 5 = 12$, then $k = 8\frac{1}{2}$. **True**

(Continue on next page.)

Cumulative Review (Chapters 1–6)

Exercises

Round to the nearest cent.

1. $12.453 **$12.45**   **2.** $39.995 **$40.00**   **3.** $160.870 **$160.87**   **4.** $.955 **$.96**

5. $821.099 **$821.10** **6.** $.006 **$.01**   **7.** $375.902 **$375.90**   **8.** $7.9048 **$7.90**

Simplify.

9. $(36 + 18)y$ **54y**   **10.** $x + 0.4x$ **1.4x**   **11.** $\frac{500r}{5}$ **100r**   **12.** $1200 \times b \times 0.3$ **360b**

13. $4(a + 5a)$ **24a**   **14.** $100n \div 2.5$ **40n**   **15.** $1.6(n - 4.2)$ **1.6n − 6.72**   **16.** $\frac{14t}{40} \times 200$ **70t**

17. $-9.7 + (-6.1)$ **−15.8**   **18.** $6.14 + (-12.5)$ **−6.36**   **19.** $-4.032 + 9.25$ **5.218**

20. $42.9 - (-3.7)$ **46.6**   **21.** $-3.4 - (-12.5)$ **9.1**   **22.** $-76 - 27.82$ **−103.82**

23. -4.23×3.5 **−14.805**   **24.** $-12.3 \times (-5.4)$ **66.42**   **25.** 13.5×24 **324**

26. $-64 \div 8$ **−8**   **27.** $-30 \div (-12)$ **2.5**   **28.** $-28 \div 0.2$ **−140**

Write the fraction in lowest terms.

29. $-\frac{84}{116}$ **$-\frac{21}{29}$**   **30.** $\frac{20}{74}$ **$\frac{10}{37}$**   **31.** $-\frac{116}{164}$ **$-\frac{29}{41}$**   **32.** $-\frac{36}{64}$ **$-\frac{9}{16}$**   **33.** $\frac{24}{148}$ **$\frac{6}{37}$**

Express as a fraction or mixed number in lowest terms.

34. 0.45 **$\frac{9}{20}$**   **35.** 0.036 **$\frac{9}{250}$**   **36.** 2.01 **$2\frac{1}{100}$**   **37.** 11.84 **$11\frac{21}{25}$**   **38.** 4.832 **$4\frac{104}{125}$**

Express as a decimal. Use a bar to indicate a repeating decimal.

39. $\frac{2}{3}$ **$0.\overline{6}$**   **40.** $\frac{5}{11}$ **$0.\overline{45}$**   **41.** $3\frac{5}{6}$ **$3.8\overline{3}$**   **42.** $2\frac{4}{9}$ **$2.\overline{4}$**   **43.** $8\frac{1}{12}$ **$8.08\overline{3}$**

Express the repeating decimal as a fraction or mixed number in lowest terms.

44. $0.\overline{4}$ **$\frac{4}{9}$**   **45.** $0.8\overline{3}$ **$\frac{5}{6}$**   **46.** $1.\overline{3}$ **$1\frac{1}{3}$**   **47.** $2.\overline{42}$ **$2\frac{14}{33}$**   **48.** $5.2\overline{13}$ **$5\frac{211}{990}$**

Solve the equation.

49. $b + 17 = 39$ **22**   **50.** $1.7 + x = 2.3$ **0.6**

51. $d - 65 = 104$ **169**   **52.** $526 - a = 438.5$ **87.5**

53. $n = 0.5 \times 38$ **19**   **54.** $1056 = r \times 22$ **48**

55. $44.688 = 0.84 \times q$ **53.2**   **56.** $2745.6 = 0.16 \times t \times 52$ **330**

226 *Chapter 6*

Problems

Problem Solving Reminders

Here are some reminders that may help you solve some of the problems on this page.

• Consider whether drawing a sketch will help.
• Check by using rounding to find an estimated answer.
• Reread the question to be sure that you have answered with the information requested.

Solve.

1. The perimeter of an equilateral triangle is 45 cm. What is the length of each side? **15 cm**

2. A photographer works 35 h a week and earns $295. What is the hourly rate to the nearest cent? **$8.43**

3. Elena commutes to work. She travels 2.6 km by subway and 1.8 km by bus. How far is that in all? **4.4 km**

4. The temperature at 11:30 P.M. was 7° below zero. By the next morning, the temperature had fallen 6°. What was the temperature then? **−13°**

5. During one week, the stock of DataTech Corporation had the following daily changes in price: Monday, up $1\frac{1}{2}$ points; Tuesday, down 2 points; Wednesday, down $\frac{3}{4}$ of a point; Thursday, up $3\frac{1}{8}$ points; Friday, up $2\frac{3}{4}$ points. What was the change in the price of the stock for the week? **up $4\frac{5}{8}$**

6. A rope 25 m long is cut into 2 pieces so that one piece is 9 m shorter than the other. Find the length of each piece. **8 m and 17 m**

7. Michael spent $16.00 on tickets to the game. Adult tickets cost twice as much as student tickets. If he bought 2 adult tickets and 4 student tickets, how much does each kind of ticket cost? **adult $4, student $2**

8. The difference between the measures of two supplementary angles is 8°. What is the measure of each angle? **86°, 94°**

9. The length of a rectangle is 5 cm greater than the width. The perimeter is 70 cm. Find the length and the width. **20 cm, 15 cm**

10. The two equal sides of an isosceles triangle are each 11 cm longer than the third side. The perimeter of the triangle is 58 cm. What is the length of each side? **23 cm, 23 cm, 12 cm**

11. The perimeter of a regular octagon is 121.6 m. What is the length of each side? **15.2 m**

Geometry **227**

25. If $\frac{r}{3} + 7 = 19$, then $r = 4$. **False**

26. If $5(8 - h) = 25$, then $h = 3$. **True**

27. If $6m = 4m - 12$, then $m = 6$. **False**

28. If $q = 5$, then $8q - 3 = 6q + 7$. **True**

What value of the variable makes the statement true?

29. $2^n = 8$ **3**

30. $3^t = \frac{1}{9}$ **−2**

31. $7^5 \div 7^9 = 7^j$ **−4**

32. $5^3 \times 5^t = \frac{1}{5}$ **−4**

33. $4a - 6 = 30$ **9**

34. $6c + 3 = 4c + 7$ **2**

Write an equivalent inequality.

Answers may vary. An example is given.

35. $4x - 7 \leq 5$ **$x \leq 3$**

36. $8 - 2y > -4$ **$y < 6$**

37. $5b + 7 \geq 12$ **$b \geq 1$**

38. $6 - 3g < 24$ **$g > -6$**

39. $4 - 3f \leq 16 + 2f$ **$f \geq -2\frac{2}{5}$**

40. $5 + 3j > 10 - 2j$ **$j > 1$**

7

Ratio, Proportion, and Percent

Before the invention of the microscope, objects appeared to consist only of those materials seen with the unaided eye. Today the ability to magnify objects, such as the salt crystals shown at the right, has enabled scientists to understand the structures of various compounds in detail. The most advanced microscopes in use at the present time are electron microscopes. Electron microscopes can magnify objects hundreds of thousands of times by using beams of focused electrons.

The visibility of fine detail in a magnification depends on several factors, including the light and the magnifying power of the microscope. For a simple microscope, the magnifying power can be expressed as this ratio:

$$\frac{\text{size of the image on the viewer's eye}}{\text{size of the object seen without a microscope}}.$$

In this chapter, you will learn how scales and ratios are used.

Career Note

When you think of photography, you probably think of it as a means of portraying people and places. When used in conjunction with a microscope (photomicrography), or with infrared or ultraviolet light, photography can become an important research tool. Scientific photographers must have a knowledge of film, filters, lenses, illuminators, and all other types of camera equipment. They must also have a thorough understanding of scale and proportion in order to find the best composition for a particular photograph.

Lesson Commentary
Chapter 7 Ratio, Proportion, and Percent

Overview

Ratio, proportion, and percent are important concepts because of their practical use and widespread application. This chapter presents an opportunity to show how mathematics can be helpful in the daily lives of your students. For students who will not take consumer mathematics courses in high school, the study of ratios, proportions, and percents becomes a necessity. As you teach this chapter, emphasize that each process is important because of its applications.

BASIC CONCEPTS

7-1 Ratio and Proportion

Objectives *for pages 230–233*

- To write a ratio in lowest terms.
- To set up and solve proportions.

Teaching Suggestions

Point out that ratios can be written as improper fractions, but not as mixed numbers.

Review how to solve equations using multiplication and division (Lesson 5-4).

Example 3 in this section indicates that words are useful when setting up a proportion. Show that the ratio of mix to water is also correct.

$$\frac{40}{3} = \frac{30}{w} \longleftarrow \text{mix} \\ \phantom{\frac{40}{3} = \frac{30}{w}} \longleftarrow \text{water}$$

Emphasize that each ratio uses the same comparison. Practice reading the proportions aloud: "If a 40-lb bag calls for 3 qt of water, a 30-lb bag will call for how many quarts of water?"

Point out that a proportion requires two equal ratios. If one ratio compares quarts of water to pounds of mix, the other must do the same.

Remind students to watch for problems involving different units of measurement. A problem might give an amount of water in quarts, for example, and ask for an answer in gallons.

Students sometimes learn to solve a proportion by cross-multiplying without learning why the procedure works. Learning from the start why the procedure works helps students avoid using the procedure inappropriately. Stress that cross-multiplying may be used to solve proportions only; it does not work for equations that are not proportions, for example $x + \frac{1}{2} = \frac{7}{8}$. Review fractions (Chapter 4) if needed.

The rest of this chapter requires that students be proficient in solving proportions. If students have difficulty with this lesson, you may want to consider spending a little extra time to ensure that students have the necessary skills for the lessons that follow.

Resource Book: Page 83 (Use After Page 233)

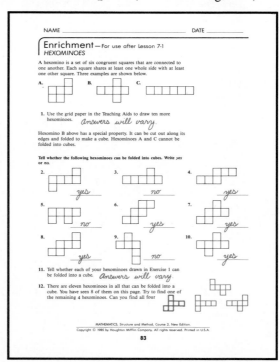

Related Activities

To relate mathematics to the real world, have students look up the meanings of the word *ratio,* its origin, and how it has been used. Also have them find examples of how ratios are used today. (Encourage special findings such as the ratio of the length to the width of the United States flag, 1.9 to 1.) Students can write up, illustrate, and display the results of their research.

7-2 Rates and Problem Solving

Objectives *for pages 234–237*

- To express unit rates.
- To use rates to solve problems.

Teaching Suggestions

Students are already familiar with many rates, such as miles per hour, miles per gallon, and dollars per pound. Point out that rates are used in many familiar situations. Ask for other rates and suggest a few, such as students per class, points per game, seats per row, days per week, and pencils per package. Students may think that only a speed is a rate; assure them that all of these examples are rates.

In Example 3, two methods of solution are shown. Students may prefer one of these methods, but they should be able to apply both of them in order to check their work and to solve problems in which one method is more easily applied.

Students should be aware that supermarkets are required to post the unit price of every item. Ask them to look for labels on shelves and counters. Emphasize the importance of looking at the unit price, not just the total price of the item. Ask for examples in which the package with the lowest unit price may not be the best choice, such as a new shampoo you may not like or food that may spoil before it is used up.

Related Activities

To provide practice using familiar items, bring several store-bought products to class and have students calculate the unit prices.

To demonstrate the importance of reading labels, bring in containers with different shapes, such as a wide jar and a tall narrow bottle. Ask students to estimate the ratio of the capacities of the containers. Then measure the capacities (by pouring water into measuring cups) and calculate the actual ratio.

7-3 Scale Drawings

Objective *for pages 238–240*

- To interpret and use scale drawings.

Teaching Suggestions

The exercises can be solved simply by solving proportions, but you may want to express the rules more formally:

$$\text{actual length} = \text{scale} \times \text{length in drawing}$$
$$\text{scale length} = \text{actual length} \div \text{scale}$$
$$\text{scale} = \text{actual length} \div \text{length in drawing}$$

Bring in some real road maps and architectural drawings to display.

To help students distinguish between the scale for an enlargement and the scale for a reduction, tell them that the first number usually represents measurements in the drawing. Thus, a scale of 1 cm : 3 cm describes a reduction to $\frac{1}{3}$ of the original size. By contrast, a scale of 3 cm : 1 cm describes an enlargement to 3 times the size of the original.

Related Activities

To relate this topic to careers, have students investigate careers in which scale drawings are used, such as cartographer, architect, engineer, designer, geologist, archeologist, and technical illustrator.

To relate mathematics to students' lives, have each student measure a room in her or his home and make a scale drawing of the room and its furnishings. Remind them to show correct placement of doors, windows, and closets.

7-4 Percents, Fractions, and Decimals

Objectives *for pages 241–244*

- To express percents as fractions and as decimals.
- To express fractions and decimals as percents.

Teaching Suggestions

The teaching suggestions and related activities for Lesson 4-7, Fractions and Decimals, also have value for this lesson. Review common fractions and decimal equivalents as you begin this section.

Emphasize that the percent symbol, %, is really a sign. This sign tells us to divide by 100, multiply by 0.01, or multiply by $\frac{1}{100}$.

Make a sign to post in the room:

$$\% = \div 100 \text{ or } \times 0.01 \text{ or } \times \frac{1}{100}$$

Explain that these operations may be used interchangeably because they say the same thing.

Another helpful visual aid is:

$$\% \text{ means } \div 100$$

(read: % means divide by 100.)

After students thoroughly grasp the meaning of the percent symbol and are ready for the shortcut of moving the decimal point, write the letters of the alphabet across the chalkboard. Point out that to move from the D, decimal, to the P, percent, requires moving to the right. Moving from the P, percent, to the D, decimal, requires moving left.

Students will find it useful to memorize certain common equivalents. If they need extra practice, you might have them fill out a table such as this:

Fraction	Decimal	Percent
$\frac{1}{2}$	0.5	50%
$\frac{1}{3}$	$0.\overline{3}$	$33\frac{1}{3}\%$
$\frac{1}{8}$	0.125	$12\frac{1}{2}\%$

Related Activities

To develop an awareness of the importance of percents in daily life, have students collect and display newspaper clippings that use percents. Headlines and bank advertisements are good places to look. Have students try to find percents greater than 100% and less than 1%, as well as decimal and fractional percents.

Resource Book: Page 84 (Use After Page 244)

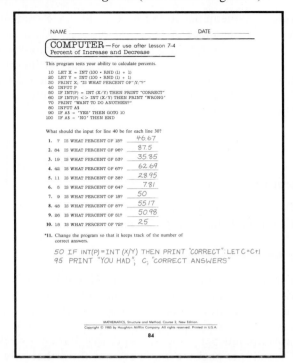

7-5 Working with Percents

Objective for pages 245–248

■ To use the percentage formula to solve problems involving percents.

Teaching Suggestions

Be sure that students do not confuse *percent* with *percentage*.

As you cover Examples 1, 2, and 3, point out that all three types of percent problems use the same formula, $p = rb$. In Example 2 we solve for r, $r = p \div b$. In Example 3 we solve for b, $b = p \div r$. The percent must always be changed to a fraction or decimal before multiplying or dividing.

Students often misplace decimal points in percent problems. Remind them to check their results. Estimation is a useful skill. Have students practice doing problems involving 1%, 10%, and 50% so that they become able to recognize a reasonable answer.

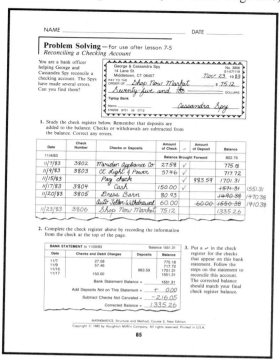

Related Activities

To provide practice in writing problems, have students write problems using the advertisements they collected for Lesson 7-4.

Some students find it helpful to replace word sentences with algebraic sentences. In each example the multiplication sign represents the word *of*.

Example 1: What is 18% of 35?
$$n = 0.18 \times 35$$

Example 2: What percent of 40 is 27?
$$n\% \times 40 = 27$$

Example 3: 48 is 16% of what number?
$$48 = 0.16 \times n$$

PERCENTS AND PROBLEM SOLVING

7-6 Percent of Increase and Decrease

Objective *for pages 249–251*

■ To solve problems involving a percent of increase or decrease.

Teaching Suggestions

Encourage alternate solutions by asking students to organize their approach with a definite plan or strategy. Writing the words before the formula is very helpful. For Example 1, the last sentence can itself become the formula.

What percent of the selling price was the tax?
$$n\% \times \$32.50 = \$33.80 - \$32.50$$

In Example 3, the first sentence can be revised before writing the formula:

$$
\begin{aligned}
\text{number who attended on Wednesday} &\longrightarrow 612 \\
\text{was} &\longrightarrow = \\
20\% \text{ lower than (or } 80\% \text{ of)} &\longrightarrow 0.80 \\
\text{number who attended on Friday} &\longrightarrow n \\
612 &= 0.80 \times n
\end{aligned}
$$

Also show students how to find increases using 100% plus the percent of increase: One hundred dollars increased by 25% can be $100 + (0.25 \times $100)$ or 100×1.25.

229d

Related Activities

To relate mathematics to personal finances, lead from Example 2 to a discussion of the stock market. Students may have studied it in social studies, and some may own stock. Have each student choose a stock to watch in the newspaper stock market listings. Each day they should record the value of the stock and calculate the percent of change from the previous day and from the first day. Interested students may want to look at a consumer mathematics textbook to learn about commission, dividend, and annual yield.

7-7 Commissions, Discounts, Royalties

Objective *for pages 252–254*

■ To solve problems involving commissions, royalties, and discounts.

Teaching Suggestions

Begin with a careful discussion of what it means to work on straight commission, to receive salary plus commission, or to be paid royalties. List occupations paid by commission and royalties. Discuss advantages and disadvantages of these methods of payment. On straight commission, for example, you might earn a lot of money or none at all.

Discount buying will be easier for the students to discuss because of their more direct involvement as consumers. Have them consider why stores give discounts and how they can give discounts and still make a profit. Explain also that many companies give their employees discounts on merchandise they produce and sell.

Related Activities

To show the range of persons who work on commission or are paid royalties, invite one or more to visit the class for an interview. Salespersons, real estate agents, authors, and freelance programmers can present many interesting facts for students to consider.

To improve students' consumer skills, have them choose 10 items sold at a "daily" discount store and compare the prices of these items on sale at another store "this week only." Ask them to look through newspapers to find sales prices and discount rates on several items, and write problems using these advertisements.

7-8 Percents and Proportions

Objective *for pages 255–259*

■ To use proportions to solve problems involving percents.

Teaching Suggestions

Word problems involving percent can be confusing to students when problems of different types are mixed. Encourage students to spend time understanding the problem before deciding what operation or proportion to use. The proportion method unifies the three types of percent problems to the single task of finding the missing term of a proportion. The definition of a percent as a ratio is the key to setting up the proportion. Notice that in each example the percent ratio is considered first before the proportion is written.

In Example 3, note that the first step of the computation is finding 25% of $59. This problem could also be solved by subtracting 25% from 100% and finding 75% of $59.

Related Activities

To relate this topic to personal finances, have students list how much money they spend each week and find the percent spent on each category (clothing, snacks, etc.). Then have them make a budget with percent goals (making sure the total is 100%) and calculate the dollar amount they could spend on each category.

7-9 Interest

Objective *for pages 260–263*

■ To solve problems involving simple and compound interest.

Teaching Suggestions

This lesson provides a real-world example of an equation to be solved by multiplication and division. Be sure that students can solve it for any variable:

$$I = Prt \qquad P = \frac{I}{rt} \qquad r = \frac{I}{Pt} \qquad t = \frac{I}{Pr}$$

Problems 1–6 provide practice in solving for all four variables.

Calculating compound interest (Example 2) is tedious, but students should do it to be sure they understand the process. A calculator, especially one with a memory, makes the work considerably easier. Ask what the value of Roy's investment would have been at simple interest. **$2650**

The answers given for the exercises in this lesson have been rounded at the last step. If your students do not use calculators, you might have them round to the nearest cent at each step.

Computers are now used to calculate compound interest. In the past, bankers used tables; you might find one in an economics textbook. Interest is often compounded daily or even continuously.

Keep this lesson current and practical. What are today's lending rates and investment rates? How much do they differ from bank to bank or between banks and savings and loan companies? What are these rates based on? How do banks make money? What services are offered by lending institutions and investment corporations? How do current interest rates affect the economy?

Be certain to include discussion about automobile loans: down payments, interest rates, finance charges, monthly payments, and insurance rates for different age groups. Also investigate advantages and disadvantages of buying on credit or in installments.

You might want to present other common chronological expressions, such as those in the table.

Common Chronological Expressions (Number of occurrences per year)		
	weekly (52)	biweekly (26)
semimonthly (24)	monthly (12)	bimonthly (6)
	quarterly (4)	
semiannually (2)	annually (1)	

Related Activities

To demonstrate the range of services offered by financial institutions, make a display of pamphlets, advertisements, and other materials.

To provide a challenge for the computer programmers in your class, suggest that they write a program to calculate compound interest.

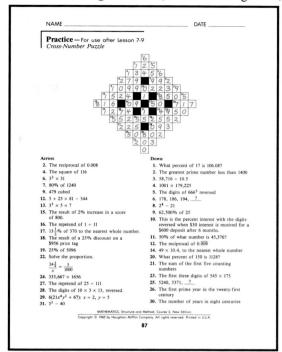

Resource Book: Pages 89-92 (Use After Page 263)

NAME ____________________ DATE __________

Quiz 7B — Lessons 7-6 through 7-9

DIRECTIONS: **Write the letter of the correct answer in the space provided.**

1. A basketball team scored 48 points in their first game and 60 in their second game. What is the percent of increase? [7-6]
   a. 20% b. 25% c. 80% d. 2.5%
2. After a 12% decrease, the price of a bicycle is $122.32. What was the old price of the bicycle?
   a. $110.32 b. $139.00 c. $107.64 d. $140.25
3. A sweater that usually sells for $34.60 is discounted 15%. How much is saved by buying the sweater at the sale price? [7-7]
   a. $29.41 b. $19.60 c. $5.19 d. $517.50
4. A real estate agent earns a 6% commission for selling houses. If her commission last week was $8520, what was the total value of her sales?
   a. $51,120 b. $14,200 c. $51,000 d. $142,000
5. Last year, 75% of the students attended the school play. If 285 students attended the school play, how many students were in the school? Which proportion would solve this problem? [7-8]
   a. $\frac{75}{285} = \frac{n}{100}$ b. $\frac{210}{b} = \frac{75}{100}$ c. $\frac{285}{b} = \frac{75}{100}$ d. $\frac{285}{360} = \frac{n}{100}$
6. The Lions have won 12 of the 15 games they have played this season. What percent of this season's games have the Lions lost? Use a proportion to solve.
   a. 80% b. 8% c. 2% d. 20%
7. Marshall borrowed $1600 for $2\frac{1}{2}$ years at 12% simple interest. What was the total amount to be repaid? [7-9]
   a. $2080 b. $480 c. $1792 d. $1850
8. You open a savings account with $600. The bank pays $5\frac{1}{2}$% interest, compounded quarterly. If you make no other deposits or withdrawals, how much is in your account at the end of nine months?
   a. $616.61 b. $625.09 c. $633.00 d. $624.75

ANSWERS

1. b (12)
2. b (13)
3. c (12)
4. d (13)
5. c (12)
6. d (13)
7. a (12)
8. b (13)

MATHEMATICS, Structure and Method, Course 2, New Edition.
Copyright © 1985 by Houghton Mifflin Company. All rights reserved. Printed in U.S.A.

89

NAME ____________________ DATE __________

Review — Chapter 7

Write each ratio as a fraction in lowest terms. [7-1]

1. $\frac{12}{20}$ $\frac{3}{5}$ 2. 60:5 $\frac{12}{1}$ 3. 2 ft to 16 in. $\frac{3}{2}$

Solve.

4. A 40-acre field yields 600 bushels of wheat. How many bushels of wheat will a 75-acre field yield? 1,125 bushels
5. A $6\frac{1}{2}$-ounce can of Sea View Tuna costs 91¢. Three 2-pound cans of Ocean Blue Tuna cost $11.52. Based on unit price alone, which brand is the better buy? Why? [7-2] Ocean Blue (12¢/ounce rather than 14¢/ounce)
6. A map uses the scale 1 cm:20 km. If the distance between two cities is 170 km, what is the difference on the map? [7-3] 8.5 cm

Express each fraction or decimal as a percent. [7-4]

7. 0.0043 0.43% 8. $5\frac{1}{5}$ 520% 9. $\frac{3}{8}$ 37.5%

Solve.

10. What percent of 80 is 16? 20% [7-5]
11. 42 is 28% of what number? 150
12. There were 132 planes on an airfield. If 75% of the planes took off for a flight, how many planes were left at the airfield? 33
13. After a 24% increase, the price of a tennis racquet was $37.82. What was the old price of the racquet? [7-6] $30.50
14. When a salesman sold a vacuum cleaner for $165, he received a commission of $13.20. What was the rate of commission? [7-7] 8%
15. Mary Karp bought a car for $8200. By the end of the year, the value of the car had decreased $2706. By what percent had the car decreased in value? Use a proportion to solve. [7-8] 33%
16. Jack Stanford deposited $280 in a Holiday Club savings account which pays $6\frac{1}{2}$% interest, compounded semiannually. If Jack makes no additional deposits, how much will be in his account at the end of a year? [7-9] $298.50

MATHEMATICS, Structure and Method, Course 2, New Edition.
Copyright © 1985 by Houghton Mifflin Company. All rights reserved. Printed in U.S.A.

90

NAME ____________________ DATE __________

Test — Chapter 7

DIRECTIONS: **Write the answers in the spaces provided.**

Write each ratio as a fraction in lowest terms. [7-1]

1. $\frac{64}{80}$ 2. 2 m to 4 cm 3. 27:24

Solve each proportion.

4. $\frac{8}{n} = \frac{15}{60}$ 5. $\frac{18}{1.5} = \frac{x}{4.5}$ 6. $\frac{90}{81} = \frac{10}{3m}$

7. A train travels 120 mi in $1\frac{1}{3}$ h. How many miles will the train go in 6 h traveling at the same rate? [7-2]
8. A scale drawing of a room uses the scale 1 in.:20 ft. Find the actual length of the room if it measures $1\frac{1}{4}$ in. in the drawing. [7-3]

Express each fraction or decimal as a percent. [7-4]

9. 0.045 10. 3.07 11. $\frac{3}{200}$ 12. $\frac{7}{8}$

13. What is 186% of 750? [7-5]
14. 0.4 is what percent of 5?
15. Mario's salary increased from $75 per week to $93 per week. What is the percent of increase? [7-6]
16. A salesman receives an 8% commission on guitar sales. If he earns $11.38 in commissions, what was the total amount of his sales? [7-7]

Use a proportion to solve Exercises 17 and 18.

17. 32,850 parts were made in a factory. When they were tested, 2% were found to be defective. How many parts were good? [7-8]
18. In a school, 60 students participate in the Bowling Club. If this is 12% of the student body, how many students are in the school?
19. If Marie deposits $320 in a bank account at $5\frac{1}{4}$% per year, how much simple interest will she earn after 2 years? [7-9]
20. Victor opens a savings account with $750. The account pays 6% interest, compounded quarterly. If he makes no other deposits or withdrawals, how much will Victor have in his account after 9 months?

ANSWERS

1. $\frac{4}{5}$ (4)
2. $\frac{50}{1}$ (4)
3. $\frac{9}{8}$ (4)
4. n = 32 (4)
5. x = 54 (4)
6. m = 3 (4)
7. 540 mi (6)
8. 25 ft (6)
9. 4.5% (4)
10. 307% (4)
11. 1.5% (4)
12. 87.5% (4)
13. 1395 (6)
14. 8% (6)
15. 24% (6)
16. $142.25 (6)
17. 32,193 (6)
18. 500 (6)
19. $33.60 (6)
20. $784.26 (6)

MATHEMATICS, Structure and Method, Course 2, New Edition.
Copyright © 1985 by Houghton Mifflin Company. All rights reserved. Printed in U.S.A.

91

NAME ____________________ DATE __________

Make-up Test — Chapter 7

DIRECTIONS: **Write the answers in the spaces provided.**

Write each ratio as a fraction in lowest terms. [7-1]

1. $\frac{75}{90}$ 2. 3 m to 6 cm 3. 35:20

Solve each proportion.

4. $\frac{12}{15} = \frac{n}{45}$ 5. $\frac{1.9}{x} = \frac{5.7}{15}$ 6. $\frac{30}{4t} = \frac{10}{24}$

7. A car travels 375 mi in $8\frac{1}{3}$ hr. At the same rate, how many miles will the car go in 12 hr? [7-2]
8. A scale drawing of a house uses the scale 1 in.:50 ft. Find the actual length of the house if it measures $1\frac{3}{5}$ in. on the drawing. [7-3]

Express each fraction or decimal as a percent. [7-4]

9. 0.032 10. 5.09 11. $\frac{9}{200}$ 12. $\frac{3}{16}$

13. What is 120% of 42? [7-5]
14. 1.2 is what percent of 8?
15. The soccer team scored 34 goals this week and 40 goals last week. What was the percent of decrease? [7-6]
16. A van is discounted 28% of the original price. What is the sale price if the original price was $16,400? [7-7]
17. A football team won 9 games, which was 60% of the games it played. How many games did the team play? [7-8]
18. Max Barker bought a suit for $185 and paid $12.95 as a sales tax. What percent was the tax?
19. How much simple interest would be earned on a savings account of $450 at $6\frac{1}{4}$% interest per year after 2 years? [7-9]
20. Jackson deposited $180 into a special savings account that pays 7% interest, compounded semiannually. If he makes no other deposits or withdrawals, how much will be in his account after 18 mo?

ANSWERS

1. $\frac{5}{6}$ (4)
2. $\frac{50}{1}$ (4)
3. $\frac{7}{4}$ (4)
4. n = 36 (4)
5. x = 5 (4)
6. t = 18 (4)
7. 540 mi (6)
8. 80 ft (6)
9. 3.2% (4)
10. 509% (4)
11. 4.5% (4)
12. 18.75% (4)
13. 50.4 (6)
14. 15% (6)
15. 15% (6)
16. $11,808 (6)
17. 15 (6)
18. 7% (6)
19. $56.25 (6)
20. $199.57 (6)

MATHEMATICS, Structure and Method, Course 2, New Edition.
Copyright © 1985 by Houghton Mifflin Company. All rights reserved. Printed in U.S.A.

92

Resource Book: Pages 93–94 (Use After Page 263)

CUMULATIVE REVIEW—Chapters 1–7
Exercises

Evaluate the expression if $f = 7$ and $g = 4$.

1. $f + g$ _11_   2. $2f - g$ _10_   3. $-g - f$ _-11_

4. $f^2 g$ _196_   5. $3f + 2g$ _29_   6. $g - f - 5$ _-8_

Write the numbers in order from least to greatest.

7. $5.2, 3.1, -4.9, -0.8, 0$ _$-4.9, -0.8, 0, 3.1, 5.2$_   8. $-26, -2.6, 2.5, 0.26$ _$-26, -2.6, 0.26, 2.5$_

Tell whether the statement is true or false for the given value of the variable.

9. $18 - 2m = 42$; 12 _F_   10. $6d \leq 2$; $\frac{1}{4}$ _T_   11. $t < -3t + 8$; -2 _T_

12. $\frac{w}{-3} > 12$; 39 _F_   13. $9 + 5x = x + 13$; 1 _T_   14. $2s + 4 = 20$; $2\frac{1}{2}$ _F_

Write the fractions as equal fractions having the least common denominator (LCD).

15. $\frac{3}{5}, \frac{5}{8}$ _$\frac{24}{40}, \frac{25}{40}$_   16. $-\frac{1}{3}, \frac{4}{9}$ _$-\frac{3}{9}, \frac{4}{9}$_   17. $\frac{5}{6}, -\frac{3}{4}$ _$\frac{10}{12}, \frac{-9}{12}$_

Solve the equation or inequality.

18. $6(p - 3) = 15$ _$p = 5\frac{1}{2}$_   19. $-8m < -24$ _$m > 3$_   20. $3f + 17 = 8f + 32$ _$f = -3$_

Complete.

21. 158% of 75 is _118.5_.   22. 15 is 30% of _50_.

23. 24 is _60_ % of 40.   24. _5.98_ is 6.5% of 92.

Solve each proportion.

25. $\frac{3}{16} = \frac{x}{80}$ _15_   26. $\frac{4.2}{d} = \frac{21}{15}$ _3_   27. $\frac{18}{6} = \frac{72}{m}$ _24_

Write a variable expression for the word phrase.

28. The product of a number r and sixty-five. _$65r$_

29. The sum of five times a number d and eighteen. _$5d + 18$_

30. The difference of forty and a number t cubed. _$40 - t^3$_

MATHEMATICS, Structure and Method, Course 2, New Edition.
Copyright © 1985 by Houghton Mifflin Company. All rights reserved. Printed in U.S.A.

CUMULATIVE REVIEW—Chapters 1–7 *(continued)*
Problems

Problem Solving Reminders
Here are some reminders that may help you solve some of the problems on this page.
- Consider whether a chart will help to organize information.
- Supply additional information if needed.
- Reread the problem to be sure that your answer is complete.

Solve.

1. This week, Ira jogged $1\frac{1}{4}$ h on Monday, $1\frac{1}{2}$ h on Wednesday, $1\frac{2}{3}$ h on Friday, and $2\frac{1}{3}$ h on Saturday. How many hours did he jog this week?   _$7\frac{1}{12}$ h_

2. Barry spent 3 h and 20 min writing a book report and playing the trumpet. He spent three times as long writing the book report as he did practicing. How long did he spend on the book report?   _$2\frac{1}{2}$ h_

3. Camera film is selling at the rate of 3 rolls for $7.47. How many rolls can you buy for $19.92?   _8 rolls_

4. Marsha bought a coat for $109.80, a hat for $5.95, and a scarf for $7.25. The tax on her purchase was $11.07. What percent of the total purchase was the tax?   _9%_

5. A savings account was opened with $3000. The bank pays $5\frac{1}{4}$% interest, compounded monthly. How much money is in the account after 3 months?   _$3,041.44_

6. The side of a square is the same length as the radius of a circle with circumference 44 m. Find the perimeter of the square. Use $\pi = \frac{22}{7}$.   _28 m_

MATHEMATICS, Structure and Method, Course 2, New Edition.
Copyright © 1985 by Houghton Mifflin Company. All rights reserved. Printed in U.S.A.

229h

Teaching Suggestions
p. 229a

Related Activities p. 229b

Reading Mathematics

Students will learn the meaning of the following mathematical terms in this lesson: *ratio, proportion, terms, extremes, means.*

Chalkboard Examples

1. Calculate your class ratio for each of the following:
   a. students to teacher
   b. tables to chairs
   c. doors to windows
2. Use proportions to solve.
   a. 13 heartbeats in 10 s. How many in 60 s? **78**
   b. 100 km in 2 h. How many in 3 h? **150**
   c. 6 apples for 53¢. How much per dozen? **$1.06**

7-1 Ratio and Proportion

A **ratio** is an indicated quotient of two numbers. For example,

$$\frac{4}{6} \qquad 4:6 \qquad 4 \text{ to } 6$$

are three ways of writing *the ratio of 4 to 6.* Note that the first number is always divided by the second. We usually write ratios in lowest terms. Because $\frac{4}{6} = \frac{2}{3}$, the ratio of 4 to 6 is the same as the ratio of 2 to 3, that is, $4:6 = 2:3$. The terms of a ratio are usually whole numbers. Because $\frac{\frac{1}{2}}{5} = \frac{1}{10}$, the ratio of $\frac{1}{2}$ to 5 is the same as the ratio of 1 to 10.

Ratios can be used to compare two quantities. Example 1 illustrates that we must use the same unit of measure to express the ratio of two quantities of the same kind.

EXAMPLE 1 An airport runway is 120 m wide and 5 km long. Use a ratio to compare its length to its width.

Solution 5 km = 5000 m

$$\begin{array}{l} \text{length} \longrightarrow \\ \text{width} \longrightarrow \end{array} \frac{5000}{120} = \frac{125}{3}$$

The ratio of length to width is $\frac{125}{3}$, or $125:3$.

Example 2 illustrates that we may use a ratio to compare quantities of different kinds.

EXAMPLE 2 Roger's car traveled 120 mi on 9 gal of gas. Express the ratio of miles to gallons in lowest terms.

Solution The ratio of miles to gallons is $\frac{120}{9}$, or $\frac{40}{3}$.

A **proportion** is a statement of equality of two ratios, for example,

$$\frac{2}{5} = \frac{6}{15} \qquad \text{or} \qquad 2:5 = 6:15. \text{ (Read } 2 \text{ is to } 5 \text{ as } 6 \text{ is to } 15.)$$

The numbers 2, 5, 6, and 15 are called the **terms** of the proportion. The numbers 2 and 15 are called the **extremes** and the numbers 5 and 6 are called the **means.** Notice that

$$2 \times 15 = 5 \times 6.$$

The product of the extremes equals the product of the means. In general,

> ### *Property*
>
> If $\frac{a}{b} = \frac{c}{d}$, or $a:b = c:d$, where $b \neq 0$ and $d \neq 0$, then $ad = bc$.

Since $ad = bc$ is an equation equivalent to the proportion $\frac{a}{b} = \frac{c}{d}$, we can use this property to *solve* a proportion. That is, we can find one term of a proportion when we know the other three terms.

EXAMPLE 3 The directions on a bag of concrete mix call for the addition of 3 qt of water to 40 lb of mix. How much water should be added if only 30 lb of mix is used?

Solution In planning the solution, ask yourself the following questions.

- What quantity is to be found?
  The amount of water needed for 30 lb of mix.
  Let w represent this quantity.
- Do the given facts involve any ratios?
  Yes, 3 qt of water to 40 lb of mix and w qt of water to 30 lb of mix.

Since ratios are involved, equate them in a proportion and solve.

$$\text{water} \longrightarrow \quad \frac{3}{40} = \frac{w}{30}$$
$$\text{mix} \longrightarrow$$
$$3 \times 30 = 40w$$
$$\frac{90}{40} = w$$
$$2\frac{1}{4} = w$$

For 30 lb of mix, $2\frac{1}{4}$ qt of water are needed.

Problem Solving Reminder

After you read a problem, it is a good idea to *ask yourself questions* to help plan your solution. Notice how the two questions in Example 3 help to identify the problem as one that can be solved by using a proportion.

Ratio, Proportion, and Percent   **231**

Class Exercises

State each ratio in lowest terms. The terms should be whole numbers.
Answers may vary in Exercises 1–7.

1. $\frac{7}{14}$ $\frac{1}{2}$
2. $8:6$ $4:3$
3. 2 to 1   2 to 1
4. $\frac{\frac{1}{4}}{6}$ $\frac{1}{24}$
5. A dozen to a pair   6 to 1

6. The number of days in a week to the number of days in June   7:30

7. The number of walls in your classroom to the number of doors

For each proportion (a) state an equivalent equation that does not involve fractions and (b) solve the equation.

8. $\frac{n}{8} = \frac{5}{2}$ a. $2n = 8 \times 5$ b. 20
9. $\frac{3}{n} = \frac{6}{10}$ a. $6n = 3 \times 10$ b. 5
10. $\frac{8}{5} = \frac{w}{15}$ a. $5w = 8 \times 15$ b. 24
11. $\frac{21}{15} = \frac{7}{r}$ 11. a. $21r = 15 \times 7$ b. 5

a. State the quantity to be represented by a variable in the problem.
b. Set up a proportion whose solution would answer the question.

12. A recipe for 20 rolls calls for 5 tablespoons of butter. How many tablespoons are needed for 30 rolls?
a. t = tablespoons needed for 30 rolls
b. $\frac{t}{30} = \frac{5}{20}$

13. A car goes 140 mi on 5 gal of gas. How many miles could it go on 7 gal?
a. m = miles car could go on 7 gal
b. $\frac{140}{5} = \frac{m}{7}$

Written Exercises

Write each ratio as a fraction in lowest terms.

A
1. 35 to 28 $\frac{5}{4}$
2. 15 to 21 $\frac{5}{7}$
3. $\frac{24}{56}$ $\frac{3}{7}$
4. $132:36$ $\frac{11}{3}$

5. $\frac{98}{49}$ $\frac{2}{1}$
6. 9 to 54 $\frac{1}{6}$
7. $\frac{5}{8}:\frac{1}{5}$ $\frac{25}{8}$
8. 1 to $\frac{1}{3}$ $\frac{3}{1}$

Compare the product of the means and the product of the extremes. Is the proportion true?

9. $\frac{4}{6} \overset{?}{=} \frac{9}{12}$ No
10. $\frac{6}{5} \overset{?}{=} \frac{12}{10}$ Yes
11. $\frac{9}{15} \overset{?}{=} \frac{12}{20}$ Yes
12. $\frac{1}{8} \overset{?}{=} \frac{7}{56}$ Yes

Solve each proportion.

13. $\frac{m}{15} = \frac{16}{20}$ 12
14. $\frac{24}{n} = \frac{8}{7}$ 21
15. $\frac{42}{14} = \frac{18}{c}$ 6
16. $\frac{2}{9} = \frac{x}{36}$ 8

17. $\frac{s}{14} = \frac{3}{4}$ $10\frac{1}{2}$
18. $\frac{8}{3} = \frac{36}{d}$ $13\frac{1}{2}$
19. $\frac{5}{4} = \frac{a}{2.4}$ 3
20. $\frac{4}{n} = \frac{15}{10}$ $2\frac{2}{3}$

B
21. $\frac{2n}{8} = \frac{7}{10}$ $2\frac{4}{5}$
22. $\frac{15}{4} = \frac{9}{2r}$ $1\frac{1}{5}$
23. $\frac{9}{10} = \frac{3b}{5}$ $1\frac{1}{2}$
24. $\frac{9}{4n} = \frac{1.5}{7}$

25. $\frac{11}{10} = \frac{x+2}{5}$ $3\frac{1}{2}$
26. $\frac{n-3}{16} = \frac{5}{8}$ 13
27. $\frac{24}{t+8} = \frac{5}{3}$ $6\frac{2}{5}$
28. $\frac{7}{8} = \frac{35}{w-1}$

24. $10\frac{1}{2}$ 28. 41

232   *Chapter 7*

232

Problems

A

1. Five cans of paint will cover 130 m² of wall space. How many cans will be needed to cover 208 m²? **8 cans**

2. To obtain the correct strength of a medicine, 5 cm³ of distilled water is added to 12 cm³ of an antibiotic. How much water should be added to 30 cm³ of the antibiotic? **12.5 cm³**

3. A recipe that serves 8 calls for 15 oz of cooked tomatoes. How many ounces of tomatoes will be needed if the recipe is reduced to serve 6? How many servings can be made with 20 oz of cooked tomatoes? **$11\frac{1}{4}$ oz; $10\frac{2}{3}$ servings**

4. A geologist found that silt was deposited on a river bed at the rate of 4 cm every 170 years. How long would it take for 5 cm of silt to be deposited? How much silt would be deposited in 255 years?
212.5 years; 6 cm

B

5. Five vests can be made from $2\frac{1}{2}$ yd of fabric. How many vests can be made from 6 yd of fabric? **12 vests**

6. A fruit punch recipe calls for 3 parts of apple juice to 4 parts of cranberry juice. How many liters of cranberry juice should be added to 4.5 L of apple juice? **6 L**

7. A bag of 3 lb of Fairlawn's Number 25 grass seed covers a 4000 ft² area. How great an area will 16 oz of the same seed cover? **$1333\frac{1}{3}$ ft²**

8. A wall hanging requires 54 cm of braided trim. How many wall hangings can be completed if 3 m of braided trim is available?
5 wall hangings

C

9. In a recent election, the ratio of votes *for* a particular proposal to votes *against* the proposal was 5 to 2. There were 4173 more votes for the proposal than against the proposal. How many votes were for and how many votes were against the proposal?
6955 for, 2782 against

10. A certain soil mixture calls for 8 parts of potting soil to 3 parts of sand. To make the correct mixture, Vern used 0.672 kg of sand and 2 bags of potting soil. How much potting soil was in each bag?
0.896 kg

Review Exercises
1. $\frac{1}{3}$ 2. $1\frac{5}{7}$ 3. $\frac{6}{7}$ 4. $1\frac{1}{2}$ 5. $\frac{11}{14}$ 6. $8\frac{11}{12}$ 7. $11\frac{2}{7}$ 8. $\frac{2}{5}$

Write as a proper fraction in lowest terms or as a mixed number in simple form.

1. $\frac{60}{180}$ 2. $\frac{48}{28}$ 3. $\frac{54}{63}$ 4. $\frac{105}{70}$ 5. $\frac{66}{84}$ 6. $\frac{107}{12}$ 7. $\frac{79}{7}$ 8. $\frac{62}{155}$

Ratio, Proportion, and Percent **233**

Suggested Assignments

Minimum
232 / 1–20
233 / Prob. 1–8
233 / Rev. 1–8

Average
232 / 2–20 even; 21–28
233 / Prob. 1–8
233 / Rev. 2–8 even

Maximum
232 / 2–20 even; 21–28
233 / Prob. 1–10

Supplementary Materials

Practice Masters, p. 31

Reading Mathematics

Students will learn the meaning of the following mathematical terms in this lesson: *rate, speed, unit price.*

Chalkboard Examples

Find the unit price of each item.
1. 5 magazines for $3.50 $.70
2. 12 eggs for $1.08 9¢
3. 3 records for $11.94 $3.98

Find the rate of speed.
4. 50 m in 8 s 6.25 m/s
5. 100 km in 2 h 50 km/h
6. 98 mi in 2 h 49 mi/h

7-2 Rates and Problem Solving

Ratios that compare quantities of different kinds are also called **rates.** A rate is usually simplified to a *per-unit* form, that is, a form involving the ratio of some number to 1. The rate is then expressed simply as a whole number, a mixed number, or a decimal.

EXAMPLE 1   If a car travels 195 km in 3 h, what is its average rate of travel?

Solution $\text{rate} = \dfrac{195}{3}$

$= \dfrac{65}{1} = 65$ (kilometers per hour)

The car traveled at an average rate of 65 kilometers per hour (km/h).

When we know the rate of travel and the time someone has traveled, we can find the distance traveled by the following formula.

Formula

The distance d, traveled in time t, at a constant rate r, is given by

$$\text{distance} = \text{rate} \times \text{time}$$
$$d = rt$$

A rate of the form *distance per unit time* is often called **speed.** In Example 1, the average speed is 65 km/h.

EXAMPLE 2   A car made a trip of 225 mi at an average speed of 50 mi/h. How long did the trip take?

Solution   Substitute 225 for d and 50 for r in the distance formula:

$$d = rt$$
$$225 = 50t$$
$$t = \frac{225}{50}$$
$$t = 4\frac{1}{2}$$

The trip took $4\frac{1}{2}$ h.

If a rate is the price of one item, it is called the **unit price**. For example, if 2 peaches sell for 78¢, the unit price is $\frac{78}{2}$, or 39, cents per peach.

EXAMPLE 3 If 5 oranges sell for 95¢, what is the cost of 12 oranges?

Solution

Method 1
You can plan to find the price of one orange and then multiply by 12 to answer the question in the problem.

unit price $= \frac{95}{5} = 19$ (cents per orange)

cost of 12 oranges $= 12 \times 19 = 228$ (cents)

Method 2
Since the facts of the problem involve a rate and a rate is a ratio, you can plan to write a proportion for the statement:

If 5 oranges cost 95¢, then 12 oranges cost __?__ ¢.

Let $c = $ cost in cents of 12 oranges.

$$
\begin{array}{l}
\text{oranges} \longrightarrow \\
\text{cents} \longrightarrow
\end{array}
\quad \frac{5}{95} = \frac{12}{c}
$$

$$5c = 95 \times 12$$

$$c = \frac{95 \times 12}{5} = 228 \text{ (cents)}$$

By either method, the cost of 12 oranges is 228¢, or $2.28.

There is often more than one correct way to solve a problem. In Example 3, one plan used a per-unit rate and the other plan used a proportion. In Example 2 a formula was used, but the problem could also have been solved using the proportion $\frac{50}{1} = \frac{225}{t}$.

Class Exercises

a. Express each rate as a fraction.
b. Write the rate in a per-unit form.

1. Three melons for $1.59

3. 6 cans of water per 2 cans of juice

5. 192.5 km in 3.5 h

7. Ten oranges for $1.65

2. Two cans of tennis balls for $5.88

4. 28 bicycles sold in 7 days

6. A dozen eggs for $1.08

8. 225 m in 25 s

Ratio, Proportion, and Percent   **235**

1. If Duane can buy one model airplane for $4.75, how many can he buy for $14.25? **3**

2. Marie can type 28 words per minute. How long will it take her to type a letter 168 words long? **6 min**

3. If 4 L of oil cost $3.88, what is the price for 1 L? **97¢**

4. If 3 tennis balls cost $2.67, what is the cost of 7 tennis balls? **$6.23**

5. If a train travels 65 km/h, about how long would it take to travel 380 km? **about 6 h**

6. A toy car travels 6 m/s. How far does the car travel in 2 min? **720 m**

Suggested Assignments

Minimum
    236/Prob. 1–12
    237/Prob. 13–14
    237/Rev. 1–8

Average
    236/Prob. 1–12
    237/Prob. 13–16
    237/Rev. 1–7 odd

Maximum
    236/Prob. 1–12
    237/Prob. 13–17

Supplementary Materials

Practice Masters, p. 32

Solve each problem by (a) using a unit rate and (b) using a proportion.

9. A hardware store sells 8 stove bolts for $1.20. How much will 11 stove bolts cost? **$1.65**

10. If 720 pencils are packaged in 5 boxes, how many pencils are packaged in 7 boxes? **1008 pencils**

11. Light bulbs are selling at the rate of 3 for $2.07. How many bulbs can you buy for $4.83? **7 bulbs**

Problems

Give the unit price of each item.

A 1. 7 oz of crackers for $1.19 **17¢**   2. 14 oz of cottage cheese for $1.19 **8.5¢**

3. 5 yd of upholstery fabric for $80 **$16**   4. 16 boxes of raisins for $5.60 **35¢**

Solve.

5. A certain kind of lumber costs $3.00 for 8 ft. At this rate, how much does a piece that is 14 ft long cost? **$5.25**

6. A package of 3 lb of ground beef costs $5.10. How much ground beef could you buy for $3.40 at this rate? **2 lb**

7. A car travels for 3 h at an average speed of 65 km/h. How far does the car travel? **195 km**

8. A boat covers 48 km in 2 h. What is the boat's average speed? **24 km/h**

9. A homing pigeon flies 180 km in 3 h. At this average speed, how far could the pigeon travel in 4 h? **240 km**

10. A bicyclist travels for 2 h at an average speed of 12 km/h. How far does the bicyclist travel? At this speed, how long will it take the bicyclist to travel 54 km? **24 km; 4.5 h**

Determine the better buy based on unit price alone.

B 11. A can of 35 oz of Best Brand Pear Tomatoes is on sale for 69¢. A can of 4 lb of Sun Ripe Pear Tomatoes costs $1.88. Which brand is the better buy? **Best Brand**

12. A can of Favorite Beef Dog Food holds $14\frac{1}{2}$ oz. Four cans cost $1.00. Three cans of Delight Beef Dog Food, each containing 12 oz, cost $.58. Which is the better buy? **Delight**

13. Three bottles of Bright Shine Window Cleaner, each containing 15 oz, cost $2.75. Two bottles of Sparkle Window Cleaner, each containing 18.75 oz, can be purchased for $1.98. Which is the better buy? Sparkle

14. A bottle of Harvest Time Apple Juice contains 64 oz and costs 99¢. Farm Fresh Juice is available in bottles that contain 1 gal for $1.88 each. Which is the better buy? Farm Fresh

Solve.

15. A car uses 3 gal of gasoline every 117 mi. During the first part of a trip, the car traveled 130 mi in 4 h. If the car continues to travel at the same average speed and the trip takes a total of 6 h, how many gallons of gasoline will be consumed? 5 gal

16. Emily Depietro purchased 3 trays of strawberry plants for $16.47. Emily also purchased 10 trays of ivy plants. If the ratio of the price per tray of strawberry plants to the price per tray of ivy plants is 3 to 2, what is the total cost of the plants? $53.07

C 17. In the time that it takes one car to travel 93 km, a second car travels 111 km. If the average speed of the second car is 12 km/h faster than the speed of the first car, what is the speed of each car? 62 km/h; 74 km/h

Review Exercises

Find the perimeter of a regular polygon whose sides have the given length.

1. pentagon, 4 cm 20 cm
2. square, 6.2 m 24.8 m
3. octagon, 10.5 cm 84 cm
4. triangle, 8.9 m 26.7 m
5. rhombus, 35.6 m 142.4 m
6. hexagon, 21.75 cm 130.5 cm
7. quadrilateral, 14.35 m 57.4 m
8. decagon, 64.87 cm 648.7 cm

Ratio, Proportion, and Percent **237**

7-3 Scale Drawings

A **scale drawing** is a drawing of a real object in which all lengths are proportional to the corresponding actual lengths. The scale of such a drawing indicates the ratio of length in the drawing to the actual length. For example, the scale

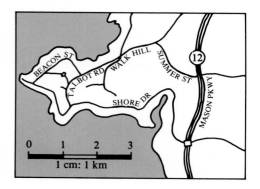

$$1 \text{ cm} : 1 \text{ km}$$

on a map means that a length of 1 cm on the map represents an actual distance of 1 km. Because 1 km = 100,000 cm, the scale ratio of distances on the map to the actual distances is $\frac{1}{100,000}$.

EXAMPLE   A scale drawing of a car chassis uses the scale 1 cm : 0.125 m. The length of the chassis is 42 cm in the drawing. What is the actual length of the chassis?

Solution   Let n = the actual length. Write a proportion.

$$\begin{array}{l} \text{length in scale drawing} \longrightarrow \\ \text{actual length} \longrightarrow \end{array} \frac{1}{0.125} = \frac{42}{n}$$

$$n = 0.125 \times 42 = 5.25$$

The length of the car chassis is 5.25 m, or 525 cm.

Class Exercises

In the scale drawing at the right, the scale is 1 cm : 2 m. Use the measurements on the drawing to find the actual length of each.

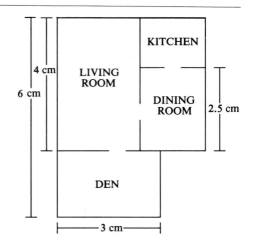

  1. living room 8 m **2.** den 6 m

  3. dining room 5 m **4.** entire house 12 m

A scale drawing uses the scale 1 cm : 4 m. Find the measurement on the drawing.

  5. The actual width is 6 m. 1.5 cm

  6. The actual length is 12 m. 3 cm

238   *Chapter 7*

Written Exercises

A scale drawing of a desk uses the scale 1 in.:2.5 in. Find the actual measurement for the given measurement in the drawing.

A 1. The width is 16 in. 40 in.

2. The height is 15 in. 37.5 in.

3. The depth is 9 in. 22.5 in.

4. The depth of the lid is 6.4 in. 16 in.

5. A leg is 0.8 in. thick. 2 in.

6. A drawer is 7 in. wide. 17.5 in.

A scale drawing of a solar heating system uses a scale of 4 cm:1 m. Find the measurement in the drawing that corresponds to the given actual measurement.

7. The width of one solar panel is 1 m. 4 cm

8. The height of one panel is 3 m. 12 cm

9. The length of a vertical section of hot water pipe is 7.5 m. 30 cm

10. The height of a hot water storage tank is 2 m. 8 cm

Solve.

11. In a drawing, the length of an amoeba is 6.3 cm. The scale of the drawing is 1 cm:0.1 mm. What was the actual length? 0.63 mm

12. A drawing of a hummingbird has the scale 5 cm:1 cm. The actual distance from the tip of the hummingbird's beak to the end of its tail feathers is 6.4 cm. What is this length in the drawing? 32 cm

B 13. A bicycle frame is to have the shape of a triangle *ABC* with the following measurements:

$m \angle A = 73°$

$AB = 60$ cm

$AC = 58$ cm

a. Make a scale drawing of this triangle using the scale 1 cm:4 cm.

b. What are the lengths in the drawing of $\overline{AB}$ and $\overline{AC}$? 15 cm; 14.5 cm

c. By measuring $\overline{BC}$ in the drawing, determine the actual length of $\overline{BC}$ to the nearest centimeter. 70 cm

Ratio, Proportion, and Percent **239**

239

14. A trestle bridge is to be constructed in the shape of an isosceles trapezoid *PQRS* with these actual measurements:

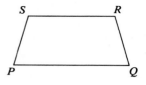

$$PQ = 40 \text{ m} \qquad PS = 12 \text{ m} \qquad QR = 12 \text{ m}$$
$$m\angle P = 70° \qquad m\angle Q = 70°$$

a. Make a scale drawing of the bridge using the scale 1 cm : 2 m.

b. Use the scale drawing to determine the actual length *RS* to the nearest meter. 32 m

Review Exercises

Round to the nearest thousandth.

1. 0.3651 0.365   **2.** 0.6977 0.698   **3.** 46.7746 46.775   **4.** 321.0055
 321.006

5. 60.0059 60.006   **6.** 4.01086 4.011   **7.** 99.9009 99.901   **8.** 6.00808
 6.008

 Computer Byte

The following program will solve a proportion. Note that −1 is used to indicate which term you want to find.

```
10   PRINT "INPUT TERMS IN THE ORDER SHOWN."
20   PRINT "USE -1 FOR THE MISSING TERM."
30   PRINT
40   PRINT  TAB( 5);"(1)"; TAB( 13);"(3)"
50   PRINT  TAB( 4);"----- = -----"
60   PRINT  TAB( 5);"(2)"; TAB( 13);"(4)"
70   PRINT
80   PRINT "INPUT TERMS";
90   INPUT A,B,C,D
100  IF A * D < 0 THEN 140
110  IF B * C > 0 THEN 20
120  LET N = (A * D) / ( - 1 * B * C)
130  GOTO 150
140  LET N = (B * C) / ( - 1 * A * D)
150  PRINT "THE MISSING TERM IS ";N
160  END
```

Use the program to solve. If your answer to Exercise 1 is not correct, check for a typing mistake.

1. $\frac{1}{2} = \frac{n}{4}$ 2   **2.** $\frac{n}{12} = \frac{6}{8}$ 9   **3.** $\frac{9}{n} = \frac{2}{3}$ 13.5   **4.** $\frac{6.4}{8.4} = \frac{8}{n}$ 10.5

7-4 Percents, Fractions, and Decimals

A **percent** is an amount *per hundred*, or a number of hundredths. The symbol for percent is %.

$$30\% = \frac{30}{100} = 0.30 \qquad\qquad 0.4\% = \frac{0.4}{100} = \frac{4}{1000} = 0.004$$

Note that

$$100\% = \frac{100}{100} = 1.$$

Percents greater than 100% name numbers greater than 1.

$$350\% = \frac{350}{100} = 3.5$$

EXAMPLE 1 Express 63.5% as (a) a fraction in lowest terms and (b) a decimal.

Solution

a. $63.5\% = \frac{63.5}{100} = \frac{635}{1000} = \frac{127}{200}$

b. $63.5\% = \frac{63.5}{100} = \frac{635}{1000} = 0.635$

Short cut: Move the decimal point two places to the left and remove the % symbol.

EXAMPLE 2 Express each as a fraction in lowest terms.

a. $\frac{7}{8}\%$ **b.** $66\frac{2}{3}\%$

Solution

a. $\frac{7}{8}\% = \dfrac{\frac{7}{8}}{100}$

$= \frac{7}{8} \times \frac{1}{100}$

$= \frac{7}{800}$

b. $66\frac{2}{3}\% = \dfrac{66\frac{2}{3}}{100}$

$= \frac{200}{3} \times \frac{1}{100}$

$= \frac{200}{300}$

$= \frac{2}{3}$

Ratio, Proportion, and Percent **241**

EXAMPLE 3 Express each as a percent.

        a. 0.036   **b.** $\frac{3}{5}$ **c.** $\frac{1}{6}$

Solution **a.** $0.036 = \frac{36}{1000} = \frac{3.6}{100} = 3.6\%$

Short cut: Move the decimal point two places to the right and add the % symbol.

b. *Method 1*

$$\frac{3}{5} = \frac{n}{100}$$

$$5n = 300$$

$$n = \frac{300}{5} = 60$$

Thus, $\frac{3}{5} = \frac{60}{100} = 60\%$.

Method 2

Divide to express as a decimal first.

$$\frac{3}{5} = 0.6$$

Now move the decimal point two places to the right and add the % symbol.

$$\frac{3}{5} = 60\%$$

c. $\frac{1}{6} = \frac{n}{100}$

$$6n = 100$$

$$n = \frac{100}{6} = 16\frac{2}{3}$$

Therefore, $\frac{1}{6} = 16\frac{2}{3}\%$.

In part (c) of Example 3, dividing the numerator of the fraction by the denominator does not result in a terminating decimal. If we divide to express such a fraction as a percent, we must round the answer before writing the decimal as a percent.

EXAMPLE 4 Express $\frac{5}{7}$ as a percent to the nearest tenth of a percent.

Solution Divide to the ten-thousandths' place to express the fraction as a decimal.

$$\frac{5}{7} \approx 0.7142$$

Round the decimal to the nearest thousandth and then write the rounded decimal as a percent.

$$0.7142 \approx 0.714 = 71.4\%$$

Class Exercises

Express each fraction as a percent.

1. $\frac{1}{2}$ 50%   **2.** $\frac{1}{3}$ $33\frac{1}{3}$% **3.** $\frac{1}{4}$ 25%   **4.** $\frac{1}{5}$ 20%   **5.** $\frac{3}{4}$ 75%   **6.** $\frac{2}{3}$ $66\frac{2}{3}$%

Express each percent as a proper fraction in lowest terms or as a mixed number in simple form.

7. 45% $\frac{9}{20}$ **8.** 8% $\frac{2}{25}$ **9.** 0.5% $\frac{1}{200}$ **10.** $\frac{3}{4}$% $\frac{3}{400}$ **11.** 175% $1\frac{3}{4}$ **12.** 2.5% $\frac{1}{40}$

Written Exercises

Express each fraction or decimal as a percent.

A

1. 0.83 83%   **2.** 3.62 362%   **3.** 0.0052 0.52%   **4.** 0.094 9.4%

5. 4.72 472%   **6.** 13.08 1308%   **7.** 0.003 0.3%   **8.** 6.003 600.3%

9. $\frac{4}{5}$ 80%   **10.** $\frac{7}{20}$ 35%   **11.** $\frac{3}{8}$ 37.5%   **12.** $\frac{5}{8}$ 62.5%

13. $\frac{11}{40}$ 27.5%   **14.** $\frac{9}{16}$ 56.25%   **15.** $\frac{5}{6}$ $83\frac{1}{3}$%   **16.** $\frac{7}{9}$ $77\frac{7}{9}$%

Express each fraction as a percent to the nearest tenth of a percent.

17. $\frac{5}{11}$ 45.5%   **18.** $\frac{9}{22}$ 40.9%   **19.** $\frac{3}{14}$ 21.4%   **20.** $\frac{7}{12}$ 58.3%

21. $\frac{15}{19}$ 78.9%   **22.** $\frac{1}{21}$ 4.8%   **23.** $\frac{6}{13}$ 46.2%   **24.** $\frac{4}{9}$ 44.4%

Express each percent as (a) a proper fraction in lowest terms or a mixed number in simple form and (b) a decimal.

25. 36%   **26.** 75%   **27.** 248%   **28.** 1.25%   **29.** 0.45%

30. 150%   **31.** 2.8%   **32.** 0.6%   **33.** 5.75%   **34.** 12.5%

Express each percent as a proper fraction in lowest terms.

35. $\frac{3}{8}$% $\frac{3}{800}$ **36.** $\frac{2}{5}$% $\frac{1}{250}$ **37.** $\frac{5}{6}$% $\frac{1}{120}$ **38.** $\frac{7}{9}$% $\frac{7}{900}$ **39.** $3\frac{1}{5}$% $\frac{4}{125}$

40. $14\frac{7}{8}$% $\frac{119}{800}$ **41.** $16\frac{2}{3}$% $\frac{1}{6}$ **42.** $33\frac{1}{3}$% $\frac{1}{3}$ **43.** $11\frac{1}{9}$% $\frac{1}{9}$ **44.** $24\frac{1}{6}$% $\frac{29}{120}$

Replace __?__ with <, >, or = to make a true statement.

B **45.** $\frac{7}{8}$ _?_ 78% >   **46.** 0.5 _?_ 50% =   **47.** 0.02 _?_ 20% <

Ratio, Proportion, and Percent **243**

Replace ? with <, >, or = to make a true statement.

48. $\frac{2}{3}$ __?__ $66\frac{2}{3}\%$ =

49. 0.25 __?__ 2.5% >

50. $\frac{5}{8}$ __?__ 62.5% =

51. 9.5 __?__ 950% =

52. 4.6 __?__ 46% >

53. $\frac{4}{9}$ __?__ $44\frac{4}{9}\%$ =

Problems

Write a fraction and a percent for each. Round to the nearest tenth of a percent when necessary.

A

1. At the Sailboat Restaurant 7 out of 10 people ordered the seafood special. $\frac{7}{10}$; 70%

2. Julia completed 8 out of 12 projects without extra help. $\frac{2}{3}$; 66.7%

3. In the hockey playoffs, the Silver Skates won 3 out of 5 games. $\frac{3}{5}$; 60%

4. In a consumer opinion survey, 400 out of 1000 people preferred liquid soap to bar soap. $\frac{2}{5}$; 40%

5. The average person spends 8 out of every 24 hours sleeping. $\frac{1}{3}$; 33.3%

6. In a class of 178 students, 49 tried out for the class play. $\frac{49}{178}$; 27.5%

Review Exercises

Solve.

1. $n - 12 = 3$ 15

2. $r + 16 = 49$ 33

3. $56.45 - p = 16.94$ 39.51

4. $y - 12.75 = 8.90$ 21.65

5. $-4 + 9 = 15 + m$ −10

6. $18 + b = 43 - 9$ 16

7. $4x + 21.50 = 5x$ 21.50

8. $t - 2t = -35.98$ 35.98

▌▌▌ Challenge

You have taken a part-time job at a nearby shopping mall. Your assignment is to hand out 500 advertising leaflets. You have decided to work in a pattern. You will hand out 1 leaflet on the first day, 2 on the second day, 4 on the third day, 8 on the fourth day, and so on. How many days will it take to complete your assignment? 9 days

244 *Chapter 7*

7-5 Working with Percents

When we say *38% of 50 is 19*, we mean

$$\frac{38}{100} \times 50 = 19 \qquad \text{or} \qquad 0.38 \times 50 = 19.$$

The percent, 38%, is called the **rate,** r.
The word "of" indicates multiplication.
The number, 50, following the word "of" is called the **base,** b.
The number, 19, that is the product of the rate and the base is called the **percentage,** p.

> ### Formula
>
> percentage = rate $\times$ base
>
> $$p = rb$$

EXAMPLE 1   What is 18% of 35?

Solution p is to be found, r is 18%, and b is 35.

$$p = 0.18 \times 35 = 6.3$$

18% of 35 is 6.3.

EXAMPLE 2   What percent of 40 is 27?

Solution r is to be found, p is 27, and b is 40.

$$27 = r \times 40$$
$$\frac{27}{40} = r$$
$$r = 0.675 = 67.5\%$$

27 is 67.5% of 40.

EXAMPLE 3   48 is 16% of what number?

Solution b is to be found, p is 48, and r is 16%.

$$48 = 0.16 \times b$$
$$b = \frac{48}{0.16} = 300$$

48 is 16% of 300.

Ratio, Proportion, and Percent   **245**

Teaching Suggestions
p. 229c

Related Activities p. 229d

Reading Mathematics

Students will learn the meaning of the following mathematical terms in this lesson: *rate, base, percentage.*

   Note the specialized meanings of *rate* and *base* used in this lesson. In percent problems the rate is the percent, the base is the whole, and the percentage is a part of the whole. Remind students that a percent is a rate, an amount *per hundred*.

Chalkboard Exercises
Solve.

1. What is 22% of 350? **77**

2. $12\frac{1}{2}$% of 36 is what number? **4.5**

3. What percent of 80 is 16? **20%**

4. 12 is what percent of 50? **24%**

5. 250 is 125% of what number? **200**

6. 16 is 10% of what number? **160**

Sometimes when we use the formula $p = rb$, it is easier to rewrite the rate as a fraction.

EXAMPLE 4   56 is $66\frac{2}{3}\%$ of what number?

Solution b is to be found, p is 56, and r is $66\frac{2}{3}\%$, or $\frac{2}{3}$.

$$56 = \frac{2}{3}b$$

$$b = \frac{56}{\frac{2}{3}} = 56 \times \frac{3}{2} = 84$$

56 is $66\frac{2}{3}\%$ of 84.

Class Exercises

Identify the given numbers as percentage, rate, or base and tell which number is to be found.

1. 12 is 4% of what number? *p*: 12; *r*: 4%; *b* is to be found

2. What is 35% of 60? *r*: 35%; *b*: 60; *p* is to be found

3. What percent of 80 is 56? *p*: 56; *b*: 80; *r* is to be found

4. 81 of 360 students at Jefferson Junior High are taking French. What percent of students are taking French? *p*: 81; *b*: 360; *r* is to be found

5. 68% of the 300 people interviewed in an opinion poll were against a tax increase. How many people were against the increase? *r*: 68%; *b*: 300; *p* is to be found

6. One day the quality control department at the Sure-Fire Sparkplug Company reported that 35 plugs were defective. This is 0.25% of the daily output. What is the daily output? *r*: 0.25%; *p*: 35; *b* is to be found

Written Exercises

Solve.

A   1. What is 24% of 550? 132

3. What percent of 500 is 35? 7%

5. 1.6 is 8% of what number? 20

7. 15 is 37.5% of what number? 40

2. 4 is 16% of what number? 25

4. What is 31% of 425? 131.75

6. What percent of 220 is 187? 85%

8. What is 32.5% of 840? 273

Additional A Exercises

Solve.

1. What is 18% of 55? 9.9

2. What percent of 132 is 11? $8\frac{1}{3}\%$

3. 20 is 62.5% of what number? 32

4. In February 36% of the 500 students who attend Jackson School were absent due to illness. How many students were absent? 180

5. Jo has saved $6 for a new calculator. If this is $37\frac{1}{2}\%$ of the amount she needs, what is the price of the calculator? $16

6. Eighteen of the twenty-five girls who tried out for the baseball team were selected for the team. What percent were *not* selected? 28%

9. What percent of 75 is 25? $33\frac{1}{3}\%$

10. What is 0.04% of 9936? 3.9744

B 11. 27 is $16\frac{2}{3}\%$ of what number? 162

12. What is $33\frac{1}{3}\%$ of 162? 54

13. What is $\frac{1}{9}\%$ of 17? $\frac{17}{900}$

14. 45 is $\frac{5}{6}\%$ of what number? 5400

15. 52 is what percent of 78? $66\frac{2}{3}\%$

16. What percent of 126 is 42? $33\frac{1}{3}\%$

17. What percent of 84 is 147? 175%

18. 33 is what percent of 4400? $\frac{3}{4}\%$

Problems

Solve.

A 1. In one game a quarterback completed 13 of 25 passes. What percent of the passes were completed? 52%

2. On a 75-question test Maureen got 84% correct. How many questions did she answer correctly? 63 questions

3. 15% of the contents of a 454 g can of dog food is protein. How many grams of protein are in the can? 68.1 g

4. A town with a population of 27,530 has voted to allot 37.5% of the entire budget to education. If the education budget is $285,000, what is the total budget? $760,000

5. 12% of the total worth of a certain pension fund is invested in oil stocks. If $45 million is invested in oil stocks, what is the total worth of the fund? $375 million

6. A stereo system is marked with a price of $479. The sales tax on the system is $28.74. What is the sales tax rate? 6%

B 7. On Saturday 78% of the breakfast customers at Mark's Restaurant ordered orange juice. If 33 customers did *not* order orange juice, how many breakfast customers were there altogether? 150 customers

8. In a state with a 5% sales tax, a tennis racket cost $60.85, including tax. What was the selling price of the racket? $57.95

9. The Masons allocated 35% of their budget for housing and insurance, 15% for food, and 15% for education. If their total budget is $52,000, how much do they spend on other items? $18,200

10. A pair of jeans costs $8.00 to manufacture. If the designer, distributor, and wholesaler each add a 50% markup of the price paid, what is the final price of the jeans? $27

Ratio, Proportion, and Percent **247**

Suggested Assignments

Minimum
Day 1: 246 / 1–8
        247 / 9–18
Day 2: 247 / Prob. 1–6
        248 / Self-Test A

Average
Day 1: 246 / 1–8
        247 / 9–18; Prob. 1–4
Day 2: 247 / Prob. 5–10
        248 / Self-Test A

Maximum
        246 / 2–8 even
        247 / 10–18 even;
          Prob. 1–10
        248 / Prob. 11–12
        248 / Self-Test A

Supplementary Materials

Practice Masters, p. 33
Test 7A, pp. 47–48

11. In a student opinion poll at Polk Junior High, 27.5% of the students who responded chose football as their favorite sport. Basketball was chosen by 17.5% of the students who responded. Other sports were chosen by 44 people in the poll.
   a. What is the total number of people who responded to the poll? 80 people
   b. How many people preferred basketball? 14 people

12. The Sound Off Siren Company tests every fifth siren for sound quality and every eighth siren for mechanical quality. The daily output is 350 sirens.
   a. What percent is tested for sound quality? 20%
   b. What percent is tested for mechanical quality? 12.5%
   c. What percent is tested for both types of quality? 2.3%

Self-Test A

Write each ratio as a fraction in lowest terms.

1. $\frac{9}{15}$ $\frac{3}{5}$ **2.** 12:4 $\frac{3}{1}$ **3.** 16 cm to 2 m $\frac{2}{25}$ [7–1]

Solve each proportion.

4. $\frac{4}{a} = \frac{24}{18}$ 3   **5.** $\frac{40}{100} = \frac{x}{6}$ 2.4   **6.** $\frac{21}{n} = \frac{7}{18}$ 54

Solve.

7. If 6 apples cost \$1.50, how much will 10 apples cost? \$2.50   [7–2]

8. Ken drives for 2 h at an average speed of 55 km/h. How far does he travel? 110 km

A map uses the scale 1 cm : 190 km. Find the actual distance for each distance on the map.

9. 3 cm 570 km   **10.** 6.5 cm 1235 km   **11.** 14 cm [7–3]
2660 km

Express each fraction or decimal as a percent.

12. 0.66 66%   **13.** 0.327 32.7%   **14.** $2\frac{1}{2}$ 250%   **15.** $\frac{1}{6}$ 16$\frac{2}{3}$% [7–4]

Solve.

16. What is 12% of 37? 4.44   **17.** 12 is 24% of what number? 50   [7–5]

18. What percent of 81 is 27? 33$\frac{1}{3}$%   **19.** What is $\frac{1}{5}$% of 885? 1.77

Self-Test answers and Extra Practice are at the back of the book.

248 *Chapter 7*

Quick Quiz A

Write each ratio as a fraction in lowest terms.

1. $\frac{15}{35}$ $\frac{3}{7}$

2. 14:2 $\frac{7}{1}$

3. 22 cm to 2 m $\frac{11}{100}$

Solve each proportion.

4. $\frac{n}{7} = \frac{15}{21}$ 5

5. $\frac{35}{100} = \frac{7}{n}$ 20

6. $\frac{10}{a} = \frac{60}{24}$ 4

Solve.

7. If 3 cans of dog food cost 99¢, how much will 5 cans cost? \$1.65

8. Jerry drove for 2 h at an average speed of 52 mi/h. How far did he travel? 104 mi

A map uses a scale of 1 cm : 80 km. Find the actual distance for each distance on the map.

9. 4 cm 320 km

10. 2.5 cm 200 km

11. 12 cm 960 km

Express as a percent.

12. 0.61 61%

13. 0.015 1.5%

14. $4\frac{1}{5}$ 420%

15. $\frac{5}{6}$ 83$\frac{1}{3}$%

Solve.

16. What is 15% of 42? 6.3

17. 25 is 80% of what number? 31.25

18. What percent of 36 is 43.2? 120%

7-6 Percent of Increase and Decrease

Many everyday problems involve the **percent of change** in a given quantity. Whether the change is an increase or a decrease, the amount of change is always a percentage of the *original* amount, not of the new amount. The formula $p = r \times b$ is easily applied:

amount of change (p) = percent of change (r) × original amount (b)

EXAMPLE 1 The selling price of a baseball glove was $32.50. After sales tax was added, the total cost was $33.80. What percent of the selling price was the tax?

Solution

Method 1
First subtract to find the amount of tax.

$$33.80 - 32.50 = 1.30$$

Then express the amount of tax as a percent of the selling price.

$$1.30 = r \times 32.50$$
$$r = \frac{1.30}{32.50}$$
$$r = 0.04 = 4\%$$

Method 2
First express the total cost as a percent of the selling price.

$$33.80 = r \times 32.50$$
$$r = \frac{33.80}{32.50}$$
$$r = 1.04 = 104\%$$

Because the total cost is 104% of the selling price, the tax is

$$104\% - 100\% = 4\%.$$

By either method, the tax is 4% of the selling price.

Problem Solving Reminder

When planning your solution, remember that there are often *alternate methods of solution.* In Example 1, one plan subtracted first to find the amount of change and then used the formula to find the percent. The other plan applied the formula first and then subtracted to find the percent.

Ratio, Proportion, and Percent **249**

Teaching Suggestions
p. 229d

Related Activities p. 229e

Reading Mathematics

Students will learn the meaning of the following mathematical terms in this lesson: *percent of change, increase, decrease.*

Problem-solving skills can be strengthened by listing words associated with increase (*grow, greater, rose,* etc.) and words associated with decrease (*dropped, lower, reduced,* etc.). Encourage students to look for these important words in problems.

Chalkboard Examples

Find the percent of increase or decrease from the first number to the second.

1. $10 to $30
   200% increase

2. 24 to 4 $83\frac{1}{3}\%$ decrease

3. 300 to 500
   $66\frac{2}{3}\%$ increase

Solve.

4. $52 decreased 20%
   $41.60

5. $14 increased 35%
   $18.90

6. 400 increased 150%
   1000

EXAMPLE 2 A share of stock in the Bonanza Gold Mine sold for $15 at the beginning of one day and dropped 32% by the end of the day. What was the price at the end of the day?

Solution   *Method 1*
First use the formula $p = rb$ to find the amount of the decrease.

$$p = 0.32 \times 15 = 4.80$$

Then subtract the decrease from the original price.

$$15 - 4.80 = 10.20$$

Method 2
Because the change is a decrease of 32%, the new price is 100% − 32%, or 68%, of the original price.

$$p = 0.68 \times 15 = 10.20$$

By either method, the price at the end of the day was $10.20.

EXAMPLE 3 The number of people who attended the Wildcats' basketball game on Wednesday was 20% lower than the number of people who attended on Friday. On Wednesday 612 people attended the game. How many people attended on Friday?

Solution   Because the change is a decrease of 20%, the number of people on Wednesday is 100% − 20%, or 80%, of the number of people on Friday. Therefore,

$$612 = 0.80b$$

$$b = \frac{612}{0.80} = 765$$

On Friday, 765 people attended the game.

Problems

A **1.** The selling price of a bicycle that had sold for $220 last year was increased by 15%. What is the new price? **$253**

2. The weight of a granola bar was decreased by 20%. What is the new weight if the original weight was 4.5 oz? **3.6 oz**

3. The membership in the Fair Oaks Chess Club increased from 256 to 288. What is the percent of increase? **12.5%**

Additional A Problems

1. In a certain area of southern California, lightning started 35 forest fires in one month. The following month the number of fires dropped to 21. What was the percent of decrease? **40%**

2. At the beginning of the school year there were 25 students in a karate class. By May, the class had increased by 20%. How many students were in the class in May? **30**

3. A $45 ski jacket is now on sale for $36. What is the percent of decrease? **20%**

4. A house was sold for $60,000 ten years ago. It has increased in value 55%. What is the value of the house now? **$93,000**

5. The population of a city is now 12,000 people. The population is expected to increase 15% in 10 years. What is the projected population? **13,800**

6. The price of a hair dryer has been reduced 50%. If the original selling price was $34, what is the sale price? **$17**

4. Orders for milling machines from Precision Machine Company dropped from 150 one year to 123 the next. What is the percent of decrease? **18%**

5. The fuel economy in the new Desert Rat 2000 compact wagon is advertised to be a 24% increase over the old model. If the new model gets 31 miles per gallon, what was the fuel economy of the old model? **25 mi/gal**

6. After a 16% increase, the price of a pair of running shoes was $40.60. What was the old price of the shoes? **$35**

7. The Calorie count of a container of Seaside Cottage Cheese was reduced by 8% to 414 Calories. What was the old Calorie count? **450 Calories**

8. The number of seats on the new Icarus 525 airliner is a 36% increase over the old model. The new plane seats 374 passengers. How many passengers did the old model seat? **275 passengers**

B   **9.** Last year the population of Spoon Forks grew from 1250 to 1300. If the population of the town grows by the same percent this year, what will the population be? **1352**

10. This year, Village Realty sold 289 homes. Last year the realty sold 340 homes. If sales decrease by the same percent next year, many homes can Village Realty expect to sell? **246 homes**

C   **11.** Contributions to the annual Grayson School fund raising campaign were 10% greater in 1984 than they were in 1983. In 1983, contributions were 15% greater than they were in 1982. If contributions for 1984 total $8855, what was the total in 1982? **$7000**

12. In July the price of a gallon of gasoline at Quick Sale Service Station rose 12%. In August it fell 15% of its final July price, ending the month at $1.19. What was its price at the beginning of July? **$1.25**

Review Exercises

Solve.

1. $p = 0.36 \times 27$ **9.72**

2. $1.89 = r \times 7$ **0.27**

3. $144.5 = 8.5n$ **17**

4. $21.65 \times 0.7 = m$ **15.155**

5. $156 = 0.3q$ **520**

6. $a \times 0.15 = 4.125$ **27.5**

7. $\frac{x}{21} = 10.5$ **220.5**

8. $91.53 \times 0.4 = t$ **36.612**

9. $\frac{324}{y} = 8100$ **0.04**

Ratio, Proportion, and Percent   **251**

Suggested Assignments

Minimum
    250/Prob. 1–3
    251/Prob. 4–8
    251/Rev. 1–9
Average
    250/Prob. 1–3
    251/Prob. 4–10
    251/Rev. 1–9 odd
Maximum
    250/Prob. 1–3
    251/Prob. 4–12

Supplementary Materials

Practice Masters, p. 33

Reading Mathematics

Students will learn the meaning of the following mathematical terms in this lesson: *commission, royalty, discount, sale price, net price.*

Chalkboard Examples

1. Sarah Joines, a real estate agent, sold a house for $85,000 and received a 5% commission. How much money did she receive? $4250

2. David Carter, a book salesman, earned $28,000 during the past year. If these earnings were based on a 12% rate of commission, what was the value of the books he sold? $233,333.33

3. If a jacket normally costs $42.00, what would it cost if discounted 20%? $33.60

7-7 Commissions, Discounts, Royalties

Percents are important in business and consumer situations. The following terms are frequently associated with percents.

Commission An amount paid to a salesperson, often in addition to a regular salary, for selling an item or service. The **rate of commission** is generally a percent of the value of the sales that the person makes.

Royalty An amount paid to the creator or owner of a musical or literary work, an invention, or a service. The **royalty rate** is a percent of the money earned by the sale of the creation or service.

Discount A reduction in the original price of an item or service. The **discount rate** is a percent of the original price. The new, lower price is called the **sale price,** or the **net price.**

EXAMPLE 1 Last year Jonathan Stubbs received a commission of $18,000 on sales of appliances totaling $225,000. What was his rate of commission?

Solution Use the formula $p = rb$.
r is to be found, p is $18,000, and b is $225,000.

$$18,000 = r \times 225,000$$

$$r = \frac{18,000}{225,000} = 0.08 = 8\%$$

Jonathan's rate of commission is 8%.

EXAMPLE 2 Nina Boldoni receives a royalty of 15% of the selling price of each of her record albums. The recording company receives the remaining portion of the selling price. What is the selling price of each album if the company receives $9.52 for each album sold?

Solution Because Nina receives 15% of the selling price, the record company receives 100% − 15%, or 85%, of the selling price. Therefore,

$$9.52 = 0.85b$$

$$b = \frac{9.52}{0.85} = 11.2, \text{ or } 11.20$$

The selling price is $11.20.

252 *Chapter 7*

EXAMPLE 3　The sale price of a clothes dryer is $252. The original price was $288. What is the discount rate?

Solution　　Subtract to find the amount of the discount.

$$288 - 252 = 36$$

Then express the amount of the discount as a percent of the original price.

$$36 = r \times 288$$
$$r = \frac{36}{288} = 0.125 = 12.5\%$$

The discount rate is 12.5%.

Problems

A
1. A pair of slacks that sold for $17.75 is on sale for $14.91. What is the discount rate? 16%

2. A video game system that sold for $135 is discounted 24%. What is the net price? $102.60

3. A carpet salesperson receives a 6% commission on her sales. If her commission was $216 last week, what was the total value of her sales? $3600

4. A guitarist earns a royalty of 22% of the selling price of a record album. If he earns $2.64 on each record album sold, what is the selling price of the album? $12

5. The author of a book on running receives a royalty of 75¢ per copy sold. If the royalty rate is 12% of the single copy price, how much money per copy does *not* go to the author? $5.50

6. The publisher of *Lost in the Jungle* receives $12.60 from each copy sold. The remaining portion of the $15 selling price goes to the author. What royalty rate does the author earn? 16%

Ratio, Proportion, and Percent　**253**

Additional A Problems

1. A gold necklace regularly sells for $76. If the necklace is on sale for 60% off, what will the sale price be? $30.40

2. Martha bought a minibike that had been discounted 60%. If she paid $96, what was the original price? $240

3. If a car salesperson sells a car for $9000 and earns a 15% commission, how much money would he earn? $1350

Suggested Assignments

Minimum
  253/Prob. 1–6
  254/Prob. 7–8
  254/Rev. 1–8

Average
  253/Prob. 1–6
  254/Prob. 7–14
  254/Rev. 1–8
  254/Calculator Key-In

Maximum
  253/Prob. 1–6
  254/Prob. 7–16
  254/Calculator Key-In

Supplementary Materials

Practice Masters, p. 34

Additional Answers
Review Exercises

Some of these words have more than one meaning. Emphasize the meaning that is used in Lesson 7-8.

1. ratio: an indicated quotient of two numbers

2. proportion: a statement of equality of two ratios

3. percent: an amount per hundred

4. rate: a ratio that compares quantities of different kinds; the percent in a percent problem

5. base: the original number of which a percent is taken

6. percentage: the number that results from taking a percent of another number

7. increase: an amount added to the original amount

8. decrease: an amount subtracted from the original amount

---

7. The discount rate on a coat at Adelphi Clothing is 30% of the original price. The sale price is $50.40. What was the original price? $72

8. The creator of a new game receives a royalty of 8% of the selling price of each game sold. The company that produces the game receives the remaining amount. If the company receives $10.10 per game, what is the selling price of the game? $10.98

B 9. A sales representative for Data Electronics earns a salary of $1314 per month plus a commission based on the total value of her sales. If she earns $1484.40 for the month and her sales totaled $5680, what is her rate of commission? 3%

10. A radio that originally sold for $59.85 was discounted 15% in April. In May, the sale price was discounted 25%. What is the new sale price in May? $38.15

A real estate agent earns a commission of 6% of the selling price of a house. If the selling price is a multiple of $100 and the owner wants to keep *at least* the following amount, what is the minimum selling price?

11. $75,000
$79,800

12. $69,000
$73,500

13. $84,000
$89,400

14. $91,000
$96,900

C 15. An insurance salesperson earns a commission of 3% of the first $5000 of insurance that he sells each week and 4% of the value in excess of $5000. One week he earned a commission of $320. What was the total value of the insurance that he sold during the week? $9250

16. At a clearance sale, a gas-powered lawnmower was discounted 32%. The lawnmower sold for $117.81, including a sales tax of 5% of the sale price. What was the original price of the mower? $165

Review Exercises

Explain the meaning of each term.

1. ratio

2. proportion

3. percent

4. rate

5. base

6. percentage

7. increase

8. decrease

 Calculator Key-In

How can you use your calculator to solve the exercise without using the percent key and using only one of the keys +, −, ×, or ÷?

1. $25.00 + (5% of $25.00) 1.05 × 25

2. $43.99 − (15% of $43.99) 0.85 × 43.99

7-8 Percents and Proportions

You have learned to solve problems involving percents by using the formula $p = rb$. You can also use proportions to solve problems involving percents. The following discussion shows how we may write a proportion that relates percentage, rate, and base.

Consider the statement *9 is 15% of 60.* Because a percent is an amount *per hundred,* we can think of 15% as 15 per hundred, or the ratio of 15 to 100:

$$15\% = \frac{15}{100}.$$

Using the formula $p = rb$, we have

$$9 = \frac{15}{100} \times 60.$$

Dividing both sides of the equation by 60, we obtain the proportion

$$\frac{9}{60} = \frac{15}{100},$$

or 9 is to 60 as 15 is to 100.

Note that $\frac{9}{60}$ is the ratio of the percentage (p) to the base (b).

Percentage, base, and rate are related as shown in the following proportion:

$$\frac{p}{b} = \frac{n}{100},$$

where $\frac{n}{100}$ is the rate expressed as an amount per hundred.

EXAMPLE 1   143 is 65% of what number?

Solution   The rate, 65%, expressed in the form $\frac{n}{100}$ is $\frac{65}{100}$.

The percentage, p, is 143. Write a proportion to find the base, b.

$$\frac{p}{b} = \frac{n}{100}$$

$$\frac{143}{b} = \frac{65}{100}$$

$$65b = 100 \times 143$$

$$b = \frac{14{,}300}{65} = 220$$

Ratio, Proportion, and Percent   **255**

Teaching Suggestions p. 229e

Related Activities p. 229e

Reading Mathematics

The prefix *semi-* is used in many expressions. Remind students of *semicircle,* page 187. When students study ellipses in a later course they will learn about semi-major and semi-minor axes. *Hemi-,* as in *hemisphere,* is a related prefix that also means "half."

Another prefix commonly used in expressions describing time is *bi-,* meaning "two." Remind students of *bisect,* page 192. *Bi-* and *semi-* are sometimes confused. *Bimonthly* means every two months, or 6 times a year; *semimonthly* means every half month, or 24 times a year.

Chalkboard Examples

Set up a proportion and use it to solve the problem.

1. Shirts are on sale for 15% off. How much is saved on a shirt that is regularly $20?
   $\frac{15}{100} = \frac{n}{20}$, $n = 3$, $3

2. A color TV, regularly $450, is on sale for $405. What is the rate of discount?
   $\frac{45}{450} = \frac{n}{100}$, $n = 10$, 10%

3. Alex saves 30% of what he earns working part time. Last month he earned $65. How much did he save?
   $\frac{30}{100} = \frac{n}{65}$, $n = 19.50, $19.50

EXAMPLE 2 In a recent survey, 38 of 120 people preferred the Bright Light disposable flashlight to other flashlights. What percent of the people surveyed preferred Bright Light?

Solution The question asks what percent, or how many people per hundred, prefer Bright Light.

Let n equal the number per hundred.
You know that p is 38 and b is 120.
Set up a proportion and then solve for n.

$$\frac{p}{b} = \frac{n}{100}$$

$$\frac{38}{120} = \frac{n}{100}$$

$$38 \times 100 = 120n$$

$$\frac{3800}{120} = n$$

$$n = 31\frac{2}{3}$$

In the survey, $31\frac{2}{3}\%$ of the people preferred Bright Light.

EXAMPLE 3 The price of a pocket cassette player has been discounted 25%. The original price was $59. What is the sale price?

Solution The question asks you to find the sale price.

First find the amount of the discount.
p is to be found, b is 59, and n is 25.
Set up a proportion and then solve for p.

$$\frac{p}{b} = \frac{n}{100}$$

$$\frac{p}{59} = \frac{25}{100}$$

$$100p = 59 \times 25$$

$$p = \frac{1475}{100} = 14.75$$

The amount of the discount is $14.75.

Next find the sale price.

$$59 - 14.75 = 44.25$$

The sale price is $44.25.

Class Exercises

For each exercise, set up a proportion to find the number or percent. Do not solve the proportion.

1. What percent of 32 is 20? $\frac{20}{32} = \frac{x}{100}$

2. 14 is 25% of what number? $\frac{14}{x} = \frac{25}{100}$

3. What is 58% of 24? $\frac{58}{100} = \frac{x}{24}$

4. A digital clock is selling at a discount of 15%. The original price was $8.98. How much money will you save by buying the clock at the sale price? $\frac{15}{100} = \frac{x}{8.98}$

5. Catherine answered 95% of the test questions correctly. If she answered 38 questions correctly, how many questions were on the test? $\frac{95}{100} = \frac{38}{x}$

6. This year, 360 people ran in the town marathon. Only 315 people finished the race. What percent of the people finished the race? $\frac{315}{360} = \frac{x}{100}$

Written Exercises

Use a proportion to solve.

A

1. What is 16% of 32? **5.12**

2. 306 is 51% of what number? **600**

3. What percent of 20 is 16? **80%**

4. What is 104% of 85? **88.4**

5. 15 is 37.5% of what number? **40**

6. What percent of 72 is 18? **25%**

Problems

Use a proportion to solve.

A

1. The Plantery received a shipment of 40 plants on Wednesday. By Friday, 33 of the plants had been sold. What percent of the plants were sold? **82.5%**

2. The Eagles have won 6 of the 8 games they have played this season. What percent of this season's games have the Eagles won? **75%**

3. The library ordered 56 new books. 87.5% of the books are nonfiction. How many books are nonfiction? **49 books**

4. This year 18.75% more students have joined the Long Hill High School Drama Club. The records show that 6 new students have joined. How many students were members last year? **32 students**

Ratio, Proportion, and Percent **257**

Suggested Assignments

Minimum
  257/1–6; Prob. 1–4
  258/Prob. 5–8
  259/Rev. 1–8

Average
  257/1–6; Prob. 1–4
  258/Prob. 5–10
  259/Rev. 2–8 even
  259/Computer Byte

Maximum
  257/2, 4, 6; Prob. 1–4
  258/Prob. 5–10
  259/Prob. 11–13
  259/Computer Byte

Supplementary Materials

Practice Masters, p. 34

5. A water purifier is discounted 20% of the original price for a saving of $6.96. What is the original price of the water purifier? What is the sale price? $34.80; $27.84

6. The original price of a Sportsmaster 300 fishing pole was $37.80. The price has now been discounted 15%. What is the amount of the discount? What is the sale price? $5.67; $32.13

B 7. Steve recently received a raise of 6% of his salary at his part-time job. He now earns $38.69 per week. How much did he earn per week before his raise? $36.50

8. Since the beginning of the year, the number of subscriptions to *New Tech Magazine* has increased by 180%. The number of subscriptions is now 140,000. What was the number of subscriptions at the beginning of the year? 50,000 subscriptions

EXAMPLE This **pie chart,** or **circle graph,** shows the distribution of the Valley Springs annual budget. Use a proportion to find the measure of the angle for the wedge for education.

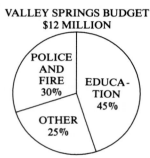

VALLEY SPRINGS BUDGET
$12 MILLION

Solution The number of degrees in a circle is 360°. The circle represents the total budget. 45% of the total budget is for education. Therefore,

$$\frac{45}{100} = \frac{n}{360}$$
$$100n = 45 \times 360$$
$$n = \frac{16,200}{100}$$
$$n = 162$$

There are 162° in the wedge for education.

Use proportions to answer these questions about the pie chart above.

9. **a.** What is the measure of the angle for the wedge for police and fire expenses? 108°
   b. How much money is budgeted for police and fire expenses? $3.6 million

10. **a.** What is the measure of the angle for the wedge for other expenses? 90°
    b. How much money is budgeted for other expenses? 3 million

258 *Chapter 7*

For Exercises 11–13, (a) use a compass and protractor to draw a pie chart to represent the budget, and (b) use proportions to find the dollar value of each expense.

11. The monthly budget of the Miller family allows for spending 25% on food, 15% on clothing, 30% on housing expenses, 10% on medical expenses, and 20% on other expenses. The budget totals $1800.

12. The weekly expenses of Daisy's Diner total $8400. Of this total, 20% is spent for employees' salaries, 60% is spent on food, 5% is spent on advertising, 10% is spent on rent, and 5% is used for other expenses.

13. The Chimney Hill school budget allows 72% for salaries, 8% for maintenance and repair, and 5% for books and supplies. The remainder is divided equally among recreation, after-school programs, and teacher training. The budget totals $680,000.

11. food $450; clothing $270; housing $540; medical $180; other $360
12. salaries $1680; food $5040; ads $420; rent $840; other $420
13. salaries $489,600; maint. $54,400; books $34,000; others $34,000 each

Review Exercises

Write as a decimal. Use a bar to indicate a repeating decimal.

1. $\frac{1}{2}$ **2.** $\frac{1}{3}$ **3.** $\frac{1}{6}$ **4.** $\frac{1}{4}$ **5.** $2\frac{1}{4}$ **6.** $\frac{2}{3}$ **7.** $\frac{3}{4}$ **8.** $1\frac{5}{12}$

0.5 $0.\overline{3}$ $0.1\overline{6}$ 0.25   2.25 $0.\overline{6}$ 0.75 $1.41\overline{6}$

▄▄▄ Computer Byte

The following program converts fractions with numerators and denominators from 1 through 15 to percents.

```
10   PRINT "FRACTION","PERCENT"
20   FOR A = 1 TO 15
30   FOR B = 1 TO 15
40   IF A < B THEN 60
50   PRINT B;"/";A; TAB( 17);100 * B / A;"%"
60   NEXT B
70   NEXT A
80   END
```

1. RUN the program to generate a list of fractions and their equivalent percents.

2. Change line 40 to IF B < A THEN 60 to generate a list of the reciprocals of the fractions in Exercise 1 and their percents.

3. Change the program to generate a list of fractions with any denominators and numerators and their percents.

Ratio, Proportion, and Percent   **259**

Reading Mathematics

Students will learn the meaning of the following mathematical terms in this lesson:
*interest, principal, rate, time,
simple interest, compound
interest.*

Chalkboard Examples

1. Find the simple interest
   due on $500 borrowed at
   5.5% for 2 years. **$55**

2. What is the interest for
   one year on $300 depos-
   ited in a savings account
   at 6.75% compounded
   semiannually? **$20.59**

3. Angela Carelli invested
   $3000 at 6% annual inter-
   est. How much must she
   invest at 7.5% annual interest for her annual interest from both investments
   to total $330? **$2000**

7-9 Interest

Interest is money that is paid for the use of money that is borrowed or
invested. If you borrow money from a bank, for example, the bank will
charge you interest for the use of the money. On the other hand, if you
deposit money in a bank or invest money in stocks or bonds, you are
lending money and you will receive interest.

The amount of interest, I, depends on the three things listed below.

P, the **principal,** the amount borrowed or invested

r, the **annual rate** of interest, a percent

t, the **time,** in years, over which the money is used

In the simplest case, we use this formula:

Formula

Interest = Principal $\times$ rate $\times$ time

$$I = Prt$$

EXAMPLE 1 Martina Lopez deposits $11,500 in a six-month savings certificate at
County Bank. She can make no additional deposits to the certificate during the six months that it is invested. At the end of six
months, Martina will receive $603.75 in interest on her original
deposit. What is the annual interest rate?

Solution Use the formula, $I = Prt$.
Because the rate of interest in the formula is the annual, or yearly,
interest, express the time, 6 months, as 0.5 year.

$$603.75 = 11,500 \times r \times 0.5$$
$$603.75 = 5750r$$
$$r = \frac{603.75}{5750} = 0.105 = 10.5\%$$

The annual rate of interest is 10.5%.

Interest paid only on the original principal, as in Example 1, is
called **simple interest.** Banks and savings-and-loan companies usually
pay **compound interest.** That is, when interest is calculated, it is added
to the original principal (or **compounded**). Thus the principal grows.
The new principal is used in the next calculation of interest.

260 *Chapter 7*

EXAMPLE 2   Roy Henderson has deposited $2500 in a special Vacation Club savings plan through his company's credit union. The plan pays 8% interest, compounded quarterly. If Roy makes no additional deposits, what is the value of his investment after 9 months?

Solution   For each interest computation, the rate is 0.08 and the time is 0.25 (one quarter of a year). Note that the principal changes after each three months.

For the first three months: $P = 2500$ $r = 0.08$ $t = 0.25$
$$I = 2500 \times 0.08 \times 0.25 = 50$$

For the second 3 months: $P = 2500 + 50 = 2550$
$$I = 2550 \times 0.08 \times 0.25 = 51$$

For the third 3 months: $P = 2550 + 51 = 2601$
$$I = 2601 \times 0.08 \times 0.25 = 52.02$$

$$2601 + 52.02 = 2653.02$$

The value of the investment after 9 months is $2653.02.

Reading Mathematics: *Vocabulary*
Interest problems often use expressions describing time. Use the meanings of common word parts, such as the prefix *semi-* ("half"), the root *-annu-* ("year"), and the suffix *-ly* ("happening each," or "once per") to remember the meanings of these terms: *annually* ("once per year"), *semiannually* ("once per half year," or "twice a year"), *quarterly* ("once per quarter," or "4 times a year"), and *monthly* ("once per month").

Problems

Complete the following table.

	Amount Borrowed	Annual Rate	Time	Simple Interest
A 1.	$4000	7.5%	2 years	? $600
2.	$150	8%	3 years	? $36
3.	$6000	? 12.5%	18 months	$1125
4.	$1250	? 16%	30 months	$500
5.	$4800	9%	? 5 years	$2160
6.	? $950	12%	3 years	$342

Ratio, Proportion, and Percent   **261**

Additional A Problems

1. A loan of $5000 at 13% simple interest is to be repaid in 3 years. What is the total amount to be repaid? $6950

2. Tom Lee invested $1600 in a 6-month savings certificate that paid simple interest. After six months he received $1698.88. What was the annual interest rate? 12.36%

3. How long will it take $1200 to earn $150 interest at 10% per year? 1.25 years

4. An investment pays 12% interest, compounded monthly. If $1000 is invested, how much money is in the account after 3 months? $1030.30

5. Anne Rose invested $2500 in a money market fund that pays 8.4% interest, compounded quarterly. How much money will be in the fund after 6 months? $2606.10

261

Suggested Assignments

Minimum
Day 1: 261/Prob. 1–6
       262/Prob. 7–12
Day 2: 262/Prob. 13–15
       263/Self-Test B

Average
Day 1: 261/Prob. 1–6
       262/Prob. 7–14
Day 2: 262/Prob. 15–17
       263/Prob. 18
       263/Self-Test B

Maximum
Day 1: 261/Prob. 1–6
       262/Prob. 7–14
Day 2: 262/Prob. 15–17
       263/Prob. 18–19
       263/Self-Test B

Supplementary Materials

Practice Masters, p. 34
Test 7B, pp. 49–50
Computer Activity 13
Computer Activity 14

7. A loan of $6400 at 12.5% simple interest is to be repaid in $4\frac{1}{2}$ years. What is the total amount to be repaid? $10,000

8. A $6500 automobile loan is to be repaid in 3 years. The total amount to be repaid is $9230. If the interest were simple interest, what would be the annual rate? 14%

9. Mac Deweese invested $3500 in a money market fund that pays 8.5% compounded quarterly. If he makes no deposits or withdrawals, how much money will be in the fund at the end of 6 months? $3650.33

10. Al Grey borrowed $8000 at 9% compounded semiannually. When the entire interest and principal are repaid at the end of two years, how much will Al owe? $9540.15

11. A savings account was opened with $4000. The bank pays $5\frac{1}{2}\%$ interest, compounded monthly. How much money is in the account after 4 months? $4073.84

12. You borrow $2500 at 16% interest, compounded semiannually. No interest is due until you repay the loan. If you repay the loan at the end of 18 months, how much will you pay? $3149.28

13. Steve Burgess and Sarah Keller each invested in 3-month savings certificates that pay simple interest. They made no other deposits or withdrawals. Steve invested $8000 at an annual rate of 8%. Sarah invested $7600 at an annual rate of 8.2%. Who had the greater amount of money after 3 months? Steve

14. Julian Dolby invested $5000 in a special savings account that pays 8% interest, compounded quarterly. How long must Julian keep his money in the account to earn at least $250 in interest? 9 months

B 15. Anita Ramirez owns two bonds, one paying 8.5% interest and the other paying 9% interest. Every six months Anita receives a total of $485 in interest from both bonds. If the 8.5% bond is worth $4000, how much is the 9% bond worth? $7000

16. Mike Robarts owns two bonds, one worth $3000, the other worth $5000. The $3000 bond pays 12% interest. Every 6 months, Mike receives a total of $530 interest from both bonds. What is the annual rate of the $5000 bond? 14%

17. Ellen Holyoke borrowed $500 for three months. Interest was charged at a rate of 18%, compounded monthly. Ellen made a payment of $200 after the interest for the second month was compounded. How much did she owe at the end of the third month? $319.84

18. David Cho deposited $10,000 in a six-month savings certificate that paid simple interest at an annual rate of 12%. After 6 months, David deposited the total value of his investment in another six-month savings certificate. David made no other deposits or withdrawals. After 6 months, David's investment was worth $11,130. What was the annual simple interest rate of the second certificate? 10%

C 19. A savings account pays 5% interest, compounded annually. Show that if $1000 is deposited in the account, the account will contain

1000×1.05 dollars after 1 year,

$1000 \times (1.05)^2$ dollars after 2 years,

$1000 \times (1.05)^3$ dollars after 3 years, and so on.

After 1 year: 1000 + 1000(0.05) = 1000 × 1.05,
after 2 years: 1000(1.05) + 1000(1.05)(0.05) = 1000(1.05)(1.05) = 1000 × (1.05)², and so on.

Self-Test B

Solve.

1. Stuart increased his typing speed from 40 to 48 words per minute. What is the percent of increase? 20%   [7-6]

2. The number of books borrowed from the library in March was 25% greater than the number borrowed in February. If 744 books were borrowed in February, how many were borrowed in March? 930 books

3. Lin Hong receives an 8% commission on the selling price of each stereo system that she sells. What is her commission on a stereo system that has a selling price of $1498? $119.84   [7-7]

4. A television that usually sells for $139 is discounted 15%. How much money do you save by buying the television at the sale price? $20.85

5. A pair of shoes with an original price of $37 has been discounted 25%. What is the amount of the discount? Use a proportion to solve. $9.25   [7-8]

6. Jake received $35 for his birthday. He has $14.70 left. What percent of the money is left? Use a proportion to solve. 42%

7. Erica borrowed $1800 for one year at 17% simple interest. What was the total amount to be repaid? $2106   [7-9]

8. You deposit money in a savings account and make no other deposits or withdrawals. How much is in the account at the end of three months if you deposit $350 at 6% interest, compounded monthly? $355.28

Self-Test answers and Extra Practice are at the back of the book.

Ratio, Proportion, and Percent **263**

Fibonacci Numbers

Enrichment Note

For further understanding of the Golden Ratio, have students draw a square 1 by 1, add another square 1 by 1, add another square 2 by 2, another 3 by 3, another 5 by 5, and so on. The side of each new square should be the next number in the Fibonacci sequence.

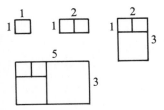

Point out that each side of each rectangle is a number in the Fibonacci sequence. After the first few rectangles, the shapes change very little as the sizes increase.

If the ratio of length to width of a rectangle is the Golden Ratio, the rectangle is called a **golden rectangle.** Have students calculate the ratios of length to width for several rectangular objects such as books, pictures, desks, index cards, and food packages. Many of these ratios will be close to the Golden Ratio.

Golden rectangles have been used in art and architecture for thousands of years. Interested students might want to calculate the ratio of length to width for paintings and the facades of buildings. (The front of the Parthenon is a classic example.) By drawing golden rectangles of various sizes on clear plastic or tracing paper, and placing one over a painting, students may discover that the artist arranged the subjects in a golden rectangle.

(Continue on next page.)

In the thirteenth century, an Italian mathematician named Leonardo of Pisa, nicknamed Fibonacci, discovered a sequence of numbers that has many interesting mathematical properties, as well as applications to biology, art, and architecture. Fibonacci defined the sequence as the number of pairs of rabbits you would have, starting with one pair, if each pair produced a new pair after two months and another new pair every month thereafter.

The diagram below illustrates the process that Fibonacci described for the first six months:

Months		Number of Pairs
1		1
2		1
3		2
4		3
5		5
6		8

The sequence formed by the numbers of pairs is called the **Fibonacci sequence.** Note that any number in the sequence is the sum of the two numbers that precede it (for example, $2 + 3 = 5$, $3 + 5 = 8$). Thus the sequence would continue

$$1, 1, 2, 3, 5, 8, 13, 21, 34, 55, 89, 144, 233, 377, 610, \ldots$$

To see one of the many mathematical properties of this sequence, study the sums of the squares of some pairs of consecutive Fibonacci numbers:

$$2^2 + 3^2 = 4 + 9 = 13$$
$$5^2 + 8^2 = 25 + 64 = 89$$
$$13^2 + 21^2 = 169 + 441 = 610$$

Note that in each case the sum is another number in the sequence.

264 *Chapter 7*

The Fibonacci sequence also relates to a historically important number called the **Golden Ratio,** or the **Golden Mean.** The Golden Ratio is the ratio of the length to the width of a "perfect" rectangle. A rectangle was considered to be "perfect" if the ratio of its length to its width was the same as the ratio of their sum to its length, as written in the proportion at the right. If we let the width of the rectangle be 1, the length is the nonterminating, nonrepeating decimal 1.61828 . . . . Thus, the Golden Ratio is the ratio 1.61828 . . . to 1.

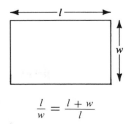

$$\frac{l}{w} = \frac{l + w}{l}$$

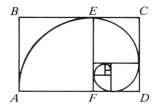

It is remarkable that the ratios of successive terms of the Fibonacci sequence get closer and closer to this number. For example,

$$\frac{8}{5} = 1.6 \qquad \frac{13}{8} = 1.625 \qquad \frac{21}{13} = 1.615384\ldots$$

$$\frac{34}{21} = 1.61904\ldots \qquad \frac{55}{34} = 1.61764\ldots \qquad \frac{89}{55} = 1.61818\ldots$$

1. Examine the fourth, eighth, twelfth, and sixteenth terms of the Fibonacci sequence. What do these numbers have in common? Try the fifth, tenth, and fifteenth terms. 3, 21, 144, and 987 are divisible by 3. 5, 55, and 610 are divisible by 5.

Find some other numerical patterns by performing these calculations with the numbers in the Fibonacci sequence listed on the previous page. Tell what you notice about each new pattern.

2. Find the difference of two numbers that are two places apart in the sequence (the first and the third terms, the second and the fourth terms, the third and the fifth terms, and so on). The original sequence.

3. Subtract the squares of two numbers that are two places apart (as in Exercise 2). Every other member of the original sequence, beginning with 3.

4. Multiply two consecutive numbers (the first and second terms), multiply the next two consecutive numbers (the second and third terms), and then add the products. Every other member of the original sequence, beginning with 3.

5. Multiply two numbers that are two places apart (begin with the second and fourth terms), multiply two other numbers that "straddle" one of these (the first and third terms), and then add the products. Every other member of the original sequence, beginning with 5.

Career Activity Botanists have discovered that Fibonacci numbers occur naturally in many plant forms. For example, a pine cone is made up of 8 spirals swirling upward in one direction and 13 spirals swirling upward in the opposite direction. Find some other instances of Fibonacci numbers that botanists have found in nature. Answers may vary. Another example is the spiral patterns of seeds in a sunflower.

Ratio, Proportion, and Percent **265**

If students draw a golden rectangle *ABCD* and mark off a square *ABEF*, the rectangle *CDFE* is also a golden rectangle.

If students continue this process and draw a circular arc in each square as shown, the curve is approximately a logarithmic spiral, similar to a snail shell. Students may want to investigate the kinds of spirals.

The golden ratio has many other names. Students who want to read more about it should also look up *golden mean, golden section, golden proportion,* and *divine proportion.*

Chapter Review

Complete.

1. If $\frac{14}{7} = \frac{8}{x}$, then $14x = $ __?__ . 56   [7-1]

2. If 3 cans of tuna cost $3.27, the unit price is __?__ . $1.09 per can   [7-2]

3. If Melissa drove 130 km at an average speed of 60 km/h, she traveled for __?__ . $2\frac{1}{6}$ h

4. A map has the scale 1 cm:0.5 km. A map distance of __?__ corresponds to an actual distance of 12 km. 24 cm   [7-3]

5. $0.625 = $ __?__ % 62.5   6. $\frac{3}{5} = $ __?__ % 60   [7-4]

7. 154% of 50 is __?__ . 77   8. 3 is 4% of __?__ . 75   [7-5]

9. 17 is __?__ % of 20. 85   10. 8.5% of 400 is __?__ . 34

11. A stock sold for $18 per share two months ago. Today its price is $15 per share. The percent of decrease is __?__ . $16\frac{2}{3}$%   [7-6]

12. The Cortells' heating bill is 24% higher this month than last month. The bill this month is $75.52. Last month the bill was __?__ . $60.90

13. The price of a jacket was $25. It has been discounted $7.50. The discount rate is __?__ . 30%   [7-7]

14. Claire Nolan receives a commission of 6% of her total sales. Last week her commission was $34.32. The total value of her sales for the week was __?__ . $572

Match the proportion to the problem.

15. The Ski Club has 50 members. If 36 members attend the ski trip, what percent attends the ski trip? B   **A.** $\frac{36}{100} = \frac{n}{50}$ [7-8]

16. There are 50 families on Jamie's paper route. If 36% receive the Sunday paper, how many families receive the Sunday paper? A   **B.** $\frac{n}{100} = \frac{36}{50}$

True or false?

17. A savings account was opened with $200. No other deposits or withdrawals were made. If the bank pays $5\frac{1}{4}$% interest compounded quarterly, $226.25 will be in the account after 3 months. False   [7-9]

18. If George's aunt gives him a loan of $650 for one year at 12% simple interest, George will owe $728 at the end of the year. True

266   *Chapter 7*

Chapter Test

State each ratio as a fraction in lowest terms.

1. $\frac{46}{60}$ $\frac{23}{30}$

2. 16 mm to 3 cm $\frac{8}{15}$

3. 18 : 15 $\frac{6}{5}$ [7–1]

Solve each proportion.

4. $\frac{n}{63} = \frac{42}{27}$ 98

5. $\frac{4.8}{r} = \frac{1.2}{3}$ 12

6. $\frac{7}{21} = \frac{t}{9}$ 3

7. A train travels 442 km in $5\frac{1}{2}$ h. Find the average speed. 80.$\overline{36}$ km/h   [7–2]

8. Country Market is selling 2 containers of yogurt for $1.18. How many containers can you buy for $2.95? 5

9. The actual distance between two cities is 340 km. A map that shows   [7–3]
the cities has a scale of 1 cm : 10 km. What is the distance on the
map? 34 cm

Express each fraction or decimal as a percent.

10. 0.93 93%

11. 0.0724 7.24%

12. $\frac{25}{1000}$ 2.5%

13. $\frac{5}{8}$ 62.5% [7–4]

14. What is 53% of 244? 129.32

15. 1.6 is 8% of what number? 20   [7–5]

16. 35 is what percent of 140? 25%

17. What is $15\frac{2}{3}$% of 60? 9.4

18. The total cost of a camera, including sales tax of 6% of the selling   [7–6]
price, is $169.55. What is the selling price? $159.95

19. Margaret Sherman's annual business expenses have increased from
$2500 to $3175. What is the percent of increase? 27%

20. A salesperson earns a salary plus a commission of 9% of total sales.   [7–7]
How much is the commission on sales totaling $1654? $148.86

21. A refrigerator was discounted 30% of the original price. The discounted price is $447.30. What was the original price? $639

Use proportions to solve Exercises 22 and 23.

22. The Pro Shop sold 6 of 20 tennis rackets in May. What percent of   [7–8]
the tennis rackets were sold? 30%

23. This term, 36% of the students in one class are on the honor roll. If
9 students are on the honor roll, how many students are in the class? 25 students

24. You invest $500 at 6% interest, compounded monthly. If you make   [7–9]
no other deposits or withdrawals, what is the value of your investment after 3 months? $507.54

Ratio, Proportion, and Percent   **267**

Additional Answers
Cumulative Review

The solutions are all the numbers:

31. greater than or equal to 1.

32. less than -9.

33. less than -3.

34. greater than or equal to -10.

35. greater than 3.

36. less than or equal to $4\frac{1}{2}$

Review for Retention
True or False?

1. $\frac{12}{15} = \frac{3}{5}$ **False**

2. $-\frac{32}{6} = -5\frac{1}{3}$ **True**

3. $-4\frac{3}{8} = \frac{35}{8}$ **False**

4. The LCD of $\frac{3}{7}$ and $\frac{2}{3}$ is 21. **True**

5. The LCD of $-\frac{1}{8}$ and $-\frac{1}{2}$ is 8. **True**

6. The LCD of $\frac{2}{5}$ and $-\frac{2}{15}$ is -15. **False**

Write the appropriate symbol.

7. A ray through point L that begins at point D $\overrightarrow{DL}$

8. A line through points J and W $\overleftrightarrow{JW}$

9. A segment with endpoints E and N $\overline{EN}$

Solve.

10. $\frac{3}{5} \times \frac{3}{8}$ $\frac{9}{40}$

11. $\frac{2}{3} + \frac{5}{6}$ $1\frac{1}{2}$

12. $\frac{3}{5} - \frac{2}{3}$ $-\frac{1}{15}$

13. $\frac{1}{8} \div \frac{4}{7}$ $\frac{7}{32}$

14. $\frac{5}{6} \div \frac{3}{8}$ $2\frac{2}{9}$

(Continue on next page.)

268

Cumulative Review (Chapters 1–7)

Exercises

Evaluate the expression if $x = 3$ and $y = 5$.

1. $x + y$ 8

2. $2x + y$ 11

3. $2y - x$ 7

4. $x + 6y$ 33

5. $y + x + 4$ 12

6. $-x - y$ -8

7. $-3x - 2y$ -19

8. $5x + (-y) - 7$ 3

9. x^2 9

10. xy^2 75

11. $(-x)^2 y$ 45

12. $-(xy)^2$ -225

Write the numbers in order from least to greatest.

13. $3, -2.5, 0, -7, 6.4, -2.2$ $-7, -2.5, -2.2, 0, 3, 6.4$

14. $4, -6.2, -7.3, 0, 3.5, 2.5$ $-7.3, -6.2, 0, 2.5, 3.5, 4$

15. $-1.6, -8.4, -3, -1.0, 0.5$ $-8.4, -3, -1.6, -1.0, 0.5$

16. $-4.7, -11.9, 1, 3.8, 0.7, -0.6$ $-11.9, -4.7, -0.6, 0.7, 1, 3.8$

Tell whether the statement is true or false for the given value of the variable.

17. $t - 3 \leq -6$; -4 True

18. $-m - 3 > 0$; -3 False

19. $2b < 3$; 1 True

20. $3 - x = 2$; 5 False

21. $n + 1 \geq -7$; -6 True

22. $r < -2r - 4$; -2 True

Write the fractions as equivalent fractions having the least common denominator (LCD).

23. $\frac{2}{3}, \frac{5}{9}$ $\frac{6}{9}, \frac{5}{9}$

24. $-\frac{3}{5}, \frac{7}{20}$ $-\frac{12}{20}, \frac{7}{20}$

25. $-\frac{8}{3}, \frac{9}{11}$ $-\frac{88}{33}, \frac{27}{33}$

26. $-\frac{5}{7}, -\frac{12}{17}$ $-\frac{85}{119}, -\frac{84}{119}$

27. $\frac{7}{3}, \frac{3}{4}$ $\frac{28}{12}, \frac{9}{12}$

28. $\frac{8}{45}, \frac{11}{75}$ $\frac{40}{225}, \frac{33}{225}$

29. $\frac{17}{32}, -\frac{3}{128}$ $\frac{68}{128}, -\frac{3}{128}$

30. $\frac{3}{34}, \frac{5}{39}$ $\frac{117}{1326}, \frac{170}{1326}$

Solve the inequality and draw its graph. Check students' graphs.

31. $x + 1 \geq 2$

32. $\frac{1}{3}a < -3$

33. $6m < -18$

34. $\frac{3}{5}n \geq -6$

35. $4t + 1 > 13$

36. $4(w - 2) \leq 10$

State which of the rigid motions are needed to match the vertices of the triangles and explain why the triangles are congruent.

37.

38.

39.

translation and rotation; ASA

translation and reflection; SAS

rotation and translation; SSS

Problems

Problem Solving Reminders

Here are some reminders that may help you solve some of the problems on this page.
- Consider whether a chart will help to organize information.
- Supply additional information if needed.
- Reread the problem to be sure that your answer is complete.

Solve.

1. Donald bought a pair of hiking boots for $35.83, a sweater for $24.65, and a backpack for $18. The tax on his purchase was $.90. How much did Donald spend? **$79.38**

2. This week, Marisa worked $1\frac{1}{2}$ h on Monday, $2\frac{1}{4}$ h on Tuesday, $1\frac{1}{3}$ h on Wednesday, and $7\frac{1}{2}$ h on Saturday. How many hours did she work this week? **$12\frac{7}{12}$ h**

3. An airplane flying at an altitude of 25,000 ft dropped 4000 ft in the first 25 s and rose 2500 ft in the next 15 s. What was the altitude of the airplane after 40 s? **23,500 ft**

4. Carolyn Cramer spent 3 h 15 min mowing and raking her lawn. She spent twice as long raking as she did mowing. How long did she spend on each task? **1 h 5 min mowing, 2 h 10 min raking**

5. At a milk processing plant 100 lb of farm milk are needed to make 8.13 lb of nonfat dry milk. To the nearest pound, how many pounds of farm milk are needed to produce 100 lb of nonfat dry milk? **1230 lb**

6. A highway noise barrier that is 120 m long is constructed in two pieces. One piece is 45 m longer than the other. Find the length of each piece. **37.5 m; 82.5 m**

7. The perimeter of a rectangle is 40 m. The length of the rectangle is 10 m greater than the width. Find the length and the width. **15 m; 5 m**

8. Oak Hill School, Longview School, and Peabody School participated in a clean-up campaign to collect scrap aluminum. Oak Hill School collected 40% more scrap aluminum than Longview School. Longview School collected 25% more than Peabody School. If the total collected by the 3 schools was 560 kg, how much did Oak Hill School collect? **245 kg**

9. Eladio invested $200 at 6% annual interest and $350 at 5.75% annual interest, both compounded annually. If he makes no deposits or withdrawals, how much will he have after two years? **$616.13**

Ratio, Proportion, and Percent **269**

Write as a decimal. Use a bar to show repeating digits.

15. $\frac{3}{16}$ **0.1875**

16. $\frac{5}{18}$ **$0.2\overline{7}$**

17. $\frac{5}{3}$ **$1.\overline{6}$**

18. $\frac{2}{11}$ **$0.\overline{18}$**

Calculate the circumference of each circle. Use $\pi \approx 3.14$.

19. $d = 8.3$ cm **26.1 cm**

20. $d = 25$ ft **78.5 ft**

21. $r = 12.7$ mm **79.8 mm**

22. $r = 14.9$ mi **93.6 mi**

Calculate the perimeter of each polygon.

23. A regular hexagon with side 16 **96**

24. A rhombus with side 42 **168**

25. A triangle with sides 18.6, 5.7, and 19.2 **43.5**

26. A rectangle with length 86.4 and width 37.9 **248.6**

27. A regular pentagon with side 15.4 **77**

In the diagram, lines g and h are parallel.

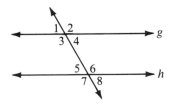

28. $\angle 4$ and $\angle\underline{\ ?\ }$ are alternate interior angles. **5**

29. $\angle 2$ and $\angle\underline{\ ?\ }$ are corresponding angles. **6**

30. If $m\angle 1 = 36°$, $m\angle 4 = \underline{\ ?\ }$ **36°**

31. If $m\angle 4 = 55°$, $m\angle 6 = \underline{\ ?\ }$ **125°**

32. If $m\angle 2 = 147°$, $m\angle 8 = \underline{\ ?\ }$ **33°**

8

The Coordinate Plane

One of the most fascinating aspects of computer science is the field of computer-aided design (C.A.D.). Computers are used to design a wide variety of goods ranging from televisions and cars to skyscrapers, airplanes, and spacecraft. Computers are also used to generate designs for decorative purposes, such as the rug pattern shown at the right. A particular advantage of using the computer is the ease with which the design can be prepared and modified. The designer may use a light pen to create the design on the computer screen and may type in commands to tell the computer to enlarge, reduce, or rotate the design. Although the actual programs for computer graphics are often complicated, the underlying idea is based on establishing a grid with labeled reference points. The grid is actually an application of the coordinate plane that is presented in this chapter.

Career Note

If you enjoy working with fabrics and drawing your own patterns, you might consider a career as a textile designer. Textile designers create the graphic designs printed or woven on all kinds of fabrics. In addition to having a good understanding of graphics, textile designers must possess a knowledge of textile production. Another important part of textile design is the ability to appeal to current tastes.

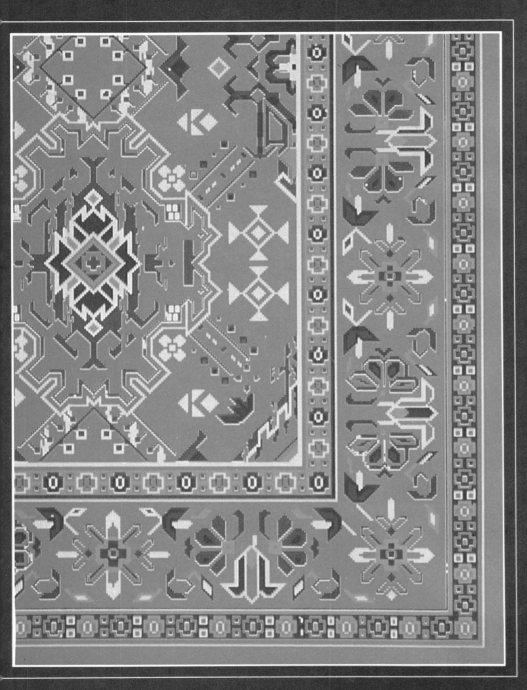

Lesson Commentary
Chapter 8   The Coordinate Plane

Overview

The coordinate, or Cartesian, plane makes it possible to unify numerical and algebraic concepts with geometric and visual concepts. By now students are prepared to deal with positive and negative coordinates, to evaluate expressions for given values of the variable, and to convert equations into forms easier to graph.

Once the basic skills of graphing equations are established, it is possible to move on to consider more advanced concepts, though at an elementary level. When equations can be graphed, there is no real difficulty in finding the intersection of two graphs, or in extending the idea of a graph to include that of an inequality.

It may be satisfying for students to realize that the concepts and skills that they acquire now will be useful and important in all further study of mathematics, as well as in science, economics, and wherever else it is necessary to represent information in graphs.

EQUATIONS AND THE COORDINATE PLANE

8-1 The Coordinate Plane

Objectives *for pages 272–275*

■ To assign coordinates to a point in the plane.
■ To graph an ordered pair of numbers in the coordinate plane.

Teaching Suggestions

Students generally consider this material to be straightforward. Conceptually, it will be important to develop the idea of one-to-one correspondence between points in the plane and pairs of real numbers. You might mention the arbitrary decisions that have been made, such as the names of the axes, positive and negative directions, and the order of the coordinates in a number pair.

To clarify the meaning of *order* in the term *ordered pair*, graph pairs such as $(-6, 3)$ and $(3, -6)$, showing

that they are not the same. It may be necessary to give special attention to points on the axes. Students are tempted to give only one coordinate for such points, rather than a pair of coordinates.

For your convenience, coordinate systems are provided in the Resource Book, pages 164–165.

Related Activities

As an example of using ordered pairs to locate points, bring in a map with an index. Show how to find, for example, a town located at C-5. A map of a city with numbered streets and avenues is also useful.

To provide a living example of a coordinate grid, assign seats one day by giving each student an ordered pair of numbers. Establish an origin and axes, and have the students seat themselves accordingly.

Resource Book: Page 95 (Use After Page 275)

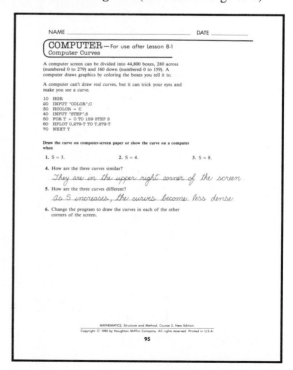

271a

NAME _____ DATE _____

| **Practice**—For use after Lesson 8-1 |
| *Pictures in the Plane* |

Graph the given ordered pairs on a coordinate plane. (Use the grid paper in the teaching aids at the back of the book.) Connect each set of points in the order listed by drawing line segments. What have you drawn?

FIGURE A	FIGURE B	FIGURE C	FIGURE D
1. (−3, 4)	1. (9, 1)	1. (−5, 10)	1. (1, −6)
2. (4, 4)	2. (5, 1)	2. (−5, 9)	2. (2, −6)
3. (−3, 11)	3. (8, 8)	3. (−7, 9)	3. (3, −7)
4. (−3, 3)	4. (11, 8)	4. (−7, 10)	4. (3, −8)
5. (−8, 3)	5. (14, 1)	5. (−12, 10)	5. (2, −9)
6. (−7, 1)	6. (10, 1)	6. (−11, 11)	6. (1, −9)
7. (4, 1)	7. (10, −6)	7. (−7, 13)	7. (0, −8)
8. (5, 3)	8. (12, −6)	8. (−4, 14)	8. (0, −7)
9. (−3, 3)	9. (12, −7)	9. (1, 14)	9. (1, −6)
sailboat	10. (7, −7)	10. (4, 13)	10. (1½, −4)
	11. (7, −6)	11. (6, 14)	11. (2, −6)
	12. (9, −6)	12. (7, 12)	12. (4, −5)
	13. (9, 1)	13. (6, 12)	13. (3, −7)
		14. (7, 11)	14. (5, 7½)
	lamp	15. (5, 11)	15. (3, −8)
Without drawing the figure, write the ordered pairs		16. (3, 10)	16. (4, −10)
for moving Figure A down 5 spaces. Then test		17. (3, 9)	17. (2, −9)
your answers by drawing the picture.		18. (1, 9)	18. (1½, −11)
FIGURE E		19. (1, 10)	19. (1, −9)
1. (−3, −1) *See answer key*		20. (−5, 10)	20. (−1, −10)
2. (4, −1) *for drawings.*			21. (0, −8)
3. (−3, 6)		*turtle*	22. (−2, −7½)
4. (−3, −2)			23. (0, −7)
5. (−8, −2)			24. (−1, −5)
6. (−7, −4)			25. (1, −6)
7. (4, −4)			
8. (5, −2)			*sun*
9. (−3, −2)			

MATHEMATICS, Structure and Method, Course 2, New Edition.

96

8-2 Equations in Two Variables

Objective *for pages 276–279*

■ To find solutions for an equation in two variables.

Teaching Suggestions

By this time students find it quite natural to substitute for variables. They need to be reminded, however, that we have agreed to the convention that ordered pairs are (x, y) pairs. Thus, when we find in Example 1 that $2(4) + (−1) = 7$ we see that $(4, −1)$ is a solution of $2x + y = 7$. This does not mean that $(4, −1)$ is a solution of $2y + x = 7$. Conversely, students should be warned to substitute correctly when checking a given number pair in an equation. In Example 1, $(4, −1)$ is a solution but $(−1, 4)$ is not because $2(−1) + 4 \neq 7$.

Although it is not necessary to point this out to students, it is worth noting that all the equations in this section are linear. Therefore they are also one-to-one functions on the real numbers; this guarantees that it is all right to substitute any value whatsoever for x (or y)

and that there will be exactly one corresponding value for y (or x).

Students are sometimes reluctant to solve an equation for a variable. Treating the equation as if it were a formula can help here. In the equation $A = lw$, we may be given A and w, and need to solve for l.

After showing how to solve for y (Example 3), point out that often certain values of x are easier to use than others. For example, in $y = 3 − \frac{2}{5}x$ it is especially easy to use 0 and multiples of 5 for x.

The definition of a function is a very precise one. Illustrate what kinds of sets are not functions. The equation $x = y^2$ is not a function because the number pairs $(4, 2)$ and $(4, −2)$ both satisfy the equation. Graphically, the definition requires that a function can not cross any vertical line more than once; this requirement is sometimes called the vertical line test.

You may want to remind students that if the same variable occurs more than once in an equation, then the same value must be substituted for each occurrence of that variable.

Related Activities

To extend the concept of ordered pairs as solutions of equations in two variables, ask students to find ordered triples that are solutions of equations in three variables. For example, find solutions of the equation $2x + 3y − z = 1$. Also, determine whether a given triple is a solution of a given equation. For example, is $(−2, 3, −1)$ a solution of $3x − y − z + 8 = 0$? (It is, since $3(−2) − 3 − (−1) + 8 = −6 − 3 + 1 + 8 = 0$.)

To reinforce their understanding of number properties, have students look for solutions to equations that are true for all x and y, such as $x + y = y + x$, $(x + 6) + y = (x + y) + 6$, and $x(3 + y) = 3x + xy$. Also, ask them to consider solutions of equations representing special situations. For example, $x + y = y$ is true for any pair $(0, y)$, regardless of the value of y; $x + y = 0$ is true for all number pairs such that the numbers are opposites; $xy = x$ is true for any pair $(0, y)$ or $(x, 1)$.

Show the utility of the ideas in this section by presenting examples of quantities that are related to each other by linear equations. Use $D = 55T$ (distance traveled at 55 mi/h) and $A = 100(1 + r)$ (value of $100 original deposit after receiving $r\%$ simple interest) as examples.

8-3 Graphing Equations in the Coordinate Plane

Objective *for pages 280–283*

■ To graph a linear equation in two variables.

Teaching Suggestions

When students are told that the set of pairs satisfying a linear equation is infinite they sometimes respond by saying, "Then you can use anything!" This is not the case. For the equation $y = 2x$, the solution set is an infinite set of number pairs, but we must have, nevertheless, only pairs where the second number is twice the first.

Encourage students to extend the lines they graph, so they do not appear to lie in only a limited part of the plane. Students typically prefer to work with positive numbers and may draw lines in only the first quadrant. You could point out that, except for vertical and horizontal lines and lines through the origin, all lines pass through three of the four quadrants.

Before working with intercepts, you may want to demonstrate that the equations of the x- and y-axes are $y = 0$ and $x = 0$ respectively. This may help when it becomes necessary to substitute 0 for y in order to find the x-intercept and vice versa.

Related Activities

To make the idea of the graph of a linear equation more concrete, number the rows and columns of your seating arrangement. Then have students stand if their coordinates satisfy a given requirement.

1. "Everyone whose column number is 2." (a vertical line)
2. "Everyone whose row number is 1." (a horizontal line)
3. "Everyone whose row number is the same as the column number." (a diagonal line bisecting the first quadrant)

You can anticipate graphs of inequalities by using requirements as follows:

4. "Everyone whose column number is more than 2." (all points to the right of the second column)
5. "Everyone whose row number is less than 3." (all points forward of the third row)

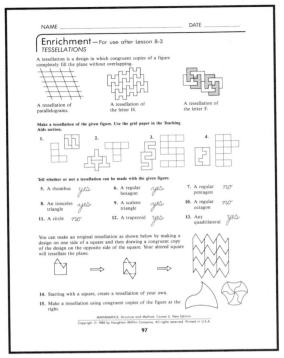

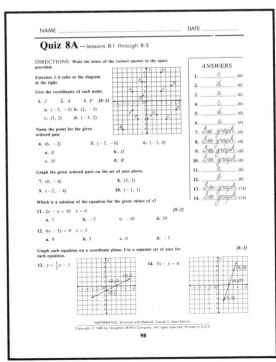

271c

To enhance understanding of intercepts, use situations where the intercepts have a specific meaning.

1. Car rental. If it costs $20 plus 10¢ per mile to rent a car, then $20 is the y-intercept, when x represents mileage and y is total cost.
2. Price vs. quantity. If we graph a relationship between the price of a product and the number of units sold, we generally have the kind of graph shown. Here the x-intercept is a price so high that no sales are made. The y-intercept would represent the number of items people would want if the product were free.

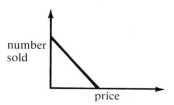

As a challenge for better students, show the graph of a line on an overhead transparency or a chalkboard coordinate grid. Have students determine an equation of the line. Remind them to check by taking two points of the line and substituting the coordinates in the equation they think is correct.

GRAPHING SYSTEMS IN THE COORDINATE PLANE

8-4 Graphing a System of Equations

Objective for pages 284–287

■ To solve systems of equations using graphs.

Teaching Suggestions

If students mastered the technique for graphing a linear equation in Section 8-3, they will have no trouble here. No new graphing skills are needed. The new skill is primarily that of locating a point of intersection of two lines and determining its coordinates.

Remind students of the ways two lines in a plane may be related. They may be parallel, they may intersect in only one point, or they may coincide. Be prepared for some debate over whether coincident lines are two lines

or one. Most people feel that there is only one line. The important point is that the same line may have any number of equations, so it is possible to have seemingly different equations whose graphs are the same line.

To strengthen students' understanding of linear equations, you might point out that not all equations are linear. Consequently it is conceivable that the graphs of two equations might intersect in more than two points, even though they do not coincide.

This is an opportunity to emphasize the importance of checking solutions. Reading solutions from a graph is a matter of approximation. You may get lucky and happen onto an exact solution, but there is no guarantee of this. Thus, after using graphs to "find" a solution, it is absolutely essential to substitute both values in both equations to verify the solution.

To demonstrate the importance of checking solutions, graph a system whose solution is not integral, such as $4x - y = 5$, $y - x = 2$. The exact solution is $(2\frac{1}{3}, 4\frac{1}{3})$. Working from the graphs, students can make a reasonable approximation such as $(2.3, 4.5)$. By substituting these coordinates in the equations, they will learn that this is not the exact solution.

Related Activities

To extend the concept of intersecting sets of points, have students consider intersections of a line and a circle and of two circles. Have them determine the possible numbers of intersections. For a line and a circle, there can be 0, 1, or 2 intersections. For two circles, there can be 0, 1, 2, or infinitely many intersections.

To provide a preview of future algebra courses, show that the system of linear equations below can be solved by using substitution.

$$(1)\ 2x + y = 5 \qquad (2)\ x - y = 4$$

a. Express (2) in terms of x.

$y = x - 4$

b. Substitute into (1).

$2x + x - 4 = 5$

c. Simplify.

$3x - 4 = 5$

d. Solve for x.

$3x = 9$

$x = 3$

e. Substitute and solve for y.

$y = x - 4$

$= 3 - 4 = -1$

f. The solution of the system:

$(3, -1)$

Have the students use substitution to solve Exercises 1–18 on pages 286–287.

To provide a challenge, have students think about the intersections of figures in space. They may want to use or visualize models, such as an orange cut in two (intersection of a plane and a sphere), a wall and a ceiling (intersection of two planes), and so on.

8-5 Using Graphs to Solve Problems

Objective for pages 288–293

■ To solve problems using graphs.

Teaching Suggestions

To help students prepare for calculating slopes, have them practice reading coordinates directly from the graph of a line. Show a graph and ask students to find the y-coordinate for a given x-coordinate and vice versa. For example, ask them to find the y-coordinate corresponding to an x-coordinate of -2, and the x-coordinate for a point with a y-coordinate of -2. This helps prepare for the work on slopes, and strengthens students' ability to read the kinds of graphs found in other courses and in magazine and newspaper articles.

The slopes in this section are positive, but you may want to point out that a slope can be negative.

In Example 1, you might ask students to find the slope; it is $2°C/h$.

In Example 2, discuss how to select intervals for graphing. It makes sense to select intervals that will let you fit all the data onto the graph. The intervals should also be easy to work with. Here, for example, whenever x is an integer y will be a multiple of 5, so 5 Calories is a more convenient interval than 4 or 6.

You may want to discuss the implications of extending a line on a graph. In Example 2 the line is not extended to the left of the y-axis because there is no running time less than 0. It is extended to the right, but this does not mean that Maryanne can run forever. Likewise, the graph in Example 1 is extended both to the left and to the right, but it would be unwise to assume that the temperature increased at the same rate for very long before 6 A.M. or after noon.

With more able groups you may want to analyze slopes of lines further. Through examples you can show that lines with positive slope slant upward to the right, and those with negative slope slant downward to the right. Point out that the slope of a horizontal line is 0, and that a vertical line has no slope. Also, students can readily understand that the greater the absolute value of the slope, the steeper the line. For example, a line whose slope is 2 is steeper than a line whose slope is 1, and a line with a slope of -3 is steeper than a line with a slope of 2.

When graphs and equations of lines are used to represent the relationship between real quantities, the numerical constants have actual meanings. In Example 2, the equation is $y = 15 + 10x$. Here the 15 is the number of Calories expended even if Maryanne does not run at all; this is a "fixed" amount. On the other hand, the 10 is a rate, specifically the rate of energy consumption per unit of time. The quantity $10x$, the energy used in running only, is a variable amount, depending on the number of minutes. Note that the rate is also the slope of the line. In general, slopes are rates.

Resource Book: Page 99 (Use After Page 293)

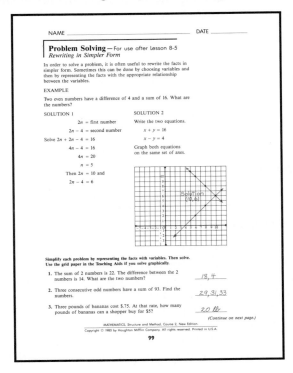

NAME _____ DATE _____

Problem Solving—For use after Lesson 8-5 (continued)
Rewriting in Simpler Form

4. Boys and girls in a fitness class began with 15 jumping jacks. Each week, 20 more were added. How many jumping jacks will the class be doing in the sixth week? _115_

5. Jean Kroll has $176.18 in her checking account at the beginning of the third week of a month. She began the month with twice that much. If she spends an equal amount each week for expenses, how much will she have left in her account at the beginning of the 4th week? _$88.09_

6. A garden is enclosed by a quadrilateral. The fencing is 107 feet long. How long is each side if one side is twice the length of the first, another side is three times the length of the first increased by 1 ft, and the fourth side is three times the first decreased by 2 ft? _12 ft, 24 ft, 37 ft, 34 ft,_

7. On June 1, the water temperature in a small lake was 59°F. On June 15, it was 62°F. If the temperature continues to rise at a constant rate, what will be the water temperature on July 20? _69°_

8. Fast Manufacturing can produce 128 machine parts in 4 h. Speedy Tool Shop can produce 112 parts in 4 h. How long will it take both shops working together to produce 1260 parts? _21 h_

9. The second year at work, Jack earned $12,950. The fifth year, his salary was up to $15,800. He earned the same dollar amount in raise each year.
   a. What was his starting salary? _$12,000_
   b. How much was he earning in his eighth year with the company? _$18,650_

10. Five cooks worked 3 days to make 1500 loaves of bread for a convention. How many loaves can 20 cooks make in 5 days? _10,000_

11. A truck ran out of gas and is slowing down at a constant rate. Fifty feet after running out of gas, the truck was traveling at 20 mi/h. In 25 more feet, it was going only 10 mi/h.
    a. What was the truck's rate of speed when it first ran out of gas? _40 mi/h_
    b. What is the total distance it rolls to a stop after running out of gas? _100 ft_

100

Related Activities

To enhance the understanding of slope, graph several parallel lines on the same set of axes. Have students determine two points on each line and calculate the slope. Ask them what seems to be true about slopes of parallel lines. **They are equal**.

8-6 Graphing Inequalities

Objective *for pages 294–297*

■ To graph a linear inequality.

Teaching Suggestions

To convince students that the graph of an inequality should be a half-plane, consider the inequality $y \geq x + 1$ (page 294). Ask students to find solutions of the form $(2, y)$. They will readily see that they can use any value of y such that $y \geq 3$. Do the same for pairs $(-3, y)$, where y must satisfy $y \geq -2$.

If these points are graphed, it soon becomes clear that we are graphing the points on and above the line $y = x + 1$.

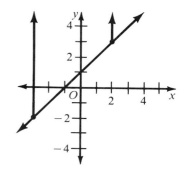

Students often make the mistake of assuming that any inequality with the symbol $>$ is an upper half-plane, and one with $<$ is always a lower half-plane. This is not true, as the inequality $2x - y < 3$ shows.

Students may find it amusing to note that in the graph at the right, A is above the line and B is below the line, even though A is below B.

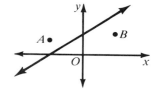

Related Activities

To provide a challenge for your abler students, introduce **linear programming,** a method used by economists to find the best combination of quantities. We need to find the maximum or minimum value of an expression on the points in a region on the coordinate plane. The region is usually defined by several inequalities. If the expression has a maximum or minimum value, it will occur at one of the corner points (the points of intersection). The ordered pair that produces the desired extreme is the solution.

Example: We intend to plant strawberries and raspberries. We want to know how many acres of each to plant in order to earn the most money. The constraints are represented by inequalities in which x represents the number of acres of strawberries, and y the number of acres of raspberries.

1. We can plant at most 2 acres of strawberries and 3 acres of raspberries. $x \leq 2$, $y \leq 3$
2. It will take 2 weeks to prepare and plant each acre of strawberries, and 1 week for each acre of raspberries. We have at most 5 weeks to do this work. $2x + y \leq 5$

On the graph, the shaded region represents the intersection of the three inequalities. The corner points are (0, 3), (1, 3), (2, 1), (2, 0), and (0, 0).

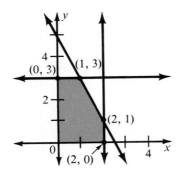

When we sell the fruit, we expect to receive $5000 per acre of strawberries, and $4000 per acre of raspberries. We want to maximize the equation $5000x + 4000y = E$, in which E represents our earnings. Substituting the coordinates of the corner points, we get: (0, 3): 12,000; (1, 3): 17,000; (2, 1): 14,000; (2, 0): 10,000. Planting 1 acre of strawberries and 3 acres of raspberries will earn the most money, $17,000.

Present the following problem: You run a factory that makes toasters and irons. You want to know how many hours per day to produce each product in order to earn the most money. Let x represent the number of hours toasters are produced, and y the number of hours irons are produced.

1. The machinery that produces toasters can be run 6 h per day. The machinery that produces irons can be run 8 h per day. Write inequalities representing these statements. **$x \le 6$; $y \le 8$**

2. The toaster machinery produces 4 toasters per hour. The iron machinery produces 2 irons per hour. The factory can produce at most 32 appliances per day. Write an inequality for the number of toasters and irons that can be produced per day. **$4x + 2y \le 32$**

3. Graph the three inequalities. What are the corner points? **(0, 8); (4, 8); (6, 4); (6, 0); (0, 0)**

4. You can sell each toaster for $20 and each iron for $15. How much do you earn per hour making toasters? making irons? Write an equation for your earnings. **$80; $30; $80x + 30y = E$**

5. Substitute the coordinates of the corner points into the equation. What are the earnings? **$240; $560; $600; $480; $0**

6. What is the maximum earnings? How many hours per day should you produce toasters? How many hours per day should you produce irons? **$600, 6 h; 4 h**

271g

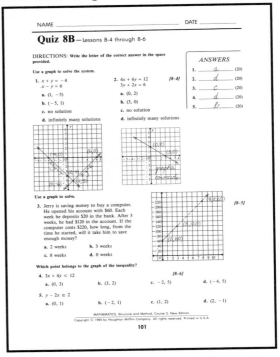

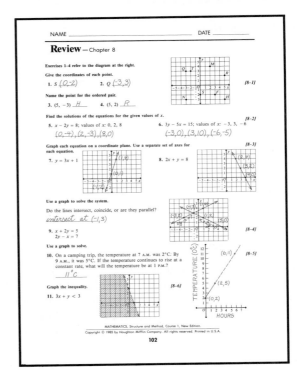

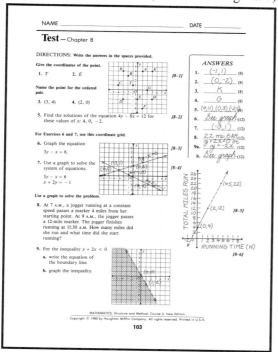

NAME _____ DATE _____

Test—Chapter 8

DIRECTIONS: Write the answers in the spaces provided.

Give the coordinates of the point.

1. *T*   2. *E*   [8-1]

Name the point for the ordered pair.

3. (3, 4)   4. (2, 0)

5. Find the solutions of the equation $4y - 8x = 12$ for these values of *x*: 4, 0, −2.   [8-2]

For Exercises 6 and 7, use this coordinate grid.

6. Graph the equation
$3y - x = 6$.   [8-3]

7. Use a graph to solve the system of equations.
$3y - x = 6$
$x + 2y = -1$ [8-4]

Use a graph to solve the problem.

8. At 7 A.M., a jogger running at a constant speed passes a marker 4 miles from her starting point. At 9 A.M., the jogger passes a 12-mile marker. The jogger finishes running at 11:30 A.M. How many miles did she run and what time did she start running?   [8-5]

9. For the inequality $y + 2x < 0$
   a. write the equation of the boundary line.
   b. graph the inequality.   [8-6]

	ANSWERS
1.	(-1, 1) (8)
2.	(0, -2) (8)
3.	K (8)
4.	G (8)
5.	(4,11),(0,3),(-2,-1) (12)
6.	See graph (12)
7.	(-3, 1) (12)
8.	22 mi, 6AM (12)
9a.	y + 2x = 0 or y = -2x (12)
b.	See graph (12)

MATHEMATICS, Structure and Method, Course 2, New Edition.
Copyright © 1985 by Houghton Mifflin Company. All rights reserved. Printed in U.S.A.

103

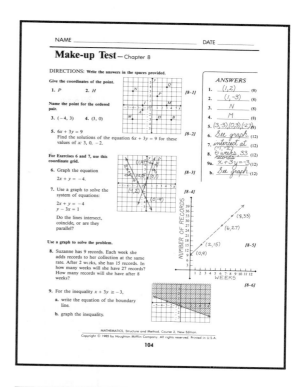

NAME _____ DATE _____

Make-up Test—Chapter 8

DIRECTIONS: Write the answers in the spaces provided.

Give the coordinates of the point.

1. *P*   2. *H*   [8-1]

Name the point for the ordered pair.

3. (−4, 3)   4. (3, 0)

5. $6x + 3y = 9$
Find the solutions of the equation $6x + 3y = 9$ for these values of *x*: 3, 0, −2.   [8-2]

For Exercises 6 and 7, use this coordinate grid.

6. Graph the equation
$2x + y = -4$.   [8-3]

7. Use a graph to solve the system of equations:
$2x + y = -4$
$y - 3x = 1$
Do the lines intersect, coincide, or are they parallel?   [8-4]

Use a graph to solve the problem.

8. Suzanne has 9 records. Each week she adds records to her collection at the same rate. After 2 weeks, she has 15 records. In how many weeks will she have 27 records? How many records will she have after 8 weeks?   [8-5]

9. For the inequality $x + 3y \geq -3$,
   a. write the equation of the boundary line.
   b. graph the inequality.   [8-6]

	ANSWERS
1.	(1, 2) (8)
2.	(1, -3) (8)
3.	N (8)
4.	M (8)
5.	(3,-3),(0,3),(-2,7)
6.	See graph (12)
7.	intersect at (-1, -2) (12)
8.	6 weeks, 33 records (12)
9a.	x + 3y = -3 (12)
b.	See graph (12)

MATHEMATICS, Structure and Method, Course 2, New Edition.
Copyright © 1985 by Houghton Mifflin Company. All rights reserved. Printed in U.S.A.

104

NAME _____ DATE _____

CUMULATIVE REVIEW—Chapters 1–8
Exercises

Complete.

1. The measure of a(n) _obtuse_ angle is between 90° and 180°.

2. A(n) _equilateral_ triangle has all sides congruent.

3. If the circumference of a circle is 12π, the radius of the circle measures _6_.

4. If the sum of the measures of two angles is _180°_, the angles are supplementary.

Round to the nearest hundredth.

5. 32.329   _32.33_   6. 148.096   _148.10_   7. 0.8949   _0.89_

Perform the indicated operation.

8. $-13.7421 - 27.399$ _-41.1411_

9. $144.9 \div -4.2$ _-34.5_

10. $-2\frac{2}{5} + 1\frac{5}{8} - 2\frac{3}{4}$ _$-3\frac{21}{40}$_

11. $\frac{3}{14} - \frac{6}{21}$ _$-\frac{3}{4}$_

12. -7.65×3.08 _23.562_

13. $-5\frac{3}{5} \times 1\frac{1}{14}$ _-6_

Write an equation or inequality for the word sentence and solve.

14. The product of *t* and 9 is seventy-two.   _$9t = 72, t = 8$_

15. The quotient of negative twelve divided by *m* is twenty-four.   _$\frac{-12}{m} = 24, m = -\frac{1}{2}$_

16. The sum of *x* and six is greater than the product of *x* and 3.   _$x + 6 > 3x$_ _$3 > x$_

Solve the proportion.

17. $\frac{x}{9.6} = \frac{0.3}{2.4}$ _1.2_   18. $\frac{16}{n} = \frac{80}{5}$ _1_   19. $\frac{23}{69} = \frac{L}{4.2}$ _1.4_

Tell whether or not the ordered pair is a solution of the given equation.

$3x + y = 16$ 20. (2, 10) _yes_   21. (6, 2) _no_   22. (0, 16) _yes_
$4a - 3b = 15$ 23. (3, 1) _no_   24. (0, −5) _yes_   25. (−3, −9) _yes_

MATHEMATICS, Structure and Method, Course 2, New Edition.
Copyright © 1985 by Houghton Mifflin Company. All rights reserved. Printed in U.S.A.

105

NAME _____ DATE _____

CUMULATIVE REVIEW—Chapters 1–8 *(continued)*
Problems

Problem Solving Reminders
Here are some reminders that may help you solve some of the problems on this page.
• Sometimes more than one method can be used to solve.
• Consider whether making a sketch will help.
• When rounding an answer to division, consider whether it is reasonable to round up or round down.

Solve.

1. Mary Foster earns $3.25 an hour working as a hospital aide. Last week she worked from 10:00 A.M. to 2:30 P.M. on Monday, Tuesday, and Wednesday. How much did she earn?   _$43.88_

2. The publisher of *Swimming Today* receives $9.30 from each copy sold. The remaining portion of the $12 selling price goes to the author. What percent does the author earn?   _22.5%_

3. Eric jogged 7 times around a circular track with a diameter of 75 yd. Did he jog 1 mi? (Hint: 1760 yd = 1 mi)   _no (1648.5 yd)_

4. The discount rate on a ski jacket is 30% of the original price. The sale price of the jacket is $47.95. What was the original price?   _$68.50_

5. A furrier is expecting a price increase of between 5% and $8\frac{1}{2}$% over last year's prices. If a certain fur coat sold for $6480 last year, what is the least it can be expected to sell for next year? the most?   _$6804, $7030.80_

6. Tony's height increased from 5 ft to 5 ft 2 in. in one year. What was the percent of increase?   _3.3%_

7. Each of the two equal sides of an isosceles triangle is 16 cm longer than the third side. If the perimeter of the triangle is 89 cm, find the lengths of the sides.   _19 cm, 35 cm, 35 cm_

MATHEMATICS, Structure and Method, Course 2, New Edition.
Copyright © 1985 by Houghton Mifflin Company. All rights reserved. Printed in U.S.A.

106

271h

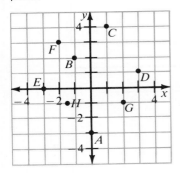
8-1 The Coordinate Plane

We describe the position of a point on a number line by stating its coordinate. Similarly, we can describe the position of a point in a plane by stating a pair of coordinates that locate it in a **rectangular coordinate system.** This system consists of two number lines perpendicular to each other at point *O*, called the **origin.** The horizontal line is called the **x-axis,** and the vertical line is called the **y-axis.** The positive direction is to the right of the origin on the *x*-axis and upward on the *y*-axis. The negative direction is to the left of the origin and downward.

Reading Mathematics: *Diagrams*
As you read text that is next to a diagram, stop after each sentence and relate what you have read to what you see in the diagram. For example, as you read the first paragraph next to the diagram below, locate point *M* on the graph, and find the vertical line from *M* to the *x*-axis.

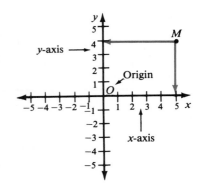

    To assign a pair of coordinates to point *M* located in the **coordinate plane,** first draw a vertical line from *M* to the *x*-axis. The point of intersection on the *x*-axis is called the **x-coordinate,** or **abscissa.** The abscissa of *M* is 5.
    Next draw a horizontal line from *M* to the *y*-axis. The point of intersection on the *y*-axis is called the **y-coordinate,** or **ordinate.** The ordinate of *M* is 4.
    Together, the abscissa and ordinate form an **ordered pair of numbers** that are the coordinates of a point. The coordinates of *M* are (5, 4).

EXAMPLE 1   Give the coordinates of each point.
                a. *F*   **b.** *S*   **c.** *P*   **d.** *T*

Solution   **a.** Point *F* has *x*-coordinate 4
                   and *y*-coordinate −3.
                   F has coordinates (4, −3).

                Similarly,

                b. *S* has coordinates (0, 2).

                c. *P* has coordinates (−3, 4).

                d. *T* has coordinates (−5, −5).

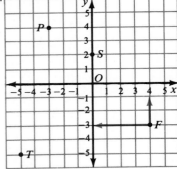

272   *Chapter 8*

Notice that $(4, -3)$ and $(-3, 4)$ are coordinates of different points. In an ordered pair of numbers the x-coordinate is listed first, followed by the y-coordinate, in the form **(x, y).**

Just as each point in the plane is associated with exactly one ordered pair, each ordered pair of numbers determines exactly one point in the plane.

EXAMPLE 2 Graph these ordered pairs: $(-6, 5)$, $(5, -4)$, $(0, 3)$, $(-3, -2)$, and $\left(2\frac{1}{2}, 1\right)$.

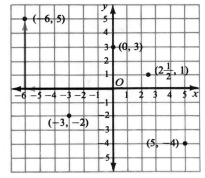

Solution First locate the x-coordinate on the x-axis. Then move up or down to locate the y-coordinate.

The x- and y-axes divide the coordinate plane into **Quadrants I, II, III,** and **IV.** The ranges of values for the x-coordinate and y-coordinate of any point in each quadrant are shown at the right.

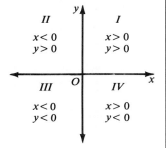

Class Exercises

Give the coordinates of the point.

1. A (2, 1)   **2.** K (5, −1)   **3.** E (0, −3)

4. J (−2, −5)   **5.** L (3, 5)   **6.** F (−1, 3)

Name the point for the ordered pair.

7. $(5, 2)$ H   **8.** $(-6, 0)$ I

9. $(4, -5)$ D   **10.** $(-4, -2)$ G

11. $(-3, 5)$ C   **12.** $(--6, 3)$ B

Name the quadrant containing the point.

13. F II   **14.** D IV   **15.** H I   **16.** J III   **17.** K IV

The Coordinate Plane **273**

Additional A Exercises

Give the coordinates of the point.

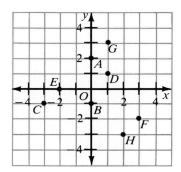

1. *A* (0, 2)
2. *C* (−3, −1)
3. *E* (−2, 0)
4. *G* (1, 3)

Name the point for the ordered pair.

5. (3, −2) *F*
6. (0, −1) *B*
7. (1, 1) *D*
8. (2, −3) *H*

Suggested Assignments

Minimum
Day 1: 274/1–18
Day 2: 274/19–22
          275/23–24
          275/Rev. 1–8

Average
Day 1: 274/1–22
Day 2: 275/23–26
          275/Rev. 1–7 odd
          275/Challenge

Maximum
Day 1: 274/1–22
          275/23–24
Day 2: 275/25–28
          275/Challenge

Supplementary Materials

Practice Masters, p. 35

Written Exercises

Throughout this chapter, answers in the form of mixed numbers or improper fractions are acceptable.

For Exercises 1–18, use the graph at the right.

Give the coordinates of the point.

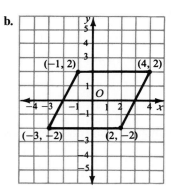

A 1. *N* (−5, −5) 2. *P* $\left(2\frac{1}{2}, -3\right)$ 3. *T* (5, 1) 4. *R* (0, 3)

5. *Q* (−3, −2) 6. *M* (0, −6) 7. *S* (−1, 4) 8. *V* (−5, 1)

Name the point for the ordered pair.

9. (4, −5) *I* 10. (−3, −2) Q

11. (−5, 1) *V* 12. $\left(\frac{5}{2}, -3\right)$ *P*

13. $\left(-\frac{7}{2}, 3\right)$ *D* 14. (1, −2) *H* 15. $\left(\frac{3}{2}, 1\right)$ *W*

16. (−1, 4) *S* 17. (0, −6) *M* 18. (0, 3) *R*

a. **Graph the given ordered pairs on a coordinate plane.**
b. **Draw line segments to connect the points in the order listed and to connect the first and last points.**
c. **Name the closed figure as specifically as you can.**

EXAMPLE (−3, −2), (−1, 2), (4, 2), (2, −2)

Solution a.   b.

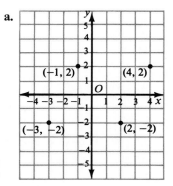

c. parallelogram

B 19. (1, −2), (3, −2), (3, 4), (1, 4) rectangle 20. (0, 1), (3, −2), (6, 1), (3, 4) square

21. (0, −5), (0, 2), (−3, 6), (−3, −1) parallelogram 22. (−5, 0), (−1, 2), (1, 6), (−3, 4) rhombus

274 *Chapter 8*

We can translate a figure on a coordinate plane by changing the ordered pairs. We can reflect a figure on a coordinate plane by changing the signs of the ordered pairs.

23–28: Check students' graphs.

a. Graph the given ordered pairs on a coordinate plane, connect the points in the order listed, and connect the first and last points.
b. Change the values of the coordinates as directed.
c. Graph and connect all the new points to form a second figure.
d. Identify the change as translation or reflection.

C 23. $(-5, 4)$, $(-2, 1)$, $(2, 1)$, $(2, 4)$
Decrease all y-coordinates by 3.
(*Hint:* $(-5, 4)$ becomes $(-5, 1)$)

24. $(1, 5)$, $(1, 1)$, $(5, 3)$
Decrease all x-coordinates by 2.

25. $(-2, -2)$, $(2, -2)$, $(4, -4)$, $(4, -6)$, $(1, -4)$, $(-1, -4)$, $(-4, -6)$, $(-4, -4)$
Increase all y-coordinates by 5.

26. $(-8, 4)$, $(-4, 4)$, $(-4, 5)$, $(-1, 3)$, $(-4, 1)$, $(-4, 2)$, $(-8, 2)$
Increase all x-coordinates by 9.

27. $(6, 5)$, $(2, 1)$, $(9, 3)$
Multiply all x-coordinates by -1.

28. $(1, 7)$, $(4, 2)$, $(7, 3)$, $(4, 8)$
Multiply all y-coordinates by -1.

23–26: translation   27, 28: reflection

Review Exercises

Complete.

1. If $x + 5 = 13$, then $x = \underline{?}$. 8

2. If $8 + x = -1$, then $x = \underline{?}$. -9

3. If $9x = 243$, then $x = \underline{?}$. 27

4. If $-4x = 52$, then $x = \underline{?}$. -13

5. If $2x + 11 = 1$, then $x = \underline{?}$. -5

6. If $99 - 9x = 18$, then $x = \underline{?}$. 9

7. If $-\frac{4}{5}x = 12$, then $x = \underline{?}$. -15

8. If $9 + \frac{2}{3}x = 15$, then $x = \underline{?}$. 9

■■■ | **Challenge**

Set up a pair of coordinate axes on graph paper. Connect the following points in the order given:

$$(-9, 3), (-4, 3), (-1.5, 1), (2, -1),$$
$$(2, -4),(8.5, -5), (9.5, -1), (2, -1)$$

Do you recognize the figure? (*Hint:* It is a well-known group of stars that is part of the constellation *Ursa Major*.) The Big Dipper

The Coordinate Plane   **275**

Reading Mathematics

Students will learn the meaning of the following mathematical term in this lesson: *function*.

The word *solution* is by now familiar. Point out that the same word may be used in slightly different ways as one progresses through mathematics. Here, a solution is a number pair, not a single number.

Chalkboard Examples

Tell whether the ordered pair is a solution of the equation.

1. $2x - y = 5$; $(4, 3)$ **Yes**

2. $3y + x = 10$; $(3, 1)$ **No**

Solve the equation for y in terms of x.

3. $4x + 2y = 5$
$y = 2\frac{1}{2} - 2x$

4. $3x - 4y = 12$
$y = \frac{3}{4}x - 3$

If $2y - x - 6 = 0$, give the value of y such that the ordered pair is a solution of the equation.

5. $x = 1$ $3\frac{1}{2}$

6. $x = -2$ **2**

7. $x = 0$ **3**

8. $x = -6$ **0**

8-2 Equations in Two Variables

The equation

$$x + y = 5$$

has two variables, x and y. A solution to this equation consists of two numbers, one for each variable. The solution can be expressed as an ordered pair of numbers, (x, y). There are many ordered pairs that satisfy this equation. Some solutions are

$$(-3, 8), (5, 0), (4, 1), (0, 5), (11, -6).$$

In fact, there are *infinitely* many ordered pairs that satisfy this equation.

EXAMPLE 1 Tell whether each ordered pair is a solution of the equation $2x + y = 7$.

  a. $(4, -1)$ **b.** $(-4, 1)$

Solution Substitute the given values of x and y in the equation.

  a. $2x + y = 7$ **b.** $2x + y = 7$
  $2(4) + (-1) \overset{?}{=} 7$ $2(-4) + 1 \overset{?}{=} 7$
  $8 - 1 \overset{?}{=} 7$ $-8 + 1 \overset{?}{=} 7$
  $7 = 7$ $-7 \neq 7$

  $(4, -1)$ is a solution. $(-4, 1)$ is not a solution.

An equation in the two variables x and y establishes a correspondence between values of x and values of y. To find a solution of a given equation in x and y, we can choose any value for x, substitute it in the equation, and solve for the corresponding value for y.

EXAMPLE 2 Give one solution of the equation $x - 3y = 2$.

Solution Choose any value for x. For example, if $x = 14$:

$$x - 3y = 2$$
$$14 - 3y = 2$$
$$-3y = 2 - 14$$
$$y = \frac{-12}{-3} = 4$$

The values $x = 14$ and $y = 4$ correspond.

$(14, 4)$ is one solution of the equation.

To find the value of y corresponding to any given value of x, we could substitute the value of x into a given equation and solve for y, as in Example 2. An easier method is to solve for y in terms of x first, and then substitute, as in Example 3.

EXAMPLE 3   Find the solutions for $2x + 3y = 6$ for the following values of x: $-9, -3, 0, 3, 6$.

Solution   First solve for y in terms of x by writing an equation with y on one side and x on the other.

$$2x + 3y = 6$$
$$3y = 6 - 2x$$
$$y = 2 - \frac{2}{3}x$$

Then substitute the values of x in the new equation and solve for the corresponding values of y.

x	$y = 2 - \frac{2}{3}x$	(x, y)
-9	$2 - \frac{2}{3}(-9) = 8$	$(-9, 8)$
-3	$2 - \frac{2}{3}(-3) = 4$	$(-3, 4)$
0	$2 - \frac{2}{3}(0) = 2$	$(0, 2)$
3	$2 - \frac{2}{3}(3) = 0$	$(3, 0)$
6	$2 - \frac{2}{3}(6) = -2$	$(6, -2)$

Thus $(-9, 8)$, $(-3, 4)$, $(0, 2)$, $(3, 0)$, and $(6, -2)$ are solutions of the equation for the given values of x.

Notice in the table above that each given value of x corresponds to exactly one value of y. In general, any set of ordered pairs such that no two different ordered pairs have the same x-coordinate is called a **function.** An equation, as the one above, that produces such a set of ordered pairs defines a function.

The Coordinate Plane   **277**

Class Exercises

Tell whether the ordered pair is a solution of the given equation.

$2x + y = 7$

1. $(2, 3)$ yes   **2.** $(1, 5)$ yes   **3.** $(7, 0)$ no   **4.** $(0, 7)$ yes

$x - 3y = 1$

5. $(2, 1)$ no   **6.** $(4, 1)$ yes   **7.** $(7, 2)$ yes   **8.** $(-2, 1)$ no

Solve the equation for y in terms of x.

9. $x - y = 5$ $y = x - 5$ **10.** $x - y = 9$ $y = x - 9$ **11.** $-3x + y = 7$ $y = 3x + 7$

If $y = x - 12$, give the value of y such that the ordered pair is a solution of the equation.

12. $(9, ?)$ -3 **13.** $(-4, ?)$ -16 **14.** $(0, ?)$ -12 **15.** $(-6, ?)$ -18

Written Exercises

Tell whether the ordered pair is a solution of the given equation.

A $-x + 3y = 15$

1. $(0, 5)$ yes   **2.** $(6, -7)$ no   **3.** $(6, 7)$ yes   **4.** $(-3, 6)$ no

$x - 4y = 12$

5. $(4, 2)$ no   **6.** $(-6, -12)$ no   **7.** $(0, 3)$ no   **8.** $\left(13, \frac{1}{4}\right)$ yes

$3x - 2y = 8$

9. $(1, 6)$ no   **10.** $(0, 4)$ no   **11.** $(4, 0)$ no   **12.** $\left(3, \frac{1}{2}\right)$ yes

$-5x - 2y = 18$

13. $(-2, -4)$ yes   **14.** $(-4, 1)$ yes   **15.** $\left(1, -\frac{23}{2}\right)$ yes   **16.** $(0, 0)$ no

Solve the equation for y in terms of x.

17. $2x + y = 7$ $y = -2x + 7$ **18.** $-8x + 5y = 10$ $y = \frac{8}{5}x + 2$ **19.** $-12x + 3y = 48$ $y = 4x + 16$

20. $4x - 9y = 36$ $y = \frac{4}{9}x - 4$ **21.** $x - \frac{3}{2}y = 3$ $y = \frac{2}{3}x - 2$ **22.** $5x - 4y = 20$ $y = \frac{5}{4}x - 5$

a. Solve the equation for y in terms of x.
b. Find the solutions of the equation for the given values of x.

23. $y - x = 7$ $y = x + 7;$ $(2, 9),$ $(-5, 2),$ $(7, 14)$
values of x: $2, -5, 7$

24. $x + y = -1$ $y = -x - 1;$ $(3, -4),$ $(1, -2),$ $(-2, 1)$
values of x: $3, 1, -2$

278   *Chapter 8*

Additional A Exercises

Tell whether the ordered pair
is a solution of the equation.

1. $-x + y = 5$
   a. $(0, 5)$ **Yes**
   b. $(5, 0)$ **No**
   c. $(-3, 2)$ **Yes**
   d. $(4, 1)$ **No**

2. $2x - 5y = -4$
   a. $(-2, 0)$ **Yes**
   b. $(3, 2)$ **Yes**
   c. $(0, 1)$ **No**
   d. $(8, 4)$ **Yes**

Solve the equation for y in
terms of x.

3. $3x - y = 10$
   $y = 3x - 10$

4. $6x + 3y = 5$
   $y = -2x + \frac{5}{3}$

25. $-x + 2y = 10$ $\quad y = \frac{1}{2}x + 5$; (4, 7),
   values of x: 4, 0, 6 $\quad$ (0, 5), (6, 8)

26. $x - 3y = 12$ $\quad y = \frac{1}{3}x - 4$; (-3, -5),
   values of x: -3, 6, 12 $\quad$ (6, -2), (12, 0)

27. $x + 4y = 20$ $\quad y = -\frac{1}{4}x + 5$; (4, 4),
   values of x: 4, -8, 0 $\quad$ (-8, 7), (0, 5)

28. $-x - 2y = 8$ $\quad y = -\frac{1}{2}x - 4$; (-6, -1),
   values of x: -6, -2, 10 $\quad$ (-2, -3), (10, -9)

B **29.** $3x - 2y = 6$ $\quad y = \frac{3}{2}x - 3$; (4, 3),
   values of x: 4, -2, -8 $\quad$ (-2, -6), (-8, -15)

30. $-2x + 3y = 12$ $\quad y = \frac{2}{3}x + 4$; (3, 6),
   values of x: 3, -3, -12 $\quad$ (-3, 2), (-12, -4)

31. $2y - x = 5$ $\quad y = \frac{1}{2}x + \frac{5}{2}$; (3, 4),
   values of x: 3, 5, -1 $\quad$ (5, 5), (-1, 2)

32. $-3y + x = 7$ $\quad y = \frac{1}{3}x - \frac{7}{3}$; (1, -2),
   values of x: 1, 7, -5 $\quad$ (7, 0), (-5, -4)

33. $2y - 5x = 6$ $\quad y = \frac{5}{2}x + 3$; (2, 8),
   values of x: 2, 1, -3 $\quad \left(1, 5\frac{1}{2}\right), \left(-3, -4\frac{1}{2}\right)$

34. $4y - 3x = 1$ $\quad y = \frac{3}{4}x + \frac{1}{4}$; (9, 7),
   values of x: 9, -1, -5 $\quad \left(-1, -\frac{1}{2}\right), \left(-5, -3\frac{1}{2}\right)$

Give any three ordered pairs that are solutions of the equation.

Answers may vary. Examples are given.

35. $y + x = -1$
   (0, -1), (-1, 0), (1, -2)

36. $x - y = 6$
   (7, 1), (0, -6), (12, 6)

37. $x + y = 0$
   (-1, 1), (1, -1), (0, 0)

38. $4y - x = 7$
   (-7, 0), (-3, 1), (1, 2)

39. $5x - y = -5$
   (-1, 0), (0, 5), (1, 10)

40. $-3x - 2y = 0$
   (0, 0), (2, -3), (-2, 3)

41. $2x - 3y = 12$
   (6, 0), (0, -4), (3, -2)

42. $-\frac{1}{4}y - x = 0$
   (0, 0), (1, -4), (-1, 4)

43. $-x + \frac{1}{2}y = 3$
   (0, 6), (-3, 0), (1, 8)

**Write an equation that expresses a relationship between the coordinates
of each ordered pair.**

EXAMPLE   (1, 4), (2, 3), (5, 0), (-1, 6)

Solution   Notice that all the coordinates share a common property: the sum of
the coordinates in each pair is 5. You can express this relationship by
the equation $x + y = 5$.

C **44.** (7, 6), (11, 10), (4, 3) $\quad x - y = 1$

45. (3, -3), (6, -6), (-4, 4) $\quad x + y = 0$

46. (-2, -4), (-3, -5), (4, 2) $\quad x - y = 2$

47. (3, -6), (-3, 0), (6, -9) $\quad x + y = -3$

Review Exercises

Solve.

1. $8a = 24$ 3

2. $6 - 5m = 11$ -1

3. $6t - 31 = 137$ 28

4. $-7x + 4 = -10$ 2

5. $9c = 18 + 3c$ 3

6. $\frac{4}{5}y = 16$ 20

7. $2 + \frac{7}{8}d = -47$ -56

8. $-10 - \frac{2}{3}f = 12$ -33

9. $5(8 + 2h) = 0$ -4

The Coordinate Plane   **279**

Suggested Assignments

Minimum
Day 1: 278/1-22
Day 2: 278/23-24
   279/25-40
   279/Rev. 1-9

Average
Day 1: 278/1-23 odd
   279/25-43 odd
Day 2: 278/2-24 even
   279/26-44 even
   279/Rev. 2-8 even

Maximum
Day 1: 278/1-23 odd
   279/25-47 odd
Day 2: 278/2-24 even
   279/26-46 even

Supplementary Materials

Practice Masters, p. 35

8-3 Graphing Equations in the Coordinate Plane

The equation in two variables

$$x + 2y = 6$$

has infinitely many solutions. The **table of values** below lists some of the solutions. When we graph the solutions on a coordinate plane, we find that they all lie on a straight line.

$x + 2y = 6$	
x	y
-2	4
0	3
6	0
10	-2

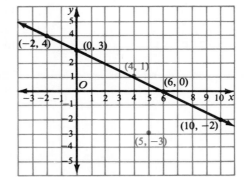

If we choose any other point on this line, we will find that the coordinates also satisfy the equation. For example, the ordered pair $(4, 1)$ is a solution:

$$x + 2y = 6$$
$$4 + 2(1) = 6$$

If we choose a point *not* on this line, such as the graph of $(5, -3)$, we find that its coordinates *do not* satisfy the equation:

$$x + 2y = 6$$
$$5 + 2(-3) \neq 6$$

The graph of an ordered pair is on the line if and only if it is a solution of the equation. The set of all points that are the graphs of solutions of a given equation is called the **graph of the equation.**

Note that the graph of $x + 2y = 6$ crosses the y-axis at $(0, 3)$. The y-coordinate of a point where a graph crosses the y-axis is called the **y-intercept** of the graph. In this case, the y-intercept is 3. Since the graph also crosses the x-axis at $(6, 0)$, the **x-intercept** of the graph is 6.

In general, any equation that can be written in the form

$$ax + by = c$$

where x and y are variables and a, b, and c are numbers (with a and b

280 *Chapter 8*

not both zero), is called a **linear equation in two variables** because its graph is always a straight line in the plane.

In order to graph a linear equation, we need to graph only two points whose coordinates satisfy the equation and then join them by means of a line. It is wise, however, to graph a third point as a check.

EXAMPLE   Graph the equation $x + 3y = 6$.

Solution   First find three points whose coordinates satisfy the equation. It is usually easier to start with the y-intercept and the x-intercept, that is, $(0, y)$ and $(x, 0)$.

If $x = 0$: $0 + 3y = 6$ If $y = 0$: $x + 3(0) = 6$
$$3y = 6$$ $$x = 6$$
$$y = 2$$

As a check, if $x = 3$: $3 + 3y = 6$
$$3y = 3$$
$$y = 1$$

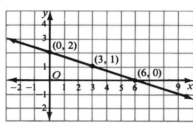

$x + 3y = 6$	
x	y
0	2
6	0
3	1

Class Exercises

Find three solutions of the linear equation. Include those that are in the form $(0, y)$ and $(x, 0)$. Answers may vary. Examples are given.

1. $x - y = 7$ **2.** $y + x = -4$ **3.** $-x - 2y = 8$

4. $3y - x = 9$ **5.** $2x + y = 10$ **6.** $3x - 2y = 3$

7. $y = x$ **8.** $y = 3x$ **9.** $y = \frac{1}{2}x$

1. (0, −7), (7, 0), (8, 1)   2. (0, −4), (−4, 0), (1, −5)   3. (0, −4), (−8, 0), (−2, −3)

4. (0, 3), (−9, 0), (3, 4)   5. (0, 10), (5, 0), (1, 8)   6. $\left(0, -1\frac{1}{2}\right)$, (1, 0), (3, 3)

7. (0, 0), (1, 1), (2, 2)   8. (0, 0), (1, 3), (2, 6)   9. (0, 0), (2, 1), (−2, −1)

Written Exercises

A 1–9. Graph each equation in Class Exercises 1–9. Use a separate set of coordinate axes for each equation. **Check students' graphs.**

The Coordinate Plane **281**

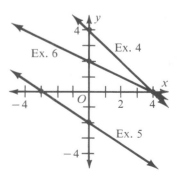

Suggested Assignments

Minimum
Day 1: 281/1–9
 282/10–15
Day 2: 282/16–25; 34–38
 283/Self-Test A

Average
Day 1: 281/1–9
 282/10–18
Day 2: 282/19–33
Day 3: 282/34–40
 283/42–45
 283/Self-Test A

Maximum
Day 1: 281/1–9
 282/10–18
Day 2: 282/19–33
Day 3: 282/34–40
 283/41–47
 283/Self-Test A

Supplementary Materials

Practice Masters, p. 36
Test 8A, pp. 53–54

Quick Quiz A

Give the coordinates of each point.

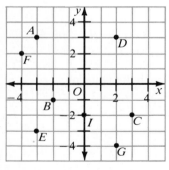

1. D (2, 3)

2. B (−2, −1)

3. I (0, −2)

4. A (−3, 3)

Name the point for the given ordered pair.

5. (−4, 2) F

6. (2, −4) G

(Continue on next page.)

Graph the equation on a coordinate plane. Use a separate set of axes for each equation. Check students' graphs.

10. $x + y = 5$

11. $x - 6 = y$

12. $y - x = 4$

13. $y + x = -3$

14. $2x - y = 10$

15. $8x + 2y = 8$

16. $3y + x = 0$

17. $3x - y = -6$

18. $-2x + 3y = 12$

19. $2y - \frac{1}{2}x = 4$

20. $\frac{1}{3}y + 2x = 3$

21. $4y - 3x = 12$

22. $4x - 3y = 6$

23. $-2x + 5y = 5$

24. $\frac{1}{2}y + 2x = 3$

B 25. $\frac{x + y}{3} = 2$

26. $\frac{x - y}{4} = -1$

27. $\frac{3x - y}{2} = 3$

28. $\frac{2x + y}{3} = 1$

29. $\frac{x - 2y}{3} = -4$

30. $\frac{x + 3}{4} = y$

31. $\frac{3x - 1}{2} = y$

32. $\frac{-3y + 2x}{4} = -2$

33. $\frac{-4x + 3y}{6} = -4$

Graph the equation. Use a separate set of axes for each equation.
Check students' graphs.

EXAMPLE $y = 6$

Solution Rewrite the equation in the form

$$y = 0x + 6.$$

Find three solutions.

If $x = -1$: $y = 0(-1) + 6 = 6$

If $x = 2$: $y = 0(2) + 6 = 6$

If $x = 3$: $y = 0(3) + 6 = 6$

Three solutions are $(-1, 6)$, $(2, 6)$, and $(3, 6)$. Graph these points and draw the line.

The graph of $y = 6$ is a horizontal line.

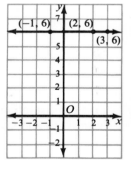

34. $y = 2$

35. $x = -4$

36. $y = 0$

37. $y = -3$

38. $x = 6$

39. $y = \frac{3}{2}$

C 40. Graph the equation $y = x^2$ by graphing the points with x-coordinates -3, -2, -1, 0, 1, 2, and 3. Join the points by means of a curved line. (This curve is called a **parabola**.)

282 *Chapter 8*

41. Graph the equation $xy = 12$ by graphing the points with x-coordinates 1, 3, 6, and 12. Join the points by means of a curved line. On the same set of axes, graph the points with x-coordinates -1, -3, -6, and -12. Join the points by means of a curved line. (This two-branched curve is called a **hyperbola.**)

Graph the equation using the following values of x: -5, -2, 0, 2, 5. Join the points by means of a straight line. Check students' graphs.

42. $y = |x|$ **43.** $y = -|x|$ **44.** $y = |x - 3|$ **45.** $y - 4 = |x|$

For what value of k is the graph of the given ordered pair in the graph of the given equation?

46. $(3, -2)$; $2y + kx = 14$ 6 **47.** $(-5, 4)$; $3x - ky = -12$ $-\frac{3}{4}$

Self-Test A

Exercises 1–6 refer to the diagram. Give the coordinates of each point.

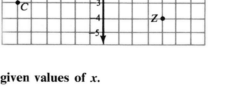

1. M (−3, 6) **2.** Z (4, −4) **3.** L (6, 6)

Name the point for the given ordered pair.

4. $(-6, -3)$ C **5.** $(2, 2)$ T **6.** $(-5, 3)$ P

Graph the given ordered pairs on one set of axes.

7. $(-3, 5)$ **8.** $(9, 7)$ **9.** $(-4, -8)$
10. $(11, -10)$ **11.** $(0, -2)$ **12.** $(-4, 2)$

Find the solutions of the equation for the given values of x.

13. $4y - x = 2$
values of x: 0, -4, 9
$\left(0, \frac{1}{2}\right)$, $\left(-4, -\frac{1}{2}\right)$, $\left(9, 2\frac{3}{4}\right)$

14. $y + 2x = 6$
values of x: -3, $\frac{1}{2}$, 11
$(-3, 12)$, $\left(\frac{1}{2}, 5\right)$, $(11, -16)$

[8-2]

Graph each equation on a coordinate plane. Use a separate set of axes for each equation. Check students' graphs.

15. $y = x - 1$ **16.** $y = 2x$ **17.** $4x - y = 9$ **18.** $x = 7$ [8-3]

Self-Test answers and Extra Practice are at the back of the book.

---

7. $(-3, -3)$ E
8. $(3, -2)$ C

Graph the ordered pairs on one set of axes.

9. $(-2, -1)$ **10.** $(4, -4)$
11. $(-1, 3)$ **12.** $(1, 2)$
13. $(-4, 1)$ **14.** $(0, -3)$

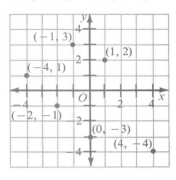

Find the solutions of the equation for the given values of x.

15. $3x - y = 5$
values of x:
0, 2, -3, -5, 4
-5, 1, -14, -20, 7

16. $-x + 2y = -3$
values of x:
3, -3, -1, 0, 7
0, -3, -2, $-1\frac{1}{2}$, 2

Graph each equation on a coordinate plane. Use a separate set of axes for each equation.

17. $y = x + 3$
18. $y = 2x - 2$
19. $3x + y = 3$
20. $y = -3$

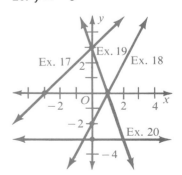

8-4 Graphing a System of Equations

Two equations in the same variables are called a **system of equations.** If the graphs of two linear equations in a system have a point in common, the coordinates of that point must be a solution of both equations. We can find a solution of a system of equations such as

$$x - y = 2$$
$$x + 2y = 5$$

by finding the *point of intersection* of the graphs of the two equations.

    The graphs of the two equations above are shown on the same set of axes. The point with coordinates (3, 1) appears to be the point of intersection of the graphs. To check whether (3, 1) satisfies the given system, we substitute its coordinates in both equations:

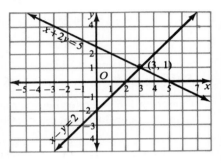

$$x - y = 2 \qquad x + 2y = 5$$
$$3 - 1 = 2 \qquad 3 + 2(1) = 5$$

Since the coordinates satisfy both equations, (3, 1) is the solution of the given system of equations.

EXAMPLE 1   Use a graph to solve the system of equations:

$$y - x = 4$$
$$3y + x = 8$$

Solution   First make a table of values for each equation, then graph both equations on one set of axes.

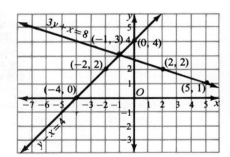

$y - x = 4$			$3y + x = 8$	
x	y		x	y
0	4		−1	3
−4	0		5	1
−2	2		2	2

The point of intersection appears to be (−1, 3).

284   *Chapter 8*

To check, substitute the coordinates $(-1, 3)$ in both equations:

$$y - x = 4 \qquad\qquad 3y + x = 8$$
$$3 - (-1) \overset{?}{=} 4 \qquad\qquad 3(3) + (-1) \overset{?}{=} 8$$
$$3 + 1 = 4 \checkmark \qquad\qquad 9 - 1 = 8 \checkmark$$

The solution for the given system is $(-1, 3)$.

EXAMPLE 2 Use a graph to solve the system of equations: $2y - x = 2$
$\qquad\qquad\qquad\qquad\qquad\qquad\qquad\qquad\qquad\qquad\qquad 2y - x = -4$

Solution Make a table of values for each equation and graph both equations on one set of axes.

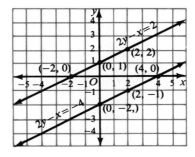

$2y - x = 2$		$2y - x = -4$	
x	y	x	y
0	1	0	-2
-2	0	4	0
2	2	2	-1

The graphs do not intersect; they are **parallel lines.** Thus, the system has *no solution.*

A system may have infinitely many solutions, as the following example illustrates.

EXAMPLE 3 Use a graph to solve the system of equations: $6x + 3y = 18$
$\qquad\qquad\qquad\qquad\qquad\qquad\qquad\qquad\qquad\qquad\qquad 2x + y = 6$

Solution Make a table of values for each equation and graph both equations on one set of axes.

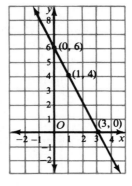

$6x + 3y = 18$		$2x + y = 6$	
x	y	x	y
0	6	0	6
3	0	3	0
1	4	1	4

The graphs *coincide.* The coordinates of all points on the line satisfy both equations. This system has *infinitely many solutions.*

The Coordinate Plane **285**

Use a graph to solve the system of equations. Do the lines intersect or coincide, or are they parallel?

1. $x + y = 3$
$x - y = 3$

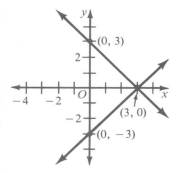

(3, 0); intersect

2. $y - 2x = -1$
$2x + y = 7$

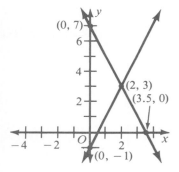

(2, 3); intersect

3. $2x - y = 5$
$y - 2x = 3$

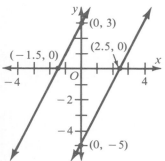

No solution; parallel

To solve a system of equations, first graph the equations on one set of axes. Then consider:

> If the graphs intersect, the system has one solution. The coordinates of the point of intersection form the solution.
>
> If the graphs are parallel, the system has no solution.
>
> If the graphs coincide, the system has infinitely many solutions.

Class Exercises

Is the ordered pair a solution of the system of equations?

1. $(4, -1)$ $x + y = 3$ **yes**
$x - y = 5$

2. $(5, -1)$ $x + y = -6$ **no**
$x - y = 4$

3. $(3, 1)$ $x + 2y = 5$ **yes**
$x - y = 2$

4. $(-4, -4)$ $2x + y = -12$ **yes**
$x - y = 0$

5. A system of two linear equations has no solution. What does the graph of this system look like? **parallel lines**

6. The coordinates $(-3, -1)$, $(0, 0)$, and $(3, 1)$ are solutions of a system of two linear equations. What does the graph of this system look like? **a single line through the origin**

7. The graphs of two equations appear to intersect at $(-4, 5)$. How can you check to see whether $(-4, 5)$ satisfies the system? **Substitute $(-4, 5)$ in both equations.**

Written Exercises

Use a graph to solve the system. Do the lines intersect or coincide, or are they parallel?

A

1. $x + y = 6$ **(3, 3);**
$x - y = 0$ **intersect**

2. $x + y = 5$ **infinitely many**
$3y + 3x = 15$ **solutions; coincide**

3. $x - y = -3$ **no solution; parallel**
$x - y = 2$

4. $x - y = 4$ **(2, −2);**
$x + y = 0$ **intersect**

5. $-2y - 2x = -6$ **infinitely**
$x + y = 3$ **many solutions; coincide**

6. $2x - y = 4$
$y + 2x = 2$
$\left(1\frac{1}{2}, -1\right)$; **intersect**

286 *Chapter 8*

286

7. $x - 2y = 8$ no solution;
$2y - x = 4$ parallel

8. $6y + 4x = 24$ infinitely many
$2x + 3y = 12$ solutions; coincide

9. $3x - y = -6$
$y - x = 6$

10. $x - 2y = -8$ (−2, 3);
$2y - 3x = 12$ intersect

11. $7x - 14y = 70$ infinitely many
$x - 2y = 10$ solutions; coincide

12. $3x + 2y = 6$
$3x + 2y = 12$

B   **13.** $2x + \frac{3}{2}y = 2$ (−2, 4);
$x + 2y = 6$ intersect

14. $x + 3y = 2$ (−1, 1);
$2x + 5y = 3$ intersect

15. $\frac{2}{3}x - y = 2$
$6y - 4x = 18$

16. $3x - 5y = 9$ (−2, −3);
$\frac{1}{2}x - 2y = 5$ intersect

17. $\frac{3}{2}x + 2y = 4$ (4, −1);
$2x + 5y = 3$ intersect

18. $-7x - 2y = 7$
$-\frac{7}{2}x - y = 1$

C   **19.** Find the value of k in the equations

$$6x - 4y = 12$$
$$3x - ky = 6$$ 2

such that the system has infinitely many solutions.

20. Find the value of k in the equations

$$5x - 3y = 15$$
$$kx - 9y = 30$$ 15

such that the system has no solution.

9. (0, 6); intersect
12. no solution; parallel
15. no solution; parallel
18. no solution; parallel

Review Exercises

Write in lowest terms.

1. $\frac{18}{16}$ $\frac{9}{8}$ or $1\frac{1}{8}$

2. $\frac{12}{27}$ $\frac{4}{9}$

3. $\frac{49}{56}$ $\frac{7}{8}$

4. $\frac{18}{81}$ $\frac{2}{9}$

5. $\frac{24}{30}$ $\frac{4}{5}$

6. $\frac{48}{144}$ $\frac{1}{3}$

7. $\frac{13}{169}$ $\frac{1}{13}$

8. $\frac{17}{101}$ $\frac{17}{101}$

   Calculator Key-In

On Roger's first birthday he received a dime from his parents. For each birthday after that, they doubled the money. How much will Roger receive for his eighteenth birthday? $^{\$}13,107.20$

The Coordinate Plane   **287**

Suggested Assignments

Minimum
Day 1: 286/1–6
     287/7–10
Day 2: 287/11–15
     287/Rev. 1–8

Average
Day 1: 286/1–6
     287/7–12
Day 2: 287/13–18
     287/Rev. 1–7 odd
     287/Calculator Key-In

Maximum
Day 1: 286/1–6
     287/7–12
Day 2: 287/13–20
     287/Calculator Key-In

Supplementary Materials

Practice Masters, p. 37

Teaching Suggestions
p. 271e

Related Activities p. 271f

Reading Mathematics

Students will learn the meaning of the following mathematical term in this lesson: *slope*.
  Many students have never dealt with problems that require this degree of analysis and persistence through several stages. You will be doing them a favor if you can encourage them to read, and re-read, problems carefully and to build up their solutions step by step.

8-5 Using Graphs to Solve Problems

In the drawing at the left below, the slope of the hill changes. It becomes steeper partway up, and then flattens out near the top.

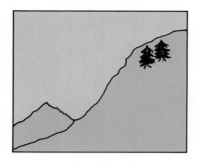
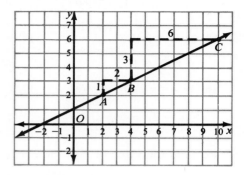

On the other hand, the slope of the straight line shown in the graph above does not change. It remains constant. The **slope of a line** is the ratio of the change in the y-coordinate to the change in the x-coordinate when moving from one point on the line to another.

Moving from A to B: slope $= \dfrac{\text{change in } y}{\text{change in } x} = \dfrac{1}{2}$

Moving from B to C: slope $= \dfrac{\text{change in } y}{\text{change in } x} = \dfrac{3}{6} = \dfrac{1}{2}$

A basic property of a straight line is that its slope is constant.

  A straight-line graph sometimes expresses the relationship between two physical quantities. For example, such a graph can represent the conditions of temperature falling at a constant rate or of a hiker walking at a steady pace. If we can locate two points of a graph that is known to be a straight line, then we can extend the graph and get more information about the relationship.

EXAMPLE 1 The temperature at 8 A.M. was 3°C. At 10 A.M. it was 7°C. If the temperature climbed at a constant rate from 6 A.M. to 12 noon, what was it at 6 A.M.? What was it at 12 noon?

Solution Set up a pair of axes.

  Let the coordinates on the horizontal axis represent the hours after 6 A.M.

  Let the vertical axis represent the temperature.

288 *Chapter 8*

Use the information given to plot the points.

At 8 A.M., or 2 h after 6 A.M., the temperature was 3°C.
This gives us the point (2, 3).

At 10 A.M., or 4 h after 6 A.M., the temperature was 7°C.
This gives us the point (4, 7).

Since we know that the temperature climbed at a constant rate, we can first graph the two points and then draw a straight line through them.

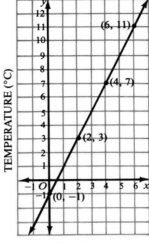

HOURS (after 6 A.M.)

We can see that the line crosses the vertical axis at −1. Therefore, at 6 A.M., or 0 h after 6 A.M., the temperature was −1°C. At 12 noon, or 6 h after 6 A.M., the temperature was 11°C.

Sometimes we are given information about the relationship between two quantities. We can use the information to write and graph an equation. We can then read additional information from the graph.

EXAMPLE 2 Maryanne uses 15 Cal of energy in stretching before she runs and 10 Cal for every minute of running time. Write an equation that relates the total number of Calories (y) that she uses when she stretches and goes for a run to the number of minutes (x) that she spends running. Graph this equation. From your graph, determine how long Maryanne must run after stretching to use a total of 55 Cal.

(*The solution is on the next page.*)

The Coordinate Plane **289**

Complete.

1. Two points on a line are (−3, 2) and (5, −2).
   The change in y is __?__.
   −4 or 4
   The change in x is __?__.
   8 or −8

   The slope is __?__. $-\frac{1}{2}$

2. The line through points (−4, 2) and (−1, 4) also contains the point (__?__, 8). **5**

Membership in the Health Club costs y dollars for x months, where
$y = 200 + 30x$.

3. What is the cost for a year? **$560**

4. How many months would be covered by a total expense of $500? **10**

5. Graph the equation. Use the graph to estimate how many months would be covered by a total of $400. $6\frac{2}{3}$

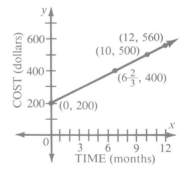

Solution   Consider the facts given:

15 Cal used in stretching

10 Cal/min used in running

Use the variables suggested.

If x = running time in minutes, then $10x$ = Cal used in running for x min.

If y = Cal used in stretching *and* running for x min, then $y = 15 + 10x$.

Make a table of values to locate two points. Because the number of Calories is large compared with the number of minutes, mark the vertical axis in intervals of 5 and the horizontal axis in intervals of 1.

$y = 15 + 10x$

x	y
0	15
2	35

Plot the points and draw the graph.

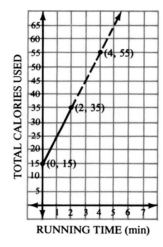

From the graph, you can see that Maryanne must run 4 min after stretching to use a total of 55 Cal.

Problem Solving Reminder

To help identify the conditions of a problem, it may be useful strategy to *rewrite the facts in simpler form.* In Example 2, we list the given facts before writing an equation based on the conditions of the problem.

Class Exercises

Complete for each graph.

1. change in y = ___?___ 2
change in x = ___?___ 4
slope = ___?___ $\frac{1}{2}$

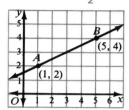

2. change in y = ___?___ 3
change in x = ___?___ 1
slope = ___?___ 3

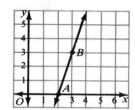

3. change in y = 2___?___
change in x = 5___?___
slope = ___?___ $\frac{2}{5}$

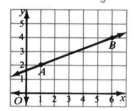

Use a straight-line graph to complete the ordered pairs, then find the slope.

4. $A(1, 3)$, $B(5, 5)$, $C(9, ?)$, $D(?, -1)$ 7; -7; $\frac{1}{2}$

5. $A(0, -3)$, $B(2, 2)$, $C(4, ?)$, $D(?, -8)$ 7; -2; $\frac{5}{2}$

6. $A(8, 4)$, $B(-1, -8)$, $C(5, ?)$, $D(?, -4)$ 0; 2; $\frac{4}{3}$

7. $A(0, 1)$, $B(2, 3)$, $C(-2, ?)$, $D(?, 0)$ -1; -1; 1

8. $A(-1, 6)$, $B(0, 4)$, $C(2, ?)$, $D(?, -4)$ 0; 4; -2

Problems

Solve. Use the same intervals for both axes.

A

1. A pack of greeting cards costs $1.50. Five packs will cost $7.50. Draw a straight-line graph to show the relationship between the number of packs and the cost. Let the x-axis represent the number of packs and the y-axis represent the cost in dollars. What is the slope of the line? $\frac{3}{2}$

2. An object of 2 g suspended from a spring stretches the spring to a length of 6 cm. An object of 5 g stretches the spring to a length of 11 cm. Draw a straight-line graph to show the relationship between the number of grams of the object and the length of the stretched spring. Let the x-axis represent grams, and the y-axis represent centimeters. What is the slope of the line? $\frac{5}{3}$

The Coordinate Plane **291**

Additional A Problem

Solve. Use the same intervals for both axes.

A tree was 2 m tall when it was 3 years old, and 3.5 m tall when it was 6 years old. Draw a straight-line graph to show the relationship between the age of the tree and the height. Let the x-axis represent the age of the tree and the y-axis represent the height in meters. What is the slope of the line? $\frac{1}{2}$

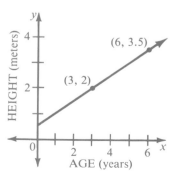

Supplementary Materials

Practice Masters, p. 38

Use a graph to solve the problem. 3–11: Students' answers may vary depending on the precision of their graphs. Accept any reasonable answers.

B **3.** At 1 A.M. the temperature was −6°C. At 5 A.M. it was −1°C. If the temperature continues to rise steadily, what will the temperature be at 9 A.M.? **4°C**

4. Hernando is saving money for a camping trip. Each week he deposits $5 in the bank. He had $25 to start the account. In 3 weeks he had $40 in the account.
a. How much money will Hernando have by the seventh week? **$60**
b. If the trip costs $85, how long will it take him to save enough money? **12 weeks**

5. At 9 A.M. a test car driving at a constant speed passes a marker 50 mi from its starting point. At noon the car is about 130 mi from the marker. If the test drive ends at 1:30 P.M., how far will the car be from its starting point? **245 mi**

6. Between 1970 and 1980, the Rockfort Corporation used a 10-year expansion plan to increase its annual earnings steadily. The corporation had earnings of $3.6 million in 1975 and $6 million in 1977.
a. About how much were the corporation's annual earnings in 1972? **0**
b. About how much did it earn by the end of the 10-year plan? **$9.6 million**

a. Write an equation relating the quantity labeled *y* to the quantity labeled *x*.
b. Graph the equation. **Check students' graphs.**
c. Use the graph to answer the question.

C **7.** A butcher charges $4.50 a pound for the best cut of beef. For an additional $2.00, any order will be delivered. Relate the total cost (*y*) to the amount of beef (*x*) ordered and delivered. How many pounds of beef can be ordered and delivered for $33.50? **a.** $y = 4.5x + 2$ **c.** 7 lb

8. It takes a work crew 15 min to set up its equipment, and 3 min to paint each square meter of a wall. Relate the number of minutes (*y*) it takes to complete a job to the number of square meters (*x*) to be painted. If it took the crew 33 hours to complete the job, about how many square meters was the wall? **a.** $y = 3x + 15$ **c.** 655 m²

292   *Chapter 8*

9. A word processor can store documents in its memory. It takes about 10 s to get the information, and about 35 s to print each page of it. Therefore, in about 360 s, or 6 min, the processor can complete a 10-page document. Relate the time (y) in minutes it takes to complete a document to the number of pages (x) to be typed. How many minutes will it take to complete an 18-page document? **a.** $y = \frac{7}{12}x + \frac{1}{6}$

c. $\frac{32}{3}$, or $10\frac{2}{3}$, min

10. Shaoli Hyatt earns a salary of $215 a week, plus a $15 commission for each encyclopedia she sells. Relate her total pay for one week (y) to the number of encyclopedias she sells during the week (x). How many encyclopedias must she sell to receive $350 for one week? **a.** $y = 15x + 215$ **c.** 9 encyclopedias

Use a graph to solve.

11. The velocity of a model rocket is 3 km/min at 1 s after takeoff. The velocity decreases to 2 km/min at 2.5 s after takeoff. When the rocket reaches its maximum height, the velocity will be 0. Assume that the decrease in velocity is constant. How long will it take the rocket to reach its maximum height? 5.5 s

Review Exercises

Solve.

1. $3x + 4 > 8$

2. $5y - 10 < 0$

3. $7 + 3y \geq -4y$

4. $2(8x + 3) < -2$

5. $6(2y + 7) \leq 42$

6. $-3\left(9x - \frac{2}{3}\right) > -7$

7. $4(9x + 10) \geq 4$

8. $5(4y + 9) \leq 15$

9. $12\left(\frac{x}{6} - \frac{5}{6}\right) > 72$

▌▌▌ Calculator Key-In

Use a calculator to find the product.

$1^2 = $ __?1__ $11,111^2 = 123454321$
$11^2 = $ __?121__ $111,111^2 = 12345654321$
$111^2 = $ __?12321__ $1,111,111^2 = 1234567654321$
$1111^2 = $ __?1234321__ $11,111,111^2 = 123456787654321$
                          $111,111,111^2 = 12345678987654321$

Use the pattern to predict the products $11,111^2$, $111,111^2$, $1,111,111^2$, $11,111,111^2$, and $111,111,111^2$.

The Coordinate Plane   **293**

8-6 Graphing Inequalities

When we graph a linear equation such as

$$y = x + 1$$

we see that the graph separates the coordinate plane into three sets of points:

(1) those above the line, such as $(-4, 5)$,

(2) those below the line, such as $(3, 1)$, and

(3) those on the line, such as $(2, 3)$.

The region *above* the line is the graph of the set of solutions of the inequality

$$y > x + 1.$$

The region *below* the line is the graph of the set of solutions of the inequality

$$y < x + 1.$$

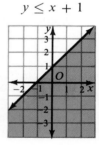

The line $y = x + 1$ forms the **boundary line** of the graphs of the inequalities $y > x + 1$ and $y < x + 1$. For any inequality we can get the boundary line by replacing the inequality symbol with the "equals" symbol.

Since the graph of an inequality consists of all the points above or below a boundary line, we use shading to indicate the region. If the boundary line is part of the graph, it is drawn with a solid line. If the boundary line is not part of the graph, use a dashed line.

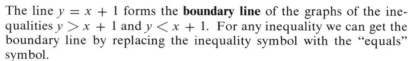

$y > x + 1$ $y \geq x + 1$ $y < x + 1$ $y \leq x + 1$

To check whether the shading is correct, choose a point in the shaded region. Then substitute its coordinates for *x* and *y* in the inequality. If the coordinates satisfy the inequality, then the shading is correct.

Any set of ordered pairs is a **relation.** Each of the open sentences

294 *Chapter 8*

$y = x + 1$, $y > x + 1$, $y \geq x + 1$, $y < x + 1$, and $y \leq x + 1$ defines a relation. The equation $y = x + 1$ is a special kind of relation because it defines a function. Not all relations are functions. Recall that for a function, every value of x has only one corresponding value of y. Notice in the shaded region of each graph above, more than one value of y may be associated with each value of x. For example, the following ordered pairs all satisfy the inequalities $y > x + 1$ and $y \geq x + 1$:

$$(-2, 0), \ (-2, 1), \ (-2, 2), \ (-2, 3)$$

Therefore, the relation defined by the inequalities $y > x + 1$ and $y \geq x + 1$ is not a function.

EXAMPLE 1   Graph $y - x < 4$.

Solution   First transform $y - x < 4$ into an equivalent inequality with y alone on one side.

$$y < 4 + x$$

Then locate the boundary line by graphing

$$y = 4 + x.$$

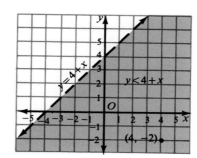

Use a dashed line to draw the boundary line, and shade the region below.

Check: Use $(4, -2)$.
$$y - x \overset{<}{} 4$$
$$-2 - 4 \overset{?}{<} 4$$
$$-6 < 4 \ \ \checkmark$$

EXAMPLE 2   Graph $x \geq -7$.

Solution   Locate the boundary line by graphing

$$x = -7.$$

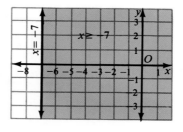

Use a solid line to draw the boundary. Shade the region to the right since all values of x greater than -7 lie to the right of the boundary line.

Supplementary Materials

Practice Masters, p. 38
Test 8B, pp. 55–56
Computer Activity 15
Computer Activity 16

Additional A Exercises

State the equation of the boundary line.

1. $2x - 5 \geq -3y$
$$y = -\frac{2}{3}x + \frac{5}{3}$$

2. $x - y < 5$ $y = x - 5$

Graph the inequality.

3. $y < x - 2$

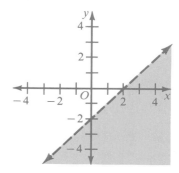

4. $2x + y \geq 4$

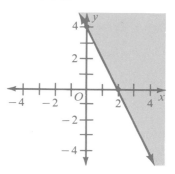

Use a graph to solve the system. State whether the lines intersect, coincide, or are parallel.

1. $y - x = -3$
$y + x = 3$
intersect

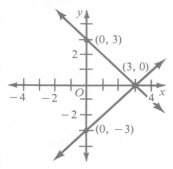

2. $2x - y = 5$
$3x + y = 5$
intersect

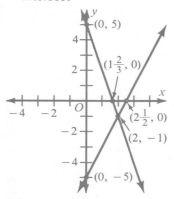

3. $2x + y = 1$
$-y - 2x = 1$
parallel

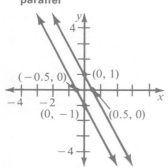

(Continue on next page.)

296

Class Exercises

Transform the inequality into an equivalent inequality with y alone on one side. State the equation of the boundary line.

$y > -\frac{1}{2}x + \frac{5}{2}$
$y = -\frac{1}{2}x + \frac{5}{2}$

1. $4x + y < 8$ $\quad y < -4x + 8$ $\quad y = -4x + 8$

2. $y - 9x < 2$ $\quad y < 9x + 2$ $\quad y = 9x + 2$

3. $4y + 2x > 10$

4. $6x - y > 0$ $\quad y < 6x$ $\quad y = 6x$

5. $3 \leq 5x + y$ $\quad y \geq -5x + 3$ $\quad y = -5x + 3$

6. $9y \geq 18$ $\quad y \geq 2$ $\quad y = 2$

State whether each point belongs to the graph of the given inequality.

7. $y \leq x + 2$ $(0, 1)$, $(3, 6)$ yes; no

8. $-x + 2y \geq 0$ $(4, 4)$, $(-2, 1)$ yes; yes

9. $x \leq -7$ $(-4, -10)$, $(-8, 0)$ no; yes

10. $5 \leq -x + y$ $(-6, -5)$, $(2, 7)$ no; yes

11. $0 \geq x + y - 5$ $(2, 1)$, $(4, 1)$ yes; yes

12. $y \geq 3$ $(9, 4)$, $(0, 8)$ yes; yes

Written Exercises

1. $y = -3x - 6$ **2.** $y = 2 - x$ **3.** $y = x - 2$
4. $y = 2$ **5.** $y = 3 - x$ **6.** $y = 3x$

State the equation of the boundary line.

A

1. $3x + y > -6$ **2.** $x + y \geq 2$ **3.** $x - y \leq 2$

4. $2y - 4 > 0$ **5.** $-x \geq y - 3$ **6.** $2y - 6x < 0$

Graph the inequality. Check students' graphs.

7. $x + y \geq 9$ **8.** $y > -3x + 3$ **9.** $-2x + y \geq 2$

10. $x + 6y \leq -5$ **11.** $4x + 2y \geq 8$ **12.** $3y - x < -3$

13. $y \geq 2x + 5$ **14.** $x + 2y \leq 6$ **15.** $3y - 4 > 2x - 5$

B **16.** $3(x - y) > 6$ **17.** $y \leq 8$ **18.** $6x + 2y + 3 < 2x - 1$

19. $4x + 3y \leq x - 3$ **20.** $3y - 6 > 0$ **21.** $x \leq -3$

22. $y > 0$ **23.** $2(x + y) < 6x + 10$ **24.** $3y - 6 \geq 3(x + 2y)$

Write an inequality for the graph shown.

25.

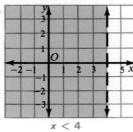

$x < 4$

26.

$x \geq -6$

27.

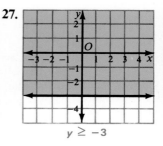

$y \geq -3$

296   *Chapter 8*

Graph the solutions of each system of inequalities. Check students' graphs.

EXAMPLE $y \geq -3 + x$
$y \leq 2 - x$

Solution   First graph $y \geq -3 + x$. Use blue to shade the region. Then graph $y \leq 2 - x$. Use gray to shade the region.

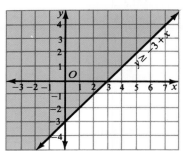 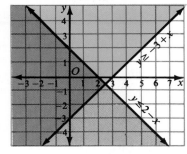

The graph of the solutions of the system is the region where the blue and gray shading overlap.

C **28.** $y \geq -4$
$x \leq 2$

29. $y > 5 - x$
$y \geq x + 5$

30. $x \leq 9 - y$
$y < x + 3$

31. $x \geq -6$
$x < 3$

Self-Test B

Use a graph to solve the system. Do the lines intersect or coincide, or are they parallel?

1. $x + y = 6$ intersect;
$y - x = -2$ (4, 2)

2. $x + 2y = 6$ coincide
$6y + 3x = 18$

3. $2x + y = 3$
$-2x - y = 2$
parallel

[8-4]

Use a graph to solve.

4. When Fritz enrolled in a speed-reading class, he read about 250 words per minute. Two weeks later, his reading speed was about 750 words per minute. If his reading speed increases steadily, how many weeks after enrollment will it take Fritz to read about 1250 words per minute? **4 weeks**

[8-5]

Graph each inequality. Check students' graphs.

5. $x + y \leq 10$

6. $3y - x > 9$

7. $x - 5y \geq 5$

[8-6]

Self-Test answers and Extra Practice are at the back of the book.

Use a graph to solve.

4. When Kim began training with the swimming team, she could swim the length of the pool in 37 s. Four weeks later it took 35 s. If her time improves steadily, how many weeks after starting to train will she reach her goal of 34 s?
6 weeks

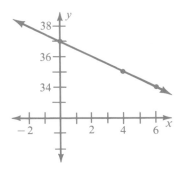

Graph each inequality.
5. $x - y \geq 4$

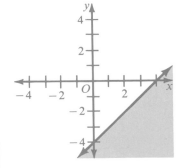

6. $y - 2x > -3$

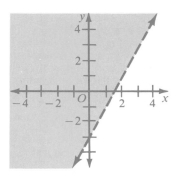

The Computer and Linear Equations

For a science project, Nina watered 6 identical lima bean gardens by different amounts. The crop yields were as recorded below.

Water applied daily in cm	0.5	1.0	1.5	2.0	2.5	3.0
Yield of lima beans in kg	1.6	1.8	2.0	2.4	2.6	2.8

Can Nina use these data to predict crop yields for other amounts of daily watering? If we plot her findings as shown on the graph at the right, we see that the points are very nearly in line.

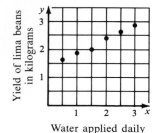

Water applied daily in centimeters

The computer program below gives the equation of the line that best fits the points on the graph. Notice how the coordinates of the points are entered in line 40.

```
10   DIM L(50)
20   PRINT "NUMBER OF POINTS ON GRAPH IS";
30   INPUT N
40   DATA .5,1.6,1,1.8,1.5,2,2,2.4,2.5,2.6,3,2.8
50   FOR I = 1 TO N
60   READ X,Y
70   LET A = A + X
80   LET B = B + Y
90   LET C = C + X * X
100  LET D = D + X * Y
110  NEXT I
120  LET Q = N * C - A * A
130  LET R =  INT (100 * (N * D - A * B) / Q + .5) / 100
140  LET S =  INT (100 * (B * C - A * D) / Q + .5) / 100
145  PRINT
150  PRINT "EQUATION OF BEST FITTING LINE IS"
155  PRINT " Y = ";R;"X";
160  IF S >  = 0 THEN 190
170  PRINT S
180  STOP
190  PRINT " ";"+ ";S
200  END
```

1. RUN the program to find the equation of the best fitting line for Nina's data. $y = 0.5x + 1.32$

2. Draw the graph of the equation. **Check students' graphs.**

298 *Chapter 8*

3. Use the graph to predict the yield if Nina applied 3.3 cm of water daily. **2.97 kg**

Use the computer program to find the equation of the best fitting line for the data given in each chart. Then graph the equation and use the graph to answer the question.

4. The chart below shows the distance a spring stretches when different masses are hung from it. $y = 5.39x + 0.97$

Mass in kg	0.3	0.6	0.9	1.2	1.5	1.8
Stretch in cm	2.1	4.9	6.0	7.1	8.9	10.8

About how much stretch would a 1 kg mass produce? **6.36 cm**

5. The chart below shows temperature changes as a cold front approached. $y = -3.3x + 20.8$

Time in hours from 1st reading	0	1	2	3	4
Temperature in °C	21	17	14	12	7

a. Estimate the temperature 1.5 hours from the first reading. **15.85°C**

b. If the temperature continues to decrease steadily, about how many hours will it take to reach 0°C? **6.3 h**

6. The chart below shows the profit earned by a bookstore on the sale of a bestseller. $y = 4.5x$

No. sold	3	4	7	9	11
Profit	$13.50	$18.00	$31.50	$40.50	$49.50

How many sales will it take to earn a profit of at least $80? **18**

7. The chart below shows the cost of college education for the past 5 years. $y = 0.59x + 7.39$

Year	1	2	3	4	5
Cost (in thousands)	$7.8	$8.6	$9.4	$9.9	$10.1

Predict the cost of college education for the next two years. **$10,930; $11,520**

The Coordinate Plane **299**

one for Y. Therefore the programmer must type a value of X, then a value of Y, then X, then Y, and so on.

Some students may wonder why INPUT is not used in the program. Point out that when all data values are known ahead, it is more efficient to use DATA statements. We could use INPUT, but there is no real need for the interactive mode employed in using INPUT.

Point out that the computer prints all numerical values as decimals. Students may not be accustomed to linear equations being written with decimal constants, but this should present no real difficulty.

In Problem 7, point out that Year 5 is this year, Year 4 is last year, and so on.

Chapter Review

True or false?

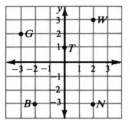

1. The coordinates of point *G* are (3, 2). **False**   **[8-1]**

2. The abscissa of point *W* is 2. **True**

3. The ordinate of point *T* is 1. **True**

4. Point *B* is associated with the ordered pair (2, −3). **False**

Match each equation with an ordered pair that satisfies the equation.

5. $2y - 7x = 4$ **C**   **A.** $(-18, 1)$ **[8-2]**

6. $10x + \frac{5}{9}y = 0$ **D**   **B.** $(9, 2)$

7. $-2x + 9y = 0$ **B**   **C.** $(2, 9)$

8. $y - \frac{1}{3}x = 7$ **A**   **D.** $(1, -18)$

Graph the equation on a coordinate plane. Use a separate set of axes for each equation. Check students' graphs.

9. $x + y = 0$ 10. $2y - 3x = -6$ 11. $y - 2x = 2$ **[8-3]**

Use a graph to solve the system of equations. Match the system with the word that describes its graphs.

12. $y + x = -3$ **A**   13. $y - 3x = -6$ **C**   14. $5y - 2x = 4$ **B**   **[8-4]**
    $2y - 3x = 4$ $y - 3x = 3$ $15y - 6x = 12$

A. intersect   **B.** coincide   **C.** parallel

Complete.

15. A basic property of a straight line is that its slope remains __?__. **constant**   **[8-5]**

16. The slope of a line is the ratio of the change in the __?__-coordinate to the change in the __?__-coordinate when moving from one point on the line to another. **y** **x**

17. The boundary line for the graph of $y > x + 6$ is a __?__ line. **dashed**   **[8-6]**

18. If the boundary line is part of the graph of an inequality, it is drawn with a __?__ line. **solid**

300   *Chapter 8*

Chapter Test

Give the coordinates of the point.

1. *I* **2.** *M* **3.** *E* **4.** *R*   [8–1]
(5, −2) (−5, 3) (−3, −5) (3, 4)

Name the point for the ordered pair.

5. (−2, 4) *T*   **6.** (1, −3) *N*

7. (−4, −2) *S*   **8.** (5, −2) *I*

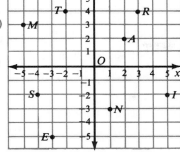

a. Solve the equation for *y* in terms of *x*.
b. Find solutions of the equation for the
given values of *x*: −3, 0, 4.

$y = 2x + \frac{1}{2}$;

$y = -7x + 23;$ (−3, 44), $y = 2x;$ (−3, −6)
9. $y + 7x = 23$ **10.** $2y − 4x = 1$ **11.** $3y − 6x = 0$ [8–2]
(0, 23), (4, −5) $\left(-3, -5\frac{1}{2}\right), \left(0, \frac{1}{2}\right), \left(4, 8\frac{1}{2}\right)$ (0, 0), (4, 8)

Graph the equation on a coordinate plane. Use a separate set of axes for
each equation. Check students' graphs.

12. $y − 3x = 7$ **13.** $4y − x = 8$ **14.** $2y + x = -10$ [8–3]

Use a graph to solve the system. Do the lines intersect or coincide, or
are they parallel?

no solution;
15. $x − 2y = 0$ (2, 1);   **16.** $3x − y = -4$ parallel **17.** $5x + y = 2$ [8–4]
$2x + y = 5$ intersect $3x − y = 3$ $10x + 2y = 4$
17. infinitely many solutions;
coincide

Use a graph to solve the problem.

18. One hour after the start of an experiment, the temperature of a   [8–5]
solution was −15°C. Three hours later it was −6°C. If the temperature continues to rise steadily, about how many hours will it
take for the temperature to reach 0°C? two more hours

19. It takes the window washers 24 min to get ready and 4 min to wash a
6 m by 6 m window.
a. Write an equation relating the total time (*y*) required on the job
to the number of windows (*x*) to be washed. $y = 4x + 24$
b. Graph the equation.
c. About how many 6 m by 6 m windows can they wash in 2 h? 24 windows

a. State the equation of the boundary line.
b. Graph the inequality.
$y = 2x + 1$ $y = -x - 4$ $y = 3x$
20. $y \geq 2x + 1$ **21.** $x + y > -4$ **22.** $y − 3x < 0$ [8–6]

The Coordinate Plane   **301**

Review for Retention

Evaluate the expression when $j = 5$ and $k = 2$.

1. $5k$ **10**
2. $3j - k$ **13**
3. j^k **25**
4. $j(k - 3) - 5$ **−10**
5. $k^2 - 2j$ **−6**

Write a related inequality.

6. $g \div 5 > 20$ $g > 100$
7. $2f - 3 \le 7$ $f \le 5$
8. $4 - 6s \ge 16$ $s \le -2$
9. $3y + 7 < 19$ $y < 4$
10. $6 - 3t > 15$ $t < -3$

Write an equation or inequality for the word sentence.

11. The sum of twelve and a number b is greater than five. $12 + b > 5$
12. The quotient of a number d divided by three equals six. $d \div 3 = 6$
13. Four less than the product of a number w and eleven equals nine. $11w - 4 = 9$
14. Three times the sum of a number h and four is less than ten. $3(h + 4) < 10$

True or False?

15. If $q = -2$, $3q + 6 = 0$. **True**
16. If $f = 3$, $4f - 8 = 20$. **False**
17. If $12 - 5j = 42$, $j = -6$. **True**
18. If $10 + 6c = 14$, $c = 4$. **False**
19. If $t = 3$, $6t + 5 > 23$. **False**
20. If $5y - 2 = 13$, $y = 3$. **True**
21. These equations are equivalent:
   $4(b - 5) = b + 7$
   $5b - 25 = 20$ **True**
22. These equations are equivalent:
   $26 - 7g = 3g - 14$
   $7 + 5g = -13$ **False**

Cumulative Review (Chapters 1–8)

Exercises

Write a variable expression for the word phrase.

1. The product of b and five **5b**   2. Eight times a number x **8x**
3. Twelve less than the sum of y and z 4. A number q divided by seven $\frac{q}{7}$
   $y + z - 12$
5. The sum of three times a number p and seven **3p + 7**

Round to the nearest hundredth.

6. 46.871 **46.87** 7. 288.005 **288.01** 8. 0.7826 **0.78**   9. 100.758 **100.76** 10. 33.663 **33.66**

Perform the indicated operation.

11. $-8.709 + 13.6001$ **4.8911** 12. $7615.7 - 333.61$ **7282.09** 13. $606.08 + (-51.99)$ **554.09**
14. $272.65 - (-0.88)$ **273.53** 15. 37.61×0.08 **3.0088** 16. $1.5798 \div 0.03$ **52.66**
17. -11.56×36.77 **−425.0612** 18. $72.5 \div 5$ **14.5** 19. $6.7 \times (-1.22)$ **−8.174**
20. $-\frac{1}{3} + \frac{4}{5}$ $\frac{7}{15}$ 21. $\frac{4}{7} \times \left(-\frac{3}{8}\right) - \frac{3}{14}$ 22. $6\frac{1}{2} \div \left(-2\frac{1}{2}\right)$ $-\frac{13}{5}$, or $-2\frac{3}{5}$
23. $\frac{7}{8} - \left(-\frac{1}{4}\right)$ $\frac{9}{8}$, or $1\frac{1}{8}$ 24. $3\frac{1}{2} - 1\frac{7}{8}$ $\frac{13}{8}$, or $1\frac{5}{8}$ 25. $-3\frac{4}{5} \times 1\frac{3}{10}$ $-\frac{247}{50}$, or $-4\frac{47}{50}$

Write an equation or inequality for the word sentence and solve.

26. The sum of x and three is seven. $x + 3 = 7$; 4
27. A number t is the product of negative three fourths and one fifth. $t = -\frac{3}{4} \times \frac{1}{5}$; $-\frac{3}{20}$
28. The quotient of negative eight divided by w is seven. $\frac{-8}{w} = 7$; $\frac{-8}{7}$, or $-1\frac{1}{7}$
29. The sum of x and twelve is greater than the product of x and 2. $x + 12 > 2x$; the solutions are all the numbers less than 12.

Find the circumference of the circle described. Use $\pi \approx 3.14$.

30. diameter $= 28$ cm **87.9 cm** 31. radius $= 3.3$ m **20.7 m** 32. diameter $= 88.5$ km **278 km**

Solve the proportion.

33. $\frac{n}{4.8} = \frac{0.4}{1.2}$ **1.6**   34. $\frac{1.5}{n} = \frac{1}{4}$ **6**   35. $\frac{13}{14} = \frac{39}{n}$ **42**   36. $\frac{1.2}{2.0} = \frac{n}{3.0}$ **1.8**

Tell whether the ordered pair is a solution of the given equation.

$2x + y = 15$ 37. $(0, 12)$ **No**   38. $(-5, 25)$ **Yes**   39. $(5, 5)$ **Yes**   40. $(4, 13)$ **No**

302   *Chapter 8*

Problems

Problem Solving Reminders

Here are some reminders that may help you solve some of the problems on this page.
- Sometimes more than one method can be used to solve.
- Consider whether making a sketch will help.
- When rounding an answer to division, consider whether it is reasonable to round up or round down.

Solve.

1. Bill Murphy earns $4.85 an hour working in a day care center. Last week he worked from 1:00 P.M. to 4:30 P.M. on Monday through Friday. How much did he earn? **$84.88**

2. "I feel like I ran a mile," gasped Marge. If Marge ran 5 times around a circular track with a diameter of 210 ft, did she really run a mile? (*Hint:* 5280 ft = 1 mi) **No**

3. Light travels at a speed of 297,600 km/s. If the circumference of Earth is about 39,800 km, about how many times could light travel around Earth in 1 s? **7 times**

4. Michael Woolsey bought $5671 worth of stock. The commission rate was $28 plus 0.6% of the dollar amount. How much was the commission? **$62.03**

5. A car dealer is expecting a price increase of between $2\frac{1}{2}\%$ and 5% over the price of last year's models. If a certain car sold for $9560 last year, what is the least it can be expected to sell for this year? the most? **$9799; $10,038**

6. Myra Daley was given an advance of $18,000 on royalties expected from a book she wrote. If the selling price of the book is $15.95 and her royalty rate is 5%, how many books must be sold before her royalties exceed her advance? **22,571 books**

7. A baby that weighed 7 lb 6 oz at birth weighed 10 lb 10 oz at 6 weeks of age. To the nearest tenth of a percent, what was the percent of increase? **44.1%**

8. It took Thomas 25 min longer to do his math homework than to do his French homework. He spent a total of 2.25 h on both subjects. How much time did he spend on math? **80 min**

9. If a microwave oven uses 1.5 kilowatt hours (kW·h) of electricity in 15 min, how much electricity does it use in 5 min? **0.5 kW·h**

The Coordinate Plane **303**

Solve each proportion.

23. $\frac{14}{49} = \frac{?}{35}$ **10**

24. $\frac{27}{45} = \frac{36}{?}$ **60**

25. $\frac{24}{108} = \frac{?}{81}$ **18**

26. $\frac{44}{99} = \frac{48}{?}$ **108**

Write as a percent.

27. 0.57 **57%**

28. 3.8 **380%**

29. 0.001 **0.1%**

30. 0.062 **6.2%**

31. $\frac{3}{5}$ **60%** 32. $1\frac{5}{8}$ **162.5%**

33. $\frac{7}{12}$ **$58\frac{1}{3}\%$** 34. $\frac{9}{40}$ **22.5%**

Write as a decimal.

35. 74.2% **0.742**

36. 846.3% **8.463**

37. 0.2% **0.002**

38. $25\frac{1}{5}\%$ **0.252**

Write as a fraction in lowest terms.

39. $6\frac{1}{4}\%$ **$\frac{1}{16}$**

40. 64.75% **$\frac{259}{400}$**

41. $16\frac{2}{3}\%$ **$\frac{1}{6}$**

42. $43\frac{3}{4}\%$ **$\frac{7}{16}$**

Solve.

43. $8\frac{1}{3}\%$ of 72 = __?__. **6**

44. $\frac{1}{4}\%$ of 800 = __?__. **2**

45. 24.7% of 80 = __?__. **19.76**

46. __?__% of 50 = 60. **120**

47. __?__% of 90 is 4.5. **5**

48. $16\frac{2}{3}\%$ of __?__ = 13. **78**

49. 40% of __?__ = 6.8. **17**

50. $2\frac{2}{3}\%$ of __?__ = 6. **225**

303

9

Areas and Volumes

Many geometric figures are symmetric with regard to a point or a line. If you imagine the petals of the flower in the photograph rotated about its center, you will recognize an illustration of symmetry. Starfish, snowflakes, butterflies, trees, and human beings are other examples of objects with symmetry that occur in nature. Symmetry can also be found in some letters of the English alphabet and other objects created by people.

In this chapter, you will learn how to determine whether figures are symmetric. You will also learn how to use symmetry in finding the areas of figures.

Career Note

Designing floral arrangements requires good color sense, a knowledge of flower care and handling, and a creative eye. Designers are usually expected to work from a customer's order that may specify color and type of flower, the occasion for the arrangement, and the amount of money to be spent.

Lesson Commentary
Chapter 9   Areas and Volumes

Overview

The first part of this chapter reviews the area formulas for plane figures that students have learned in previous courses. This review includes an explanation of the concept of area itself.

In the second part of the chapter students use the basic formulas for plane figures to find the volumes and surface areas of geometric solids. Careful attention will be given to understanding what volume is as well as how it is calculated using a formula. The same is true of surface area. A section is also included on finding the mass of an object of a given density.

AREAS OF PLANE FIGURES

9-1 Areas of Rectangles and Triangles

Objective *for pages 306–311*

■ To find the areas of rectangles and triangles.

Teaching Suggestions

Before developing the formulas given in this section, use grid paper (Resource Book pages 162–163) or geoboards to review what area is by having students actually count the number of square centimeters a polygon encloses. After counting square centimeters on several polygons, students should look for easier methods or general patterns for special polygons such as the rectangle and triangle. This will lead to the discussion of the development and use of formulas or equations by mathematicians to find areas of special polygons. Note that in Written Exercises 1–6 the figures are on unit squares.

In discussing the height of triangles, explain that the height may be from any vertex to the opposite side or an extension of the opposite side. Thus in Example 1 the leg of length 3 could be used as the base; the height would then be 4. Written Exercises 15 and 16 continue this concept. Draw several triangles and show the possible ways of drawing the heights and bases.

Related Activities

To help students relate mathematics to their own lives, have them write, illustrate, and solve their own problems about area. Encourage them to look for everyday situations when the area of a polygon might be needed. Ask for problems that go beyond "find the area," such as cost of new carpet.

Resource Book: Page 107 (Use After page 311)

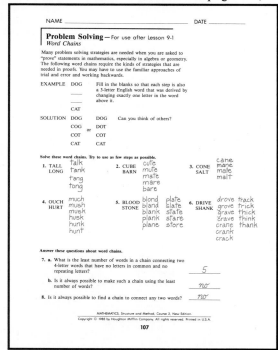

9-2 Areas of Quadrilaterals

Objective *for pages 312–316*

■ To find the areas of parallelograms and trapezoids.

Teaching Suggestions

After developing the formula for the area of a parallelogram show how the formula for the rectangle,

$A = l \times w$, and the square, $A = s^2$, can be derived from the general formula, $A = b \times h$.

An alternate approach to developing the formula for the area of a trapezoid is to divide the trapezoid into two triangles. The area of the trapezoid is equal to the sum of the areas of the triangles.

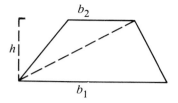

$$\text{Area} = \frac{1}{2}b_1h + \frac{1}{2}b_2h$$
$$= \frac{1}{2}(b_1 + b_2)h$$

Related Activities

To provide more practice, give students worksheets with several irregular polygons and have them divide each into simpler regions. Have students measure the necessary bases and heights, then find the areas. Provide transparent grid paper for students to use to check their areas by counting the square units.

9-3 Areas of Circles

Objective *for pages 317–320*

■ To find the areas of circles and of regions involving circles.

Teaching Suggestions

Students have probably studied the areas of circles in an earlier course. If they have not, or if they have difficulty with the formula, you might show them the following demonstration. Draw a large circle on paper. Cut the circle into 16 or more narrow wedges, and arrange the wedges zigzag fashion into a figure that is almost a parallelogram. The height of this figure is r. The base is half the circumference of the circle, or πr. Therefore the area is πr^2. Students may be interested to learn that a method similar to this is used in calculus.

You could relate the area of a circle to the area of a square. Draw a circle inscribed in a square. If the radius of the circle is r, then the side of the square is $2r$ and the area of the square is $4r^2$. The area of the circle is less than this; use grid paper to estimate it.

Remind students to round to 3 digits when calculating with π. In multiple-step problems students should round only in the last step.

Related Activities

To relate geometry to algebra, challenge students to explain this area formula for a circle : $A = 0.785d^2$. (The formula is found by substituting $\frac{d}{2}$ for r in $A = \pi r^2$.)

9-4 Areas of Symmetric Figures

Objective *for pages 321–325*

■ To use point and line symmetry in finding the areas of figures.

Teaching Suggestions

The concept of symmetry is made easier if students can actually manipulate objects. Have them fold a sheet of paper and cut it to produce a symmetrical figure. Using a figure with one or more lines of symmetry such as a square, they can fold it along each line of symmetry to see that the halves match.

To demonstrate symmetry with respect to a point, cut a figure like the one on page 322 from colored paper and trace it on white paper. Attach the white paper to the bulletin board, then put the colored figure on the tracing with a tack through its point of symmetry. Turn the figure 180° and show that it matches the tracing.

When students work problems for which several solutions are possible, have them organize their work so that all who read it can understand what approach was used. Show students how to use words and formulas, as in the solution to Example 2, to present their work.

Related Activities

To demonstrate natural examples of symmetry, have students prepare a display of pictures or objects illustrating symmetry. This can be done as a class project.

To provide practice in a different way, have students classify the capital letters of the alphabet as having vertical symmetry, horizontal symmetry, vertical and horizontal symmetry, or no symmetry. Have them write some symmetric words such as WOW or HIDE.

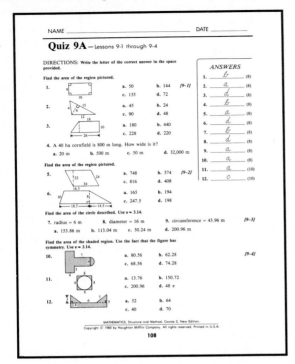

VOLUMES AND AREAS OF SOLIDS

9-5 Volumes of Prisms and Cylinders

Objective *for pages 326–330*

■ To find the volumes and capacities of prisms and cylinders.

Teaching Suggestions

Divide the class into groups of two or three students and provide each group with a rectangular box and a can. Have students measure the length, width, and height of the box to the nearest centimeter and calculate the volume using $V = l \times w \times h$. Remind them that the symbol for cubic centimeter is cm^3. Give each group at least one cubic-centimeter model to remind them of its size.

For the can, have students measure the diameter of the bottom and the height. Ask them to calculate the volume by using $V = \pi r^2 h$.

Provide some rice or sand and a graduated liter beaker for each group to check the accuracy of their measurements and calculations using the important metric relationship that one liter contains $1000 \ cm^3$. Show that this relationship is factual by pouring a liter of rice or sand into a cube 10 cm by 10 cm by 10 cm.

The formulas for finding volumes are very straightforward. You might review the formulas for finding the areas of polygons, as this is usually where errors occur.

Resource Book page 166 has patterns for a cone and a cylinder.

Related Activities

To emphasize the practical importance of this material, give students problems like those below and have them write some of their own.

1. Find the volume of a cylindrical oil tank if the diameter of the base is 3 m and the height is 4 m. Use $\pi \approx 3.14$. **28.3 m³**
2. A fish tank in the form of a rectangular prism is 50 cm by 40 cm by 36 cm. Find the number of liters of water it will hold. **72 L**

9-6 Volumes of Pyramids and Cones

Objective *for pages 331–334*

■ To find the volumes and capacities of pyramids and cones.

Teaching Suggestions

Have available several examples of prisms and pyramids with the same base and height, and cylinders and cones of the same base and height. Demonstrate again the relationship $V = \frac{1}{3}Bh$ by pouring rice or sand into the models as explained in the teaching suggestions for Section 9-5.

Be sure students understand that the height of a pyramid or a cone is the perpendicular distance from its vertex to its base, not the slant height.

Related Activities

To provide a change of pace, supply patterns for the geometric solids such as the tetrahedron, octahedron, dodecahedron, and icosahedron and have students make attractive mobiles using these patterns. Through research on Archimedes and Plato students can discover historical meanings and uses of these solid shapes.

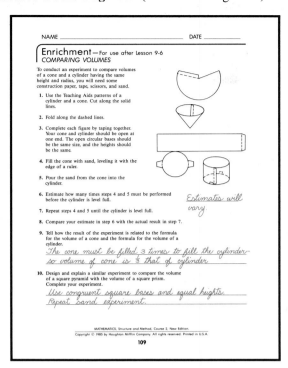

Understanding the concept of surface area is more important than memorizing the formulas in this lesson. Students who understand surface area can use easier formulas for plane figures to develop the formulas for solid figures.

Point out that the lateral surface of a prism is all the lateral faces. A triangular prism such as the one on page 335 has three lateral faces.

Related Activities

To expand on this topic, have students develop a formula for the surface area of a pyramid. Suggest that one important measurement is the slant height of a lateral face. (For a regular pyramid, if the slant height is h, the length of one side of the base is a, and the number of sides is n, the lateral area is $\frac{1}{2}nah$.)

To provide a challenge, suggest that students write computer programs to calculate the volumes and surface areas of prisms and cylinders, and the volumes of pyramids and cones.

9-7 Surface Areas of Prisms and Cylinders

Objective for pages 335–339

■ To find the surface areas of prisms and cylinders.

Teaching Suggestions

Visualization is very important when discussing this section. Begin by cutting a rectangular box open and laying it flat as in Written Exercise 12 to show students the six rectangles that make up the box. Cover the flattened box with a transparent centimeter grid to show the number of square centimeters in each rectangle. Students will notice three pairs of two identical rectangles, the top and bottom, the back and front, and the two sides.

Also take an empty juice can or an oatmeal box and cut the lateral surface perpendicular to the bases to produce the flattened figure shown on page 335. A biscuit can opens "naturally" into a parallelogram and two circles. This is another excellent model to use while explaining the formulas.

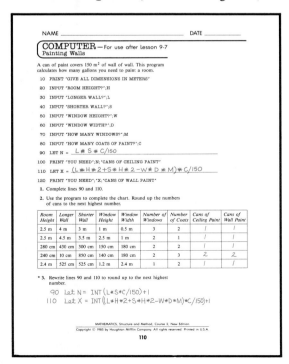

9-8 Volumes and Surface Areas of Spheres

Objective *for pages 340–343*

■ To find the surface areas and volumes of spheres.

Teaching Suggestions

Draw a sphere that fits snugly into a cylinder as shown. (If students may have trouble visualizing this, demonstrate with a balloon and an oatmeal box.) If the radius of the sphere is r, then the height of the cylinder is $2r$. Thus the volume of the cylinder is $\pi r^2 h = \pi r^2(2r) = 2\pi r^3$.

The volume of the sphere is less than the volume of the cylinder. As shown on page 340, it is $\frac{4}{3}\pi r^3$, which is two-thirds of $2\pi r^3$.

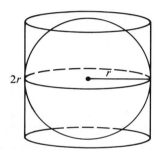

The surface area of a sphere is four times the area of the great circle (the circle whose radius is the same as the radius of the sphere) or $4\pi r^2$.

Remind students of the order of operations requirement for doing exponents before multiplication. To simplify calculations of volume, suggest that if the radius or height is not divisible by 3, then all computations should be done before the division by 3.

If students do the Calculator Key-In on page 343, note that on some calculators the exponent entry key is marked EE rather than EXP. The display will vary depending on the type of calculator used.

Related Activities

To relate mathematics to other subjects and provide practice using scientific notation, have students calculate the surface areas of Earth and the other planets. These areas can be used for other calculations, such as dividing the area of Earth by the human population.

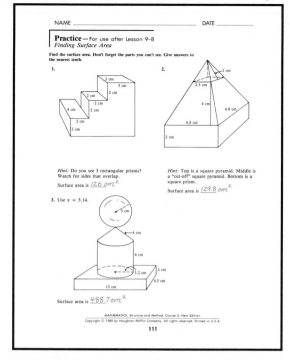

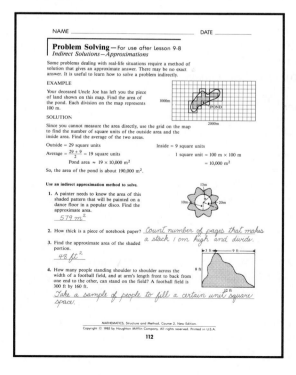

9-9 Mass and Density

Objective *for pages 344–347*

■ To find the mass of an object of a given density.

Teaching Suggestions

Most students have some idea of the meaning of *mass*, but may confuse it with *weight*. Explain to students that weight depends on the amount of gravitational pull on an object. As the force of gravity on an object decreases, the weight of an object decreases. Mass, however, remains constant and is the measure of the amount of matter an object contains. A rock will weigh less on the moon than on Earth because the gravity on the moon is less. The mass of the rock is the same whether it is on Earth, on the moon, or in space.

Demonstrate why the multiplier in Table 1 is 1,000,000:

$$1 \text{ m}^3 = (100 \text{ cm})^3 = 1,000,000 \text{ cm}^3$$
$$1 \text{ t} = 1000 \text{ kg} = 1000(1000 \text{ g}) = 1,000,000 \text{ g}$$

Related Activities

To relate mathematics to social studies, have students find out what units of measurement and measuring instruments have been used in the past and in various parts of the world. They could also find out the standards for the units of measurement that are used now.

To provide experience in measuring, have students measure the masses and volumes of objects. (If they are studying physical science, they may already have done this.) A spring scale may be marked in grams, but it actually measures the weight of an object; its reading would be less on the moon. A pan balance measures may be comparing the weight of an object with the weights of standard masses; its reading would be the same on the moon. To find the volume of a block of wood, students can measure the dimensions and multiply. To find the volume of an irregular object, read the water level in a graduated container, drop the object in, read the water level again, and subtract. When students calculate the density of an object, ask whether it would float in water and let them test the prediction. You might have other liquids available, such as vegetable oil (density about 0.9 g/cm³) or concentrated sugar solution (density about 1.2 g/cm³).

NAME _____ DATE _____

Quiz 9B — Lessons 9-5 through 9-9

DIRECTIONS: Write the letter of the correct answer in the space provided.

Use π = 3.14 unless told to do otherwise.

1. Triangular prism: base area = 32.5 cm², height = 6.5 cm. *[9-5]*
   What is the volume?
   a. 211.25 cm³   b. 186.55 cm³   c. 5 cm³   d. 39 cm³

2. Cylinder: base radius = 3 m, height = 6 m.
   What is its volume?
   a. 18 m³   b. 339.12 m³   c. 169.56 m³   d. 54 m³

3. A pyramid has a base area of 15 m² and a height *[9-6]*
   of 12 m. It has a volume of __?__.
   a. 30 m²   b. 60 m³   c. 90 m³   d. 180 m³

4. A cone with base diameter 10 m and height 6 m has a
   volume of __?__.
   a. 471 m³   b. 1884 m   c. 157 m³   d. 628 m³

5. A cylinder with base diameter 28 and height 4 has a *[9-7]*
   lateral area of __?__. Use π = 22/7.
   a. 352   b. 1232   c. 704   d. 1584

6. A rectangular prism has base 8 by 10 and height 5. Find
   the total surface area.
   a. 260   b. 340   c. 400   d. 800

7. Find the surface area of a sphere with diameter 17 cm. *[9-8]*
   Leave your answer in terms of π.
   a. 6551 π   b. 17 π   c. 1156 π   d. 289 π

8. A sphere has radius 6 cm. Find its volume. Leave your
   answer in terms of π.
   a. 288 π   b. 36 π   c. 144 π   d. 12 π

9. Find the mass of a sphere of ice with radius of 3 cm, *[9-9]*
   density of 0.92 g/cm³.
   a. 25 g   b. 35 g   c. 104 g   d. 9 g

ANSWERS		
1. _a_	(8)
2. _c_	(12)
3. _b_	(8)
4. _c_	(12)
5. _a_	(12)
6. _b_	(12)
7. _d_	(12)
8. _a_	(12)
9. _c_	(12)

113

NAME _____ DATE _____

Review — Chapter 9

1. The area of a triangle is 96. If the base of the triangle is 16,
   find the height.   _12_   *[9-1]*

2. A stone walk 2 ft wide surrounds a rectangular garden which is
   4 ft by 8 ft. Find the area of the walk.   _64 ft²_

3. Find the area of the parallelogram.   _108_   4. Find the area of the trapezoid.   _145_   *[9-2]*

5. Find the area of a circle whose circumference is 34π m.
   Use π = 3.14.   _907.46 m²_   *[9-3]*

6. Find the area of the
   shaded figure. Use the
   fact that the figure
   has symmetry. Use π = 3.14.   _126.5_   *[9-4]*

7. Find the volume of a cylinder with a base diameter of 28 cm
   and a height of 7 cm. Use π = 22/7.   _4,312 cm³_   *[9-5]*

8. A pyramid has a square base 9 m on a side. If the volume is
   216 m³, find the height.   _8 m_   *[9-6]*

9. A cone-shaped storage bin has diameter 3 ft and height 5 ft.
   What is its volume? Use π = 3.14.   _11.775 ft³_

10. Find (a) the lateral area and (b) the total surface area of a
    rectangular prism with base 10 by 13 and height 6.   *[9-7]*
    (a) _276_   (b) _536_

11. Find (a) the surface area and (b) the volume of a sphere having
    diameter 6 m. Leave your answers in terms of π.   *[9-8]*
    (a) _36π m²_   (b) _36π m³_

12. A steel block measures 20 cm by 25 cm by 5 cm, with density
    7.82 g/cm³. Find its mass.   _19,550 g_   *[9-9]*

114

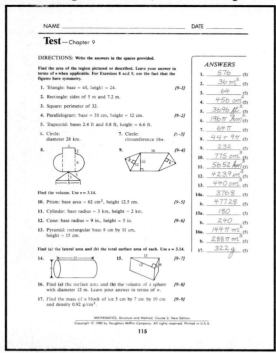

NAME _____ DATE _____

Test — Chapter 9

DIRECTIONS: Write the answers in the spaces provided.

Find the area of the region pictured or described. Leave your answer in terms of π when applicable. For Exercises 8 and 9, use the fact that the figures have symmetry.

1. Triangle: base = 48, height = 24. *[9-1]*
2. Rectangle: sides of 5 m and 7.2 m.
3. Square: perimeter of 32.
4. Parallelogram: base = 38 cm, height = 12 cm. *[9-2]*
5. Trapezoid: bases 2.4 ft and 8.8 ft, height = 6.6 ft.
6. Circle: diameter 28 km.   7. Circle: circumference 16π. *[9-3]*
8.   9. *[9-4]*

Find the volume. Use π ≈ 3.14.

10. Prism: base area = 62 cm², height 12.5 cm. *[9-5]*
11. Cylinder: base radius = 3 km, height = 2 km.
12. Cone: base radius = 9 in., height = 5 in. *[9-6]*
13. Pyramid: rectangular base 8 cm by 11 cm, height = 15 cm.

Find (a) the lateral area and (b) the total surface area of each. Use π ≈ 3.14.

14.   15. *[9-7]*

16. Find (a) the surface area and (b) the volume of a sphere with diameter 12 m. Leave your answer in terms of π. *[9-8]*

17. Find the mass of a block of ice 5 cm by 7 cm by 10 cm and density 0.92 g/cm³. *[9-9]*

ANSWERS
1. 576 (5)
2. 36 m² (5)
3. 64 (5)
4. 456 cm² (5)
5. 3696 ft² (5)
6. 196 π km² (5)
7. 64 π (5)
8. 44 + 9π (5)
9. 232 (5)
10. 775 cm³ (5)
11. 56.52 km³ (5)
12. 423.9 in³ (5)
13. 440 cm³ (5)
14a. 3768 (5)
b. 4772.8 (5)
15a. 180 (5)
b. 240 (5)
16a. 144 π m² (5)
b. 288 π m³ (5)
17. 322 g (5)

MATHEMATICS, Structure and Method, Course 2, New Edition.

115

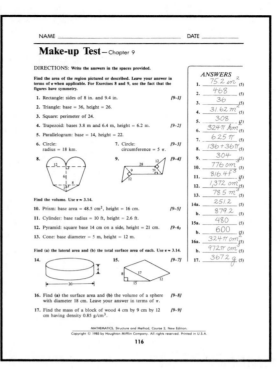

NAME _____ DATE _____

Make-up Test — Chapter 9

DIRECTIONS: Write the answers in the spaces provided.

Find the area of the region pictured or described. Leave your answer in terms of π when applicable. For Exercises 8 and 9, use the fact that the figures have symmetry.

1. Rectangle: sides of 8 in. and 9.4 in. *[9-1]*
2. Triangle: base = 36, height = 26.
3. Square: perimeter of 24.
4. Trapezoid: bases 3.8 m and 6.4 m, height = 6.2 m. *[9-2]*
5. Parallelogram: base = 14, height = 22.
6. Circle: radius = 18 km.   7. Circle: circumference = 5 π. *[9-3]*
8.   9. *[9-4]*

Find the volume. Use π ≈ 3.14.

10. Prism: base area = 48.5 cm², height = 16 cm. *[9-5]*
11. Cylinder: base radius = 10 ft, height = 2.6 ft.
12. Pyramid: square base 14 cm on a side, height = 21 cm. *[9-6]*
13. Cone: base diameter = 5 m, height = 12 m.

Find (a) the lateral area and (b) the total surface area of each. Use π ≈ 3.14.

14.   15. *[9-7]*

16. Find (a) the surface area and (b) the volume of a sphere with diameter 18 cm. Leave your answer in terms of π. *[9-8]*

17. Find the mass of a block of wood 4 cm by 9 cm by 12 cm having density 0.85 g/cm³. *[9-9]*

ANSWERS
1. 75.2 in² (5)
2. 468 (5)
3. 36 (5)
4. 31.62 m² (5)
5. 308 (5)
6. 324 π km² (5)
7. 6.25 π (5)
8. 136 + 36π (5)
9. 304 (5)
10. 776 cm³ (5)
11. 816.4 ft³ (5)
12. 1,372 cm³ (5)
13. 78.5 m³ (5)
14a. 251.2 (5)
b. 879.2 (5)
15a. 480 (5)
b. 600 (5)
16a. 324 π cm² (5)
b. 972π cm³ (5)
17. 367.2 g (5)

MATHEMATICS, Structure and Method, Course 2, New Edition.

116

NAME _____ DATE _____

CUMULATIVE REVIEW — Chapters 1–9
Exercises

Evaluate the expression if p = 4, q = 0.5, and r = 12.

1. $pq + r$ 14
2. pqr 24
3. $3r - 8p$ 4
4. $r^2 + p^3$ 208
5. pq^2 1
6. $10q - r$ -7

Solve.

7. $46 > 3x - 17$ $x < 21$
8. $3r + 23 = 68$ $r = 15$
9. $\frac{d}{4} \le 12$ $d \le 48$
10. $4t \div 9 = 8$ $t = 18$
11. $7 - 2w < 15$ $w > -4$
12. $2m + 12 = 5m - 15$ $m = 9$

Complete.

13. The area of a trapezoid having bases 14 and 24 and height 8 is   152.
14. The area of a circle with a diameter 8 m is   16 π.
15. The volume of a pyramid of height 16 cm having a 6-cm by 10-cm rectangle as a base   320 cm³
16. A cylinder with base radius 3 and height 8 has a lateral area of   48 π   and a surface area of   66 π.
17. 24 is 32% of what number?   75
18. What is $20\frac{1}{2}$% of 620?   127.1
19. 30.69 is what percent of 68.2?   45%
20. 91 is 140% of what number?   65

Solve the equation for y in terms of x.

21. $3x + y = 15$ $y = 15 - 3x$
22. $xy = 42$ $y = 42 - x$
23. $\frac{x}{3} + y = 12$ $y = 12 - \frac{x}{3}$
24. $2x + 2y = 10$ $y = 5 - x$
25. $y - x^2 = 49$ $y = 49 + x$
26. $3y - x = 5x$ $y = 2x$

Find the area of the figure described. Leave your answer in terms of π if necessary.

27. Circle with radius 5 cm.   25 π cm²
28. Triangle with height 7 m and base 12 m.   42 m²
29. Parallelogram with height 5 in. and base 16 in.   80 in²
30. Circle with diameter 34 cm.   289 π cm²

MATHEMATICS, Structure and Method, Course 2, New Edition.

117

NAME _____ DATE _____

CUMULATIVE REVIEW — Chapters 1–9 (continued)
Problems

Problem Solving Reminders
Here are some reminders that may help you solve some of the problems on this page.
- Determine what information is necessary to solve the problem.
- Consider whether drawing a sketch will help.
- If more than one method can be used to solve a problem, use one method to solve and one to check.

Solve.

1. A cylindrical storage tank 6 m in diameter is 4 m high. What is the volume of the tank? Use π ≈ 3.14.   113.04 m³

2. An insurance agent earns a commission of $3\frac{1}{4}$% of the first $8000 of insurance she sells each week and 5% of the value in excess of $8000. One week she sold $17,540 of insurance. How much did she earn? $757

3. After a 12% increase, the price of a warm-up suit was $43.40. What was the old price of the suit? $38.75

4. Mark's living room measures 14 ft by 18 ft. How much will it cost to carpet the room if carpet costs $15.95 per square yard, padding costs $2.50 per square yard, and installation is $3.00 per square yard? (Hint: 9 ft² = 1 yd²) $600.60

5. Amy purchased soccer cleats costing $14.95, shin guards costing $10.50, and two pair of soccer socks costing $2.75 each. There was a 6% tax on her purchases. How much did she get after paying with two twenty-dollar bills? $7.19

6. Jack Nissen purchased a piece of wood that he cut into two sections for shelving. One section was 5 in. longer than twice the length of the other. If the piece of wood measured 2 ft 8 in., how long was each section?   9 in, 23 in

7. The cost of piano sheet music rose from $1.95 to $2.60 in three years. What was the percent of increase? $33\frac{1}{3}$%

MATHEMATICS, Structure and Method, Course 2, New Edition.

118

NAME _____ DATE _____

CUMULATIVE TEST — Chapters 7–9

DIRECTIONS: Write the answer in the space provided.

Chapter 7

Solve each proportion.

1. $\frac{d}{18} = \frac{72}{81}$ 2. $\frac{8}{6} = \frac{46}{n}$ 3. $\frac{8}{2x} = \frac{20}{35}$

Solve.

4. Ten shirts can be made from $17\frac{1}{2}$ yd of fabric. How many shirts can be made from 28 yd of fabric?

5. A scale drawing of a bridge uses a scale of 4 cm:1 m. If the length of the bridge in the drawing is 460 cm, what is the actual length of the bridge?

6. What is 135% of 92? 7. 18 is 37.5% of what number?

8. The membership in the Far Hills Jogging Club increased from 75 to 87. What was the percent of increase?

9. A piano sales representative earns a 7% commission on his sales. If his commission was $243.60 last week, what was the total value of his sales?

10. The original price of a Browning baseball mitt was $33.80. If the price is now discounted 15%, what is the sale price?

11. How much simple interest would be earned on $325 at 8.5% interest for 4 years?

Chapter 8

Tell whether the ordered pair is a solution of the given equation.

$x - 4y = 2$

12. (0, −2) 13. (2, 0) 14. (−2, −1)

Solve the equation for y in terms of x.

15. $\frac{2}{3}x - y = 6$ 16. $3x + 4y = 12$ 17. $2y - 8x = 6$

Complete.

18. To find the solution of a system of equations, find the point of ___?___ of the graphs of the two equations.

(Continue on next page.)

119

ANSWERS

1. $d = 16$ (1)
2. $n = 345$ (1)
3. $x = 7$ (1)
4. 16 (4)
5. $115\ m$ (4)
6. 124.2 (4)
7. 48 (4)
8. 16% (4)
9. $\$3480$ (4)
10. $\$28.73$ (4)
11. $\$110.50$ (4)
12. no (1)
13. yes (1)
14. yes (1)
15. $y = \frac{2}{3}x - 6$ (4)
16. $y = \frac{12 - 3x}{4}$ or $y = 3 - \frac{3}{4}x$ (4)
17. $y = 3 + 4x$ (4)
18. $intersection$ (2)

NAME _____ DATE _____

CUMULATIVE TEST — Chapters 7–9 (continued)

19. If the graphs of two linear equations coincide, this system has ___?___ solution(s).

Is the ordered pair a solution of the system of equations?

20. (4, −2) $x + y = 2$
                $x - y = 6$

21. (2, −6) $2x + y = -3$
                $x - y = 9$

Complete.

22. A basic property of a straight line graph is that its slope remains ___?___.

23. The boundary line for the graph $y > x + 5$ is shown as a ___?___ line.

24. It takes a marathon runner 25 minutes to warm up and $6\frac{1}{2}$ minutes to run a mile. Write an equation relating the total time (t) required for running practice to the number of miles (d) to be run.

Chapter 9

Find the area of the region described. Use $\pi \approx \frac{22}{7}$ if necessary.

25. Trapezoid: bases 8.5 and 12.5, height 14.

26. Circle: radius = 14 m.

27. Parallelogram: base 18, height 24.5.

28. Circle: circumference = 7π.

Find the volume. Use $\pi \approx \frac{22}{7}$ if necessary.

29. Prism: base area = 36 cm², height = 8.5 cm.

30. Cone: base diameter = 8 m, height = 3 m.

Solve.

31. A carpet remnant is on sale for $828. If the carpet piece measures 8 ft by 9 ft, what is the cost per square foot?

32. Find the lateral area and the total surface area of a cylinder with a radius of 7 m and a height of 20 m. Use $\pi \approx \frac{22}{7}$.

33. The area of a sphere is $900\ \pi$ m². What is the diameter?

120

ANSWERS

19. $infinitely\ many$ (4)
20. yes (2)
21. no (2)
22. $constant$ (4)
23. $dashed$ (4)
24. $t = 25 + 6\frac{1}{2}d$ (8)
25. 147 (1)
26. $616\ m^2$ (1)
27. 441 (1)
28. 38.5 (4)
29. $306\ cm^3$ (1)
30. $50.29\ m^3$ (4)
31. $\$11.50$ (4)
32. $880\ m^2,\ 1188\ m^2$ (4)
33. $30\ m$ (4)

305h

9-1 Areas of Rectangles and Triangles

By the **area** of a polygon, we mean the measure of the part of the plane that the polygon encloses. We can find the area of the rectangle at the right by counting the unit squares it contains. The area is 12 cm². The same result can be found by multiplying the length of the rectangle by the width of the rectangle, as shown below.

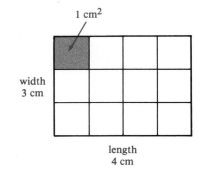

$$\text{Area} = 4 \times 3 = 12 \ (\text{cm}^2).$$

This example suggests a formula for finding the area of any rectangle.

> ### *Formula*
> Area of rectangle = length × width
> $$A = lw$$

When a rectangle is a square, all sides have equal measures. We usually use the simpler formula $A = s^2$, where s is the measure of a side.

To find a formula for the area of a triangle, choose any side to be the **base.** The word *base* is also used for the length of the base. The **height** of the triangle is the perpendicular distance from the opposite vertex to the base line.

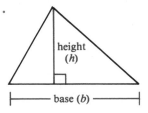

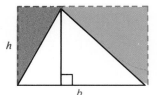

If you were to complete a rectangle around the triangle as shown at the right above, you would find that the areas of the red and blue regions together match exactly the area of the original triangle. Thus the triangle's area is exactly half the rectangle's area, which is *bh.*

Formula

Area of triangle $= \frac{1}{2} \times$ base $\times$ height

$$A = \frac{1}{2}bh$$

In the first paragraph, we used the square centimeter (cm^2) as the unit of area. In other cases we may use smaller or larger units, for example, the square millimeter (mm^2), square meter (m^2), or square kilometer (km^2). When a unit of length is not specified, we simply measure area in *square units*. We will usually not write the labels *units* and *square units*.

EXAMPLE 1   Find the area of the region pictured.

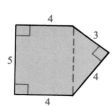

Solution   The dashed line divides the region into a 5-by-4 rectangle and a triangle having base 4 and height 3. Notice that in a right triangle, one of the perpendicular sides can be considered the base. The length of the other perpendicular side can be considered the height.

First find the area of the rectangle.

$$A = bh = 5 \times 4 = 20$$

Then find the area of the triangle.

$$A = \frac{1}{2}bh = \frac{1}{2} \times 4 \times 3 = 6$$

Thus the total area is $20 + 6 = 26$ (square units).

To measure plots of land such as farms, the **hectare** (ha) can be used.

$$1 \text{ ha} = 10,000 \text{ m}^2 = 0.01 \text{ km}^2$$

EXAMPLE 2   A wheat field is a rectangle 5 km by 2.5 km. Find its area in hectares.

Solution $A = 5 \times 2.5 = 12.5$ (km^2)
Since $1 \text{ km}^2 = 100$ ha, $12.5 \text{ km}^2 = 1250$ ha.
The area of the field is 1250 ha.

Areas and Volumes   **307**

Class Exercises

Find the area of the shaded region.

1.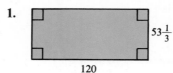
$53\frac{1}{3}$
120
6400

2.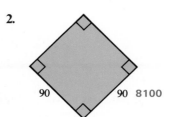
90   90   8100

3.
18
117
13

4.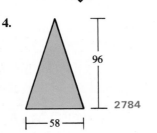
96
2784
58

5. Find the perimeters of the shaded regions in Exercises 1 and 2. $346\frac{2}{3}$; 360

6. What is the area of a square whose perimeter is 20 cm? **25 cm²**

Complete.

7. 1 m = ___?___ cm **100**

8. 1 km = ___?___ m **1000**

9. 0.01 km² = ___?___ ha $\frac{1}{100}$

1 m² = ___?___ cm² **10,000**

1 km² = ___?___ m² **1,000,000**

1 km² = ___?___ ha

10. Choose a rectangular wall of your classroom and estimate its area in
square meters. **Answers may vary.**

Written Exercises

Find the area of each shaded region.

A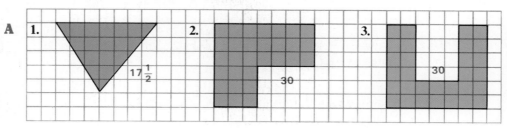

1. $17\frac{1}{2}$

2. 30

3. 30

308 *Chapter 9*

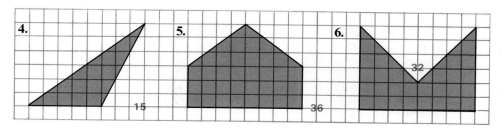

4. 15

5. 36

6. 32

Find the perimeter and the area of the polygon.

7.
220 m
480 m
1400 m; 105,600 m²

8.
16 km
64 km; 256 km²
16 km

9.
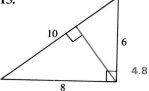
25 cm   28 cm
15 cm
70 cm; 210 cm²
17 cm

10.
9 m
17 m
36 m; 36 m²
10 m
8 m

11. How many hectares are in a square field 27 km on a side?   72,900

12. How many hectares are in a rectangular field 360 m by 140 m?   5.04

13. A 2000 ha field is 2.5 km long. How wide is it?   8 km

14. A 36 ha field is 480 m wide. How long is it?   750 m

Find the length of the segment printed in red.

15.
10
6
8
4.8

16.
8
3
4
6

Areas and Volumes   **309**

Suggested Assignments

Minimum
Day 1: 308/1–3
        309/4–16
        310/17–18
Day 2: 310/Prob. 1–4
        311/Prob. 5–8
        311/Rev. 1–8

Average
Day 1: 308/1–3
        309/4–16
        310/17–20
Day 2: 310/Prob. 1–4
        311/Prob. 5–10
        311/Rev. 2–8 even

Maximum
Day 1: 308/1–3
        309/4–16
        310/17–22
Day 2: 310/Prob. 1–4
        311/Prob. 5–11

Supplementary Materials

Practice Masters, p. 39

In Exercises 17 and 18, dimensions of several rectangles are given. Copy and complete the tables.

17.

Dimensions	Perimeter	Area
10 by 10	? 40	? 100
12 by 8	? 40	? 96
18 by 2	? 40	? 36
19 by 1	? 40	? 19

18.

Dimensions	Perimeter	Area
8 by 8	? 32	?64
16 by 4	? 40	?64
32 by 2	? 68	?64
64 by 1	? 130	?64

Use the evidence of Exercises 17 and 18 to complete these statements.

B **19.** Of all rectangles with a given perimeter, the square has the greatest __?__. **area**

20. Of all rectangles with a given area, the square has the least __?__. **perimeter**

C **21.** Use Exercise 19 or 20 to explain why there can be no rectangle having perimeter 20 and area 36. The greatest possible area for a rectangle with perimeter 20 is $\left(\frac{20}{4}\right)^2 = 25$.

22. If the dimensions of a triangle are doubled, the perimeter is multiplied by __?__, and the area is multiplied by __?__. **2; 4**

Problems

A **1.** A particular carpet sells for $7 per square foot. What is the cost of the carpet needed to cover a floor 12 ft by 27 ft? **$2268**

2. One can of paint will cover 24 m². How many cans should you buy to be sure that you have enough to cover a 16 m by 8 m ceiling? (You may have paint left over.) **6 cans**

3. A 21 ha field is 350 m wide. How long is it? **600 m**

4. A piece of land 1.2 km by 3.6 km is for sale at $1500 per hectare. What is the price of the land? **$648,000**

5. Sixty meters of fencing enclose a square corral. What is the area of the corral? **225 m²**

6. A field 480,000 m² is 160 m wide. What length of fencing is needed to enclose it? **6320 m**

7. Find the total area of the sails shown below. **39.6 m²**

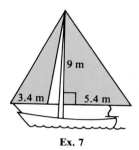

Ex. 7

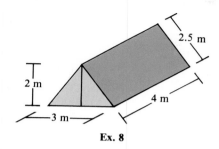

Ex. 8

8. The ends of the tent shown above are mosquito netting costing $3.50 per square meter, and the rest of the tent, including the floor, is canvas costing $15 per square meter. What is the total cost of these materials? **$501**

B **9.** A brick walk 2 m wide surrounds a rectangular pool that is 3 m by 5 m. Find the area of the walk. **48 m²**

10. How many square vinyl tiles, 20 cm on a side, are needed to cover a floor 6 m by 5 m? **750 tiles**

C **11.** How many square tiles, 9 in. on a side, are needed to cover a floor 12 ft by 21 ft? **448 tiles**

Review Exercises

Evaluate each expression using the given values of the variables.

$a + b$ **1.** $a = 119$, $b = 61$ **180**   **2.** $a = 5.7$, $b = 0.65$ **6.35**

$2x + 2y$ **3.** $x = 18$, $y = 26$ **88**   **4.** $x = 16.5$, $y = 4.9$ **42.8**

$\frac{1}{2}(c + d)$ **5.** $c = 12$, $d = 22$ **17**   **6.** $c = 5.6$, $d = 3.1$ **4.35**

$\frac{1}{2}(x + y)z$ **7.** $x = 4$, $y = 11$, $z = 8$ **60**   **8.** $x = 12.3$, $y = 6.44$, $z = 8.2$ **76.834**

Chalkboard Examples

Find the area and perimeter of each parallelogram.

1.

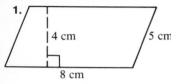

$A = 32 \text{ cm}^2, P = 26 \text{ cm}$

2.

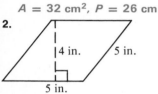

$A = 20 \text{ in.}^2, P = 20 \text{ in.}$

Find the area and perimeter of each trapezoid.

3.

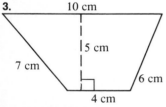

$A = 35 \text{ cm}^2, P = 27 \text{ cm}$

4.

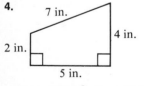

$A = 15 \text{ in.}^2, P = 18 \text{ in.}$

9-2 Areas of Quadrilaterals

Either pair of parallel sides of a parallelogram can be taken to be the **bases.** The **height** is the perpendicular distance between the base lines.

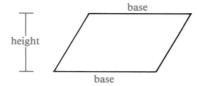 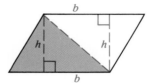

The parallelogram at the right above has base b and height h. A diagonal divides the parallelogram into two congruent triangles, each having area $\frac{1}{2}bh$. Therefore, the area of the parallelogram is two times $\frac{1}{2}bh$, that is, bh.

> ### *Formula*
>
> Area of parallelogram = base × height
>
> $$A = bh$$

EXAMPLE 1 Find (a) the perimeter and (b) the area of the parallelogram.

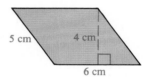

Solution

a. Since opposite sides of a parallelogram are congruent,

$$p = (2 \times 5) + (2 \times 6) = 22.$$

The perimeter is 22 cm.

b. $A = bh$
$$= 6 \times 4 = 24$$

The area is 24 cm².

The **height** of a trapezoid is the perpendicular distance between its parallel sides, which are called its **bases.** Let us find a formula for the area of a trapezoid having bases b_1 and b_2 and height h. This trapezoid and a congruent copy of it can be put together to form a parallelogram as shown on the next page.

312 *Chapter 9*

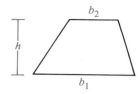 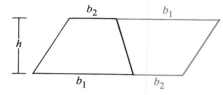

The parallelogram has area $(b_1 + b_2)h$, and this is twice the area of the original trapezoid. Therefore:

> ### Formula
>
> Area of trapezoid $= \frac{1}{2} \times$ (sum of bases) $\times$ height
>
> $$A = \frac{1}{2}(b_1 + b_2)h$$

EXAMPLE 2   Find the area of a trapezoid with height 5 m and bases 2 m and 4 m.

Solution
$$A = \frac{1}{2}(b_1 + b_2)h$$

$$= \frac{1}{2}(2 + 4) \times 5 = 15$$

The area of the trapezoid is 15 m².

EXAMPLE 3   Find the area of the quadrilateral $ABCD$.

Solution   Subtract the areas of the corner triangles from the area of rectangle $PQRS$.

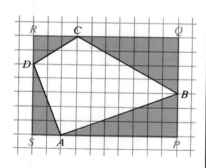

Area $PQRS = 10 \times 7 = 70$

Area $\triangle APB = \frac{1}{2} \times 8 \times 3 = 12$

Area $\triangle BQC = \frac{1}{2} \times 7 \times 4 = 14$

Area $\triangle CRD = \frac{1}{2} \times 3 \times 2 = 3$

Area $\triangle DSA = \frac{1}{2} \times 2 \times 5 = 5$

Area $PQRS$ − areas of triangles $= 70 - (12 + 14 + 3 + 5) = 36$

Class Exercises

Find the area of the figure. For Exercises 5 and 6, give your answers in hectares.

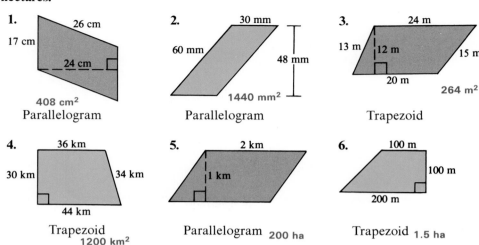

1. 26 cm / 17 cm / 24 cm / **408 cm²** / Parallelogram

2. 30 mm / 60 mm / 48 mm / **1440 mm²** / Parallelogram

3. 24 m / 13 m / 12 m / 15 m / 20 m / **264 m²** / Trapezoid

4. 36 km / 30 km / 34 km / 44 km / Trapezoid / **1200 km²**

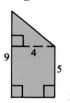

5. 2 km / 1 km / Parallelogram / **200 ha**

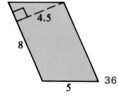

6. 100 m / 100 m / 200 m / Trapezoid / **1.5 ha**

Written Exercises

Find the area of the trapezoid or parallelogram.

A

1. 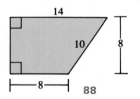 14 / 10 / 8 / 8 / **88**

2. 9 / 4 / 5 / **28**

3. 4.5 / 8 / 5 / **36**

4. A parallelogram with base 15 cm and height 6 cm **90 cm²**

5. A trapezoid with height 8 m and bases 18 m and 12 m **120 m²**

6. A trapezoid with height 12 cm and bases 14.5 cm and 5.5 cm **120 cm²**

7. A parallelogram with height 5.2 km and base 11.4 km **59.28 km²**

Exercises 8 and 9 refer to parallelograms. Complete.

8. Area = 360 km², base = 15 km, height = __?__ **24 km**

9. Area = 175 cm², height = 12.5 cm, base = __?__ **14 cm**

314 *Chapter 9*

Additional A Exercises

1. Find the area of this parallelogram.

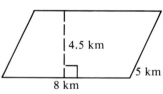

4.5 km / 5 km / 8 km

36 km²

2. Find the area of this trapezoid.

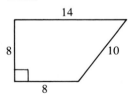

14 / 8 / 10 / 8

88 square units

3. A rhombus has a perimeter of 44 cm. If the height of the rhombus is 9 cm, what is the area of the rhombus? **99 cm²**

4. A trapezoid has an area of 120 cm², a base of 14.5 cm, and a height of 12 cm. What is the length of the other base? **5.5 cm**

314

Exercises 10 and 11 refer to trapezoids. Complete.

10. Area = 336 m², bases = 7 m and 14 m, height = __?__ 32 m

11. Area = 132 m², height = 12 m, one base = 16 m, other base = __?__ 6 m

12. Gina and Tom found the area of parallelogram *ABCD* in different ways. Who was correct? **both**

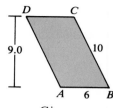 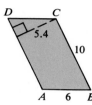

Gina   Tom

$A = 6 \times 9.0$ $A = 10 \times 5.4$

Find the area of each quadrilateral.

B

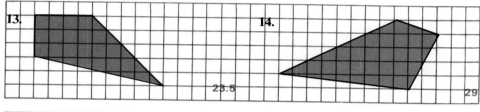

13.   14.   23.5   29

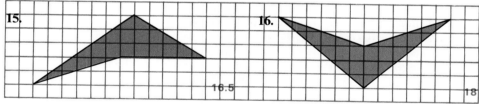

15.   16.   16.5   18

Find the length of the segment printed in red in the parallelogram.

17.   **18.**

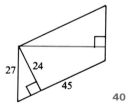   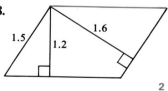

Suggested Assignments

Minimum
  314/1–9
  315/10–12
  316/Rev. 1–10

Average
  314/2–8 even
  315/10, 12–18
  316/19–23
  316/Rev. 1–9 odd

Maximum
  314/2–8 even
  315/10, 12–18
  316/19–24

Supplementary Materials

Practice Masters, p. 39

19. The diagonals of a rhombus are perpendicular and bisect each other. Find the area of a rhombus whose diagonals are 8 cm and 20 cm long. **80 cm²**

Find the area of the figure by first dividing it into simpler regions. The figure in Exercise 21 has three pairs of parallel sides.

20.

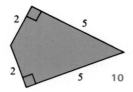
2   5
2   5   10

21.

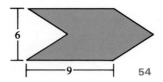
6
9   **54**

Refer to the diagrams below. Express each ratio in lowest terms.

22. a. $RS:OP$ **5:3**   **b.** $ST:PQ$ **5:3**   **c.** $TR:QO$ **5:3**
   d. Perimeter of $\triangle RST$:Perimeter of $\triangle OPQ$ **5:3**
   e. Area of $\triangle RST$:Area of $\triangle OPQ$ **25:9**

T
17   8| 10
R   21   S

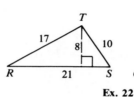
4.8   Q
10.2   6
O   12.6   P

A   5.5   D
15   12
B   14.5   C

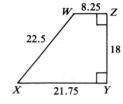
W   8.25   Z
22.5   18
X   21.75   Y

Ex. 22   **Ex. 23**

23. a. $AB:WX$ **2:3**   **b.** $BC:XY$ **2:3**   **c.** $CD:YZ$ **2:3**   **d.** $AD:WZ$
   e. Perimeter of $ABCD$:Perimeter of $WXYZ$ **2:3**   **2:3**
   f. Area of $ABCD$:Area of $WXYZ$ **4:9**

C   24. Two figures have the same shape but not the same size. The lengths of their corresponding sides are in the ratio given below. What is the ratio of their perimeters? What is the ratio of their areas? (*Hint:* Refer to Exercises 22 and 23.)
   a. 2:1 **2:1; 4:1**   **b.** 3:4 **3:4; 9:16**

Review Exercises **1.** 1 **2.** 25 **3.** 64 **4.** 0.09 **5.** 1.44 **6.** 4; −4
7. 7; −7 **8.** 10; −10 **9.** 0.6; −0.6 **10.** 1.1; −1.1

Complete.

1. $1^2 =$ ___?___   **2.** $5^2 =$ ___?___   **3.** $8^2 =$ ___?___   **4.** $0.3^2 =$ ___?___   **5.** $1.2^2 =$ ___?___

6. ___?___ $^2 = 16$ **7.** ___?___ $^2 = 49$ **8.** ___?___ $^2 = 100$ **9.** ___?___ $^2 = 0.36$ **10.** ___?___ $^2 = 1.21$

316   *Chapter 9*

9-3 Areas of Circles

We know that the circumference, C, of a circle of radius r is given by the formula $C = 2\pi r$. Two approximations for the number π are $\pi \approx 3.14$ and $\pi \approx \frac{22}{7}$.

The area of a circle is given by this formula:

> ### Formula
> Area of circle $= \pi \times$ (radius)^2
>
> $A = \pi r^2$

EXAMPLE 1   Find the area of the shaded region. Use $\pi \approx 3.14$.

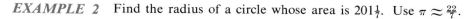

Solution   Subtract the area of the small circle from the area of the large circle.

Area of large circle $= \pi \times 5^2$
$$\approx 3.14 \times 25 = 78.5$$

Area of small circle $= \pi \times 3^2 \approx 3.14 \times 9 = 28.26$

Area of shaded region $\approx 78.5 - 28.26 = 50.24$

Rounded to three digits, the area of the shaded region is approximately 50.2.

EXAMPLE 2   Find the radius of a circle whose area is $201\frac{1}{7}$. Use $\pi \approx \frac{22}{7}$.

Solution   Substitute $201\frac{1}{7}$ for A in the formula $A = \pi r^2$.

$$201\frac{1}{7} = \pi r^2$$

$$201\frac{1}{7} \approx \frac{22}{7} \times r^2$$

$$\frac{1408}{7} \times \frac{7}{22} \approx \frac{22}{7} \times \frac{7}{22} \times r^2$$

$$64 \approx r^2$$

Since $8^2 = 64$, $r \approx 8$.

To avoid approximations when working with circles, we often give answers *in terms of* π. Any time we need a decimal answer, we can replace π by 3.14 or some other approximation.

Areas and Volumes   **317**

EXAMPLE 3 Find (a) the radius and (b) the circumference of a circle whose area is 49π. Leave your answer in terms of π.

Solution   **a.** Substitute 49π for A in the formula for area.

$$A = \pi r^2$$
$$49\pi = \pi r^2$$
$$\frac{49\pi}{\pi} = \frac{\pi r^2}{\pi}$$
$$49 = r^2$$

Since $7^2 = 49$, $r = 7$.

b. Use $r = 7$ in the formula for circumference.

$$C = 2\pi r$$
$$= 2\pi \times 7$$
$$= 14\pi$$

The circumference is 14π.

Throughout this chapter when the approximation of 3.14 is used for π, answers are rounded to 3 digits.

Class Exercises

1. Find the area of a circle whose radius is 7 cm. Use $\pi \approx \frac{22}{7}$. **154 cm²**

2. Find the area of a circle whose diameter is 20 km. Use $\pi \approx 3.14$. **314 km²**

3. A circle has radius 8. What is the area? Use $\pi \approx 3.14$. **201**

4. A circle has diameter 10. What is the area? Use $\pi \approx \frac{22}{7}$. $\frac{550}{7}$, **or** $78\frac{4}{7}$

5. The circumference of a circle is 12π.
   a. Find the radius. **6**   **b.** Find the area. **36π**

6. The circumference of a circle is 2π.
   a. Find the radius. **1**   **b.** Find the area. **π**

Additional A Exercises

Find the area of the circle described. Use $\pi \approx \frac{22}{7}$.

1. diameter = 70 cm
   3850 cm²

2. radius = $1\frac{3}{4}$ in. $9\frac{5}{8}$ in.²

Find the area of the circle described. Use $\pi \approx 3.14$.

3. radius = 16 cm **804 cm²**

4. diameter = 3 mm
   7.07 mm²

5. The area of a circle is 154 cm². Find the radius.
   about 7 cm

6. The area of a circle is 530 m². Find the diameter. **about 26 m**

Written Exercises

Find the area of the circle described. Use $\pi \approx \frac{22}{7}$.

A   **1.** radius = 21 km **1386 km²**   **2.** diameter = 21 km **346.5 km²**

   3. diameter = 1.4 cm **1.54 cm²**   **4.** radius = 1.4 cm **6.16 cm²**

318   *Chapter 9*

Find the area of the circle described. Use $\pi \approx 3.14$.

5. radius = 4 m   50.2 m²

6. radius = 10 m   314 m²

7. diameter = 10 cm   78.5 cm²

8. diameter = 12 cm   113 cm²

9. circumference = 94.2 m   707 m²

10. circumference = 6.28 m   3.14 m²

In Exercises 11 and 12, use $\pi \approx 3.14$.

11. The area of a circle is 314 cm². Find the radius.   10 cm

12. The area of a circle is 12.56 m². Find the radius.   2 m

The table gives data about circles. Copy and complete it, leaving your answers in terms of π.

B

	13.	14.	15.	16.	17.	18.
Radius	7	? 9	? 4	? 15	? 5	? 10
Diameter	? 14	18	? 8	? 30	? 10	? 20
Circumference	? 14π	? 18π	8π	30π	? 10π	? 20π
Area	? 49π	? 81π	? 16π	? 225π	25π	100π

19. If the radius of a circle is doubled, the area is multiplied by __?__.   4

20. If the radius of a circle is tripled, the area is multiplied by __?__.   9

Find the area of the shaded region. Leave your answer in terms of π.

21.
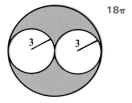
18π

22.
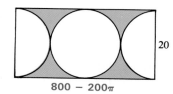
$800 - 200\pi$

C 23.
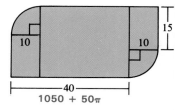
$1050 + 50\pi$

24.
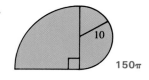
150π

Suggested Assignments

Minimum
318/1–4
319/5–14, 21
320/Prob. 1–2
320/Rev. 1–6

Average
318/1, 3
319/5–11 odd; 13–22
320/Prob. 1–6
320/Rev. 1–6

Maximum
318/1, 3
319/5–17 odd; 19–24
320/Prob. 1–8

Supplementary Materials

Practice Masters, p. 40

Problems

In this chapter, answers to exercises and problems may vary slightly due to rounding.

Solve. Use $\pi \approx 3.14$.

A **1.** A circular pond 12 m in diameter is surrounded by a brick walk 3 m wide. Find the areas of the pond and the walk. **113 m²; 141 m²**

2. The bull's eye of an archery target is 10 cm in diameter, and each ring is 5 cm wide. Find the areas of the first, second, and third rings. **236 cm²; 393 cm²; 550 cm²**

Ex. 2

Problems 3–6 refer to the running track pictured at the right.

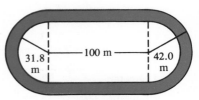

B **3.** Find the inside perimeter of the track. **400 m**

4. Find the outside perimeter of the track. **464 m**

5. Find the area of the region inside the track. **9540 m²**

6. Find the area of the track surface. **4400 m²**

Exs. 3–6

C **7.** A circle is inscribed in a square (four points of the circle are on the square). What percent of the area of the square is outside the circle? **21.5%**

8. A square is inscribed in a circle (all vertices of the square are on the circle). What percent of the area of the circle is outside the square? **36.3%**

Review Exercises

State which of the rigid motions (translation, rotation, or reflection) are needed to match the vertices of the congruent figures.

1.
translation

2. rotation

3.
reflection

4.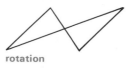
rotation, or
rotation and translation

5.
rotation, or
rotation and translation

6.
reflection and translation, or
rotation and reflection

320 *Chapter 9*

9-4 Areas of Symmetric Figures

If we could fold the figure at the right along the dot-dash line l, the shaded region would fall exactly on the region that is not shaded. We say that the figure is **symmetric with respect to the line** l and that l is a **line of symmetry.** A figure can have more than one line of symmetry, as illustrated below.

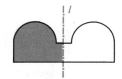

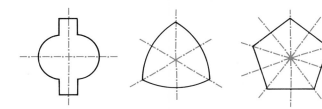

Often we can take advantage of symmetry when finding areas of figures.

EXAMPLE 1 Find the area of the figure pictured at the right. The dot-dash line is a line of symmetry.

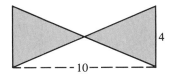

Solution We can think of the region as a rectangle with two trapezoids removed.

First find the area of the rectangle.

$$A = bh = 25 \times 15 = 375$$

Then find the area of one trapezoid. One base has length 10. The other base has length

$$25 - (5 + 5) = 15.$$

The height is 5.

$$A = \tfrac{1}{2}(b_1 + b_2)h = \tfrac{1}{2}(10 + 15)5 = 62.5$$

Because of symmetry, the trapezoids have equal areas. Subtract the areas of the two trapezoids from the area of the rectangle.

$$\text{Area of region} = 375 - (2 \times 62.5) = 250$$

Areas and Volumes **321**

Teaching Suggestions p. 305b

Related Activities p. 305b

Reading Mathematics

Students will learn the meaning of the following mathematical terms in this lesson: *symmetric, symmetric with respect to a line, line of symmetry, symmetric with respect to a point, point of symmetry.*

Chalkboard Exercises

Draw the lines and points of symmetry for the figure.

1.

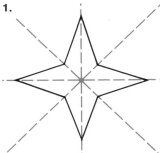

Find the area of the shaded region. Use the fact that the figure has symmetry. Use $\pi \approx 3.14$.

2. 20 square units

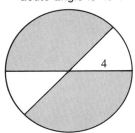

3. The measure of each acute angle is 45°.

37.7 square units

Additional A Exercises

Find the area of the shaded region. Use the fact that the figure has symmetry. Use $\pi \approx 3.14$.

1.

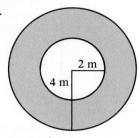

37.7 m²

2.

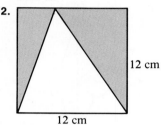

12 cm

12 cm

72 cm²

3.

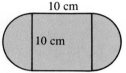

10 cm

10 cm

179 cm²

4.

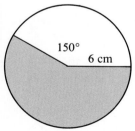

150°

6 cm

65.9 cm²

A figure is **symmetric with respect to a point** O if for every point P on the figure, there is an "opposite" point Q on the figure such that O is the midpoint of $\overline{PQ}$.

If a figure is symmetric with respect to a point O, then any line through O divides it into two congruent figures.

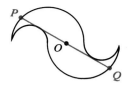

EXAMPLE 2   The figure at the right is symmetric with respect to point O. Find the area of the shaded region. Use $\pi \approx 3.14$.

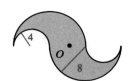

Solution   A horizontal line through the point of symmetry divides the figure into two congruent parts and therefore two parts of equal area. To find the area of one part, subtract the area of the small semicircle from the area of the large semicircle. Recall that a semicircle is half of a circle so the area of a semicircle is half the area of a circle.

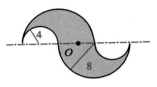

Large semicircle:
$$A = \tfrac{1}{2}\pi r^2 \approx \tfrac{1}{2} \times 3.14 \times 8^2 = \tfrac{1}{2} \times 3.14 \times 64 = 100.48$$

Small semicircle:
$$A = \tfrac{1}{2}\pi r^2 \approx \tfrac{1}{2} \times 3.14 \times 4^2 = \tfrac{1}{2} \times 3.14 \times 16 = 25.12$$

Area of part $\approx 100.48 - 25.12 = 75.36$

To find the area of the entire shaded region, multiply by 2.

Area of region $\approx 2 \times 75.36 = 150.72$

Rounded to three digits, the area is approximately 151.

Class Exercises

1. Draw a square and all of its lines of symmetry. Is it symmetric with respect to a point? Yes; the point is the intersection of the diagonals.

2. Draw an equilateral triangle and all of its lines of symmetry. Is it symmetric with respect to a point? No.

3. Does a circle have one, two, or infinitely many lines of symmetry? Is it symmetric with respect to a point? infinitely many. Yes; the center.

322   *Chapter 9*

Complete. In each of the two figures below, the red and blue regions are congruent because of symmetry.

Ex. 4

Ex. 5

4. The sum of the areas of the red and blue regions is __?__. Therefore the area of each is __?__. $\pi;\ \frac{\pi}{2}$

5. The sum of the areas of the red and blue regions is __?__. Therefore the area of each is __?__. 12; 6

Written Exercises

Copy the figure. Draw dashed lines to represent all lines of symmetry (if any) and mark each point of symmetry (if any) with a •.

A 1.

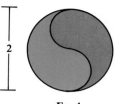

2.

3.

4.

5.

6.

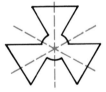

Find the area of the shaded region. Use the fact that the figure has symmetry. Use $\pi \approx 3.14$.

7.

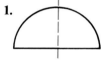

12

452

8.

6

2

3

2   18

9.

10

20

800

Areas and Volumes **323**

Suggested Assignments

Minimum
Day 1: 323/1–9
Day 2: 324/10–12
      325/Self-Test A

Average
Day 1: 323/1–9
      324/10–11
Day 2: 324/12–15
      324/Challenge
      325/Self-Test A

Maximum
Day 1: 323/1–9 odd
      324/10–15
Day 2: 324/16–18
      324/Challenge
      325/Self-Test A

Supplementary Materials

Practice Masters, p. 40
Test 9A, pp. 59–60

Find the area of the shaded region. Use the fact that the figure has symmetry. Use $\pi \approx 3.14$.

B 10.

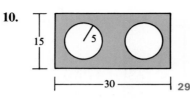

293

11.

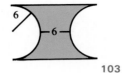

103

12.

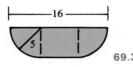

69.3

13.

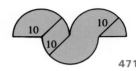

471

14.

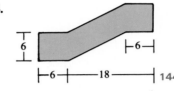

144

15.

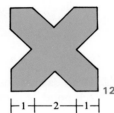

12

C 16.

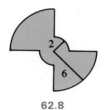

62.8

17.

98.1

18.

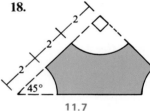

11.7

Quick Quiz A

Find the area of the region pictured.

1.

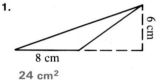

8 cm

6 cm

24 cm²

2.

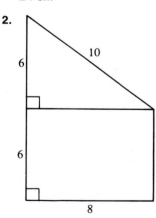

6

10

6

8

72 square units

3.   5 m

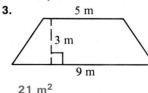

3 m

9 m

21 m²

(Continue on next page.)

Challenge

Draw a square and then add a congruent square to one of its sides. Add a third congruent square to a side of one of the first two squares. There are exactly two ways (shown) to connect the three squares so that the resulting figures are not congruent.

There are exactly five possibilities for connecting four congruent squares. Can you sketch them? Check students' drawings.

There are twelve possibilities for connecting five congruent squares. Can you sketch them all? Check students' drawings.

324 *Chapter 9*

Self-Test A

Find the area of the region pictured.

[9–1]

1.

56
48
1344

2.

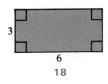

3
18
6

3.

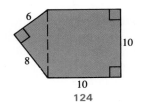

6
10
8
10
124

4. The area of a rectangular field is 140 ha. The field is 350 m wide. How long is it? **4000 m**

5. The area of a parallelogram is 120 cm². The base is 16 cm. What is the height? **7.5 cm**

6. The area of a parallelogram is 406 cm². The height is 14 cm. What is the base? **29 cm**

Find the area of the region pictured.

[9–2]

7.

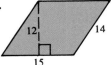

12
14
15

Parallelogram **180**

8.

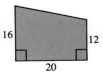

16
12
20

Trapezoid **280**

Find the area of the circle described. Use π ≈ 3.14.

[9–3]

9. radius = 2.5 cm **10.** diameter = 18 m **11.** circumference = 37.68 m
19.6 cm² **254 m²** **113 m²**

Find the area of the shaded region. Use the fact that the figure has symmetry. Use π ≈ 3.14.

[9–4]

12.

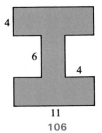

4
6
4
11
106

13.

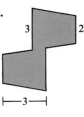

3
2
3
15

14.

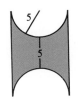

5
5
71.5

Self-Test answers and Extra Practice are at the back of the book.

Areas and Volumes **325**

4. The area of a parallelogram is 72 cm². The base is 16 cm. What is the height? **4.5 cm**

5. The area of a rectangular field is 120 ha. The field is 4000 m long. How wide is it? **300 m**

Find the area of the circle described. Use π ≈ 3.14.

6. radius = 3.4 cm
36.3 cm²

7. circumference = 94.2 cm
707 cm²

Find the area of the shaded region. Use the fact that the figure has symmetry. Use π ≈ 3.14.

8.

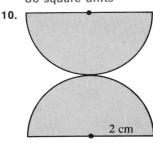

1
3
3
1
4
9 square units

9.

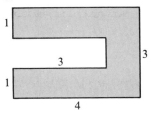

8
10
80 square units

10.

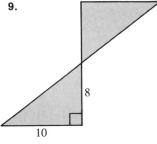

2 cm
12.6 cm²

325

Teaching Suggestions
p. 305c

Related Activities p. 305c

Reading Mathematics

Students will learn the meaning of the following mathematical terms in this lesson: *polyhedron, prism, bases, height, solid, volume, cylinder, capacity, liter, milliliter.*

9-5 Volumes of Prisms and Cylinders

A **polyhedron** is a figure formed of polygonal parts of planes, called **faces,** that enclose a region of space. A **prism** is a polyhedron that has two congruent faces, called **bases,** that are parallel. The other faces are regions bounded by parallelograms. The bases may also be parallelograms. Prisms are named according to their bases. Unless otherwise stated, we will only consider prisms whose faces are rectangles.

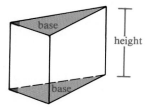

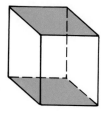

Triangular Prism   **Square Prism**

In each figure above, the bases are shaded. The perpendicular distance between the bases is the **height** of the prism.

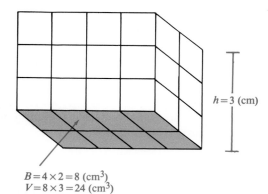

A polyhedron together with the region inside it is called a **solid.** The measure of the space occupied by a solid is called the **volume** of the solid. The prism at the right, filled with 3 layers of 8 unit cubes, has 24 unit cubes. In this case, each unit cube is a cubic centimeter (cm³). Thus the volume of the cube is 24 cm³.

This example suggests a formula for finding the volume of any prism.

$h = 3$ (cm)

$B = 4 \times 2 = 8$ (cm³)
$V = 8 \times 3 = 24$ (cm³)

> ## *Formula*
> Volume of prism = Base area × height
>
> $V = Bh$

326   *Chapter 9*

EXAMPLE 1 A watering trough is in the form of a trapezoidal prism. Its ends have the dimensions shown. How long is the trough if it holds 12 m³?

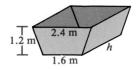

Solution Examine the diagram carefully to determine which regions are the bases. In this diagram, one of the bases is at the front. You know that the volume is 12 m³. Find the area of the base.

$$B = \frac{1}{2}(1.6 + 2.4) \times 1.2 = 2.4 \ (\text{m}^2)$$

Then, use the formula.

$$V = Bh$$
$$12 = 2.4h$$
$$5 = h$$

The length of the trough is 5 m.

A **cylinder** is like a prism except that its bases are circles instead of polygons. The area of the base, B, is πr^2. Thus:

Formula

Volume of cylinder = Base area × height

$$V = \pi r^2 h$$

The volume of a container is often called its **capacity.** The capacity of containers of fluids is usually measured in **liters** (L) or **milliliters** (mL).

$$1 \ \text{L} = 1000 \ \text{cm}^3 \qquad 1 \ \text{mL} = 1 \ \text{cm}^3$$

It is easy to show that $1 \ \text{m}^3 = 1000 \ \text{L}$.

EXAMPLE 2 A cylindrical storage tank 1 m in diameter is 1.2 m high. Find its capacity in liters. Use $\pi \approx 3.14$.

Solution Use the formula $V = \pi r^2 h$. The height is 1.2 m and, because the diameter is 1 m, the radius is 0.5 m.

$$V \approx 3.14 \times (0.5)^2 \times 1.2 = 0.942 \ (\text{m}^3)$$

Since $1 \ \text{m}^3 = 1000 \ \text{L}$, $0.942 \ \text{m}^3 = 942 \ \text{L}$. The capacity of the tank is approximately 942 L.

Areas and Volumes **327**

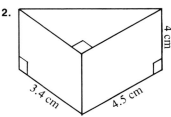
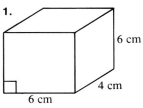
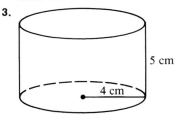
327

Find the volume of the solid. In Exercises 5 and 6, leave your answer in terms of π.

1.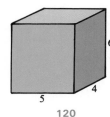
120

2.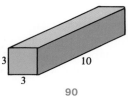
90

3.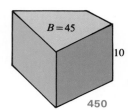
B = 45
10
450

4.
B = 20
3
60

5.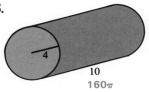
4
10
160π

6.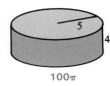
5
4
100π

7. a. 1 m = __?__ cm 100
   b. 1 m^3 = __?__ cm^3 1,000,000
   c. 1000 L = __?__ cm^3 1,000,000

8. a. 1 cm = __?__ mm 10
   b. 1 cm^3 = __?__ mm^3 1000
   c. 1 mL = __?__ mm^3 1000

Written Exercises

In this exercise set, use $\pi \approx 3.14$ unless told to do otherwise. Find the volume of the solid.

A

1.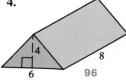
3
12
5
90

2.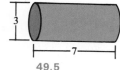
3
7
49.5

3.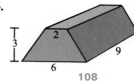
2
3
6
9
108

4.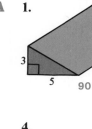
4
6
8
96

5.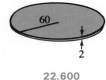
60
2
22,600

6.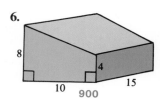
8
4
10
15
900

328 *Chapter 9*

Additional A Exercises

Find the volume of the solid. Use $\pi \approx 3.14$.

1.
12
8
9
432 cubic units

2.
20 ft
9 ft
2830 ft^3

3.
7 in.
7 in.
7 in.
343 in.^{3}

Find the capacity in liters of the prism or cylinder.

4. Prism: base area 120 cm^2, height 16 cm **1.92 L**

5. Cylinder: base diameter 1 m, height 1.2 m **942 L**

7.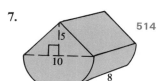

514

5
10
8

8.

1220

7

7

7

Find the capacity in liters of the prism or cylinder.

9. Square prism: 25 cm by 25 cm by 80 cm 50 L

10. Prism: base area = 1.2 m², height = 2.3 m 2760 L

11. Cylinder: base radius = 1.2 m, height = 1.4 m 6330 L

12. Cylinder: base diameter = 1 m, height = 75 cm 589 L

The table below refers to cylinders. Copy and complete it. Leave your answers in terms of π.

B

	13.	14.	15.	16.	17.	18.
Volume	12π	150π	100π	20π	18π	100π
base radius	2	5	? 5	? 2	? 3	? 2
Base area	? 4π	? 25π	25π	4π	? 9π	? 4π
height	? 3	? 6	? 4	? 5	2	25

Find the volume of the prism if the pattern were folded.

19.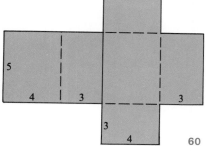

5
4
3
3
3
4
60

20.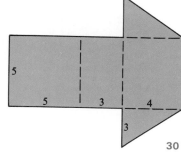

5
5
3
4
3
30

C 21. What happens to the volume of a cylinder if this change is made?
  a. The radius is doubled. quadrupled   **b.** The height is halved. halved
  c. The radius is doubled and the height is halved. doubled

22. What happens to the volume of a cylinder if this change is made?
  a. The radius is halved. quartered   **b.** The height is doubled. doubled
  c. The radius is halved and the height is doubled. halved

Areas and Volumes **329**

In an *oblique prism,* the bases are *not* perpendicular to the other faces. The volume formula $V = Bh$ still applies, where h is the perpendicular distance between the bases. Find the volume of each figure shown in red.

23.

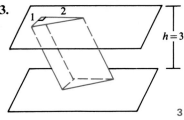

$h = 3$

3

24.

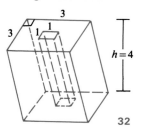

3

$h = 4$

32

Problems

Solve. Use $\pi \approx 3.14$.

A **1.** Find the capacity in liters of the V-shaped trough shown below.

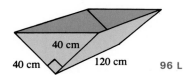

40 cm

40 cm   120 cm

96 L

2. Find the capacity in liters of the half-cylinder trough shown below.

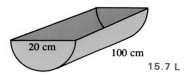

20 cm   100 cm

15.7 L

B **3.** Find the volume of metal in the copper pipe shown below.

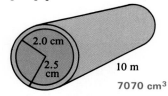

2.0 cm

2.5 cm

10 m

7070 cm³

4. Find the volume of concrete in the construction block shown below.

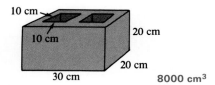

10 cm

10 cm

20 cm

20 cm

30 cm

8000 cm³

C **5.** A cylindrical water bottle is 28 cm in diameter. How many centimeters does the water level drop when one liter is drawn off? 1.62 cm

Review Exercises

Solve for x.

1. $x = \frac{1}{3} \times 6.4 \times 15$

32

2. $x = \frac{1}{2}(7.2) \times 3$

10.8

3. $3.38 = 4x$

0.845

4. $\frac{1}{3}x = 11$

33

5. $3.14 \times 20^2 = x$

1256

6. $(0.8)^2 x = 5.12$

8

7. $314 = 3.14x^2$

10; -10

8. $x^2 = 169$

13; -13

330 *Chapter 9*

9-6 Volumes of Pyramids and Cones

If we shrink one base of a prism to a point, we obtain a **pyramid** with that point as its **vertex.** A **cone** is obtained in the same way from a cylinder. In each case, the **height** of the solid is the perpendicular distance from its vertex to its base. As for a prism, the shape of the base of a pyramid determines its name. All other faces of a pyramid are triangles. A cone is like a pyramid except that its base is a circle instead of a polygon.

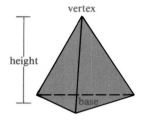

Triangular Pyramid or Tetrahedron

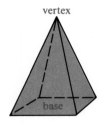

Square Pyramid

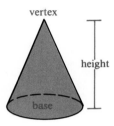

Cone

The volume of a pyramid can be found using this formula:

> ### Formula
>
> Volume of pyramid $= \frac{1}{3} \times$ Base area $\times$ height
>
> $$V = \frac{1}{3}Bh$$

EXAMPLE 1   Find the volume of the square pyramid shown at the right.

Solution   First find the base area. Since the base is a square,

$$B = 12^2 = 144 \text{ (cm}^2).$$

Then use the volume formula.

$$V = \frac{1}{3}Bh$$

$$= \frac{1}{3} \times 144 \times 25 = 1200 \text{ (cm}^3)$$

Areas and Volumes   **331**

Teaching Suggestions p. 305c

Related Activities p. 305c

Reading Mathematics

Students will learn the meaning of the following mathematical terms in this lesson: *pyramid, vertex, cone, height, base.*

Chalkboard Examples

Find the volume of the solid. Use $\pi \approx 3.14$.

1. A square pyramid of height 15 cm and base edge 12 cm. **720 cm³**

2. A cone of height 8 cm and base radius 6 cm. **301 cm³**

3. A cone of base diameter 5 cm and height 11.5 cm. **75.2 cm³**

Find the capacity in liters of the cone or pyramid described.

4. A pyramid of height 16 cm having a 15 cm by 6 cm rectangle as base **0.48 L**

5. A cone of height 12 m and base diameter 10 m **314,000 L**

For a cone, the base area is given by the formula $B = \pi r^2$.

Formula

Volume of cone $= \frac{1}{3} \times$ Base area $\times$ height

$$V = \frac{1}{3}\pi r^2 h$$

EXAMPLE 2 A conical container is 20 cm across the top and 21 cm deep. Find its capacity in liters. Use $\pi \approx 3.14$.

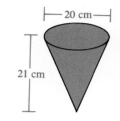

Solution The diameter of the base of the cone is 20 cm, so the radius is 10 cm.

$$V = \frac{1}{3}\pi \times 10^2 \times 21$$

$$\approx \frac{1}{3} \times 3.14 \times 100 \times 21 = 2198$$

Rounding the product to three digits, the volume is approximately 2200 cm³. Because 1000 cm³ equals 1 L, the capacity of the conical container is approximately 2.2 L.

Reading Mathematics: *Vocabulary*
Words that we use in everyday speech may have different meanings in mathematics. For example, the everyday word *base* often refers to the part of an object that it is resting on. The geometrical term *base* refers to a particular face of a figure that may appear at the top, the side, or the end of the figure in a drawing. In Example 2, above, the base appears at the top of the container.

Class Exercises

Find the volume of the solid. In Exercise 3, the base is a square. In Exercise 4, leave your answer in terms of π.

1.
$h = 10$
$B = 30$
100

2.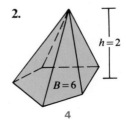
$h = 2$
$B = 6$
4

3.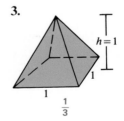
$h = 1$
1
1
$\frac{1}{3}$

4.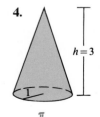
$h = 3$
π

Complete.

5. Except for the base, the shapes of all the faces of a pyramid are __?__. triangles

6. The shapes of all the faces of a tetrahedron are __?__. triangles

7. A cone has base radius 3 and height 6. The volume of the cone is __?__ π. 18

Written Exercises

For Exercises 1–10, use $\pi \approx 3.14$ when needed. Find the volume of the solid pictured.

A **1.**
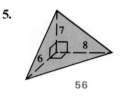
72

2.
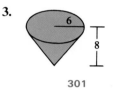
63

3.
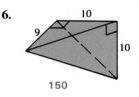
301

4.
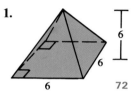
1700

5.
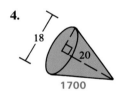
56

6.
150

Find the capacity in liters of the cone or pyramid described.

7. A pyramid of height 12 cm having a 5 cm by 8 cm rectangle as base 0.16 L

8. A pyramid having height 10 m and a square base 15 m on a side 750,000 L

9. A cone having base radius 0.8 m and height 1.5 m 1000 L

10. A cone of height 24 cm and base diameter 11 cm 0.76 L

Copy and complete the table for pyramids.

	11.	**12.**	**13.**	**14.**	**15.**	**16.**
Base area, *B*	5	33	4	13	? 3	? 4
height, *h*	6	12	? 6	? 3	10	15
Volume, *V*	? 10	? 132	8	13	10	20

Areas and Volumes **333**

Additional A Exercises

Find the volume of the solid. Use $\pi \approx 3.14$.

1. A pyramid of height 12 in. having a rectangular base 4 in. by 5 in. 80 in.³

2. A cone with height 10 cm and radius 6 cm. 377 cm³

3. Find the height of a rectangular pyramid whose base area is 192 m² and whose volume is 960 m³. 15 m

Find the capacity in liters of the cone or pyramid described.

4. A pyramid of height 22 m having a 12 m by 8 m rectangle as base 704,000 L

5. A cone of height 30 cm and base diameter 18 cm 2.54 L

Suggested Assignments

Minimum
Day 1: 333/1–16
Day 2: 334/17–20
    334/Prob. 1–2
    334/Rev. 1–8

Average
Day 1: 333/1–16
    334/17–20
Day 2: 334/Prob. 1–4
    334/Rev. 1–8

Maximum
Day 1: 333/1–16
    334/17–20
Day 2: 334/21–22
    334/Prob. 1–4

Supplementary Materials

Practice Masters, p. 41

Copy and complete the table for cones.

B

	17.	18.	19.	20.
radius, r	1	2	?3	?1
height, h	?15	?9	4	15
Volume, V	5π	12π	12π	5π

Complete.

C **21.** A cone has volume 6 cm³. The volume of a cylinder having the same base and same height is __?__ cm³. **18**

22. A cylinder of height 2 m has the same base and same volume as a cone. The cone's height is __?__ m. **6**

Problems

Solve. Use $\pi \approx 3.14$.

A **1.** The Pyramid of Cheops in Egypt has a square base approximately 230 m on a side. Its original height was approximately 147 m. What was its approximate volume originally? **2,592,100 m³**

2. A volcano is in the form of a cone approximately 1.8 km high and 12 km in diameter. Find its volume. **67.8 km³**

B **3.** Find the volume of this buoy.

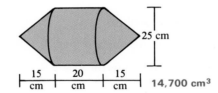

25 cm

| 15 cm | 20 cm | 15 cm |

14,700 cm³

4. Find the volume of this tent. The floor of the tent is square.

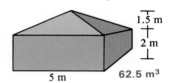

1.5 m

2 m

5 m

62.5 m³

Review Exercises

2. 20 cm   **4.** 44 m   **6.** 124.06 km
8. 31.45 m

Find the perimeter of the figure whose sides have the given lengths.

1. rhombus: 9 m per side **36 m**

2. trapezoid: 4 cm, 4 cm, 5 cm, 7 cm

3. triangle: 35 cm per side **105 cm**

4. parallelogram: 15 m, 7 m, 15 m, 7 m

5. square: 12.8 km per side **51.2 km**

6. rectangle: 24.63 km by 37.40 km

7. square: 145.2 km per side **580.8 km**

8. triangle: 3.70 m, 12.90 m, 14.85 m

9-7 Surface Areas of Prisms and Cylinders

The **surface area** of every prism and cylinder is made up of its two **bases** and its **lateral surface** as illustrated in the figures below. The lateral surface of a prism is made up of its **lateral faces.** Each lateral face is a rectangle.

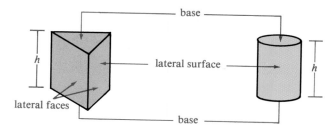

If we were to cut open and flatten out the prism and cylinder shown above, the bases and the lateral surfaces of the figures would look like this:

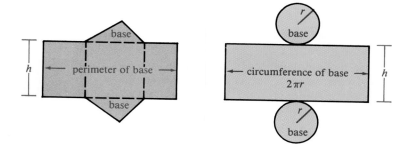

In each of the figures above, the area of the lateral surface, called the **lateral area,** is the product of the perimeter of the base and the height of the figure. To find the **total surface area** of a prism or cylinder, we simply add the area of the two bases to the lateral area of the figure.

Formulas

For a prism or cylinder,

lateral area = perimeter of base × height

total surface area = lateral area + area of bases

Areas and Volumes **335**

Teaching Suggestions
p. 305d

Related Activities p. 305d

Reading Mathematics

Students will learn the meaning of the following mathematical terms in this lesson: *surface area, bases, lateral surface, lateral faces, lateral area, total surface area.*

Find the total surface area of a rectangular prism having the given dimensions.

1. 2.7 cm by 4.8 cm by 5.3 cm **105.42 cm²**

2. 10 m by 9 m by 6 m **408 m²**

Find the lateral surface area and the total surface area of each cylinder. Use $\pi \approx 3.14$.

3. A cylinder having height 4 m and base radius 1.5 m. **37.7 m², 51.8 m²**

4. A cylinder having base diameter 10 cm and height 11 cm **345 cm², 502 cm²**

EXAMPLE 1   Find (a) the lateral area, (b) the area of the bases, and (c) the total surface area of the prism shown.

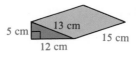

Solution

a. perimeter of base = 5 + 12 + 13 = 30 (cm)
height = 15 cm
lateral area = 30 × 15 = 450 (cm²)

b. area of bases = $2 \times \left(\frac{1}{2} \times 12 \times 5\right) = 60$ (cm²)

c. total surface area = 450 + 60 = 510 (cm²)

In a cylinder of base radius r, the perimeter (circumference) of the base is $2\pi r$. Thus:

Formulas

For a cylinder,

lateral area $= 2\pi rh$

area of bases $= 2\pi r^2$

total surface area $= 2\pi rh + 2\pi r^2$

EXAMPLE 2   A can of paint will cover 50 m². How many cans are necessary to paint the inside (top, bottom, and sides) of the storage tank shown? Use $\pi \approx 3.14$.

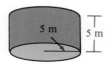

Solution

Since $r = 5$ and $h = 5$,
total surface area = $(2\pi \times 5 \times 5) + (2\pi \times 5^2)$
$\approx (3.14 \times 50) + (3.14 \times 50) = 314$

The total surface area is approximately 314 m².

The number of cans of paint is 314 ÷ 50, or 6.28. Rounding *up* to the nearest whole number, the answer is 7 cans.

Problem Solving Reminder

For problems whose answers are the result of division, take time to consider whether it is reasonable *to round up or round down*. In Example 2, the answer to the division was 6.28 cans of paint. Because paint cannot be purchased in hundredths of a can, the answer was rounded up to the nearest whole number. If the answer had been rounded down, there would not have been enough paint to cover the interior of the tank.

Class Exercises

1. If a prism has hexagonal bases, how many lateral faces does it have? How many faces does it have in all? 6; 8

Find the lateral area and the total surface area. Use $\pi \approx 3.14$.

2.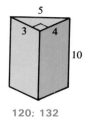

120; 132

3.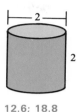

12.6; 18.8

4.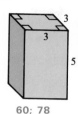

60; 78

5. If each edge of a cube is one unit long, what is the total surface area in square units? 6

Written Exercises

Find the total surface area of a rectangular prism having the given dimensions.

A **1.** 45 cm by 30 cm by 20 cm 5700 cm²   **2.** 5 cm by 18 cm by 25 cm 1330 cm²

3. 2.5 m by 1.6 m by 0.8 m 14.56 m²   **4.** 1.8 m by 0.6 m by 2.0 m 11.76 m²

Find (a) the lateral area and (b) the total surface area of the cylinder or prism. Use $\pi \approx 3.14$.

5. A cylinder having base radius 12 cm and height 22 cm 1660 cm²; 2560 cm²

6. A cylinder having base diameter 6 m and height 4.5 m 84.8 m²; 141 m²

7.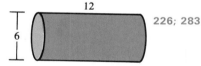

226; 283

8.

25.1; 126

9.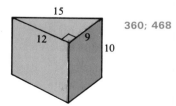

360; 468

10.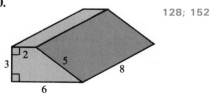

128; 152

Additional A Exercises

Find the total surface area of a rectangular prism having the given dimensions.

1. 8 cm by 8 cm by 8 cm
384 cm²

2. 5 cm by 8 cm by 13 cm
418 cm²

3. 3 cm by 4 cm by 5 cm
94 cm²

Find the lateral surface area and the total surface area of each cylinder. Use $\pi \approx 3.14$.

4. A cylinder having base radius 3 m and height 0.5 m 9.42 m², 65.9 m²

5. A cylinder having base diameter 8 cm and height 19 cm 477 cm², 577 cm²

If the patterns below were drawn on cardboard, they could be folded along the dotted lines to form prisms. Find (a) the volume and (b) the total surface area of each.

B 11.

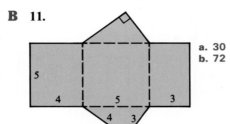

a. 30
b. 72

12.

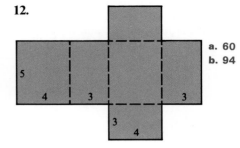

a. 60
b. 94

13. Find the length of the edge of a cube whose total area is 150 cm². **5 cm**

14. Three faces of a box have a common vertex and their combined area is 20 cm². What is the total surface area of the box? **40 cm²**

15. One can of varnish will cover 64 m² of wood. If you want to put one coat of varnish on each of 24 wooden cubes with the dimensions shown at the right, how many cans of varnish should you buy? **6 cans**

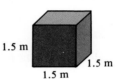

1.5 m
1.5 m
1.5 m

16. You have two cans of red paint, each of which will cover 100 m². Which of the two cylinders pictured below can you paint completely using just the paint that you have? **B**

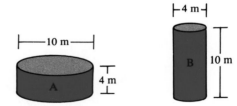

17. A prism of height 3 m has bases that are right triangles with sides 6 m, 8 m, and 10 m. Find the lateral area and the total surface area. (Be sure to draw and label a sketch.) **72 m²; 120 m²**

18. A prism of height 10 cm has bases that are right triangles with sides 5 cm, 12 cm, and 13 cm. Find the lateral area and the surface area. (Be sure to draw and label a sketch.) **300 cm²; 360 cm²**

19. If the number of faces of a prism is represented by n, write an algebraic expression to represent the number of lateral faces. **$n - 2$**

338 *Chapter 9*

C **20.** The lateral surface of a cone is made up of many small wedges like the one shown in color. Thinking of the wedge as a triangle of base b and height s, we see that its area is $\frac{1}{2}bs$. When we add all these areas together, we obtain $\frac{1}{2}(2\pi r)s$, or πrs, because the sum of all the b's is $2\pi r$, the circumference of the base. Thus, for a cone:

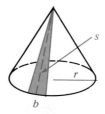

$$\text{lateral area} = \pi rs$$

$$\text{area of base} = \pi r^2$$

$$\text{total surface area} = \pi rs + \pi r^2$$

The length s is called the **slant height** of the cone.

Find the total surface area of each figure.

a.

298

b.

94.2

c.

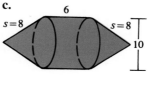

440

Review Exercises

Find the radius of the circle with the given circumference C or diameter d. Use $\pi \approx 3.14$.

1. $d = 12$ **6**   **2.** $C = 62.8$ **10**   **3.** $d = 210$ **105**   **4.** $C = 83.6$ **13.3**

5. $C = 220$ **35**   **6.** $d = 25$ **12.5**   **7.** $d = 76$ **38**   **8.** $C = 2.42$ **0.385**

Challenge

1. Copy the square at the right and cut it into four pieces along the dashed lines. Re-form the four pieces into a larger square with a "hollow" square at the center.

2. Repeat step 1 several times, assigning different values to a and b each time. In each case, what is the area of the "hollow" square?

$(b - a)^2$

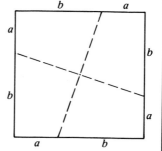

Areas and Volumes **339**

9-8 Volumes and Surface Areas of Spheres

The **sphere** with **radius** r and **center** at C consists of all points at the distance r from point C. The word *radius* also is used for any segment having C as one endpoint and a point of the sphere as another (for example, $\overline{CP}$ in the figure). The word **diameter** is also used in two ways: for a *segment* through C having its endpoints on the sphere (for example, $\overline{AB}$), and for the *length* of such a segment.

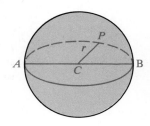

The following formulas for the surface area and volume of a sphere can be proved using higher mathematics.

Formulas

For any sphere of radius r,

Area $= 4\pi \times (\text{radius})^2$ Volume $= \frac{4}{3}\pi \times (\text{radius})^3$

$A = 4\pi r^2$ $V = \frac{4}{3}\pi r^3$

The surface area of a sphere is usually referred to simply as the *area* of the sphere.

> **Reading Mathematics:** *Diagrams*
> Reading diagrams correctly is an important reading skill in mathematics. When three-dimensional objects are pictured on a two-dimensional page, the lines used to draw congruent segments may be of different lengths. For example, in the drawing above, you understand that all radii of a sphere are congruent and that $CP = CB$. Yet these radii cannot be drawn to be of equal length if the picture is to look realistic.

EXAMPLE 1   Find (a) the surface area and (b) the volume of a sphere having diameter 18. Leave your answer in terms of π.

Solution   The radius equals $\frac{1}{2}$ the diameter, so $r = 9$.
  a. $A = 4\pi r^2 = 4\pi \times 9^2 = 4\pi \times 81 = 324\pi$

  b. $V = \frac{4}{3}\pi r^3 = \frac{4}{3}\pi \times 9^3 = \frac{4}{3}\pi \times 729 = 972\pi$

340   *Chapter 9*

EXAMPLE 2   The area of a sphere is 1600π cm². What is the radius?

Solution   Substitute 1600π for A in the formula $A = 4\pi r^2$.

$$1600\pi = 4\pi r^2$$
$$\frac{1600\pi}{4\pi} = \frac{4\pi r^2}{4\pi}$$
$$400 = r^2$$

Since $20^2 = 400$, $r = 20$ cm.

Class Exercises

Complete. In Exercises 1 and 2, give your answers in terms of π.

1. The area of a sphere of radius 1 is __?__ , and the volume is __?__ . 4π; $\frac{4}{3}\pi$
2. The area of a sphere of radius 2 is __?__ , and the volume is __?__ . 16π; $\frac{32}{3}\pi$
3. If the radius of a sphere is doubled, the area is multiplied by __?__ . 4
4. If the radius of a sphere is doubled, the volume is multiplied by 8 __?__ .
5. If $\overline{AB}$ is a diameter of a sphere having center C, then $\overline{AC}$ and $\overline{BC}$ are __?__ of the sphere. radii

Complete the following analogies with choice a, b, c, or d.

6. Sphere: Circle = Cube: __?__   c
   a. Pyramid   **b.** Prism   **c.** Square   **d.** Cylinder
7. Cone: Pyramid = Cylinder: __?__   b
   a. Sphere   **b.** Prism   **c.** Circle   **d.** Triangle

Written Exercises

Copy and complete the table below. Leave your answers in terms of π.

A

	1.	2.	3.	4.	5.	6.
radius of sphere	3	5	6	9	10	12
surface area	? 36π	? 100π	? 144π	? 324π	? 400π	? 576π
volume	? 36π	? $\frac{500}{3}\pi$	? 288π	? 972π	? $\frac{4000}{3}\pi$	? 2304π

Areas and Volumes **341**

Additional A Exercises

Leave your answers in terms of π.

1. Find the surface area and volume of a sphere having radius 9. 324π, 972π
2. The surface area of a sphere is 100π cm². What is its radius? 5 cm
3. The volume of a sphere is 36π m³. What is its diameter? 6 m
4. Find the area of the curved surface of a hemisphere of radius 7. 98π

Half of a sphere is called a *hemisphere*. Solve. Leave your answers in terms of π.

7. Find the volume of a hemisphere of radius 2. $\frac{16}{3}\pi$

8. Find the area of the curved surface of a hemisphere of radius 8. 128π

9. Find the area of the curved surface of a hemisphere of radius 2.2. 9.68π

10. Find the volume of a hemisphere of radius 3.3. 23.958π

Copy and complete the table below. Leave your answers in terms of π.

B

	11.	12.	13.	14.	15.	16.
radius of sphere	3.6	? 4	? 9	4.5	? 8	? 6
surface area	? 51.84π	64π	? 324π	? 81π	256π	? 144π
volume	?	?	972π	?	?	288π

62.208π $\frac{256}{3}\pi$ 121.5π $\frac{2048}{3}\pi$

Solve. Leave your answers in terms of π.

17. The observatory building shown at the right consists of a cylinder surmounted by a hemisphere. Find its volume. 324π m³

18. The water tank at the right consists of a cone surmounted by a cylinder surmounted by a hemisphere. Find its volume. 456π m³

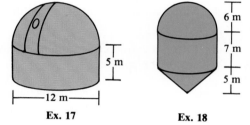

Ex. 17   Ex. 18

19. Earth's diameter is about $3\frac{2}{3}$ times that of the moon. How do their volumes compare? Earth's volume is about 49.3 times that of the moon.

20. The sun's diameter is about 110 times that of Earth. How do their volumes compare? The sun's volume is about 1,331,000 times that of Earth.

342   *Chapter 9*

If a sphere fits snugly inside a cylinder it is said to be *inscribed* in the cylinder. Use the diagram at the right for Exercises 21 and 22.

C   21. a. A sphere of radius 4 is inscribed in a cylinder of height 8. What is the ratio of the volume of the sphere to the volume of the cylinder? 2:3

b. A sphere of radius 5 is inscribed in a cylinder of height 10. What is the ratio of the volume of the sphere to the volume of the cylinder? 2:3

c. A sphere of radius r is inscribed in a cylinder. What is the ratio of the volume of the sphere to the volume of the cylinder? $4r:3h$, or 2:3

22. a. A sphere of radius 6 is inscribed in a cylinder of height 12. What is the ratio of the surface area of the sphere to the lateral area of the cylinder? 1:1

b. A sphere of radius 7 is inscribed in a cylinder of height 14. What is the ratio of the surface area of the sphere to the lateral area of the cylinder? 1:1

c. A sphere of radius r is inscribed in a cylinder. What is the ratio of the surface area of the sphere to the lateral area of the cylinder? $2r:h$, or 1:1

Review Exercises

Simplify these in your head if you can. Write down the answers.

1. 7×0.3 2.1

2. 4×5.1 20.4

3. 0.8×0.8 0.64

4. 23.3×100 2330

5. $3500 \div 1000$ 3.5

6. $10.75 \div 100$ 0.1075

7. 300×2.7 810

8. 0.0004×0.2 0.00008

 Calculator Key-In

The surface area of Earth is approximately 510,070,000 km². The surface area of Jupiter is approximately 64,017,000,000 km². About how many times greater than the surface area of Earth is the surface area of Jupiter? 126

If you try to enter the numbers as they are shown above on your calculator, you may find it will not accept more than eight digits. Many calculators have a key marked *EXP* that allows you to use scientific notation to express very large (or very small) numbers. For example, you can enter 510,070,000 by thinking of the number as 5.1007×10^8 and entering 5.1007 [EXP] 8. Your calculator may show 5.1007   08.

Try to find a calculator that will accept scientific notation and solve the problem above.

Areas and Volumes **343**

Reading Mathematics

Students will learn the meaning of the following mathematical terms in this lesson: *mass, gram, kilogram, metric ton, weight, density.*

9-9 Mass and Density

The **mass** of an object is a measure of the amount of matter it contains. In the metric system, units of mass are the **gram (g),** the **kilogram (kg),** and the **metric ton (t).**

> 1 g = mass of 1 cm³ of water under standard conditions
> (Standard conditions are 4°C at sea-level pressure.)
>
> 1 kg = 1000 g
>
> 1 t = 1000 kg

The *weight* of an object is the force of gravity acting on it. While the mass of an object remains constant, its weight would be less on a mountaintop or on the moon than at sea level. In a given region, mass and weight are proportional (so that mass can be found by weighing).

The tables below give the masses of unit volumes (1 cm³) of several substances.

TABLE 1

Substance	Mass of 1 cm³	Mass of 1 m³
Pine	0.56 g	0.56 t
Ice	0.92 g	0.92 t
Water	1.00 g	1.00 t
Aluminum	2.70 g	2.70 t
Steel	7.82 g	7.82 t
Gold	19.3 g	19.3 t

TABLE 2

Substance	Mass of 1 cm³	Mass of 1 L
Helium	0.00018 g	0.00018 kg
Air	0.0012 g	0.0012 kg
Gasoline	0.66 g	0.66 kg
Water	1.00 g	1.00 kg
Milk	1.03 g	1.03 kg
Mercury	13.6 g	13.6 kg

The mass per unit volume of a substance is its **density.** In describing densities we use a slash (/) for the word *per.* For example, the density of gasoline is 0.66 kg/L.

EXAMPLE   Find the mass of a block 3 cm by 5 cm by 10 cm made of wood having density 0.8 g/cm³.

Solution   The volume of the block is 3 × 5 × 10, or 150, cm³.

Since 1 cm³ of the wood has mass 0.8 g, 150 cm³ has mass 0.8 × 150, or 120, g.

Chalkboard Examples

Use the tables in the text to find the mass of the following.

1. 3 L of water **3 kg**

2. 800 mL of mercury **10.88 kg**

3. 2 cm³ of gold **38.6 g**

4. 1000 cm³ of steel **7.82 kg**

Give the density of the following using the tables in the text.

5. Pine **0.56 g/cm³**

6. Milk **1.03 kg/L**

The example illustrates the following formula.

> ## *Formula*
> Mass = Density × Volume

In Table 2, the number of grams per cubic centimeter is the same as the number of kilograms per liter. This is because there are 1000 g in a kilogram and 1000 cm³ in a liter. Similarly in Table 1, the number of grams per cubic centimeter is the same as the number of metric tons per cubic meter.

Class Exercises

Complete.

1. 1 t = _?_ kg 1000

2. 1 kg = _?_ g 1000

3. 1 t = _?_ g 1,000,000

4. 2400 kg = _?_ t 2.4

5. 0.62 kg = _?_ g 620

6. 400 g = _?_ kg 0.4

Use the tables in this lesson to give the mass of the following.

7. 2 L of water 2.00 kg

8. 10 cm³ of gasoline 6.6 g

9. 100 cm³ of milk 103 g

10. 4 L of gasoline 2.64 kg

11. helium filling a 1000 L tank 0.18 kg

12. a cube of ice 2 cm on each edge 7.36 g

13. the block of steel shown

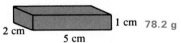 2 cm, 5 cm, 1 cm 78.2 g

Written Exercises

Complete.

A

1. 6.3 kg = _?_ g 6300

2. 2500 kg = _?_ t 2.5

3. 4.3 t = _?_ kg 4300

Use the tables in this lesson to find the mass of the following.

4. 50 cm³ of gold 965 g

5. 300 cm³ of aluminum 810 g

6. 25 L of gasoline 16.5 kg

7. 2.5 L of mercury 34 kg

8. 500 m³ of water 500 t

9. 500 m³ of ice 460 t

10. 1 m³ of air 1200 g

11. 1 m³ of helium 180 g

12. 4 L of milk 4.12 kg

Areas and Volumes **345**

Additional A Exercises

Use the tables in this lesson to find the mass of the following.

1. 5 L of milk 5.15 kg

2. 2.5 L of mercury 34 kg

3. 50 cm³ of ice 46 g

4. 3000 cm³ of aluminum 8.1 kg

5. A bar of gold measuring 25 cm by 15 cm by 10 cm 72.375 kg

6. Milk filling a rectangular container 10 cm by 10 cm by 16 cm. 1.648 kg

Suggested Assignments

Minimum
Day 1: 345/1–2
       346/13–15
Day 2: 346/Prob. 1–4
       347/Self-Test B

Average
Day 1: 345/1–12
       346/13–18
Day 2: 346/Prob. 1–5
       347/Prob. 6
       347/Self-Test B

Maximum
Day 1: 345/1–12
       346/13–18
Day 2: 346/Prob. 1–5
       347/Prob. 6
       347/Self-Test B

Supplementary Materials

Practice Masters, p. 42
Test 9B, pp. 61–62
Computer Activity 17
Computer Activity 18

In Exercises 13–15, the solid pictured is made of the specified material. Use the tables in this lesson to find the mass of the solid. Use $\pi \approx 3.14$.

13.
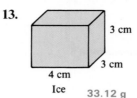
4 cm
3 cm
3 cm
Ice
33.12 g

14.
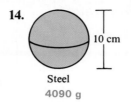
10 cm
Steel
4090 g

15.
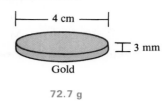
4 cm
3 mm
Gold
72.7 g

Use the tables in this lesson to find the mass of the named content of the container pictured. Use $\pi \approx 3.14$.

16.
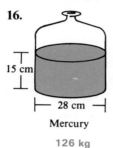
15 cm
28 cm
Mercury
126 kg

17.
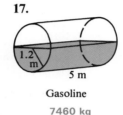
1.2 m
5 m
Gasoline
7460 kg

18.
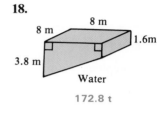
8 m
8 m
1.6 m
3.8 m
Water
172.8 t

Problems

Solve. Use the tables in this lesson if no density is given. Use $\pi \approx 3.14$.

A

1. A solid gold bar has dimensions of approximately 17 cm by 9 cm by 4.5 cm. Find its mass in kilograms.
   13.28805 kg

2. A solid pine board has dimensions of approximately 100 cm by 30 cm by 1.5 cm. Find the mass of the board in grams. 2520 g

3. The optical prism shown at the right is made of glass having density 4.8 g/cm³. Find its mass. 81.12 g

4. A piece of ice is in the form of a half-cylinder 5 cm in radius and 3 cm high. What is its mass?
   108 g

B

5. What is the mass in metric tons of the steel I-beam shown at the right? 3.91 t

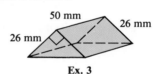
50 mm
26 mm
26 mm
Ex. 3

Ex. 4

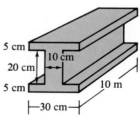
5 cm
10 cm
20 cm
5 cm
30 cm
10 m
Ex. 5

Quick Quiz B

Complete the following. Use $\pi \approx 3.14$.

1. Pentagonal prism: base area = 60 cm², height = 9 cm, volume = __?__ cm³ 540

(Continue on next page.)

6. The drawing at the right shows the cross-section of a two-kilometer-long tunnel that is to be dug through a mountain. How many metric tons of earth must be removed if its density is 2.8 t/m³? **253,000 t**

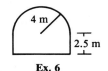

Ex. 6

Self-Test B

Use $\pi \approx 3.14$ unless told to do otherwise.

Complete.

1. Triangular prism: base area = 7.6 m², height = 5.5 m, volume = _?_ m³ **41.8** [9–5]

2. Cylinder: base diameter = 38 cm, height = 24 cm, volume = _?_ cm³ **27,200**

3. Square prism: 17 cm by 17 cm by 32 cm, volume = _?_ cm³, **9248** capacity = _?_ L **9.248**

Find the volume of the solid.

4. A cone with base radius 0.5 m and height 1.2 m **0.314 m³** [9–6]

5. A pyramid with base of 180 m² and height 20 m **1200 m³**

6. A square pyramid with base 26 cm on a side and height 48 cm **10,816 cm³**

Find (a) the lateral area and (b) the total surface area of the solid.

7. A rectangular prism with base 4 by 3 and height 7 **a. 98 b. 122** [9–7]

8. A cylinder with base diameter 10 and height 3 **a. 94.2 b. 251**

9. A square prism with height 42 and base 18 per side **a. 3024 b. 3672**

Find (a) the surface area and (b) the volume of a sphere with the given dimensions. Leave your answers in terms of π.

10. radius = 18 cm **a. 1296π cm² b. 7776π cm³**   **11.** diameter = 12 m **a. 144π m² b. 288π m³** [9–8]

Find the mass of the solid. **12. 8240 g   13. 181.76 g**

12. A sphere of aluminum with diameter 18 cm, density 2.70 g/cm³ [9–9]

13. A 4 cm by 4 cm by 20 cm block of pine, density of 0.568 g/cm³

Self-Test answers and Extra Practice are at the back of the book.

Areas and Volumes **347**

---

2. A cylinder: base diameter = 10 m, height = 6 m, volume = _?_ m³ **471**

3. A rectangular prism: 12 cm by 8 cm by 11 cm, volume = _?_ cm³, capacity = _?_ L **1056, 1.056**

Find the volume of the solid.

4. A cone with base radius 4 m and height 7 cm **117 cm³**

5. A pyramid with base area 60 cm² and height 7 cm **140 cm³**

6. A square pyramid with base 4.5 m on a side and height 5 m **33.75 m³**

Find the lateral area and the total surface area of the solid.

7. A rectangular prism with base 6 cm by 2 cm and height 3 cm **48 cm², 72 cm²**

8. A cylinder with base diameter 8 cm and height 20 cm **502 cm², 602 cm²**

9. A square prism with height 60 cm and base 9 cm per side **2160 cm², 2322 cm²**

Find the surface area and the volume of a sphere with the given dimensions. Leave your answers in terms of π.

10. radius = 21 m **1764π m², 12,348π m³**

11. diameter = 18 cm **324π cm², 972π cm³**

Find the mass of the solid.

12. a 2 cm by 20 cm by 4 cm block of pine, density 0.56 g/cm³ **89.6 g**

13. A sphere of aluminum with diameter 10 cm, density 2.70 g/cm³ **1.41 kg**

Locating Points on Earth

We can think of Earth as a sphere rotating on an axis that is a diameter with endpoints at the North Pole (N) and South Pole (S). A **great circle** on a sphere is the intersection of the sphere with a plane that contains the center of the sphere. The great circle whose plane is perpendicular to Earth's axis is called the **equator.** The equator divides Earth into the Northern and Southern Hemispheres.

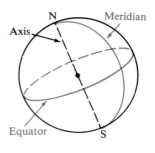

Semicircles with endpoints at the North and South Poles are called **meridians.** The meridian that passes through Greenwich, England, is called the **prime meridian.** The great circle on which the prime meridian lies divides Earth into the Eastern and Western Hemispheres.

The prime meridian and the equator are important parts of a degree-coordinate system that we use to describe the location of points on Earth. A series of circles whose planes are parallel to the equator, called **parallels of latitude,** identify the **latitude** of a point as a number of degrees between 0° and 90° *north* or *south of the equator.* The meridians identify the **longitude** of a point as the number of degrees between 0° and 180° *east* or *west of the prime meridian.*

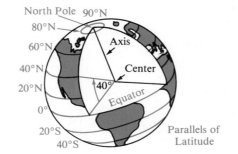

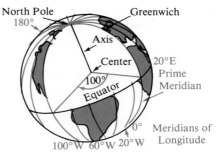

Thus, each point on the surface of Earth can be assigned an ordered pair of degree-coordinates: (latitude, longitude).

The flat map below, called a **Mercator projection,** shows the meridians and parallels of latitude marked off in 10° intervals as perpendicular lines. Notice that the city of Paris, France, is located at about 48°N, 2°E.

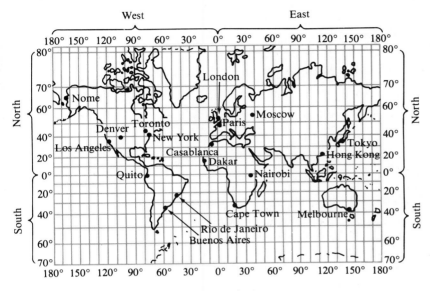

Mercator projection

Use the map above to name the major city at the location specified.

New York
1. 40°N, 74°W

Buenos Aires
2. 34°S, 58°W

Rio de Janeiro
3. 23°S, 43°W

Cape Town
4. 34°S, 18°E

5. 55°N, 37°E

6. 37°S, 145°E

7. 33°N, 7°W

8. 34°N, 118°W

Moscow

Melbourne

Casablanca

Los Angeles

Give the latitude and longitude of the following cities to the nearest 5°.

40°N, 105°W
9. Denver

0°, 35°E
10. Nairobi

55°N, 0°
11. London

0°, 80°W
12. Quito

13. Dakar

14. Toronto

15. Nome

16. Hong Kong

15°N, 15°W

45°N, 80°W

65°N, 165°W

20°N, 115°E

Career Activity

Ancient navigators determined their position by observing the sun and the stars. Modern navigators use much more sophisticated methods. If you were a navigator today what are some of the instruments and methods you might use?

Areas and Volumes **349**

Chapter Review

True or false?

1. A triangle with base 26 cm and height 36 cm has area 936 cm². **False**   [9–1]

2. A rectangular field that is 7 km by 12.8 km has area 8960 ha. **True**

3. A parallelogram with area 308 cm² and height 14 cm has base 22 cm. **True**   [9–2]

4. A trapezoid with bases 23 m and 37 m and height 25 m has area 1500 m². **False**

5. A circle with diameter 24 has area 576 π. **False**   [9–3]

6. A semicircle with radius 18 has area 162 π. **True**

7. A figure cannot have more than one line of symmetry. **False**   [9–4]

8. If a figure is symmetric with respect to a point, then any line drawn through the point of symmetry divides the figure into two parts of equal area. **True**

Complete. Use $\pi \approx 3.14$ when needed.

9. A rectangular prism has a base 12 cm by 14 cm and height 23 cm. Its volume is __?__. **3864 cm³**   [9–5]

10. A cylinder has base radius 4 cm and height 15 cm. Its capacity is __?__ liters. **0.754 L**

11. A cone with base diameter 6 and height 4.8 has volume __?__. **45.2**   [9–6]

12. A pyramid with base area 160 cm² and height 24 cm has volume __?__. **1280 cm³**

13. A cylinder with base radius 7 and height 12 has lateral area __?__ π **168** and surface area __?__ π. **266**   [9–7]

14. A prism has height 16. Its bases are triangles with base 15, height 12, and remaining side 18. Its total surface area is __?__. **900**

15. A sphere with radius 24 has surface area __?__ π and volume __?__ π.   [9–8]

16. A sphere with radius 32 has surface area __?__ π and volume __?__ π.

17. A rectangular storage tank has dimensions 14 m by 6 m by 4 m. It is filled with helium of density 0.00018 kg/L. The mass of the helium is __?__. **60.48 kg**   [9–9]

15. 2304; 18,432   16. 4096; 43,690 $\frac{2}{3}$

350   *Chapter 9*

Chapter Test

Find the area of the region pictured or described. Leave your answers in terms of π when applicable. For Exercises 7 and 8, use the fact that the figures have symmetry.

1. Triangle: base = 56, height = 30 840   [9-1]

2. Rectangle: sides of 14 m and 23 m 322 m²

3. Trapezoid: bases 10.5 and 20, height = 15 228.75   [9-2]

4. Parallelogram: base = 34, height = 26 884

5. Circle: radius = 11 m 121π m²   **6.** Circle: Circumference = 12 π 36π   [9-3]

7. 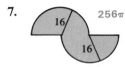 256π   **8.**  6π + 4   [9-4]

Find the volume. Use π ≈ 3.14.

9. Cylinder: base radius = 7.2 m, height = 5.8 m 944 m³   [9-5]

10. Prism: base area = 45 cm², height = 33 cm 1485 cm³

11. Cone: base diameter = 6 cm, height = 14 cm 132 cm³   [9-6]

12. Pyramid: square base 17 cm on a side, height = 21 cm 2023 cm³

Find (a) the lateral area and (b) the total surface area of each. Use π ≈ 3.14.

13. 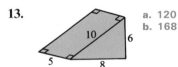 a. 120 b. 168   **14.** 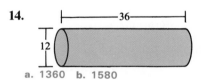 a. 1360 b. 1580   [9-7]

Find (a) the surface area and (b) the volume of a sphere with the given dimensions. Leave your answer in terms of π.

15. diameter = 18 cm a. 324π cm² b. 972π cm³   **16.** radius = 45 m a. 8100π m² b. 121,500π m³   [9-8]

17. Find the mass of a sphere with diameter 20 cm and density 8.9 g/cm³. Use π ≈ 3.14. 37,300 g   [9-9]

18. Find the mass of a cube 9 cm on each edge with density 0.56 g/cm³. 408.24 g

Areas and Volumes **351**

Cumulative Review (Chapters 1–9)

Exercises

Evaluate the expression if $a = 0.5$, $b = 5$, and $c = 2$.

1. abc 5

2. $a + b + c$ 7.5

3. $b \div a$ 10

4. $3a - 3b$ -13.5

5. ab^2 12.5

6. $c^2 + b^3$ 129

7. $6(a^2 - c^2)$ -22.5

8. $10a - \dfrac{b}{c}$ 2.5

Evaluate the expression if $x = \frac{1}{3}$, $y = 2\frac{3}{4}$, and $z = -\frac{3}{5}$.

9. $x + y$ $\frac{37}{12}$, or $3\frac{1}{12}$

10. xz $-\frac{1}{5}$

11. $3x + z$ $\frac{2}{5}$

12. $5z - x$ $-\frac{10}{3}$, or $-3\frac{1}{3}$

13. $x + 4y - 10z$ $\frac{52}{3}$, or $17\frac{1}{3}$

14. $6x + 8y + z$ $\frac{117}{5}$, or $23\frac{2}{5}$

15. $20z - (-y)$ $-\frac{37}{4}$, or $-9\frac{1}{4}$

16. $12x \div z$ $-\frac{20}{3}$, or $-6\frac{2}{3}$

Solve.

17. $15n + 7 > 52$

18. $6 - 2x < 21$

19. $38 \geq x - 2$

20. $\frac{n}{8} > 3$

21. $27 \leq 3x$

22. $3b + 5 < 56$

23. $4x + 7 = 35$ 7

24. $-y + 10 = 26$ -16

25. $\frac{3w}{7} = 9$ 21

26. Find the measure of each angle of an equilateral triangle.   60°, 60°, 60°

27. The measure of one angle in an isosceles triangle is 90°. Find the measures of the other angles.   45°, 45°

28. An equilateral triangle has perimeter 37.5 cm. Find the length of each side.   12.5 cm, 12.5 cm, 12.5 cm

29. What is 18% of 45?   8.1

30. 8 is what percent of 4000?   0.2%

31. 6.48 is what percent of 27?   24%

32. 105 is 42% of what number?   250

33. 316 is 0.5% of what number?   63,200

34. What is $34\frac{1}{2}$% of 1100?   379.5

Solve the equation for y in terms of x.

35. $4x + y = 18$ $y = 18 - 4x$

36. $x + 2y = 15$ $y = 7\frac{1}{2} - \frac{1}{2}x$

37. $6x - 6y = 50$ $y = -8\frac{1}{3} + x$

38. $\frac{x}{2} + y = 17$ $y = 17 - \frac{x}{2}$

39. $xy = 20$ $y = \frac{20}{x}$

40. $x^2 + y = 100$ $y = 100 - x^2$

Find the area of the circle described. Leave your answer in terms of π.

41. radius 14 cm 196π cm²

42. diameter 46 mm 529π mm²

43. radius 125 km $15{,}625\pi$ km²

44. diameter 286 m $20{,}449\pi$ m²

45. radius 1805 cm $3{,}258{,}025\pi$ cm²

46. diameter 305.6 m $23{,}347.84\pi$ m²

352   *Chapter 9*

Find the surface area and volume for the sphere described. Leave your answer in terms of π.

47. radius 8 256π; $\dfrac{2048}{3}\pi$ **48.** radius 15 900π; 4500π **49.** radius 36 5184π; $62{,}208\pi$

Problems

> **Problem Solving Reminders**
> Here are some reminders that may help you solve some of the problems on this page.
> - Determine what information is necessary to solve the problem.
> - Consider whether drawing a sketch will help.
> - If more than one method can be used to solve a problem, use one method to solve and one to check.

Solve.

1. The Aleutian Trench in the Pacific Ocean is 8100 m deep. Each story of an average skyscraper is about 4.2 m high. How many stories would a skyscraper as tall as the Aleutian Trench have? Round your answer to the nearest whole number. **1929 stories**

2. Beryl's Bike Repair Shop occupies an area that is 25 ft long and 35 ft wide. Beryl pays a monthly fee of $1.75 per square foot for rent. What is her monthly rent? **$1531.25**

3. A rancher bought 15 fence sections at $58 each to complete one side of a corral. If the length of the side is 375 m and each section is the same length, what is the length of a section? **25 m**

4. George had 15 flat tires last year. The cost of repairing each tire was $6.35 plus 5% tax. How much did George spend on tire repairs for the year? **$100.05**

5. A boat salesperson receives a commission of 4.5% of sales. What would be the commission on sales of $135,000? **$6075**

6. Gus is canning tomato sauce. He has 20 jars that have a diameter of 9 cm and height of 9 cm. If he must leave one centimeter of air space at the top of each jar, what volume of sauce can a jar hold? Use $\pi \approx 3.14$ and round the answer to three digits. **509 cm³**

7. The cost of an average basket of groceries rose from $78.80 in April to $82.74 in June. What was the percent of increase? **5%**

8. A roll of 36-exposure film costs $5.85. Processing for color prints costs $.42 per print. What is the total cost for film and processing of 36 prints? **$20.97**

Areas and Volumes   **353**

Find the circumference of the circle. Use $\pi \approx 3.14$.

17. $d = 8.25$ in.   **25.9 in.**

18. $d = 16.3$ cm   **51.2 cm**

19. $r = 10$ ft   **62.8 ft**

20. $r = 29.38$ km   **185 km**

Find the perimeter of each figure.

21. A regular pentagon with side 12.   **60**

22. A parallelogram with length 17 and width 8.   **50**

23. A regular octagon with side 3.8   **30.4**

24. A rhombus with side 16.   **64**

Complete.

25. In triangle ABC, $m\angle A = 63°$, $m\angle B = 46°$, and $m\angle C = \underline{\ ?\ }$ **71°**

26. In isosceles triangle RST, $m\angle R = 106°$, $m\angle S = \underline{\ ?\ }$, and $m\angle T = \underline{\ ?\ }$ **37°, 37°**

27. $\angle G$ and $\angle H$ are complementary. If $m\angle G$ is 14° less than $m\angle H$, $m\angle G = \underline{\ ?\ }$ **38°**

28. $\angle M$ and $\angle N$ are supplementary. If $m\angle M$ is 36° less than $m\angle N$, $m\angle N = \underline{\ ?\ }$.   **108°**

Match each equation with an ordered pair that satisfies the equation.

A. $(6, -4)$ B. $(-6, 6)$
C. $(-5, -4)$ D. $(-1, -2)$

29. $2y - 3x = 7$ **C**

30. $6 - 5y = 4x$ **B**

31. $2x - 4 = 3y$ **D**

32. $4x + 3y = 12$ **A**

State the equation of the boundary line.

33. $y \geq 4x - 3$ $y = 4x - 3$

34. $2y - 6x < 0$ $y = 3x$

10

Square Roots and Right Triangles

Suppose that the string attached to a kite, like the one shown in the photograph, was held nearly taut. Suppose also that you knew the length of the kite string and the angle that the string made with the ground. You could then find the height of the kite by using a ratio from trigonometry.

Trigonometric ratios can be used to determine angles and distances, both large and small. A method known as trigonometric parallax, for example, can be used to measure distances as great as those from Earth to stars neighboring our solar system. Trigonometry can also be used to describe certain phenomena such as the passage of light through transparent objects.

In this chapter, you will extend your knowledge of triangles and learn about trigonometric ratios. You will study some methods for finding angles and lengths.

Career Note

The job of surveyor is a career in which knowledge of right triangles and trigonometry plays an important role. Surveyors are responsible for establishing legal land boundaries. About half of their time is spent on location measuring sites and collecting data for maps and charts. The remaining part of their time is spent preparing reports, drawing maps, and planning future surveys.

354

Lesson Commentary
Chapter 10   Square Roots and Right Triangles

Overview

This chapter unifies virtually all of the major topics that have been presented up to this point. In particular, it builds on the earlier material covering positive and negative numbers, decimals, triangles, and area.

For most students, this will be the first introduction to square roots. They encounter the meaning of the term *square root,* and become familiar with the radical sign. They will learn to evaluate rational square roots. For irrational square roots, students will be able to approximate, using both an arithmetic method and a table of square roots.

Square root concepts and skills lead to the study of right triangles through the Pythagorean theorem. On the formal level, similar triangles will be a new concept for most students, and will require careful development. Similar triangles provide the basis for defining the basic trigonometric ratios. Finally, the process of solving a right triangle brings all the concepts of the chapter together in a single context. Solving a right triangle can involve the Pythagorean theorem, squares and square roots, trigonometric ratios, and the use of tables, all in one problem.

SQUARE ROOTS

10-1 Square Roots

Objective *for pages 356–357*

■ To estimate the positive square root of a positive number by determining the two consecutive integers between which the square root lies.

Teaching Suggestions

It will help to review arithmetic of positive and negative numbers before starting on square roots. This will make it easier to see that every positive number has two square roots, while a negative number has no real-number square root.

As an aid to understanding square roots, point out that, since the number $\sqrt{a}$ is the square root of a ($a \geq 0$), this means that $(\sqrt{a})^2 = a$. This provides a way to test whether $\sqrt{a}$ has a given value.

Students often find it interesting to realize that $\sqrt{a}$, where a is an integer, is rational only when a is the square of an integer. This has a bearing, among other things, on which entries in the square root table are exact and which are approximate. You may wish to point out that the relation between numbers and their square roots is not a linear one. This means that, for example, although 17 is halfway between 9 and 25, $\sqrt{17}$ is not 4, which is halfway between $\sqrt{9}$ and $\sqrt{25}$.

Related Activities

To strengthen understanding of squares and prime numbers, have students find the number of prime factors (page 111) of each integer from 1 to 25. Then have students categorize integers according to the number of prime factors. The only integers with one factor are primes. Have students examine the prime factors of perfect squares such as 9, 3×3, and 16, $2 \times 2 \times 2 \times 2$. They should be able to predict that

$$36 = 2 \times 2 \times 3 \times 3$$

is a perfect square but

$$32 = 2 \times 2 \times 2 \times 2 \times 2$$

is not.

To enhance understanding of the fact that $\sqrt{a^2} = |a|$, have students fill in a chart headed as shown.

a	a^2	$\sqrt{a^2}$	$|a|$
2	4	2	2
−2	4	2	2

Use a variety of both positive and negative numbers for a. Students should notice that when a is positive, $\sqrt{a^2} = a$; when a is negative, $\sqrt{a^2} = -a$. But in all cases, $\sqrt{a^2} = |a|$.

121

122

10-2 Approximating Square Roots

Objective for pages 358–360

■ To use the "divide-and-average" method to approximate the square root of a number.

Teaching Suggestions

Although the focus here is primarily on the divide-and-average algorithm itself, the concept behind it is one that students readily grasp. In essence, the idea is that if x is an approximation of $\sqrt{a}$, and $y = \frac{a}{x}$, then if $x < \sqrt{a}$, then $y > \sqrt{a}$, and the average of x and y is closer to $\sqrt{a}$ than either x or y is. This gives us a quick and manageable method for approximating $\sqrt{a}$. Moreover, it is a process that can be reiterated any number of times to achieve whatever degree of accuracy is desired for $\sqrt{a}$.

There are, of course, other techniques for approximating square roots. For example, in the "guess-and-correct" method one guesses a value for $\sqrt{a}$, then checks by squaring the guess. If the result is greater than a, the next guess should be lower, and vice versa. Some teachers may have learned a computational algorithm for approximating $\sqrt{a}$, in which digits are marked off in pairs, and so on. This algorithm is no longer encountered very often.

In this lesson we are approximating square roots to the tenths' place, not to the nearest tenth. The answers given are not rounded up, even when the digit in the next place is 5 or greater.

Related Activities

To extend students' understanding of irrational numbers, mention that irrational numbers are those that can be written as nonrepeating, nonterminating decimals. Encourage students to "invent" their own irrational numbers, such as 0.121221222 . . . and 1.213141516 . . .

To provide a challenge, have students prove that $\sqrt{2}$ is irrational. If $\sqrt{2}$ were rational, there would be integers p and q such that $\sqrt{2} = \frac{p}{q}$ where p and q have no common factor. Then $p^2 = 2q^2$. Consider the prime factorization of p^2 and $2q^2$. Since p^2 is a multiple of 2, it is even, and p must also be even. Since p and q have no common factor, q must be odd. If p is even, $p = 2m$, where m is

355b

an integer. Then $p^2 = 4m^2$ and $2q^2 = 4m^2$, so that $q^2 = 2m^2$. Now we have q^2 and therefore q is even, contradicting the earlier conclusion that q is odd. Thus the original supposition that $\sqrt{2}$ is rational is false, and $\sqrt{2}$ is irrational.

10-3 Using a Square Root Table

Objective for pages 361–363

■ To use a table or interpolation to find the approximate square root of a number.

Teaching Suggestions

It would be worthwhile to make it clear that every non-negative number has a nonnegative square root. This includes integers that are not perfect squares, as well as decimals and fractions. Some students have difficulty accepting the fact that $\sqrt{78}$, for example, is indeed a real number.

It may heighten understanding of the meaning of a square root to show that the square root table is also a table of squares, that is, if we locate a given number x in the column headed $\sqrt{N}$, then x^2 will be the entry in the N column. Inform students that very few entries in the square root table are exact values. In fact, only the square roots of numbers that are squares of integers $(1, 4, 9, 16, 25, \ldots)$ are exact. All other entries in the table are decimal approximations of irrational numbers.

Some students may benefit from organizing interpolation in a tabular format, as in the following determination of $\sqrt{7.3}$.

$$
\begin{array}{ccc}
 & x & \sqrt{x} \\
 & 8 & 2.828 \\
1.0 \begin{bmatrix} 7.3 \\ 0.3 \begin{bmatrix} \\ 7 \end{bmatrix} \end{bmatrix} & & \begin{bmatrix} ? \\ \\ 2.646 \end{bmatrix} d \; 0.182
\end{array}
$$

$$
\frac{0.3}{1.0} = \frac{d}{0.182} \qquad d = 0.3(0.182) = 0.0546
$$

$$
\sqrt{7.3} \approx 2.646 + d = 2.7006 \approx 2.701
$$

Square roots found by interpolation from a table may differ from those given by a calculator. Answers in each section of this chapter reflect the method taught in the lesson.

Related Activities

To put tables into a more general context, bring in a variety of tables for students to practice reading. These could include income tax and sales tax tables, tables of population growth, and so on.

To improve students' graphing skills, have them graph the equation $y = \sqrt{x}$, using the table of square roots to find the values.

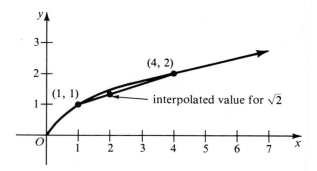

The graph is a "smooth" curve. Tell students that a curve shaped like this is said to be concave downward. Ask whether a segment joining two points on the curve will lie below or above the curve. Below Then point out that interpolation, basically, approximates a portion of the curve with a segment. Ask how the interpolated square root of a number compares to the actual square root. The interpolated value is always less.

10-4 The Pythagorean Theorem

Objective for pages 364–367

■ To use the Pythagorean theorem and its converse.

Teaching Suggestions

The Pythagorean theorem is probably the single best-known proposition of mathematics. It is used for such varied purposes as finding the distance between points in the coordinate plane, laying out playing fields, and calculating the lengths of roof rafters.

Demonstrate that the longest side of a triangle is always opposite the largest angle. A right angle in a triangle is always the largest angle, so the hypotenuse is the longest side.

Many students will not be familiar with the term *converse*. The conditional sentence "If p, then q" can be represented as $p \rightarrow q$. For this sentence we have the following related sentences, where $\sim p$ is the negation of p, read "not p."

Converse	$q \rightarrow p$	If q, then p.
Inverse	$\sim p \rightarrow \sim q$	If not p, then not q.
Contrapositive	$\sim q \rightarrow \sim p$	If not q, then not p.

Logically, the contrapositive is equivalent to the original sentence. The sentences $p \rightarrow q$ and $\sim q \rightarrow \sim p$ have the same meaning. If $p \rightarrow q$ is true, then $\sim q \rightarrow \sim p$ must also be true. The converses or inverses of some true sentences are true, but those of some true sentences are false. The Pythagorean theorem happens to be a proposition whose converse is true. The converse is useful for testing the given measures of the sides of a triangle to see if it is a right triangle.

As an example of a true conditional whose converse is not true, consider the statement

$$\text{If } x = 3, \text{ then } x^2 = 9.$$

The converse is

$$\text{If } x^2 = 9, \text{ then } x = 3,$$

which is false because $(-3)^2$ is also 9.

It may be helpful to develop two alternative forms of the Pythagorean theorem. If

$$c^2 = a^2 + b^2,$$

then we can also say

$$a^2 = c^2 - b^2 \quad \text{and} \quad b^2 = c^2 - a^2.$$

These forms of the theorem are suited for use when the objective is to solve for the length of a leg rather than the length of the hypotenuse.

In some of these exercises, such as Written Exercises 19–21 and Problems 1, 3, 4, 6, and 7, students need to find the square roots of numbers greater than 100. If students do not use calculators, refer them to Written Exercises 32–37 on page 363.

The introduction to Written Exercises 22–24 shows how to find Pythagorean Triples. The Computer Byte on page 387 presents a program for producing Pythagorean Triples.

Related Activities

To reinforce the meaning of the converse of the Pythagorean theorem, knot a piece of string 12 ft long to form a loop. Make a mark every foot. Ask one student to hold the string at any mark, another to hold it 3 ft from the first, and another to hold it 4 ft from the second. Have them pull the string until it is taut, and examine the resulting triangle. It is a right triangle because $3^2 + 4^2 = 5^2$. It has been said that the ancient Egyptians used such strings to lay out right angles when surveying their fields, although there is some question whether the historic evidence supports this assertion. Students interested in the history of mathematics might want to read Chapter 5 of *The Ascent of Man* by Jacob Bronowski.

To extend the Pythagorean theorem, consider triangles that are not right triangles. If the sides of a triangle have lengths a, b, and c, and the angle opposite the side of length c is obtuse, then $c^2 > a^2 + b^2$; if the angle is acute, then $c^2 < a^2 + b^2$. Determine whether the angle opposite side c is acute, right, or obtuse.

1. $a = 8$, $b = 5$, $c = 10$ obtuse
2. $a = 20$, $b = 21$, $c = 29$ right
3. $a = 7$, $b = 10$, $c = 14$ obtuse
4. $a = 2$, $b = 3$, $c = \sqrt{10}$ acute

Resource Book: Page 123 (Use After Page 367)

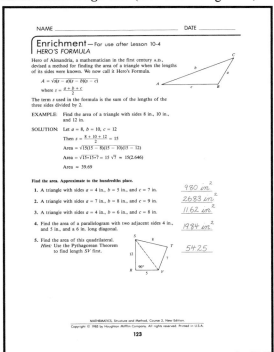

Resource Book: Page 124 (Use After Page 367)

NAME ______________________ DATE __________

Quiz 10A — Lessons 10-1 through 10-4

DIRECTIONS: **Write the letter of the correct answer in the space provided.**

If the given symbol names an integer, state the integer. If not, name the two consecutive integers between which the number lies.

1. $\sqrt{60}$ *[10–1]*
   a. 8, 9 b. 8 c. 7, 8 d. 7
2. $^{-}\sqrt{121}$
   a. $^{-}12$ b. $^{-}11$ c. 11, 12 d. $^{-}10$, $^{-}11$
3. $\sqrt{144} + \sqrt{81}$
   a. 225 b. 15 c. 12 d. 21
4. $^{-}\sqrt{84 - 16}$
   a. $^{-}8$ b. $^{-}7$, 8 c. $^{-}9$ d. $^{-}8$, $^{-}9$
5. Use the divide-and-average method to approximate $\sqrt{43.8}$ to the nearest tenth. *[10–2]*
   a. 6.6 b. 6.7 c. 6.5 d. 6.4

Use the table on page 498 of the student text and interpolation to approximate each square root to the nearest tenth.

6. $\sqrt{23}$ *[10–3]*
   a. 4.79 b. 4.8 c. 4.7 d. 4.796
7. $3\sqrt{52}$
   a. 12.2 b. 18.8 c. 7.2 d. 21.6
8. $\sqrt{8.2}$
   a. 2.9 b. 2.8 c. 2.7 d. 3.0

A right triangle has sides of lengths a, b, and c, with c the length of the hypotenuse. Find the length of the missing side.

9. $a = 15$, $b = 20$ *[10–4]*
   a. $c = 30$ b. $c = 25$ c. $c = 35$ d. $c = 625$
10. $b = 60$, $c = 68$
    a. $a = 90.69$ b. $a = 1024$ c. $a = 16$ d. $a = 32$

ANSWERS

1. c (10)
2. b (10)
3. d (10)
4. d (10)
5. a (10)
6. b (10)
7. d (10)
8. a (10)
9. b (10)
10. d (10)

MATHEMATICS, Structure and Method, Course 2, New Edition.

124

RIGHT TRIANGLES

10-5 Similar Triangles

***Objective** for pages 368–372*

■ To apply facts about similar triangles.

Teaching Suggestions

Similarity as a formal concept is not familiar to most students. To give a general flavor, discuss various sized photo enlargements, maps of the same area with different scales, and scale models. These are all examples of similar figures.

Two triangles are similar if they have three pairs of congruent angles. (In fact, if two pairs of angles are congruent, the third pair must be congruent.) Do not imply, however, that pairs of equal angles guarantee similarity for other figures. A square and a rectangle have four pairs of equal angles but may easily not be similar. On the other hand, all squares are similar.

Students are sometimes reluctant to accept that the way similarity is expressed makes a difference. Referring to the triangles in the diagram on page 368, it is certainly true that $\triangle DEF$ can also be called $\triangle DFE$, $\triangle FDE$, and so on. However, if we intend to convey information about correspondence of sides and angles, we are not free to use any name for this triangle once a name has been chosen for the other triangle. We can state any of the following similarities:

$$\triangle ABC \sim \triangle DEF \qquad \triangle ACB \sim \triangle DFE$$
$$\triangle BCA \sim \triangle EFD \qquad \triangle BAC \sim \triangle EDF$$
$$\triangle CAB \sim \triangle FDE \qquad \triangle CBA \sim \triangle FED$$

You may want to show how much information is contained in a statement of similarity even without reference to a diagram. For example, if $\triangle FOR \sim \triangle NXT$, then:

$$\angle F \cong \angle N \qquad \angle O \cong \angle X \qquad \angle R \cong \angle T$$

and $\frac{FO}{NX} = \frac{OR}{XT} = \frac{FR}{NT}$.

If you assign Written Exercise 20, ask why the triangles are similar. You may need to review parallel lines, page 200. $\overline{PQ} \parallel \overline{AB}$, so

$$\angle CPQ \cong \angle CAB \text{ and } \angle PQC \cong \angle ABC$$

because they are alternate interior angles.

$$\angle QCP \cong \angle BCA$$

because they are vertical angles.

Related Activities

To apply similar triangles to a practical problem, use similar triangles for "indirect measurement," that is, to find the heights of objects that cannot actually be measured. At any given time, the triangles determined by objects and their shadows are similar. To find a, the unknown height of object A, use an object B of known height b, such as a meter stick. Measure c, the length of A's shadow, and d, the length of B's shadow. Then since $\frac{a}{c} = \frac{b}{d}$, we have $a = \frac{bc}{d}$ and can readily determine the height a.

To illustrate the idea of similar figures in general, use an opaque projector to project the same picture from several different distances. Trace the image on paper or on the chalkboard. This will give several similar copies of the same original, all of different sizes.

10-6 Special Right Triangles

Objective *for pages 373–377*

■ To find the lengths of missing sides of a 45° right triangle, and of a 30°-60° right triangle, given the length of one side.

Teaching Suggestions

Although the point was made in the last section, it would be worth repeating that any two right triangles with one pair of equal acute angles must be similar to each other. This gives us, in the current section, a property that is true of all 45° right triangles and another that is true of all 30°-60° right triangles. This similarity property is also involved later, when we define trigonometric ratios as functions of angles and not of particular triangles.

For the sake of thoroughness, you might present an example of a 45° right triangle for which the hypotenuse is known and a leg is to be found. Here, since the hypotenuse is $\sqrt{2}$ times the leg, it becomes necessary to divide by $\sqrt{2}$ to find the leg. Similarly, you might give the leg opposite the 60° angle in a 30°-60° right triangle. Then this leg is divided by $\sqrt{3}$ to find the shorter leg, which is in turn doubled to find the hypotenuse.

Students may not realize at first that it matters which leg is involved in a 30°-60° right triangle problem. Emphasize that the hypotenuse is twice the leg opposite the 30° angle, not just any leg. Conversely, the leg opposite the 30° angle is half the hypotenuse.

The rule against radicals in denominators is a convention, an agreement people have made about how something is done. As such it is similar to the order of operations convention and the convention that $-\frac{1}{2}$ is preferred to $\frac{-1}{2}$ or $\frac{1}{-2}$. Do not try to justify the procedure as one that makes calculation easier. With a calculator it is no more difficult to calculate $\frac{6}{\sqrt{3}}$ than $2\sqrt{3}$. The original intent of the rule may have been to make quick decimal approximations easy to find using mental arithmetic. In this case, $2\sqrt{3} \approx 2(1.73) = 3.46$.

When an expression with a radical in the denominator is rewritten, the equivalent expression is often a fraction. For example, $\frac{3}{\sqrt{5}} = \frac{3\sqrt{5}}{5}$.

In Class Exercise 12, most students will use the same procedure as in Example 1: $x = 10\sqrt{2}$; $y = 10\sqrt{2} \div \sqrt{2} = 10$. Some students may realize that each triangle is isosceles, so the length of the unmarked leg of the lower triangle is 10. Since the measure of each unmarked angle is 45°, the quadrilateral is a rectangle; since two consecutive sides are congruent it is a square and $y = 10$. Thus $x = 10\sqrt{2}$.

Related Activities

To give concrete meaning to irrational numbers and increase facility with the Pythagorean theorem, have students use rulers and protractors to construct a spiral as shown.

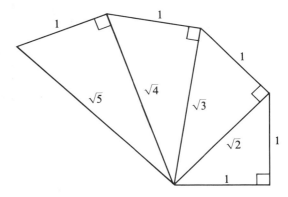

Choose a unit and construct a second leg of the same length perpendicular to it. Then draw the hypotenuse and determine its length using the Pythagorean theorem. Using this hypotenuse as a leg, construct another unit leg, and find the new hypotenuse. This process produces a spiral with a series of hypotenuses of lengths $\sqrt{2}$, $\sqrt{3}$, $\sqrt{4}$, $\sqrt{5}$, ...

10-7 Trigonometric Ratios

Objective *for pages 378–381*

■ To calculate the sine, cosine, and tangent of an acute angle of a right triangle, given the lengths of two sides.

Teaching Suggestions

Students need to realize that a particular side of a right triangle is not always the opposite side, for example. The leg that is the opposite side for one acute angle is the adjacent side for the other. For this reason we see that if $\angle A$ and $\angle B$ are the acute angles of a right triangle, then $\sin A = \cos B$ and $\cos A = \sin B$. Make sure students realize that our definitions apply only to the acute angles, not the right angle.

Some students assume that $\sin 30°$, $\cos 45°$, and so on are variables. Actually these are numbers. Point out that for any x between $0°$ and $90°$ both the cosine and the sine of x are real numbers between 0 and 1. With more able students you might investigate the behavior of $\tan x$ near $0°$ and $90°$. Since the tangent is $\frac{\text{opposite}}{\text{adjacent}}$, then as x approaches $90°$, $\tan x$ approaches infinity. (Opposite becomes larger, adjacent becomes smaller.) Conversely, as x approaches $0°$, $\tan x$ approaches 0. (Opposite becomes smaller, adjacent becomes larger.)

Remind students that they can use square root tables if necessary to approximate ratios containing radicals. Of course, some students will prefer to use a calculator.

Many students find the mnemonic SOH CAH TOA useful for remembering the definitions: $\sin x = \frac{\text{opposite}}{\text{hypotenuse}}$, $\cos x = \frac{\text{adjacent}}{\text{hypotenuse}}$, $\tan x = \frac{\text{opposite}}{\text{adjacent}}$.

The purpose of Written Exercises 15–17 is to apply the right triangle properties and trigonometric ratios to obtain an unknown value of a trigonometric ratio from one that is known. Answers will vary slightly depending on when students round.

Related Activities

By completing the chart below, students can discover that $\sin^2 A + \cos^2 A = 1$.

A	sin A	cos A	(sin A)²	(cos A)²
30°	0.5	$\frac{\sqrt{3}}{2}$	0.25	0.75
45°	$\frac{\sqrt{2}}{2}$	$\frac{\sqrt{2}}{2}$	0.5	0.5
60°	$\frac{\sqrt{3}}{2}$	0.5	0.75	0.25

To approximate trigonometric functions of angles besides $30°$, $45°$, and $60°$, have students draw x- and y-axes, and a large circle with center at the origin and radius 1. Use a scale so that 10 graph paper squares represent a unit.

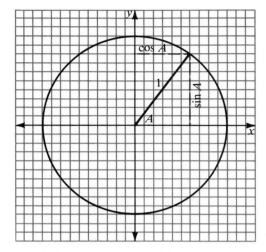

To evaluate functions of a given angle A, use a protractor to draw the angle in standard position. Since the radius of the circle is 1, $\sin A$ is the y-coordinate of the point where the second ray of the angle crosses the circle. These values can be approximated fairly accurately directly from the graph, and will give students an idea of where the values in trigonometric tables, introduced in the next section, come from.

To provide a challenge, ask students to predict the range of values each trigonometric function can have. The sine and cosine must be between 0 and 1 because the hypotenuse is longer than either leg. The tangent can have any value. In later courses students will learn that trigonometric ratios can be applied to angles larger than $90°$ and to triangles that are in quadrants II, III, and IV of the coordinate plane.

10-8 Solving Right Triangles

Objective for pages 382–387

■ To solve a right triangle by using a trigonometric table.

Teaching Suggestions

A triangle is said to have six "parts": the three angles and the three sides. The parts of $\triangle ABC$ are $\angle A$, $\angle B$,

$\angle C$, $\overline{AB}$, $\overline{BC}$, and $\overline{AC}$. Solving a triangle means to find the measures of all of these parts. To solve a right triangle, we must be given at least two parts besides the right angle. In a right triangle we must only account for five of the six parts, since we already know that one angle is a right angle. Emphasize, as suggested earlier, that an expression like sin 75° or tan 25° is a number, or constant, not an unknown, or variable. To solve for a part of a right triangle we must find a relationship involving only one unknown term. For example, we can use $\tan A = \dfrac{\text{opposite}}{\text{adjacent}}$ when the opposite side is not known but the measures of $\angle A$ and the adjacent side are known.

Examination of the trigonometric table on page 499 can be interesting. Observe that the cosine column is just the reverse of the sine column, and that both vary between 0 and 1. Tangents run from nearly zero to a very large number indeed. The table does not use 0 before decimal points, as the rest of this book does. This is to familiarize students with this type of notation, which is generally used in tables of trigonometric functions.

For the Computer Byte on page 387, refer students back to the definition of Pythagorean Triples on page 366. In Exercise 5 they will discover that the smallest triple is 3, 4, 5.

Related Activities

To illustrate the pattern of variation of the sine function, have students graph the sines of angles from 0° to 90°.

To provide a challenge, have students use the sine function to derive an area formula for triangles that does not require knowing the altitude. Suppose $\triangle ABC$ is as shown.

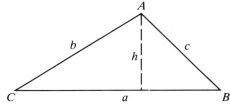

Then $\sin C = \dfrac{h}{b}$, or $h = b \sin C$. Also, area of $\triangle ABC = \frac{1}{2}ah = \frac{1}{2}ab \sin C$. Thus we can find areas of triangles directly from the sides and angles of the triangle, with no need to determine the altitude.

Resource Book: Pages 125–126 (Use After Page 387)

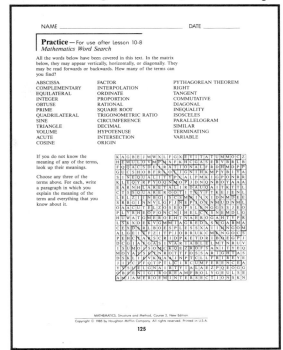

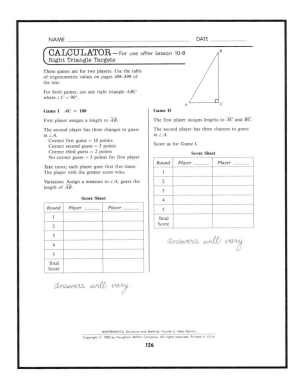

NAME _____   DATE _____

Quiz 10B — Lessons 10-5 through 10-8

DIRECTIONS: Write the letter of the correct answer in the space provided.

Exercises 1–4 refer to the diagram below. △QMT ~ △QVR. Complete.

1. $\frac{QT}{QR} = \frac{?}{QV}$ **[10-5]**
   a. MT   b. QM   c. VR   d. QT

2. $\frac{VR}{?} = \frac{QR}{QT}$
   a. QV   b. QT   c. MT   d. QM

3. QT = $\frac{?}{}$
   a. 4   b. 10   c. 6   d. 15

4. MV = $\frac{?}{}$
   a. 6   b. 24   c. 21   d. 15

In Exercises 5 and 6, give answers in terms of radicals with the radical in the numerator.

5. The hypotenuse of an isosceles right triangle is 8.2 in.   **[10-6]**
   long. What is the length of each leg?
   a. 16.4   b. 8.2√2   c. 4.1√2   d. 8.2√2

6. A ladder 12 m long that leans against a building makes an angle of 60° with the ground. How far up the wall does it reach?
   a. 6√2 m   b. 12√3 m   c. 6 m   d. 6√3 m

Exercises 7–8 refer to the diagram at the right. Complete.

7. sin M = $\frac{?}{}$ **[10-7]**
   a. $\frac{l}{i}$ b. $\frac{m}{i}$ c. $\frac{m}{f}$ d. $\frac{i}{m}$

8. tan F = $\frac{?}{}$
   a. $\frac{l}{i}$ b. $\frac{l}{f}$ c. $\frac{f}{m}$ d. $\frac{m}{i}$

Find the measure of the angle to the nearest degree and the length to the nearest tenth. Use the table on page 499 of the student text.

9. If l = 9 and m = 7, then f = $\frac{?}{}$ and ∠ M = $\frac{?}{}$ **[10-8]**
   a. 5.7, 39°   b. 11.4, 51°   c. 11.4, 39°   d. 5.7, 51°

ANSWERS
1. _b_ (10)
2. _c_ (10)
3. _b_ (10)
4. _a_ (10)
5. _c_ (15)
6. _d_ (15)
7. _b_ (10)
8. _c_ (10)
9. _d_ (10)

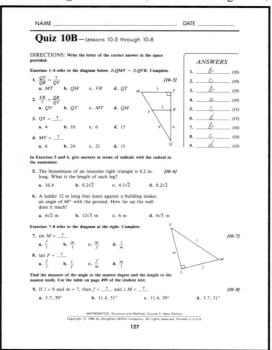

NAME _____   DATE _____

Review — Chapter 10

If the given symbol names an integer, state the integer. If not, name the two consecutive integers between which the number lies.

1. ⁻√169 _-13_   2. √88 _9,10_   3. √100 − 25 _8,9_ **[10-1]**

4. Use the divide-and-average method to approximate √110 to the nearest tenth. _10.5_   **[10-2]**

Use the table on page 498 of the student text and interpolation to approximate each square root to the nearest tenth.

5. 5√29 _26.9_   6. $\frac{1}{10}$√13 _0.4_   7. √14.6 _3.8_ **[10-3]**

The lengths of the sides of a triangle are given. Is it a right triangle?

8. 8, 20, 25 _no_   9. 24, 45, 51 _yes_ **[10-4]**

Solve. Give your answer to the nearest tenth.

10. Find the length of a diagonal of a 9-cm by 9-cm square. _12.7cm_

Exercises 12–14 refer to the diagram at the right. △ABC ~ △EDC. Complete.

11. $\frac{AC}{EC} = \frac{BC}{?}$ _DC_ **[10-5]**
12. ED = _15_
13. BD = _48_

Solve.

14. One day, Daniel, who is 160 cm tall, cast a shadow 200 cm long while Bob's shadow was 220 cm long. How tall is Bob? _176 cm_ **[10-6]**

Exercises 15–18 refer to the diagram at the right. Give all ratios in lowest terms.

15. x = _24_   16. sin T = $\frac{4}{5}$ **[10-7]**
17. cos T = $\frac{3}{5}$ 18. tan S = $\frac{3}{4}$

Exercises 19–22 refer to the diagram at the right. Find the measures of the angles to the nearest degree and the lengths to the nearest tenth. Use the tables on pages 498–499 in the student text.

19. If h = 14 and f = 10, find g. _9.8_ **[10-8]**
20. If h = 9 and ∠ F = 54°, find f. _7.3_
21. If f = 6 and ∠ G = 25°, find h. _6.6_
22. If f = 6 and g = 14, find ∠ F. _23°_

NAME _____   DATE _____

Test — Chapter 10

DIRECTIONS: Write the correct answer in the space provided.

If the given symbol names an integer, state the integer. If not, name the two consecutive integers between which the number lies.

1. ⁻√169   2. √400 − √144   3. √29 + 43   **[10-1]**

4. Use the divide-and-average method to approximate √28.6 **[10-2]** to the nearest tenth.

Solve. Give your answer to the nearest tenth.

5. Using interpolation and the table on page 498 in the **[10-3]** student text, √78.9 _?_ .

6. The area of a square wall is 90 m². What is the length of one side?

Is the triangle with sides of the given lengths a right triangle?

7. 8, 10, 12   8. 24, 45, 51   9. 5, 12, 14   **[10-4]**

Exercises 10–13 refer to the diagram at the right. △FGH ~ △NMP.

10. $\frac{FG}{MN} = \frac{HF}{?}$ **[10-5]**
11. Find the length of HF.
12. Find the length of MP.
13. Find the measure of ∠ F.

Give answers in terms of radicals with the radical in the numerator.

14. The hypotenuse of an isosceles right triangle has a length **[10-6]** of 16. How long is each leg?

15. Find the height of an equilateral triangle with sides 6 cm long.

Exercises 16–18 refer to the diagram at the right. Give all ratios in lowest terms.

16. sin P   17. tan R   18. cos R   **[10-7]**

Each of the equal legs of an isosceles triangle is 30 and the perimeter of the triangle is 96.

19. Find the length of the third leg of the isosceles triangle.

ANSWERS
1. _-13_ (5)
2. _8_ (5)
3. _8,9_ (5)
4. _5.3_ (5)
5. _8.9_ (5)
6. _9.5 m_ (5)
7. _no_ (5)
8. _yes_ (5)
9. _no_ (5)
10. _PN_ (5)
11. _9_ (5)
12. _16_ (5)
13. _108°_ (5)
14. _8√2_ (5)
15. _3√3_ (6)
16. $\frac{4}{5}$ (6)
17. $\frac{5}{3}$ (6)
18. $\frac{4}{5}$ (6)
19. _36_ (6)

NAME _____   DATE _____

Make-up Test — Chapter 10

DIRECTIONS: Write the correct answer in the space provided.

If the given symbol names an integer, state the integer. If not, name the two consecutive integers between which the number lies.

1. ⁻√49   2. √900 + √100   3. √170 − 43   **[10-1]**

4. Use the divide-and-average method to approximate √40.2 to **[10-2]** the nearest tenth.

Solve. Give the answer to the nearest tenth.

5. A square floor has an area of 47 m². Find the length of **[10-3]** one side.

6. Using interpolation and the table on page 498 in the student text, √56.8 _?_ .

Is the triangle with sides of the given lengths a right triangle?

7. 6, 9, 12   8. 5, 11, 13   9. 40, 75, 85   **[10-4]**

Exercises 10–13 refer to the diagram at the right. △ABC ~ △RST.

10. $\frac{AB}{SR} = \frac{?}{TS}$ **[10-5]**
11. Finish the length of TS.
12. Find the length of AC.
13. Find the measure of ∠ T.

Give answers in terms of radicals with the radical in the numerator.

14. The height of an equilateral triangle with sides **[10-6]** 14 cm long.

15. The hypotenuse of a 45° right triangle has a length of 24. How long is each leg?

Exercises 16–18 refer to the diagram at the right. Give all ratios in lowest terms.

16. tan G   17. cos F   18. sin G   **[10-7]**

Each of the base angles of an isosceles triangle is 37° and each of the equal sides is 30.

19. Find the perimeter of the isosceles triangle.   **[10-8]**
20. Find the vertex angle of the isosceles triangle.

ANSWERS
1. _-7_ (5)
2. _40_ (5)
3. _11,12_ (5)
4. _6.3_ (5)
5. _6.9 m_ (5)
6. _7.5_ (5)
7. _no_ (5)
8. _no_ (5)
9. _yes_ (5)
10. _BC_ (5)
11. _15_ (5)
12. _6_ (5)
13. _87°_ (5)
14. _7√3_ (5)
15. _12√2_ (5)
16. $\frac{5}{8}$ (5)
17. $\frac{15}{17}$ (5)
18. $\frac{15}{17}$ (5)
19. _108_ (5)
20. _106°_ (5)

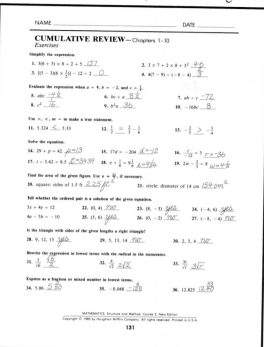

NAME _____ DATE _____

CUMULATIVE REVIEW—Chapters 1–10
Exercises

Simplify the expression.

1. $3(6 + 5) \times 8 \div 2 + 5$ 137

2. $3 \times 7 + 2 \times 8 + 3^2$ 46

3. $[(5 - 3)(6 \times \frac{1}{2})] - 12 \div 2$ 0

4. $4(7 - 9) \div (-8 - 4)$ $\frac{2}{3}$

Evaluate the expression when $a = 9$, $b = -2$, **and** $c = \frac{1}{4}$.

5. abc $-4\frac{1}{2}$

6. $bc + a$ $8\frac{1}{2}$

7. $ab \div c$ -72

8. c^2 $\frac{1}{16}$

9. $b^2 a$ 36

10. $-16bc$ 8

Use >, <, or = to make a true statement.

11. $5.324 \; \underline{<} \; 5.33$

12. $\frac{1}{2} \; \underline{=} \; \frac{2}{3} - \frac{1}{6}$

13. $-\frac{2}{5} \; \underline{>} \; -\frac{3}{4}$

Solve the equation.

14. $29 + p = 42$ $p = 13$

15. $17d = -204$ $d = -12$

16. $\frac{r}{-12} = 3$ $r = -36$

17. $t \div 3.62 = 9.5$ $t = 34.39$

18. $e + \frac{1}{8} = 9\frac{1}{6}$ $e = 9\frac{1}{24}$

19. $2w - \frac{2}{5} = 8$ $w = 4\frac{1}{5}$

Find the area of the given figure. Use $\pi \approx \frac{22}{7}$, **if necessary.**

20. square: sides of 1.5 ft $2.25 \, ft^2$

21. circle: diameter of 14 cm $154 \, cm^2$

Tell whether the ordered pair is a solution of the given equation.

$3x + 4y = 12$

22. $(0, 4)$ no

23. $(8, -3)$ yes

24. $(-4, 6)$ yes

$4a - 5b = -10$

25. $(5, 6)$ yes

26. $(0, -2)$ no

27. $(-8, -4)$ no

Is the triangle with sides of the given lengths a right triangle?

28. 9, 12, 15 yes

29. 5, 13, 14 no

30. 2, 3, 4 no

Rewrite the expression in lowest terms with the radical in the numerator.

31. $\frac{3}{\sqrt{6}}$ $\frac{\sqrt{6}}{2}$

32. $\frac{4}{\sqrt{2}}$ $2\sqrt{2}$

33. $\frac{3r}{\sqrt{r}}$ $3\sqrt{r}$

Express as a fraction or mixed number in lowest terms.

34. 5.06 $5\frac{3}{50}$

35. -0.048 $-\frac{6}{125}$

36. 12.825 $12\frac{33}{40}$

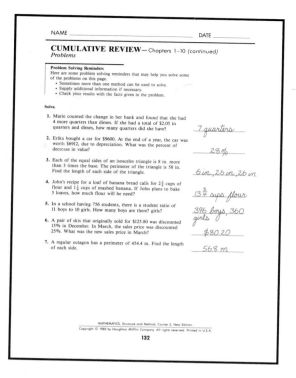

NAME _____ DATE _____

CUMULATIVE REVIEW—Chapters 1–10 *(continued)*
Problems

Problem Solving Reminders
Here are some problem solving reminders that may help you solve some of the problems on this page.
- Sometimes more than one method can be used to solve.
- Supply additional information if necessary.
- Check your results with the facts given in the problem.

Solve.

1. Marie counted the change in her bank and found that she had 4 more quarters than dimes. If she had a total of $2.05 in quarters and dimes, how many quarters did she have? *7 quarters*

2. Erika bought a car for $9600. At the end of a year, the car was worth $6912, due to depreciation. What was the percent of decrease in value? *28%*

3. Each of the equal sides of an isosceles triangle is 8 in. more than 3 times the base. The perimeter of the triangle is 58 in. Find the length of each side of the triangle. *6 in., 26 in., 26 in.*

4. John's recipe for a loaf of banana bread calls for $2\frac{3}{4}$ cups of flour and $1\frac{1}{4}$ cups of mashed banana. If John plans to bake 5 loaves, how much flour will he need? *$13\frac{3}{4}$ cups flour*

5. In a school having 756 students, there is a student ratio of 11 boys to 10 girls. How many boys are there? girls? *396 boys, 360 girls*

6. A pair of skis that originally sold for $125.80 was discounted 15% in December. In March, the sales price was discounted 25%. What was the new sales price in March? *$80.20*

7. A regular octagon has a perimeter of 454.4 m. Find the length of each side. *56.8 m*

355j

10-1 Square Roots

Recall that we can write $b \times b$ as b^2 and call it the *square* of *b*. The **square root** of b^2 is the factor *b*. A given number *a* has *b* as a square root if

$$b^2 = a.$$

Thus 9 has 3 as a square root because $3^2 = 9$.

Every positive number has two square roots, and these are opposites of each other. For example, the square roots of 25 are 5 and -5 because

$$5^2 = 5 \times 5 = 25 \quad \text{and} \quad (-5)^2 = (-5) \times (-5) = 25.$$

The only square root of 0 is 0 because $b \times b = 0$ only when $b = 0$.

In this chapter we will work mostly with positive square roots. We use $\sqrt{a}$ to denote the *positive* square root of *a*. Thus $\sqrt{25} = 5$, not -5. A symbol such as $2\sqrt{25}$ means *2 times the positive square root of 25*. The negative square root of 25 is $-\sqrt{25}$, or -5.

Negative numbers have no real-number square roots because no real number has a square that is negative.

If $\sqrt{a}$ is an integer, we call *a* a **perfect square.** For example, 36 is a perfect square because $\sqrt{36}$ is the integer 6. Also, 144 is a perfect square because $\sqrt{144} = 12$.

If *a* is not a perfect square, we can estimate $\sqrt{a}$ by finding the two consecutive integers between which the square root lies. In the process, we use the fact that the smaller of two positive numbers has the smaller positive square root.

EXAMPLE Between which two consecutive integers does $\sqrt{40}$ lie?

Solution 40 lies between the consecutive perfect squares 36 and 49.

$$36 < 40 < 49$$
$$\sqrt{36} < \sqrt{40} < \sqrt{49}$$
$$\text{Thus} \quad 6 < \sqrt{40} < 7.$$

Class Exercises

Read each symbol.

1. "The positive square root of 7"
2. "3 times the positive square root of 10"
3. "The negative square root of 81"
4. "The positive square root of 64"
5. "2 times the positive square root of 14"

1. $\sqrt{7}$ 2. $3\sqrt{10}$ 3. $-\sqrt{81}$ 4. $\sqrt{64}$ 5. $2\sqrt{14}$

356 *Chapter 10*

If the given symbol names an integer, state the integer. If not, name the two consecutive integers between which the number lies.

6. $\sqrt{16}$ 4   **7.** $-\sqrt{36}$ −6   **8.** $\sqrt{21}$ 4 and 5   **9.** $\sqrt{70}$ 8 and 9   **10.** $\sqrt{50}$ 7 and 8

11. $-\sqrt{49}$ −7   **12.** $\sqrt{81}$ 9   **13.** $\sqrt{69}$ 8 and 9   **14.** $-\sqrt{144}$ −12   **15.** $\sqrt{169}$ 13

Written Exercises

If the given symbol names an integer, state the integer. If not, name the two consecutive integers between which the number lies.

A   **1.** $\sqrt{43}$ 6 and 7   **2.** $\sqrt{64}$ 8   **3.** $-\sqrt{16}$ −4   **4.** $\sqrt{24}$ 4 and 5   **5.** $\sqrt{1}$ 1

6. $\sqrt{0}$ 0   **7.** $-\sqrt{6^2}$ −6   **8.** $\sqrt{13}$ 3 and 4   **9.** $\sqrt{54}$ 7 and 8   **10.** $\sqrt{9}$ 3

11. $\sqrt{30}$ 5 and 6   **12.** $\sqrt{48}$ 6 and 7   **13.** $\sqrt{15}$ 3 and 4   **14.** $\sqrt{8^2}$ 8   **15.** $\sqrt{2}$ 1 and 2

16. $\sqrt{25} + \sqrt{16}$ 9   **17.** $\sqrt{100} - \sqrt{49}$ 3   **18.** $\sqrt{144} + \sqrt{25}$ 17

19. $\sqrt{79 - 61}$ 4 and 5   **20.** $-\sqrt{66 - 2}$ −8   **21.** $\sqrt{100 - 19}$ 9

Replace the __?__ with $<$, $>$, or $=$ to make a true statement.

EXAMPLE $\sqrt{9} + \sqrt{25} \underline{\ \ ?\ \ } \sqrt{9 + 25}$

Solution $\sqrt{9} + \sqrt{25} = 3 + 5 = 8; \ \sqrt{9 + 25} = \sqrt{34} < 8.$
Thus $\sqrt{9} + \sqrt{25} > \sqrt{9 + 25}.$

B   **22.** $\sqrt{9} + \sqrt{16} \underline{\ \ ?\ \ }^{>} \sqrt{9 + 16}$ **23.** $\sqrt{16} + \sqrt{4} \underline{\ \ ?\ \ }^{>} \sqrt{16 + 4}$

24. $\sqrt{16} - \sqrt{9} \underline{\ \ ?\ \ }^{<} \sqrt{16 - 9}$ **25.** $\sqrt{25} - \sqrt{9} \underline{\ \ ?\ \ }^{<} \sqrt{25 - 9}$

26. $\sqrt{4} \times \sqrt{9} \underline{\ \ ?\ \ }^{=} \sqrt{4 \times 9}$ **27.** $\sqrt{25} \times \sqrt{4} \underline{\ \ ?\ \ }^{=} \sqrt{25 \times 4}$

28. $2\sqrt{2} \underline{\ \ ?\ \ }^{>} \sqrt{2 \times 2}$ **29.** $3\sqrt{12} \underline{\ \ ?\ \ }^{>} \sqrt{3 \times 12}$

Evaluate the expression.

C   **30.** $(\sqrt{25})^2$ 25   **31.** $(\sqrt{81})^2$ 81   **32.** $(\sqrt{49})^2$ 49   **33.** $(\sqrt{11})^2$ 11   **34.** $(\sqrt{2})^2$ 2

Review Exercises

Divide. Round to the nearest hundredth.

1. $44 \div 6.7$ 6.57   **2.** $35 \div 5.9$ 5.93   **3.** $72 \div 8.3$ 8.67   **4.** $96 \div 9.5$ 10.11

5. $147 \div 12.3$ 11.95   **6.** $230 \div 14.7$ 15.65   **7.** $0.0165 \div 0.13$ 0.13   **8.** $0.68 \div 0.81$ 0.84

Square Roots and Right Triangles   **357**

Additional A Exercises

If the given symbol names an integer, state the integer. If not, name the two consecutive integers between which the number lies.

1. $-\sqrt{16}$ −4

2. $\sqrt{61}$ 7 and 8

3. $\sqrt{6^2}$ 6

4. $\sqrt{18}$ 4 and 5

5. $\sqrt{75}$ 8 and 9

6. $-\sqrt{81}$ −9

7. $\sqrt{90}$ 9 and 10

Suggested Assignments

Minimum
  357/1–25
  357/Rev. 1–8

Average
  357/1–32
  357/Rev. 1–7 odd

Maximum
  357/1–34

Supplementary Materials

Practice Masters, p. 45

Reading Mathematics

Students will learn the meaning of the following mathematical terms in this lesson: *divide and average method, irrational number, real number.*

Chalkboard Examples

Between which two integers does the number lie?

1. $\sqrt{72}$ **8, 9**

2. $\sqrt{39}$ **6, 7**

3. $\sqrt{21.6}$ **4, 5**

Give the next estimate for the square root.

4. $\sqrt{42}$ $6\overline{)42}$ **6.5**

5. $\sqrt{31.7}$ $5.7\overline{)31.7}$ **5.63**

Approximate to the tenths' place.

6. $\sqrt{18}$ **4.2**

7. $\sqrt{87}$ **9.3**

10-2 Approximating Square Roots

To get a close approximation of a square root, we can use the *divide-and-average* method. This method is based on the fact that

$$\text{if } \sqrt{a} = b, \text{ then } a = b \times b \text{ and } \frac{a}{b} = b.$$

In other words, when we divide a number a by its square root b, the quotient is b. When we use an estimate for b that is *less* than b for a divisor, the quotient is then *greater* than b. The average of the divisor and quotient can be used as a new estimate for b.

EXAMPLE 1   Approximate $\sqrt{55}$ to the tenths' place.

Solution

Step 1   To estimate $\sqrt{55}$, first find the two integers between which $\sqrt{55}$ lies.

$$\begin{array}{ccccc} 49 & < & 55 & < & 64 \\ \sqrt{49} & < & \sqrt{55} & < & \sqrt{64} \\ 7 & < & \sqrt{55} & < & 8 \end{array}$$

Since 55 is closer to 49 than to 64, you might try 7.3 as an estimate of $\sqrt{55}$.

Step 2   Divide 55 by the estimate, 7.3. Compute to one more place than you want in the final answer.

$$\begin{array}{r} 7.53 \\ 7.3\overline{)55.0\,00} \\ \underline{51\ 1} \\ 3\ 90 \\ \underline{3\ 65} \\ 2\ 50 \\ \underline{2\ 19} \\ 31 \end{array}$$

Step 3   Average the divisor and quotient.

$$\frac{7.3 + 7.53}{2} \approx 7.42$$

Use the average as the next estimate and repeat Steps 2 and 3 until your divisor and quotient agree in the tenths' place.

In this case, use 7.42 as your next estimate and divide.

$$\begin{array}{r} 7.41 \\ 7.42\overline{)55.00\,00} \\ \underline{51\ 94} \\ 3\ 06\ 0 \\ \underline{2\ 96\ 8} \\ 9\ 20 \\ \underline{7\ 42} \\ 1\ 78 \end{array}$$

As you can see, $\sqrt{55} \approx 7.4$ to the tenths' place.

358   *Chapter 10*

We can approximate $\sqrt{55}$ to whatever decimal place we wish by repeating the steps shown in Example 1 on the previous page. Because $\sqrt{55}$ is a nonterminating, nonrepeating decimal, we say that $\sqrt{55}$ is an **irrational number.** Together, irrational and rational numbers form the set of **real numbers.** Other irrational numbers are discussed on page 133.

To find the square root of a number that is not an integer by the divide-and-average method, we use the same steps as in Example 1. The first step, finding the two integers between which a square root lies, is shown below.

EXAMPLE 2 Complete the first step in estimating each square root.

        a. $\sqrt{12.3}$ **b.** $\sqrt{0.7}$

Solution The first step in estimating a square root is to find the two integers between which it lies.

a.
$$9 < 12.3 < 16$$
$$\sqrt{9} < \sqrt{12.3} < \sqrt{16}$$
$$3 < \sqrt{12.3} < 4$$

b.
$$0 < 0.7 < 1$$
$$\sqrt{0} < \sqrt{0.7} < \sqrt{1}$$
$$0 < \sqrt{0.7} < 1$$

Class Exercises

Give the first digit of the square root.

1. $\sqrt{7}$ 2   **2.** $\sqrt{11}$ 3   **3.** $\sqrt{30}$ 5   **4.** $\sqrt{50}$ 7   **5.** $\sqrt{94}$
                                                                                          9

Give the next estimate for the square root of the dividend.

EXAMPLE
$$3.8\overline{)15.0\,00} \quad \text{quotient } 3.95$$

Solution
$$\frac{3.8 + 3.95}{2} \approx 3.88$$

Thus 3.88 is the next estimate.

6. $2\overline{)4.8}$ quotient 2.4   2.2   **7.** $3\overline{)11}$ quotient 3.7   3.35   **8.** $5\overline{)28.5}$ quotient 5.7   5.35   **9.** $4.3\overline{)21.0\,00}$ quotient 4.59   4.88

10. $14\overline{)225}$ quotient 16   15   **11.** $0.7\overline{)0.53}$ quotient 0.76   0.73   **12.** $0.6\overline{)0.3}$ quotient 0.5   0.55   **13.** $0.9\overline{)0.83}$ quotient 0.92   0.91

Square Roots and Right Triangles   **359**

Additional A Exercises

Approximate to the tenths' place.

1. $\sqrt{11}$ 3.3
2. $\sqrt{44}$ 6.6
3. $\sqrt{8.1}$ 2.8
4. $\sqrt{86}$ 9.2
5. $\sqrt{2.5}$ 1.5
6. $\sqrt{56.8}$ 7.5

Suggested Assignments

Minimum
Day 1: 360/1–12
Day 2: 360/13–22
      360/Rev. 1–8

Average
Day 1: 360/1–19 odd; 21–24
Day 2: 360/25–34
      360/Rev. 2–8 even
      360/Calculator Key-In

Maximum
Day 1: 360/1–19 odd; 21–24
Day 2: 360/25–36
      360/Calculator Key-In

Supplementary Materials

Practice Masters, p. 45

Written Exercises

Approximate to the tenths' place.

A
1. $\sqrt{11}$ 3.3
2. $\sqrt{13}$ 3.6
3. $\sqrt{33}$ 5.7
4.8 **4.** $\sqrt{23}$

5. $\sqrt{8}$ 2.8
6. $\sqrt{5}$ 2.2
7. $\sqrt{26}$ 5.1
6.4 **8.** $\sqrt{42}$

9. $\sqrt{57}$ 7.5
10. $\sqrt{75}$ 8.6
11. $\sqrt{91}$ 9.5
8.3 **12.** $\sqrt{69}$

13. $\sqrt{5.7}$ 2.3
14. $\sqrt{7.5}$ 2.7
15. $\sqrt{9.1}$ 3.0
2.6 **16.** $\sqrt{6.9}$

17. $\sqrt{8.2}$ 2.8
18. $\sqrt{4.6}$ 2.1
19. $\sqrt{3.5}$ 1.8
1.2 **20.** $\sqrt{1.6}$

B
21. $\sqrt{152}$ 12.3
22. $\sqrt{285}$ 16.8
23. $\sqrt{705}$ 26.5
18.1 **24.** $\sqrt{328}$

25. $\sqrt{15.2}$ 3.9
26. $\sqrt{28.5}$ 5.3
27. $\sqrt{70.5}$ 8.4
5.6 **28.** $\sqrt{32.4}$

29. $\sqrt{0.4}$ 0.6
30. $\sqrt{0.6}$ 0.7
31. $\sqrt{0.05}$ 0.2
0.4 **32.** $\sqrt{0.21}$

Approximate to the hundredths' place.

33. $\sqrt{2}$ 1.41
34. $\sqrt{3}$ 1.73
35. $\sqrt{5}$ 2.23
3.16 **36.** $\sqrt{10}$

Review Exercises

Simplify.

1. $4(11 - 2) + 3(2) + 2(5 + 3)$ 58
2. $5(81 \div 9) - 36 + 11$ 20

3. $7.3 + (9.14 - 6.91) - 2.81$ 6.72
4. $11.32 - 67(8.01 - 7.92)$ 5.29

5. $3.617 + 0.7(5.301 - 4.911)$ 3.89
6. $14.95 + 5(3.2 + 14) - 90.84$ 10.11

7. $(72 - 65) + 11(8.76 - 0.89)$ 93.57
8. $5.143 + 0.3(8.914 - 7.126)$ 5.6794

▌▌▌ Calculator Key-In

On many calculators there is a square root key. If you have access to such a calculator, use it to complete the exercises below.

1. a. $\sqrt{1}$ 1
b. $\sqrt{100}$ 10
c. $\sqrt{10,000}$ 100

2. a. $\sqrt{7}$ 2.6457513
b. $\sqrt{700}$ 26.457513
c. $\sqrt{70,000}$ 264.57513

3. a. $\sqrt{70}$ 8.3666002
b. $\sqrt{7000}$ 83.666002
c. $\sqrt{700,000}$ 836.66002

4. a. $\sqrt{0.08}$ 0.2828427
b. $\sqrt{8}$ 2.8284271
c. $\sqrt{800}$ 28.284271

5. a. $\sqrt{0.54}$ 0.7348469
b. $\sqrt{54}$ 7.3484692
c. $\sqrt{5400}$ 73.484692

360 *Chapter 10*

10-3 Using a Square-Root Table

Part of the Table of Square Roots on page 498 is shown below. Square roots of integers are given to the nearest thousandth.

Number	Positive Square Root	Number	Positive Square Root	Number	Positive Square Root	Number	Positive Square Root
N	$\sqrt{N}$	N	$\sqrt{N}$	N	$\sqrt{N}$	N	$\sqrt{N}$
1	1	26	5.099	51	7.141	76	8.718
2	1.414	27	5.196	52	7.211	77	8.775
3	1.732	28	5.292	53	7.280	78	8.832
4	2	29	5.385	54	7.348	79	8.888

We can use the table to approximate the square roots of integers from 1 to 100. For example, to find $\sqrt{78}$, first locate 78 under a column headed "Number." Then read off the value beside 78 in the "Square Root" column.

$$\sqrt{78} \approx 8.832$$

Reading Mathematics: *Tables*

Some tables may have many columns of information. When you are reading a table, use a ruler to help guide your eyes across the page or down a column. This way you can be sure to find the correct entry.

To find an approximate square root of a number that lies between two entries in the column headed "Number," we can use a process called **interpolation**. The interpolation process may cause an error in the last digit of the approximation.

EXAMPLE 1 Approximate $\sqrt{3.8}$ by interpolation.

Solution On a number line $\sqrt{3.8}$ lies between $\sqrt{3}$ and $\sqrt{4}$. We can assume that $\sqrt{3.8}$ is about 0.8 of the distance between $\sqrt{3}$ and $\sqrt{4}$.

$$\sqrt{3.8} \approx \sqrt{3} + 0.8(\sqrt{4} - \sqrt{3})$$
$$\approx 1.732 + 0.8(2.000 - 1.732)$$
$$\approx 1.732 + 0.2144 = 1.9464$$

Thus, rounded to the thousandths' place, $\sqrt{3.8} = 1.946$.

Square Roots and Right Triangles **361**

Reading Mathematics

Students will learn the meaning of the following mathematical term in this lesson: *interpolation*.

Students may not have much experience reading tables. Show them that in this table we look for a number in the N column, then find its square root in the $\sqrt{N}$ column. Encourage students to study the table to see some patterns. As N increases, so does $\sqrt{N}$, but not as rapidly.

Chalkboard Examples

Use the table on page 498 to find the approximate square root.

1. $\sqrt{68}$ 8.246
2. $\sqrt{39}$ 6.245
3. $5\sqrt{22}$ 23.45

Find two decimals in the table between which the square root lies.

4. $\sqrt{21.6}$ 4.583, 4.690
5. $\sqrt{73.4}$ 8.544, 8.602
6. The area of a square roof is 89.5 m². Find the length of a side to the nearest hundredth of a meter. 9.46 m

EXAMPLE 2 The area of a square display room is 71 m². Find the length of a side to the nearest hundredth of a meter.

Solution Recall that the formula for the area of a square is $A = s^2$.

$$s^2 = 71$$
$$s = \sqrt{71}$$

Using the table on page 498, we see that $\sqrt{71} = 8.426$.
To the nearest hundredth of a meter, the length of a side is 8.43 m.

Class Exercises

Use the table on page 498 to find the approximate square root.

1. $\sqrt{39}$ 6.245
2. $\sqrt{83}$ 9.110
3. $\sqrt{20}$ 4.472
4. $\sqrt{95}$ 9.747
5. $\sqrt{34}$ 5.831
6. $\sqrt{49}$ 7
7. $\sqrt{11}$ 3.317
8. $\sqrt{52}$ 7.211
9. $10\sqrt{87}$ 93.27
10. $\frac{1}{10}\sqrt{22}$ 0.469

Find two decimals in the table on page 498 between which the square root lies.

11. $\sqrt{54.3}$ 7.348 and 7.416
12. $\sqrt{1.7}$ 1 and 1.414
13. $\sqrt{60.7}$ 7.746 and 7.810
14. $\sqrt{4.5}$ 2 and 2.236
15. $\sqrt{28.6}$ 5.292 and 5.385

Written Exercises

For Exercises 1–37, refer to the table on page 498.

Approximate to the nearest hundredth.

A

1. $\sqrt{65}$ 8.06
2. $\sqrt{31}$ 5.57
3. $\sqrt{56}$ 7.48
4. $\sqrt{13}$ 3.61
5. $\sqrt{97}$ 9.85

6. $10\sqrt{37}$ 60.83
7. $10\sqrt{41}$ 64.03
8. $\frac{1}{10}\sqrt{83}$ 0.91
9. $\frac{1}{10}\sqrt{75}$ 0.87
10. $\frac{1}{10}\sqrt{24}$ 0.49

11. $3\sqrt{55}$ 22.25
12. $2\sqrt{30}$ 10.95
13. $6\sqrt{19}$ 26.15
14. $4\sqrt{18}$ 16.97
15. $7\sqrt{72}$ 59.40

B

16. $\sqrt{39} + \sqrt{16}$ 10.25
17. $\sqrt{28} + \sqrt{53}$ 12.57
18. $\sqrt{71} - \sqrt{25}$ 3.43

19. $\sqrt{91} - \sqrt{84}$ 0.37
20. $2\sqrt{56} - \sqrt{4}$ 12.97
21. $\sqrt{37} - 2\sqrt{8}$ 0.43

Approximate to the nearest hundredth by interpolation.

22. $\sqrt{13.2}$ 3.63
23. $\sqrt{5.9}$ 2.43
24. $\sqrt{14.7}$ 3.83
25. $\sqrt{81.6}$ 9.03
26. $\sqrt{24.3}$ 4.93

27. $\sqrt{8.7}$ 2.95
28. $\sqrt{69.2}$ 8.32
29. $\sqrt{50.9}$ 7.13
30. $5\sqrt{84.4}$ 45.94
31. $3\sqrt{81.9}$ 27.15

362 *Chapter 10*

Approximate the square root to the nearest hundredth.

32. $\sqrt{700}$ (*Hint:* $\sqrt{100 \times 7} = \sqrt{100} \times \sqrt{7} = 10\sqrt{7}$)
26.46

33. $\sqrt{500}$ 22.36 34. $\sqrt{1100}$ 33.17

35. $\sqrt{380}$ (*Hint:* $\sqrt{100 \times 3.8} = \sqrt{100} \times \sqrt{3.8} = 10\sqrt{3.8}$) 19.46
36. $\sqrt{420}$ 20.47 37. $\sqrt{3470}$ 58.91

Problems

Solve.

A 1. The area of a square is 85 m². Find the length of a side to the nearest hundredth of a meter. 9.22 m

2. A square floor has an area of 32 m². Find the length of a side to the nearest tenth of a meter. 5.7 m

3. The area of a square room measures 225 ft². How much will it cost to put molding around the ceiling at $.35 per foot? $21

B 4. An isosceles right triangle has an area of 13.5 cm². Find the length of the equal sides to the nearest tenth of a centimeter. 5.2 cm

5. A circle has an area of 47.1 cm². Find its radius to the nearest hundredth of a centimeter. (Use $\pi \approx 3.14$.) 3.87 cm

6. The height of a parallelogram is half the length of its base. The parallelogram has an area of 67 cm². Find the height to the nearest tenth of a centimeter. 5.8 cm

C 7. The total surface area of a cube is 210 m². Find the length of an edge to the nearest hundredth of a meter. 5.92 m

8. One base of a trapezoid is three times as long as the other base. The height of the trapezoid is the same as the shorter base. The trapezoid has an area of 83 cm². Find the height to the nearest tenth of a centimeter. 6.4 cm

Review Exercises

Write the value of the product.

1. 0.9^2 0.81   2. 0.05^2 0.0025   3. 0.06^2 0.0036   4. 0.7^2 0.49   5. 3.7^2 13.69   6. 1.9^2 3.61   7. 24.3^2 590.49   8. 5.03^2 25.3009

Square Roots and Right Triangles **363**

Suggested Assignments

Minimum
  362/1–21
  363/Prob. 1–5
  363/Rev. 1–8

Average
  362/2–14 even; 16–31
  363/Prob. 1–6
  363/Rev. 1–7 odd

Maximum
  362/2–30 even
  363/32–37
  363/Prob. 1–8

Supplementary Materials

Practice Masters, p. 46

Reading Mathematics

Students will learn the meaning of the following mathematical terms in this lesson: *hypotenuse, leg, Pythagorean theorem, converse, Pythagorean Triple.*

Chalkboard Examples

Is the triangle with sides of the given lengths a right triangle?

1. 3, 3, 4 No

2. 6, 8, 10 Yes

3. 3, 5, 6 No

4. 1, 1, $\sqrt{2}$ Yes

5. 10, 24, 26 Yes

6. 6, 7, 9 No

A right triangle has sides of length a, b, and c, with c the length of the hypotenuse. Find the length of the missing side.

7. $a = 9$, $b = 12$ $c = 15$

8. $b = 15$, $c = 17$ $a = 8$

10-4 The Pythagorean Theorem

The longest side of a right triangle is opposite the right angle and is called the **hypotenuse.** The two shorter sides are called **legs.**

About 2500 years ago, the Greek mathematician Pythagoras proved the following useful fact about right triangles.

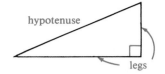

The Pythagorean Theorem

If the hypotenuse of a right triangle has length c, and the legs have lengths a and b, then

$$c^2 = a^2 + b^2.$$

The figure at the right illustrates the Pythagorean theorem. We see that the area of the square on the hypotenuse equals the sum of the areas of the squares on the legs:

$$25 = 9 + 16,$$

$$\text{or } 5^2 = 3^2 + 4^2.$$

The converse of the Pythagorean theorem is also true. It can be used to test whether a triangle is a right triangle.

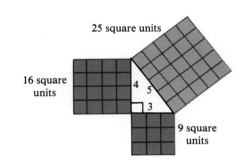

Converse of the Pythagorean Theorem

If the sides of a triangle have lengths a, b, and c, such that $c^2 = a^2 + b^2$, then the triangle is a right triangle.

EXAMPLE 1   Is the triangle with sides of the given lengths a right triangle?
         a. 4, 5, 7   **b.** 5, 12, 13

Solution **a.** $4^2 = 16$, $5^2 = 25$, $7^2 = 49$
             No, since $16 + 25 \neq 49$. The triangle with sides of lengths 4, 5, and 7 *cannot* be a right triangle.

364   *Chapter 10*

b. $5^2 = 25$, $12^2 = 144$, $13^2 = 169$

Yes, since $25 + 144 = 169$. The triangle with sides of lengths 5, 12, and 13 is a right triangle.

Sometimes it may be necessary to solve for the length of a missing side of a right triangle. The example below illustrates the steps involved.

EXAMPLE 2 For right triangle ABC, find the length of the missing side to the nearest hundredth. Use the table on page 498.

a. $a = 3$, $b = 7$ **b.** $a = 4$, $c = 9$

Solution Using the equation $c^2 = a^2 + b^2$:

a. $c^2 = 3^2 + 7^2$
$ = 9 + 49 = 58$
$c = \sqrt{58}$
$c \approx 7.62$

b. $9^2 = 4^2 + b^2$
$9^2 - 4^2 = b^2$
$81 - 16 = b^2$
$65 = b^2$
$\sqrt{65} = b$
$b \approx 8.06$

Class Exercises

Without actually counting them, tell how many unit squares there are in the shaded square.

1.

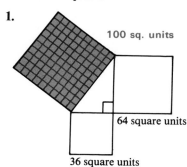

100 sq. units

64 square units

36 square units

2.

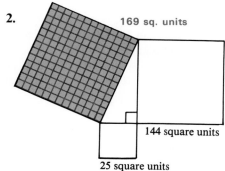

169 sq. units

144 square units

25 square units

Replace ? with = or ≠ to make a true statement.

3. $6^2 \underline{\ ?\ } \neq 4^2 + 5^2$ **4.** $5^2 \underline{\ ?\ } = 3^2 + 4^2$ **5.** $10^2 \underline{\ ?\ } = 6^2 + 8^2$

The lengths of the sides of a triangle are given. Is it a right triangle?

6. 3, 4, 5 Yes   **7.** 7, 24, 25 Yes   **8.** 5, 10, 12 No   **9.** 10, 24, 26 Yes

Square Roots and Right Triangles **365**

Suggested Assignments

Minimum
Day 1: 366/1–17
Day 2: 366/Prob. 1
367/Prob. 2–5
367/Self-Test A

Average
Day 1: 366/1–21
Day 2: 366/Prob. 1
367/Prob. 2–7
367/Self-Test A

Maximum
Day 1: 366/1–24
Day 2: 366/Prob. 1
367/Prob. 2–8
367/Self-Test A

Supplementary Materials

Practice Masters, p. 47
Test 10A, pp. 67–68

Written Exercises

Find the area of the square.

A   **1.** 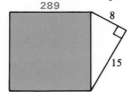   **2.** 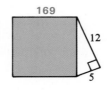   **3.**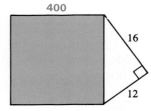

Is the triangle with sides of the given lengths a right triangle?

4. 6, 8, 10   Yes   **5.** 8, 15, 17   Yes

6. 16 cm, 30 cm, 34 cm   Yes   **7.** 9 m, 12 m, 15 m   Yes

8. 1.5 mm, 2.0 mm, 2.5 mm   Yes   **9.** 0.6 km, 0.8 km, 1.0 km   Yes

10. 9 m, 21 m, 23 m   No   **11.** 20 cm, 21 cm, 29 cm   Yes

12. 9 km, 40 km, 41 km   Yes   **13.** 8 m, 37 m, 39 m   No

A right triangle has sides of lengths a, b, and c, with c the length of the hypotenuse. Find the length of the missing side. If necessary, use the table on page 498 for the square root values and round answers to the nearest hundredth. Answers to Exercises 14–18 found by interpolation.

B   **14.** $a = 2$, $b = 1$ **15.** $a = 8$, $b = 6$ **16.** $a = 4$, $c = 9$ **17.** $b = 5$, $c = 6$
      $c = 2.24$ $c = 10$ $b = 8.06$ $a = 3.32$

      18. $a = 5$, $b = 12$ **19.** $a = 9$, $b = 7$ **20.** $b = 11$, $c = 19$ **21.** $a = 24$, $c = 74$
          $c = 13$ $c = 11.24$ $a = 15.41$ $b = 70$

A Pythagorean Triple consists of three positive integers a, b, and c that satisfy the equation $a^2 + b^2 = c^2$. You can find as many Pythagorean Triples as you wish by substituting positive integers for m and n (such that $m > n$) in the following expressions for a, b, and c.

$$a = m^2 - n^2 \qquad b = 2mn \qquad c = m^2 + n^2$$

Find Pythagorean Triples using the given values of m and n.

C   **22.** $m = 5$, $n = 1$ **23.** $m = 6$, $n = 3$ **24.** $m = 4$, $n = 2$
       $a = 24$ $a = 27$ $a = 12$
       $b = 10$ $b = 36$ $b = 16$
       $c = 26$ $c = 45$ $c = 20$

Problems

In this chapter, answers may vary slightly due to rounding and methods used to find square roots.

Solve. Give your answer to the nearest tenth.

A   **1.** A plane flies 90 km due east and then 60 km due north. How far is it then from its starting point?   108.2 km

Additional A Exercises

1. Find the area of the square.   185 square units

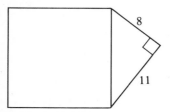

Is the triangle with sides of the given lengths a right triangle?

2. 2, 3, 4   No

3. 12, 16, 20   Yes

4. 0.1, 0.24, 0.26   Yes

5. 6, 9, 11   No

2. The foot of a 6 m ladder is 2.5 m from the base of a wall. How high up the wall does the ladder reach? 5.5 m

3. The figure shows two cables bracing a television tower. What is the distance between the points where the cables touch the ground? 55.7 m

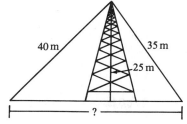

4. Find the length of a diagonal of a 10 cm by 10 cm square. 14.1 cm

B **5.** A square has diagonals 10 cm long. Find the length of a side. 7.1 cm

6. The diagonals of a rhombus are perpendicular and bisect each other. Find the length of a side of a rhombus whose diagonals have lengths 12 m and 18 m. 10.8 m

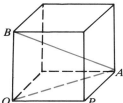

C **7.** Find the length of a diagonal of a 10 by 10 by 10 cube. (*Hint:* First find *AQ* using right triangle *PQA*. Then find the required length *AB* using right triangle *AQB*.) 17.3

8. Find the length of a diagonal of a box having dimensions 2 by 3 by 6. (See the *Hint* for Problem 7.) 7.0

Self-Test A

If the given symbol names an integer, state the integer. If not, name the two consecutive integers between which the number lies.

1. $\sqrt{56}$ 7 and 8 **2.** $-\sqrt{81}$ −9 **3.** $\sqrt{9} + \sqrt{25}$ 8 **4.** $\sqrt{106 - 57}$ 7 [10-1]

5. Use the divide-and-average method to approximate $\sqrt{86.4}$ to the nearest tenth. 9.3 [10-2]

Use the table on page 498 and interpolation to approximate each square root to the nearest tenth.

6. $\sqrt{18}$ 4.2 **7.** $\sqrt{50}$ 7.1 **8.** $\sqrt{9.8}$ 3.1 **9.** $\sqrt{5.6}$ 2.4 [10-3]

A right triangle has sides of lengths *a*, *b*, and *c*, with *c* the length of the hypotenuse. Find the length of the missing side.

10. $a = 3$, $b = 4$ $c = 5$ **11.** $b = 96$, $c = 100$ $a = 28$ **12.** $c = 20$, $a = 12$ $b = 16$ [10-4]

Self-Test answers and Extra Practice are at the back of the book.

Square Roots and Right Triangles **367**

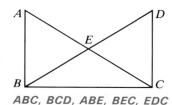
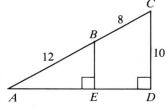
10-5 Similar Triangles

As you know, we say that two figures are congruent when they are identical in both shape and size. When two figures have the same shape, but do not necessarily have the same size, we say that the figures are **similar.**

  For two *triangles* to be similar it is enough that the measures of their corresponding angles are equal.

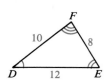

To indicate that the triangles shown above are similar, we can write the following.

$$\triangle ABC \sim \triangle DEF$$

The symbol ∼ means *is similar to.* Note that when we write expressions such as the one above, we list corresponding vertices in the same order.

  In triangles *ABC* and *DEF*, we see that the lengths of the corresponding sides have the same ratio:

$$\frac{AB}{DE} = \frac{18}{12} = \frac{3}{2} \qquad \frac{BC}{EF} = \frac{12}{8} = \frac{3}{2} \qquad \frac{CA}{FD} = \frac{15}{10} = \frac{3}{2}$$

Therefore,

$$\frac{AB}{DE} = \frac{BC}{EF} = \frac{CA}{FD}.$$

Because the ratios are equal, we say that the lengths of the corresponding sides are *proportional.*

  In general, we can say the following.

> For two similar triangles,
>
>   corresponding angles are congruent
>
>   and
>
>   lengths of corresponding sides are proportional.

368   *Chapter 10*

EXAMPLE 1 If $\triangle RUN \sim \triangle JOG$, find the lengths marked x and y.

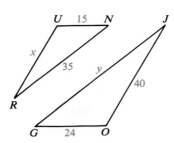

Solution Since the corresponding vertices are listed in the same order, we know the following.

$$\angle R \cong \angle J$$

$$\angle U \cong \angle O$$

$$\angle N \cong \angle G$$

$$\frac{RU}{JO} = \frac{UN}{OG} = \frac{NR}{GJ}$$

Substituting the values that are given in the diagram, we obtain

$$\frac{x}{40} = \frac{15}{24} = \frac{35}{y}.$$

Therefore, we can set up one proportion involving x and another involving y.

$$\frac{x}{40} = \frac{15}{24} \qquad\qquad \frac{15}{24} = \frac{35}{y}$$

$$24x = 15 \times 40 \qquad\qquad 15y = 35 \times 24$$

$$x = \frac{15 \times 40}{24} \qquad\qquad y = \frac{35 \times 24}{15}$$

$$x = \frac{600}{24} = 25 \qquad\qquad y = \frac{840}{15} = 56$$

The length of x is 25 and the length of y is 56.

In the two *right triangles* shown at the right, the measures of two acute angles are equal. Since all right angles have equal measure, 90°, the two remaining acute angles must also have equal measure. (Recall that the sum of the angle measures of any triangle is 180°.) Thus the two right triangles are similar.

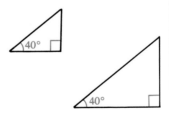

If an acute angle of one *right* triangle is congruent to an angle of a second *right* triangle, then the triangles are similar.

Suggested Assignments

Minimum
 371/1–13
 372/17
 372/Rev. 1–9

Average
 371/1–16
 372/17–20
 372/Rev. 2–8 even

Maximum
 371/1–13 odd; 14–16
 372/17–25

Supplementary Materials

Practice Masters, p. 47

EXAMPLE 2 At the same time a tree on level ground casts a shadow 48 m long, a 2 m pole casts a shadow 5 m long. Find the height, h, of the tree.

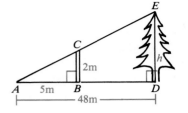

Solution In the diagram, right triangles ABC and ADE share acute $\angle A$ and thus are similar. Since $\frac{AD}{AB} = \frac{DE}{BC} = \frac{EA}{CA}$, we can set up a proportion to solve for h.

$$\frac{h}{2} = \frac{48}{5}$$

$$5h = 48 \times 2$$

$$h = \frac{48 \times 2}{5} = 19.2$$

The height of the tree is 19.2 m.

Reading Mathematics: *Diagrams*

To help you read a diagram that has overlapping triangles, you can redraw the diagram, pulling apart the individual triangles. For example, $\triangle ADE$ above can be separated as shown below.

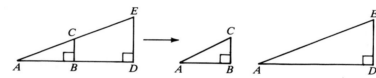

Class Exercises

In Exercises 1–4, $\triangle LOG \sim \triangle RIT$.

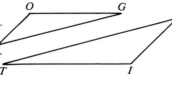

1. Name all pairs of corresponding angles. $\angle L, \angle R;$ $\angle O, \angle I;$ $\angle G, \angle T$

2. Name all pairs of corresponding sides. $\overline{LO}, \overline{RI};$ $\overline{OG}, \overline{IT};$ $\overline{GL}, \overline{TR}$

3. $\frac{OL}{IR} = \frac{OG}{?}$ IT

4. $\frac{LG}{?} = \frac{GO}{TI}$ RT

True or false?

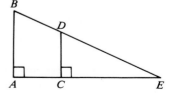

5. $\triangle BAE$ and $\triangle DCE$ are right triangles. True

6. $m\angle ABE = m\angle CDE$ True **7.** $\triangle BAE \sim \triangle DCE$ True

8. $\frac{CE}{AE} = \frac{BA}{DE}$ False

9. $\frac{BA}{DC} = \frac{BE}{DE}$ True

370 *Chapter 10*

Written Exercises

Exercises 1–5 refer to the diagram at the right. $\triangle ABC \sim \triangle PQR$.

A **1.** $\dfrac{PR}{AC} = \dfrac{?}{CB}$ RQ

2. $\dfrac{BA}{?} = \dfrac{CB}{RQ}$

QP

3. Find the length of $\overline{RQ}$. 9

4. Find the length of $\overline{AC}$. 10

5. m$\angle A = 47°$ and m$\angle Q = 29°$,
m$\angle C = \underline{\ ?\ }°$. 104°

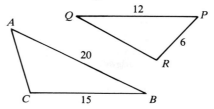

Exercises 6–10 refer to the diagram at the right. $\triangle AED \sim \triangle ACB$.

6. The length of $\overline{AE} = \underline{\ ?\ }$. 48

7. The length of $\overline{AB} = \underline{\ ?\ }$. 25

8. The length of $\overline{AD} = \underline{\ ?\ }$. 50

9. If m$\angle A = 25°$, then m$\angle ABC = \underline{\ ?\ }°$
and m$\angle ADE = \underline{\ ?\ }°$.
65, 65

10. If $\dfrac{BC}{DE} = \dfrac{1}{2}$, then $\dfrac{AB}{AD} = \underline{\ ?\ }$. $\dfrac{1}{2}$

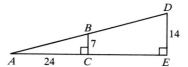

Find the lengths marked x and y.

11. $\triangle MAB \sim \triangle SRO$

12. $\triangle DIP \sim \triangle MON$

13. $\triangle RST \sim \triangle RUV$

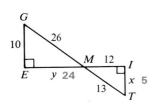

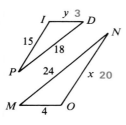

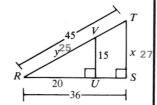

B **14.** $\triangle GEM \sim \triangle TIM$

15. $\triangle PAR \sim \triangle PBT$

16. $\triangle ART \sim \triangle ABC$

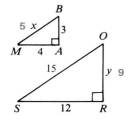

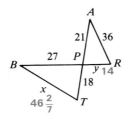

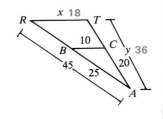

Square Roots and Right Triangles **371**

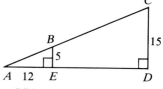

$\triangle BEA \sim \triangle CDA$.

1. The length of $\overline{AD} = \underline{\ ?\ }$
36

2. The length of $\overline{ED} = \underline{\ ?\ }$
24

3. The length of $\overline{AB} = \underline{\ ?\ }$
13

4. The length of $\overline{AC} = \underline{\ ?\ }$
39

5. If m$\angle A = 23°$,
then m$\angle ACD = \underline{\ ?\ }°$ 67

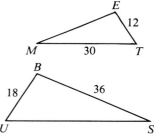

$\triangle MET \sim \triangle SBU$.

6. The length of $\overline{ME} = \underline{\ ?\ }$.
24

7. The length of $\overline{SU} = \underline{\ ?\ }$.
45

17. One day Jessica, who is 150 cm tall, cast a shadow that was 200 cm long while her father's shadow was 240 cm long. How tall is her father? **180 cm**

18. A person 1.8 m tall standing 7 m from a streetlight casts a shadow 3 m long. How high is the light? **6 m**

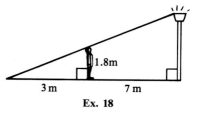

Ex. 18

19. Find (a) the perimeter and (b) the area of the shaded trapezoid in the figure at the left below.

(a) **18**
(b) **18**

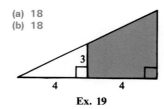

Ex. 19

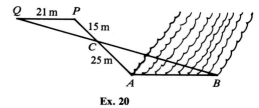

Ex. 20

20. To find the distance *AB* across a river, surveyors laid off $\overline{PQ}$ parallel to $\overline{AB}$ and created 2 similar triangles. They made the measurements shown in the figure at the right above. Find the length of $\overline{AB}$. **35 m**

Exercises 21–22 refer to the diagram at the right.

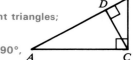

C **21.** Explain why $\triangle ADC \sim \triangle ACB$. △ADC and △ACB are right triangles; ∠A ≅ ∠A; so

22. Explain why $\triangle ADC \sim \triangle CDB$. ∠B ≅ ∠DCA
∠CDA ≅ ∠CDB; m∠BCD + m∠B = 90°, m∠BCD + m∠DCA = 90°,
so m∠B = m∠DCA; ∠B ≅ ∠DCA, so ∠A ≅ ∠BCD **Ex. 21, 22**

23. If $\triangle MNO \sim \triangle PQR$ and $\triangle PQR \sim \triangle STU$, is $\triangle MNO \sim \triangle STU$? Explain your answer. Yes; angles congruent, sides proportional

24. If $\triangle MNO \cong \triangle PQR$, is $\triangle MNO \sim \triangle PQR$? Explain your answer. Yes. If they're congruent, their angles are congruent.

25. If $\triangle MNO \sim \triangle PQR$, is $\triangle MNO \cong \triangle PQR$? Explain your answer. No. The lengths of the sides may differ.

Review Exercises

Multiply.

1. 300×1.73 **519**

2. 500×3.9 **1950**

3. 7.81×200 **1562**

4. 16.34×120 **1960.8**

5. 2.18×1.03 **2.2454**

6. 3.17×6.01 **19.0517**

7. 54.2×0.09 **4.878**

8. 683×2.48 **1693.84**

9. 71.4×52.4 **3741.36**

10-6 Special Right Triangles

In an *isosceles right triangle* the two acute angles are congruent. Since the sum of the measures of these two angles is 90°, each angle measures 45°. For this reason, an isosceles right triangle is often called a **45° right triangle.**

In the diagram each leg is 1 unit long. If the hypotenuse is c units long, by the Pythagorean theorem we know that $c^2 = 1^2 + 1^2 = 2$ and thus

$$c = \sqrt{2}.$$

Every 45° right triangle is similar to the one shown. Since corresponding sides of similar triangles are proportional, we have the following property.

> If each leg of a 45° right triangle is a units long, then the hypotenuse is $a\sqrt{2}$ units long.

EXAMPLE 1 A square park measures 200 m on each edge. Find the length, d, of a path extending diagonally from one corner to the opposite corner. Use $\sqrt{2} \approx 1.414$.

Solution Since the park is square, we can apply the property of 45° right triangles to solve for d. We use the fact that d is the hypotenuse of the right triangle and that each side measures 200 m.

$$d = 200\sqrt{2} \approx 200 \times 1.414 = 282.8$$

Thus the path measures approximately 282.8 m.

A **30°-60° right triangle,** such as $\triangle ACB$, may be thought of as half an equilateral triangle. If hypotenuse $\overline{AB}$ is 2 units long, then the shorter leg $\overline{AC}$ (half of $\overline{AD}$) is 1 unit long. To find BC, we use the Pythagorean theorem:

$$(AC)^2 + (BC)^2 = (AB)^2$$
$$1^2 + (BC)^2 = 2^2$$
$$(BC)^2 = 2^2 - 1^2 = 3$$
$$BC = \sqrt{3}$$

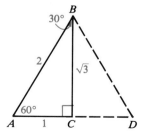

Square Roots and Right Triangles **373**

Teaching Suggestions
p. 355f

Related Activities p. 355f

Reading Mathematics

Students will learn the meaning of the following mathematical terms in this lesson: *45° right triangle, 30°–60° right triangle, radical sign, radical.*

Chalkboard Examples

1. Each leg of a 45° right triangle is 3 units long. Find the length of the hypotenuse. **$3\sqrt{2}$**
2. The hypotenuse of a 45° right triangle is 6 units long. Find the length of each leg. **$3\sqrt{2}$**

Use the diagram for Exercises 3–5.

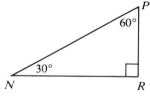

3. If $PR = 4$, then $PN =$ __?__. **8**
4. If $PR = 2$, then $NR =$ __?__. **$2\sqrt{3}$**
5. If $PN = 10$, then $RN =$ __?__. **$5\sqrt{3}$**

Every 30°–60° right triangle is similar to the one above, and since corresponding sides of similar triangles are proportional, we have the following property.

If the shorter leg of a 30°–60° right triangle is *a* units long, then the longer leg is $a\sqrt{3}$ units long, and the hypotenuse is 2*a* units long.

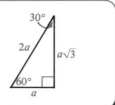

EXAMPLE 2   The hypotenuse of a 30°–60° right triangle is 8 cm long. Find the lengths of the legs.

Solution   Using the 30°–60° right triangle property, we know that
$$2a = 8,\ a = 4,\ \text{and}\ a\sqrt{3} = 4\sqrt{3}.$$
Thus the lengths of the legs are 4 cm and $4\sqrt{3}$ cm.

The symbol $\sqrt{}$ is called the **radical sign.** An expression such as $\sqrt{3}$ or $\sqrt{x}$ is called a **radical.** We often leave answers *in terms of radicals* with the radical in the numerator. To rewrite expressions such as $\frac{6}{\sqrt{3}}$ so that the radical appears in the numerator, we may use the fact that $\sqrt{x} \times \sqrt{x} = x$.

EXAMPLE 3   Rewrite $\frac{6}{\sqrt{3}}$ in lowest terms with the radical in the numerator.

Solution   If we multiply the numerator and denominator by $\sqrt{3}$, we will find an equivalent fraction with the radical in the numerator.

$$\frac{6}{\sqrt{3}} = \frac{6 \times \sqrt{3}}{\sqrt{3} \times \sqrt{3}}$$

$$= \frac{6\sqrt{3}}{3}$$

$$= 2\sqrt{3}$$

Thus, $2\sqrt{3}$ is equivalent to $\frac{6}{\sqrt{3}}$ in lowest terms with the radical in the numerator.

374   *Chapter 10*

Class Exercises

Rewrite the expression in lowest terms with the radical in the numerator.

1. $\dfrac{1}{\sqrt{3}}$ $\dfrac{\sqrt{3}}{3}$ 2. $\dfrac{2}{\sqrt{3}}$ $\dfrac{2\sqrt{3}}{3}$ 3. $\dfrac{2}{\sqrt{2}}$ $\sqrt{2}$ 4. $\dfrac{6}{\sqrt{2}}$ $3\sqrt{2}$ 5. $\dfrac{1}{\sqrt{x}}$ $\dfrac{\sqrt{x}}{x}$ 6. $\dfrac{\sqrt{x}}{x}$ $\dfrac{\sqrt{x}}{\sqrt{x}}$

Find the lengths marked x and y in the triangle. Give your answer in terms of radicals when radicals occur.

7.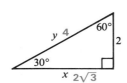

8.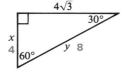

9.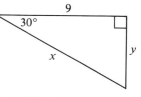

10.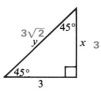

11.

12.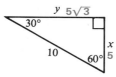

Written Exercises

Rewrite the expression in lowest terms with the radical in the numerator.

1. $\dfrac{6}{\sqrt{10}}$ $\dfrac{3\sqrt{10}}{5}$ 2. $\dfrac{12}{\sqrt{13}}$ $\dfrac{12\sqrt{13}}{13}$ 3. $\dfrac{3}{\sqrt{3}}$ $\sqrt{3}$ 4. $\dfrac{1}{\sqrt{2}}$ $\dfrac{\sqrt{2}}{2}$ 5. $\dfrac{2}{\sqrt{x}}$ $\dfrac{2\sqrt{x}}{x}$ 6. $\dfrac{3x}{\sqrt{x}}$ $3\sqrt{x}$

A

Approximate the lengths marked x and y to the nearest tenth.
Use $\sqrt{2} \approx 1.414$ and $\sqrt{3} \approx 1.732$.

7.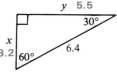

8.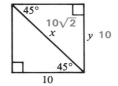

9.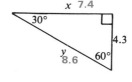

10.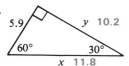

11.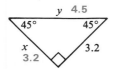

12.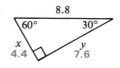

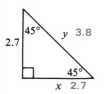

In Exercises 13–16, give answers in terms of radicals with the radical in the numerator.

B **13.** The hypotenuse of an isosceles right triangle has length 4. How long is each leg? $2\sqrt{2}$

14. The hypotenuse of a 45° right triangle has length 10. How long is each leg? $5\sqrt{2}$

15. The longer leg of a 30°–60° right triangle has length 15. How long are the other sides? $5\sqrt{3}$, $10\sqrt{3}$

16. The side opposite the 60° angle of a right triangle has length 3. How long are the other sides? $\sqrt{3}$, $2\sqrt{3}$

In Exercises 17–22, $\angle C$ is a right angle in $\triangle ABC$. Find the length of the missing side to the nearest tenth.

17. $AC = 2$, $BC = 5$ $AB = 5.4$

18. $AB = 18$, $AC = 9$ $BC = 15.6$

19. $AB = 6\sqrt{2}$, $AC = 6$ $BC = 6$

20. $AC = CB = x$ $AB = 1.4x$

C **21.** $\frac{1}{2}BA = CA = y$ $BC = 1.7y$

22. $2BC = BA = z$ $AC = 0.9z$

Note: Exercise 17 is solved by the Pythagorean theorem, Exercises 18–22 are solved by special right triangles.

Approximate the lengths marked x and y to the nearest tenth.

23.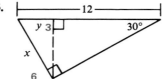

24.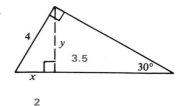

Problems

Solve. Give answers to the nearest tenth.

A **1.** A ladder 10 m long resting against a wall makes a 60° angle with the ground. How far up the wall does it reach? 8.7 m

2. A baseball diamond is a square 90 ft on each side. How far is it diagonally from home plate to second base? 127.3 ft

3. A hillside is inclined at an angle of 30° with the horizontal. How much altitude has Mary gained after hiking 40 m up the hill?   20 m

4. The diagram on the right shows the roof of a house. Find the dimensions marked x and y. $x = 6$ m; $y = 10.4$ m

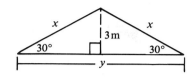

B **5.** A checkerboard has 8 squares on each side. If one side of a square is 5 cm long, how far is it from one corner of the board to the opposite corner? 56.6 cm

6. Find the height of an equilateral triangle with sides 12 cm long. 10.4 cm

7. Find the perimeters of the two squares shown in the diagram. larger: 40; smaller: 28.3

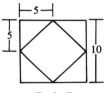

Prob. 7

8. An equilateral triangle has sides 10 units long. Find (a) the height and (b) the area.
(a) 8.7 units (b) 43.3 units²

C **9.** An equilateral triangle has sides r units long. Find both (a) the height and (b) the area in terms of r. (a) 0.9r units (b) 0.4r^2 units²

10. The area of a square pan is 900 cm². What is the length of a diagonal of the pan? 42.4 cm

11. A 10 m pole is supported in a vertical position by three 6 m guy wires. If one end of each wire is fastened to the ground at a 60° angle, how high on the pole is the other end fastened? 5.2 m

12. A rhombus has angles of 60° and 120°. Each side of the rhombus is 8 cm long. What are the lengths of the diagonals? (*Hint:* The diagonals bisect the angles of the rhombus.) short: 8 cm
long: 13.9 cm

Review Exercises

Write the fraction as a decimal. Use a bar to show a repeating decimal.

1. $\frac{5}{4}$ 1.25 **2.** $\frac{3}{5}$ 0.6 **3.** $\frac{2}{9}$ 0.$\overline{2}$ **4.** $\frac{7}{12}$ 0.583$\overline{3}$ **5.** $\frac{11}{10}$ 1.1 **6.** $\frac{3}{16}$ **7.** $\frac{1}{6}$ 0.1$\overline{6}$ **8.** $\frac{4}{11}$
0.1875   0.$\overline{36}$

Square Roots and Right Triangles **377**

377

Reading Mathematics

Students will learn the meaning of the following mathematical terms in this lesson: *trigonometric ratios, sine, sin A, cosine, cos A, tangent, tan A.*

Chalkboard Examples

Give each trigonometric ratio as a decimal to the nearest hundredth.

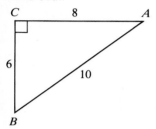

1. cos B 0.60
2. tan A 0.75
3. sin A 0.60
4. tan B 1.33
5. Evaluate cos 60° to the nearest hundredth. 0.50
6. Evaluate sin 45° to the nearest hundredth. 0.71

10-7 Trigonometric Ratios

Since each of the three triangles in the diagram below contains ∠ A and a right angle, the triangles are *similar* and their sides are *proportional*. Thus, the ratios written below for the smallest triangle apply to all three triangles.

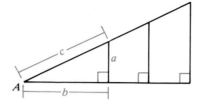

$$\frac{\text{length of side opposite } \angle A}{\text{length of hypotenuse}} = \frac{a}{c}$$

$$\frac{\text{length of side adjacent to } \angle A}{\text{length of hypotenuse}} = \frac{b}{c}$$

$$\frac{\text{length of side opposite } \angle A}{\text{length of side adjacent to } \angle A} = \frac{a}{b}$$

These ratios, called the **trigonometric ratios,** are so useful that each has been given a special name.

$\frac{a}{c}$ is called the **sine** of ∠ A, or **sin A.**

$\frac{b}{c}$ is called the **cosine** of ∠ A, or **cos A.**

$\frac{a}{b}$ is called the **tangent** of ∠ A, or **tan A.**

It is important to understand that each trigonometric ratio depends only on the measure of ∠ A and *not* on the size of the right triangle.

The following shortened forms of the definitions may help you remember the trigonometric ratios.

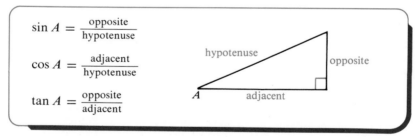

$$\sin A = \frac{\text{opposite}}{\text{hypotenuse}}$$

$$\cos A = \frac{\text{adjacent}}{\text{hypotenuse}}$$

$$\tan A = \frac{\text{opposite}}{\text{adjacent}}$$

EXAMPLE 1 For ∠ A find the value of each trigonometric ratio in lowest terms.

a. sin A   **b.** cos A   **c.** tan A

Solution   To find the value of the trigonometric ratios for ∠ A, first find the value of x. By the Pythagorean theorem:

$$x^2 + 5^2 = 6^2$$
$$x^2 + 25 = 36$$
$$x^2 = 36 - 25$$
$$x^2 = 11$$
$$x = \sqrt{11}$$

a. $\sin A = \dfrac{\text{opposite}}{\text{hypotenuse}} = \dfrac{5}{6}$

b. $\cos A = \dfrac{\text{adjacent}}{\text{hypotenuse}} = \dfrac{\sqrt{11}}{6}$

c. $\tan A = \dfrac{\text{opposite}}{\text{adjacent}} = \dfrac{5}{\sqrt{11}} = \dfrac{5 \times \sqrt{11}}{\sqrt{11} \times \sqrt{11}} = \dfrac{5\sqrt{11}}{11}$

EXAMPLE 2   Find the sine, cosine, and tangent of a 30° angle to the nearest thousandth.

Solution   To find the values of these trigonometric ratios, first draw a 30°–60° right triangle. Let the shorter leg be 1 unit long and write in the lengths of the other sides according to the property of 30°–60° triangles that you learned in the previous lesson.

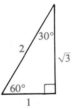

$$\sin 30° = \frac{1}{2} = 0.500$$

$$\cos 30° = \frac{\sqrt{3}}{2} \approx 0.866$$

$$\tan 30° = \frac{1}{\sqrt{3}} = \frac{\sqrt{3}}{3} \approx 0.577$$

Class Exercises

Find the value of the trigonometric ratio.

1. $\sin A$ $\frac{4}{5}$

2. $\cos A$ $\frac{3}{5}$

3. $\tan A$ $\frac{4}{3}$

4. $\sin B$ $\frac{3}{5}$

5. $\cos B$ $\frac{4}{5}$

6. $\tan B$ $\frac{3}{4}$

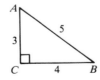

Square Roots and Right Triangles   **379**

Give the value as a fraction in lowest terms.

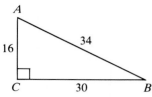

1. $\sin A$ $\dfrac{15}{17}$

2. $\tan B$ $\dfrac{8}{15}$

3. $\cos B$ $\dfrac{15}{17}$

4. $\cos A$ $\dfrac{8}{17}$

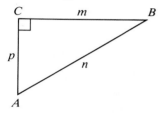

5. $\cos B$ $\dfrac{m}{n}$

6. $\tan A$ $\dfrac{m}{p}$

7. $\tan B$ $\dfrac{p}{m}$

8. $\sin A$ $\dfrac{m}{n}$

Find the value of the trigonometric ratio.

7. $\sin P$ $\dfrac{y}{z}$

8. $\cos P$ $\dfrac{x}{z}$

9. $\tan P$ $\dfrac{y}{x}$

10. $\sin R$ $\dfrac{x}{z}$

11. $\cos R$ $\dfrac{y}{z}$

12. $\tan R$ $\dfrac{x}{y}$

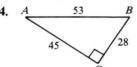

1. $\sin A = \dfrac{3}{5}$; $\cos A = \dfrac{4}{5}$; $\tan A = \dfrac{3}{4}$; $\sin B = \dfrac{4}{5}$; $\cos B = \dfrac{3}{5}$; $\tan B = \dfrac{4}{3}$

2. $\sin A = \dfrac{15}{17}$; $\cos A = \dfrac{8}{17}$; $\tan A = \dfrac{15}{8}$; $\sin B = \dfrac{8}{17}$; $\cos B = \dfrac{15}{17}$; $\tan B = \dfrac{8}{15}$

Written Exercises

Give the value of the sine, cosine, and tangent of $\angle A$ and $\angle B$. Give all ratios in lowest terms.

A 1.

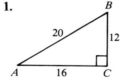

2.

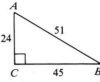

3.

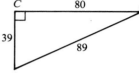

3. $\sin A = \dfrac{80}{89}$; $\cos A = \dfrac{39}{89}$; $\tan A = \dfrac{80}{39}$; $\sin B = \dfrac{39}{89}$; $\cos B = \dfrac{80}{89}$; $\tan B = \dfrac{39}{80}$

4.

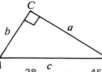

5.

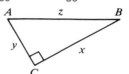

6.

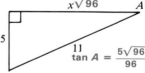

4. $\sin A = \dfrac{28}{53}$; $\cos A = \dfrac{45}{53}$; $\tan A = \dfrac{28}{45}$; $\sin B = \dfrac{45}{53}$; $\cos B = \dfrac{28}{53}$; $\tan B = \dfrac{45}{28}$

B In Exercises 7–12, give all ratios in lowest terms and with the radical in the numerator.

Find the value of x. Then find $\tan A$.

7.

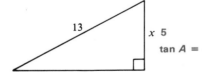

x 5 $\tan A = \dfrac{5}{12}$

8.

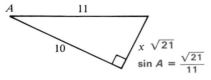

$\tan A = \dfrac{5\sqrt{96}}{96}$

5. $\sin A = \dfrac{a}{c}$; $\cos A = \dfrac{b}{c}$; $\tan A = \dfrac{a}{b}$; $\sin B = \dfrac{b}{c}$; $\cos B = \dfrac{a}{c}$; $\tan B = \dfrac{b}{a}$

Find the value of x. Then find $\sin A$.

9.

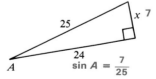

$x \ \sqrt{21}$ $\sin A = \dfrac{\sqrt{21}}{11}$

10.

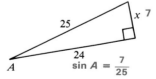

$\sin A = \dfrac{7}{25}$

6. $\sin A = \dfrac{x}{z}$; $\cos A = \dfrac{y}{z}$; $\tan A = \dfrac{x}{y}$; $\sin B = \dfrac{y}{z}$; $\cos B = \dfrac{x}{z}$; $\tan B = \dfrac{y}{x}$

Find the value of x. Then find $\cos A$.

11.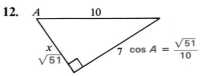
A x 24   10 $\cos A = \dfrac{12}{13}$
26

12. A 10 x $\sqrt{51}$ 7 $\cos A = \dfrac{\sqrt{51}}{10}$

Find the sine, cosine, and tangent. Write the answer both as a fraction and as a decimal to the nearest thousandth. (*Hint:* See Example 2.)

13. **a.** $\sin 60°$ **b.** $\cos 60°$ **c.** $\tan 60°$
$\dfrac{\sqrt{3}}{2}$; 0.866 $\dfrac{1}{2}$; 0.500 $\sqrt{3}$; 1.732

14. **a.** $\sin 45°$ **b.** $\cos 45°$ **c.** $\tan 45°$
$\dfrac{\sqrt{2}}{2}$; 0.707 $\dfrac{\sqrt{2}}{2}$; 0.707   1; 1.000

Give answers to the nearest tenth. Answers for parts (b) and (c) of Exercises 15–17 are found by using rounded answers obtained in preceding parts.

C 15. $\sin 67° = 0.9205$
a. $x = $?   6.4
b. $y = $?   2.8
c. $\sin 23° = $?   0.4

y | 67°   7
x

16. $\tan 40° = 0.8391$
a. $m = $?   12.6
b. $n = $?   19.6
c. $\cos 50° = $?   0.6

m n
40°
15

17. $\cos 65° = 0.4226$
a. $e = $?   3.8
b. $f = $?   8.2
c. $\tan 25° = $?   0.5

f
e | 65°   9

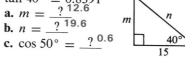

Review Exercises

Select the number that is closest to the one given.

1. 0.3765   b
   a. 0.3774   **b.** 0.3759

2. 8.1443   b
   a. 8.1430   **b.** 8.1451

3. 0.9004   a
   a. 0.9019   **b.** 0.8954

4. 1.8040   b
   a. 1.829   **b.** 1.788

5. 0.2126   b
   a. 0.2666   **b.** 0.1986

6. 11.4301   a
   a. 12.0801   **b.** 10.6801

7. 0.1758   b
   a. 0.1744   **b.** 0.1764

8. 3.2709   a
   a. 3.2712   **b.** 3.2705

▌▌▌ Challenge

Leslie is considering two job offers. Alloid Metals pays an hourly wage of $7.30. Acme Steel Company pays an annual salary of $14,040. Both jobs have a 40-hour work week. Which job offers a better salary? Alloid

Square Roots and Right Triangles   **381**

Suggested Assignments
Minimum
   380 / 1–10
   381 / 11–12
   381 / Rev. 1–8
Average
   380 / 1–10
   381 / 11–15
   381 / Rev. 2–8 even
   381 / Challenge
Maximum
Day 1: 380 / 1–10
       381 / 11–12
Day 2: 381 / 13–17
       381 / Challenge

Supplementary Materials

Practice Masters, p. 48

Teaching Suggestions
p. 355g

Related Activities p. 355h

Reading Mathematics

Students will learn the meaning of the following mathematical term in this lesson: *solve a right triangle.*

Chalkboard Examples

Use the table on page 499 to find each value.

1. tan 72° **3.0777**

2. sin 17° **0.2924**

3. Find the measure of ∠*A* to the nearest degree, if cos *A* = 0.732. **43°**

Find each measure for △*ABC*. Round lengths to the nearest tenth and angle measures to the nearest degree.

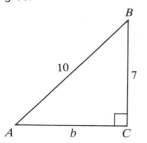

4. *b* **7.1**

5. m∠*A* **44°**

6. m∠*B* **46°**

10-8 Solving Right Triangles

The table on page 499 gives approximate values of the sine, the cosine, and the tangent of angles with measure 1°, 2°, 3°, . . . , 90°. To find sin 45°, look down the column headed "Angle" to 45°. To the right of it in the column headed "Sine," you see that sin 45° ≈ 0.7071.

The values in the table on page 499 are, in general, accurate to only four decimal places. However, in computational work with sine, cosine, and tangent, it is customary to use = instead of ≈. In this lesson, we will write *sin 45° = 0.7071* instead of *sin 45° ≈ 0.7071*.

We can use the values in the table to **solve right triangles,** that is, to find approximate measures of all the sides and all the angles of any right triangle.

EXAMPLE 1 Solve △*ABC* by finding each measure.
a. *c* to the nearest tenth
b. m∠*A*
c. m∠*B*

Solution **a.** The diagram indicates that ∠*C* is a right triangle, therefore by the Pythagorean theorem:

$$c^2 = 7^2 + 5^2 = 74$$
$$c = \sqrt{74} = 8.6$$

To the nearest tenth, *c* = 8.6.

b. $\tan A = \frac{7}{5} = 1.4$

In the tangent column in the table, the closest entry to 1.4 is 1.3764, for angle measure 54°. Thus, to the nearest degree, m∠*A* = 54°.

c. m∠*A* + m∠*B* + m∠*C* = 180°
54° + m∠*B* + 90° = 180°
m∠*B* = 180° − 90° − 54°
m∠*B* = 36°

Problem Solving Reminder

To solve some problems, you might need to *use previously obtained solutions* in order to complete the answer. In Example 1, it was convenient to use the m∠*A* found in part *b* to solve for the m∠*B*.

EXAMPLE 2 Solve △ABC by finding each measure.

      a. m ∠ B

      b. *a* to the nearest tenth

      c. *b* to the nearest tenth

Solution

a. m ∠ A + m ∠ B + m ∠ C = 180°

      38° + m ∠ B + 90° = 180°

      m ∠ B = 180° − 90° − 38° = 52°

b. $\sin 38° = \dfrac{a}{6.5}$

    $a = \sin 38° \times 6.5$

      $= 0.6157 \times 6.5 = 4.00205$

To the nearest tenth, $a = 4.0$.

c. $\cos 38° = \dfrac{b}{6.5}$

    $b = \cos 38° \times 6.5$

      $= 0.7880 \times 6.5 = 5.122$

To the nearest tenth, $b = 5.1$.

Class Exercises

State whether you would use the sine, cosine, or tangent ratio to find *x* in each diagram.

1. 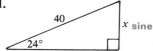 *x* sine

2. 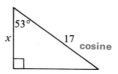 cosine

3. *x* tangent

4. 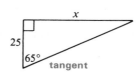 tangent

For Exercises 5–18, use the table on page 499.

Find a value for the trigonometric ratio.

5. cos 8° 0.9903   **6.** sin 67° 0.9205   **7.** tan 36° 0.7265   **8.** tan 82° 7.1154

9. sin 15° 0.2588   **10.** cos 75° 0.2588   **11.** cos 20° 0.9397   **12.** sin 70° 0.9397

Square Roots and Right Triangles **383**

Find the measure of $\angle A$ to the nearest degree.

13. sin A = 0.4 24°

14. tan A = 1.6 58°

15. cos A = 0.85 32°

16. cos A = 0.19 79°

17. tan A = 0.819 39°

18. sin A = 0.208 12°

1. 0.4226; 0.9063; 0.4663 2. 0.9703; 0.2419; 4.0108 3. 0.9994; 0.0349; 28.6363
4. 0.1908; 0.9816; 0.1944 5. 0.6293; 0.7771; 0.8098 6. 0.6691; 0.7431; 0.9004

Written Exercises

For Exercises 1–40, use the tables on page 498 and page 499.

Find sin A, cos A, and tan A for the given measure of $\angle A$.

A **1.** 25° **2.** 76° **3.** 88° **4.** 11° **5.** 39° **6.** 42°
7. 0.9613; 0.2756; 3.4874 8. 0.2250; 0.9744; 0.2309 9. 0.6428; 0.7660; 0.8391
7. 74° **8.** 13° **9.** 40° **10.** 52° **11.** 65° **12.** 81°
10. 0.7880; 0.6157; 1.2799 11. 0.9063; 0.4226; 2.1445 12. 0.9877; 0.1564; 6.3138

Find the measure of $\angle A$ to the nearest degree.

13. sin A = 0.9877 81°

14. cos A = 0.9205 23°

15. tan A = 0.0175 1°

16. cos A = 0.8572 31°

17. tan A = 4.0108 76°

18. sin A = 0.2250 13°

Find the measure of the angle to the nearest degree or the length of the side to the nearest whole number.

19. m $\angle A$ 30°

20. x 7

21. m $\angle B$ 60°

22. m $\angle L$ 35°

23. t 6

24. u 7

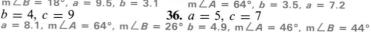

Find the measure of $\angle A$ to the nearest degree.

B **25.** sin A = 0.8483 58°

26. cos A = 0.2758 74°

27. tan A = 0.4560 25°

28. sin A = 0.6559 41°

29. tan A = 2.7500 70°

30. cos A = 0.5148 59°

Solve $\triangle ABC$. Round angle measures to the nearest degree and lengths to the nearest tenth.

31. $a = 5$, $b = 8$
$c = 9.4$, m $\angle A$ = 32°, m $\angle B$ = 58°

32. $a = 4$, $b = 7$
$c = 8.1$, m $\angle A$ = 30°, m $\angle B$ = 60°

33. m $\angle A$ = 72°, $c = 10$
m $\angle B$ = 18°, $a = 9.5$, $b = 3.1$

34. m $\angle B$ = 26°, $c = 8$
m $\angle A$ = 64°, $b = 3.5$, $a = 7.2$

35. $b = 4$, $c = 9$
$a = 8.1$, m $\angle A$ = 64°, m $\angle B$ = 26°

36. $a = 5$, $c = 7$
$b = 4.9$, m $\angle A$ = 46°, m $\angle B$ = 44°

37. m $\angle B$ = 20°, $b = 15$
m $\angle A$ = 70°, $c = 43.9$, $a = 41.2$

38. m $\angle A$ = 80°, $a = 9$
m $\angle B$ = 10°, $b = 1.6$, $c = 9.1$

39. m $\angle A$ = 58°, $b = 12$
m $\angle B$ = 32°, $a = 19.2$, $c = 22.6$

40. m $\angle B$ = 39°, $a = 20$
m $\angle A$ = 51°, $b = 16.2$, $c = 25.7$

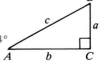

Problems

Give angle measures to the nearest degree and lengths to the nearest tenth.

A

1. How tall is the tree in the diagram below?

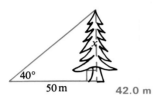

50 m   40°   42.0 m

2. How tall is the flagpole in the diagram below?

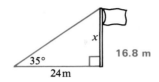

35°   24 m   x   16.8 m

3. In the diagram below, the road rises 20 m for every 100 m traveled horizontally. What angle does it make with the horizontal?

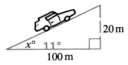

x° 11°   20 m   100 m

4. What angle does the rope make with the horizontal in the diagram below?

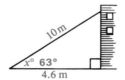

10 m   x° 63°   4.6 m

B

5. a. How tall is the building in the diagram below?

b. How tall is the antenna?

a. 42.5 m
b. 10.7 m

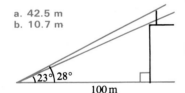

23° 28°   100 m

6. What is the height of the child in the diagram below? 1.3 m

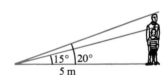

15° 20°   5 m

7. In △ABC, $\overline{AC}$ is 8 cm long. The length of the altitude to $\overline{AB}$ is 5 cm. Find the measure of ∠A. **39°**

8. Triangle MNO is an isosceles triangle with $\overline{MO}$ congruent to $\overline{NO}$. The third side of the triangle, $\overline{MN}$, is 36 cm long. The perimeter of the triangle is 96 cm.

a. Find the lengths of $\overline{MO}$ and $\overline{NO}$. **30 cm**

b. The altitude from O to $\overline{MN}$ bisects $\overline{MN}$. Find the measure of ∠OMN. **53°**

Square Roots and Right Triangles **385**

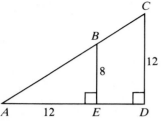

1. $\triangle DCA \sim \triangle$ __?__ **EBA**

2. $\dfrac{AE}{AD} = \dfrac{?}{AC}$ **AB**

3. $AD =$ __?__ **18**

4. $m\angle ACD = m\angle$ __?__
ABE

Give answers in terms of radicals with the radical in the numerator.

5. The hypotenuse of a 45° right triangle is 8 cm long. How long is a leg? **4√2 cm**

6. The longer leg of a 30°–60° right triangle is 15 units long. How long is the shorter leg? **5√3 units**

Complete in terms of *r*, *s*, and *t*.

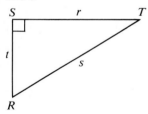

7. tan R $\dfrac{r}{t}$

8. cos T $\dfrac{r}{s}$

9. sin T $\dfrac{t}{s}$

(Continue on next page.)

Give angle measures to the nearest degree and lengths to the nearest tenth.

9. A surveyor is determining the direction in which tunnel $\overline{AB}$ is to be dug through a mountain. She locates point C so that $\angle C$ is a right angle, the length of $\overline{AC}$ is 1.5 km, and the length of $\overline{BC}$ is 3.5 km. Find the measure of $\angle A$. **67°**

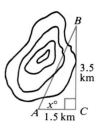

C **10.** In $\triangle RST$, the measure of $\angle S$ is 142°. The length of $\overline{RS}$ is 10. Find the length of the altitude from vertex R. **6.2**

Self-Test B

Exercises 1–4 refer to the diagram below. Complete.

1. $\triangle TOY$ __?__ $\triangle TIN$ [10-5]

2. $\dfrac{TI}{TO} = \dfrac{IN}{OY} = \dfrac{?}{?}$ $\dfrac{TN}{TY}$

3. $TY =$ __?__ $7\frac{1}{2}$

4. $m\angle TIN$ __?__ $\overset{=}{m}\angle TOY$

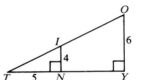

In Exercises 5 and 6, give answers in terms of radicals with the radical in the numerator.

5. The hypotenuse of a 45° right triangle is 6.2 cm long. What is the length of each leg? **3.1√2 cm**   [10-6]

6. The longer leg of a 30°–60° right triangle has length 12. What are the lengths of the shorter leg and the hypotenuse? **4√3, 8√3**

Exercises 7–13 refer to the diagram at the right.

Complete in terms of *p*, *q*, and *r*.

7. sin P = __?__ $\dfrac{p}{q}$ **8.** cos P = __?__ $\dfrac{r}{q}$ [10-7]

9. tan P = __?__ $\dfrac{p}{r}$

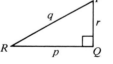

Find the measure of the angles to the nearest degree and the lengths to the nearest tenth. Use the tables on page 498 and page 499. m∠R = 12°

10. $r = 3$, $q = 6$ m∠P = 60° p = 5.2   **11.** m∠P = 78°, r = 5   [10-8]
                          m∠R = 30°   q = 24.1, p = 23.5,

12. m∠R = 23°, p = 8   **13.** m∠R = 57°, q = 24
          m∠P = 67°, r = 3.4, q = 8.7   m∠P = 33°, p = 13.1, r = 20.1

Self-Test answers and Extra Practice are at the back of the book.

386   *Chapter 10*

Computer Byte

The following program produces a Pythagorean Triple using any counting number greater than 2.

```
10   PRINT "INPUT THE DESIRED NUMBER";
20   INPUT N
30   IF N * (N − 1) * (N − 2) < > 0 THEN 60
40   PRINT "THERE IS NO SUCH TRIPLE."
50   GOTO 150
60   IF INT (N / 2) < > N / 2 THEN 120
70   IF N = 4 THEN 110
80   LET N = N / 2
90   LET C = C + 1
100   GOTO 60
110   LET N = 3
120   PRINT "A PYTHAGOREAN TRIPLE IS:"
130   LET B = INT (N ↑ 2 / 2)
140   PRINT 2 ↑ C * N,2 ↑ C * B,2 ↑ C * (B + 1)
150   END
```

4. 6, 8, 10
   7, 24, 25
   6, 8, 10
   11, 60, 61
   17, 144, 145
   24, 32, 40
   101, 5100, 5101

1. Use the program to find a triple with the number 3. Does it give you the triple you had expected? 3, 4, 5

2. Use the program to find a triple with the number 4. Does it give you the triple you had expected? 3, 4, 5

3. Now try 5. Is the output what you had expected? 5, 12, 13

4. Input each of these numbers to produce Pythagorean Triples:

   6, 7, 8, 11, 17, 24, 101

   Check three of your answers by multiplying.

5. Try 1 or 2 in the program. Can you explain why this output is true?
   Output: THERE IS NO SUCH TRIPLE. Neither 1^2 nor 2^2 can equal the difference of the squares of two other integers.

 ## Challenge

Trace the two squares as they are shown at the right. Can you draw one line that will divide each of the squares into two parts of equal area?
Locate centers of squares (by finding points where diagonals intersect). Connect them.

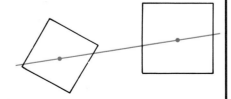

Square Roots and Right Triangles   **387**

In right triangle *JKL* find lengths to the nearest tenth and angles to the nearest degree.

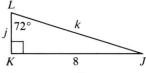

10. m∠*J* = __?__ 18°
11. *j* = __?__ 2.6
12. *k* = __?__ 8.4

Other Roots and Fractions as Exponents

As you learned earlier, $\sqrt{49} = 7$ because $7^2 = 49$. Recall that we chose 7 and not -7 since 7 is the positive square root of 49.

We can extend the idea of square roots to other roots. The fourth root of 16, denoted $\sqrt[4]{16}$, is 2 since $2^4 = 16$. In general,

> For any positive *even* integer n, and positive integer c,
>
> $$\sqrt[n]{a} = c, \text{ if } c^n = a.$$

The third root, or cube root, of a number may be positive or negative depending on the sign of the number

For example, $\sqrt[3]{64} = 4$ because $4^3 = 64$

and $\sqrt[3]{-27} = -3$ because $(-3)^3 = -27$.

In general,

> For any positive *odd* integer n, and any integers a and c,
>
> $$\sqrt[n]{a} = c, \text{ if } c^n = a.$$

The following cases will complete our discussion of roots.

If $a = 0$, then $\sqrt[n]{a} = 0$ because $a^n = 0^n = 0$.

If a is a negative number and n is *even,* there is no real nth root of a.

388 *Chapter 10*

Recall that you add exponents when multiplying powers of the same base.

$$9^1 \times 9^2 = 9^{1+2} = 9^3$$

When this rule is applied to fractional exponents, we have

$$9^{\frac{1}{2}} \times 9^{\frac{1}{2}} = 9^{\frac{1}{2}+\frac{1}{2}} = 9^1 = 9.$$

This example suggests that we define $9^{\frac{1}{2}}$ as $\sqrt{9}$, since $(\sqrt{9})^2 = 9$.

In general,

$$a^{\frac{1}{n}} = \sqrt[n]{a}.$$

7 and 8: There is no square root because a is negative and n is even.

Find the root. If the root does not exist, explain why.

1. $\sqrt[3]{27}$ 3

2. $\sqrt[6]{0}$ 0

3. $\sqrt[4]{16}$ 2

4. $\sqrt[3]{1000}$ 10

5. $\sqrt[3]{64}$ 4

6. $\sqrt[3]{-27}$ -3

7. $\sqrt{-49}$

8. $\sqrt[4]{-16}$

9. $\sqrt[3]{-1000}$ -10

10. $\sqrt[5]{-32}$ -2

11. $\sqrt[3]{125}$ 5

12. $\sqrt[7]{-1}$ -1

Write the expression without exponents.

13. $36^{\frac{1}{2}}$ 6

14. $27^{\frac{1}{3}}$ 3

15. $64^{\frac{1}{3}}$ 4

16. $64^{\frac{1}{6}}$ 2

17. $16^{\frac{1}{4}}$ 2

18. $1000^{\frac{1}{3}}$ 10

19. $81^{\frac{1}{4}}$ 3

Calculator Activity

Most scientific calculators have a $\boxed{\sqrt[x]{y}}$ key that can be used to approximate roots that are not integers. For example, to obtain $\sqrt[4]{7}$, enter $\boxed{7}$ $\boxed{\sqrt[x]{y}}$ $\boxed{4}$ $\boxed{=}$ to get 1.6265766. On some calculators, the $\boxed{\sqrt[x]{y}}$ key may be a second function. In this case, push the $\boxed{\text{2nd F}}$ key to activate the root function.

Other calculators have a $\boxed{y^x}$ and a $\boxed{1/x}$ key. In this case, we can obtain $\sqrt[4]{7}$ by calculating $7^{\frac{1}{4}}$ in the following way.

$\boxed{7}$ $\boxed{y^x}$ $\underbrace{\boxed{4} \quad \boxed{1/x}}$ $\boxed{=}$

This is $\frac{1}{4}$.

Use a calculator to approximate the following. Answers will vary.

1. $\sqrt[3]{10}$ 2.1544347

2. $\sqrt[3]{4}$ 1.5874011

3. $\sqrt[5]{50}$ 2.1867241

4. $\sqrt[4]{44}$ 2.5755096

5. $5^{\frac{1}{4}}$ 1.4953488

6. $11^{\frac{1}{3}}$ 2.2239801

7. The volume of a sphere is related to its radius by the formula $V = \frac{4}{3}\pi r^3$. Use the formula to find the radius of a balloon that has a volume of 3500 ft³. Use $\pi \approx 3.14$. About 9.4203395 ft

Square Roots and Right Triangles   **389**

Chapter Review

Complete.

1. A positive number has exactly __?_ 2 different square root(s). [10–1]

2. $\sqrt{169}$ is 13, therefore 169 is a __?_ perfect square.

3. If 5.2 is used as an estimate for $\sqrt{28.6}$ in the divide-and-average [10–2]
   method, the next estimate will be __?_ 5.35

4. Using the divide-and-average method, $\sqrt{53} = $ __?_ 7.2 to the nearest
   tenth.

5. In the table on page 498, $\sqrt{24.6}$ lies between __?_ 4.899 and __?_ 5. [10–3]

6. Using interpolation and the table on page 498, $\sqrt{5.7} = $ __?_ 2.39 to the
   nearest hundredth.

True or false?

7. The Pythagorean theorem applies to all triangles. False [10–4]

8. The hypotenuse is the longest side of a right triangle and is opposite
   the right angle. True

9. The measure of the diagonal of a 5 cm by 5 cm square is 50 cm. False

Exercises 10–12 refer to the diagram below.
$\triangle ABC \sim \triangle DEF$. **Complete.**

10. $\dfrac{BA}{?\ ED} \equiv \dfrac{AC}{DF}$ 11. $\angle C \cong \angle$ __?_ F [10–5]

12. $\overline{BC}$ corresponds to __?_ $\overline{EF}$.

13. An isosceles right triangle is also called a __?_ 45 ° right triangle. [10–6]

14. An equilateral triangle with sides 16 cm long has an altitude of
    $8\sqrt{3}$ __?_ cm.

15. The legs of an isosceles right triangle are 7 cm long. The length of
    the hypotenuse is __?_ $7\sqrt{2}$ cm.

Exercises 16–21 refer to the diagram at the right. Match.

16. $\sin F$ C   17. $\cos F$ A   A. $\dfrac{x}{7}$ B. $\cos 42° \times 7$ [10–7]

18. $\tan N$ E   19. y D   C. $\dfrac{y}{7}$ D. $\sin 42° \times 7$ [10–8]

20. x B   21. $m \angle N$ F   E. $\dfrac{x}{y}$ F. $48°$

390   *Chapter 10*

Chapter Test

Supplementary Materials
Test Chapter 10, pp. 71–72

If the given symbol names an integer, state the integer. If not, name the
two consecutive integers between which the number lies.

1. $\sqrt{16}$ 4   **2.** $-\sqrt{144}$ **3.** $\sqrt{169} - \sqrt{121}$ **4.** $\sqrt{38 + 43}$ [10–1]

                      -12 2   9

Solve. Give your answer to the nearest tenth.

5. Use the divide-and-average method to approximate $\sqrt{13.7}$. 3.7   [10–2]

6. Using interpolation and the table on page 498, $\sqrt{12.6} \approx \underline{\ ?\ }$. 3.5   [10–3]

7. The area of a square deck is 65.6 m². Find the length of the side.

                                             8.1 m

Is the triangle with sides of the given lengths a right triangle?

8. 6, 8, 10   Yes   **9.** 7, 11, 19   No   **10.** 8, 15, 17   Yes   [10–4]

Exercises 11–13 refer to the diagram at the right.
$\triangle MNO \sim \triangle XYZ$.

11. If $\frac{MN}{XY} = \frac{3}{4}$, then $\frac{NO}{YZ} = \underline{\ ?\ }$. $\frac{3}{4}$ [10–5]

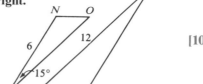

12. Find the length of $\overline{MO}$. 9

13. Find the measure of $\angle N$. 120°

Give answers in terms of radicals with the radical in the numerator.

14. In a 30°–60° right triangle, the shorter leg has length 5. How long is   [10–6]
(a) the longer leg and (b) the hypotenuse? (a) $5\sqrt{3}$

                            (b) 10

15. The hypotenuse of a 45° right triangle has a
length of 36. How long is each leg? $18\sqrt{2}$

Exercises 16–19 refer to the diagram at the right.
Find a value for the trigonometric ratio.

16. $\cos A$ $\frac{4}{5}$ **17.** $\tan A$ $\frac{3}{4}$ **18.** $\cos B$ $\frac{3}{5}$ **19.** $\sin B$ $\frac{4}{5}$ [10–7]

$\triangle KLM$ is an isosceles triangle with $\overline{KL} \cong \overline{LM}$. The third side, $\overline{KM}$, is
42 cm long. The perimeter of $\triangle KLM$ is 112 cm.

                                         28 cm

20. Find the lengths of $\overline{KL}$ and $\overline{LM}$.   **21.** Find the height of $\triangle KLM$.   [10–8]

                  35 cm

22. Find m $\angle K$ and m $\angle M$ to the nearest degree. Use the table on page
499.   53°, 53°

Square Roots and Right Triangles   **391**

Review for Retention

Complete. Use $=$, $>$, or $<$ to make a true statement.

1. $7 \underline{\ ?\ }|-7|$ $=$
2. $|-5| \underline{\ ?\ }|-2|$ $>$
3. $-3.5 + 4.2 \underline{\ ?\ }$
   $|21.7 - 18.1|$ $<$
4. $6.4 - (-2.1) \underline{\ ?\ }$
   $-7.2 + 15.7$ $=$

Evaluate the expression when $a = -3$ and $b = -4.2$.

5. $-b + a$ **1.2**
6. $a - (-b)$ **−7.2**
7. $-|a + b|$ **−7.2**

Solve each proportion.

8. $\frac{16}{80} = \frac{4}{x}$ **20**
9. $\frac{x}{7} = \frac{5.1}{21}$ **1.7**
10. $\frac{42}{18} = \frac{x}{3}$ **7**

Express each fraction or decimal as a percent.

11. 0.57 **57%**
12. $\frac{5}{16}$ **31.25%**
13. 1.025 **102.5%**
14. $\frac{5}{1000}$ **0.5%**

Find the area of the region described. Leave your answers in terms of π when applicable.

15. Triangle: base $= 72$ m
    height $= 40$ m **1440 m²**
16. Rectangle: sides of 50 m
    and 21 m **1050 m²**
17. Circle: radius 7 m
    49π m²
18. Circle: circumference
    22π m **121π m²**

Find the product or quotient.

19. $17(-32)$ **−544**
20. $(-5.7)(-2.1)$ **11.97**
21. $52 \div 1.3$ **40**
22. $-76 \div 0.4$ **−190**
23. $-2(-1.8)(-7)$ **−25.2**

(Continue on next page.)

Cumulative Review (Chapters 1–10)

Exercises

Simplify the expression.

1. $(8 + 2) \div (3 \times 9)$ $\frac{10}{27}$
2. $15 \div 8 + 7 \div 9$ $2\frac{47}{72}$
3. $[48(2 + 5) - 6] \times 10$ **3300**
4. $-26 - 7 + 9 \times 3$ **−6**
5. $2(10 + 5) \div (-3 - 6)$ $-3\frac{1}{3}$
6. $[(7 - 5)(3 \times 5)] - 5$ **25**

Name the property illustrated.

7. $57.89 + 0 = 0 + 57.89$ **Commutative**
8. $46 \times 8 = (40 \times 8) + (6 \times 8)$ **Distributive**
9. $(36 \times 20)15 = 36(20 \times 15)$ **Associative**
10. $88 \times 59 = 59 \times 88$ **Commutative**
11. $(5 \times 175) + (8 \times 175) = 13(175)$ **Distributive**
12. $7861 \times 1 = 7861$ **Multiplicative Prop. of 1**

Evaluate the expression when $a = 10$, $b = -10$, and $c = 0.5$.

13. ab **−100**
14. ac **5**
15. $a + b$ **0**
16. $a - b$ **20**
17. $2ab$ **−200**
18. b^2 **100**
19. ac^2 **2.5**
20. a^2c **50**
21. $\frac{b}{a}$ **−1**
22. $\frac{ab}{c}$ **−200**

Replace $\underline{\ ?\ }$ with $<$, $>$, or $=$ to make a true statement.

23. $\frac{1}{2} \underline{\ ?\ } \frac{3}{8}$ **>**
24. $\frac{1}{5} \underline{\ ?\ } \frac{2}{8}$ **<**
25. $-\frac{4}{5} \underline{\ ?\ } \frac{3}{4}$ **<**
26. $-\frac{1}{3} \underline{\ ?\ } -\frac{7}{9}$ **>**

Solve the equation.

27. $12 + a = 50$ **38**
28. $x - 27 = 56$ **83**
29. $43m = 107.5$ **2.5**
30. $\frac{n}{38.6} = 15$ **579**
31. $z + \frac{2}{3} = 8$ $7\frac{1}{3}$
32. $w - \frac{1}{5} = 12$ $12\frac{1}{5}$

Find the perimeter of the given polygon.

33. square: sides of 2.9 ft **11.6 ft**
34. triangle: 7.11 in., 8.11 in., 12.45 in. **27.67 in.**

Complete the proportion.

35. $\frac{n}{15} = \frac{12}{45}$ **4**
36. $\frac{6}{7} = \frac{n}{35}$ **30**
37. $\frac{8}{n} = \frac{32}{40}$ **10**
38. $\frac{3}{5} = \frac{24}{n}$ **40**

Graph each equation on a separate coordinate plane. Check students' graphs.

39. $x + 2y = 7$
40. $2x + 2y = 9$
41. $x + \frac{1}{5}y = 1$

Find the volume of a cylinder with the given dimensions. Leave your answer in terms of π.

42. radius: 7   height: 12 **588π**
43. radius: 2.3   height: 10.5 **55.545π**

392   *Chapter 10*

Rewrite the expression in lowest terms with the radical in the numerator.

44. $\dfrac{4}{\sqrt{10}}$ $\dfrac{2\sqrt{10}}{5}$

45. $\dfrac{5}{\sqrt{2}}$ $\dfrac{5\sqrt{2}}{2}$

46. $\dfrac{18}{\sqrt{37}}$ $\dfrac{18\sqrt{37}}{37}$

47. $\dfrac{2n}{\sqrt{n}}$ $2\sqrt{n}$

48. $\dfrac{6m}{\sqrt{m}}$ $6\sqrt{m}$

Problems

> **Problem Solving Reminders**
> Here are some problem solving reminders that may help you solve some of the problems on this page.
> - Sometimes more than one method can be used to solve.
> - Supply additional information if necessary.
> - Check your results with the facts given in the problem.

Solve.

1. Evan is a parking lot attendant at the Lonestar Garage. When counting his tips from Monday he discovered he had 12 more quarters than dimes and 3 fewer nickels than quarters. If Evan earned a total of $19.45 in tips, how many of each type of coin did he have?
40 dimes, 52 quarters, 49 nickels

2. A regular pentagon has a perimeter of 378.5 m. Find the length of each side. **75.7 m**

3. A discount store has an automatic markdown policy. Every 7 days, the price of an item is marked down 25% until the item is sold or 4 weeks have elapsed. If the first price of an item is $40 on September 17, what will the price be on October 1? **$22.50**

4. A window washer uses a vinegar and water solution in the ratio of one-half cup of vinegar to three cups of water. How much vinegar will be in two gallons of solution? $4\frac{4}{7}$ **cups**

5. Lavender soap is sold in boxes of 3 bars for $6.50. To the nearest cent, what is the cost of one bar? **$2.17**

6. Bertha Magnuson had purchased 2500 shares of ABC stock for $3.50 per share. When she sold the stock, its value had gone down to $\frac{5}{8}$ of the purchase price per share. How much did Bertha lose?
$3281.25

7. The area of a square table is 1936 in.^{2}. What will be the dimensions of a square tablecloth that drops 4 in. over each side of the table?
52 in. × 52 in.

8. Mary has $300 to spend on new boots and a winter coat. She expects to spend $\frac{2}{5}$ as much for boots as for a coat. What is the most she can spend on boots? **$85.71**

Square Roots and Right Triangles **393**

---

24. $(-6.4) \div (-0.4)$ **16**

25. Find the total cost of a product if the selling price is $140, and the sales tax is 7%. **$149.80**

26. A suit was discounted 15% of the original price. The original price was $196. How much was the discount? **$29.40**

27. A cylinder has a base radius of 3 cm and a height of 12 cm. What is its surface area? **90π cm^2**

28. What is the volume of the cylinder described in Exercise 27? **108π cm^3**

29. A pyramid has a square base 20 m on a side and a height of 24 m. What is its volume? **3200 m^3**

Write the numbers in order from least to greatest.

30. $-0.45, 0.54, -4.50,$ $5.04, -4.05$ **$-4.50,$ $-4.05, -0.45, 0.54,$ 5.04**

31. $-0.4, -4.65, 0.56,$ $-656, -0.65$ **$-656,$ $-4.65, -0.65, -0.4,$ 0.56**

Write the expression without exponents.

32. -7^{-3} $-\dfrac{1}{343}$

33. $(-4)^{-4}$ $\dfrac{1}{256}$

34. $(-2) \times (-2)^{-4}$ $-\dfrac{1}{8}$

35. $(5)^{-5} \times 5^3$ $\dfrac{1}{25}$

State each ratio as a fraction in lowest terms.

36. $34:51$ $\dfrac{2}{3}$

37. $9:72$ $\dfrac{1}{8}$

38. $18:42$ $\dfrac{3}{7}$

393

11

Probability

The force of hurricane winds is dramatized in this photograph taken at Palm Beach, Florida. Winds from these tropical storms range from 116 to 320 km/h. In the southeastern area of the United States, the hurricane season lasts from June through October. September is the month in which hurricanes are most probable.

These storms develop over the ocean and get their energy from the water beneath them. As they approach land, their energy and wind velocity diminish quickly. Then they are reclassified as heavy rain storms. Though the number of hurricanes varies from year to year, the average number of hurricanes in the Atlantic region is seven per year.

In this chapter, you will learn about the probability or chance that a certain event will happen and how to calculate that probability.

Career Note

Meteorologists use sophisticated tracking equipment plus historical climatic patterns to predict the weather. A career in meteorology, the science dealing with weather and weather conditions, is an interesting one. Colleges offer programs that will give the necessary scientific background. A knowledge of mathematics is basic.

Lesson Commentary
Chapter 11   Probability

Overview

Probability is a subject that most students enjoy. With the increased use of probabilistic models in science, business, and so on, it is a subject receiving considerable attention. The chapter provides a thorough introduction to probability. Although the treatment is elementary, all the standard topics are included. The first half of the chapter defines and applies probability and odds. The second half presents the more advanced concepts of mutually exclusive and independent events.

The arithmetic background required for this chapter is not especially demanding. Students will need sound skills with fractions and decimals to express and use probabilities. It might be a good idea to review fractions and decimals before beginning the work with probability.

SIMPLE PROBABILITIES

11-1 Permutations

Objective *for pages 396–400*

- To determine the number of permutations that can be made from a group of objects.

Teaching Suggestions

Although the counting principle may seem obvious and a matter of common sense, it is probable that students have never considered it formally. When presenting examples, it would be a good idea to actually list the possible choices or arrangements of things. It is important to emphasize that, if there are m ways to do one thing and n ways to do another, then there are n ways to do the second thing for each of the m ways of doing the first. If this point is not clarified there will be students who want to add m and n rather than multiplying.

When discussing permutations, make the point that the word *arrangement* is synonymous with *permutation*.

There are many possible permutations of a given set of objects, even though the objects are the same in each case. Students may realize that they can determine the number of permutations of a given set by using the counting principle, and that memorizing the permutations formula may not be mandatory.

Venn diagrams, which are introduced on page 400, can represent collections of data. If you present this material, show that if there were no red sedans the circles would not overlap. Draw a Venn diagram showing the number of students in two school activities.

Resource Book: Page 133 (Use After Page 400)

Related Activities

To provide a challenge, ask students to solve problems such as the following.

1. Find the number of different license plates possible if each plate has three digits followed by three letters. **17,576,000**
2. Find out how many telephone numbers can be made if no number begins with zero and each telephone has a seven-digit number. **9,000,000**

To provide practice with a calculator or computer, have students investigate factorial numbers. Evaluate $n!$ for many values of n. Students are usually impressed to find how quickly these numbers become very large. To display factorials larger than $11!$ an 8-digit calculator uses scientific notation.

Most calculators cannot go beyond $69!$, since $70!$ exceeds 10^{100} and thus the capacity of the calculator. Students may also notice that each factorial from $5!$ on ends in zero; this is because 2 and 5 are factors.

11-2 Combinations

Objective *for pages 401–403*

■ To determine the number of combinations that can be made from a group of objects.

Teaching Suggestions

Emphasize the difference between combinations and permutations. For a given combination there are many permutations. It can be useful to call permutations "arrangements" and combinations "selections." To help illustrate the distinction, discuss electing officers, where order matters, and choosing a committee, where order doesn't matter.

Try to make the need for dividing by $_rP_r$ in the combinations formula as clear as possible. The reason is that otherwise we would be counting many permutations of the same combination. Why, specifically, is it $_rP_r$ that we divide by? Precisely because this is the number of arrangements of any one selection of r objects. In Example 1 on page 401, if we use the permutations formula then we would be counting ABCD, ABDC, ACBD, and so on separately. However, we should count all of these as only one combination. For any such 4-letter combination, there are $_4P_4$, or 24, permutations, so we divide by $_4P_4$ in order to count all of these permutations as only one combination.

Related Activities

To expand this topic, show students how to form Pascal's Triangle. Each entry is the sum of the numbers above and to the left and right. For example, $3 = 2 + 1$.

$$
\begin{array}{ccccccccc}
& & & & 1 & & & & \\
& & & 1 & & 1 & & & \\
& & 1 & & 2 & & 1 & & \\
& 1 & & 3 & & 3 & & 1 & \\
1 & & 4 & & 6 & & 4 & & 1 \\
\end{array}
$$

Ask students to find the number of combinations of four things taken four at a time, three at a time, and so on. Compare the resulting numbers to the fourth row of Pascal's Triangle, which is the same series of numbers. Explain that this is true for each row; the nth row of the triangle is the number of combinations of n things.

11-3 The Probability of an Event

Objective *for pages 404–408*

■ To determine the probability of an event when the outcomes are equally likely.

Teaching Suggestions

When all possible outcomes are equally likely, we can assign probabilities and use the formula on page 404. Students may ask about experiments for which all outcomes are not equally likely. An example would be a game cube that is "loaded," or a spinner with sectors that are not all the same size.

Point out that the sum of the probability of the possible outcomes must equal 1. In the case of the five cards at the top of page 404,

$$P(\text{heart}) + P(\text{club}) + P(\text{diamond}) + P(\text{spade}) =$$
$$\tfrac{2}{5} + \tfrac{1}{5} + \tfrac{1}{5} + \tfrac{1}{5} = 1.$$

Be sure to take enough time to develop the lattice of points to represent the outcome when rolling two game cubes. Students are generally ready to agree that there are eleven possible sums, but they may not realize that there are 36 possible outcomes until they remember the counting principle in Lesson 11-1. It may be helpful to demonstrate that there are several different ways of rolling some sums. For example, there are three ways of rolling 4: (1, 3), (2, 2), and (3, 1). You may want to refer to the chart on page 432.

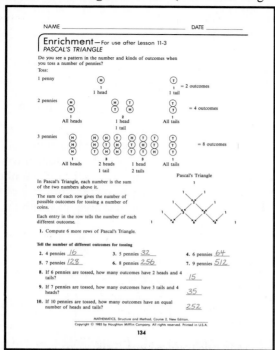

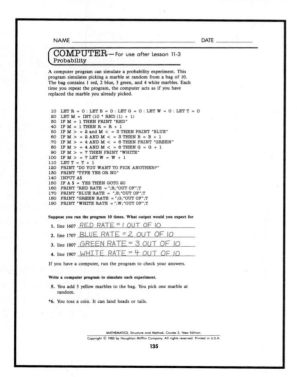

Related Activities

To simulate probability experiments using random numbers, use a telephone directory. Students might choose the last number on each page. To simulate tossing a game cube, look at the last two digits of each number. Reject any number if the last two digits contain 0, 7, 8, or 9. Record 60 numbers. Find the sum of the two digits of each number. How many sevens are there? The probability of a seven is $\frac{1}{6}$.

11-4 Odds in Favor and Odds Against

Objective for pages 409–412

■ To determine the odds in favor of an event and the odds against an event.

Teaching Suggestions

Many students have the mistaken impression that odds and probability are the same concept. Point out that probability is a ratio of *numbers* (whole) of outcomes, but odds are a ratio of *probabilities*. In most cases, to find the odds for or odds against an event happening, we must find the quotient of two fractions. Emphasize that the value of a probability ranges from 0 to 1, whereas the value of odds may be greater than 1.

The sum of the probabilities of all the possible outcomes must be 1; that is, it is certain that the result of an experiment must be one of the possible outcomes. In experiments with n equally likely outcomes the probability of each outcome is $\frac{1}{n}$; there is a sum of $n\left(\frac{1}{n}\right) = 1$ for all n outcomes. A consequence of this is that if $P(A) = p$, then $P(\text{not } A) = 1 - p$, since all outcomes must be in either A or not A.

Odds of 1 to 1 are called even odds. This occurs when $\frac{p}{1 - p} = 1$, or $p = 1 - p$. By applying some simple algebra, show your class that $p = 1 - p$ can occur only when $p = \frac{1}{2}$. Thus even, or 1 to 1, odds are the same as a probability of $\frac{1}{2}$, as in flipping a coin. When an event has more than an even chance the odds are greater than 1. If there is less than an even chance the odds are less than 1. Point out that the odds in favor of an event and the odds against the event are reciprocals of each other.

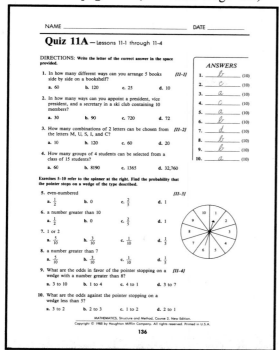

Quiz 11A — Lessons 11-1 through 11-4

Teaching Suggestions

Be sure that students understand mutually exclusive events. For the pointer shown on page 413, events O and E are mutually exclusive because they cannot both occur at once. Events R and O are not mutually exclusive because they both occur when the pointer stops on a red wedge that is odd-numbered.

The formula for mutually exclusive events on page 413 is actually a special case of the more general formula

$$P(A \text{ or } B) = P(A) + P(B) - P(A \text{ and } B),$$

which is presented in the next lesson (page 416). The general formula applies to any two events A and B. If A and B also happen to be mutually exclusive, then $P(A \text{ and } B) = 0$, and we have the formula for mutually exclusive events,

$$P(A \text{ or } B) = P(A) + P(B).$$

It may seem to students that this should be the general formula. However, A and B have a nonempty intersection when they are not mutually exclusive, so adding $P(A)$ and $P(B)$ would actually count some outcomes twice.

Related Activities

To provide a challenge, ask students to determine which event has the better odds. They will have to devise a method for answering; an example would be to divide b into a, when odds are a to b, and express the odds as a decimal.

		Odds in Favor	
	Event A	Event B	
1.	18 to 11 1.$\overline{63}$	23 to 14 1.64	B better
2.	7 to 16 0.44	8 to 19 0.42	A better
3.	37 to 48 0.77	40 to 53 0.75	A better

COMBINED PROBABILITIES

11-5 Mutually Exclusive Events

Objective *for pages 413–415*

■ To identify mutually exclusive events and apply the formula for the probability of "A or B" where A and B are mutually exclusive events.

Related Activities

To provide a challenge, present the following problem. A clinic is staffed by doctors and nurses. There are always 1, 2, or 3 doctors and 1, 2, or 3 nurses. The possible combinations are shown in the diagram.

1. Describe in words the event indicated.
  a. A 1 nurse, 1 or 2 doctors
  b. B total staff 3
  c. C 2 nurses
  d. D total staff 4
  e. E 3 nurses or 3 doctors

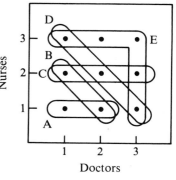

2. Are the following pairs of events mutually exclusive?
  a. A and B No   **b.** A and C Yes   **c.** B and C No
  d. B and D Yes   **e.** B and E Yes   **f.** C and D No
  g. C and E No   **h.** A and D Yes   **i.** A and E Yes

395d

11-6 "Overlapping" Events

Objective for pages 416–419

- To identify overlapping events and apply the formula for the probability of "A or B" where A and B are overlapping events.

Teaching Suggestions

It is possible that two or more events have outcomes in common. This, of course, would mean that the events are not mutually exclusive. In this case the events have a nonempty intersection. If we were to list the outcomes in one event, and then list the outcomes in the other event, some outcomes would be listed twice. For example, if two people give birthday presents to Terry, they might each give Terry a cassette player.

The same kind of thing happens when we deal with probabilities. If we add $P(A)$ and $P(B)$ we are counting the outcomes in the intersection of A and B twice. This is the reason that we must subtract $P(A \text{ and } B)$; this eliminates one of the two countings of the outcomes in the intersection, so that all outcomes are now counted only once.

You might want to relate this formula to the one in Lesson 11-5 (page 413). The formula on page 416 is the more general one. If A and B are mutually exclusive we have $P(A \text{ and } B) = 0$. The general formula leads to the special case for mutually exclusive events:

$$P(A \text{ or } B) = P(A) + P(B) - P(A \text{ and } B)$$
$$= P(A) + P(B) - 0$$
$$= P(A) + P(B)$$

Related Activities

To provide additional practice in problem solving, present the following problem. The probability that Fran will go to the movies is 0.39. The probability that Fran will go swimming is 0.18. The probability that Fran will go to the movies or go swimming is 0.42.

1. What is the probability that Fran will go to the movies and go swimming? **0.15**
2. What is the probability that Fran will go to the movies but not go swimming?
   P(movies and not swimming)
   = P(movies) − P(movies and swimming)
   = 0.39 − 0.15 = 0.24

11-7 Independent Events

Objective for pages 420–423

- To identify independent events and apply the formula for the probability of "A and B" where A and B are independent events.

Teaching Suggestions

There are two ways to look at the meaning of independent events. On the one hand, we say that independent events are those that do not affect each other. Conversely, we may use the formula to define the term: A and B are independent events if and only if

$$P(A \text{ and } B) = P(A) \times P(B).$$

Students may ask if independent events are the same as mutually exclusive events. Assure them that this is not the case. For example, when rolling a red and a green game cube, rolling 6 on the red is independent of rolling 5 on the green. $P(\text{red } 6) = \frac{1}{6}$, $P(\text{green } 5) = \frac{1}{6}$, and $P(\text{red } 6 \text{ and green } 5) = \frac{1}{36}$. The events are not, of course, mutually exclusive.

Although students will probably realize it on their own, if necessary you can point out the significance of replacing or not replacing marbles in the marble drawing experiment. With replacement, events are independent; without, they are not.

Written Exercises 13 and 14 provide an opportunity to dissuade students of any fallacious belief in the so-called "Law of Averages." This "law" is widely believed, but patently untrue. If a coin has come up heads five times in a row, $P(\text{heads}) = \frac{1}{2}$ for the sixth toss, as for each toss. Although the probability of heads on any given toss is $\frac{1}{2}$, it is true that $P(6 \text{ heads in a row})$ is $\left(\frac{1}{2}\right)^6 = \frac{1}{64}$, which is certainly a low probability.

Related Activities

To apply the skills learned in this section, present the following problem: Jackson School has 100 boys and 100 girls in each of grades 7, 8, and 9. One of these students will be chosen at random for an interview. What is the probability that the student is:

1. a girl? $\frac{1}{2}$
2. a 9th grade boy? $\frac{1}{6}$
3. an 8th grader? $\frac{1}{3}$
4. a 7th grader or a girl? $\frac{2}{3}$

11-8 Dependent Events

Objective *for pages 424–427*

■ To identify dependent events and apply the formula for the probability of "*A* and *B*" where *A* and *B* are dependent events.

Teaching Suggestions

It would be helpful to point out that once we accept that an event *A* has occurred, we must recompute the probability of *B* in light of the occurrence of *A*. Of course, this is what we mean by $P(B|A)$ and it is possible for $P(B|A)$ to be the same as, greater than, or less than $P(B)$. Given that *A* occurs, this may raise or lower the chances of *B* occurring, or leave this chance unchanged.

In discussing conditional probability, you may want to point out that the formula applies whether or not *A* and *B* are dependent. Even when *A* and *B* are independent, we have

$$P(A \text{ and } B) = P(A) \times P(B|A),$$

since $P(B|A) = P(B)$ in this case, so that the formula is equivalent to

$$P(A \text{ and } B) = P(A) \times P(B),$$

which we have seen is true for independent events.

Related Activities

To provide a challenge for your ablest students, present the following problem. A bag contains many red and blue marbles. You draw two marbles. If they are the same color, put one red marble into the bag. If they are different colors, put one blue marble into the bag. Keep doing this until there is only one marble left in the bag. Is it possible to predict what color the last marble will be? If so, what would you have to know about the original numbers of marbles? **Each time you draw two marbles and replace one, the number of red marbles in the bag changes from odd to even or vice versa. The number of blue marbles removed is always either 0 or 2, so the number of blue marbles in the bag always remains odd or even, whichever it was originally. Therefore the color of the last marble depends on whether the original number of blue marbles is even or odd. If it was even, the number of blue marbles in the bag is always even, so a lone marble must be red. If the original number of blue marbles was odd, the number in the bag is always odd, so a lone marble must be blue.**

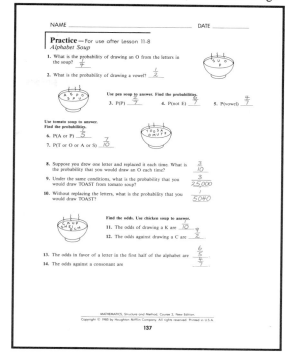

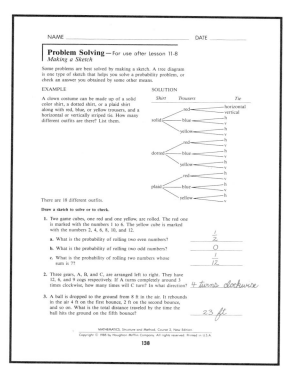

11-9 Estimating Probabilities

Objective *for pages 428–431*

■ To estimate the probability of an event on the basis of repeated observations or random samples.

Teaching Suggestions

It may not be immediately obvious to students why sampling is a desirable way to determine information. Explain about such factors as expense and time, which could be prohibitive if we were to use only 100% "samples" of a population.

To make the case for sampling a bit more dramatically, suggest a product for which the testing procedure destroys the item being tested. Ask students to consider what would happen if every flashbulb manufactured were tested to see if it works.

The question of how to select a "random," or truly representative, sample is not a trivial one. This question occupies a major place in statistics. Care must be taken so that the samples taken do not give distorted results.

You might want to mention the Law of Large Numbers in connection with sampling. Informally, this law states that the larger the sample, the more closely sample statistics will approximate the statistics for the entire population. This may be what some people have in mind when they refer to the "Law of Averages."

In the solution of Example 2, note that in part **a** we calculated the ratio of the number defective in a sample to the number in the sample as 0.03. We assume that this ratio applies to any number of calculators, including the total daily output of 5000 calculators.

Related Activities

To build appreciation of the sampling process, have students develop a method for selecting a sample of 100 students in your school to obtain a representative opinion on a current school issue or policy.

To relate mathematics to science, present the following example of sampling. To find out how many fish of a certain species live in a lake, biologists catch 100 fish, tag them, and release them back into the lake. A few days later they catch 100 fish, and count how many are tagged. What is a good estimate of the number of fish in the lake if the number of tagged fish in the second catch is (a) 100? **100**   (b) 10? **1000**   (c) 1? **10,000**

395g

NAME _____ DATE _____

Test — Chapter 11

DIRECTIONS: Write the correct answer in the space provided.

1. In how many different ways can you arrange the letters in the word THEORY? *[11-1]*

2. How many different three-digit whole numbers can you make with the digits 2, 4, 6, and 8 if no digit appears more than once in each number?

3. In how many ways can a science student choose 4 experiments to perform out of 7? *[11-2]*

Exercises 4–8 refer to the spinner shown at the right. Find the probability that the pointer will stop on a wedge of the described type.

4. odd-numbered 5. a number less than 9 *[11-3]*

6. 9 7. a number greater than 5

8. What are the odds against the pointer stopping on a wedge with a number less than 5? *[11-4]*

9. Events Q and R are mutually exclusive. $P(R) = 0.34$, $P(Q \text{ or } R) = 0.52$. Find $P(Q)$. *[11-5]*

Both dials are spun. Find each probability.

10. 2 comes up. 11. 2 and L comes up. *[11-6]*

12. L comes up. 13. 2 or L comes up.

A bag contains 5 purple discs and 10 green discs. A disc is drawn and replaced. Then a second disc is drawn. Find the probability of each event.

14. Both discs are purple. *[11-7]*

A box contains 2 blue marbles and 6 yellow marbles. A marble is drawn and is not replaced. Then a second marble is drawn. Find the probability of each event.

15. The first marble is yellow and the second is blue. *[11-8]*

A factory turns out 6000 digital watches a day. Of a random sample of 40 watches, 1 was found to be defective.

16. How many watches in a day's output are likely to be defective? *[11-9]*

ANSWERS	
1. 720	(6)
2. 24	(6)
3. 35	(6)
4. $\frac{1}{2}$	(6)
5. 1	(6)
6. 0	(6)
7. $\frac{3}{8}$	(6)
8. 3 to 5	(6)
9. 0.18	(6)
10. $\frac{1}{4}$	(6)
11. $\frac{1}{20}$	(6)
12. $\frac{1}{5}$	(6)
13. $\frac{1}{20}$	(6)
14. $\frac{1}{9}$	(7)
15. $\frac{3}{14}$	(7)
16. 150	(8)

NAME _____ DATE _____

Make-up Test — Chapter 11

DIRECTIONS: Write the correct answer in the space provided.

1. In how many different ways can 5 students be lined up for a group picture? *[11-1]*

2. How many different three-digit whole numbers can you make with the digits 1, 3, 5, 7, and 9 if no digit appears more than once in each number?

3. How many groups of 3 stereo tapes can be selected from 10 tapes? *[11-2]*

Exercises 4–8 refer to the spinner shown at the right. Find the probability that the pointer will stop on a wedge of the type described.

4. even-numbered 5. a number greater than 5 *[11-3]*

6. 10 7. numbered with a multiple of 3

8. What are the odds in favor of the pointer stopping on a wedge with a number less than 7? *[11-4]*

9. Events F and G are mutually exclusive. $P(F) = 0.43$, $P(G) = 0.38$. Find $P(F \text{ or } G)$. *[11-5]*

Both dials are spun. Find each probability.

10. F comes up. 11. F and 4 comes up. *[11-6]*

12. 4 comes up. 13. F or 4 comes up.

A box contains 4 black checkers and 8 red checkers. A checker is drawn and replaced. Then a second checker is drawn. Find the probability of each event.

14. Both checkers are red. *[11-7]*

A bag contains 3 green marbles and 7 white marbles. A marble is drawn and is not replaced. Then a second marble is drawn. Find the probability of each event.

15. The first marble is white and the second is green. *[11-8]*

16. Both marbles are green.

Mr. Karis received a shipment of 1500 light bulbs. He picked 20 bulbs at random and discovered that 1 was defective.

17. Of the 1500 light bulbs, about how many are defective? *[11-9]*

ANSWERS	
1. 120	(6)
2. 60	(6)
3. 120	(6)
4. $\frac{1}{2}$	(6)
5. $\frac{3}{8}$	(6)
6. 0	(6)
7. $\frac{1}{4}$	(6)
8. 3 to 1	(6)
9. 0.81	(6)
10. $\frac{1}{6}$	(6)
11. $\frac{1}{24}$	(6)
12. $\frac{1}{4}$	(6)
13. $\frac{1}{3}$	(6)
14. $\frac{4}{9}$	(7)
15. $\frac{7}{30}$	(7)
16. $\frac{1}{15}$	(6)
17. 75	(4)

NAME _____ DATE _____

CUMULATIVE REVIEW — Chapters 1–11
Exercises

Simplify.

1. $7(4 + 5) + 20 \div 2 + 3$ 76
2. $3(x + 2) + x - 8$ $4x - 2$
3. $(3^3 - 5) \times (23 - 4^2)$ 154
4. $4x + 3y - x + 2y - 2x$ $x + 5y$
5. $40.2 + (4^3 \div 16)$ 442
6. $3a^2 \times 4a^3 \times 2b^2$ $24a^5b^2$

Write an equation or inequality for the word sentence.

7. Three less than five times a number is thirty-seven. $5x - 3 = 37$

8. Thirteen increased by the product of v and nine is greater than forty-eight. $13 + 9v > 48$

9. The quotient when a number q is divided by four is equal to the sum of the number and six. $q \div 4 = q + 6$

Complete. Use $\pi = \frac{22}{7}$ if necessary.

10. If the circumference of a circle is 308, the radius is 49 .
11. If the area of a square is 144 m², a side of the square is 12 m .
12. If the diameter of a circle is 14, the area is 154 .
13. You can choose 35 combinations of 4 colors from 7 colors.

Solve.

14. $5x + 9 = 8x + 12$ $x = -1$ 15. $t + \frac{2}{3} > 2\frac{1}{3}$ $t > 2\frac{1}{2}$ 16. $18 - 3x < 0$ $x > 6$

17. What is 132% of 70? 92.4
18. What percent of 40 is 26? 65%
19. 48 is 75% of what number? 64
20. What is $\frac{1}{2}$% of 8? 0.04

Write the fraction in lowest terms.

21. $\frac{18}{216}$ $\frac{1}{12}$ 22. $-\frac{32}{128}$ $-\frac{1}{4}$ 23. $\frac{13}{260}$ $\frac{1}{20}$ 24. $-\frac{45}{60}$ $-\frac{3}{4}$

Find the volume of a cylinder with the given dimensions. Leave your answer in terms of π.

25. radius: 5, height: 8 200π
26. radius: 3.4, height: 10 115.6π

Find the value of each factorial.

27. 3! 6 28. 1! 1 29. 5! 120 30. 2! 2

NAME _____ DATE _____

CUMULATIVE REVIEW — Chapters 1–11 (continued)
Problems

Problem Solving Reminders
Here are some problem solving reminders that may help you solve some of the problems on this page.
- Some steps in your plan may not involve operations.
- Consider whether a chart will help to organize information.
- Check by using rounding to find an estimated answer.

Solve.

1. Three coins are tossed at the same time. What is the probability of getting three heads? $\frac{1}{8}$

2. Evan Bormanski purchased a pair of hockey skates for $39.95, a hockey stick for $18.90, a hat for $7.25, gloves for $4.80, and thermal socks for $5.45. There was a 5% sales tax on his purchases. What was the total cost? $80.17

3. Wendy is 4 years younger than Jane. Scott is 2 years younger than twice Jane's age. The sum of their ages is 50. What is each person's age? Jane = 14, Wendy = 10, Scott = 26

4. A jar contains four $1 bills, three $5 bills, and five $10 bills. If a bill is drawn from the jar, what is the probability of picking either a $5 or $10? $\frac{2}{3}$

5. When the pool is winterized, water runs out at the rate of $1\frac{1}{3}$ gal/h. How long will it take for 36 gal to run out? 27 h

6. A case of Kitty Pretty Cat Food is on sale for $17.64. There are 36 cans in a case. The original price was 3 cans for $1.79. How much is saved by buying 3 cases at the sale price? $11.52

7. Marsha Malbin bought 75 shares of Max Oil (MO) stock and 50 shares of Thinger Brands (TB) stock. Quarterly, MO paid a dividend of $1.35 per share and TB paid a dividend of $1.62 per share. At the end of one year, what was the total that Marsha received in dividends? $729.00

11-1 Permutations

After school, Vilma plans to go to the music store and then to the pool. She can take any one of 3 routes from school to the music store and then take either of 2 routes from the store to the pool. In how many different ways can Vilma go from school to the pool?

To answer, consider that for each route Vilma can take from school to the music store, she has a choice of either of 2 routes to continue from there. Thus, she has a choice of 3×2, or 6, possible different ways to go from school to the pool.

This example illustrates a general counting principle:

> If there are m ways to do one thing and n ways to do another, then there are $m \times n$ ways to do both things.

In mathematics, an arrangement of a group of things in a particular order is called a **permutation.** The counting principle can help you count the number of different permutations of any group of items.

EXAMPLE 1 In how many different ways can you arrange the three cards shown at the right if you arrange them side by side in a row?

Solution Notice that there are 3 possibilities for the first card: A, B, or C. After the first card is selected, there are 2 possibilities for the second card. After the first and second cards have been selected, there is just 1 possibility for the third card.

Applying the counting principle, there are $3 \times 2 \times 1$, or 6, possible ways to arrange the three cards.

To check, list the permutations: A B C   B A C   C A B
A C B   B C A   C B A

Notice that the number of permutations of 3 things is $3 \times 2 \times 1$. We can write 3! (read *3 factorial*) to represent the expression $3 \times 2 \times 1$. In general, the number of permutations of n things is

$$n \times (n - 1) \times (n - 2) \times \cdots \times 3 \times 2 \times 1.$$

We can write this expression as $n!$.

396 *Chapter 11*

If we let $_nP_n$ represent the number of permutations of a group of n things when using all n things, we can write the following formula.

Formula

For the number of permutations of n things taken n at a time,

$$_nP_n = n \times (n - 1) \times (n - 2) \times \cdots \times 3 \times 2 \times 1 = n!$$

EXAMPLE 2 How many four-digit whole numbers can you write using the digits 1, 2, 3, and 4 if no digit appears more than once in each number?

Solution You need to find the number of permutations of 4 things taken 4 at a time.
Using the formula,

$$_4P_4 = 4! = 4 \times 3 \times 2 \times 1 = 24.$$

Therefore, 24 four-digit whole numbers can be written using the given digits.

Sometimes we work with arrangements that involve just a portion of the group at one time.

EXAMPLE 3 This year, 7 dogs are entered in the collie competition at the annual Ridgedale Kennel Club show. In how many different ways can first, second, and third prizes be awarded in the competition?

Solution You want to find the number of permutations of 7 things taken 3 at a time. There are 7 choices for first prize, 6 for second, and 5 for third. Thus,

$$7 \times 6 \times 5 = 210.$$

There are 210 possible ways to award the prizes.

If we let $_nP_r$ represent the number of permutations of n objects taken r at a time, we can write the following formula.

Formula

For the number of permutations of n things taken r at a time, we use the following formula carried out to r factors:

$$_nP_r = n \times (n - 1) \times (n - 2) \times \cdots$$

Using the formula in Example 3 above, we find $_7P_3 = 7 \times 6 \times 5 = 210$.

Class Exercises

Find the value of each.

1. 4! 24 **2.** 3! 6 **3.** 2! 2 1 **4.** 1!

5. $_5P_5$ 120 **6.** $_3P_3$ 6 **7.** $_5P_4$ 120 120 **8.** $_6P_3$

Solve.

9. In wrapping a gift, you have a choice of 3 different boxes and 4 different wrapping papers. In how many different ways can you wrap the gift? 12

10. There are 3 roads from Craig to Hartsdale, 2 roads from Hartsdale to Lee, and 4 roads from Lee to Trumbull. In how many different ways can you travel from Craig to Trumbull by way of Hartsdale and Lee? 24

Use the formula to answer. Then list all of the permutations to check.

11. In how many different ways can you arrange the letters in the word CAR? 6

12. In how many different ways can you arrange the 4 cards shown at the right if you take 3 at a time and arrange them side by side? 24

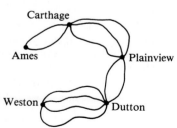

Written Exercises

Find the value of each.

A **1.** 5! 120 **2.** 6! 720 **3.** 7! 5040 40,320 **4.** 8!

5. $_6P_6$ 720 **6.** $_7P_7$ 5040 **7.** $_8P_8$ 40,320 120 **8.** $_5P_5$

9. $_6P_4$ 360 **10.** $_8P_4$ 1680 **11.** $_{43}P_3$ 74,046 506 **12.** $_{23}P_2$

Problems

Exercises 1–4 refer to the map at the right. Tell how many different ways you can travel from one city to the other.

A **1.** Ames to Plainview 6 **2.** Carthage to Dutton 6

3. Carthage to Weston 24 **4.** Ames to Dutton 12

398 *Chapter 11*

Additional Answers
Class Exercises

11. CAR, CRA, RAC, RCA, ARC, ACR

12. RYG, RGY, RYB, RBY, RBG, RGB, YGB, YBG, YBR, YRB, YRG, YGR, GRB, GBR, GYR, GRY, GYB, GBY, BYR, BRY, BRG, BGR, BYG, BGY

Additional A Exercises

Find the value of each.

1. $_5P_2$ 20

2. $_6P_5$ 720

3. $_8P_3$ 336

A four-digit number is to be made using the digits 1, 3, 5, and 8.

4. How many numbers can be made if repeated digits are allowed? 256

5. How many numbers can be made if all digits must be different? 24

6. How many even numbers can be made if all digits must be different? 6

5. A furniture store sells couches that are available in 3 different styles, 7 different colors, and 2 different sizes. How many different couches are available? 42

6. How many different sandwiches can you make using one kind of bread, one kind of meat, and one kind of cheese with these choices?

Bread: white, rye, whole wheat 18
Cheese: Swiss, cheddar
Meat: turkey, chicken, roast beef

Use a formula to solve. List the permutations to check your answer.

7. In how many different ways can you arrange the 4 books shown side by side on a shelf? 24

8. In how many different ways can Carla, Dean, and Ellen be seated in a row of 3 chairs? 6

9. How many different two-digit whole numbers can you make with the digits 1, 3, 5, and 7 if no digit appears more than once in each number? 12

10. In how many different ways can you arrange the letters in the word RING if you take the letters 3 at a time? 24

Solve.

B **11.** In how many different ways can 7 books be arranged side by side on a shelf? 5040

12. In how many different ways can 6 students stand in a row of 6? 720

13. In how many different ways can you arrange the letters in the word ANSWER if you take the letters 5 at a time? 720

14. How many different four-digit numbers can you make using the digits 1, 2, 3, 5, 7, 8, and 9 if no digit appears more than once in a number? 840

Using the digits 1, 2, 4, 5, 7, and 8, how many different three-digit numbers can you form according to each of the following rules?

C **15.** Each digit may be repeated any number of times in a number. 216

16. The numbers are even numbers and no digit appears more than once in a number. 60

17. There is a 5 in the ones' place and no digit appears more than once in a number. 20

Probability **399**

Suggested Assignments

Minimum
398/1–12
398/Prob. 1–4
399/Prob. 5–12
399/Rev. 1–8

Average
398/1–12
398/Prob. 1–4
399/Prob. 5–17
400/Rev. 2–8 even
400/Challenge

Maximum
398/1–11 odd
398/Prob. 1–4
399/Prob. 5–17
400/Prob. 18–20
400/Challenge

Supplementary Materials

Practice Masters, p. 49

Additional Answers Problems

7. BYRW, BYWR, BWRY, BWYR, BRYW, BRWY, WRBY, WRYB, WYRB, WYBR, WBYR, WBRY, RYBW, RYWB, RWBY, RWYB, RBYW, RBWY, YBRW, YBWR, YWBR, YWRB, YRBW, YRWB

8. CDE, CED, DEC, DCE, EDC, ECD

9. 13, 15, 17, 31, 35, 37, 51, 53, 57, 71, 73, 75

10. RIN, RNI, RGN, RNG, RIG, RGI, NIR, NRI, NIG, NGI, NRG, NGR, GRN, GNR, GIR, GRI, GNI, GIN, IRG, IGR, ING, IGN, IRN, INR

18. In how many different ways can you arrange the letters in the word ROOT? (*Hint:* Notice that two of the letters are indistinguishable.) **12**

19. In how many different ways can you arrange the letters in the word NOON? **6**

The diagram at the right, called a **Venn diagram,** illustrates the following statement.

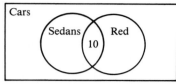

> Of 100 cars, 35 are sedans, 25 are red, and 10 are red sedans.

The rectangular region represents the number of cars. One circular region represents the number of sedans; the other represents the number of red cars. The overlapping portion of the two circular regions represents the number of cars that are red and sedans. The number of red cars that are not sedans is 25 − 10, or 15.

Draw a Venn diagram to illustrate the statement. Then answer the questions.

20. Of 240 knit caps, 110 are striped, 65 are blue, and 45 are striped and blue.
   a. How many are striped but not blue? **65**
   b. How many are blue but not striped? **20**
   c. How many are striped or blue (striped, or blue, or both)? **130**
   d. How many are neither striped nor blue? **110**

Review Exercises

Simplify.

1. $\frac{70}{5} \times \frac{1}{2}$ **7**

2. $\frac{15}{12} \times \frac{36}{60}$ **$\frac{3}{4}$**

3. $\frac{21}{5} \times \frac{10}{14}$ **3**

4. $\frac{27}{51} \times \frac{17}{3}$ **3**

5. $\frac{9 \times 8}{3 \times 2}$ **12**

6. $\frac{7 \times 6}{4 \times 3}$ **$\frac{7}{2}$**

7. $\frac{11 \times 10 \times 9}{3 \times 2 \times 1}$ **165**

8. $\frac{23 \times 22 \times 21 \times 20}{4 \times 3 \times 2 \times 1}$ **8855**

▌▌▌ Challenge

You and a friend have decided to jog through Peachtree Park. The park has five entrance gates and several paths as shown in the diagram at the right. To jog along all of the paths without covering any path more than once, through which gate would you enter? **Gate 1 or Gate 4**

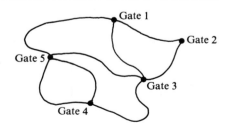

11-2 Combinations

Sometimes we select groups of objects from a larger group without regard to the order of the objects selected. Such groups in which the order is not considered are called **combinations.**

Suppose there is a group of 4 students—Jon, Lin, Meg, and Ray—who wish to go to the computer center today. If only 3 of them may go today, what are the possible combinations of these students who may be selected to go? To find any one combination, just leave out 1 student from the group of 4. The possible combinations are listed below.

Jon, Lin, Meg   Jon, Lin, Ray   Jon, Meg, Ray   Lin, Meg, Ray

The number of groups of 3 students that can be selected from a group of 4 students is 4.

Here is another way to approach the problem.

$$\begin{bmatrix} \text{number of groups} \\ \text{of 3 students you} \\ \text{can select from 4} \end{bmatrix} \times \begin{bmatrix} \text{number of ways of} \\ \text{arranging 3 stu-} \\ \text{dents in a group} \end{bmatrix} = \begin{bmatrix} \text{number of ways of} \\ \text{arranging 3 out} \\ \text{of 4 students} \end{bmatrix}$$

$$N \quad\quad\quad \times \quad\quad\quad {}_3P_3 \quad\quad\quad = \quad\quad\quad {}_4P_3$$

Solving for N, we find that

$$N = \frac{{}_4P_3}{{}_3P_3} = \frac{4 \times 3 \times 2}{3 \times 2 \times 1} = 4.$$

This formula gives us the same answer that we found by showing and counting the number of combinations of 3 students that may be selected from a group of 4 students.

EXAMPLE 1 How many combinations of 4 cards can be chosen from the cards shown at the right?

Solution Use the formula to find the number of combinations of 6 cards taken 4 at a time.

$$N = \frac{{}_6P_4}{{}_4P_4} = \frac{\overset{3}{\cancel{6}} \times 5 \times \overset{1}{\cancel{4}} \times \overset{1}{\cancel{3}}}{\underset{1}{\cancel{4}} \times \underset{1}{\cancel{3}} \times \underset{1}{\cancel{2}} \times 1} = \frac{15}{1} = 15$$

List the combinations to check.

A B C D	A B D E	A C D E	A D E F	B C E F
A B C E	A B D F	A C D F	B C D E	B D E F
A B C F	A B E F	A C E F	B C D F	C D E F

Probability **401**

Teaching Suggestions p. 395b

Related Activities p. 395b

Reading Mathematics

Students will learn the meaning of the following mathematical term in this lesson: *combination.*

Chalkboard Examples

Find the value of each.

1. ${}_6C_3$ 20

2. ${}_7C_5$ 21

3. ${}_8C_5$ 56

Five club members have agreed to serve on a committee, but only three are needed. Those willing to serve are Ann, Bill, Carla, Dana, and Emil.

4. List all the possible combinations of people who could be chosen for the committee.
ABC ABD ABE ACD
ACE ADE BCD BCE
BDE CDE

5. How many possible combinations are there for the committee members? 10

Suppose Ann, Carla, and Emil are chosen for the committee.

6. A committee head is to be chosen. How many choices are there? 3

7. A publicity subcommittee is chosen, to consist of two of the committee members. How many combinations of people are possible for this subcommittee? 3

In general, if we let $_nC_r$ represent the number of combinations of n things taken r at a time, we can use the following formula.

> ## Formula
>
> For the number of combinations of n things taken r at a time,
>
> $$_nC_r = \frac{_nP_r}{_rP_r} = \frac{n \times (n-1) \times \cdots \text{(to } r \text{ factors)}}{r!}$$

EXAMPLE 2 Four of 7 students who have volunteered will be chosen to hand out programs at the drama club performance. How many combinations of these students can be selected?

Solution We wish to find the number of combinations of 7 students taken 4 at a time.
Using the formula, we find

$$_7C_4 = \frac{_7P_4}{_4P_4} = \frac{7 \times 6 \times 5 \times 4}{4 \times 3 \times 2 \times 1} = \frac{35}{1} = 35.$$

Class Exercises

Find the value of each.

1. $_5C_3$ 10 **2.** $_5C_4$ 5 **3.** $_6C_2$ 15 **4.** $_7C_2$ 21 **5.** $_8C_4$ 70 **6.** $_8C_6$ 28 **7.** $_{12}C_3$ 220 **8.** $_{20}C_2$ 190

Use the formula to solve. List the combinations to check your answer.

9. How many combinations of 2 cards can be chosen from the cards shown at the right? 6

10. How many combinations of 3 letters can be chosen from the letters A, B, C, D, and E? 10

Problems

A **1.** How many combinations of 4 books can you choose from 6 books? 15

2. How many groups of 3 types of plants can be selected from 6 types? 20

3. How many straight lines can be formed by connecting any 2 of 6 points, no 3 of which are on a straight line? 15

402 *Chapter 11*

402

4. How many groups of 4 fabrics can be selected from 7 fabrics? 35

B **5.** How many ways can a class of 21 students select 2 of its members as class representatives for student government? 210

6. The school photographer wants to photograph 3 students from a club with 14 members. How many combinations can be made? 364

7. Kristen must answer 5 of 10 questions on her quiz. How many combinations of questions are possible? 252

8. Philip wishes to check 2 books out of his school library. If the library contains 800 books, in how many ways might Philip make his choice of books? 319,600

9. You have a total of 4 coins: a penny, a nickel, a dime, and a quarter. How many different amounts of money can you form using the given number of these coins?
 a. 1 coin   **b.** 2 coins   **c.** 3 coins   **d.** 4 coins   **e.** one or more coins
 4   6   4   1   15

10. There are three books left in the sale rack: a book about sailing, a cookbook, and a book about baseball. How many combinations can be formed using the given number of these books?
 a. 1 book   **b.** 2 books   **c.** 3 books 1   **d.** one or more books 7
 3   3

C **11.** In how many ways can a five-member committee of 3 seniors and 2 juniors be selected from a group of 14 seniors and 8 juniors? (*Hint:* Find the number of combinations of each type and determine their product.) 10,192

12. A basketball squad has 17 members. The coach has designated 3 members to play center, 6 to play guard, and 8 to play forward. How many ways can the coach select a starting team of 1 center, 2 guards, and 2 forwards? (*Hint:* See the hint in Exercise 11.) 1260

Review Exercises

Explain the meaning of each term.

1. factor   **2.** multiple   **3.** even number   **4.** odd number

5. cube   **6.** at least one   **7.** at most one   **8.** exactly one

Probability   **403**

Suggested Assignments

Minimum
  402/Prob. 1–3
  403/Prob. 4–10
  403/Rev. 1–8

Average
  402/Prob. 1–3
  403/Prob. 4–11
  403/Rev. 1–8

Maximum
  402/Prob. 1–3
  403/Prob. 4–12

Supplementary Materials

Practice Masters, p. 49

Additional Answers
Review Exercises

1. factor: any of two or more numbers that are multiplied together

2. multiple: the product of a given whole number and any whole number

3. even number: a whole number that is a multiple of 2

4. odd number: a whole number that is not a multiple of 2

5. cube: a rectangular solid in which all edges are equal

6. at least one: one or more occurrences of an event

7. at most one: one or fewer occurrences of an event

8. exactly one: one and only one occurrence of an event

Teaching Suggestions
p. 395b

Related Activities p. 395c

Reading Mathematics

Students will learn the meaning of the following mathematical terms in this lesson: *outcome, probability, random, impossible, certain.*

In mathematics, some words have different meanings from their ordinary usage, but some words such as *certain* and *impossible* mean the same as they do in ordinary language.

11-3 The Probability of an Event

In a simple game, the five cards shown are turned face down and mixed so that all choices are *equally likely.*

You then draw a card. If the card is a heart, you win a prize. To find your chance of winning, notice that there are 5 possible **outcomes.** Notice, too, that 2 of the outcomes are hearts. We say that 2 of the outcomes **favor** the event of drawing a heart. The **probability,** or chance, of drawing a heart is $\frac{2}{5}$. If we let H stand for the event of drawing a heart, we may write $P(H) = \frac{2}{5}$. This statement is read as *the probability of event H is $\frac{2}{5}$.*

In general we have the following:

> ### Formula
>
> The probability of an event E is
>
> $$P(E) = \frac{\text{number of outcomes favoring event } E}{\text{number of possible outcomes}}$$
>
> for equally likely outcomes.

When all outcomes are equally likely, as in drawing one of the cards in the game described above, we say that the outcomes occur *at random,* or *randomly.*

In this chapter, we shall often refer to *experiments* such as drawing cards, drawing marbles from a bag, or rolling game cubes. We shall always assume that the outcomes of these experiments occur at random. When we refer to spinners like the one shown at the right, we shall always assume that the pointer stops at random but not on a division line.

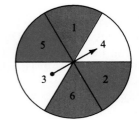

Often it is helpful to list all possible outcomes of an experiment. We could show the possible outcomes for the spinner shown above by using letters to represent the colors and by writing the following:

R1	B2	W3
R6	B5	W4

404 *Chapter 11*

EXAMPLE 1 Find the probability that the pointer of the spinner shown on the preceding page stops on a wedge of the type described.
  a. even-numbered   **b.** odd-numbered
  c. red   **d.** not red
  e. even-numbered *and* red   **f.** green
  g. not green

Solution The number of possible outcomes is 6.

a. $P(\text{even-numbered}) = \frac{3}{6} = \frac{1}{2}$

b. $P(\text{odd-numbered}) = \frac{3}{6} = \frac{1}{2}$

c. $P(\text{red}) = \frac{2}{6} = \frac{1}{3}$

d. $P(\text{not red}) = \frac{4}{6} = \frac{2}{3}$

e. $P(\text{even-numbered and red}) = \frac{1}{6}$

f. $P(\text{green}) = \frac{0}{6} = 0$

g. $P(\text{not green}) = \frac{6}{6} = 1$

The events in parts (f) and (g) of the example illustrate these facts:

> The probability of an impossible event is 0.
> The probability of a certain event is 1.

Sometimes it is useful to picture the possible outcomes of an experiment. Consider the experiment of rolling the two game cubes that are shown at the right. One cube is blue, one cube is red. The numbers 1 through 6 are printed on each cube, one number per face. An outcome can be represented by an ordered pair of numbers. The array at the right shows the 36 possible outcomes when the two cubes are rolled. The encircled dot stands for the outcome of a 5 on the top face of the red cube and a 3 on the top face of the blue cube, or the ordered pair (5, 3).

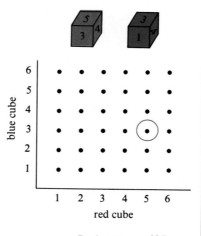

Probability   **405**

EXAMPLE 2   Two game cubes are rolled.

    a. Find the probability that one cube *or* the other cube shows a 5 (that is, that the number 5 is on the top face of either or both cubes).

    b. Find the probability that the sum of the top faces is 5.

Solution   First, make a sketch to show the possible outcomes. Then circle the event.

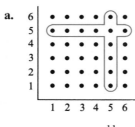

$$P(\text{a } 5) = \frac{11}{36} \qquad\qquad P(\text{sum} = 5) = \frac{4}{36} = \frac{1}{9}$$

Problem Solving Reminder

Sometimes *making a sketch* can help you solve a problem. In Example 2, above, picturing an outcome as the graph of an ordered pair simplifies the problem.

Class Exercises

Two red, one white, and three blue marbles are put into a bag. Find each probability for a marble chosen at random.

1. $P(\text{red})$ $\frac{1}{3}$ **2.** $P(\text{white})$ $\frac{1}{6}$ **3.** $P(\text{blue})$ $\frac{1}{2}$ **4.** $P(\text{green})$
                                                                                                   0

5. $P(\text{not green})$ 1   **6.** $P(\text{red or white})$ $\frac{1}{2}$

7. $P(\text{white or blue})$ $\frac{2}{3}$ **8.** $P(\text{red or blue})$ $\frac{5}{6}$

Exercises 9–12 refer to the spinner at the right. Find the probability that the pointer stops on a wedge of the type described.

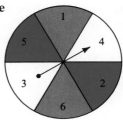

9. numbered with a factor of 6 $\frac{2}{3}$

10. numbered with a multiple of 3 $\frac{1}{3}$

11. even-numbered or blue $\frac{2}{3}$

12. even-numbered and blue $\frac{1}{6}$

406   *Chapter 11*

Written Exercises

Find the probability of each roll if you use a single game cube.

A **1.** a 5 $\frac{1}{6}$

2. an odd number $\frac{1}{2}$

3. a number less than 5 $\frac{2}{3}$

4. a number greater than 3 $\frac{1}{2}$

5. a 7 0

6. a number less than 7 1

Each of the 20 cards shown at the right has a letter, a number, and a color. Each card is equally likely to be drawn. Find each probability.

A 1	A 2	A 3	A 4	A 5
B 1	B 2	B 3	B 4	B 5
C 1	C 2	C 3	C 4	C 5
D 1	D 2	D 3	D 4	D 5

7. $P(C)$ $\frac{1}{4}$

8. $P(A)$ $\frac{1}{4}$

9. $P(1)$ $\frac{1}{5}$

10. $P(2)$ $\frac{1}{5}$

11. $P(\text{red})$ $\frac{1}{2}$

12. $P(\text{blue})$ $\frac{1}{2}$

13. $P(\text{not A})$ $\frac{3}{4}$

14. $P(\text{not D})$ $\frac{3}{4}$

15. $P(1 \text{ or } 2)$ $\frac{2}{5}$

16. $P(1, 2, 3, \text{ or } 4)$ $\frac{4}{5}$

17. $P(\text{neither 1 nor 2})$ $\frac{3}{5}$

18. $P(\text{not 1, or 2, or 3, or 4})$ $\frac{1}{5}$

Exercises 19–28 refer to the spinner below. Find the probability that the pointer stops on a wedge of the type described.

19. red $\frac{1}{3}$

20. white or blue $\frac{2}{3}$

21. numbered with a factor of 12 $\frac{1}{2}$

22. even-numbered $\frac{1}{2}$

23. numbered with a multiple of 3 $\frac{1}{3}$

24. numbered with a multiple of 4 $\frac{1}{4}$

25. odd-numbered or red $\frac{2}{3}$

26. odd-numbered and red $\frac{1}{6}$

27. red and a factor of 6 $\frac{1}{12}$

28. blue and a multiple of 5 0

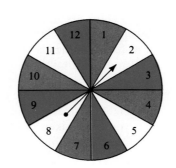

Two game cubes are rolled. Find the probability that this sum shows.

B **29.** 7 $\frac{1}{6}$

30. 12 $\frac{1}{36}$

31. 3 $\frac{1}{18}$

32. 9 $\frac{1}{9}$

33. 7 or 11 $\frac{2}{9}$

34. 2 or 12 $\frac{1}{18}$

35. less than 7 $\frac{5}{12}$

36. 6, 7, or 8 $\frac{4}{9}$

Probability **407**

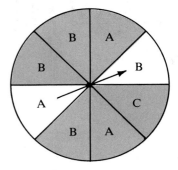

For Exercises 37 and 38, use a *tree diagram* to picture the possible outcomes of the random experiment.

EXAMPLE   Two coins are tossed. Find the probability of obtaining at least one head.

Solution   Let H stand for heads and T stand for tails.

First Coin	Second Coin	Outcomes

There are 4 possible outcomes. Three of the outcomes have one or more heads.
$$P(\text{at least one H}) = \frac{3}{4}$$

37. You have two bags of marbles, each of which holds one blue marble, one red marble, and one green marble. You choose one marble at random from each bag. Find the probability of obtaining the following.
    a. two red marbles $\frac{1}{9}$ b. at least one blue marble $\frac{5}{9}$ c. no green marbles $\frac{4}{9}$
    d. at most one green marble $\frac{8}{9}$ e. exactly one red marble $\frac{4}{9}$

38. Three coins are tossed. Find the probability of obtaining the following.
    a. at least two heads $\frac{1}{2}$ b. three heads $\frac{1}{8}$ c. no heads $\frac{1}{8}$
    d. at most two tails $\frac{7}{8}$ e. exactly one head $\frac{3}{8}$

C 39. You have one penny, one nickel, one dime, and one quarter in your pocket. You select two coins at random. What is the probability that you have taken at least 25¢ from your pocket? $\frac{1}{2}$

Review Exercises

Evaluate each expression using the given values of the variable.

$1 - x$

1. $x = 10$ 2. $x = \frac{1}{2} \quad \frac{1}{2}$ 3. $x = \frac{2}{3} \quad \frac{1}{3}$ 4. $x = -1 \quad 2$

$\dfrac{x}{1 - x}$

5. $x = \frac{1}{3} \quad \frac{1}{2}$ 6. $x = \frac{2}{3} \quad 2$ 7. $x = \frac{3}{7} \quad \frac{3}{4}$ 8. $x = \frac{4}{7} \quad \frac{4}{3}$

408   *Chapter 11*

11-4 Odds in Favor and Odds Against

EXAMPLE 1 A game is played with the spinner shown at the right. To win the game, the pointer must stop on a wedge that shows a prime number. Find each probability.

a. You win.   **b.** You do not win.

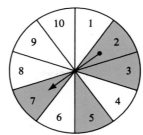

Solution   There are 10 possible outcomes. For you to win, the pointer must stop on 2, 3, 5, or 7. Therefore:

a. $P(\text{win}) = \frac{4}{10} = \frac{2}{5}$

b. $P(\text{not win}) = \frac{6}{10} = \frac{3}{5}$

Example 1 illustrates this general fact:

> If the probability that an event occurs is p, then the probability that the event does not occur is $1 - p$.

In Example 1 there are 4 ways of winning and 6 ways of not winning. We therefore say:

a. The *odds in favor* of winning are 4 to 6, or 2 to 3.

b. The *odds against* winning are 6 to 4, or 3 to 2.

> ## Formula
>
> If the probability that an event occurs is p (where $p \neq 0$ and $p \neq 1$), then:
>
> $$\text{Odds in favor of the event} = \frac{p}{1-p}$$
>
> $$\text{Odds against the event} = \frac{1-p}{p}$$

Odds are usually expressed in the form "x to y," where x and y are integers having no common factor.

EXAMPLE 2 Find the odds (a) in favor of and (b) against rolling a sum of 6 with two game cubes.

Solution From the array of possible outcomes, we see that:

$$P(\text{sum} = 6) = \frac{5}{36} = p$$

$$P(\text{sum} \neq 6) = 1 - p = 1 - \frac{5}{36} = \frac{31}{36}$$

a. Odds in favor $= \dfrac{p}{1-p}$

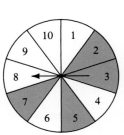

$$\frac{\frac{5}{36}}{\frac{31}{36}} = \frac{5}{36} \div \frac{31}{36} = \frac{5}{36} \times \frac{36}{31} = \frac{5}{31}$$

Odds in favor are 5 to 31.

b. Odds against are 31 to 5.

EXAMPLE 3 The chance of rain tomorrow is 40%. What are the odds against its raining?

Solution The probability of rain is $p = 40\% = 0.4$.

Odds against rain $= \dfrac{1-p}{p} = \dfrac{1 - 0.4}{0.4} = \dfrac{0.6}{0.4} = \dfrac{3}{2}$

Odds against rain are 3 to 2.

Class Exercises

1. The chance of rain tomorrow is 20%. Find the odds against rain. **4 to 1**

2. Find the odds against rolling a 4 with one game cube. **5 to 1**

Exercises 3–6 refer to the spinner at the right. Find the odds (a) in favor of and (b) against the pointer stopping on a wedge of the type described.

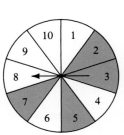

3. an odd number **1 to 1; 1 to 1**   4. a multiple of 3 **3 to 7; 7 to 3**

5. a factor of 10 **2 to 3; 3 to 2**   6. a number less than 7 **3 to 2; 2 to 3**

7. The odds are 1 to 1 that an event will occur. What is the probability that the event will occur? $\frac{1}{2}$

8. The probability that an event will occur is $\frac{1}{2}$. What are the odds against the event? **1 to 1**

Written Exercises

Exercises 1–6 refer to a bag containing 6 red, 2 white, and 4 blue marbles. Find the odds in favor of drawing a marble of the type described.

A **1.** red 1 to 1

2. white 1 to 5

3. blue 1 to 2

4. white or blue 1 to 1

5. blue or red 5 to 1

6. red or white 2 to 1

7. The chance of rain tomorrow is 60%. What are the odds against rain? 2 to 3

8. The probability of snow next week is 75%. What are the odds in favor of snow? 3 to 1

9. The probability that the Lions football team will win the next game is 0.6. What are the odds that it will win? 3 to 2

10. The Student Union Party has a 30% chance of winning in the next school election. What are the odds against its winning? 7 to 3

In Exercises 11–16 a card has been drawn at random from the 20 cards that are shown. Find the odds against drawing a card of the type described.

11. an A 3 to 1

12. a blue card 1 to 1

13. a red card 1 to 1

14. a C 3 to 1

15. a 1, 2, or 3 2 to 3

16. B2, B3, B4, or B5 4 to 1

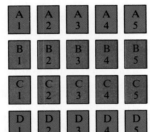

Two game cubes are rolled. Find the odds against obtaining the sum described.

17. 7 5 to 1

18. 11 17 to 1

19. 7 or 11 7 to 2

20. 2 or 12 17 to 1

21. greater than 7 7 to 5

22. less than 6 13 to 5

B **23. a.** even 1 to 1   **b.** odd 1 to 1

24. a. divisible by 3 2 to 1   **b.** not divisible by 3 1 to 2

Probability **411**

1. In how many different ways can you arrange 5 framed photographs in a row for an exhibit? **120**

2. How many different auto part codes can be made if each code is a 3-digit number, the digits 1, 2, 6, 7, 8, and 9 can be used, and no digit can be used more than once in a code? **120**

3. The Lees are planning a trip to New England. The trip will include 4 of the New England states (Maine, Vermont, New Hampshire, Massachusetts, Connecticut, Rhode Island). How many combinations of states are there? **15**

4. How many committees of 4 people can be appointed from a class of 12 students? **495**

A card is drawn. Find the probability of drawing the kind of card described.

5. blue $\frac{1}{2}$

6. red $\frac{1}{2}$

7. not a star $\frac{2}{3}$

8. star $\frac{1}{3}$

9. What are the odds in favor of drawing a blue triangle from the cards above? **1 to 5**

10. What are the odds against drawing a star? **2 to 1**

The two game cubes are rolled again. Find the odds in favor of the event described.

25. Exactly one 5 shows. **5 to 13**

26. At least one 5 shows. **11 to 25**

27. Two even numbers show. **1 to 3**

28. At least one odd number shows. **3 to 1**

29. The numbers showing differ by 2. **2 to 7**

30. The product of the numbers showing is 6. **1 to 8**

C 31. The odds in favor of the Melodies winning the music competition are 5 to 3. What is the probability that the Melodies will win? $\frac{5}{8}$

32. The odds in favor of drawing a red marble at random from a bag of marbles are 1 to 8. What is the probability of drawing a red marble? $\frac{1}{9}$

Self-Test A

1. In how many different ways can you arrange 4 boxes side by side on a shelf? **24** [11–1]

2. How many different three-digit numbers can you make with the digits 1, 2, 3, 4, and 5 if no digit appears more than once in each number? **60**

3. How many combinations of 3 letters can be chosen from the letters A, B, C, D, and E? **10** [11–2]

4. In how many ways can a committee of 2 people be selected from a group of 15 people? **105**

Find the probability that the pointer on the spinner shown at the right stops on a wedge of the type described.

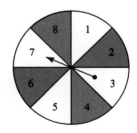

5. 3 $\frac{1}{8}$

6. odd-numbered $\frac{1}{2}$

7. red $\frac{1}{4}$

8. a number less than 9 **1**

9. What are the odds in favor of the pointer on the spinner shown stopping on a wedge with a number greater than 6? **1 to 3**

10. What are the odds against the pointer on the spinner shown stopping on a blue wedge? **3 to 1**

[11–3]

[11–4]

Self-Test answers and Extra Practice are at the back of the book.

11-5 Mutually Exclusive Events

The pointer shown at the right stops at random but not on a division line. Consider the following events.

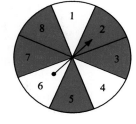

R: The pointer stops on a red wedge.

B: The pointer stops on a blue wedge.

O: The pointer stops on an odd-numbered wedge.

E: The pointer stops on an even-numbered wedge.

Events *R* and *B* cannot both occur at once. Such events are said to be **mutually exclusive.** Notice that events *B* and *E* are *not* mutually exclusive because they both occur when the pointer stops on a blue wedge that is even-numbered.

In the spinner above, five of the eight wedges are colored red or blue. Therefore,

$$P(R \text{ or } B) = \frac{5}{8}.$$

Notice that

$$P(R) = \frac{1}{4}, \ P(B) = \frac{3}{8}, \text{ and } P(R) + P(B) = \frac{1}{4} + \frac{3}{8} = \frac{5}{8}.$$

Thus, $P(R \text{ or } B) = P(R) + P(B)$.

If *A* and *B* are mutually exclusive events, then

$$P(A \text{ or } B) = P(A) + P(B)$$

EXAMPLE The probability that a randomly chosen car is green is 0.15 and that it is red is 0.25.
a. Find the probability that the next car you see will be red or green.
b. Find the odds against its being red or green.

Solution **a.** The events described are mutually exclusive. Thus,

$$P(\text{red or green}) = P(\text{red}) + P(\text{green})$$
$$= 0.25 + 0.15 = 0.40$$

b. Odds against red or green $= \frac{1 - 0.40}{0.40} = \frac{0.6}{0.4} = \frac{3}{2}$

The odds against the next car's being red or green are 3 to 2.

Teaching Suggestions
p. 395d

Related Activities p. 395d

Reading Mathematics

Students will learn the meaning of the following mathematical term in this lesson: *mutually exclusive.*

Chalkboard Examples

Two game cubes are tossed. One is red, the other green. Are events *A* and *B* mutually exclusive?

1. *A:* The total is even.
   B: The total is odd. **Yes**

2. *A:* The green cube shows 2.
   B: The total is 8. **No**

3. *A:* The red cube shows 6.
   B: The total is 6. **Yes**

4. *A:* The green cube shows 3.
   B: The red cube shows 4. **No**

A and *B* are mutually exclusive events. Complete.

5. $P(A \text{ and } B) = \underline{\ ?\ }$ **0**

6. If $P(A) = \frac{1}{5}$ and
   $P(A \text{ or } B) = \frac{7}{10}$, then
   $P(B) = \underline{\ ?\ }$ $\frac{1}{2}$

7. If $P(A) = P(B) = \frac{3}{8}$, then
   $P(A \text{ or } B) = \underline{\ ?\ }$ $\frac{3}{4}$

413

Class Exercises

Are events *A* and *B* mutually exclusive?

1. You take a test. **Yes**
A: You pass it.
B: You fail it.

2. You take a test. **No**
A: You score less than 9.
B: You score more than 6.

3. Two coins are tossed. **Yes**
A: Two heads result.
B: Two tails result.

4. Two game cubes are rolled. **Yes**
A: The sum is 5.
B: A 5 shows on one cube.

5. Two game cubes are rolled. **Yes**
A: Cubes show the same number.
B: The sum is 7.

6. Two game cubes are rolled. **No**
A: Cubes show the same number.
B: The sum is 8.

A and B are mutually exclusive events. Find P(A or B).

7. $P(A) = \frac{1}{4}$, $P(B) = \frac{3}{8}$ $\frac{5}{8}$

8. $P(A) = 0.2$, $P(B) = 0.5$ 0.7

9. $P(A) = \frac{1}{2}$ and $P(B) = \frac{2}{3}$. Are *A* and *B* mutually exclusive events? **No**

Written Exercises

A and B are mutually exclusive events.

A

1. $P(A) = \frac{1}{5}$, $P(B) = \frac{2}{3}$. Find $P(A \text{ or } B)$. $\frac{13}{15}$

2. $P(A) = 0.32$, $P(B) = 0.45$. Find $P(A \text{ or } B)$. **0.77**

3. $P(A) = 0.4$, $P(A \text{ or } B) = 0.7$. Find $P(B)$. **0.3**

4. $P(B) = \frac{1}{3}$, $P(A \text{ or } B) = \frac{3}{4}$. Find $P(A)$. $\frac{5}{12}$

In Exercises 5–10, find the probability that the pointer stops on a wedge of the type described.

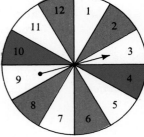

5. a. red $\frac{1}{3}$ **b.** white $\frac{1}{2}$ **c.** red or white $\frac{5}{6}$

6. a. blue $\frac{1}{6}$ **b.** red $\frac{1}{3}$ **c.** blue or red $\frac{1}{2}$

7. a. blue $\frac{1}{6}$ **b.** not blue $\frac{5}{6}$

8. a. white $\frac{1}{2}$ **b.** not white $\frac{1}{2}$

9. a. odd-numbered $\frac{1}{2}$ **b.** red $\frac{1}{3}$ **c.** odd-numbered or red $\frac{5}{6}$

10. a. odd-numbered $\frac{1}{2}$ **b.** blue $\frac{1}{6}$ **c.** odd-numbered or blue $\frac{2}{3}$

414   *Chapter 11*

Additional A Exercises

A and *B* are mutually exclusive events. Complete.

1. If $P(A) = \frac{1}{4}$ and $P(B) = \frac{1}{2}$, then $P(A \text{ or } B) = $ __?__ $\frac{3}{4}$

2. If $P(A \text{ or } B) = 0.83$ and $P(B) = 0.59$, then $P(A) = $ __?__ **0.24**

3. If $P(A) = P(B)$ and $P(A \text{ or } B) = 0.48$, then $P(B) = $ __?__ **0.24**

4. If $P(A) = P(B) = \frac{5}{12}$, then $P(A \text{ or } B) = $ __?__ $\frac{5}{6}$

5. If $P(A) \times P(B) = 0.15$ and $P(A) = 0.3$, then $P(A \text{ or } B) = $ __?__ **0.8**

414

Exercises 11–14 refer to the cards at the right. Find the probability that a card drawn at random is of the type described.

A 1	A 2	A 3	A 4	A 5
B 1	B 2	B 3	B 4	B 5
C 1	C 2	C 3	C 4	C 5
D 1	D 2	D 3	D 4	D 5

11. a. a 5 $\frac{1}{5}$ **b.** less than 3 $\frac{2}{5}$
c. a 5 or less than 3 $\frac{3}{5}$

12. a. a 2 $\frac{1}{5}$ **b.** greater than 3 $\frac{2}{5}$
c. a 2 or greater than 3 $\frac{3}{5}$

13. a. a D $\frac{1}{4}$ **b.** a red card greater than 2 $\frac{3}{10}$
c. a D or a red card greater than 2 $\frac{11}{20}$

14. a. a B $\frac{1}{4}$ **b.** a blue card greater than 3 $\frac{1}{5}$
c. a B or a blue card greater than 3 $\frac{9}{20}$

Two game cubes are rolled. Find the probability of the event described.

B 15. a. The sum is 9. $\frac{1}{9}$ **b.** The roll is a double (for example, $\boxed{3}$ $\boxed{3}$). $\frac{1}{6}$
c. The sum is 9 or a double is rolled. $\frac{5}{18}$

16. a. The sum is 7. $\frac{1}{6}$ **b.** The roll is a double. $\frac{1}{6}$
c. The sum is 7 or a double is rolled. $\frac{1}{3}$

17. Joe's batting average (the probability of his getting a hit) is 0.350. What are the odds against his getting a hit? 13 to 7

18. The probability of Jan's team winning the next softball game is 55%. Find the odds that the team will lose. 9 to 11

C 19. The probability that the next soup ordered will be chicken is 0.45; that it will be tomato is 0.35. What are the odds against its being chicken or tomato? 1 to 4

20. At West High School the probability that a randomly chosen student is a senior is 0.20. The probability that the student is a junior is 0.25. Find the odds against the student's being a junior or senior.
11 to 9

Review Exercises

Solve for x.

1. $x = \frac{1}{5} + \frac{2}{3}$ $\frac{13}{15}$

2. $x = \frac{3}{8} + \frac{1}{2} - \frac{1}{4}$ $\frac{5}{8}$

3. $\frac{1}{4} + \frac{1}{3} - \frac{1}{12} = x$ $\frac{1}{2}$

4. $x + \frac{7}{8} = \frac{1}{12}$ $-\frac{19}{24}$

5. $1 = x + \frac{3}{8}$ $\frac{5}{8}$

6. $\frac{5}{18} + x = \frac{3}{8} + \frac{7}{15}$ $\frac{203}{360}$

7. $x - 0.2 = 0.9$ 1.1

8. $0.51 + x = 1$ 0.49

9. $0.7 = 0.4 + 0.6 - x$
0.3

Probability **415**

Suggested Assignments

Minimum
  414/1–10
  415/11–14
  415/Rev. 1–9

Average
  414/1–10
  415/11–18
  415/Rev. 2–8 even

Maximum
  414/1–10
  415/11–20

Supplementary Materials

Practice Masters, p. 51

Reading Mathematics

The way *or* is used in mathematics is contrary to everyday use of the word. In common usage people usually mean an exclusive *or*, that is, "*A* or *B*" would mean *A* or *B*, but not both.

Chalkboard Examples

A card is drawn at random from those shown below. Find the probability that the card is of the type described.

A   B   C

1. circle $\frac{2}{3}$

2. blue $\frac{2}{3}$

3. circle and blue $\frac{1}{3}$

4. circle or blue 1

5. Are drawing a circle and drawing a blue card mutually exclusive events? No

6. If $P(A) = \frac{3}{5}$, $P(B) = \frac{4}{5}$, and $P(A \text{ and } B) = \frac{1}{2}$, find $P(A \text{ or } B)$. $\frac{9}{10}$

11-6 "Overlapping" Events

On the spinner at the right, there are 5 wedges that are blue (*B*) or even-numbered (*E*) or both. Thus,

$$P(B \text{ or } E) = \frac{5}{8}.$$

On the other hand,

$$P(B) + P(E) = \frac{3}{8} + \frac{1}{2} = \frac{7}{8},$$

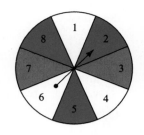

so that $P(B \text{ or } E) \neq P(B) + P(E)$. This is because events *B* and *E* are *not* mutually exclusive. (Both events occur when the pointer stops on a blue wedge numbered 2 or 8; we call this event "*B* and *E*.") The rule that covers this "overlapping event" case is this:

> For *any* two events *A* and *B*,
> $$P(A \text{ or } B) = P(A) + P(B) - P(A \text{ and } B)$$

Applying this formula to the spinner above, we have

$$P(B \text{ or } E) = P(B) + P(E) - P(B \text{ and } E) = \frac{3}{8} + \frac{1}{2} - \frac{1}{4} = \frac{5}{8}.$$

EXAMPLE 1 Both dials are spun. Find the probabilities of these events. (In the illustration, 3 and B have come up.)

    a. 3 comes up.
    b. C comes up.
    c. 3 and C come up.
    d. 3 or C comes up.

Solution From the array of 12 possible outcomes we see that

    a. $P(3) = \frac{3}{12} = \frac{1}{4}$

    b. $P(C) = \frac{4}{12} = \frac{1}{3}$

    c. $P(3 \text{ and } C) = \frac{1}{12}$

    d. $P(3 \text{ or } C) = P(3) + P(C) - P(3 \text{ and } C) = \frac{1}{4} + \frac{1}{3} - \frac{1}{12} = \frac{1}{2}$

416   *Chapter 11*

Reading Mathematics: *Vocabulary*

In mathematics *or* means "and/or."

  A or B means *A* occurs, or *B* occurs, or both *A* and *B* occur.
  A and B means that *both A* and *B* must occur.

EXAMPLE 2 Based on past history, the probability that the Hawks will win the first game of a double header is $\frac{2}{3}$, that they will win the second game is $\frac{1}{2}$, and that they will win both is $\frac{1}{3}$. Find the probability that they will win at least one game.

Solution $P(\text{win at least one}) = P(\text{win first}) + P(\text{win second}) - P(\text{win both})$

$$= \frac{2}{3} + \frac{1}{2} - \frac{1}{3} = \frac{5}{6}$$

EXAMPLE 3 The probability that a randomly chosen marble is red is 0.4, that it is striped is 0.6, and that it is red or striped is 0.7. What is the probability that the marble is red and striped?

Solution
$$P(\text{red or striped}) = P(\text{red}) + P(\text{striped}) - P(\text{red and striped})$$
$$0.7 = 0.4 + 0.6 - P(\text{red and striped})$$
$$0.7 = 1.0 - P(\text{red and striped})$$
$$P(\text{red and striped}) = 0.3$$

Class Exercises

In Exercises 1–4, find $P(A \text{ or } B)$.

1. $P(A) = 0.4$, $P(B) = 0.5$, $P(A \text{ and } B) = 0.2$ **0.7**

2. $P(A) = \frac{1}{2}$, $P(B) = \frac{1}{2}$, $P(A \text{ and } B) = \frac{1}{3}$ **$\frac{2}{3}$**

3. $P(A) = \frac{1}{2}$, $P(B) = \frac{3}{4}$, $P(A \text{ and } B) = \frac{3}{8}$ **$\frac{7}{8}$**

4. $P(A) = 75\%$, $P(B) = 50\%$, $P(A \text{ and } B) = 30\%$ **95%**

5. If two events, *A* and *B*, are mutually exclusive, what is the value of $P(A \text{ and } B)$? What does the formula at the beginning of this lesson become? **0; $P(A \text{ or } B) = P(A) + P(B)$**

6. Is the following a true statement? **Yes**

$$P(A \text{ or } B) + P(A \text{ and } B) = P(A) + P(B)$$

Explain.

Additional Answers
Class Exercises

6. $P(A \text{ and } B)$ has been added to both sides of the equation on page 416.

Written Exercises

Solve.

A **1.** $P(A) = 0.35$, $P(B) = 0.55$, $P(A \text{ and } B) = 0.20$. Find $P(A \text{ or } B)$. 0.7

2. $P(A) = \frac{3}{8}$, $P(B) = \frac{3}{4}$, $P(A \text{ and } B) = \frac{1}{4}$. Find $P(A \text{ or } B)$. $\frac{7}{8}$

3. $P(A) = \frac{1}{3}$, $P(B) = \frac{1}{2}$, $P(A \text{ and } B) = \frac{1}{4}$. Find $P(A \text{ or } B)$. $\frac{7}{12}$

4. $P(A) = 0.45$, $P(B) = 0.75$, $P(A \text{ and } B) = 0.30$. Find $P(A \text{ or } B)$. 0.9

5. $P(A) = 0.65$, $P(A \text{ or } B) = 0.85$, $P(A \text{ and } B) = 0.30$. Find $P(B)$. 0.5

6. $P(A) = 0.75$, $P(A \text{ or } B) = 0.80$, $P(A \text{ and } B) = 0.15$. Find $P(B)$. 0.2

The two dials shown are spun. Find the probabilities of the events described. To answer parts (a), (b), and (c), sketch the array of possible outcomes as in Example 1. Use the formula to answer part (d).

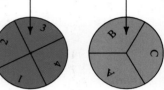

7. a. 4 comes up. $\frac{1}{4}$ **b.** B comes up. $\frac{1}{3}$
    c. 4 and B come up. $\frac{1}{12}$ **d.** 4 or B comes up. $\frac{1}{2}$

8. a. 1 comes up. $\frac{1}{4}$ **b.** A comes up. $\frac{1}{3}$
    c. 1 and A come up. $\frac{1}{12}$ **d.** 1 or A comes up. $\frac{1}{2}$

9. a. An odd number comes up. $\frac{1}{2}$ **b.** C comes up. $\frac{1}{3}$
    c. An odd number and C come up. $\frac{1}{6}$ **d.** An odd number or C comes up. $\frac{2}{3}$

10. a. An even number comes up. $\frac{1}{2}$ **b.** A comes up. $\frac{1}{3}$
    c. An even number and A come up. $\frac{1}{6}$ **d.** An even number or A comes up. $\frac{2}{3}$

A card is drawn at random from those shown at the right. Find the probability that the card is of the type described.

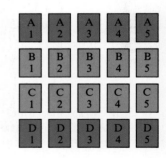

B **11.** a C or a number greater than 3 $\frac{11}{20}$

12. a D or a number greater than 2 $\frac{7}{10}$

13. a blue card or a number greater than 3 $\frac{7}{10}$

14. a red card or a number greater than 2 $\frac{4}{5}$

In Exercises 15–18, two game cubes are rolled. Find (a) the probability of the event described and (b) the odds against its occurring.

C **15.** The sum is 6 or a double is rolled.   **16.** The sum is 10 or a double is rolled.

                                                    $\frac{5}{18}$; 13 to 5 $\frac{2}{9}$; 7 to 2

17. The sum is 8 or exactly one 6 shows. **18.** The sum is 7 or exactly one 3 shows.

$\frac{13}{36}$; 23 to 13

$\frac{7}{18}$; 11 to 7

Suggested Assignments

Minimum
   418/1–10
   419/Prob. 1–3
   419/Rev. 1–8
Average
   418/1–14
   419/Prob. 1–4
   419/Rev. 1–7 odd
Maximum
Day 1: 418/1–16
   419/17–18
Day 2: 419/Prob. 1–5

Supplementary Materials

Practice Masters, p. 51

Problems

A **1.** The chance (probability) of rain tomorrow is 80%, the chance of snow is 40%, and the chance of rain and snow is 30%. What is the chance that it will rain or snow? **90%**

2. The probability that a randomly chosen car is a convertible is 0.09, that it is red is 0.25, and that it is a red convertible is 0.03. What is the probability that the next car to come along is red or a convertible? **0.31**

B **3.** In a certain neighborhood, 60% of the homes receive the *Daily Reporter*, 90% receive the *Daily Reporter* or the *Weekly Times,* and 50% receive the *Daily Reporter* and the *Weekly Times.* Find the probability that a home chosen at random receives the *Weekly Times.* **80%**

4. The probability that a randomly chosen adult resident of Bayview City owns a boat is 0.15, that the adult rents an apartment is 0.30, and that the adult owns a boat or rents an apartment is 0.40. Find the probability that the adult owns a boat and rents an apartment. **0.05**

C **5.** Of 32 marbles in a bag, 18 are green, 9 are spotted, and 11 are neither green nor spotted. What is the probability that a marble chosen at random is green and spotted? Draw a Venn diagram, as on page 400, to illustrate the problem, and then answer the question. $\frac{3}{16}$

Review Exercises

Write your answer in lowest terms.

1. $\frac{5}{6} \times \frac{1}{6}$ $\frac{5}{36}$

2. $\frac{4}{5} \times \frac{2}{7}$ $\frac{8}{35}$

3. $\frac{1}{4} \times \frac{2}{3}$ $\frac{1}{6}$

4. $\frac{1}{6} \times \frac{1}{2}$ $\frac{1}{12}$

5. $\frac{2}{5} \times \frac{3}{5}$ $\frac{6}{25}$

6. $\frac{5}{7} \times \frac{5}{7}$ $\frac{25}{49}$

7. $1 - \frac{13}{25}$ $\frac{12}{25}$

8. $1 - \frac{11}{21}$ $\frac{10}{21}$

Probability **419**

Reading Mathematics

Students will learn the meaning of the following mathematical term in this lesson: *independent events*.

Chalkboard Examples

Are events *A* and *B* independent? If they are, find the probability that they both occur.

1. Two coins are tossed.
   A: The nickel comes up heads.
   B: The penny comes up tails. **Yes;** $\frac{1}{4}$

2. Two game cubes are tossed.
   A: A 6 comes up on the red cube.
   B: The total is 12. **No**

3. A bag contains 3 orange and 4 purple marbles. A marble is drawn and replaced. Then a marble is drawn again.
   A: The first marble is orange.
   B: The second marble is purple. **Yes;** $\frac{12}{49}$

4. Same as Exercise 3 except that the first marble is not replaced. **No**

11-7 Independent Events

A coin is tossed and a game cube rolled. Consider these events.

A: The coin shows heads.
B: The cube shows 2, 3, 4, or 5.

Neither of these events has any effect on the other. For example, the probability that *B* will occur is not affected by whether or not *A* occurs. Such events are said to be **independent.** What is $P(A \text{ and } B)$ in the experiment described above? One way to find out is to list the 12 possible outcomes as shown below.

H1 (H2) (H3) (H4) (H5) H6

T1 T2 T3 T4 T5 T6

Notice that 4 of the possible outcomes favor the combined event "*A* and *B*." Thus,

$$P(A \text{ and } B) = \frac{4}{12} = \frac{1}{3}.$$

An easier way to find $P(A \text{ and } B)$ is to use this general principle:

> If *A* and *B* are independent events, then
> $$P(A \text{ and } B) = P(A) \times P(B)$$

In the experiment considered above, we know that $P(A) = \frac{1}{2}$ and $P(B) = \frac{4}{6} = \frac{2}{3}$. Thus,

$$P(A \text{ and } B) = P(A) \times P(B)$$
$$= \frac{1}{2} \times \frac{2}{3} = \frac{1}{3}.$$

EXAMPLE A bag contains 2 red and 3 blue marbles. A marble is drawn and replaced. Then a marble is drawn again. Find the probability of each event. (Recall that the marbles are drawn at random.)
   a. The first marble is red, and the second one is blue.
   b. The first marble is blue, and the second one is red.
   c. Both marbles are red.
   d. Both marbles are blue.

Solution   Because the first marble drawn is replaced, the second-draw events are independent of the first-draw events.

$$P(\text{red}) = \tfrac{2}{5};\ P(\text{blue}) = \tfrac{3}{5}$$

a. $P(\text{red, then blue}) = P(\text{red}) \times P(\text{blue}) = \tfrac{2}{5} \times \tfrac{3}{5} = \tfrac{6}{25}$

b. $P(\text{blue, then red}) = P(\text{blue}) \times P(\text{red}) = \tfrac{3}{5} \times \tfrac{2}{5} = \tfrac{6}{25}$

c. $P(\text{red, red}) = P(\text{red}) \times P(\text{red}) = \tfrac{2}{5} \times \tfrac{2}{5} = \tfrac{4}{25}$

d. $P(\text{blue, blue}) = P(\text{blue}) \times P(\text{blue}) = \tfrac{3}{5} \times \tfrac{3}{5} = \tfrac{9}{25}$

The example can be continued to find the probability that the two marbles drawn have the same color and the probability that they have different colors. The events "red, red" and "blue, blue" are mutually exclusive. Therefore,

$$P(\text{same color}) = P(\text{red, red}) + P(\text{blue, blue}) = \tfrac{4}{25} + \tfrac{9}{25} = \tfrac{13}{25}.$$

We can find $P(\text{different colors})$ in a similar way by adding the probabilities in parts (a) and (b) of the example.

Class Exercises

Are events A and B independent? If they are, find the probability that they both occur.

1. A coin is tossed twice. Yes; $\tfrac{1}{4}$
   A: Heads come up on the first toss.   *B:* Heads come up on the second toss.

2. A bag contains 1 red marble and 2 blue marbles. A marble is drawn and replaced. Then a marble is drawn again. Yes; $\tfrac{1}{9}$
   A: The first marble is red.   *B:* The second marble is red.

3. Same as Exercise 2 except that the first marble is not replaced. No

4. A game cube is rolled twice. Yes; $\tfrac{1}{36}$
   A: A 3 comes up on the first roll.   *B:* A 5 comes up on the second roll.

5. A red game cube and a green game cube are rolled. Yes; $\tfrac{1}{36}$
   A: A 6 comes up on the red cube.   *B:* A 6 comes up on the green cube.

6. One game cube is rolled. No
   A: An odd number comes up.   *B:* A prime number comes up.

A number is chosen at random from the integers from 10 to 99. Find the probability of the event described.

1. the tens' digit is 5 $\frac{1}{9}$

2. The ones' digit is 5 $\frac{1}{10}$

3. both digits are 5 $\frac{1}{90}$

4. either digit is 5 $\frac{1}{5}$

5. neither digit is 5 $\frac{4}{5}$

Written Exercises

For Exercises 1–16, find the probabilities of the events that are described.

A   **1.** Two coins are tossed.
   A: Both show heads. $\frac{1}{4}$
   B: Both show tails. $\frac{1}{4}$
   C: Exactly one head shows. $\frac{1}{2}$

2. A game cube is rolled twice.
   A: Both rolls come up 6.
   B: Neither roll comes up 6.
   C: Exactly one 6 comes up.
   A: $\frac{1}{36}$; *B:* $\frac{25}{36}$; *C:* $\frac{5}{18}$

In Exercises 3 and 4, a marble is drawn and replaced. Then a marble is drawn again.

3. A bag contains 1 red marble and 3 blue marbles.
   A: Both marbles are red. $\frac{1}{16}$
   B: Both marbles are blue. $\frac{9}{16}$
   C: Both marbles are the same color. $\frac{5}{8}$
   D: The marbles are different colors. $\frac{3}{8}$

4. A bag contains 4 red and 2 blue marbles. Events *A*, *B*, *C*, and *D* are the same as in Exercise 3. $P(A) = \frac{4}{9}$; $P(B) = \frac{1}{9}$; $P(C) = \frac{5}{9}$; $P(D) = \frac{4}{9}$

5. The two dials pictured at the right are spun.
   A: Both dials show a 3. $\frac{1}{9}$
   B: The red dial shows an odd number and the blue dial shows an even number. $\frac{2}{9}$
   C: One dial shows an odd number and the other shows an even number. $\frac{4}{9}$

6. Chris and Lee each pick one of the digits, 0, 1, 2, . . . , 9, at random.
   A: Lee's digit is 5, and Chris's is 6. $\frac{1}{100}$
   B: Lee's digit is odd, and Chris's is even. $\frac{1}{4}$
   C: One of their digits is odd and the other is even. $\frac{1}{2}$

In Exercises 7 and 8, a card is drawn at random from those shown at the right and is replaced. Then a card is drawn again.

7. *A:* Both cards are C's. $\frac{1}{16}$
   B: Neither card is a C. $\frac{9}{16}$
   C: At least one card is a C. $\frac{7}{16}$
   D: One card is a C and the other is not. $\frac{3}{8}$

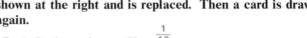

8. *A:* Both cards show numbers greater than 3. $\frac{4}{25}$
   B: Neither card shows a number greater than 3. $\frac{9}{25}$
   C: At least one card shows a number greater than 3. $\frac{16}{25}$
   D: One card shows a number greater than 3 and the other does not. $\frac{12}{25}$

422   *Chapter 11*

EXAMPLE A coin is tossed 5 times.

  A: Heads come up each time. *B:* No heads come up.

Solution The general principle for finding $P(A$ and $B)$ can be extended to more than two independent events.

Therefore, $P(A) = \frac{1}{2} \times \frac{1}{2} \times \frac{1}{2} \times \frac{1}{2} \times \frac{1}{2} = \frac{1}{32}$

$P(B) = \frac{1}{2} \times \frac{1}{2} \times \frac{1}{2} \times \frac{1}{2} \times \frac{1}{2} = \frac{1}{32}$

B 9. Four coins are tossed.

  A: Four tails come up. $\frac{1}{16}$

  B: No tails come up. $\frac{1}{16}$

10. A game cube is rolled three times.

  A: All of the rolls come up 6. $\frac{1}{216}$

  B: None of the rolls comes up 6. $\frac{125}{216}$

11. The probability that the Buffalos will win any given game is 0.6.

  A: They win three in a row. 0.216

  B: They lose three in a row. 0.064

12. Amy is taking 4 courses. The probability that she makes an A in any given course is 0.8.

  A: She makes no A's. 0.0016

  B: She makes all A's. 0.4096

13. A coin has been tossed five times and a head has come up each time.

  A: A head comes up on the sixth toss. $\frac{1}{2}$

14. A game cube has been rolled five times and no 6 has come up.

  A: A 6 comes up on the sixth roll. $\frac{1}{6}$

Exercises 15 and 16 refer to the cards in Exercises 7 and 8. Three cards are drawn, each one being replaced before the next one is drawn.

C 15. *A:* Three C's are drawn. $\frac{1}{64}$

  B: The first card drawn is a C and the others are not. $\frac{9}{64}$

  C: Exactly one C is drawn. $\frac{27}{64}$

16. *A:* No C's are drawn. $\frac{27}{64}$

  B: The first two cards drawn are C's and the third is not. $\frac{3}{64}$

  C: Exactly two C's are drawn. $\frac{9}{64}$

Review Exercises

Find the value.

1. $_4C_2$ 6

2. $_4C_3$ 4

3. $_5C_2$ 10

4. $_6C_5$ 6

5. $_6C_4$ 15

6. $_7C_3$ 35

7. $_8C_5$ 56

8. $_{10}C_3$ 120

Probability **423**

Suggested Assignments

Minimum
  422/1–8
  423/9–10
  423/Rev. 1–8
Average
  422/2–8 even
  423/9–14
  423/Rev. 2–8 even
Maximum
Day 1: 422/1–8
  423/9–10
Day 2: 423/11–16

Supplementary Materials

Practice Masters, p. 52

Reading Mathematics

Students will learn the meaning of the following mathematical terms in this lesson: *dependent events, conditional probability.*

Chalkboard Exercises

A bag contains 3 orange marbles and 5 purple marbles. A marble is drawn and is not replaced. Then a second marble is drawn. Find $P(B|A)$ for events A and B described below.

1. *A:* An orange marble is drawn.
   B: A purple marble is drawn. $\frac{5}{7}$

2. *A:* A purple marble is drawn.
   B: An orange marble is drawn. $\frac{3}{7}$

Use the formula to find the probability of the events described.

3. The first marble is orange and the second is purple.
   $\frac{15}{56}$

4. Both marbles are orange.
   $\frac{3}{28}$

5. They are different colors.
   $\frac{15}{28}$

Use combinations to find the probability of the events described.

6. Both marbles are purple.
   $\frac{5}{14}$

7. They are different colors.
   $\frac{15}{28}$

11-8 Dependent Events

A bag contains 2 red and 3 blue marbles. One marble is drawn, and then a second marble is drawn. If the first marble drawn is *not* replaced, then the first-draw events and second-draw events are **dependent** events. That is, the result of the first draw affects the result of the second draw.

For example, suppose that the first marble drawn is red and it is not replaced. Now the bag contains 1 red marble and 3 blue marbles, so the probability of obtaining a blue marble on the second draw is $\frac{3}{4}$, not $\frac{3}{5}$.

On the other hand, suppose that the first marble drawn is blue. Then the bag contains 2 red and 2 blue marbles, so the probability of obtaining a blue marble on the second draw is $\frac{2}{4} = \frac{1}{2}$.

We write $P(blue \mid red)$, read *the probability that the second is blue given that the first is red,* to denote the **conditional probability** of drawing a blue marble after a red one has been drawn. Thus, $P(blue \mid red) = \frac{3}{4}$, and $P(blue \mid blue) = \frac{1}{2}$. We will still use the symbol $P(blue)$ to denote the probability that the *first* marble drawn is blue; thus, $P(blue) = \frac{3}{5}$.

If we write $P(B \mid A)$ to represent the probability that event B will occur given that event A has occurred, we have the following formula:

> For two events A and B, not necessarily independent,
>
> $$P(A \text{ and } B) = P(A) \times P(B \mid A)$$

EXAMPLE 1 A bag contains 2 red and 3 blue marbles. A marble is drawn and is not replaced. A second marble is drawn. Find the probability of these events.
  a. The first marble is red, and the second one is blue.
  b. The first marble is blue, and the second one is red.
  c. Both marbles are red.
  d. Both marbles are blue.
  e. They are different colors.

Solution

$P(\text{red}) = \frac{2}{5}$　　　　　　$P(\text{blue}) = \frac{3}{5}$

$P(\text{blue} \mid \text{red}) = \frac{3}{4}$　　　　$P(\text{red} \mid \text{blue}) = \frac{2}{4} = \frac{1}{2}$

$P(\text{red} \mid \text{red}) = \frac{1}{4}$　　　　$P(\text{blue} \mid \text{blue}) = \frac{2}{4} = \frac{1}{2}$

424　*Chapter 11*

a. $P(\text{red, then blue}) = P(\text{red}) \times P(\text{blue} \mid \text{red}) = \frac{2}{5} \times \frac{3}{4} = \frac{3}{10}$

b. $P(\text{blue, then red}) = P(\text{blue}) \times P(\text{red} \mid \text{blue}) = \frac{3}{5} \times \frac{1}{2} = \frac{3}{10}$

c. $P(\text{red, red}) = P(\text{red}) \times P(\text{red} \mid \text{red}) = \frac{2}{5} \times \frac{1}{4} = \frac{1}{10}$

d. $P(\text{blue, blue}) = P(\text{blue}) \times P(\text{blue} \mid \text{blue}) = \frac{3}{5} \times \frac{1}{2} = \frac{3}{10}$

e. $P(\text{different colors}) = P(\text{red, then blue}) + P(\text{blue, then red})$
$$= \frac{3}{10} + \frac{3}{10} = \frac{3}{5}$$

Sometimes we can use what we know about combinations to compute probabilities.

EXAMPLE 2   Use combinations to solve Example 1, parts (d) and (e).

Solution   **d.** Because there are 3 blue marbles in the bag, the number of possible ways of drawing 2 blue marbles is

$$_3C_2 = \frac{3 \times 2}{2 \times 1} = 3.$$

Since the bag contains a total of 5 marbles, the number of possible ways of drawing 2 marbles from the bag is

$$_5C_2 = \frac{5 \times 4}{2 \times 1} = 10.$$

Use the probability formula.

$$P(\text{blue, blue}) = \frac{\text{number of ways of drawing 2 blue marbles}}{\text{number of ways of drawing 2 marbles of any color}}$$
$$= \frac{3}{10}$$

e. Since there are 2 red marbles, there are $_2C_1$, or 2, ways of drawing 1 red marble. For each of these ways, there are $_3C_1$, or 3, ways of drawing 1 blue marble.

Using the counting principle, there are 2×3, or 6, ways of drawing 1 red and 1 blue marble. Therefore, the probability of drawing 1 red and 1 blue marble is

$$P = \frac{\text{number of ways of drawing 1 red and 1 blue marble}}{\text{number of ways of drawing 2 marbles of any color}}$$
$$= \frac{6}{10} = \frac{3}{5}.$$

Suggested Assignments

Minimum
    426/1–9
    427/10–15
    427/Rev. 1–10

Average
    426/1–9
    427/10–18
    427/Rev. 1–9 odd

Maximum
Day 1: 426/1–9
    427/10–12
Day 2: 427/13–20

Supplementary Materials

Practice Masters, p. 52

Class Exercises

A bag contains 5 yellow marbles and 4 green marbles. A marble is drawn and is not replaced. Then a second marble is drawn.

Find $P(B \mid A)$ for events A and B described below.

1. *A:* A yellow marble is drawn.   *B:* A green marble is drawn. $\frac{1}{2}$

2. *A:* A yellow marble is drawn.   *B:* A yellow marble is drawn. $\frac{1}{2}$

3. *A:* A green marble is drawn.   *B:* A green marble is drawn. $\frac{3}{8}$

4. *A:* A green marble is drawn.   *B:* A yellow marble is drawn. $\frac{5}{8}$

Use the formula to find the probability of the events described.

5. The first marble is yellow and the second is green. $\frac{5}{18}$

6. The first marble is green and the second is yellow. $\frac{5}{18}$

7. Both marbles are green. $\frac{1}{6}$ **8.** They are different colors. $\frac{5}{9}$

Use combinations to find the probability of the events described.

9. Both marbles are green. $\frac{1}{6}$ **10.** They are different colors. $\frac{5}{9}$

Written Exercises

A bag contains 4 red marbles and 6 blue marbles. A marble is drawn and is not replaced. Then a second marble is drawn.
a. Identify the first and second events.
b. Find P(second event | first event).

A   1. Both marbles are red.   2. Both marbles are blue.

3. The first marble is blue and the second marble is red.

4. The first marble is red and the second marble is blue.

A bag contains 3 orange and 7 green marbles. A marble is drawn and is not replaced. Then a second marble is drawn. Use the formula to find the probability of the events described.

5. Both marbles are orange. $\frac{1}{15}$ **6.** Both marbles are green. $\frac{7}{15}$

7. The first marble is orange and the second is green. $\frac{7}{30}$

8. The first marble is green and the second is orange. $\frac{7}{30}$

9. They are different colors. $\frac{7}{15}$

426   *Chapter 11*

A bag contains 6 yellow and 5 red marbles. A marble is drawn and is not replaced. Then a second marble is drawn. Use combinations to find the probability of the events described.

B 10. Both marbles are yellow. $\frac{3}{11}$

11. Both marbles are red. $\frac{2}{11}$

12. They are different colors. $\frac{6}{11}$

Two of the five cards shown are drawn at random at the same time. Find the probability of the events described. (*Hint:* Drawing two at once is the same as drawing one at a time and not replacing the first one drawn.)

13. They are both odd. $\frac{3}{10}$

14. They are both even. $\frac{1}{10}$

15. One is even and the other is odd. $\frac{3}{5}$

Two letters are chosen at random at the same time from the word TRIANGLE. Find the probability of the events described. (*Hint:* Choosing two at once is the same as choosing one letter and then choosing another from the letters that remain.)

16. Both letters are vowels. $\frac{3}{28}$

17. Both letters are consonants. $\frac{5}{14}$

18. One letter is a vowel and one is a consonant. $\frac{15}{28}$

A bag contains 4 red marbles, 5 blue marbles, and 6 green marbles. Three marbles are drawn one at a time without replacement. Find the probability of the events described.

C 19. The first marble is green, the second is blue, and the third is red. $\frac{4}{91}$

20. All three marbles are green. $\frac{4}{91}$

Review Exercises

Write as a decimal.

1. $\frac{3}{4}$ 0.75
2. $\frac{4}{5}$ 0.8
3. $\frac{7}{8}$ 0.875
4. $\frac{3}{20}$ 0.15
5. $\frac{5}{16}$ 0.3125
6. $\frac{21}{140}$ 0.15
7. $\frac{12}{300}$ 0.04
8. $\frac{180}{250}$ 0.72
9. $\frac{54}{1000}$ 0.054
10. $\frac{1308}{2000}$ 0.654

Probability **427**

427

Teaching Suggestions
p. 395g

Related Activities p. 395g

Reading Mathematics

Students will learn the meaning of the following mathematical terms in this lesson: *sampling methods, sample.*

Chalkboard Examples

Of 300 rural water wells tested in Madison County, 180 had hard water. The rest had soft water.

1. What is the probability that a rural well has hard water? **0.6**

2. What is the probability that a rural well has soft water? **0.4**

3. There are 4500 rural water wells in Madison County. How many are likely to have hard water? **2700**

4. How many of the 4500 wells are likely to have soft water? **1800**

5. In an area with only 250 wells, how many are likely to have hard water? **150**

11-9 Estimating Probabilities

Experiments such as drawing a card or rolling a game cube are of a special kind. We know all of the possible outcomes and are able to assign an equal probability to each. In many real-life situations, however, we can only estimate probabilities based on experience.

EXAMPLE 1   Up to now Mark has sunk 75 out of 120 free throws. Find the probability that he will succeed in sinking the next free throw he attempts.

Solution   We use "past history" to estimate the probability.

$$P(\text{success}) = \frac{\text{number of past successes}}{\text{number of past attempts}} = \frac{75}{120} = \frac{5}{8} = 0.625$$

We say that Mark's *free-throw average* is 0.625.

Often we can use **sampling methods** to estimate probabilities. In such cases, a sample is chosen at random and conclusions are drawn based on an analysis of the sample.

EXAMPLE 2   A factory turns out 5000 digital calculators a day. To control quality, a daily random sample of 200 is taken and tested. Of these, 6 are found to be defective.
  a. Find the probability that a randomly chosen calculator will be defective.
  b. How many calculators in a day's output are likely to be defective?

Solution   **a.** We assume that the random sample is representative of the day's output.

$$P(\text{defective}) = \frac{\text{number defective in a sample}}{\text{number in sample}} = \frac{6}{200} = 0.03$$

  b. It is possible that only 6 of the entire output of 5000 calculators are defective, but this is very unlikely. We assume that the following proportion is close to the actual situation:

$$\frac{\text{number defective}}{\text{total number}} = \frac{\text{number defective in sample}}{\text{number in sample}}$$

Thus, $\dfrac{\text{number defective}}{5000} = 0.03$

$$\text{number defective} = 0.03 \times 5000 = 150$$

In a day's output, 150 calculators are likely to be defective.

428   *Chapter 11*

Note that a random sample was specified in Example 2. If the sample were not random, the information obtained from the sample would not be as reliable. For instance, if the sample consisted of the first 200 calculators made that day, the results could be biased by machinery that needed adjustment.

In general, the larger the size of a random sample, the more reliable it is. But the reliability of a large sample must be balanced against the cost and time involved in taking it.

Class Exercises

1. Sarah has been at bat 30 times this season and has hit safely 9 times. Estimate the probability that she will hit safely the next time she is at bat. 0.3

2. Thus far this season, 18 of the junior varsity team's 25 free-throw attempts have been successful. Estimate the probability that the next free-throw is successful. 0.72

3. In the last 50 years it has snowed on Valentine's Day 15 times. Estimate the probability that it will snow on next Valentine's Day. 0.3

4. A quarterback has completed 9 of the last 15 passes he has thrown. Estimate the probability that he will complete his next pass. 0.6

5. A weather announcer predicted correctly 990 times out of 1000. Estimate the probability that her next prediction will be correct. 0.99

Problems

Estimate the probabilities for these problems.

One thousand golf balls, some white, some green, and some yellow, are put into a barrel. As they are drawn out, their colors are tallied. Using the tally shown, find the probability that the next ball will be this color:

green	₩₩ ₩₩ ₩₩ I
white	₩₩ ₩₩ ₩₩ ₩₩ III
yellow	₩₩ ₩₩ I

A
1. green 0.32   2. white 0.46   3. yellow 0.22

4. white or yellow 0.68   5. yellow or green 0.54   6. green or white 0.78

7. Of the 1000 golf balls described above, about how many are white? 460

8. Of the 1000 golf balls described above, about how many are yellow? 220

Probability **429**

Suggested Assignments

Minimum
429 / Prob. 1–8
430 / Prob. 9–12
431 / Self-Test B

Average
Day 1: 429 / Prob. 1–8
430 / Prob. 9–14
Day 2: 431 / Prob. 15–16
431 / Self-Test B

Maximum
Day 1: 429 / Prob. 1–8
430 / Prob. 9–14
Day 2: 431 / Prob. 15–16
431 / Self-Test B

Supplementary Materials

Practice Masters, p. 52
Test 11B, pp. 75–76
Computer Activity 21
Computer Activity 22

Quick Quiz B

1. Events A and B are mutually exclusive.
$P(A) = 0.45$.
$P(A \text{ or } B) = 0.8$.
Find $P(B)$. **0.35**

2. Events A and B are mutually exclusive.
$P(A \text{ or } B) = 0.9$.
$P(A) = P(B)$. Find $P(A)$.
0.45

3. $P(A \text{ or } B) = 0.71$,
$P(A \text{ and } B) = 0.22$, and
$P(B) = 0.6$. Find $P(A)$.
0.33

4. Find the probability that the spinner stops on a wedge containing a 3 or an A. $\frac{1}{2}$

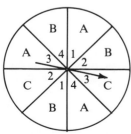

(Continue on next page.)

430

9. It is halfway through the season and José has hit safely 42 times out of 120 times at bat.
  a. What is the probability that he will hit safely on his next time at bat? **0.35**
  b. About how many hits can he expect to get during his next 40 times at bat? **14 hits**

10. The County Department of Agriculture caught a random sample of 5000 fruit flies. Of these, 40 were harmful to crops.
  a. What is the probability that the next fruit fly caught will be harmful? **0.008**
  b. Of an estimated 40 billion fruit flies in the county, about how many are harmful?
    320 million fruit flies

B   **11.** Before it can be shipped, a quality-control inspector must approve each shipment of parts made on an assembly line. She cannot give her approval to a shipment if the probability that a randomly chosen part will be defective is greater than 0.5%. When 300 parts were randomly selected from one shipment, 2 were found to be defective. Will the shipment be approved? **No**

12. The Dynamos have completed 15 of their last 24 passes. **5 to 3**
  a. What are the odds that the team's next pass will be completed?
  b. About how many of its next five passes can the team expect to complete? **about 3 passes**

13. A traffic engineer monitoring a freeway interchange found that of 180 cars, 75 continued straight on, 60 took the left-bound exit ramp, and 45 took the right-bound exit ramp.
  a. What are the odds that the next car will go straight? go left? go right? **5 to 7; 1 to 2; 1 to 3**
  b. Of the 40,000 cars that use the freeway daily, about how many go left at this interchange? **about 13,333 cars**

14. A recent survey of 250 randomly selected people indicated that 140 read Thursday's edition of the local newspaper. Among the 140, 70% had seen an advertisement for a particular product in the newspaper. What is the probability that a randomly selected person has seen the advertisement in Thursday's newspaper? **0.392**

430   *Chapter 11*

C **15.** Testing of a random sample of products from an assembly line resulted in 7 defective products out of 2000. What is the probability that a buyer of the product made by this company will not get a defective product? 0.9965

16. A certain ballot measure requires a 60% favorable vote to pass. Of a random sample of 500 voters, 291 favored passage, 166 were opposed, and 43 were undecided.
a. On the basis of this sample, is the measure likely to pass? Give a reason for your answer. Yes, if 21% of those undecided favor it.
b. Assuming that 120,000 people will vote, about how many in the undecided group must support the measure to ensure its passage? about 2160 voters

Self-Test B

1. Events A and B are mutually exclusive. $P(A) = \frac{5}{12}$. $P(B) = \frac{1}{6}$. [11-5]
Find $P(A \text{ or } B)$. $\frac{7}{12}$

2. Events A and B are mutually exclusive. $P(A) = 0.5$. $P(A \text{ or } B) = 0.7$. Find $P(B)$. 0.2

3. $P(A) = 0.45$, $P(A \text{ or } B) = 0.65$, and [11-6]
$P(A \text{ and } B) = 0.3$. Find $P(B)$. 0.5

4. A card is drawn at random from those shown at the right. Find the probability that the card is a C or a number less than 4. $\frac{4}{5}$

5. A game cube is rolled twice. Find the probability of each event. [11-7]
a. Both rolls come up 3. $\frac{1}{36}$
b. Exactly one 3 comes up. $\frac{5}{18}$
c. At least one 3 comes up. $\frac{11}{36}$
d. Neither roll comes up 3. $\frac{25}{36}$

6. A bag contains 4 red marbles and 5 blue marbles. A marble is [11-8] drawn at random and is not replaced. Then a second marble is drawn. Find the probability of each event.
a. The first is red and the second is blue. $\frac{5}{18}$
b. Both are red. $\frac{1}{6}$

7. Of a random sample of 275 plants, 11 showed signs of a particular [11-9] disease.
a. Estimate the probability that another randomly selected plant will show signs of the disease. 0.04
b. Of 1400 plants in the greenhouse, about how many will show signs of the disease? 56 plants

Self-Test answers and Extra Practice are at the back of the book.

Probability **431**

5. A game cube is rolled twice. Find the probability of each event.
a. Both rolls show an even number. $\frac{1}{4}$
b. Both rolls show an odd number. $\frac{1}{4}$
c. Both rolls show a number greater than 2. $\frac{4}{9}$
d. Neither roll shows a number greater than 2. $\frac{1}{9}$

6. A bag contains 5 yellow marbles and 3 green marbles. A marble is drawn at random and is not replaced. Then a second marble is drawn. Find the probability of each event.
a. Both marbles are yellow. $\frac{5}{14}$
b. Both marbles are green. $\frac{3}{28}$
c. The first marble is green and the second is yellow. $\frac{15}{56}$

7. Of a sample of 240 athletes, 72 have been injured in the past two years.
a. What is the estimated probability that an athlete has been injured in the past two years? $\frac{3}{10}$
b. Of 3000 athletes in the Sports Congress, how many are likely to have been injured in the past two years? 900

Enrichment Note

After calculating the probabilities in Exercise 1, students can determine the predicted number of times each value of S will occur. For example, since $P(3) = \frac{1}{18}$, we would expect about $\frac{1}{18} \times 300$, or approximately 17, threes out of 300 trials. These predictions can then be compared to the actual results when the program is run. These predicted numbers of occurrences are, of course, the expected values that are studied in Chapter 12.

The computer prints both the 300 values of X obtained randomly and a bar graph showing how many times each value occurs. The bar graph is a visual display of the data, making trends and patterns easily apparent. We expect the bar graph to "peak" at 7 and to taper off on either side of this peak. In Chapter 12 students will learn that this kind of bar graph is called a histogram.

This experiment is an example of a computer simulation. With suitable changes in the way S is determined we can simulate other probabilistic experiments, such as tossing coins, drawing cards, and so on. In fact, any experiment can be simulated by the computer provided we have a way to assign probabilities to the possible outcomes. Computer games, educational simulations, and sophisticated business and economic models all use this basic technique.

Depending on the model of computer your students use, they may have to use a slightly different command in line 295, such as PRINT TAB (4 * N). Check your computer handbook.

ENRICHMENT

The Computer and Random Experiments

You have learned how to determine the probability of an outcome in a random experiment. Of course, probability does not enable you to know in advance what the outcome of a random experiment will be on a single trial. How well does probability work? A good way to find out is to perform a random experiment many times and to compare the results of the experiment with what your knowledge of probability would lead you to expect.

Consider the random experiment of rolling two number cubes. Let S stand for the sum of the numbers on the top faces of the cubes. The table below shows the sum S for each of the 36 equally likely ways the pair can turn up.

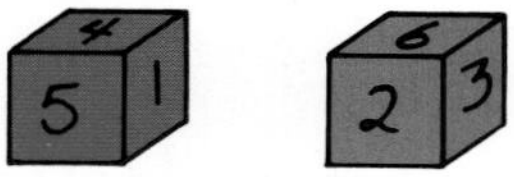

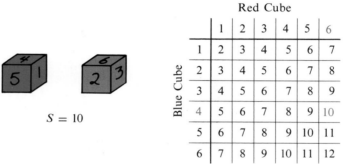

$S = 10$

Red Cube

Blue Cube	1	2	3	4	5	6
1	2	3	4	5	6	7
2	3	4	5	6	7	8
3	4	5	6	7	8	9
4	5	6	7	8	9	10
5	6	7	8	9	10	11
6	7	8	9	10	11	12

Sum S for a Pair of Number Cubes

The probability of obtaining a sum of 3 is $\frac{2}{36}$, or $\frac{1}{18}$. The probability of obtaining a sum of 5 is $\frac{4}{36}$, or $\frac{1}{9}$. Based on these probabilities, you would expect that if you were to repeat this experiment several hundred times you would obtain a sum of 5 more frequently than you would obtain a sum of 3.

Of course, it would take you a great deal of time to repeat the experiment several hundred times. The computer, however, can simulate a random experiment, repeat it many times at high speed, and organize the results of the experiment. The BASIC program shown on the next page simulates the experiment of rolling two number cubes and repeats it 300 times. The program also records the sum of the numbers on each trial and prints a bar graph that shows the number of times that each sum occurred.

1. Before you run the program, find the probability of each possible value of S. 2 or 12: $\frac{1}{36}$; 3 or 11: $\frac{1}{18}$; 4 or 10: $\frac{1}{12}$; 5 or 9: $\frac{1}{9}$; 6 or 8: $\frac{5}{36}$; 7: $\frac{1}{6}$

2. Run the computer program twice. (Note: Check your computer handbook on the use of the RND function.) Answers will vary.

  a. What similarities do you see in the shapes of the two graphs?

  b. Which value of S occurred most often in each graph? Probably 6, 7, or 8

  c. Which value of S occurred least often in each graph? Probably 2 or 12

  d. How do the results of these experiments compare with what you expected based on your answer to Exercise 1? Explain.

  a. In most graphs the center bars are tallest.

  d. The results are similar to Exercise 1, but not exact because of the limited number of rolls.

```
10   PRINT  TAB( 25);"SUM OF CUBES"
15   PRINT
20   FOR Z = 1 TO 300
25   LET S =  INT (6 *  RND (1)) +  INT (6 *  RND (1)) + 2
30   PRINT S;" ";
35   ON S - 1 GOTO 40,50,60,70,80,90,100,110,120,130,140
40   LET A = A + 1
45   GOTO 145
50   LET B = B + 1
55   GOTO 145
60   LET C = C + 1
65   GOTO 145
70   LET D = D + 1
75   GOTO 145
80   LET E = E + 1
85   GOTO 145
90   LET F = F + 1
95   GOTO 145
100  LET G = G + 1
105  GOTO 145
110  LET H = H + 1
115  GOTO 145
120  LET I = I + 1
125  GOTO 145
130  LET J = J + 1
135  GOTO 145
140  LET K = K + 1
145  NEXT Z
150  PRINT
152  PRINT
155  PRINT  TAB( 25);"BAR GRAPH"
160  PRINT
165  LET L = A
170  GOSUB 280
175  LET L = B
180  GOSUB 280
185  LET L = C
190  GOSUB 280
195  LET L = D
200  GOSUB 280
205  LET L = E
210  GOSUB 280
215  LET L = F
220  GOSUB 280
225  LET L = G
230  GOSUB 280
235  LET L = H
240  GOSUB 280
245  LET L = I
250  GOSUB 280
255  LET L = J
260  GOSUB 280
265  LET L = K
270  GOSUB 280
275  STOP
280  LET M = M + 1
285  PRINT M + 1;
290  FOR N = 1 TO L
295  PRINT  TAB( 4);"*";
300  NEXT N
305  PRINT
310  RETURN
315  END
```

Probability **433**

Chapter Review

True or false?

1. You can arrange the letters in the word DRAW in 4 different ways if you take the letters 3 at a time. false [11-1]

2. A group of 3 people can be selected from 8 people in 56 ways. true [11-2]

3. The probability of rolling a 4 with a single game cube is $\frac{2}{3}$. false [11-3]

4. When a single game cube is rolled, the probability that the roll shows a number greater than 3 is $\frac{1}{2}$. true

5. If the chance of snow is 30%, the odds against snow are 7 to 1. false [11-4]

6. The odds in favor of rolling a 2 with a single game cube are 1 to 5. true

Complete.

7. If events A and B cannot both occur at the same time, they are said to be __?__ events. mutually exclusive [11-5]

8. For two mutually exclusive events, the probability of drawing a red card is $\frac{1}{4}$ and the probability of drawing a blue card is $\frac{1}{2}$. The probability of drawing a red card or a blue card is __?__. $\frac{3}{4}$

9. $P(A) = \frac{1}{2}$, $P(B) = \frac{1}{2}$, and $P(A \text{ and } B) = \frac{1}{6}$. $P(A \text{ or } B) = $ __?__. $\frac{5}{6}$ [11-6]

10. If $P(A) = \frac{1}{3}$, $P(A \text{ and } B) = \frac{1}{9}$, and $P(A \text{ or } B) = \frac{5}{9}$, $P(B) = $ __?__. $\frac{1}{3}$

The dials shown at the right are spun.

11. The probability that the blue dial shows an even number and the red dial shows an odd number is __?__. $\frac{2}{9}$ [11-7]

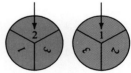

12. The probability that one dial shows an odd number and one dial shows an even number is __?__. $\frac{4}{9}$

13. A bag contains 7 red marbles and 5 yellow marbles. A marble is drawn and is not replaced. Then a second marble is drawn. [11-8]
    a. The probability that the first is yellow and the second is red is __?__. $\frac{35}{132}$
    b. The probability that the marbles are different colors is __?__. $\frac{35}{66}$

14. Of a random sample of 65 cassette holders, 13 were defective. [11-9]
    a. The probability that a randomly selected cassette holder is defective is __?__. 0.2
    b. Of 2400 produced, about __?__ of the cassette holders are defective. 480

434 *Chapter 11*

Chapter Test

1. In how many different ways can 3 people sit in a row of 5 seats? [11–1]
   60
2. How many combinations of 3 colors can you choose from 7 colors? [11–2]
   35

Exercises 3–7 refer to the spinner shown below at the right. Find the probability that the pointer will stop on a wedge of the type described.

3. blue $\frac{1}{6}$ 4. odd-numbered and red $\frac{1}{3}$ 5. green 0 [11–3]

6. What are the odds in favor of the pointer stopping on a red wedge? 1 to 2 [11–4]

7. What are the odds against the pointer stopping on a wedge with a number less than 5? 1 to 2

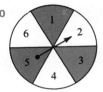

8. Two game cubes are rolled. Are events A and B mutually exclusive? Yes [11–5]
   A: The sum is 4. B: A 4 shows on one cube.

9. Events A and B are mutually exclusive. $P(A) = \frac{1}{3}$. $P(B) = \frac{5}{12}$.
   Find $P(A$ or $B)$. $\frac{3}{4}$

10. The two dials are spun. Find each probability. [11–6]
    a. 2 comes up. $\frac{1}{4}$
    b. B comes up. $\frac{1}{4}$
    c. 2 and B come up. $\frac{1}{16}$
    d. 2 or B comes up. $\frac{7}{16}$

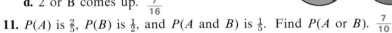

11. $P(A)$ is $\frac{2}{5}$, $P(B)$ is $\frac{1}{2}$, and $P(A$ and $B)$ is $\frac{1}{5}$. Find $P(A$ or $B)$. $\frac{7}{10}$

12. A bag contains 3 red marbles and 4 blue marbles. A marble is [11–7]
    drawn at random and replaced. Then a second marble is drawn.
    Find the probability of each event.
    a. The first marble is blue and the second is red. $\frac{12}{49}$
    b. Both marbles are blue. $\frac{16}{49}$

13. A bag contains 4 green marbles and 2 yellow marbles. A marble is [11–8]
    drawn at random and is not replaced. Then a second marble is
    drawn. Find the probability of each event.
    a. The first marble is yellow and the second is green. $\frac{4}{15}$
    b. Both marbles are green. $\frac{2}{5}$

14. Of a random sample of 600 tires, 3 were found to be defective. [11–9]
    a. What is the probability that the next tire chosen will be defective? 0.005
    b. Of 7000 tires made, about how many are defective?
       about 35 tires

Probability **435**

Review for Retention

Complete.

1. $7 \times \underline{\ ?\ } = \frac{14}{15}$ $\frac{2}{15}$

2. $9 \times (-13) = \underline{\ ?\ }$
-117

3. $-9 \div 7 = \underline{\ ?\ }$ $-1\frac{2}{7}$

4. $\frac{1}{2} \div \frac{1}{4} = \underline{\ ?\ }$ 2

Add, subtract, multiply, or divide. Write the answer as a proper fraction in lowest terms or as a mixed number in simple form.

5. $\frac{9}{16} - \frac{1}{3}$ $\frac{11}{48}$

6. $-\frac{3}{8} \div \frac{1}{2}$ $-\frac{3}{4}$

7. $1\frac{2}{3} + \frac{11}{12}$ $2\frac{7}{12}$

8. $2\frac{1}{4} - 1\frac{1}{16}$ $1\frac{3}{16}$

9. $4\frac{1}{5} \times 2\frac{1}{2}$ $10\frac{1}{2}$

10. $3\frac{3}{5} \div 1\frac{2}{7}$ $2\frac{4}{5}$

Give the coordinates of the given points. Name the points for the ordered pairs.

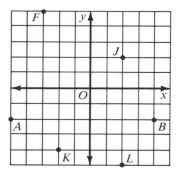

11. A $(-5, -2)$

12. $(-3, 5)$ F

13. J $(2, 2)$

14. L $(2, -5)$

15. $(4, -2)$ B

16. $(-2, -4)$ K

(Continue on next page.)

436

Cumulative Review (Chapters 1–11)

Exercises

Simplify.

1. $5.4 + (7 \times 6.3)$ 49.5

2. $\frac{16 + 9}{32 + 8}$ 0.625, or $\frac{5}{8}$

3. $13(9.2 \div 16)$
7.475

4. $4x - y + xy + 3y$
$4x + xy + 2y$

5. $2m + 2n - m + n$
$m + 3n$

6. $3p^2(p + 5)$
$3p^3 + 15p^2$

Perform the indicated operation. Write the answer as a proper fraction in lowest terms or as a mixed number in simple form.

7. $\frac{3}{5} + \frac{4}{7}$ $1\frac{6}{35}$

8. $\frac{8}{11} - \frac{1}{3}$ $\frac{13}{33}$

9. $\frac{3}{4} \times \frac{7}{8}$ $\frac{21}{32}$

10. $-1\frac{1}{2} \div -2\frac{1}{2}$
$\frac{3}{5}$

Solve.

11. $6x = -4 + (-18)$ $-3\frac{2}{3}$

12. $-3 - 7 = x + 1$ -11

13. $x(4 - 2) = 40$
20

14. $x + (-9) > -2$
All the numbers greater than 7.

15. $4 + (-12) \leq x - 6$
All the numbers greater than or equal to -2.

16. $11 - x > 0$
All the numbers less than 11.

Find the radius of a circle with the given circumference. Use $\pi \approx \frac{22}{7}$.

17. $C = 264$ 42

18. $C = 343.2$ 54.6

19. $C = 83.6$ 13.3

20. $C = 897.6$
142.8

Solve.

21. What is 39% of 120? 46.8

22. What is 125% of 89? 111.25

23. What percent of 60 is 12? 20%

24. What percent of 75 is 35? $46\frac{2}{3}$%, or $46.\overline{6}$%

25. 18 is 50% of what number? 36

26. 35 is 8% of what number? 437.5

Use a straight-line graph to complete the ordered pairs, then find the slope.

27. $A(7, 0)$, $B(5, 1)$, $C(-1, ?)$, $D(?, 7)$
$4, -7; -\frac{1}{2}$

28. $A(0, 0)$, $B(2, 1)$, $C(4, ?)$, $D(?, 3)$
$2, 6; \frac{1}{2}$

Find the perimeter and the area of the polygon described.

29. A rectangle with sides 136.5 m and 97.5 m 468 m; 13,308.75 m²

30. A parallelogram with base 15 cm, one side 7 cm, and height 6 cm 44 cm; 90 cm²

31. A triangle with base 63 m, sides 51 m and 30 m, and height 24 m 144 m; 756 m²

Is the triangle with sides of the given lengths a right triangle?

32. 12, 16, 20 Yes

33. 4, 6, 9 No

34. 9, 12, 15 Yes

436 *Chapter 11*

Find the value of each factorial.

35. 2! 2 **36.** 5! 120 **37.** 3! 6 **38.** 7! 5040 **39.** 1! 1

Problems

> **Problem Solving Reminders**
> Here are some problem solving reminders that may help you solve some of the problems on this page.
> - Some steps in your plan may not involve operations.
> - Consider whether a chart will help to organize information.
> - Check by using rounding to find an estimated answer.

Solve.

1. Rosalie has 2 ten-dollar bills. She would like to buy a book for $6.95, some puzzles for a total cost of $12.50, and birthday cards for a total cost of $3.60. Does she have enough money? no

2. A faucet leaks at the rate of $\frac{1}{4}$ cup of water per hour. How much water will leak in 24 hours? 6 cups

3. A Rosebud rocking chair can be purchased for $245.70 in a furniture store or for $189 at a factory store. What is the percent of markup for the furniture store? 30% markup

4. In order for two elements to combine, the sum of their valence numbers must be 0. One atom of carbon has a valence number of 4, and one atom of fluorine has a valence number of -1. How many atoms of fluorine are needed to combine with 1 atom of carbon? 4 atoms

5. A student from the eighth grade class will be selected at random to represent the Heath School at the governor's conference on schools. If there are 78 boys and 82 girls in the class, what is the probability that a girl will be chosen? $\frac{41}{80}$

6. Find the area of a rectangular yard that has one side of length 12 m and perimeter 54 m. 180 m²

7. You can buy whole chickens at Sal's Market for $1.09 per pound. For an additional $.25 per pound, the butcher will cut up the chicken and remove the bones. If chicken is sold in tenths of a pound, how much boneless chicken can be purchased for $7.50? about 5.6 lb

8. A rectangular painting is 5 ft wide and has an area of 15 ft². The frame around the painting is 3 in. wide. What are the dimensions of the framed painting? $5\frac{1}{2}$ ft by $3\frac{1}{2}$ ft

Probability **437**

---

a. Solve the equation for y in terms of x.

b. Find solutions of the equation for the given values of x: $-5, 2, 8$.

17. $5x + y = 15$
$y = 15 - 5x$;
40, 5, -25

18. $-7x + y = 3$
$y = 3 + 7x$;
-32, 17, 59

19. $2x = 1 - y$
$y = 1 - 2x$;
11, -3, -15

Solve. Give your answer to the nearest tenth.

20. Use the divide-and-average method to approximate $\sqrt{40}$. 6.3

21. Use interpolation and the table on page 498 to approximate $\sqrt{27.5}$. 5.2

22. Use the divide-and-average method to approximate $\sqrt{11}$. 3.3

23. Use interpolation and the table on page 498 to approximate $\sqrt{77.8}$. 8.8

Is the triangle with sides of the given lengths a right triangle?

24. 5, 11, 13 No

25. 8, 15, 17 Yes

26. 6, 7, 9 No

27. 10, 24, 26 Yes

Give answers in terms of radicals with the radical in the numerator.

28. A leg of a 45° right triangle has a length of 17. How long is the hypotenuse? $17\sqrt{2}$

29. In a 30°–60° right triangle, the shorter leg has a length of 11. How long is the hypotenuse? 22

30. In a 30°–60° right triangle, the hypotenuse has a length of 12. How long is the longer leg? $6\sqrt{3}$

437

12

Statistics

For ecological and other reasons, it is sometimes important to determine the size and geographical location of a group of migrating birds such as those shown in the photograph. A total count of a particular kind of bird obviously poses a difficult problem. By using a sample count, however, only a small part of the bird population needs to be counted. The total number of birds in the entire area can then be estimated from the number in the sampled area.

The simplest method of counting birds and studying migration is direct observation. Because of the disadvantages of this method, more sophisticated methods are being developed and used. These include banding, radio tracking, and radar observation. With the help of computers, this data can be quickly collected and examined.

In this chapter, you will learn some methods for gathering and analyzing data.

Career Note

Statisticians collect, analyze, and interpret numerical results of surveys and experiments. They may use the information that is gathered to determine suitable choices, evaluate a report, or redesign an existing program. Statisticians are usually employed in manufacturing, finance, or government positions. A thorough knowledge of mathematics and a background in economics or natural science is needed.

439

Lesson Commentary
Chapter 12 Statistics

Overview

Statistics is a branch of mathematics that finds application in virtually every field of endeavor. As even the previously nontechnical fields use statistics more and more, it becomes important to have an early introduction to statistics.

Understanding bar and line graphs is a life skill for your students. They will encounter these graphs all their lives in newspapers, magazines, manuals, and so on. A mathematically literate person must know how to read and interpret the data in these graphs.

The standard statistical measures are introduced: range, mean, median, and mode. The range is a measure of "spread," or dispersion; the mean, median, and mode are the standard measures of central tendency, which describe the middle of the data. For large quantities of data, we use frequency distributions to summarize the information conveniently. The mean, median, mode, and range are calculated from the table or histogram of a frequency distribution. Frequency distributions and their associated frequency polygons sometimes hint at normal distributions, or bell curves, a topic students may encounter later in their study of mathematics.

GRAPHS AND STATISTICAL MEASURES

12-1 Bar Graphs

Objective *for pages 440–444*

■ To read and make single and double bar graphs.

Teaching Suggestions

Most of the material in this lesson will be review for students. They should be able to interpret and make bar graphs. Remind them to space the bars equally and to choose a uniform scale on the vertical axis.

The real value of a bar graph, like that of all graphs, is its visual impact. Be sure that students can look at one and tell the item with the greatest value and the one with the least value.

Some students may wonder why the bars are required to be of uniform width. Is this a question of aesthetics, or one of mathematics? Point out that bars of equal heights but unequal widths have different areas, and thus really should not be used to represent equal quantities. If bars are of equal width, then height and area are proportional, and any quantity proportional to height is also proportional to area.

Some pointers about vertical scales would be helpful. A uniform scale is necessary, or unintended distortions of data occur. You should make it clear, too, that the vertical axis does not always begin from zero. This is usually shown by a zigzag at the bottom of the axis.

Sliding bar graphs are often used for data that include positive and negative numbers. Emphasize the zero at the center of the horizontal axis. Similar graphs are called floating column charts, gain and loss charts, and bilateral bar charts. They can be used to depict companies' gains and losses or people's income and spending.

Related Activities

To see how graphs are found in everyday use, have students bring in and explain bar graphs found in magazines and newspapers.

To illustrate how one can "lie" with statistics, show students these two bar graphs of the same data.

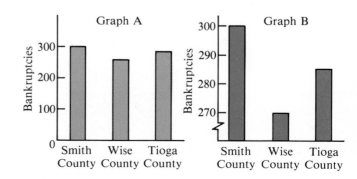

1. Which graph emphasizes the similarity of the three counties? **A**
2. Which graph emphasizes the difference among the counties? **B**

Suppose the counties are trying to attract new businesses.

3. Which graph would Smith County be likely to use? **A**
4. Which graph would Wise County use? **B**

Interested students might like to read *How to Lie with Statistics* by Darrell Huff and Irving Geis.

Resource Book: Page 145 (Use After Page 444)

NAME _____ DATE _____

Problem Solving — For use after Lesson 12-1
Review

This page reviews different types of problem solving situations.

| Making a Model or Sketch | Not Enough Information | Logic |
| Working Within Limits | Too Much Information | Identifying a Subgoal |

Identify the type of problem solving situation and then solve the problem.

1. At Peninsula High School, it is estimated from previous years that about 73% of the seniors will continue their schooling. 75% of these will attend a 4-year college. It is also estimated that 5% of the seniors will enter the service and 22% will go directly into the work force. From a class of 188, about how many seniors will go to a 4-year college?
   103 (too much inf.) (subgoal)

2. John and Pete are allowed to work with the computer at school during any study period and/or lunch period that is directly before or after one of their study periods. If periods are 48 min long, passing time between classes is 4 min, and lunch periods are 35 min, what is the maximum time they can spend with the computer?
   87 min (limits)

3. The width of a river is 321 m at the point where it is spanned by a bridge. 25% of the bridge is on one side of the river, and 21½% is on the other side of the river. How long is the bridge?
   600 m (sketch)

4. East Hamilton recycles about 26% of the material received at the local landfill. 85% of East Hamilton's 3820 families dispose of waste there. How much of the material is recycled each year?
   not enough information

5. What are the options for a new sports car if the list at the right shows all the models?
   Red, Blue, or Maroon, 2-door or 4-door. Red, Maroon - 2-tone

   | Red, 2-door, 2-tone |
   | Blue, 4-door |
   | Blue, 2-door |
   | Red, 4-door |
   | Maroon, 4-door, 2-tone |
   | Red, 4-door, 2-tone |
   | Maroon, 2-door, 2-tone |
   | Maroon, 2-door |
   | Red, 2-door |
   | Maroon, 4-door |

6. The sketch shows how two parallelograms can be formed by 7 toothpicks. What is the greatest number of parallelograms of the same size that can be formed in a design of 27 toothpicks?
   10 (sketch)

7. Lynn, Jesse, and Dean play basketball, soccer, and softball, not necessarily in that order. Lynn does not play with a bat. The basketball player and Lynn are cousins. Jesse practices with Lynn's cousin. Who plays which game?
   See answer key for chart. Jesse - softball, Lynn - soccer, Dean - basketball (logic)

MATHEMATICS, Structure and Method, Course 2, New Edition.
Copyright © 1985 by Houghton Mifflin Company. All rights reserved. Printed in U.S.A.

145

12-2 Line Graphs

Objective for pages 445–448

■ To read and make line graphs.

Teaching Suggestions

Students may wonder when to make a bar graph and when to make a line graph, especially if the horizontal axis is to be labeled with numbers. Line graphs are generally used when the value of the data change continuously from one point to the next. Otherwise a bar graph is more appropriate. For Exercise 9 on page 443, for example, the data should be presented as a bar graph because it would make no sense to infer that there are 20.2 million 2½-member families.

For the data on page 445, a line graph is appropriate because it is fair to assume that the data change smoothly; a guess that the enrollment in 1982 was 45 million students would probably be close to correct. Point out that the more data we have, the more accurate the graph would be. If we made a graph using only the figures from 1960, 1970, 1980, and 1990, a reader would guess 1965 enrollment to be about 2 million lower than it actually was, and would miss the 1985 dip completely.

Line graphs can be used for data that change smoothly even if time is not involved. Some examples would be the cost of various amounts of Swiss cheese, the amount of sugar that dissolves in water at different temperatures, or a graph that is used to convert from pints to gallons.

Emphasize that, although we may use different scales on the two axes of a line graph, the scale on either given axis should be uniform.

Point out that the vertical scale of the graph on page 445 begins at 40 million students rather than at 0. This emphasizes the differences between the enrollments. The graph could have been made with 0 below 40 and a zigzag line between 0 and 40.

A line graph, like a bar graph, can show at a glance the greatest and least values of the quantity in question. Line graphs are especially useful, however, for showing changes and rates of change. We can use a line graph to show when the quantity increases or decreases, and when it changes the most, the least, or perhaps not at all. You might want to mention that it is slope that is involved. Steepness and direction are intuitively clear to students.

Double line graphs should be clear to students who understand single line graphs. When making a double line graph, be sure that the two lines are easy to distinguish and clearly labeled.

Related Activities

To show that line graphs are in everyday use, have students bring in and explain line graphs found in magazines and newspapers.

To illustrate the effects of the choice of scales for a line graph, have students use the data on page 445 to make the following graphs. For each graph they should use one graph paper square per interval. Graph paper with 4 × 4 squares per square inch is suitable. Ask how each graph differs from graph 1.

1. Horizontal interval: 5 years, from 1960 to 1995, Vertical interval: 2 million students, from 40 million to 52 million. **This is the graph on page 445.**
2. Horizontal interval: $2\frac{1}{2}$ years, from 1960 to 1995. Vertical interval: same as graph 1. **The graph is twice as wide and the slopes are halved.**
3. Horizontal interval: same as graph 1. Vertical interval: 1 million students, from 40 million to 52 million. **The graph is twice as high and the slopes are doubled.**
4. Horizontal interval: same as graph 1. Vertical interval: 10 million students, from 0 to 60 million. **The graph is the same height but the graph line is only in the top third. The slopes are $\frac{1}{5}$ of what they were.**

12-3 Statistical Measures

Objective *for pages 449–452*

■ To calculate the range, mean, median, and mode.

Teaching Suggestions

The range is a measure, although a very crude one, of the degree to which the data are scattered or dispersed. For example, consider the following set of data: 5, 21, 21, 25, 28, 30, 45. The extreme values (5 and 45) can be dropped without changing the mean (25) median (25), and mode (21). In later courses students may learn about variance and standard deviation, more refined measures of dispersion.

Students have probably used the mean before, but they may not have used the median and mode. Encourage students to list data in order if they are asked to find the median or mode. Some sets of data have no mode, such as the set in Example 2.

The mean, median, and mode are called measures of central tendency because they describe the middle of the set of data. Of course, no statistic is really adequate to describe a set of data. Many wildly different sets of data can have the same mean and range. It is partly for this reason that the standard deviation is used with the mean

in later courses to more completely characterize data. Students will learn about standard deviation in the Enrichment, page 464.

You might want to mention the uses and limitations of statistics. For example, suppose you are a student in Class *A* of Example 1. The teacher has announced that the students with the top six grades will get A's. Your grade is 93. Knowing the mean, median, or mode would tell you that you may get an A, but you cannot be sure.

Related Activities

To show that statistics are in broad use, have students bring in newspaper or magazine articles that use the statistical measures studied here. They are most likely to find references to means, or averages, and medians. These terms are used frequently, for example, in articles about economics.

To understand the effect of extreme values on the statistics, have students find the median and mode of a set of 9 numbers with a range of 10. Then replace the smallest number with one ten times as great, and calculate the mean, median, and mode again.

Resource Book: Page 146 (Use After Page 452)

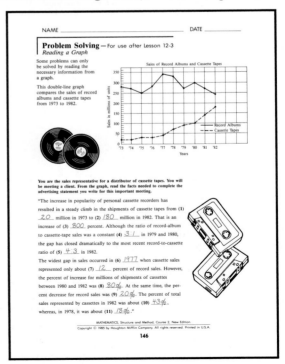

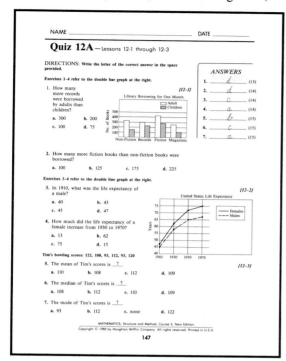

---

frequencies, starting from either the smallest or the largest data item, until we find the frequency that gives a total equal to or greater than the number of the middle item. In Example 2, the median is in the interval 40–49.

When it is time for students to make their own frequency tables with data grouped into intervals, be prepared to give a bit more guidance than usual. Students are likely to want to be told what intervals to use. If you plan to leave the decision to them, be prepared for variation in the intervals chosen. There is no "right" interval. In Example 2, intervals of five years would have involved more work but would have been more useful for some purposes.

Related Activities

To give students some experience with collecting data to produce a frequency table, take a tally of the number of school clubs each student belongs to or the number of children in each student's family. From the tally students can make a frequency table, and then calculate the mean, median, and mode for the data.

FREQUENCY AND EXPECTED VALUE

12-4 Frequency Distributions

Objective for pages 453–456

■ To read and make frequency distributions.

Teaching Suggestions

It is important to take the time to explain the columns in the frequency tables that are headed "$x \times f$." Be sure students realize that each of these entries is actually a partial sum. Since each row has f data items, each one of which is x, the sum of these items is $x \times f$. By adding all the numbers in the "$x \times f$" column we have the total of all the data items. Point out that the sum of the numbers in the frequency column is the total number of data items, so finding a mean requires division by this sum.

In using grouped data in a frequency table to determine means, medians, and modes, take extra care to explain how the median is found. The idea is to add

---

NAME _____ DATE _____

CALCULATOR — For use after Lesson 12-4
Weighted Means

Often, when you find the mean for a frequency distribution, different quantities have different frequencies. A **weighted mean** takes into account the relative importance of each quantity.

EXAMPLE At a sale, Julio bought 9 records at $1.98 each, 4 at $2.50 each, and 3 at $5.18 each. What was the mean cost per record?

SOLUTION Mean $= \dfrac{9(\$1.98) + 4(\$2.50) + 3(\$5.18)}{9 + 4 + 3}$

$= \dfrac{\$17.82 + \$10.00 - \$15.54}{16}$

$= \dfrac{\$43.36}{16} = \$2.71$

To find a weighted mean, multiply each quantity times its frequency, then divide the sum of the products by the sum of the frequencies.

Use your calculator to find each mean.

1. Marie invested $100 at 7% interest, $50 at 9%, and $200 at 8%. What is her average rate of interest? _7.9%_

2. A group of people donated a television set to the youth center. Six people each gave $15, 4 gave $25 each, 2 gave $50 each, and 1 gave $75. What was the average donation? _$28.08_

3. Carrie scored 70, 80, 90, and 75 on a quiz, a test, a midterm, and a final exam. Her teacher considers the test twice as important as the quiz, the midterm twice as important as the test, and the final exam twice as important as the midterm. What is Carrie's average for the term? _79.3_

4. Hugo ran 6 mi on each of 3 days, 5 mi on each of 5 days, and 7 mi on each of 6 days. What was the average distance he ran during this time? _6.07 mi_

12-5 Histograms and Frequency Polygons

Objective *for pages 457–460*

- To read and make histograms and frequency polygons.

Teaching Suggestions

There are hints of some sophisticated statistical concepts in this section. By drawing frequency polygons, we hint at the continuous probability distributions of advanced statistics. Also, many of the examples and exercises roughly resemble normal distributions, or "bell" curves. Furthermore, since the area under a frequency polygon is the same as the area of the histogram, this area is the same as the sum of all the items in the distribution.

Note that in Example 1, each bar represents one score. In the histogram each number on the horizontal axis labels the center of a bar. The graph of the frequency polygon is connected to the vertical lines that represent scores. In Example 2 each bar represents an interval of scores. In the histogram the tallest bar, for example, represents scores between 70 and 80. The graph of the frequency polygon is connected to the midpoints of the intervals.

To illustrate the relationships that can exist among means, medians, and modes, consider the frequency polygons shown. We have two skewed distributions, one with a tail to the right, the other with a tail to the left. In the first graph the tail causes the mean to be less than the median. When the tail is on the left, as in the second graph, the mean is greater than the median.

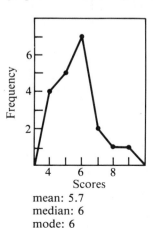

mean: 5.7
median: 6
mode: 6

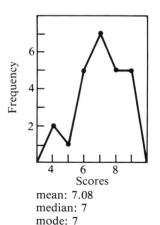

mean: 7.08
median: 7
mode: 7

Students may notice that the mode corresponds to the tallest bar of a histogram and the highest point on the frequency polygon. Point out that the median corresponds to the value on the horizontal axis such that a vertical line can be drawn that divides the histogram or frequency polygon into two parts of equal area.

Resource Book: Page 149 (Use After Page 460)

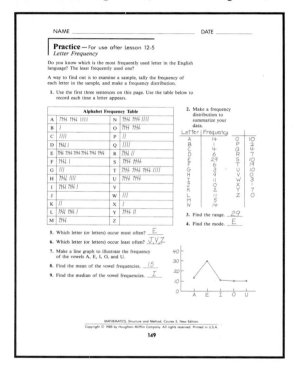

Related Activities

To provide practical experience, have students prepare a histogram and a frequency polygon of the enrollment by grade in your school. Determine the mean number of students per grade.

To extend the idea of a frequency polygon, convert a frequency polygon into a relative frequency polygon. This will indicate what fractional part (expressed as a decimal) each data value represents of the whole set of data. For example, consider the data in Written Exercise 15. Since there are 20 items, a frequency of 2 corresponds to a relative frequency of $\frac{2}{20}$, or 0.1. We can add a scale to show both frequencies and relative frequencies, as shown on the next page.

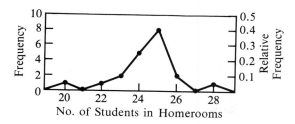

No. of Students in Homerooms

12-6 Expected Value of a Random Variable

Objective *for pages 461–463*

■ To find the expected value of a random variable.

Teaching Suggestions

Students can use a formal statement of the meaning of expected value, but they will appreciate the concept better if they have a clear intuitive grasp of it. The easiest context in which to understand expected value is to think of the long run. By the long run we mean repeating the experiment numerous times. In the long run, the expected value is the average value of the random variable. In terms of the game used to introduce the section, the expected value is the average amount won per play of the game, if we were to play enough times so that the proportions of $5's, $10's, and $15's would be $\frac{1}{3}$, $\frac{1}{2}$, and $\frac{1}{6}$, respectively.

You will recognize that an expected value is quite similar to a weighted average, or weighted mean. In this instance the weights are the probabilities of the various outcomes. In a situation in which all outcomes have equal probabilities, the expected value is simply the mean of all the possible outcomes. This is also the case for a weighted average when all weights are equal.

Be sure students understand that the expression for the mean on page 461,

$$5 \times \frac{27}{80} + 10 \times \frac{39}{80} + 15 \times \frac{14}{80} = 9.19,$$

is not expected to be equal to the expression on page 462,

$$5 \times \frac{2}{6} + 10 \times \frac{3}{6} + 15 \times \frac{1}{6} = 9\frac{1}{6}, \text{ or } 9.17.$$

The second expression is a theoretical prediction based on the assumption that the pointer is equally likely to stop on any of the six sections of the spinner. The first expression is based on the results of an experiment. The experimental value might have come out the same as the theoretical value, or it might have been quite different (especially if the pointer is actually not equally likely to stop on any of the six sections).

Related Activities

To give a realistic example of expected value, present the following problem: In a raffle, 1000 tickets are sold. First prize is a color television set worth $650; second prize is a home computer worth $150; third prize is a tape deck worth $50.

1. What is the probability of any given ticket being drawn for first prize? 0.001 for second prize? 0.001 for third prize? 0.001
2. What is the probability that any given ticket is not drawn to win any prize? 0.997
3. What is the total value of all the prizes? $850
4. What is the average value of the winnings per ticket? $.85
5. What is the expected value of each ticket? $.85
6. What is the most that a "logical" person would be willing to spend on a ticket? $.85

Resource Book: Page 150 (Use After Page 463)

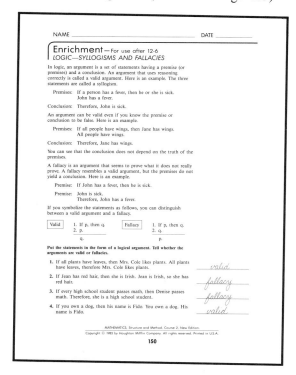

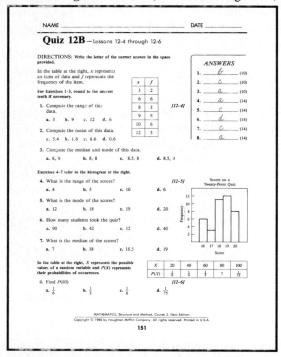

NAME _____ DATE _____

Quiz 12B — Lessons 12-4 through 12-6

DIRECTIONS: Write the letter of the correct answer in the space provided.

In the table at the right, x represents an item of data and f represents the frequency of the item.

For Exercises 1–3, round to the nearest tenth if necessary.

x	f
3	2
6	6
8	3
9	8
10	6
12	5

[12-4]

1. Compute the range of this data.
   a. 3 b. 9 c. 12 d. 6

2. Compute the mean of this data.
   a. 5.4 b. 1.6 c. 8.6 d. 0.6

3. Compute the median and mode of this data.
   a. 8, 9 b. 8, 8 c. 8.5, 8 d. 8.5, 9

Exercises 4–7 refer to the histogram at the right. [12-5]

4. What is the range of the scores?
   a. 4 b. 5 c. 10 d. 6

5. What is the mode of the scores?
   a. 12 b. 18 c. 19 d. 20

6. How many students took the quiz?
   a. 90 b. 42 c. 12 d. 40

7. What is the median of the scores?
   a. 7 b. 18 c. 18.5 d. 19

In the table at the right, X represents the possible values of a random variable and $P(X)$ represents their probabilities of occurrence.

X	20	40	60	80	100
$P(X)$	$\frac{1}{6}$	$\frac{1}{4}$	$\frac{1}{3}$	?	$\frac{1}{12}$

8. Find $P(80)$. [12-6]
   a. $\frac{1}{6}$ b. $\frac{1}{3}$ c. $\frac{1}{8}$ d. $\frac{1}{75}$

ANSWERS
1. _b_ (10)
2. _c_ (10)
3. _a_ (10)
4. _a_ (14)
5. _c_ (14)
6. _d_ (14)
7. _c_ (14)
8. _a_ (14)

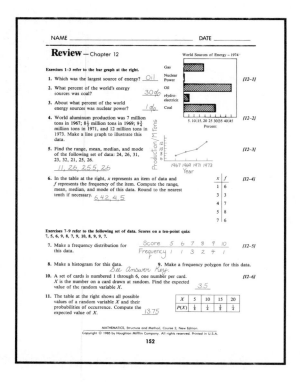

NAME _____ DATE _____

Review — Chapter 12

Exercises 1–3 refer to the bar graph at the right.

1. Which was the largest source of energy? _Oil_ [12-1]

2. What percent of the world's energy sources was coal? _30%_

3. About what percent of the world energy sources was nuclear power? _1%_

4. World aluminum production was 7 million tons in 1967; $8\frac{1}{4}$ million tons in 1969; $9\frac{1}{4}$ million tons in 1971, and 12 million tons in 1973. Make a line graph to illustrate this data. [12-2]

5. Find the range, mean, median, and mode of the following set of data: 24, 26, 31, 23, 32, 21, 25, 26. [12-3]
   _11, 26, 25.5, 26_

6. In the table at the right, x represents an item of data and f represents the frequency of the item. Compute the range, mean, median, and mode of this data. Round to the nearest tenth if necessary. [12-4] _6, 4.2, 4.5_

x	f
1	6
3	3
4	7
5	8
7	6

Exercises 7–9 refer to the following set of data. Scores on a ten-point quiz:
7, 5, 6, 9, 8, 7, 9, 10, 8, 9, 9, 7.

7. Make a frequency distribution for this data. [12-5]

Score	5	6	7	8	9	10
Frequency	1	1	3	2	4	1

8. Make a histogram for this data.   9. Make a frequency polygon for this data.
   See Answer Key.

10. A set of cards is numbered 1 through 6, one number per card. X is the number on a card drawn at random. Find the expected value of the random variable X. [12-6] _3.5_

11. The table at the right shows all possible values of a random variable X and their probabilities of occurrence. Compute the expected value of X. _13.75_

X	5	10	15	20
$P(X)$	$\frac{1}{4}$	$\frac{1}{4}$	$\frac{3}{8}$	$\frac{1}{8}$

World Sources of Energy – 1974

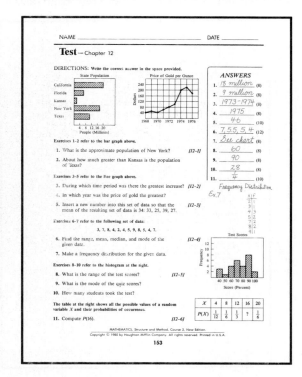

NAME _____ DATE _____

Test — Chapter 12

DIRECTIONS: Write the correct answer in the space provided.

State Population — Price of Gold per Ounce

Exercises 1–2 refer to the bar graph above.

1. What is the approximate population of New York? [12-1]

2. About how much greater than Kansas is the population of Texas?

Exercises 3–5 refer to the line graph above.

3. During which time period was there the greatest increase? [12-2]

4. In which year was the price of gold the greatest?

5. Insert a new number into this set of data so that the mean of the resulting set of data is 34: 33, 25, 39, 27. [12-3]

Exercises 6–7 refer to the following set of data:
3, 7, 8, 4, 2, 4, 5, 9, 8, 5, 4, 7.

6. Find the range, mean, median, and mode of the given data. [12-4]

7. Make a frequency distribution for the given data.

Exercises 8–10 refer to the histogram at the right.

8. What is the range of the test scores? [12-5]

9. What is the mode of the quiz scores?

10. How many students took the test?

The table at the right shows all the possible values of a random variable X and their probabilities of occurrence.

X	4	8	12	16	20
$P(X)$	$\frac{1}{12}$	$\frac{1}{6}$	$\frac{1}{3}$	?	$\frac{1}{6}$

11. Compute $P(16)$. [12-6]

ANSWERS
1. _18 million_ (8)
2. _9 million_ (8)
3. _1973–1974_ (8)
4. _1975_ (8)
5. _46_ (10)
6. _7, 5.5, 5, 4_ (12)
7. _See chart_ (8)
8. _60_ (8)
9. _90_ (8)
10. _28_ (8)
11. _$\frac{1}{4}$_ (10)

Frequency Distribution Ex. 7

x	f
3	1
4	3
5	2
7	2
8	2
9	1

Test Scores

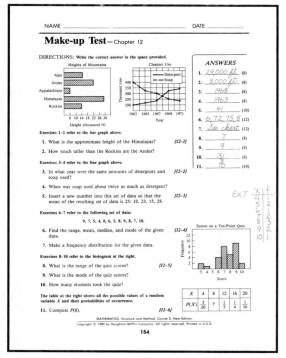

NAME _____ DATE _____

Make-up Test — Chapter 12

DIRECTIONS: Write the correct answer in the space provided.

Heights of Mountains — Cleanser Use

Exercises 1–2 refer to the bar graph above.

1. What is the approximate height of the Himalayas? [12-1]

2. How much taller than the Rockies are the Andes?

Exercises 3–4 refer to the line graph above.

3. In what year were the same amounts of detergents and soap used? [12-2]

4. When was soap used about twice as much as detergent?

5. Insert a new number into this set of data so that the mean of the resulting set of data is 25: 18, 23, 15, 28. [12-3]

Exercises 6–7 refer to the following set of data:
9, 7, 5, 4, 8, 6, 5, 8, 9, 8, 7, 10.

6. Find the range, mean, median, and mode of the given data. [12-4]

7. Make a frequency distribution for the given data.

Exercises 8–10 refer to the histogram at the right.

8. What is the range of the quiz scores? [12-5]

9. What is the mode of the quiz scores?

10. How many students took the quiz?

The table at the right shows all the possible values of a random variable X and their probabilities of occurrence.

X	4	8	12	16	20
$P(X)$	$\frac{3}{20}$	?	$\frac{1}{5}$	$\frac{1}{4}$	$\frac{1}{10}$

11. Compute $P(8)$. [12-6]

ANSWERS
1. _29,000 ft_ (8)
2. _3,000 ft_ (8)
3. _1968_ (8)
4. _1963_ (8)
5. _41_ (10)
6. _6, 7.2, 7.5, 8_ (12)
7. _See chart_ (12)
8. _7_ (8)
9. _9_ (8)
10. _31_ (8)
11. _$\frac{3}{10}$_ (10)

Ex. 7

x	f
4	1
5	2
6	1
7	2
8	3
9	2
10	1

Scores on a Ten-Point Quiz

Page 155

NAME _____ DATE _____

CUMULATIVE REVIEW—Chapters 1-12
Exercises

Evaluate the expression if $a = 4$, $b = 12$, and $c = \frac{1}{4}$.

1. $a + bc$ *7*
2. $-3a + 8c$ *-10*
3. $a^2 - b$ *4*
4. $(-b)^2$ *144*
5. $(-ac)^3$ *-1*
6. $a - b - 3$ *-11*

Solve for y in terms of x.

7. $3x + y = 7$ $y = 7 - 3x$
8. $4x + 2y = 10$ $y = 5 - 2x$
9. $2x - y = 1$ $y = 2x - 1$

Express as a percent.

10. $\frac{1}{5}$ *20%*
11. $\frac{5}{8}$ *62½%*
12. $\frac{7}{4}$ *175%*
13. $\frac{2}{3}$ *66⅔%*

Find the perimeter and area of the polygon described.

14. A square with side 2.5 m. $P = 10\,m$, $A = 6.25\,m^2$
15. A rhombus with base 16 cm and height 12 cm. $P = 64\,cm$, $A = 192\,cm^2$
16. A right triangle with legs 5 in. and 12 in. $P = 30\,in$, $A = 30\,in^2$

Use >, <, or = to make a true statement.

17. 53.465 _<_ 53.47
18. -3.07 _<_ -2.98
19. $-\frac{3}{5}$ _>_ $-\frac{7}{9}$

Round to the place specified.

20. hundreds: 732.894   _700_
21. tenths: 67.493   _67.5_
22. thousandths: 3.8995   _3.900_
23. hundredths: 431.087   _431.09_

For Exercises 24-27, refer to the table on page 498. Approximate the square root to the nearest hundredth.

24. $\sqrt{45}$ _6.71_
25. $\sqrt{60}$ _7.75_
26. $\sqrt{10}$ _3.16_
27. $3\sqrt{91}$ _28.62_

Complete. For Exercises 28-32, refer to the following set of data:
6, 9, 4, 5, 8, 6, 5, 9, 8, 6.

28. The range is _5_.
29. The mean is _6.6_.
30. The median is _6_.
31. The mode is _6_.
32. If you choose a number at random from the given set of data, the probability of picking an 8 is $\frac{2}{5}$.

155

Page 156

NAME _____ DATE _____

CUMULATIVE REVIEW—Chapters 1-12 (continued)
Problems

Problem Solving Reminders
Here are some problem solving reminders that may help you solve some of the problems on this page.
- Sometimes more than one method can be used to solve a problem.
- Consider whether drawing a sketch will help.
- When rounding an answer to division, consider whether it is reasonable to round up or round down.

Solve.

1. Sheila has a Happy Time laundry-powder coupon for "buy three, get one free." If she purchases 14 boxes of laundry powder, how many boxes will she receive free?   _4 boxes_

2. Keith scored 96, 89, 88, 91, and 99 on chemistry tests. What is the least he can score on the next test if he wants to maintain a 92 average?   _89_

3. Angela has 6 different skirts and 8 different sweaters. How many outfit combinations does she have?   _48_

4. Mark bought a backyard swing set for $79.95, a sandbox for $39.50, and 8 lb of sand costing $1.45 per pound. There was an assembly charge of $8.00 for the swing set and 6% sales tax on the sand. What was the total cost of Mark's purchases?   _$139.75_

5. Leslie bought 45 packs of baseball cards for 96¢ a pack. Each pack contained 32 cards. He later sold all the cards for $115.20. How much profit did he make per card?   _5¢ per card_

6. Two game cubes are tossed at the same time. Each cube has sides numbered 1 to 6. What is the probability that the sum of the two sides showing is greater than nine? $\frac{1}{6}$

   greater than twelve?   _0_

156

Page 157

NAME _____ DATE _____

CUMULATIVE TEST—Chapters 10-12

DIRECTIONS: Write the answer in the space provided.

Chapter 10

Replace the _?_ with >, <, or = to make a true statement.

1. $-\sqrt{100}$ _?_ $-\sqrt{64}$
2. $\sqrt{16} + \sqrt{9}$ _?_ $\sqrt{16 + 9}$
3. $\sqrt{4} \times \sqrt{9}$ _?_ $\sqrt{4 \times 9}$

Solve. Use interpolation and the table on page 498.

4. A square floor has an area of 68.8 m². Find the length of a side to the nearest tenth of a meter.

5. Find the length of a diagonal of a 15-cm by 15-cm square to the nearest tenth of a centimeter.

Solve. Give the answer in terms of radicals with the radical in the numerator.

6. A ladder 8 ft long resting against a house makes a 60° angle with the ground. How far up the house does it reach?

$\triangle ABC$ is a right triangle with $\angle C = 90°$, $BC = 24$ and $AB = 26$. Give all ratios in lowest terms.

7. Find the length of $\overline{AC}$.
8. Find sin A.
9. Find tan A.
10. Find m $\angle A$ to the nearest degree. Use the table on page 498.

Chapter 11

11. In how many different ways can you arrange the letters in the word THINK if you take the letters 3 at a time?

12. A game cube is rolled. Find the probability that the faces showing will be a number less than 5.

13. The probability of snow tomorrow is 60%. What are the odds in favor of snow?

14. Two game cubes are rolled at the same time. Find the probability that a 4 or 2 shows up.

ANSWERS	
1. _<_	(4)
2. _>_	(4)
3. _=_	(4)
4. _8.3 m_	(4)
5. _21.2_	(4)
6. _4√3 ft_	(4)
7. _10_	(4)
8. $sin A = \frac{12}{13}$	(4)
9. $tan A = \frac{12}{5}$	(4)
10. _67°_	(4)
11. _60_	(4)
12. $\frac{2}{3}$	(4)
13. _3:2_	(4)
14. $\frac{1}{9}$	(4)

(Continue on next page.)

157

Page 158

NAME _____ DATE _____

CUMULATIVE TEST—Chapters 10-12 (continued)

For Exercises 15-16, use a bag that contains 6 green marbles and 4 red marbles.

15. A marble is drawn at random and replaced. Then a second marble is drawn. Find the probability that both marbles are red.

16. A marble is drawn and is not replaced. Then a second marble is drawn. Find the probability that both marbles are green.

17. Of a random sample of 750 disc cameras, 3 were found to be defective. What is the probability that the next camera will be defective?

Chapter 12

Exercises 18-22 use the fact that goals scored by the soccer team in this season's games were 8, 2, 7, 3, 8, 3, 8, 5, 7, 8, 4, 9.

18. Find the range of the data.
19. Find the mean.
20. Find the median.
21. Find the mode.
22. Insert a new number into the set of data so that the mean becomes 7.

Complete.

23. A table that pairs each item of data with the number of times that item occurs is called a _?_.

24. A _?_ is a bar graph that provides a visual display of statistical data.

25. A box contains 6 nickels, 8 dimes, and 2 quarters. You are allowed to select one coin without looking. If V = the value in cents of the coin you select, what is the expected value of V?

ANSWERS	
15. $\frac{4}{23}$	(4)
16. $\frac{1}{3}$	(4)
17. _0.004_	(4)
18. _7_	(4)
19. _6_	(4)
20. _7_	(4)
21. _8_	(4)
22. _19_	(4)
23. _frequency distribution_	(4)
24. _histogram_	(4)
25. _10¢_	(4)

158

12-1 Bar Graphs

Everyday life produces masses of numerical facts that we refer to as **data.** Often there is a need to analyze some of these data in order to draw conclusions, and so we organize the data into a table, chart, or graph. This process of organizing and analyzing data is part of the branch of mathematics that is called **statistics.**

When we wish to have a *visual* display of data, we use various kinds of graphs. One type of graph that is used frequently is the **bar graph.** In a bar graph, data are represented by bars that are drawn to an appropriate length using a scale along one of two axes.

EXAMPLE 1   Make a bar graph to illustrate the data in this table.

Coal Production in One Year	
Country	**Million Metric Tons**
China	620
Poland	163
Soviet Union	487
United Kingdom	128
United States	698

Solution   Draw perpendicular axes. Mark off regular intervals on the vertical axis. Since all the numbers in the table are hundreds, start at zero and label each interval in increments of 100. Label the horizontal axis with the names of the countries. Then, using the vertical axis as a scale, draw a bar of the appropriate height for each country.

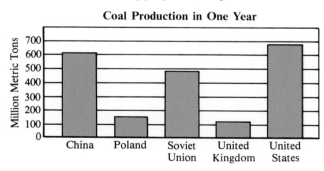

440   *Chapter 12*

Reading Mathematics: *Titles and Labels*

A graph must be easy to read to be useful. Therefore, each part of a graph should be clearly identified. In the bar graph for Example 1 on page 440, notice that each bar was labeled along the horizontal axis with the name of the country it represents and that the scale on the vertical axis was labeled *Million Metric Tons.* Notice too that the entire graph was given the title *Coal Production in One Year.*

There are many kinds of bar graphs. In a **double bar graph,** two bars may be used to display two related types of data at the same time. A **legend** is usually placed on the graph to identify the type of data that each bar represents. Example 2, below, illustrates how we interpret a double bar graph.

EXAMPLE 2   Using the double bar graph below, determine the following.

     a. The approximate value of United States exports to Africa

     b. The approximate value of United States imports from Asia

United States Trade by Geographic Area in One Year

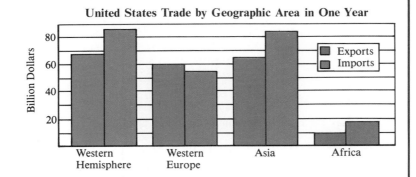

Solution

    a. From the colors in the legend on the graph you see that, in each pair of bars on the graph, the bar at the left represents exports. Locate *Africa* on the horizontal axis. The top of the bar at the left of this pair lies at about 10 on the scale of the vertical axis. These numbers represent billion dollars, so we conclude that the value of United States exports to Africa was about 10 billion dollars.

    b. The bar at the right of each pair represents imports. For Asia, the top of this bar lies about halfway between 80 and 90 on the vertical scale. Thus the value of United States imports from Asia was about 85 billion dollars.

Statistics **441**

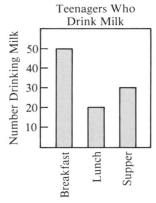

1. How many drink milk at breakfast? **50 teenagers**

2. At which meal do the fewest drink milk? **lunch**

3. How many drink milk at supper? **30 teenagers**

4. How many people are represented by each mark on the vertical scale? **10 people**

5. How many more drink milk at breakfast than at lunch? **30 teenagers**

6. How many people were in the survey? **Can't tell because many people are included in several categories.**

441

Exercises 1–6 refer to the double bar graph below.

Annual Transactions

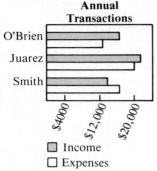

☐ Income
☐ Expenses

1. Which family had the greatest income? **Juarez**

2. Which family had the greatest expenses? **Juarez**

3. Which family had more expenses than income? **Smith**

4. About how much did the families earn altogether? **about $51,000**

5. Which family had the greatest excess of income over expenses? **O'Brien**

6. About how much did the families spend altogether? **about $49,000**

Class Exercises

Exercises 1–5 refer to the single bar graph.

1. How many categories of imports are displayed? **4**

2. What is represented by the numbers along the horizontal axis?
Amount of imports in billions of dollars

3. For which category is the amount of United States imports the least? **Chemicals** the greatest? **Fuel**

4. What is the approximate amount of United States imports of machinery? of food?
About $68 billion; about $17 billion

5. The table at the right lists the amounts of United States *exports* for these same categories. Use these data and the data from the graph above to make a *double* bar graph. Title this graph *United States Trade by Category.*
Check students' graphs.

United States Imports by Category

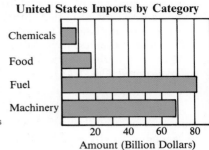

United States Exports	
Category	**Amount (Billion Dollars)**
Chemicals	21
Food	33
Fuel	10
Machinery	96

Written Exercises

Exercises 1–6 refer to the double bar graph below.

A **1.** What is represented by the numbers along the horizontal axis? **Percent of students employed**

2. What is represented by the bar at the bottom of each pair?
Percent of seniors employed

3. Which job is held by the most sophomores? seniors?
Babysitting; store sales

4. Which jobs are held by more seniors than sophomores?
Store sales and food service

5. For which job is there the greatest difference between sophomores and seniors? **Babysitting**

6. About what percent of the sophomores do odd jobs? **8%**

Jobs Held by High School Students

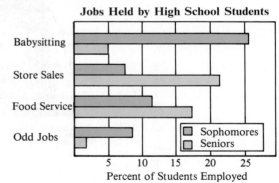

☐ Sophomores
☐ Seniors

Percent of Students Employed

442 *Chapter 12*

Make a bar graph to illustrate the data. For Exercises 7–10, make a single bar graph. For Exercises 11 and 12, make a double bar graph. Check students' graphs.

7.

Spending by Consumers Younger than 25 Years of Age

Item	Percent of Spending
Food at Home	28
Food Away from Home	21
Health/Personal Care	5
Housekeeping	3
Transportation/Utilities	31
Other	12

8.

World's Largest Countries

Country	Area (Million Km²)
Australia	7.7
Brazil	8.5
Canada	10.0
People's Republic of China	9.6
Soviet Union	22.4
United States	9.4

9.

United States Families

Family Size	Number of Families (Millions)
1	18.9
2	25.8
3	14.6
4	12.8
5	6.1
6	2.5
7 or more	1.6

10.

Outdoor Recreation

Activity	Participants (Millions)
Bicycling	79
Camping	88
Downhill Skiing	12
Fishing	91
Hiking	48
Horseback Riding	25
Sailing	19

B 11.

Family Use of Time on the Microcomputer (Percent)

Activity	Adult	Teen
Accounting	15	0
Education	15	27
Entertainment	21	53
Programming	7	10
Word Processing	34	8
Work	8	2

12.

New Book Titles Published in One Year (Hundreds)

Subject	Hardbound	Paperbound
Biography	13.5	5.1
Fiction	18.6	38.0
Juvenile	26.6	4.4
Science	27.8	6.0
Sports	7.4	70.6
Travel	2.5	2.2

Statistics **443**

Suggested Assignments

Minimum
Day 1: 442/1–6
　　　443/7–9
Day 2: 443/10–12
　　　444/Rev. 1–10

Average
Day 1: 442/1–6
　　　443/7–10
Day 2: 443/11–12
　　　444/Rev. 1–9 odd
　　　444/Challenge

Maximum
Day 1: 442/1–6
　　　443/7–10
Day 2: 443/11–12
　　　444/13–14
　　　444/Challenge

Supplementary Materials

Practice Masters, p. 53

The graph at the right is called a **sliding bar graph.** Notice that 0 is at the middle of the horizontal axis and that a scale of numbers extends both to the left and to the right. Graphs such as this are often used to illustrate data concerning gains and losses, highs and lows, and the like.

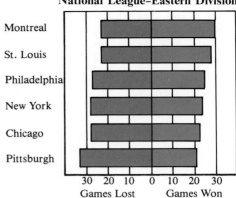

National League–Eastern Division

Montreal
St. Louis
Philadelphia
New York
Chicago
Pittsburgh

30 20 10 0 10 20 30
Games Lost   Games Won

Make a sliding bar graph to illustrate the given data. Check students' graphs.

C 13.

National League Western Division

Club	Games Won	Games Lost
Houston	33	20
Cincinnati	31	21
San Francisco	29	23
Los Angeles	27	26
Atlanta	25	27
San Diego	18	36

14.

Record Extreme Temperatures (°C)

Continent	Low	High
Antarctica	−88.3	14.4
Asia	−68	53.9
North America	−62.8	56.7
Europe	−45	46
South America	−32.8	48.9
Africa	−23.9	58
Australia	−22	53.1

Review Exercises

Express (a) as a decimal and (b) as a fraction in lowest terms.

1. 18% 0.18; $\frac{9}{50}$
2. 1.25% 0.0125; $\frac{1}{80}$
3. 9% 0.09; $\frac{9}{100}$
4. 0.4% 0.004; $\frac{1}{250}$
5. 82.5% 0.825; $\frac{33}{40}$

6. $12\frac{1}{2}\%$ 0.125; $\frac{1}{8}$
7. $33\frac{1}{3}\%$ $0.\overline{3}$; $\frac{1}{3}$
8. 0.08% 0.0008; $\frac{1}{1250}$
9. $25\frac{1}{2}\%$ 0.255; $\frac{51}{200}$
10. $16\frac{2}{3}\%$ $0.1\overline{6}$; $\frac{1}{6}$

444 *Chapter 12*

▮▮▮	**Challenge**

Replace each ? with +, −, ×, ÷, or = to make a true statement.

1. $\frac{5}{7}$? $\frac{2}{7}$? $\frac{6}{7}$? $\frac{3}{7}$
− = −

2. $\frac{2}{5}$? $\frac{2}{5}$? $\frac{3}{5}$? $\frac{2}{5}$
÷ = +
or ÷ − =

3. $\frac{2}{3}$? $\frac{2}{3}$? $\frac{7}{9}$? $\frac{1}{3}$
× = −

12-2 Line Graphs

When you need to show how data vary over a period of time, it is sometimes better to use a **line graph** than a bar graph. In a line graph the given data are represented by points plotted on a set of coordinate axes, and the points are connected by line segments. The resulting graph clearly displays changes such as increases and decreases and may make it easier to analyze the data.

EXAMPLE 1 Make a line graph to illustrate the data in this table.

School Enrollment in the United States								
Year	1960	1965	1970	1975	1980	1985	1990	1995
Students (Millions)	42.2	48.5	51.3	49.8	45.8	43.7	46.1	50.5

Solution   Mark off regular intervals on a set of coordinate axes. Label the horizontal axis with the years listed on the table. To choose a scale for the data, notice that the least number is 42.2 and the greatest number is 51.3. Therefore, it is sufficient to label the vertical axis in increments of 2 from 40 to 52. Now consider the data in the table as ordered pairs: (1960, 42.2), (1965, 48.5), (1970, 51.3), and so on. Plot these points on the set of coordinate axes and use line segments to join these points in order from left to right.

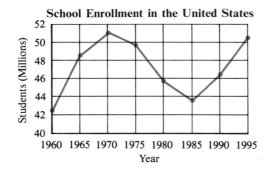

Different types of line graphs are used depending on the purpose of graphing the data. A **double line graph** is often used when the purpose is to make comparisons between two groups of data. Example 2 on the following page illustrates how we interpret double line graphs.

Statistics   **445**

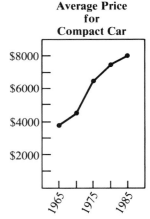

Suggested Assignments

Minimum
Day 1: 447/1–7
Day 2: 447/8
      448/9
      448/Rev. 1–6

Average
Day 1: 447/1–8
Day 2: 448/9–10
      448/Rev. 1–6
      448/Challenge

Maximum
Day 1: 447/1–8
Day 2: 448/9–11
      448/Challenge

Supplementary Materials

Practice Masters, p. 53

EXAMPLE 2   Using the double line graph below, answer the following.

    a. Approximately how great were the rural and urban populations of the United States in 1960?

    b. In what year were the rural and urban populations of the United States approximately equal?

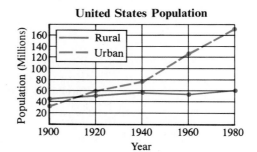

United States Population

Solution

    a. The solid line represents the rural population and the dashed line represents the urban population. Locate the points along these lines that have 1960 as their horizontal coordinate. Using the vertical coordinates of these points, you see that the rural population was about 50 million and the urban population was about 125 million.

    b. The solid and dashed lines intersect at a point with a horizontal coordinate near 1915. Therefore, the rural and urban populations were approximately equal in the year 1915.

Class Exercises

Exercises 1 and 2 refer to the graph for Example 1 on page 445.

1. In which year was the enrollment the greatest? the least? 1970; 1960

2. Between which two years was there the greatest increase in enrollment? the greatest decrease? 1960–1965; 1975–1980

Exercises 3–5 refer to the graph for Example 2 above.

3. In which year was the urban population about 75 million? 1940

4. About how great were the rural and urban populations in 1920?
Rural 51 million, urban 58 million. (Answers may vary slightly.)
5. During what time period was the rural population greater than the urban? 1900–1920

446 *Chapter 12*

Written Exercises

Exercises 1–4 refer to the graph at the right.

Supermarket Shoppers in One Day

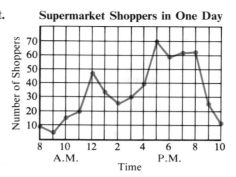

A
1. When was there the greatest number of shoppers? 5 P.M.

2. When was there the least number of shoppers? 9 A.M.

3. During which period was there the greatest increase in the number of shoppers? 4 P.M.–5 P.M.

4. During which time period did the number of shoppers remain about the same? 7 P.M.–8 P.M.

Make a single line graph to illustrate the given data. Check students' graphs.

5.

United States Population					
Year	1900	1920	1940	1960	1980	2000
Population (Millions)	76	106	132	178	227	268 (estimated)

6.

Reported Volcanic Activity in the World									
Year	1900	1910	1920	1930	1940	1950	1960	1970	1980
Number of Active Volcanoes	27	35	34	40	38	50	45	50	57

7.

Running Practice								
Week	1	2	3	4	5	6	7	8
Time to Run One Mile (Min)	10.0	9.7	9.2	8.8	8.3	8.0	7.5	7.0

8.

Normal Temperatures for Milwaukee, Wisconsin												
Month	J	F	M	A	M	J	J	A	S	O	N	D
Average Temperature (°C)	−7	−5	−1	7	12	18	21	20	16	11	3	−4

Additional A Exercises

Make a single line graph to illustrate the given data.

Snowfall in Weston County	
Year	**Inches of Snow**
1975	153
1976	168
1977	202
1978	238
1979	115
1980	129

Snowfall in Weston County

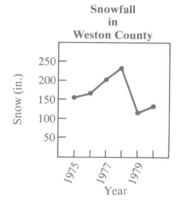

Statistics **447**

447

Make a double line graph to illustrate the given data. Check students' graphs.

B 9.

United States Energy Consumption (Percent of Total)

Year	1880	1900	1920	1940	1960	1980
Coal	41	71	73	50	23	20
Petroleum and Natural Gas	2	5	16	41	74	72

10.

Money Spent on Recreation in the United States (Million Dollars)

Year	1940	1950	1960	1970	1980
Motion Pictures	735	1367	956	1536	2899
Spectator Sports	98	223	354	1173	2314

C 11. Make a *triple* line graph to illustrate the data in this table.

Amount of United States Passenger Traffic (Billion Miles)

Year	Air	Bus	Rail
1940	1	1	24
1950	10	26	32
1960	34	19	22
1970	119	25	11
1980	219	28	12

Check students' graphs.

Review Exercises

Evaluate the expression when $x = -2.8$ and $y = 6.5$.

1. xy **2.** $3x - y$ **3.** $-x + y$ **4.** $5x - (-y)$ **5.** x^2y **6.** $-y^2 - x$
    −18.2   −14.9   9.3   −7.5   50.96   −39.45

 Challenge

A sightseer at Breathless Gorge dropped his sandwich from a gondola. The object fell at the rate of 9.8 meters per second (m/s) after the first second, 19.6 m/s after the second second, and 29.4 m/s after the third second. How fast will the sandwich be falling at 4 s? 39.2 m/s

12-3 Statistical Measures

Graphing is not the only statistical technique used to analyze numerical data. The *range*, the *mean*, the *median*, and the *mode* are four **statistical measures** that are also used for this purpose. To understand these measures, let's use them to analyze the two sets of test scores shown below at the right.

The **range** of a set of data is the difference between the greatest and the least numbers.

$$\text{range of Class } A = 99 - 59 = 40$$
$$\text{range of Class } B = 100 - 47 = 53$$

The **mean** is the sum of the data in a set divided by the number of items of data. The mean is frequently referred to as the **average.**

$$\text{mean of Class } A = \frac{2077}{25} \approx 83.1$$
$$\text{mean of Class } B = \frac{1922}{26} \approx 73.9$$

When the data are arranged in numerical order, the middle number is called the **median.** If the number of items of data is even, the median is the mean of the *two* middle numbers.

$$\text{median of Class } A = 85$$
$$\text{median of Class } B = \frac{75 + 72}{2} = 73.5$$

The **mode** is the number that occurs most often. A set of data can have more than one mode or no mode.

$$\text{mode of Class } A: 85$$
$$\text{modes of Class } B: 84, 65$$

Class A	Class B
99	100
98	96
98	93
96	88
93	88
93	86
91	84
89	84
87	84
87	80
85	78
85	75
85	75
85	72
83	70
82	69
79	66
78	66
78	65
75	65
73	65
70	63
66	58
63	54
59	51
2077	47
	1922

Now let's use these statistical measures to compare the data. For Class *A* the range of scores was only 40 points, the mean score was 83.1, the median was 85, and the mode was 85. For Class *B* the range of scores was 53 points, the mean score was only 73.9, the median score was only 73.5, and the modes were 84 and 65. An overall analysis of the data would be that the performance of Class *A* on this test was better than the performance of Class *B*.

Statistics **449**

Teaching Suggestions p. 439c

Related Activities p. 439c

Reading Mathematics

Students will learn the meaning of the following mathematical terms in this lesson: *statistical measures, range, mean, average, median, mode, measure of central tendency, statistic.*

Of the new terms, some have clear, familiar meanings. *Range* is one of these; *median* should be clear, too, if students think of median strips which are in the middle of a highway. The term *mean* will be clearer if you point out that it is synonymous with the more familiar term *average*. *Mode* is probably new and requires memorization.

The heights in centimeters of
several horses are given to
the nearest ten centimeters.
150 cm, 170 cm, 140 cm,
150 cm, 160 cm, 180 cm,
150 cm, 160 cm

1. List the heights in order,
   from smallest to largest.
   140 cm, 150 cm,
   150 cm, 150 cm,
   160 cm, 160 cm,
   170 cm, 180 cm

2. What is the least height?
   the greatest?
   140 cm; 180 cm

3. What is the range of the
   heights? **40 cm**

4. How many horses were
   150 cm tall? **3**

5. What is the mode of the
   heights? **150 cm**

6. What is the median
   height? **155 cm**

7. What is the mean height?
   157.5 cm

As you can see, the mean, median, and mode are helpful in locating the "center" of a set of data. For this reason, these measures are often referred to as **measures of central tendency.**

EXAMPLE 1 Find the range, mean, median, and mode of the following set of data. Round to the nearest tenth if necessary.

$$12, \ 15, \ 9, \ 8, \ 4, \ 15, \ 3, \ 15, \ 16, \ 7, \ 11, \ 12$$

Solution Note that there are twelve items of data in all. Rewrite these numbers in order from greatest to least.

$$16, \ 15, \ 15, \ 15, \ 12, \ 12, \ 11, \ 9, \ 8, \ 7, \ 4, \ 3$$

Then find the statistical measures.

$$\text{range} = 16 - 3 = 13$$

$$\text{mean} = \frac{16 + 15 + 15 + 15 + 12 + 12 + 11 + 9 + 8 + 7 + 4 + 3}{12}$$

$$= \frac{127}{12} \approx 10.6$$

$$\text{median} = \frac{12 + 11}{2}$$

$$= \frac{23}{2} = 11.5$$

$$\text{mode} = 15$$

EXAMPLE 2 Insert a new number into this set of data so that the mean of the resulting set of data is 17: 12, 15, 21.

Solution Use x to represent the new number. Write and solve an equation.

$$\frac{12 + 15 + 21 + x}{4} = 17$$

$$4\left(\frac{12 + 15 + 21 + x}{4}\right) = 4(17)$$

$$12 + 15 + 21 + x = 68$$

$$48 + x = 68$$

$$48 + x - 48 = 68 - 48$$

$$x = 20$$

The new number is 20.

A statistical measure such as the range, mean, median, or mode is often more simply called a **statistic.**

Class Exercises

Exercises 1–4 refer to the table below.

High Temperatures for June 10

Year	1890	1900	1910	1920	1930	1940	1950	1960	1970	1980
Temperature (°C)	10	16	9	12	16	10	16	21	15	13

1. **a.** What is the lowest temperature listed? 9°C
   b. What is the highest temperature listed? 21°C
   c. What is the range of the temperatures? 12°C

2. **a.** What is the sum of the temperatures? 138°C
   b. What is the mean of the temperatures? 13.8°C

3. **a.** List the temperatures in order from lowest to highest. Which two temperatures are at the middle of the list?
   b. What is the median of the temperatures? 14°C

4. **a.** Which temperatures occurred more than once? 10°C, 16°C
   b. What is the mode of the temperatures? 16°C

   3a. 9°C, 10°C, 10°C, 12°C, 13°C, 15°C, 16°C, 16°C, 16°C, 21°C;
   13°C, 15°C

Written Exercises

Find the range, mean, median, and mode of each of the following sets of data. Round to the nearest tenth if necessary.

A

1. 12, 10, 8, 4, 3, 3, 2 10; 6; 4; 3
2. 50, 48, 35, 32, 31, 30   20; 37.7; 33.5; none
3. 89, 102, 75, 85, 116, 62   54; 88.2; 87; none
4. 83, 118, 143, 99, 194, 210, 153   127; 142.9; 143; none
5. 12.6, 11.0, 10.1, 9.7, 8.9, 8.3   4.3; 10.1; 9.9; none
6. 21.6, 30.2, 15.1, 28.8, 19.5   15.1; 23.0; 21.6; none
7. 14, −9, −11, 23, 2, 0, −9   34; 1.4; 0; −9
8. 4.6, 2.3, 0, −1.2, −3.1, −5.6   10.2; −0.5; −0.6; none

9. Points scored by the Basketeers in their most recent games:
   98, 100, 96, 101, 99, 98, 101, 101, 100, 102 6; 99.6; 100; 101

10. Earned runs allowed by one pitcher in this season's games:
    3, 2, 2, 4, 1, 0, 3, 3, 5, 2, 0, 0, 3, 5, 7, 2, 2, 1, 3, 4 7; 2.6; 2.5; 2, 3

Insert a new number into the set of data so that the mean becomes the indicated number.

11. 3, 9, 14; mean = 11 18
12. 5, 7, 10, 14; mean = 8 4
13. 6.3, 0.8, 1.2; mean = 4.7 10.5
14. −1, 0, 5, −7; mean = −7 −32

Statistics **451**

Suggested Assignments

Minimum
    451 / 1–12
    452 / 15–16
    452 / Self-Test A

Average
    451 / 1–13 odd
    452 / 15–18
    452 / Self-Test A

Maximum
Day 1: 451 / 1–14
Day 2: 452 / 15–20
    452 / Self-Test A

Supplementary Materials

Practice Masters, p. 54
Test 12A, pp. 79–80

Additional A Exercises

Find the range, mean, median, and mode of each of the following sets of data. Round to the nearest tenth if necessary.

1. 2, 3, 3, 4, 5 3; 3.4; 3; 3
2. 15, 18, 16, 18, 15, 20, 19 5; 17.3; 18; modes 15, 18
3. 25, 25, 100, 50, 75, 50, 25 75; 50; 50; 25
4. 8, 20, 13, 20, 14, 9, 8, 20, 17, 11 12; 14; 13.5; 20

Insert a new number into the set of data so that the mean becomes the indicated number.

5. 6, 8, 11, 16; mean = 10 9
6. 573, 487, 628; mean = 553.5 526

Exercises 1 and 2 refer to
the double line graph below.

Gasoline Mileage

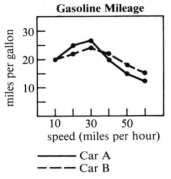

1. What is the gasoline mileage of Car A at 40 mi/h?
20 mi/gal

2. At what speed does Car B
get 18 mi/gal? **50 mi/h**

3. A computer was down for
30 min on Monday, 20 min
on Tuesday, 30 min on
Wednesday, 40 min on
Thursday, and 60 min on
Friday. Make a bar graph
to illustrate these data.

**Computer
Down Time**

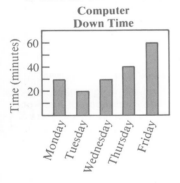

4. Find the range, mean,
median, and mode of the
following set of data: 180,
207, 191, 180, 195, 191,
202, 203, 191, 200.
27; 194; 193; 191

5. Insert a new number into
this set of data so that the
mean of the resulting set
of data is 27: 22, 19, 38.
29

Solve.

B **15.** The heights of four of the starting players on the basketball team are
183 cm, 178 cm, 174 cm, and 185 cm. If the mean height of all five
starting players is 182 cm, what is the height of the fifth starting
player? **190 cm**

16. A student's scores on the first four mathematics tests of the year
were 80, 95, 92, and 89. What must the student score on the fifth test
so that the mean score for all five tests is 90? **94**

17. Insert another number into the set of data 11, 14, 16, 19 so that the
median of the data is not changed. **15**

18. Replace one of the numbers in the set of data 11, 14, 16, 19 so that
the median of the data becomes 16. **Replace 11 or 14 with 16.**

C **19.** Suppose that each number in a set of data is decreased by 5. How is
the median of the data affected? **It is decreased by 5.**

20. Suppose that each number in a set of data is multiplied by 2. How is
the mean of the data affected? **It is multiplied by 2.**

Self-Test A

Exercises 1 and 2 refer to the double bar graph at the right.

1. Which state had the greatest income from
crops and livestock together? **California**

2. About how much was the income from
crops in Iowa? **$4.5 billion**

Farm Income in One Year

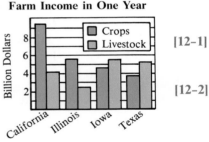

[12–1]

[12–2]

3. There were 19 million telephones in the
United States in 1940; 39 million in 1950;
66 million in 1960; 105 million in 1970;
and 157 million in 1980. Make a line
graph to illustrate these data. **Check students' graphs.**

4. Find the range, mean, median, and mode of the following set of
data: 100, 103, 102, 103, 105, 102, 101, 102. **5; 102.25; 102; 102**

[12–3]

5. Insert a new number into this set of data so that the mean of the
resulting set of data is 15: 13, 21, 10. **16**

Self-Test answers and Extra Practice are at the back of the book.

452   *Chapter 12*

12-4 Frequency Distributions

When you need to analyze a large amount of data, a statistic that is often used is **frequency.** The frequency of an item of data is the number of times that the item occurs. A table that pairs each item of data with its frequency is called a **frequency distribution.**

For example, the data below are the weights in kilograms of a group of sixty middle-school students. The table to the right shows the same data listed in a frequency distribution.

41	38	42	39	40	40
43	39	40	41	41	42
44	40	39	40	41	42
41	39	39	39	40	41
42	37	40	39	41	38
42	41	40	39	38	40
38	43	43	41	42	42
39	40	40	42	42	40
44	41	43	42	39	40
41	41	40	43	39	41

Weight x	Frequency f	$x \times f$
37	1	37
38	4	152
39	11	429
40	14	560
41	13	533
42	10	420
43	5	215
44	2	88
Total	60	2434

The numbers in the third column of the table are obtained by multiplying each item by its frequency. Example 1 shows how we use these numbers to compute statistical measures for the given data.

EXAMPLE 1   Find the range, mean, median, and mode of the data above.

Solution   The least weight is 37 and the greatest weight is 44. Therefore, the *range* of the weights is $44 - 37 = 7$.

In the third column, 2434 is the total of all 60 weights. Thus,

$$mean = \frac{2434}{60} \approx 40.6.$$

By adding the frequencies of the weights in the table beginning at 37, the least weight, we find that there are exactly 30 weights of 40 kg or less. It follows that the 30th weight in order must be 40, the 31st weight must be 41, and

$$median = \frac{40 + 41}{2} = 40.5.$$

From the frequency column of the table we see that the weight that occurred most often was 40. Therefore, the *mode* is 40.

Statistics   **453**

Teaching Suggestions p. 439d

Related Activities p. 439d

Reading Mathematics

Students will learn the meaning of the following mathematical terms in this lesson: *frequency, frequency distribution.*

Chalkboard Examples

The number of years of education beyond high school was recorded for a group of adults. The data are shown below.

0 4 1 2 4 3 1 4 5 2 1 0 5 4
3 0 4 6 1 4 0 1 4 1 0 2 1 4

1. Complete the frequency distribution.

Years x	Frequency f	$x \times f$
0	? 5	? 0
1	? 7	? 7
2	? 3	? 6
3	? 2	? 6
4	? 8	? 32
5	? 2	? 10
6	? 1	? 6
Total	? 28	? 67

2. Find the following statistics for the data above. Round to the nearest hundredth.
   a. range 6
   b. mean 2.39
   c. median 2
   d. mode 4

Suggested Assignments

Minimum
    455/2–14 even
    456/16, 18
    456/Rev. 1–8

Average
    455/2–14 even
    456/16–20
    456/Rev. 2–8 even

Maximum
Day 1: 455/1–12
Day 2: 455/13–14
    456/15–22

Supplementary Materials

Practice Masters, p. 55

When a set of data has a very large range, it is usually more convenient to make a frequency distribution by grouping the data into *intervals*.

EXAMPLE 2   The data below are the ages of a group of fifty people who answered a survey. Make a frequency distribution for these data.

27	54	18	22	73	32	48	55	30	35
62	70	45	39	18	33	25	29	65	42
20	55	38	42	36	41	19	24	58	49
37	71	54	22	69	31	43	38	45	64
39	21	71	46	35	67	53	65	42	48

Solution   Notice that the ages range from 18 to 73. If you made a table with an entry for *each* age in this range, you would need 56 entries in the table. Therefore, it is probably more efficient to record the data in intervals. Choose seven intervals of ten ages: 10–19, 20–29, 30–39, . . . , 70–79. The table at the right shows the resulting frequency distribution.

Age	Frequency
10–19	3
20–29	8
30–39	12
40–49	11
50–59	6
60–69	6
70–79	4

Class Exercises

The data below represent the scores of a class of 24 students who took a 5-point quiz. Exercises 1 and 2 refer to these data.

5	5	2	4	5	3	3	3	4	2	5	4
3	4	4	3	2	4	4	2	3	2	3	5

1. Complete the frequency distribution shown at the right.

2. Find the following statistics for these data.

    a. range 3

    b. mean 3.5

    c. median 3.5

    d. mode 3, 4

Score x	Frequency f	$x \times f$
1	? 0	? 0
2	? 5	? 10
3	? 7	? 21
4	? 7	? 28
5	? 5	? 25
Total	24	? 84

454   *Chapter 12*

Written Exercises Check students' frequency distributions.

Make a frequency distribution for the given data.

A　**1.** 5, 6, 6, 6, 6, 7, 7, 7, 8, 8, 8, 9

　2. 6, 6, 7, 7, 7, 7, 9, 9, 9, 10, 10, 10

　3. 6, 6, 9, 9, 9, 9, 12, 12, 12, 12, 12, 15

　4. 6, 9, 9, 9, 9, 9, 12, 12, 12, 12, 18, 18

　5. 10, 8, 8, 6, 8, 2, 4, 4, 6, 4, 10, 2

　6. 15, 20, 15, 10, 30, 5, 10, 10, 20, 15, 15, 5

For Exercises 7–10, _x_ represents an item of data and _f_ represents the frequency of the item. Compute the following.
a. range　　　　**b. mean**　　　　**c. median**　　　　**d. mode**

7.

x	f	
6	2	a. 4
7	6	b. 7.8
8	7	c. 8
9	4	d. 8
10	1	

8.

x	f	
0	2	a. 12
3	3	b. 6
6	5	c. 6
9	3	d. 6
12	2	

9.

x	f	
2	3	a. 10
4	5	b. 7.12
6	4	c. 8
8	5	d. 4, 8
10	4	
12	4	

10.

x	f	
4	2	a. 5
5	6	b. 6.25
6	2	c. 6.5
7	6	d. 5, 7
8	3	
9	1	

Check students' frequency distributions.

Make a frequency distribution for the given data, then use it to compute the range, mean, median, and mode of the data.

11. Numbers of puppies in fourteen litters:　　　6; 5; 4.5; 4

3, 5, 4, 4, 7, 8, 5, 3, 4, 6, 7, 8, 2, 4

12. Numbers of peas in sixteen pods:

6, 5, 2, 9, 12, 6, 5, 6, 11, 9, 6, 4, 7, 8, 10, 6　　　10; 7; 6; 6

13. Occupants per car passing through a checkpoint:

2, 1, 1, 4, 3, 1, 2, 2, 6, 1, 1, 4, 2, 5, 1, 4, 4, 2, 4, 2　　　5; 2.6; 2; 1, 2

14. Persons per household surveyed:

3, 2, 2, 3, 6, 1, 2, 1, 4, 3, 5, 2, 2, 4, 2, 1, 1, 5, 3, 2, 3, 5, 2, 4, 2, 4, 1, 4, 3, 2　　　5; 2.8; 2.5; 2

Statistics **455**

Complete the frequency distribution for the given data.

15. Distance in kilometers from shoppers' homes to the mall:

18	2	5	12	7	2	13	16
4	4	15	3	10	9	4	2
3	13	17	1	11	5	4	6

Distance (Kilometers)	Frequency
1–3	? 6
4–6	? 7
7–9	? 2
10–12	? 3
13–15	? 3
16–18	? 3

16. Amount in dollars of shoppers' grocery bills:

24	51	14	46	6	37	59	42
27	9	34	12	44	20	25	53
45	31	21	39	5	10	42	37

Amount (Dollars)	Frequency
0–10	? 4
11–20	? 3
21–30	? 4
31–40	? 5
41–50	? 5
51–60	? 3

Make a frequency distribution for the given data. Check students' frequency distributions.

B **17.** Scores on a mathematics test:
75, 89, 72, 97, 84, 87, 100, 58, 66, 75, 85, 77, 93, 74, 98, 64, 78, 74, 86, 92, 69, 77, 62, 88

18. Students' heights in centimeters:
143, 157, 161, 155, 146, 153, 148, 144, 147, 155, 152, 169, 164, 142, 146, 156, 159, 168, 150, 163

19. The mean of 10 numbers is 15. What is the sum of the numbers? 150

20. The sum of a set of numbers is 120 and the mean is 10. How many numbers are in this set? 12

Exercises 21 and 22 refer to a class that consists of 15 girls and 25 boys.

C **21.** On test A, the mean of the girls' scores was 80 and the mean of the boys' scores was 70. What was the class mean? 73.75

22. On test B, the class mean was 80 and the mean of the girls' scores was 75. What was the mean of the boys' scores? 83

Review Exercises

a. Solve for y in terms of x.   **b. Find solutions for $x = 0$ and $x = 2$.**

1. $x - 2y = 3$ **2.** $2x + 3y = 6$ **3.** $x + y = -3$ **4.** $x - y = -1$

5. $x + 2y = 4$ **6.** $3x + 2y = 6$ **7.** $2x - y = 4$ **8.** $4y - 5x = -10$

456 *Chapter 12*

12-5 Histograms and Frequency Polygons

Graphs are often used to provide a visual display of the data in a frequency distribution. A bar graph that is used for this purpose is called a **histogram.** A line graph that is used for this purpose is called a **frequency polygon.**

For example, the frequency distribution at the right lists a set of scores on a ten-point quiz. The graph below at the left is a histogram that pictures these data. To the right of the histogram is a frequency polygon for the same data.

Score	Frequency
3	1
4	1
5	3
6	5
7	10
8	9
9	4
10	2

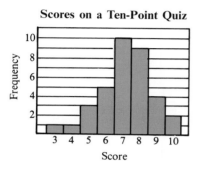

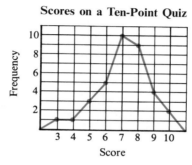

Notice that the histogram is different from the bar graphs that we made previously in that no space is left between the bars. Also note that, in the frequency polygon, the graph is connected to the horizontal axis at both ends.

EXAMPLE   Use the histogram and the frequency polygon just given to find the range, mean, median, and mode of the set of quiz scores.

Solution   The *range* is the difference between the least and the greatest numbers along the horizontal axis. Thus, the range is $10 - 3 = 7$.

To find the *mean,* multiply each item of data by its frequency, add the results, then divide by the sum of the frequencies.

$$\frac{3(1) + 4(1) + 5(3) + 6(5) + 7(10) + 8(9) + 9(4) + 10(2)}{1 + 1 + 3 + 5 + 10 + 9 + 4 + 2} \approx 7.1$$

The mean is 7.1.

Since there are 35 items, the *median* is the 18th item, which is 7.

The *mode* is represented by the tallest bar of the histogram and the highest point of the frequency polygon. Thus the mode is 7.

Statistics   **457**

Teaching Suggestions
p. 439e

Related Activities p. 439e

Reading Mathematics

Students will learn the meaning of the following mathematical terms in this lesson: *histogram, frequency polygon.*

Chalkboard Examples

Exercises 1–7 refer to the histogram below.

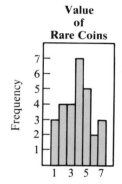

Value (dollars)

Estimate the frequency of the indicated value.

1. $6   **2**

2. $3   **4**

3. $4   **7**

4. What is the range of the values?   **$6**

5. What is the mean of the values?   **$3.89**

6. What is the median of the values?   **$4**

7. What is the mode of the values?   **$4**

Suggested Assignments

Minimum
 459/1–11, 13
 460/15
 460/Rev. 1–8

Average
Day 1: 459/1–12
Day 2: 459/13–14
 460/15–16
 460/Rev. 1–7 odd

Maximum
Day 1: 459/1–14
Day 2: 460/15–19

Supplementary Materials

Practice Masters, p. 55

When the data in a frequency distribution are listed by intervals, the bars of a histogram for the data are drawn between the endpoints of the intervals. In making a frequency polygon for such data, the points are located at the *midpoints* of the intervals.

Test Scores (Percent)	Frequency
40–49	1
50–59	2
60–69	4
70–79	12
80–89	7
90–100	5

As an example, the frequency distribution above lists a set of test scores. Below are a histogram and a frequency polygon for these data.

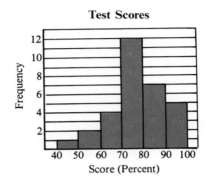

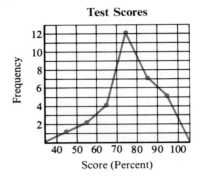

Class Exercises

Exercises 1–9 refer to the histogram at the right.

1. What is the range of the scores? 8

2. What is the mode of the scores? 8

3. How many students received scores of 8? 10? 3? 5? 10; 4; 0; 5

4. How many students received scores less than 7? 15

5. How many students took the quiz? 40

6. What is the sum of all the scores? 284

7. What is the mean of the scores? 7.1

8. What is the median of the scores? 7

9. Make a frequency polygon for the data. Check students' graphs.

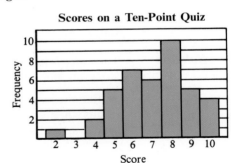

458 *Chapter 12*

Written Exercises

Exercises 1–10 refer to the frequency polygon at the right.

A **1.** How many people surveyed receive exactly 2 magazines? 9

2. How many people surveyed receive 4 or more magazines? 34

3. How many people were surveyed? 58

4. What is the median of the data? 4

5. What is the greatest number of magazines received? 8

6. What is the range of the data? 7

Magazine Subscriber Survey

Frequency

Number of Magazines Received Regularly

7. What is the number of magazines received by the fewest people? 7

8. What is the mode of the data? 4, 5

9. What is the total number of magazines received regularly? 226

10. To the nearest tenth, what is the mean number of magazines received? 3.9

For Exercises 11–14, x represents an item of data and f represents the frequency of the item. Make the following. Check students' graphs.
a. a histogram **b. a frequency polygon**

11.

x	f
5	1
6	3
7	4
8	9
9	7
10	2

12.

x	f
20	2
21	8
22	12
23	6
24	0
25	1

B **13.**

x	f
30–39	1
40–49	0
50–59	2
60–69	6
70–79	12
80–89	8
90–99	4

14.

x	f
0–25	5
26–50	9
51–75	16
76–100	22
101–125	25
126–150	11
151–175	3

Statistics **459**

Additional A Exercises

The frequency polygon shows the number of days that the given number of school buses were out of service in March.

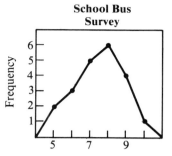

School Bus Survey

Frequency

Buses out of service

1. On how many days were 7 buses out of service? **5 days**

2. On how many days were 8 or more buses out of service? **11 days**

3. What is the mode of the data? **8**

4. At least how many buses were out of service on a given day? **5 buses**

5. How many school days were there in March? **21 days**

6. Altogether, how many times were buses reported to be out of service? **157 times**

7. What is the mean of the data rounded to the nearest tenth? **7.5**

8. What is the range of the data? **5**

9. What is the median of the data? **8**

Make a histogram and a frequency polygon for each set of data.

Check students' graphs.

15. Students in the homerooms at Valley Junior High:

24 23 20 25 25 24 25
24 25 24 25 28 23 22
26 25 26 25 25 24

16. Runs scored by the Bluebirds in this season's games:

1 1 2 0 3 3 0 2 4 3
2 0 5 3 0 8 2 0 3 5
2 3 4 1 2 4 1 3 0 3

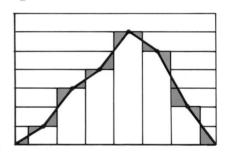

C 17. Visitors to the aquarium in the last two weeks:

946 518 402 473 553 672 850
979 436 541 622 705 814 902

18. Daily high temperatures in April (°C):

2   4   2   6   5   1   0   −3   −7   −5
−9   −5   0   3   1   6   6   9   12   14
17   19   18   15   12   9   6   4   5   2

19. The figure at the right shows a histogram and a frequency polygon for the same data drawn on a single set of coordinate axes. Explain why the area under the frequency polygon is equal to the area of the bars of the histogram. (*Hint:* Compare the area of the red triangles with the area of the blue triangles.) Each red triangle is congruent to a blue triangle.

Review Exercises

Two game cubes, each labeled with the numbers 1–6, are rolled. Find the probability of each.

1. A 5 shows. $\frac{11}{36}$

2. A 6 shows. $\frac{11}{36}$

3. An odd number shows. $\frac{3}{4}$

4. The sum is 5. $\frac{1}{9}$

5. The sum is 11. $\frac{1}{18}$

6. The sum is even. $\frac{1}{2}$

7. The sum is less than 4. $\frac{1}{12}$

8. The sum is 3 or a 3 shows. $\frac{13}{36}$

12-6 Expected Value of a Random Variable

Suppose that you play a game by spinning the spinner shown at the right, and you win as a prize the amount of money indicated by the pointer. Assume that the pointer never stops on a line between two sections of the spinner. What amount might you expect to win?

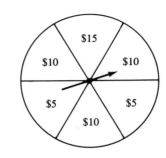

One way to estimate this amount is to make a large number of trial spins in order to collect some data and then find the mean of these data. For example, suppose that you make 80 trial spins: $5 comes up 27 times, $10 comes up 39 times, and $15 comes up 14 times. By recording the data in a frequency distribution such as the one at the right, you can readily calculate the mean of your trial spins.

$$\text{mean} = \frac{735}{80} \approx 9.19$$

Thus you have determined experimentally that the expected value of your prize is about $9.19. Although you cannot win $9.19 *exactly,* it is the average amount you would win if you played many times.

Let's consider another way to find this expected value. Choose a variable such as X to represent the amount indicated by the pointer. Since the value of X is determined randomly, X is called a **random variable.** We can now construct a table of all possible values of X and their probabilities of occurrence.

Amount (Dollars) x	Frequency f	$x \times f$
5	27	135
10	39	390
15	14	210
Total	**80**	**735**

X	5	10	15
$P(X)$	$\frac{2}{6}$	$\frac{3}{6}$	$\frac{1}{6}$

There is no way to know in advance what the *exact* value of a random variable will be in a single trial. However, it is possible to compute the *mean* value of a random variable over a large number of trials. By computing the mean value of our random variable X, we can find the expected value of the prize after spinning the spinner. To understand how this can be done, let's take another look at the data from the 80 trials above. Note that the mean could be represented by the following calculation.

$$\text{mean} = \frac{5(27) + 10(39) + 15(14)}{80}$$

$$= 5 \times \frac{27}{80} + 10 \times \frac{39}{80} + 15 \times \frac{14}{80}$$

Statistics **461**

Suggested Assignments

Minimum
     463/1–5
     463/Self-Test B

Average
     463/1–6
     463/Self-Test B

Maximum
Day 1: 463/1–5
Day 2: 463/6–7
     463/Self-Test B

Supplementary Materials

Practice Masters, p. 56
Test 12B, pp. 81–82
Computer Activity 23
Computer Activity 24

Additional A Exercises

X represents the possible
values of a random variable
and P(X) represents their
probabilities of occurrence.
Find the expected value of X.

1.

X	10	20	30
P(X)	$\frac{1}{2}$	$\frac{1}{3}$	$\frac{1}{6}$

$16\frac{2}{3}$, or $16.\overline{6}$

2.

X	5	10	15	20
P(X)	0.1	0.2	0.3	0.4

15

3.

X	−2	0	2	4
P(X)	$\frac{1}{4}$	$\frac{1}{8}$	$\frac{3}{8}$	$\frac{1}{4}$

$1\frac{1}{4}$, or 1.25

Consider the 80 trial spins as a random sample of the type discussed in Chapter 11. If we assume that this is a representative sample of the results of spinning the spinner, we can conclude the following.

$$\frac{27}{80} = \frac{\text{number of fives in sample}}{\text{number in sample}} = P(5) \qquad \frac{39}{80} = \frac{\text{number of tens in sample}}{\text{number in sample}} = P(10)$$

$$\frac{14}{80} = \frac{\text{number of fifteens in sample}}{\text{number in sample}} = P(15)$$

We can then make the following substitutions.

$$\begin{aligned}
\text{mean} &= 5 \times \frac{27}{80} + 10 \times \frac{39}{80} + 15 \times \frac{14}{80} \\
&= 5 \times P(5) + 10 \times P(10) + 15 \times P(15) \\
&= 5 \times \frac{2}{6} + 10 \times \frac{3}{6} + 15 \times \frac{1}{6} = 9\frac{1}{6}, \text{ or } 9.17
\end{aligned}$$

Therefore, the expected value of the random variable is about 9.17, and the expected value of your prize is about $9.17. Notice that this is only slightly different from the expected value of $9.19 that we computed experimentally. Since both expected values are approximations, this difference is not significant.

> To find the expected value of a random variable, multiply each possible value by its probability and add the results.

EXAMPLE A box contains 4 nickels, 6 dimes, and 2 quarters. You are allowed to select one coin without looking. If $V =$ the value in cents of the coin you select, what is the expected value of V?

Solution List all the possible values of V and their probabilities of occurrence. Multiply each value by its probability, then add.

V	5	10	25
P(V)	$\frac{4}{12}$	$\frac{6}{12}$	$\frac{2}{12}$

$$5 \times \frac{4}{12} + 10 \times \frac{6}{12} + 25 \times \frac{2}{12} = \frac{130}{12}$$
$$\approx 10.8$$

The expected value of V is 10.8 cents.

Class Exercises 1. pennies, nickels, dimes, and quarters

$V =$ **the value of a coin to be selected at random.**
1. What types of coins are there?
2. If there are 8 coins in all, how many are nickels? 1
3. What is the expected value of V?

$\frac{87}{8}$, or 10.875, cents

V	1	5	10	25
P(V)	$\frac{1}{4}$	$\frac{1}{8}$	$\frac{3}{8}$	$\frac{1}{4}$

462 *Chapter 12*

Written Exercises

X represents the possible values of a random variable and *P(X)* represents their probabilities of occurrence. Find the expected value of *X*. $42\frac{1}{2}$, or 42.5

A **1.**

X	10	20	30	40
P(X)	$\frac{1}{4}$	$\frac{1}{8}$	$\frac{3}{8}$	$\frac{1}{4}$

$26\frac{1}{4}$, or 26.25

2.

X	15	30	45	60	75
P(X)	$\frac{1}{6}$	$\frac{1}{4}$	$\frac{1}{3}$	$\frac{1}{12}$	$\frac{1}{6}$

3.

X	2	5	10
P(X)	0.3	0.5	0.2

5.1

4.

X	−20	−40	0	20
P(X)	0.1	0.2	0.3	0.4

−2

Find the expected value of the random variable *X*.

B **5.** The faces of a cube are numbered 0 through 5. *X* is the number on the face that comes up when the cube is thrown. $2\frac{1}{2}$, or 2.5

6. In a set of envelopes, 2 are empty, 4 contain \$1, 3 contain \$5, and 1 contains \$10. *X* is the amount in an envelope selected at random. \$2.90

C **7.** Karen throws a cube with faces numbered from 1 through 6. If it comes up an odd number, she loses that number of points. If it comes up an even number, she wins that number of points. About how many points is she likely to have after 100 throws? 50 points

---

Self-Test B Check students' tables and graphs.

Exercises 1–3 refer to the following set of data.

13, 10, 10, 11, 12, 12, 13, 14, 11, 13, 11, 14, 12, 12, 12

1. Make a frequency distribution for the data and use it to compute the range, mean, median, and mode of the data. 4; 12; 12; 12 [12-4]

2. Make a histogram for the data. [12-5]

3. Make a frequency polygon for the data.

4. In the table at the right, *X* represents the possible values of a random variable and *P(X)* represents their probabilities of occurrence. Find the expected value of *X*. $8\frac{8}{9}$, or $8.\overline{8}$ [12-6]

X	4	8	12	16
P(X)	$\frac{1}{6}$	$\frac{5}{9}$	$\frac{1}{6}$	$\frac{1}{9}$

Self-Test answers and Extra Practice are at the back of the book.

Exercises 1–3 refer to the following set of data.
7, 10, 8, 7, 10, 9, 11, 8, 7, 11, 9, 9, 10

1. Make a frequency distribution for the data and use it to compute the range, mean, median, and mode of the data. Round to the nearest hundredth.

x	f
7	3
8	2
9	3
10	3
11	2

range: 4
mean: 8.92
median: 9
modes: 7, 9, 10

2. Make a histogram for the data.

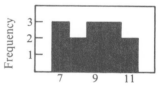

3. Make a frequency polygon for the data.

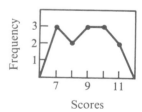

4. In the table below, *X* represents the possible values of a random variable and *P(X)* represents their probabilities of occurrence. Find the expected value of *X*. $\frac{45}{4}$, or $11\frac{1}{4}$

X	5	10	15	20
P(X)	$\frac{1}{4}$	$\frac{3}{8}$	$\frac{1}{4}$	$\frac{1}{8}$

Standard Deviation

Enrichment Note

To describe a set of data, we use two kinds of statistics: those that measure central tendency, such as the mean and median, and those that measure dispersion, or spread. A measure of each kind is necessary for an adequate characterization of the data.

As the examples on page 464 show, widely different data sets can have the same mean and range. In fact, the range is of such limited use that it is seldom considered to be of real interest.

To provide a more useful measure of dispersion, we are led to the progressively more useful and sophisticated measures called deviation, variance, and standard deviation. Each of these statistics was derived as a means of expressing the difference, on the average, of the individual data values and the average, or mean, value.

The deviation is not a useful approach to describing dispersion. Because positive and negative values can counter each other, a widely dispersed set of data can have a deceptively small total deviation. No such problem exists with the variance. Since deviations are squared, there is no cancelling of positive and negative deviations. A new problem arises, however, because the units of the variance are not consistent with those of the original data. The standard deviation is found by taking the square root of the variance; thus we return to the same unit used with the original data.

If students study statistics later, they will find that the mean and the standard deviation are the two statistics

(Continue on next page.)

For many purposes the *range* of a set of data is a poor measure of its spread. Consider, for example, the frequency distributions and histograms below for the mass in kilograms of various rocks found by three groups of rock collectors.

Group A		Group B		Group C	
Mass (kg)	Frequency	Mass (kg)	Frequency	Mass (kg)	Frequency
1	4	1	1	1	1
3	1	3	3	3	2
7	1	5	2	5	4
9	4	7	3	7	2
		9	1	9	1

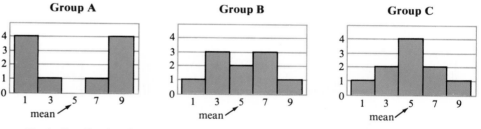

Each distribution has a range of 8. But a glance at each histogram reveals that distribution A is more spread out around its center, or mean, than are distributions B and C.

A more useful measure of the spread of a distribution is the **deviation** from the mean. Suppose a bowler has scores of 198, 210, and 156. The mean score is 188. The table at the right shows how much each score varies, or *deviates*, from the mean.

Score	Deviation
198	+10
210	+22
156	−32

The **variance** and **standard deviation** are two commonly used measures of how data are scattered around the mean. The variance is computed by squaring each deviation from the mean, adding these squares, and dividing the sum by the number of entries in the distribution. The standard deviation is found by computing the positive square root of the variance. The standard deviation is a more useful statistic than the variance because comparisons are being made of common units. For example, when data are given in meters, the variance will be in square meters, but the standard deviation will be in meters.

The table below shows the calculation of the variance and standard deviation for each frequency distribution on the preceding page. In each case, x is the mass and m is the mean, which is 5. Notice that the more a distribution is spread out from its mean, the larger its standard deviation.

most frequently used to describe data. In fact, for a normal distribution (a bell curve) the mean and standard deviation together give a complete characterization of the data.
Rather than squaring the deviations we could use their absolute values. The mean of these absolute values is called the average deviation. It is much less widely used than the standard deviation in advanced work.

Students are sometimes intimidated by the elaborate calculations needed to figure a standard deviation. This would be an excellent place to suggest the use of a calculator or computer. The calculations may be arduous, but the procedure, or algorithm, is straightforward. We repeat the same sequence of operations over and over. This makes the standard deviation a prime candidate for a computer program in BASIC; this should be within the ability of an able student.

Group A			Group B			Group C		
	deviation			deviation			deviation	
x	$(x - m)$	$(x - m)^2$	x	$(x - m)$	$(x - m)^2$	x	$(x - m)$	$(x - m)^2$
1	-4	16	1	-4	16	1	-4	16
1	-4	16	3	-2	4	3	-2	4
1	-4	16	3	-2	4	3	-2	4
1	-4	16	3	-2	4	5	0	0
3	-2	4	5	0	0	5	0	0
7	2	4	5	0	0	5	0	0
9	4	16	7	2	4	5	0	0
9	4	16	7	2	4	7	2	4
9	4	16	7	2	4	7	2	4
9	4	16	9	4	16	9	4	16
		136 kg²			56 kg²			48 kg²

variance $= \frac{136}{10} = 13.6$ kg²   variance $= \frac{56}{10} = 5.6$ kg²   variance $= \frac{48}{10} = 4.8$ kg²

standard
deviation $= \sqrt{13.6}$ standard
deviation $= \sqrt{5.6}$ standard
deviation $= \sqrt{4.8}$

≈ 3.7 kg ≈ 2.4 kg ≈ 2.2 kg

Find (a) the mean, (b) the deviation, (c) the variance, and (d) the standard deviation of the given data. Use the table on page 498, or approximate the square root to the nearest hundredth by interpolation.

1. From a sample of four dairy cows, a farmer recorded the following yields for one day: 11 gal, 13 gal, 9 gal, and 15 gal.
   a. 12 gal   **b.** -1, 1, -3, 3   **c.** 5 gal²   **d.** 2.24 gal
2. In a survey of local stores, the following prices were quoted for a World watch: $34, $27, $41, and $38.
   a. $35   **b.** -1, -8, 6, 3   **c.** 27.5 dollars²   **d.** $5.24
3. The fuel efficiency ratings of five new cars were 20, 19, 20, 22, and 33 mi/gal.   **a.** 22.8 mi/gal   **b.** -2.8, -3.8, -2.8, -0.8, 10.2
   c. 26.96 (mi/gal)²   **d.** 5.19 mi/gal

Chapter Review

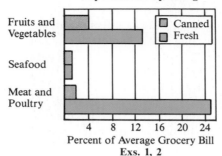

Supermarket Spending

Canned
Fresh

Fruits and
Vegetables

Seafood

Meat and
Poultry

4   8   12   16   20   24
Percent of Average Grocery Bill
Exs. 1, 2

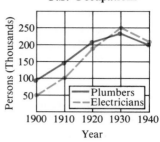

U.S. Occupations

Persons (Thousands)

250
200
150
100
50

Plumbers
Electricians

1900 1910 1920 1930 1940
Year
Exs. 3, 4

Exercises 1 and 2 refer to the double bar graph above. True or false?

1. More money is spent on fresh meat and poultry than on canned and fresh fruits and vegetables together. **True** [12–1]

2. Approximately 5% is spent on fresh seafood. **False**

Exercises 3 and 4 refer to the double line graph above. Complete.

3. There was approximately the same number of plumbers and electricians in the year ___?___. **1924 (Answers may vary slightly.)** [12–2]

4. In 1910 the number of electricians was approximately ___?___. **100,000**

Exercises 5–11 refer to the following set of data.

    14, 18, 12, 10, 12, 16, 15, 20, 17, 12,
    13, 19, 17, 14, 11, 18, 16, 15, 12, 14

Compute the following for the given data.

5. range **10**   6. mean **14.75**   7. median **14.5**   8. mode **12**   [12–3]

Make the following for the given data. Check students' tables and graphs.

9. a frequency distribution   [12–4]

10. a histogram   11. a frequency polygon   [12–5]

The table shows all possible values of a random variable X and their probabilities of occurrence. Compute the following.

X	2	4	6	8
$P(X)$	$\frac{1}{12}$	$\frac{1}{3}$	?	$\frac{1}{4}$

12. $P(6)$ **$\frac{1}{3}$**   13. the expected value of X
        $5\frac{1}{2}$, or 5.5

[12–6]

466   *Chapter 12*

Chapter Test

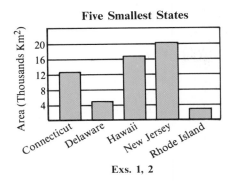

Exs. 1, 2

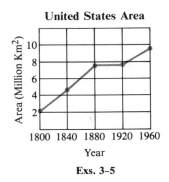

Exs. 3–5

Exercises 1 and 2 refer to the bar graph above. Answers may vary slightly.

1. What is the approximate area of Delaware? 5 thousand km² [12-1]

2. About how much smaller than New Jersey is Rhode Island?
18 thousand km²

Exercises 3–5 refer to the line graph above.

3. During which time period was there no increase in area? 1880–1920 [12-2]

4. During which 80 years was there the greatest increase? 1800–1880

5. What was the approximate area of the United States in 1840? 4.75 million km²

Exercises 6 and 7 refer to the following set of data.
8, 5, 7, 6, 10, 9, 8, 7, 6, 7, 9, 8

6. Find the range, mean, median, and mode of the given data. 5; 7.5; 7.5; 7, 8 [12-3]

7. Make a frequency distribution for the given data. [12-4]
Check students' frequency distributions.

Exercises 8 and 9 refer to the histogram at the right.

Scores on a Twenty-Point Quiz

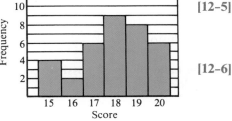

8. What is the range of the quiz scores? 5 [12-5]

9. Make a frequency polygon for this same set of quiz scores.
Check students' graphs.

10. A set of 10 cards is numbered 1 through 10, one number per card. X is the number on a card drawn at random. Find the expected value of the random variable X. 5.5 [12-6]

Statistics **467**

Review for Retention

Use one of the properties of equality to form a true sentence.

1. If $c + 5 = -13$, then $c = \underline{}$. **−18**

2. If $3 + k = 1$, then $k = \underline{}$. **−2**

3. If $4y = -28$, then $y = \underline{}$. **−7**

Use transformations to solve the equations.

4. $v + 7 = -12$ **−19**

5. $m - 13 - 18 = -29$ **2**

6. $-7x = -63$ **9**

7. $8y - 3 = -43$ **−5**

8. $\frac{d}{18} = -5$ **−90**

9. $-\frac{1}{4}f + 6 = 4$ **8**

Use transformations to solve the inequalities.

10. $a + 8 \leq 2$ **All the numbers less than or equal to −6**

11. $-12 > 4p$ **All the numbers less than −3**

Use an equation to solve.

12. Sven earned $123 last week. If he earned $\frac{1}{3}$ of his salary on Saturday, how much did he earn the rest of the week? **$82**

Find the area of the region described. Leave your answers in terms of π when applicable.

13. Triangle: base = 12.4 m, height = 7 m **43.4 m²**

14. Trapezoid: bases 18 and 14, height = 5 **80 square units**

15. Circle: diameter = 60 mm **900π mm²**

(Continue on next page.)

468

Cumulative Review (Chapters 1–12)

Exercises

Write the decimal number that is equal to each of the following.

1. $|-3.79|$ **3.79** 2. $|-65.8|$ **65.8** 3. $|1.301|$ **1.301** 4. $|0.123|$ **0.123** 5. $|-100.01|$ **100.01**

Write as a proper fraction in lowest terms.

6. $0.666\ldots$ $\frac{2}{3}$ 7. $0.58\overline{3}$ $\frac{7}{12}$ 8. $0.2777\ldots$ $\frac{5}{18}$ 9. $0.\overline{18}$ $\frac{2}{11}$

Write an equation for the word sentence and solve. Variables may be represented by any letter.

10. Eight less than the product of a number and three is seven. $3x - 8 = 7$; **5**

11. The sum of one half a number and twelve is negative six. $\frac{x}{2} + 12 = -6$; **−36**

12. The quotient of a number divided by eight is two. $\frac{x}{8} = 2$; **16**

13. A number minus nine equals five minus the number. $x - 9 = 5 - x$; **7**

14. The product of the sum of a number and eight, times five, is twenty. $5(x + 8) = 20$; **−4**

Find the measure of the third angle of a triangle having the following measures for the other two angles.

15. 77°, 41° **62°** 16. 85.5°, 40.5° **54°** 17. 110°, 35° **35°** 18. 22.5°, 135° **22.5°**

Express as a percent.

19. $\frac{2}{5}$ **40%** 20. $\frac{1}{8}$ **12$\frac{1}{2}$%** 21. $\frac{3}{500}$ **$\frac{3}{5}$%** 22. $\frac{1}{12}$ **8$\frac{1}{3}$%** 23. $\frac{5}{4}$ **125%** 24. $\frac{1}{3}$ **33$\frac{1}{3}$%**

Use a graph to solve the system. Do the lines intersect or coincide, or are they parallel? Check students' graphs.

25. $x - y = 7$ **Intersect**
    $x + y = 7$ **at (7, 0)**

26. $2x + 3y = 5$
    $4x + 6y = 10$ **Coincide**

27. $y = -2x + 1$
    $y + 8 = -2x$ **Parallel**

Find the capacity in liters of the prism or cylinder. Use $\pi \approx 3.14$ and round the answer to three digits.

28. Prism: base area = 1627.5 m²
    height = 50 m **81,375,000 L**

29. Cylinder: base radius = 3.75 cm
    height = 5.50 cm **0.243 L**

For Exercises 31–35, refer to the table on page 498. Approximate the square root to the nearest hundredth.

30. $\sqrt{38}$ **6.16** 31. $\sqrt{47}$ **6.86** 32. $\sqrt{7}$ **2.65** 33. $\sqrt{11.1}$ **3.33** 34. $4\sqrt{18}$ **16.97**

468 *Chapter 12*

If you choose a letter at random from the word EXCELLENT, what is the probability of the following outcomes?

35. a vowel $\frac{1}{3}$ **36.** a consonant $\frac{2}{3}$ **37.** the letter B 0 **38.** the letter L $\frac{2}{9}$

Find the range, mean, median, and mode of the set of numbers. Round to the nearest tenth if necessary.

39. 67, 85, 26, 26, 38
59; 48.4; 38; 26

40. 0.5, 1.7, 0.8, 2.6, 1.4
2.1; 1.4; 1.4; none

41. 100, 101, 110, 90, 99, 99
20; 99.8; 99.5; 99

Problems

Problem Solving Reminders
Here are some problem solving reminders that may help you solve some of the problems on this page.
- Sometimes more than one method can be used to solve a problem.
- Consider whether drawing a sketch will help.
- When rounding an answer to division, consider whether it is reasonable to round up or round down.

Solve.

1. J-Stores sells exercise bicycles for $169.95. This month the bicycles are offered at a 15% discount, followed by a rebate of $15.00. What is the total price to customers after the discount and rebate? $129.46

2. The price of Stuffed Shirt Starch Company stock went down $\frac{5}{8}$ on Monday, down $1\frac{1}{8}$ on Tuesday, and down $1\frac{3}{4}$ on Wednesday before going up $2\frac{7}{8}$ on Thursday. The stock went up $1\frac{1}{4}$ on Friday. What was the total loss or gain for the week? $\frac{5}{8}$ gain

3. A ferryboat travels from Eric's Island to Pearltown to Bonneville and back to Eric's Island. The course forms a right triangle with the route from Pearltown to Bonneville forming the hypotenuse. If the distance from Bonneville to Eric's Island is 45 km and the distance from Eric's Island to Pearltown is 80 km, what is the approximate distance from Pearltown to Bonneville? Use the table on page 498.
92 km, to the nearest kilometer

4. Christopher is required to take a history course and a language course. He can choose from American, European, or ancient history, and French, Spanish, or Italian language. How many combinations of two courses does Christopher have? 9

5. Zachary scored 83, 82, 75, 70, and 88 on biology quizzes. What is the least he can score on his next quiz if he wants to maintain an 80 average? 82

Statistics **469**

Find the volume. Use $\pi \approx 3.14$.

16. Cylinder:
base radius = 6 m,
height = 4 m 452 m³

17. Pyramid:
base area = 126 m²,
height = 20 m 840 m³

18. Find the surface area and the volume of a sphere with radius 9 cm. Leave your answers in terms of π.
324π cm²; 972π cm³

19. Find the mass of a steel ball with diameter 10 cm. Use $\pi \approx 3.14$. The density of steel is 7.82 g/cm³. 4090 g

20. In how many different ways can 4 cars park in 7 spaces? 840

21. In how many different ways can a team of 3 students be selected from 15 students? 455

22. The chance of snow tomorrow is 45%. What are the odds that it will not snow tomorrow? 11 to 9

23. Events A and B are mutually exclusive. $P(A) = \frac{1}{4}$. $P(B) = \frac{1}{3}$. Find $P(A \text{ or } B)$. $\frac{7}{12}$

24. $P(A)$ is $\frac{3}{5}$, $P(B)$ is $\frac{1}{2}$, and $P(A \text{ and } B) = \frac{3}{10}$. Find $P(A \text{ or } B)$. $\frac{4}{5}$

25. One game cube is rolled three times. Find the probability of each.
a. A 4 comes up on each of the rolls. $\frac{1}{216}$
b. None of the rolls come up 4. $\frac{125}{216}$
c. Exactly two 4's come up. $\frac{5}{72}$

Skill Review

Addition

46.7
+ 8.31
55.01

14.71
3.009
+ 291.681
309.400

Add.

1. 34.3
+ 23.5
57.8

2. 2.536
+ 7.019
9.555

3. 8.7
+ 0.5
9.2

4. 48.37
+ 12.6
60.97

5. 83.55
+ 8.617
92.167

6. 299.1
+ 68.33
367.43

7. 24.6251
+ 9.88
34.5051

8. 933.068
+ 724.3997
1657.4677

9. 19.6
2.71
+ 33.5
55.81

10. 58.71
6.8
+ 3.59
69.1

11. 118.7
4.91
+ 30.08
153.69

12. 90.71
219.65
+ 3.34
313.7

13. 5.4
12.137
1.25
+ 306.49
325.277

14. 1.6256
6.006
9.36
+ 1.49
18.4816

15. 24.603
18.4
2.9
+ 0.216
46.119

16. 911.34
0.52
26.1
+ 83.192
1021.152

17. 899.08 + 3.7 **902.78**

18. 14.6 + 5.99 **20.59**

19. 11.87 + 49.3 **61.17**

20. 38.75 + 116.6 **155.35**

21. 0.051 + 16.88 **16.931**

22. 578.57 + 12.1 **590.67**

23. 73.6 + 18.07 **91.67**

24. 63.583 + 8.09 **71.673**

25. 27.0564 + 281.4 **308.4564**

26. 3.51032 + 14.99 **18.50032**

27. 11.2 + 0.9013 **12.1013**

28. 84.1 + 0.062 **84.162**

29. 6.8 + 37.51 + 108.2 **152.51**

30. 89.71 + 5.5 + 0.62 **95.83**

31. 43.6 + 12.1 + 0.008 **55.708**

32. 2.4 + 3.183 + 9 **14.583**

33. 4 + 0.463 + 43.4 **47.863**

34. 116.04 + 2.57 + 12.38 **130.99**

35. 7 + 112.4 + 0.06 **119.46**

36. 121.2 + 18 + 0.12 **139.32**

37. 16.24 + 5.6 + 18.09 + 6.7 **46.63**

38. 2.55 + 0.34 + 0.42 + 3.57 **6.88**

39. 61.476 + 14.1 + 0.59 + 366 **442.166**

40. 90.072 + 32.4 + 24 + 8.6 **155.072**

41. 193.7 + 4.08 + 11.5 + 1.9026 **211.1826**

42. 0.428 + 83.7 + 6.999 + 7.06 **98.187**

43. 37.7 + 0.6 + 6.834 + 16 **61.134**

44. 1165 + 0.08 + 17.1 + 94.028 **1276.208**

45. 570.2 + 74.4 + 6.553 + 9.2 **660.353**

46. 7.8118 + 27.6 + 5.302 + 14 **54.7138**

Skill Review

Subtraction

$$\begin{array}{r} 983.210 \\ -\ \ 86.541 \\ \hline 896.669 \end{array}$$

$$\begin{array}{r} 300.710 \\ -\ \ 46.008 \\ \hline 254.702 \end{array}$$

Subtract.

1. $\begin{array}{r} 18.636 \\ -\ 13.435 \\ \hline 5.201 \end{array}$ **2.** $\begin{array}{r} 234.86 \\ -\ \ \ 9.25 \\ \hline 225.61 \end{array}$ **3.** $\begin{array}{r} 27.954 \\ -\ 16.21 \\ \hline 11.744 \end{array}$ **4.** $\begin{array}{r} 326.5822 \\ -\ \ 14.001 \\ \hline 312.5812 \end{array}$

5. $\begin{array}{r} 71.5 \\ -\ 16.3 \\ \hline 55.2 \end{array}$ **6.** $\begin{array}{r} 46.53 \\ -\ 21.46 \\ \hline 25.07 \end{array}$ **7.** $\begin{array}{r} 8.434 \\ -\ 6.297 \\ \hline 2.137 \end{array}$ **8.** $\begin{array}{r} 35.061 \\ -\ \ 9.875 \\ \hline 25.186 \end{array}$

9. $\begin{array}{r} 6.952 \\ -\ 5.06 \\ \hline 1.892 \end{array}$ **10.** $\begin{array}{r} 583.86 \\ -\ 279.9 \\ \hline 303.96 \end{array}$ **11.** $\begin{array}{r} 214.005 \\ -\ \ 63.26 \\ \hline 150.745 \end{array}$ **12.** $\begin{array}{r} 83.56 \\ -\ 31.235 \\ \hline 52.325 \end{array}$

13. $\begin{array}{r} 453 \\ -\ \ 17.46 \\ \hline 435.54 \end{array}$ **14.** $\begin{array}{r} 55.7 \\ -\ \ 3.9 \\ \hline 51.8 \end{array}$ **15.** $\begin{array}{r} 206.771 \\ -\ 160.48 \\ \hline 46.291 \end{array}$ **16.** $\begin{array}{r} 126.328 \\ -\ \ 9.4078 \\ \hline 116.9202 \end{array}$

17. $\begin{array}{r} 0.081 \\ -\ 0.007 \\ \hline 0.074 \end{array}$ **18.** $\begin{array}{r} 80.09 \\ -\ 12.763 \\ \hline 67.327 \end{array}$ **19.** $\begin{array}{r} 2.0056 \\ -\ 0.918 \\ \hline 1.0876 \end{array}$ **20.** $\begin{array}{r} 219.33 \\ -\ 184.925 \\ \hline 34.405 \end{array}$

21. $55.7 - 3.9$ **51.8**

22. $48.08 - 7.95$ **40.13**

23. $279.5 - 33.7$ **245.8**

24. $46.08 - 7.05$ **39.03**

25. $605.01 - 31.23$ **573.78**

26. $0.065 - 0.009$ **0.056**

27. $22.916 - 17.4$ **5.516**

28. $25.006 - 3.98$ **21.026**

29. $175.6 - 28.51$ **147.09**

30. $88.71 - 13.9$ **74.81**

31. $518.2 - 327.41$ **190.79**

32. $2.7736 - 0.1531$ **2.6205**

33. $800.6 - 315$ **485.6**

34. $0.9001 - 0.035$ **0.8651**

35. $207.001 - 44.62$ **162.381**

36. $91.003 - 17.6$ **73.403**

37. $388.5 - 29.62$ **358.88**

38. $56 - 7.88$ **48.12**

39. $68 - 51.3$ **16.7**

40. $276.1 - 8.39$ **267.71**

41. $584.32 - 16.9056$ **567.4144**

42. $104.6 - 27.83$ **76.77**

43. $9.8 - 6.88$ **2.92**

44. $53.405 - 27.3$ **26.105**

45. $212 - 0.511$ **211.489**

46. $106.8 - 36.47$ **70.33**

47. $11.92 - 4.6679$ **7.2521**

48. $137.05 - 8.6$ **128.45**

49. $307.85 - 26.138$ **281.712**

50. $6007.2 - 27.158$ **5980.042**

Skill Review

Multiplication

$$\begin{array}{r} 371.6 \\ \times\ 0.27 \\ \hline 26012 \\ 7432 \\ \hline 100.332 \end{array}$$

1 place
2 places

3 places

Multiply.

1. $\begin{array}{r}785\\ \times\ 1.2\\ \hline 942\end{array}$	**2.** $\begin{array}{r}6.61\\ \times\ 3\\ \hline 19.83\end{array}$	**3.** $\begin{array}{r}808\\ \times\ 17.2\\ \hline 13{,}897.6\end{array}$	**4.** $\begin{array}{r}22.5\\ \times\ 8.9\\ \hline 200.25\end{array}$
5. $\begin{array}{r}89.06\\ \times\ 0.5\\ \hline 44.53\end{array}$	**6.** $\begin{array}{r}37.5\\ \times\ 0.28\\ \hline 10.5\end{array}$	**7.** $\begin{array}{r}212.8\\ \times\ 0.67\\ \hline 142.576\end{array}$	**8.** $\begin{array}{r}93.65\\ \times\ 4.11\\ \hline 384.9015\end{array}$
9. $\begin{array}{r}0.16\\ \times\ 8.34\\ \hline 1.3344\end{array}$	**10.** $\begin{array}{r}37.44\\ \times\ 5.9\\ \hline 220.896\end{array}$	**11.** $\begin{array}{r}5.37\\ \times\ 0.012\\ \hline 0.06444\end{array}$	**12.** $\begin{array}{r}4.806\\ \times\ 7.03\\ \hline 33.78618\end{array}$
13. $\begin{array}{r}54.72\\ \times\ 0.9\\ \hline 49.248\end{array}$	**14.** $\begin{array}{r}812.77\\ \times\ 514\\ \hline 417{,}763.78\end{array}$	**15.** $\begin{array}{r}0.462\\ \times\ 0.93\\ \hline 0.42966\end{array}$	**16.** $\begin{array}{r}0.653\\ \times\ 207\\ \hline 135.171\end{array}$
17. $\begin{array}{r}61.437\\ \times\ 5.82\\ \hline 357.56334\end{array}$	**18.** $\begin{array}{r}9148.2\\ \times\ 6.35\\ \hline 58{,}091.07\end{array}$	**19.** $\begin{array}{r}0.0025\\ \times\ 0.602\\ \hline 0.001505\end{array}$	**20.** $\begin{array}{r}0.0007\\ \times\ 0.923\\ \hline 0.0006461\end{array}$

21. 11.6×38.51 **446.716**

22. 47.3×6.05 **286.165**

23. 86.9×121.75 **10,580.075**

24. 36.91×0.57 **21.0387**

25. 874.6×1.1 **962.06**

26. 27.5×40.1 **1102.75**

27. 0.05×0.003 **0.00015**

28. 20.35×3.7 **75.295**

29. 3.807×6.9 **26.2683**

30. 13.405×21.3 **285.5265**

31. 24.4×0.61 **14.884**

32. 643.21×1.626 **1045.85946**

33. 52.303×0.96 **50.21088**

34. 0.837×25 **20.925**

35. 10.01×45.33 **453.7533**

36. 71.7×3.02 **216.534**

37. 854.6×2.19 **1871.574**

38. 41.6×212.5 **8840**

39. 0.75×436 **327**

40. 362.008×24.7 **8941.5976**

41. 573×7.62 **4366.26**

42. 11.3×6.4372 **72.74036**

43. 66.7×5.329 **355.4443**

44. 16.3×85.004 **1385.5652**

45. 5129.36×0.008 **41.03488**

46. 814×93.11 **75,791.54**

47. 9.8413×16.55 **162.873515**

48. 6.8×3.7592 **25.56256**

49. 87.51×98.663 **8633.99913**

50. 251×0.0783 **19.6533**

Skill Review

Division

```
       12.51
6.8)85.068
     68
    170
    136
     346
     340
       68
       68
        0
```

Divide.

1. $4)\overline{140.8}$ 35.2

2. $7)\overline{160.3}$ 22.9

3. $1.8)\overline{13.68}$ 7.6

4. $5.06)\overline{47.564}$ 9.4

5. $3.8)\overline{59.66}$ 15.7

6. $8.1)\overline{423.63}$ 52.3

7. $0.25)\overline{22.175}$ 88.7

8. $0.9)\overline{131.04}$ 145.6

9. $11.42)\overline{41.112}$ 3.6

10. $21.73)\overline{52.152}$ 2.4

11. $0.8)\overline{200}$ 250

12. $6.4)\overline{1152}$ 180

Divide. Round to the nearest tenth.

13. $7.3)\overline{4001}$ 548.1

14. $6.9)\overline{117}$ 17.0

15. $0.56)\overline{27.8}$ 49.6

16. $3775 \div 15.6$ **242.0**

17. $6.3 \div 2.4$ **2.6**

18. $11.9 \div 4.6$ **2.6**

19. $0.86 \div 1.5$ **0.6**

20. $27.69 \div 37.5$ **0.7**

21. $88.01 \div 0.6$ **146.7**

22. $47.611 \div 0.4$ **119.0**

23. $78.9 \div 41.3$ **1.9**

24. $44.7 \div 22.1$ **2.0**

25. $3.96 \div 1.57$ **2.5**

26. $54 \div 3.07$ **17.6**

27. $2.61 \div 39$ **0.1**

28. $260.13 \div 19.1$ **13.6**

29. $565.29 \div 11.8$ **47.9**

30. $1.0472 \div 0.66$ **1.6**

31. $247.863 \div 7.04$ **35.2**

32. $36.15 \div 1.09$ **33.2**

33. $2.8927 \div 2.8$ **1.0**

Divide. Round to the nearest hundredth.

34. $8.7553 \div 0.28$ **31.27**

35. $96.14 \div 2.6$ **36.98**

36. $0.0361 \div 0.46$ **0.08**

37. $88.92 \div 1.91$ **46.55**

38. $1.4357 \div 0.047$ **30.55**

39. $3.5156 \div 0.028$ **125.56**

40. $90.068 \div 1.73$ **52.06**

41. $361.57 \div 20.7$ **17.47**

42. $0.92 \div 6.03$ **0.15**

43. $0.054 \div 1.86$ **0.03**

44. $26.923 \div 1.001$ **26.90**

45. $560 \div 74.73$ **7.49**

46. $270 \div 269.5$ **1.00**

47. $11.99 \div 12.1$ **0.99**

To round a quotient to a particular place, divide to one place beyond the place specified and then round.

```
        22.988
2.71)62.30000
     54 2
      8 10
      5 42
      2 680
      2 439
        2410
        2168
        2420
        2168
         252
```

Rounded to the nearest hundredth, the quotient is 22.99.

Extra Practice: *Chapter 1*

Simplify the numerical expression.

1. $44.23 - 1.6$ 42.63   **2.** 83×6 498   **3.** $4.80 \div 30$ 0.16   **4.** $74 + 116$ 190

Evaluate the expression when $d = 6$ and $y = 4$.

5. $y - 3$ 1   **6.** $d + d$ 12   **7.** $2y \times 3$ 24   **8.** $y + d + 2$ 12

Simplify the numerical expression.

9. $18 \div (2 \times 3) + 6$ 9   **10.** $5 \times (5 - 2) \div 3$ 5   **11.** $\dfrac{8 - 2 \times 3}{(6 - 4)(5 + 1)}$ $\frac{1}{6}$

Evaluate the expression when $x = 4.2$ and $y = 9$.

12. $4(x + y)$ 52.8   **13.** $5y - x$ 40.8   **14.** $(y - x)(x + y)$ 63.36

Evaluate the expression when $a = 5$ and $b = 10$.

15. $3a - \dfrac{a}{5}$ 14   **16.** $a(b - 2) \div 3$ $\frac{40}{3}$, or $13\frac{1}{3}$ **17.** $\dfrac{ab - 20}{a + b}$ 2

Find the solution of the equation for the given replacement set.

18. $q + 9 = 17$; $\{8, 9, 10\}$ 8   **19.** $b - 12 = 35$; $\{45, 46, 47\}$ 47

20. $x \div 14 = 8$; $\{110, 112, 114\}$ 112   **21.** $53 + m = 66$; $\{13, 15, 17\}$ 13

22. $8f = 56$; $\{5, 6, 7\}$ 7   **23.** $17t = 102$; $\{7, 8, 9\}$ no solution

24. $2g - 8 = 14$; $\{10, 11, 12\}$ 11   **25.** $4(a + 6) = 36$; $\{1, 2, 3\}$ 3

Replace ? with =, >, or < to make a true statement.

26. 31 _?_ 61 <   **27.** 18×4 _?_ 82 <   **28.** 47 _?_ $49 - 9$ >

Use > or < to write a true statement with the given numbers. 208 < 280 < 802, or 802 > 280 > 208

29. 35, 18, 6 6 < 18 < 35, or 35 > 18 > 6   **30.** 59, 41, 95 41 < 59 < 95, or 95 > 59 > 41   **31.** 208, 802, 280

Graph the solutions of the inequality. The replacement set for a is $\{0, 1, 2, 3, 4, 5, 6, 7, 8, 9, 10\}$.

32. $a < 14$ **33.** $a \geq 8$ **34.** $a + 6 > 9$ **35.** $10 - a \leq 5$

Find the solutions of the inequality. The replacement set for x is the set of whole numbers.

36. $x < 11$ **37.** $7 > x$ 0, 1, 2, 3, 4, 5, 6   **38.** $x \geq 9$ 9, 10, 11, and so on   **39.** $4 \geq x \geq 1$ 1, 2, 3, 4
0, 1, 2, 3, 4, 5, 6, 7, 8, 9, 10

Use inverse operations to solve.

40. $k + 16 = 28$ 12 **41.** $n \div 6 = 122$ 732 **42.** $7p = 217$ 31 **43.** $p - 11 = 41$ 52

44. $m \div 12 = 204$ 2448 **45.** $17 + z = 53$ 36 **46.** $6m = 240$ 40 **47.** $a - 35 = 41$ 76

48. $b \div 7 \le 14$ **49.** $f - 18 \ge 92$ **50.** $5a < 35$ **51.** $d + 9 > 27$

52. $3x - 7 = 32$ 13 **53.** $2b + 19 = 37$ 9 **54.** $(y \div 4) + 8 = 12$ 16

Additional Answers

The solutions are all the numbers:

48. less than or equal to 98.

49. greater than or equal to 110.

50. less than 7.

51. greater than 18.

Write a variable expression for the word phrase.

55. The difference when a number t is subtracted from eighteen $18 - t$

56. Five added to the product of a number x and nine $9x + 5$

57. Forty divided by a number m, decreased by sixteen $(40 \div m) - 16$

58. The remainder when a number q is subtracted from two hundred $200 - q$

59. Eleven more than three times a number y $3y + 11$

60. The sum of a number r and six, divided by twelve $(r + 6) \div 12$

Write an equation or inequality for the word sentence. **64–65:** Any letter may represent the number.

61. Twenty less than a number k is thirty-six. $k - 20 = 36$

62. The quotient when a number t is divided by thirteen is greater than nine. $t \div 13 > 9$

63. The sum of a number y and the product of eight and six is less than or equal to fifty. $y + (8 \times 6) \le 50$

64. Fifteen more than the quotient of a number divided by two is sixty. $x \div 2 + 15 = 60$

65. The remainder when the product of six and a number is subtracted from twenty is less than twelve. $20 - 6x < 12$

Solve, using the five-step plan.

66. Recently, Ken ran a 400 m race in 52.3 s. This was 0.2 s slower than the school record. What is the school record? 52.1 s

67. On July 1, Kay had $542.07 in her savings account. On September 1, she had $671.82 in her account. How much did she save between July 1 and September 1? $129.75

68. A machine produces 3 plastic parts each minute that it runs. If the machine runs for 7 h, how many parts will it produce? 1260 parts

69. Exercise World is buying 4 new exercise bicycles for $129.95 each and 6 exercise mats for $47.85 each. What is the total cost? $806.90

Extra Practice **475**

Extra Practice: Chapter 2

Simplify the expression.

1. 3^4 **81** **2.** 4^3 **64** **3.** $5^2 + 8^2$ **89** **4.** $2^3 + 3^3$ **35**

5. $(8 + 17)^0$ **1** **6.** $(4 \times 6)^2$ **576** **7.** $6^2 \times 18^0$ **36** **8.** $4^2 \times 4^2$ **256**

Write as a single power of the given base.

9. $3^8 \times 3^4$ **3¹²** **10.** $7^2 \times 7$ **7³** **11.** $k^5 \times k^{13}$ **k¹⁸** **12.** $m^2 \times m^0$ **m²**

Evaluate the expression if $a = 4$, $b = 2$, and $c = 6$.

13. $5c^3$ **1080** **14.** $(4b)^3$ **512** **15.** $2ab^4$ **128** **16.** $2a^3$ **128**

17. $3(ab)^2$ **192** **18.** $(3c)^b$ **324** **19.** $a^2 - b^4$ **0** **20.** c^2a **144**

21. ac^b **144** **22.** $(ab)^0$ **1** **23.** a^3b^2c **1536** **24.** $b^3 \times b^4$ **128**

Write the decimal in expanded form.

25. 734 **26.** 516.21 **27.** 0.024 **28.** 25.2

29. 2138 **30.** 91.9 **31.** 0.38 **32.** 307.009

Write as a decimal.

33. 18 and 21 hundredths **18.21** **34.** 5 and 4 thousandths **5.004** **35.** 242 and 6 tenths **242.6**

36. 9 and 9 ten-thousandths **9.0009** **37.** 85 thousandths **0.085** **38.** 6 ten-thousandths **0.0006**

Additional Answers

25. $(7 \times 100) + (3 \times 10) + 4$

26. $(5 \times 100) + (1 \times 10) + 6 + (2 \times 0.1) + (1 \times 0.01)$

27. $(2 \times 0.01) + (4 \times 0.001)$

28. $(2 \times 10) + 5 + (2 \times 0.1)$

29. $(2 \times 1000) + (1 \times 100) + (3 \times 10) + 8$

30. $(9 \times 10) + 1 + (9 \times 0.1)$

31. $(3 \times 0.1) + (8 \times 0.01)$

32. $(3 \times 100) + 7 + (9 \times 0.001)$

54. Addition Property of Zero

55. Commutative and Associative Properties

56. Distributive Property

57. Associative Property and Multiplication Property of Zero

58. Commutative and Associative Properties

59. Distributive Property

Replace __?__ with the symbols =, <, or > to make a true statement.

39. 48.2 __?__ 4.82 **>** **40.** 0.03 __?__ 0.031 **<** **41.** 1.452 __?__ 1.425 **>**

42. 0.008 __?__ 0.06 **<** **43.** 21.74 __?__ 217.4 **<** **44.** 7.44 __?__ 7.444 **<**

Round to the place specified.

45. hundreds; 871.21 **900** **46.** tenths; 113.93 **113.9** **47.** thousandths; 1.00414 **1.004**

48. hundredths; 0.0577 **0.06** **49.** tens; 382.45 **380** **50.** hundredths; 45.552 **45.55**

51. thousandths; 3.4279 **3.428** **52.** hundreds; 84 **100** **53.** tenths; 74.991 **75.0**

Use the properties to simplify the expression. Name the property or properties used.

54. $3(0 + 4.1)$ **12.3** **55.** $5.4 + 3.8 + 1.6$ **10.8** **56.** $9 \times 4.3 + 9 \times 0.7$ **45**

57. $8.51 \times 0 \times 712$ **0** **58.** $1.625 \times 1.3 \times 8$ **16.9** **59.** $4(32.5 + 2.8)$ **141.2**

What value of the variable makes the statement true?

60. $7.4 \times n = 1.84 \times 7.4$ **1.84**

61. $6.81 = r + 6.81$ **0**

62. $8.726z = z$ **0**

63. $3.4(5.12 + 9.4) = (5.12 + 9.4)p$ **3.4**

64. $(79 \times k) + (79 \times 4) = 79 \times 12$ **8**

65. $a \times 24.5 = 24.5$ **1**

66. $(6.4 \times h)12 = (12 \times 5.1) \times 6.4$ **5.1**

67. $(5.3 + 8) + y = 5.3 + 8$ **0**

Simplify the expression.

68. $(6^2 + 34) \div 7$ **10**

69. $8 + 6 \times 5^2$ **158**

70. $4 + (2.7 \div 0.3^2)$ **34**

71. $4.2 \times 7 - 1.1 \times 2^3$ **20.6**

72. $\dfrac{8.2 + 7.3 - 3.1 \times 2}{(7.9 + 4.5) \div 2^2}$ **3**

73. $\dfrac{(3.89 + 1.6)}{(14 \div 7)(5^2 - 4^2)}$ **0.305**

74. $3a^2 + (12 - 3^2)a^2$ **6a²**

75. $10k(k + 50) + 5[k^2 - (2 \times 5)^2 k + 6]$ **15k² + 30**

Evaluate the expression when $a = 2.5$, $b = 3$, and $c = 1.6$.

76. $3c + b^2$ **13.8**

77. $a^2 + bc$ **11.05**

78. $(a^3 + b - 3c)^0$ **1**

79. $a + 2b^3 - c$ **54.9**

80. $3a + 0.5b^2$ **12**

81. $b(a - c)^2$ **2.43**

82. $[4a + 2(b - c)^2] \div 8$ **1.74**

83. $(2b)^2 \times [(a + b) \div 11]$ **18**

Solve. Check your answer.

84. In a track meet, points are distributed in the following way: first place, 5 points; second place, 3 points; third place, one point. If the Centerville High track team received 4 first-place awards, 6 second-place awards, and 4 third-place awards in a recent meet, how many points did the team score? **42 points**

85. Three hundred fifty people attended the drama club's Friday evening performance. On Saturday evening, 20 fewer people attended the performance. If the cost of each ticket was $4.75, how much money did the club take in? **$3230**

86. At the beginning of the week, the odometer on Tom's bike read 321 km. If he rides his bike 68 km this week and twice that amount next week, what will the odometer on his bike then read? **525 km**

87. Cindy bought a camera for $125.60, a zoom lens for $75.50 and two rolls of film for $8.35 each. How much money did she spend? **$217.80**

88. Last week Pearl and Amy drove from their home to Seattle. In going to Seattle, Pearl drove 185 km and Amy drove 35 km more than Pearl. For the return trip, they decided to divide the driving evenly. How much did each person drive on the entire trip? **Pearl drove 387.5 km; Amy drove 422.5 km.**

Extra Practice **477**

Extra Practice: Chapter 3

Express as an integer.

1. $|^-3|$ 3   **2.** $|5|$ 5   **3.** $|1|$ 1   **4.** $|0|$ 0   **5.** $|^-6|$ 6

6. $|4|$ 4   **7.** $|^-2|$ 2   **8.** $|^-7|$ 7   **9.** $|9|$ 9   **10.** $|^-8|$ 8

Graph the number and its opposite on the same number line. Check students' graphs.

11. 6   **12.** $^-9$ **13.** 8   **14.** 5   **15.** $^-1$

Write the integers in order from least to greatest.

16. 0, 4, $^-4$, 3, $^-3$ $^-4, ^-3, 0, 3, 4$ **17.** 5, 0, $^-2$, $^-8$, 6 $^-8, ^-2, 0, 5, 6$ **18.** 7, $^-3$, $^-2$, 1, 9 $^-3, ^-2, 1, 7, 9$

19. $^-1$, 3, $^-7$, 5, $^-4$ $^-7, ^-4, ^-1, 3, 5$ **20.** $^-6$, $^-7$, 0, $^-5$, $^-2$ $^-7, ^-6, ^-5, ^-2, 0$ **21.** $^-4$, 5, 4, $^-5$, 0 $^-5, ^-4, 0, 4, 5$

List the integers that can replace x to make the statement true.

22. $|x| = 5$ $^-5, 5$ **23.** $|x| = 2$ $^-2, 2$ **24.** $|x| = 0$ 0

25. $|x| = 4$ $^-4, 4$ **26.** $|x| \le 6$ $^-6, ^-5, ^-4, \ldots, 6$ **27.** $|x| \le 3$ $^-3, ^-2, ^-1, \ldots, 3$

Graph the numbers in each exercise on the same number line. Check students' graphs.

28. 1, $^-1.5$, 0, $^-2$ **29.** $^-2$, $^-4$, 2.5, $^-3.5$ **30.** 3, 1.2, $^-2.4$, $^-5$

31. 7.6, $^-6.7$, 6, $^-7$ **32.** 1, 1.5, $^-2$, 2.5   **33.** 2, $^-1.8$, $^-2.1$, 0

Write the numbers in order from least to greatest.

34. $^-4.74$, $^-4$, $^-5$, 4.74, 4 $^-5, ^-4.74, ^-4, 4, 4.74$ **35.** 8.3, $^-8.3$, 8.03, $^-8.83$, $^-8$ $^-8.83, ^-8.3, ^-8, 8.03, 8.3$

36. 26.5, $^-26$, $^-2.65$, 2.6, $^-0.26$ $^-26, ^-2.65, ^-0.26, 2.6, 26.5$ **37.** $^-0.5$, 0.05, $^-5.5$, $^-5.05$, 5 $^-5.5, ^-5.05, ^-0.5, 0.05, 5$

38. 11.9, $^-12$, $^-11.9$, 11.09, 11 $^-12, ^-11.9, 11, 11.09, 11.9$ **39.** $^-42.6$, 42.06, $^-4.26$, 4.206, $^-0.42$ $^-42.6, ^-4.26, ^-0.42, 4.206, 42.06$

Draw an arrow to represent the decimal number described.

40. The number 5, with starting point $^-4$

41. The number $^-8$, with starting point 6

42. The number 6, with starting point $^-5$

43. The number $^-6$, with starting point 3

Find the sum.

44. $2.7 + 7.2$ 9.9   **45.** $^-4.9 + ^-7.6$ $^-12.5$ **46.** $^-2.25 + 2.25$ 0

47. $^-3.8 + ^-3.8$ $^-7.6$ **48.** $^-148 + ^-256$ $^-404$ **49.** $6.1 + ^-2.3$ 3.8

50. $^-0.6 + {}^-2.3$ -2.9

51. $18.12 + 1.66$ 19.78

52. $^-5.2 + 2.9$ -2.3

53. $^-2.8 + {}^-3.9$ -6.7

54. $1.9 + 19$ 20.9

55. $^-14.75 + 9.94$
-4.81

56. $^-3.7 + {}^-1.3$ -5

57. $0.31 + 19.14$ 19.45

58. $4.038 + {}^-6$
-1.962

Find the difference.

59. $30.5 - 18$ 12.5

60. $16 - 24.3$ -8.3

-0.6
61. $10.6 - 11.2$

62. $16.2 - (-7)$ 23.2

63. $5 - (-15.3)$ 20.3

27.7
64. $18 - (-9.7)$

65. $-8.3 - 5.2$ -13.5

66. $-7 - 14.6$ -21.6

-20.3
67. $-12.3 - 8$

68. $43.4 - (-136)$ 179.4

69. $-3 - (-8.2)$ 5.2

70. $-12.9 - (-4.5)$
-8.4

Evaluate when $x = -3.2$ and $y = -5.7$.

71. $-y$ 5.7

72. $-x$ 3.2

73. $-|x|$ -3.2

74. $-|y|$ -5.7

75. $y - x$ -2.5

76. $-x - y$ 8.9

77. $x - (-y)$ -8.9

78. $-x - (-y)$ -2.5

79. $-y - (-x)$ 2.5

Find the product.

80. $2.4(-1.2)$ -2.88

81. $-1.4(3.4)$ -4.76

-7.65
82. $4.5(-1.7)$

83. $-8.2(-6.1)$ 50.02

84. $-4.3(-3.4)$ 14.62

32.86
85. $-6.2(-5.3)$

86. $-2.15(1.15)$ -2.4725

87. $3.14(-8.1)$ -25.434

-42.3342
88. $-5.22(8.11)$

89. $4.25(-3.14)$ -13.345

90. $1.11(-1.11)$ -1.2321

-15.66
91. $-6.75(2.32)$

92. $-4.6(2.8)(-5.4)$ 69.552

93. $7.85(-15)(0)$ 0

94. $-8(9.2)(-20)$
1472

Find the quotient.

95. $-15.5 \div 0.5$ -31

96. $-16.4 \div 4$ -4.1

-20
97. $-150 \div 7.5$

98. $36.6 \div -0.06$ -610

99. $38 \div -0.4$ -95

-0.91
100. $8.19 \div -9$

101. $-3.038 \div (-7)$ 0.434

102. $-63.7 \div (-0.007)$ 9100

410
103. $-246 \div (-0.6)$

104. $-0.003 \div (1)$ -0.003

105. $0 \div (-0.85)$ 0

106. $-0.9 \div (-1.8)$
0.5

Write the expression without exponents.

107. 7^{-3} $\frac{1}{343}$ **108.** $(-4)^{-2}$ $\frac{1}{16}$ **109.** 2^{-5} $\frac{1}{32}$ **110.** $(-6)^{-4}$ $\frac{1}{1296}$ **111.** 8^{-1} $\frac{1}{8}$

112. $(-9)^{-2}$ $\frac{1}{81}$ **113.** 5^{-4} $\frac{1}{625}$ **114.** $(-1)^{-7}$ -1   **115.** 3^{-6} $\frac{1}{729}$ **116.** $(-5)^{-3}$

117. $8^5 \times 8^{-7}$ $\frac{1}{64}$ **118.** $10^4 \times 10^{-3}$ 10   **119.** $5^9 \times 5^{-9}$ 1   **120.** $4^{-2} \times 4^0$

121. $9^{17} \times 9^{-17}$ 1   **122.** $3^{-6} \times 3^4$ $\frac{1}{9}$ **123.** $6^{-2} \times 6^5$ 216   **124.** $2^{10} \times 2^{-8}$

116. $-\frac{1}{125}$ **120.** $\frac{1}{16}$ **124.** 4   *Extra Practice* **479**

Extra Practice: Chapter 4

Express in two other ways.

1. $-\frac{3}{5}$ $\frac{-3}{5}, \frac{3}{-5}$
2. $\frac{-4}{13}$ $-\frac{4}{13}, \frac{4}{-13}$
3. $-\frac{8}{7}$ $\frac{-8}{7}, \frac{8}{-7}$
4. $\frac{6}{-11}$ $-\frac{6}{11}, \frac{-6}{11}$
5. $\frac{-9}{14}$ $-\frac{9}{14}, \frac{9}{-14}$
6. $-\frac{7}{10}$ $\frac{-7}{10}, \frac{7}{-10}$

Complete.

7. $\frac{1}{4}+\frac{1}{4}+\frac{1}{4}+\frac{1}{4}=\underline{\ ?\ }$ 1

8. $\underline{\ ?\ }\times\frac{1}{3}=-\frac{2}{3}$ -2

9. $5\times\underline{\ ?\ }=-1$ $-\frac{1}{5}$

10. $\frac{3}{10}=3\div\underline{\ ?\ }$ 10

11. $\left(-\frac{1}{7}\right)+\left(-\frac{1}{7}\right)=\underline{\ ?\ }$ $-\frac{2}{7}$

12. $4\times\underline{\ ?\ }=\frac{4}{9}$ $\frac{1}{9}$

Complete.

13. $\frac{2}{5}=\frac{?}{20}$ 8

14. $\frac{-8}{9}=\frac{?}{27}$ -24

15. $-\frac{12}{30}=-\frac{2}{?}$ 5

16. $\frac{20}{-36}=\frac{?}{-9}$ 5

17. $3=\frac{12}{?}$ 4

18. $-4=\frac{-28}{?}$ 7

Write as a proper fraction in lowest terms or as a mixed number in simple form.

19. $\frac{15}{45}$ $\frac{1}{3}$
20. $-\frac{22}{64}$ $-\frac{11}{32}$
21. $\frac{7}{5}$ $1\frac{2}{5}$
22. $\frac{180}{240}$ $\frac{3}{4}$
23. $-\frac{144}{96}$ $-1\frac{1}{2}$
24. $-\frac{58}{12}$ $-4\frac{5}{6}$
25. $\frac{75}{125}$ $\frac{3}{5}$
26. $\frac{-145}{95}$ $-1\frac{10}{19}$
27. $\frac{14}{-8}$ $-1\frac{3}{4}$
28. $\frac{32}{28}$ $1\frac{1}{7}$
29. $\frac{-63}{81}$ $-\frac{7}{9}$
30. $-\frac{48}{54}$ $-\frac{8}{9}$

Write as an improper fraction.

31. $5\frac{2}{3}$ $\frac{17}{3}$
32. $3\frac{4}{5}$ $\frac{19}{5}$
33. $-4\frac{3}{10}$ $-\frac{43}{10}$
34. $-15\frac{1}{6}$ $-\frac{91}{6}$
35. $-7\frac{1}{8}$ $-\frac{57}{8}$
36. $9\frac{3}{25}$ $\frac{228}{25}$
37. $6\frac{1}{4}$ $\frac{25}{4}$
38. $-5\frac{11}{12}$ $-\frac{71}{12}$

Write the set of fractions as equivalent fractions with the least common denominator (LCD).

39. $\frac{5}{6}, \frac{3}{8}$ $\frac{20}{24}, \frac{9}{24}$
40. $\frac{4}{5}, -\frac{3}{10}$ $\frac{8}{10}, -\frac{3}{10}$
41. $\frac{4}{8}, \frac{5}{12}$ $\frac{6}{12}, \frac{5}{12}$
42. $-\frac{8}{15}, -\frac{7}{20}$ $-\frac{32}{60}, -\frac{21}{60}$
43. $-\frac{11}{28}, \frac{17}{42}$ $-\frac{33}{84}, \frac{34}{84}$
44. $\frac{7}{30}, \frac{19}{70}$ $\frac{49}{210}, \frac{57}{210}$
45. $\frac{1}{4}, \frac{7}{12}, \frac{5}{18}$ $\frac{9}{36}, \frac{21}{36}, \frac{10}{36}$
46. $-\frac{5}{18}, -\frac{7}{75}, -\frac{7}{10}$ $-\frac{125}{450}, -\frac{42}{450}, -\frac{315}{450}$
47. $\frac{4}{15}, \frac{8}{35}, \frac{1}{10}$ $\frac{56}{210}, \frac{48}{210}, \frac{21}{210}$

Add or subtract. Write the answer as a proper fraction in lowest terms or as a mixed number in simple form.

48. $\frac{5}{13} + \frac{4}{13}$ $\frac{9}{13}$

49. $-\frac{7}{8} - \frac{5}{8}$ $-1\frac{1}{2}$

50. $\frac{5}{12} - \frac{1}{12}$ $\frac{1}{3}$

51. $-\frac{4}{15} + \frac{1}{5}$ $-\frac{1}{15}$

52. $-\frac{6}{14} - \frac{12}{21}$ -1

53. $\frac{3}{16} - \frac{5}{8}$ $-\frac{7}{16}$

54. $\frac{5}{9} + \left(-\frac{1}{4}\right)$ $\frac{11}{36}$

55. $-\frac{9}{14} - \frac{5}{32}$ $-\frac{179}{224}$

56. $\frac{3}{7} - \left(-\frac{4}{5}\right)$ $1\frac{8}{35}$

57. $-4\frac{1}{12} + 2\frac{4}{5}$ $-1\frac{17}{60}$

58. $5\frac{2}{3} - 2\frac{5}{8}$ $3\frac{1}{24}$

59. $-3\frac{7}{12} + 7\frac{5}{16}$

60. $2\frac{3}{7} - \left(-4\frac{5}{6}\right)$ $7\frac{11}{42}$

61. $-1\frac{3}{28} + \left(-4\frac{10}{21}\right)$ $-5\frac{7}{12}$

62. $-15\frac{1}{2} - \left(-8\frac{3}{4}\right)$

63. $\frac{3}{25} + \frac{2}{15} + \frac{7}{10}$ $\frac{143}{150}$

64. $2\frac{7}{12} + \frac{1}{5} + 1\frac{1}{6}$ $3\frac{19}{20}$

65. $\frac{9}{11} - \frac{3}{5} - 1\frac{1}{2}$

$-1\frac{31}{110}$

59. $3\frac{35}{48}$ 62. $-6\frac{3}{4}$

Multiply or divide. Write the answer as a proper fraction in lowest terms or as a mixed number in simple form.

66. $-\frac{3}{4} \times \frac{4}{5}$ $-\frac{3}{5}$

67. $\frac{21}{56} \times \frac{20}{25}$ $\frac{3}{10}$

68. $\frac{7}{8} \times \left(-\frac{4}{7}\right)$ $-\frac{1}{2}$

69. $-\frac{9}{14} \times \frac{18}{45}$ $-\frac{9}{35}$

70. $-\frac{15}{16} \times \left(-\frac{56}{25}\right)$ $2\frac{1}{10}$

71. $-\frac{21}{52} \times \left(-\frac{13}{15}\right)$

72. $6\frac{3}{4} \times -1\frac{1}{3}$ -9

73. $-2\frac{5}{8} \times \left(-\frac{16}{19}\right)$ $2\frac{4}{19}$

74. $-4\frac{2}{7} \times 2\frac{1}{4}$ $-9\frac{9}{14}$

75. $\frac{4}{9} \div \frac{2}{9}$ 2

76. $-\frac{3}{8} \div \left(-\frac{5}{16}\right)$ $1\frac{1}{5}$

77. $-\frac{8}{15} \div \left(-2\frac{2}{7}\right)$

78. $-3\frac{3}{5} \div \left(2\frac{4}{15}\right)$ $-1\frac{10}{17}$

79. $-\frac{5}{6} \div 4\frac{1}{2}$ $-\frac{5}{27}$

80. $3\frac{5}{9} \div (-32)$ $-\frac{1}{9}$

81. $-16 \div 2\frac{10}{11}$ $-5\frac{1}{2}$

82. $\frac{3}{7} \div \frac{9}{20}$ $\frac{20}{21}$

83. $-\frac{11}{13} \div \left(-\frac{23}{52}\right)$

71. $\frac{7}{20}$ 77. $\frac{7}{30}$ $1\frac{21}{23}$

Write as a terminating or repeating decimal. Use a bar to show a repeating decimal.

91. $-0.\overline{851}$ -0.3125

84. $\frac{3}{8}$ 0.375

85. $\frac{3}{5}$ 0.6

86. $\frac{21}{22}$ $0.95\overline{4}$

87. $-\frac{5}{16}$

88. $\frac{1}{6}$ $0.1\overline{6}$

89. $-\frac{5}{9}$ $-0.\overline{5}$

90. $-\frac{8}{15}$ $-0.5\overline{3}$

91. $-\frac{161}{189}$

92. $\frac{287}{385}$ $0.7\overline{45}$

93. $3\frac{5}{12}$ $3.41\overline{6}$

94. $-2\frac{3}{11}$ $-2.\overline{27}$

95. $4\frac{1}{18}$

$4.0\overline{5}$

Write as a proper fraction in lowest terms or as a mixed number in simple form.

$-3\frac{1}{40}$

96. 0.6 $\frac{3}{5}$

97. -0.04 $-\frac{1}{25}$

98. 1.34 $1\frac{17}{50}$

99. -4.22 $-4\frac{11}{50}$

100. -3.025

$-2\frac{1}{6}$

101. $0.\overline{6}$ $\frac{2}{3}$

102. $-2.\overline{09}$ $-2\frac{1}{11}$

103. $1.\overline{7}$ $1\frac{7}{9}$

104. $8.2121\ldots$ $8\frac{7}{33}$

105. $-2.1666\ldots$

Extra Practice   **481**

Extra Practice: Chapter 5

Use one of the properties of equality to form a true sentence.

1. If $r + 8 = 15$, then $r = $ __?__. 7   **2.** If $13 = w + 5$, then __?__ $= w$. 8

3. If $-8e = -32$, then $e = $ __?__. 4   **4.** If $6f = -54$, then $f = $ __?__. -9

5. If $14 = -9 + u$, then __?__ $= u$. 23   **6.** If $c + 13 = 10$, then $c = $ __?__. -3

Simplify the expressions on both sides of the equation to obtain an equivalent equation.

7. $n - 7 + 4 + 10 = 42 \div 6$ $n + 7 = 7$ **8.** $3 \times 18 \div 9 = 14 + k - 2$ $6 = k + 12$

9. $47 = 6v + 7 + 2v$ $47 = 8v + 7$ **10.** $5y - 4 + 2y - 3y = 32$ $4y - 4 = 32$

11. $3(h + 8) = 39$ $3h + 24 = 39$ **12.** $-28 = -7(g - 2)$ $-28 = -7g + 14$

Use transformations to solve the equation. Write down all the steps.

13. $d + 9 = 24$ 15   **14.** $-22 = t + 10$ -32   **15.** $j - 7 = 13$ 20

16. $-14 = r - 3$ -11   **17.** $-5 + b + 11 = 26$ 20   **18.** $-8 + g - 12 = -16$ 4

19. $-6 = 7 + 13 + t$ -26   **20.** $18 = q + 4 - 15$ 29   **21.** $s + 8\frac{2}{3} = 12$ $3\frac{1}{3}$

22. $-4\frac{2}{5} + w = 6$ $10\frac{2}{5}$ **23.** $9 = u - 7.6$ 16.6   **24.** $3.4 + e = -5$ -8.4

25. $56 = 8t$ 7   **26.** $-4m = 36$ -9   **27.** $-55 = 11x$ -5   **28.** $-7k = -42$ 6

29. $\frac{a}{4.2} = -13$ -54.6   **30.** $5 = \frac{y}{23.1}$ 115.5   **31.** $\frac{c}{-0.6} = -14$ 8.4   **32.** $3 = \frac{n}{-412}$ -1236

33. $16 = \frac{1}{3}g$ 48   **34.** $\frac{7}{8}f = -21$ -24   **35.** $12 = \frac{4}{-5}a$ -15   **36.** $\frac{-9}{2}h = -27$ 6

37. $-3.7 = 0.01z$ -370   **38.** $8.5m = 25.5$ 3   **39.** $\frac{-2}{3}b = \frac{4}{-5}$ $1\frac{1}{5}$ **40.** $\frac{5}{14} = \frac{-3}{7}d$ $-\frac{5}{6}$

41. $8 - 6x = 37 - 3$ $-4\frac{1}{3}$ **42.** $5e + 9 = -33 + 7$ -7   **43.** $14 + \frac{w}{3} = 26$ 36

44. $15 = \frac{-1}{4}m - 7$ -88   **45.** $4a = a + 25$ $\frac{25}{3}$, or $8\frac{1}{3}$ **46.** $22 - 2c = 9c$ 2

47. $\frac{4}{3}u + 8 = u$ -24   **48.** $v = 6 - \frac{5}{4}v$ $\frac{8}{3}$, or $2\frac{2}{3}$ **49.** $-10 = \frac{2}{7}(s - 21)$ -14

50. $\frac{5}{6}(n + 24) = 13$ $-\frac{42}{5}$, or $-8\frac{2}{5}$ **51.** $0.5(k + 18) = 14$ 10   **52.** $-44 = (m - 10)2.2$ -10

Use transformations to solve the inequality. Write down all the steps.

53. $y + 5 \leq -17$ **54.** $q - 8 > 24$ **55.** $5\frac{1}{6} - \frac{1}{3} < k$

482   *Extra Practice*

482

56. $7.8 + 4.3 \geq m$ **57.** $f < (17 - 3)0.5$ **58.** $z \leq \frac{1}{2}(25 - 7)$

59. $6e > 42$ **60.** $-5a \leq 45$ **61.** $28 < -7u$

62. $52 \geq 4x$ **63.** $\frac{w}{-3} > 21$ **64.** $\frac{c}{4} \geq 17$

65. $-11 \leq \frac{a}{5}$ **66.** $\frac{e}{-2} < -23$ **67.** $10 > \frac{v}{7}$

68. $-5x + 7 + 2x - 13 < 9$ **69.** $-22 \geq 10d - 4 - 3d + 12$

70. $2 > \frac{4}{5}n + 3 - \frac{1}{5}n + 6$ **71.** $5 + \frac{3}{7}u - 8 + \frac{2}{7}u \leq 5$

72. $-w + 8 \leq 4w - 17$ **73.** $-6s - 4 < s + 31$

74. $10 + \frac{2}{3}h > -\frac{5}{3}h + 6$ **75.** $8 - \frac{1}{6}p \geq 4 - \frac{1}{3}p$

76. $4(m + 3) \geq 48$ **77.** $35 < -5(x + 2)$

78. $34 < (18t - 6)\frac{1}{3}$ **79.** $\frac{-1}{7}(14 + 21u) \geq 7$

Write a problem that the equation could represent. Answers will vary.

80. $67 + x = 75$ **81.** $x - 9 = 32$ **82.** $45 - x = 38$ **83.** $x + 17 = 22$

84. $7x = 93$ **85.** $5x = 135$ **86.** $\frac{x}{12} = 5$ **87.** $\frac{1}{9}x = 7$

Follow the five-step plan for using an equation to solve.

88. Leroy's homeroom has sold $262.50 worth of tickets to the school play. If each ticket costs $3.50, how many more tickets must be sold to take in a total of $651? 111 more tickets

89. The dining hall staff is setting up tables for a new group of campers. There is room for 12 people at each table. If 75 girls, 69 boys, and 19 counselors must be fed, how many tables are needed? 14 tables

90. It took Alfredo $3\frac{3}{4}$ h to ride his bicycle to and from the beach. The return trip was uphill and took him twice as long as the ride to the beach. How long will he spend riding in each direction? $1\frac{1}{4}$ h going, $2\frac{1}{2}$ h returning

91. On a visit to Sacramento, Cornelia saw $4.55 worth of 35¢ picture postcards that she liked. If she could spend only $2.80, how many of the postcards was she unable to buy? 5 postcards

92. Brightwood High sponsored a cheerleading contest in which 53 teams competed. If each team had five students, and 185 of the students were from within the state, how many teams were from other states? 16 teams

Extra Practice **483**

Extra Practice: Chapter 6

Check students' work.

1. Draw any segment *AB* and construct $\overline{CD}$ congruent to $\overline{AB}$.

Draw a labeled diagram to illustrate each description. Check students' diagrams.

2. $\overrightarrow{XY}$ and point *A* on $\overrightarrow{XY}$ but not on $\overline{XY}$

3. $\overleftrightarrow{AB}$ and point *R* on $\overleftrightarrow{AB}$ but not on $\overrightarrow{AB}$

4. A circle with center *A*, radii $\overline{AM}$ and $\overline{AN}$, and chord $\overline{PQ}$

5. A circle with center *G*, diameter $\overline{KL}$, and radius $\overline{GN}$

Find the circumference of the circle with the given radius or diameter. Use $\pi \approx 3.14$.

6. *r* = 57 cm   358 cm **7.** *r* = 14.5 m   91.1 m **8.** *d* = 23 km   72.2 km **9.** *d* = 7.03 m   22.1 m

10. Draw any acute angle *J*. Construct an angle congruent to $\angle J$.   Check students' work.

11. Draw any obtuse angle *A*. Construct a bisector of $\angle A$.

The measures of two angles in the diagram are given. Find the measure of the third angle.

12. m$\angle ABC$ = 56°, m$\angle CBE$ = 41°, m$\angle ABE$ = __?__°   97

13. m$\angle ABC$ = 17°, m$\angle ABE$ = 83°, m$\angle CBE$ = __?__°   66

14. m$\angle CBE$ = 24°, m$\angle ABE$ = 72°, m$\angle ABC$ = __?__°   48

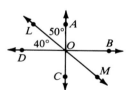

Find the measure of each angle in the diagram at the right.

15. $\angle COM$ 50°   **16.** $\angle MOB$ 40°

17. $\angle AOB$ 90°   **18.** $\angle DOC$ 90°

19. Two angles are complementary. The measure of one is 4 times the measure of the other. What are the measures of the angles?   18°, 72°

20. Two angles are supplementary. The measure of one is 16° greater than the measure of the other. What are the measures of the angles?   82°, 98°

In the diagram at the right, *l* ∥ *n*.

21. Name two pairs of alternate interior angles. $\angle 3, \angle 6; \angle 4, \angle 5$

22. Name four pairs of corresponding angles. $\angle 1, \angle 5; \angle 2, \angle 6;$ $\angle 3, \angle 7; \angle 4, \angle 8$

23. m$\angle 8$ = 100°. Find the measures of the other angles.

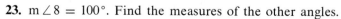

m$\angle 1$ = m$\angle 4$ = m$\angle 5$ = 100°; m$\angle 2$ = m$\angle 3$ = m$\angle 6$ = m$\angle 7$ = 80°

24. If the measure of one angle of a right triangle is 30°, what are the measures of the other angles? 90°, 60°

25. An isosceles triangle has one angle that measures 110°. What are the measures of the other angles? 35°, 35°

26. What is a triangle with three sides that are not congruent called? Scalene

27. The angles of a triangle measure 75°, 65°, and 40°. Is the triangle an obtuse triangle or an acute triangle? Acute triangle

28. How many acute angles does a right triangle have? 2

True or false?

29. A square is also a rhombus. True

30. Every quadrilateral has at least two parallel sides. False

31. An isosceles trapezoid has two sides that are congruent. True

32. Opposite angles of a parallelogram are congruent. True

33. A trapezoid is a special type of parallelogram. False

34. A segment that connects opposite vertices of a quadrilateral is called a diameter. False

35. What is the perimeter of a square with one side 65 mm? 260 mm

36. One side of a regular decagon is 7.8 cm. What is the perimeter? 78 cm

37. A triangle has sides of length 64.3 mm, 28.7 mm, and 56.2 mm. What is the perimeter? 149.2 mm

38. One side of a rectangle is 2.8 m. The perimeter of the rectangle is 17.2 m. What are the lengths of the other sides? 2.8 m, 5.8 m, 5.8 m

39. A regular pentagon has perimeter 14.5 cm. What is the length of each side? 2.9 cm

Are the triangles in each pair congruent? If so, name the triangles that are congruent and explain why they are congruent.

40.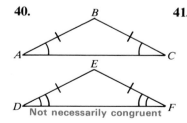
Not necessarily congruent

41.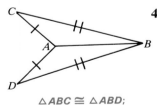
△ABC ≅ △ABD;
SSS

42.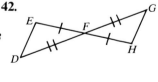
△DEF ≅ △GHF;
SAS

Extra Practice: Chapter 7

Write the ratio as a fraction in lowest terms.

1. $\frac{9}{36}$ $\frac{1}{4}$ **2.** 17 to 7 $\frac{17}{7}$ **3.** 15:35 $\frac{3}{7}$ **4.** 56 to 63 $\frac{8}{9}$ **5.** $\frac{1}{2}:\frac{2}{3}$ $\frac{3}{4}$

Solve the proportion.

6. $\frac{8}{16}=\frac{x}{78}$ 39   **7.** $\frac{27}{x}=\frac{6}{2}$ 9   **8.** $\frac{125}{25}=\frac{60}{x}$ 12   **9.** $\frac{x}{18}=\frac{17}{51}$ 6

Solve.

10. In order to make 4 servings, a recipe calls for 3 eggs to be used. How many eggs will be needed to make 32 servings? **24 eggs**

11. Charlie runs 5 mi in 37 min. If he could maintain the same speed, how long would it take him to run 15 mi? **1 h 51 min**

12. A dozen apples cost $1.80. What is the unit price? **15¢**

13. A car travels 234 km in 4.5 h. What is the car's average speed? **52 km/h**

14. A floor plan with the scale 1 cm = 2 m shows a room as 2 cm wide and 5 cm long. What are the actual width and length? **4 m, 10 m**

15. A certain map uses a scale of 1 cm = 6 km. If the distance from Hopeville to Breda is 150 km, how far apart are they on the map? **25 cm**

Express as a percent.

16. $\frac{7}{8}$ **87.5%**   **17.** 1.73 **173%**   **18.** $\frac{1}{4}$ **25%**   **19.** 0.05 **5%**   **20.** 0.375 **37.5%**

21. $\frac{3}{5}$ **60%**   **22.** $\frac{1}{10}$ **10%**   **23.** $\frac{7}{28}$ **25%**   **24.** 0.57 **57%**   **25.** $\frac{2}{3}$ **66$\frac{2}{3}$%**

Express as a percent to the nearest tenth of a percent.

26. $\frac{1}{6}$ **16.7%**   **27.** $\frac{5}{9}$ **55.6%**   **28.** $\frac{6}{17}$ **35.3%**   **29.** $\frac{7}{15}$ **46.7%**   **30.** $\frac{21}{33}$ **63.6%**

Express as (a) a proper fraction in lowest terms or as a mixed number in simple form and (b) a decimal.

31. 0.7% $\frac{7}{1000}$; 0.007   **32.** 27% $\frac{27}{100}$; 0.27   **33.** 1.3% $\frac{13}{1000}$; 0.013   **34.** 44% $\frac{11}{25}$; 0.44

35. 135% $1\frac{7}{20}$; 1.35   **36.** 15.5% $\frac{31}{200}$; 0.155   **37.** 0.3% $\frac{3}{1000}$; 0.003   **38.** 1% $\frac{1}{100}$; 0.01

Express as a fraction in lowest terms.

39. $\frac{1}{8}$% $\frac{1}{800}$ **40.** $\frac{5}{6}$% $\frac{1}{120}$ **41.** 83$\frac{1}{3}$% $\frac{5}{6}$ **42.** 22$\frac{1}{6}$% $\frac{133}{600}$

Solve. Round to the nearest tenth if necessary.

43. What is 40% of 75? 30

44. What is 20% of 81? 16.2

45. What is 17% of 108? 18.4

46. 5 is what percent of 50? 10%

47. 12 is what percent of 30? 40%

48. 56 is 112% of what number? 50

49. 27 is $33\frac{1}{3}$% of what number? 81

50. What is $11\frac{1}{9}$% of 1000? 111.1

51. 36 is what percent of 28? 128.6%

52. 325 is 1.3% of what number? 25,000

53. 19 is 190% of what number? 10

54. 47 is what percent of 70? 67.1%

Solve.

55. Carol has 60 boxes of light bulbs. If she sells 15% of the boxes today, how many will be left? 51 boxes

56. A calculator costs $6.25 plus $.25 sales tax. What is the sales tax rate? 4%

57. At a pet store, fish that usually cost $1.25 each are on sale for $.75 each. What is the percent of decrease? 40%

58. A restaurant raises its price for the salad bar 20% to $1.50. What did the salad bar cost before? $1.25

59. The band concert drew an audience of 270 on Thursday. On Friday, attendance increased 30%. How many people attended on Friday? 351 people

60. The discount rate at an appliance store sale is 15%. What is the sale price of a dishwasher if the original price was $600? $510

61. Nancy Allen earns a 12% commission on her sales. Last month she earned $4800. What was the total value of her sales? $40,000

62. Last Friday, 720 people at Data Tech drove cars to work. Of these, 585 bought gas on the way home. What percent of the drivers bought gas on the way home? Use a proportion to solve. 81.25%

63. How much does a $53.00 iron cost if it is taxed at 5%? Use a proportion to solve. $55.65

64. Jill has $525 in a savings account that pays 6% simple interest. How much will she have in the account after 1 year, if she makes no deposits or withdrawals? $556.50

65. Holly has a savings account that pays 6.5% interest, compounded monthly. If she started the account with $750 and makes no deposits or withdrawals, how much will be in the account after 3 months? $762.25

Extra Practice **487**

487

Extra Practice: Chapter 8

For Exercises 1–6, give the coordinates of the point.

1. A (−6, 2)   **2.** B (5, −4)   **3.** C (4, 4)

4. D (−3, −2)   **5.** E (−2, 4)   **6.** F (1, 1)

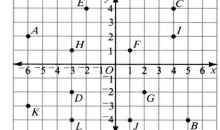

Name the point for the ordered pair.

7. (2, −2) G   **8.** (−3, −4) L

9. (4, 2) I   **10.** (−6, −3) K

11. (1, −4) J   **12.** (−3, 1) H

a. Graph the given ordered pairs on a coordinate plane. Check students' graphs.

b. Connect all the points in the order listed by means of line segments to produce a closed figure.

c. Name the figure as specifically as you can.

13. (3, 3), (3, 0), (−2, 0), (−5, 0), (−5, 3), (3, 3) Rectangle

14. (2, −2), (2, −6), (−2, −6), (−2, −2), (0, −2), (2, −2) Square

15. (1, 5), (−2, 2), (−5, −1), (0, −1), (6, −1), (1, 5) Triangle

16. (0, 7), (3, 5), (2, 2), (−2, 2), (−3, 5), (0, 7) Pentagon

17. (7, −4), (4, −1), (2, 1), (1, 2), (1, −4), (7, −4) Right triangle

Tell whether the ordered pair is a solution of the given equation.

$-x + 2y = 4$

18. (4, 0) No   **19.** (−4, 0) Yes   **20.** (2, 3) Yes   **21.** (−2, 3) No

$x + 3y = 6$

22. (0, 2) Yes   **23.** (6, 0) Yes   **24.** (2, 1) No   **25.** (3, 1) Yes

$2x + y = 5$

26. (3, 1) No   **27.** (2, 1) Yes   **28.** (1, 3) Yes   **29.** (0, 5) Yes

a. Solve the equation for y in terms of x.

b. Find the solutions of the equation for the given values of x.

30. $2x + y = 8$ $y = 8 - 2x$; (−1, 10), (0, 8), (1, 6)
values of x: −1, 0, 1

31. $y - 3x = 4$ $y = 3x + 4$; (−5, −11), (0, 4), (5, 19)
values of x: −5, 0, 5

32. $-x + y = 1$ $y = x + 1$; (−1, 0), $\left(\frac{1}{2}, 1\frac{1}{2}\right)$, (2, 3)
values of x: −1, $\frac{1}{2}$, 2

33. $3x - 2y = -6$ $y = \frac{3}{2}x + 3$; (−2, 0), (0, 3), (2, 6)
values of x: −2, 0, 2

488 *Extra Practice*

34. $2x + y = 6$ $y = 6 - 2x$; (0, 6),
values of x: 0, 3, 1 (3, 0), (1, 4)

35. $x - y = 3$ $y = x - 3$; (6, 3),
values of x: 6, -1, -3 (-1, -4),
(-3, -6)

Graph the equation on a coordinate plane. Use a separate set of axes for each equation. Check students' graphs.

36. $2x + y = 4$

37. $x - 3y = -3$

38. $x + 2y = -4$

39. $3x + 4y = 12$

40. $2x + 5y = 10$

41. $-x + y = -1$

42. $x + y = 2$

43. $3x - y = 3$

44. $4x - 2y = 3$

45. $2x = y - 2$

46. $y = x - 3$

47. $-3x + 4y = 12$

Use a graph to solve the system. Do the lines intersect, coincide, or are they parallel?

48. $x - y = -2$ Intersect
$2x + y = 5$ at (1, 3)

49. $x - y = 6$ Intersect
$2x + y = 0$ at (2, -4)

50. $2x + y = -2$ Intersect at (-2, 2)
$x - y = -4$

51. $2x + y = 2$ Parallel
$2x + y = -3$

52. $6x + 3y = 6$ Coincide
$2x + y = 2$

53. $3x + y = -6$
$2x - y = 1$
Intersect at (-1, -3)

54. A parking lot attendant charges \$3 for the first hour and \$1 for each extra hour after that. Write an equation that relates the total cost of parking (y) to the number of extra hours a car is parked (x). Graph the equation. What is the slope of the graph? From your graph determine how much it would cost to park a car for 5 h after the initial hour. $y = x + 3$; check students' graphs; slope = 1; \$8

55. The initial charge for a phone call to Jonesboro is 25¢ for the first 3 min. After that the charge is 5¢ for every additional minute. Write an equation that relates the total cost of a phone call (y) to the number of additional minutes on the phone (x). Graph the equation. What is the slope of the graph? From the graph determine the cost of a call requiring 7 min beyond the initial 3.
$y = 5x + 25$; check students' graphs; slope = 5; 60¢

56. The temperature in a town rose at a constant rate from 5 A.M. to 12 noon. At 9 A.M. the temperature was 17°C. At 11 A.M. the temperature was 21°C. Use this information to draw a graph and determine what the temperature was at 5 A.M. and at 12 noon.
Check students' graphs; 9°C at 5 A.M., 23°C at 12 noon.

Graph the inequality. Check students' graphs.

57. $x + 2y < 4$

58. $2x - y < 1$

59. $6x + y \geq 7$

60. $-x + 3y < 0$

61. $2x + y \geq 1$

62. $3x + y \leq -2$

Extra Practice: Chapter 9

Use $\pi \approx 3.14$ when needed. Answers involving π have been rounded to 3 digits.

1. What is the area of a square with a side that is 16 cm long? 256 cm²

2. What is the area of a triangle with base 72 mm and height 53 mm? 1908 mm²

3. A square has a perimeter of 88 m. What is its area? 484 m²

4. The legs of a right triangle are 28 cm and 35 cm. What is the area of the triangle? 490 cm²

5. Find the length of a rectangle with area 9720 m² and width 67.5 m. 144 m

6. Find the height of a triangle with area 4122.5 mm² and base 85 mm. 97 mm

7. A parallelogram has base 60 mm and height 40 mm. Find its area. 2400 mm²

8. Find the area of a parallelogram with height 15 cm and base 24 cm. 360 cm²

9. A trapezoid has height 18 cm and bases 113 cm and 121 cm. Find its area. 2106 cm²

10. A parallelogram with area 1176 m² has height 56 m. Find its base. 21 m

11. A trapezoid with bases 51 m and 33 m has area 630 m². Find its height. 15 m

12. A parallelogram with base 45 cm has area 1440 cm². Find its height. 32 cm

13. What is the area of a circle whose diameter is 140 cm? 15,400 cm²

14. A circle has radius 12 m. Find its area. 452 m²

15. What is the radius of a circle whose area is 803.84 mm²? 16.0 mm

16. The circumference of a circle is 43.96 m. Find the area. 154 m²

17. Find the diameter of a circle with an area of 379.94 m². 22.0 m

18. Find the area of a circle whose diameter is 36 cm. 1020 cm²

Tell whether the figure is symmetric with respect to a point, to a line, or to both. Use the fact that the figure has symmetry to find the area.

19.

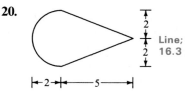

Both; 32.6

20.

Line; 16.3

21. A prism with height 5 m has base area 173 m². Find the volume. 865 m³

22. Find the volume of a cylinder with height 82 cm and base area 50 cm². 4100 cm³

23. A right triangle with legs 15 mm and 7 mm is the base of a prism with height 24 mm. Find the volume of the prism. 1260 mm³

24. Find the volume of a cylinder with height 300 cm and diameter 15 cm. 53,000 cm³

25. The volume of a triangular prism is 2340 cm³. Find the height of the prism if the base area is 78 cm². 30 cm

26. A cone with base area 234 mm² is 82 mm high. Find its volume and its capacity in liters. 6400 mm³; 0.006 L

27. A pyramid with height 52 cm has a rectangular base measuring 12 cm by 17 cm. Find the volume. 3536 cm³

28. The base of a cone has diameter 70 cm. If the height of the cone is 120 cm, what is the volume? 154,000 cm³

For Exercises 29–32, find (a) the lateral surface area and (b) the total surface area of the figure described.

29. A prism of height 15 cm whose bases are right triangles with sides 15 cm, 36 cm, and 39 cm 1350 cm²; 1890 cm²

30. A cylinder with radius 4 cm and height 11 cm 276 cm²; 377 cm²

31. A cube with edges that are 15 cm 900 cm²; 1350 cm²

32. A rectangular prism of height 27 cm and base 15 cm by 12 cm 1458 cm²; 1818 cm²

For Exercises 33–36, leave your answers in terms of π.

33. Find the surface area of a sphere with radius 18 cm. 1296π cm²

34. Find the volume of a sphere with diameter 30 cm. 4500π cm³

35. Find the radius of a sphere whose surface area is 576π m². 12 m

36. Find the volume of a sphere whose radius is 16 cm. $\frac{16,384}{3}\pi$, or $5461\frac{1}{3}\pi$, cm³

37. If the mass of 1 L of gasoline is 0.66 kg, what is the mass of 4 L? 2.64 kg

38. Each edge of a cube of steel measures 12 cm. Find the mass of the cube if the mass of 1 cm³ of steel is 7.82 g. 13,512.96 g

39. A rectangular prism of aluminum is 15 cm long, 7 cm wide, and 30 cm high. Find the mass of the prism if the mass of 1 cm³ of aluminum is 2.708 g. 8530.2 g

Extra Practice: Chapter 10

If the given symbol names an integer, state the integer. If not, name the two consecutive integers between which the number lies.

1. $\sqrt{9}$ 3
2. $\sqrt{39}$ 6, 7
3. $-\sqrt{27}$ −6, −5
4. $\sqrt{10}$ 3, 4
5. $\sqrt{17}$ 4, 5
6. $\sqrt{5}$ 2, 3
7. $\sqrt{81}$ 9
8. $-\sqrt{12}$ −4, −3
9. $\sqrt{60}$ 7, 8
10. $-\sqrt{78}$ −9, −8
11. $\sqrt{25}$ 5
12. $\sqrt{19}$ 4, 5
13. $\sqrt{16}$ 4
14. $\sqrt{43}$ 6, 7
15. $\sqrt{84}$ 9, 10
16. $\sqrt{64}$ 8

Approximate to the tenths' place, using the divide-and-average method.

17. $\sqrt{24}$ 4.8
18. $\sqrt{30}$ 5.4
19. $\sqrt{92}$ 9.5
20. $\sqrt{74}$ 8.6
21. $\sqrt{51}$ 7.1
22. $\sqrt{29}$ 5.3
23. $\sqrt{10}$ 3.1
24. $\sqrt{86}$ 9.2
25. $\sqrt{37}$ 6.0
26. $\sqrt{80}$ 8.9
27. $\sqrt{5.6}$ 2.3
28. $\sqrt{9.8}$ 3.1

For Exercises 29–53, refer to the table on page 498.
Approximate the square root to the nearest hundredth.

29. $\sqrt{8}$ 2.83
30. $\sqrt{19}$ 4.36
31. $\sqrt{5}$ 2.24
32. $\sqrt{11}$ 3.32
33. $\sqrt{24}$ 4.90
34. $\sqrt{52}$ 7.21
35. $\sqrt{39}$ 6.25
36. $\sqrt{2}$ 1.41
37. $\sqrt{31}$ 5.57
38. $2\sqrt{18}$ 8.49
39. $\sqrt{58}$ 7.62
40. $5\sqrt{45}$ 33.54

Approximate the square root to the nearest hundredth by interpolation.

41. $\sqrt{15.8}$ 3.97
42. $\sqrt{6.3}$ 2.51
43. $\sqrt{21.4}$ 4.63
44. $\sqrt{83.6}$ 9.14

State whether or not a triangle with sides of the given lengths is a right triangle.

45. 2, 3, 4 No
46. 3, 4, 5 Yes
47. 10, 20, 24 No
48. 8, 15, 17 Yes
49. 10, 12, 15 No
50. 6, 8, 10 Yes
51. 30, 40, 50 Yes
52. 7, 9, 12 No
53. 12, 16, 20 Yes

A right triangle has sides of lengths a, b, and c, with c the length of the hypotenuse. Find the length of the missing side. If necessary, use the table on page 498 for the square root values and round answers to the nearest hundredth.

54. $a = 5$, $b = 8$ 9.43
55. $a = 4$, $b = 5$ 6.40
56. $a = 3$, $c = 5$ 4
57. $b = 12$, $c = 15$ 9
58. $b = 15$, $c = 17$ 8
59. $a = 7$, $b = 7$ 9.90

60. $a = 6,\ c = 10$ 8

61. $b = 8,\ c = 17$ 15

62. $a = 13,\ c = 14$
5.20

Find the lengths marked x and y. In each exercise, the triangles are similar.

63.

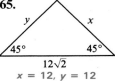

$x = 20$ $y = 40$

64.

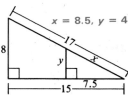

$x = 8.5,\ y = 4$

Find the lengths marked x and y in the triangle. Give your answer in terms of radicals when radicals occur.

65.

$x = 12,\ y = 12$

66.

$x = 5\sqrt{3},\ y = 10$

67.

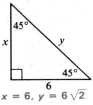

$x = 20,\ y = 10$

68.

$x = 6,\ y = 6\sqrt{2}$

Rewrite the expression in lowest terms with the radical in the numerator.

69. $\dfrac{2}{\sqrt{3}}$ $\dfrac{2\sqrt{3}}{3}$

70. $\dfrac{5}{\sqrt{x}}$ $\dfrac{5\sqrt{x}}{x}$

71. $\dfrac{x}{\sqrt{2a}}$ $\dfrac{x\sqrt{2a}}{2a}$

72. $\dfrac{7}{\sqrt{4}}$
$\dfrac{7}{2}$, or $3\dfrac{1}{2}$

Use the diagram to name each ratio.

73. $\tan A$ $\dfrac{x}{y}$

74. $\sin A$ $\dfrac{x}{z}$

75. $\cos A$ $\dfrac{y}{z}$

76. $\tan B$ $\dfrac{y}{x}$

77. $\cos B$ $\dfrac{x}{z}$

78. $\sin B$ $\dfrac{y}{z}$

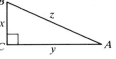

For Exercises 79–88, use the tables on pages 498 and 499.
Find $\sin A$, $\cos A$, and $\tan A$ for the given measure of $\angle A$.
0.0872, 0.9962, 0.0875

79. $27°$
0.4540, 0.8910, 0.5095

80. $68°$
0.9272, 0.3746, 2.4751

81. $89°$
0.9998, 0.0175, 57.2900

82. $5°$

Find the measure of $\angle A$ to the nearest degree.
53°

83. $\sin A = 0.436$ 26°

84. $\cos A = 0.224$ 77°

85. $\tan A = 1.35$

Refer to the diagram at the right.

86. Find the value of x. 5

87. Find $\angle D$ to the nearest degree. 23°

88. Find $\angle E$ to the nearest degree. 67°

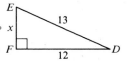

Extra Practice **493**

Extra Practice: Chapter 11

Find the value of each.

1. 6! 720
2. 3! 6
3. 10! 3,628,800
4. 2! 2
5. 5! 120

6. $_2P_2$ 2
7. $_4P_4$ 24
8. $_9P_3$ 504
9. $_{15}P_2$ 210
10. $_{28}P_4$ 491,400

11. An auto dealer has 3 models on sale. Each is available in 5 colors, with or without air-conditioning. How many different cars are available? 30

12. In how many different ways can you arrange the letters in the word DIRECT if you take the letters 3 at a time? 120

Find the value of each.

13. $_4C_2$ 6
14. $_{10}C_3$ 120
15. $_6C_3$ 20
16. $_{12}C_2$ 66
17. $_{10}C_5$ 252

18. How many combinations of 3 fish can you choose from 7 fish? 35

19. There are 52 basketball teams entered in a tournament. How many combinations can make it to the final game? 1326

A bag contains 3 green, 2 blue, 1 red, and 1 white marble. Find the probability for a marble chosen at random.

20. P(red) $\frac{1}{7}$
21. P(white) $\frac{1}{7}$
22. P(not red) $\frac{6}{7}$

23. P(green) $\frac{3}{7}$
24. P(not green) $\frac{4}{7}$
25. P(yellow) 0

26. P(not yellow) 1
27. P(green or red) $\frac{4}{7}$
28. P(red, white, or green) $\frac{5}{7}$

Kate has 24 albums: 4 by the Deltas, 6 by the Squares, 6 by the Tuscon Band, 3 by Eliot Smith, 3 by the Marks, and 2 by the Deep River Quartet. She selects one at random.

29. Find the odds in favor of selecting a record by the following.
    a. the Marks $\frac{1}{7}$ **b.** the Deep River Quartet $\frac{1}{11}$ **c.** the Squares $\frac{1}{3}$

30. Find the odds against selecting a record by the following.
    a. Eliot Smith $\frac{7}{1}$ **b.** the Tuscon Band $\frac{3}{1}$ **c.** the Squares $\frac{3}{1}$

Two game cubes are rolled. Find the probability of each.

31. **a.** The cubes show the same number. $\frac{1}{6}$
    b. The sum is 3. $\frac{1}{18}$
    c. The cubes show the same number or the sum is 3. $\frac{2}{9}$

32. **a.** The difference is 1. $\frac{5}{18}$
    b. The sum is 12. $\frac{1}{36}$
    c. The difference is 1 or the sum is 12. $\frac{11}{36}$

33. $P(A) = 0.40$, $P(B) = 0.60$, $P(A \text{ and } B) = 0.24$. Find $P(A \text{ or } B)$. 0.76

34. Find the probability that a month, chosen at random, begins with the letter J or has 30 days. $\frac{1}{2}$

35. $P(A) = 0.25$, $P(B) = 0.20$, $P(A \text{ and } B) = 0.05$. Find $P(A \text{ or } B)$. 0.40

36. Two game cubes are rolled. Find the probability of each event.
    a. The cubes show the same number. $\frac{1}{6}$ **b.** The sum is 8. $\frac{5}{36}$
    c. The cubes show the same number and the sum is 8. $\frac{1}{36}$
    d. The cubes show the same number or the sum is 8.
                                                      $\frac{5}{18}$

Are A and B independent events? If they are, find $P(A \text{ and } B)$.

37. A white game cube and a red game cube are rolled.
    $A:$ An even number comes up on the white cube.
    $B:$ A 2 comes up on the red cube. Yes, $\frac{1}{12}$

38. A bag contains 4 green marbles and 3 white marbles. A marble is drawn at random and replaced. Then a marble is drawn again.
    $A:$ The first marble is green.
    $B:$ The second marble is white. Yes, $\frac{12}{49}$

A bag contains 3 dimes, 4 nickels, and 5 pennies. One of the coins is drawn at random and is not replaced. Then a second coin is drawn. Find the probability of the events described.

39. Both coins are dimes. $\frac{1}{22}$

40. The first coin is a nickel and the second is a penny. $\frac{5}{33}$

41. The first coin is a nickel and the second is a dime. $\frac{1}{11}$

42. Both coins are nickels. $\frac{1}{11}$

A bag contains 26 cards, each with a different letter of the alphabet. One card is drawn and is not replaced. Then another card is drawn. Find the probability of the events. Assume y is a vowel.

43. Two vowels are drawn. $\frac{3}{65}$ **44.** Two consonants are drawn. $\frac{38}{65}$

45. George has had 52 hits in 125 times at bat. Estimate the probability that George will get a hit on his next time at bat. 0.416

46. An inspector on an assembly line chose 200 condensers at random out of 4000 condensers. Of the 200, 6 were defective.
    a. What is the probability that a condenser will be defective? 0.03
    b. About how many defective condensers would you expect to find in the 4000 condensers? 120 defective condensers

Extra Practice: Chapter 12

Construct a bar graph to illustrate the data in the table. Check students' graphs.

1.

Water Usage	
Activity	**Liters**
5 min shower	100
dishwasher load	50
bath	125
15 min lawn watering	275

2.

Electricity Usage	
Appliance	**Watts**
radio	75
electric shaver	15
knife sharpener	40
stereo	100

3. Using the double bar graph, determine the following. **$19 billion**
   a. The approximate amount of U.S. exports to Japan
   b. The approximate amount of U.S. imports from Canada **$38 billion**
   c. The country with the greatest difference between imports and exports **Japan**
   d. The total amount of U.S. exports to Mexico and France **$16 billion**

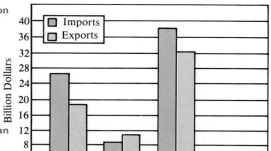

Trade with U.S. (1979)

4. Construct a line graph to illustrate the data in the table. Check students' graphs.

Rollerskating Rink Association Membership								
Year	1940	1945	1950	1955	1960	1965	1970	1975
Membership	147	200	287	328	610	522	555	963

5. Using the double line graph, determine the following.
   a. In which year were the two league pennant winners closest in percent of games won? farthest apart? **1941; 1961**
   b. In which year did the National League pennant winner win a larger percent of games? **1901**

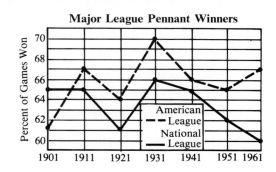

Major League Pennant Winners

Find the range, mean, median, and mode of each set of data. Round to the nearest tenth if necessary.

6. 14, 9, 7, 5, 4, 4, 1 13; 6.3; 5; 4

7. 40, 55, 37, 34, 30, 42 25; 39.7; 38.5; none

8. 106, 109, 84, 111, 95 27; 101; 106; none

9. 18.2, 11.6, 9.5, 12.3, 16.1, 12.5 8.7; 13.4; 12.4; none

Insert a new number into each set of data so that the mean of the resulting set is 13.

10. 10, 18, 22 2

11. 5, 8, 12 27

12. 6, 11, 15 20

Use the following data to make a frequency distribution. Then find the range, mean, median, and mode. Round to the nearest tenth if necessary. Check students' frequency distributions.

13. 8, 7, 9, 9, 8, 10, 11, 12, 7, 7, 7, 10, 9, 10, 8, 10, 11, 9, 12, 9 5; 9.2; 9; 9

14. 25, 35, 30, 25, 35, 35, 40, 25, 40, 45, 35, 45, 45 20; 35.4; 35; 35

Exercises 15–18 refer to the histogram at the right.

15. How many kilograms of wool were produced in all? 292 kg

16. How many shearings produced less than 10 kg of wool? 6 shearings

17. Find the range, mean, median, and mode of the data. Round to the nearest tenth if necessary. 8; 10.4; 10; 12

18. Make a frequency polygon for the data. Check students' graphs.

Wool Production of Merino Sheep

X represents the possible values of a random variable and $P(X)$ represents their probabilities of occurrence. Find the expected value of X.

19.

X	5	10	15	20
P(X)	$\frac{1}{8}$	$\frac{2}{8}$	$\frac{3}{8}$	$\frac{2}{8}$

$13\frac{3}{4}$, or 13.75

20.

X	−2	1	3	5
P(X)	0.1	0.2	0.3	0.4

2.9

21. A set of cards is numbered 1 through 8, one number per card. X is the number on a card drawn at random. $4\frac{1}{2}$ or 4.5

Extra Practice　**497**

Table of Square Roots of Integers from 1 to 100

Number	Positive Square Root	Number	Positive Square Root	Number	Positive Square Root	Number	Positive Square Root
N	$\sqrt{N}$	N	$\sqrt{N}$	N	$\sqrt{N}$	N	$\sqrt{N}$
1	1	26	5.099	51	7.141	76	8.718
2	1.414	27	5.196	52	7.211	77	8.775
3	1.732	28	5.292	53	7.280	78	8.832
4	2	29	5.385	54	7.348	79	8.888
5	2.236	30	5.477	55	7.416	80	8.944
6	2.449	31	5.568	56	7.483	81	9
7	2.646	32	5.657	57	7.550	82	9.055
8	2.828	33	5.745	58	7.616	83	9.110
9	3	34	5.831	59	7.681	84	9.165
10	3.162	35	5.916	60	7.746	85	9.220
11	3.317	36	6	61	7.810	86	9.274
12	3.464	37	6.083	62	7.874	87	9.327
13	3.606	38	6.164	63	7.937	88	9.381
14	3.742	39	6.245	64	8	89	9.434
15	3.873	40	6.325	65	8.062	90	9.487
16	4	41	6.403	66	8.124	91	9.539
17	4.123	42	6.481	67	8.185	92	9.592
18	4.243	43	6.557	68	8.246	93	9.644
19	4.359	44	6.633	69	8.307	94	9.695
20	4.472	45	6.708	70	8.367	95	9.747
21	4.583	46	6.782	71	8.426	96	9.798
22	4.690	47	6.856	72	8.485	97	9.849
23	4.796	48	6.928	73	8.544	98	9.899
24	4.899	49	7	74	8.602	99	9.950
25	5	50	7.071	75	8.660	100	10

Exact square roots are shown in red. For the others, rational approximations are given correct to three decimal places.

Table of Trigonometric Ratios

Angle	Sine	Cosine	Tangent	Angle	Sine	Cosine	Tangent
1°	.0175	.9998	.0175	46°	.7193	.6947	1.0355
2°	.0349	.9994	.0349	47°	.7314	.6820	1.0724
3°	.0523	.9986	.0524	48°	.7431	.6691	1.1106
4°	.0698	.9976	.0699	49°	.7547	.6561	1.1504
5°	.0872	.9962	.0875	50°	.7660	.6428	1.1918
6°	.1045	.9945	.1051	51°	.7771	.6293	1.2349
7°	.1219	.9925	.1228	52°	.7880	.6157	1.2799
8°	.1392	.9903	.1405	53°	.7986	.6018	1.3270
9°	.1564	.9877	.1584	54°	.8090	.5878	1.3764
10°	.1736	.9848	.1763	55°	.8192	.5736	1.4281
11°	.1908	.9816	.1944	56°	.8290	.5592	1.4826
12°	.2079	.9781	.2126	57°	.8387	.5446	1.5399
13°	.2250	.9744	.2309	58°	.8480	.5299	1.6003
14°	.2419	.9703	.2493	59°	.8572	.5150	1.6643
15°	.2588	.9659	.2679	60°	.8660	.5000	1.7321
16°	.2756	.9613	.2867	61°	.8746	.4848	1.8040
17°	.2924	.9563	.3057	62°	.8829	.4695	1.8807
18°	.3090	.9511	.3249	63°	.8910	.4540	1.9626
19°	.3256	.9455	.3443	64°	.8988	.4384	2.0503
20°	.3420	.9397	.3640	65°	.9063	.4226	2.1445
21°	.3584	.9336	.3839	66°	.9135	.4067	2.2460
22°	.3746	.9272	.4040	67°	.9205	.3907	2.3559
23°	.3907	.9205	.4245	68°	.9272	.3746	2.4751
24°	.4067	.9135	.4452	69°	.9336	.3584	2.6051
25°	.4226	.9063	.4663	70°	.9397	.3420	2.7475
26°	.4384	.8988	.4877	71°	.9455	.3256	2.9042
27°	.4540	.8910	.5095	72°	.9511	.3090	3.0777
28°	.4695	.8829	.5317	73°	.9563	.2924	3.2709
29°	.4848	.8746	.5543	74°	.9613	.2756	3.4874
30°	.5000	.8660	.5774	75°	.9659	.2588	3.7321
31°	.5150	.8572	.6009	76°	.9703	.2419	4.0108
32°	.5299	.8480	.6249	77°	.9744	.2250	4.3315
33°	.5446	.8387	.6494	78°	.9781	.2079	4.7046
34°	.5592	.8290	.6745	79°	.9816	.1908	5.1446
35°	.5736	.8192	.7002	80°	.9848	.1736	5.6713
36°	.5878	.8090	.7265	81°	.9877	.1564	6.3138
37°	.6018	.7986	.7536	82°	.9903	.1392	7.1154
38°	.6157	.7880	.7813	83°	.9925	.1219	8.1443
39°	.6293	.7771	.8098	84°	.9945	.1045	9.5144
40°	.6428	.7660	.8391	85°	.9962	.0872	11.4301
41°	.6561	.7547	.8693	86°	.9976	.0698	14.3007
42°	.6691	.7431	.9004	87°	.9986	.0523	19.0811
43°	.6820	.7314	.9325	88°	.9994	.0349	28.6363
44°	.6947	.7193	.9657	89°	.9998	.0175	57.2900
45°	.7071	.7071	1.0000	90°	1.0000	.0000	Undefined

Summary of Formulas

Circumference

$C = \pi d$

$C = 2\pi r$

Area

Rectangle: $A = lw$

Triangle: $A = \frac{1}{2}bh$

Parallelogram: $A = bh$

Trapezoid: $A = \frac{1}{2}(b_1 + b_2)h$

Circle: $A = \pi r^2$

Volume

Prism: $V = Bh$

Cylinder: $V = \pi r^2 h$

Pyramid: $V = \frac{1}{3}Bh$

Cone: $V = \frac{1}{3}\pi r^2 h$

Sphere: $V = \frac{4}{3}\pi r^3$

Lateral Area

Prism: lateral area = perimeter of base × height

Cylinder: lateral area = $2\pi rh$

Surface Area

Prism: total surface area = lateral area + area of bases

Cylinder: total surface area = $2\pi rh + 2\pi r^2$

Sphere: $A = 4\pi r^2$

Mass

Mass = Density × Volume

Distance

distance = rate × time

Percentage

percentage = rate × base

Interest

Interest = Principal × rate × time

APPENDIX A: Estimation

Sometimes solving a problem involves long and repetitive calculations. To avoid doing these, it is often possible to use **estimation.** We *estimate* when we need to find only an approximate answer to a problem or to test the reasonableness of the calculated answer. For example, suppose that we want to find the total number of rainy days this summer, and it rained 7 days in June, 12 days in July, and 9 days in August. To find the sum we approximate each number. Notice that the numbers all *cluster* around, or are close to, 10. Thus the sum is about 10 + 10 + 10, or 30. There were approximately 30 rainy days this summer.

Estimation strategies that are frequently used include *rounding, clustering, front-end estimation,* and choosing *compatible numbers.* The example above illustrates the use of *clustering* in estimation. The **clustering** method is appropriate to use when finding a sum in which the addends are all close to the same number.

EXAMPLE 1 Estimate the total grocery bill for the following items.
$2.19, $1.88, $1.79, $2.31, $1.74, $1.98, $2.08, $2.26

Solution Each item costs about $2.00.
The total grocery bill will be close to 8 × $2.00, or $16.00.

Front-end estimation helps us to add or subtract numbers quickly. Determine the highest place value shown for the given numbers. Add or subtract all the digits in that place value. Then adjust the answer by calculating with the digits in the next highest place value.

EXAMPLE 2 Fabric remnants are on sale for $.50 per yard. One bundle has 3 pieces of fabric, all having the same width but with lengths $1\frac{2}{3}$ yd, $1\frac{5}{8}$ yd, and 1 yd. About how much does the bundle cost?

Solution When working with fractions, first add the whole numbers.

$$1\frac{2}{3}$$
$$1\frac{5}{8}$$
$$\underline{+1}$$
$$3$$

Then compensate for the fractions. Both $\frac{2}{3}$ and $\frac{5}{8}$ are close to $\frac{1}{2}$ so that the sum $\frac{2}{3} + \frac{5}{8}$ is about equal to the sum $\frac{1}{2} + \frac{1}{2}$, or 1. Thus the bundle contains around 3 + 1, or 4, yards. Since each yard costs $.50, the bundle costs about 4 × $.50, or $2.00.

Rounding is a common way of estimating. Refer to pages 48–49 for a detailed explanation of rounding. When rounding more than one number in order to estimate an answer, round each number to its highest place value. This allows for fast computation.

EXAMPLE 3   Denise Crosby earns a salary of $214.33 each week. Deductions of $20.28 for federal income tax, $7.94 for state income tax, and $14.61 for Social Security are taken from her pay. About how much money does Denise take home each week?

Solution   Round each deduction and then add the deductions.
Round $20.28 to $20, $7.94 to $8, and $14.61 to $10.

$$20 + 8 + 10 = 38$$

The total deductions are close to $38.

Subtract the total from the salary.

Round $214.33 to $200 and $38 to $40.

$$200 - 40 = 160$$

Denise takes home about $160 each week.

Choosing **compatible numbers** makes solving multiplication and division problems simpler. Select numbers that are easy to multiply or divide and that are close to the actual numbers.

EXAMPLE 4   A recent survey shows that about 23% of a class will vote for Bill Donnway for class treasurer. If 768 students vote, about how many can be expected to vote for Bill?

Solution   Find an estimate for 23% of 768. First change the percent to one that is close to 23% and that can be converted easily to a fraction. 23% is about 25%, or $\frac{1}{4}$. Then choose a number close to 768 that has 4 as a factor. Pick 800.

$$23\% \text{ of } 768 \longrightarrow \tfrac{1}{4} \times 800 = 200$$

About 200 students will vote for Bill Donnway.

Exercises

Select the best estimate.

A   **1.** 0.16 + 2.34 + 9.5

   a. 0.12   **b.** 1.2   **c.** 12   **d.** 120

   2. 4.01 × 8.2

   a. 0.32   **b.** 3.2   **c.** 12   **d.** 32

Select the best estimate.

3. $72,197 - 38,846$
   a. 300
   b. 3000
   c. 30,000 ✓
   d. 300,000

4. $4213 \div 6.7$
   a. 0.6
   b. 6.0
   c. 60
   d. 600 ✓

B 5. $489.233 + 256.1 + 133.26$
   a. 90
   b. 900 ✓
   c. 9000
   d. 90,000

6. $\dfrac{7}{16} \times 6104$
   a. 30
   b. 300
   c. 3000 ✓
   d. 30,000

7. 18% of 3477
   a. 0.7
   b. 7
   c. 70
   d. 700 ✓

8. $\dfrac{7}{12} + \dfrac{4}{10}$
   a. 1 ✓
   b. 2
   c. 11
   d. 22

C 9. $\$32.14 \div 0.78$
   a. $.04
   b. $4
   c. $40 ✓
   d. $400

10. $0.04 + 0.0006 + 1.009$
   a. 0.019
   b. 0.05
   c. 0.1
   d. 1 ✓

Problems

Estimate each answer.   Answers may vary. Accept reasonable answers.

A 1. Garth takes $1\frac{7}{12}$ hours to ride his bicycle to the lake. He rides around the lake in $2\frac{2}{3}$ hours. About how much more time does he take to ride around the lake than to the lake?   **1 hour**

2. What is the greatest number of cassette tapes costing $6.45 each that Carolyn can buy with $20.00?   **3 tapes**

B 3. The digits in the product of 3.008×2.79 are 839232. Where should the decimal point be placed?   **8.39232**

4. At Parts Inc. 0.023 of the parts built are defective. About how many of the 4140 parts built in an average day are defective?   **100 parts**

C 5. A $489.66 VCR is on sale for 18% off. Approximately what is the sale price?   **$400**

6. To get the most for his money, should Adam buy 60 vitamins for $6.82 or 90 of the same vitamins for $8.85?   **90 vitamins for $8.85**

Glossary

Absolute value (p. 72) The distance from 0 to the graph of a number on the number line.

Acute angle (p. 191) An angle with measure between 0° and 90°.

Acute triangle (p. 204) A triangle with three acute angles.

Adjacent angles (p. 192) Two angles with a common side and a common vertex, but with no common points in their interiors.

Alternate interior angles (p. 200) One of two pairs of angles formed when a transversal intersects two lines. In the diagram, $\angle 1$ and $\angle 4$ are one such pair, and $\angle 2$ and $\angle 3$ are the other.

Angle (p. 191) A figure formed by two rays with a common endpoint.

Annual rate of interest (p. 260) A percent of the principal figured on a yearly basis.

Arc (p. 187) A part of a circle.

Area (p. 306) Amount of surface, measured in square units.

Base of a geometric figure (pp. 306, 312, 326, 331) A selected side or face.

Base, numerical (p. 40) A number that is raised to some power. In 5^3, 5 is the base.

Base, in percent relationship (p. 245) The number of which a percent is taken.

Bisect (p. 192) To divide a geometric figure into two congruent parts.

Capacity (p. 327) A measure of the volume of a container.

Center (pp. 187, 340) The point that lies equidistant from all points on a circle or a sphere.

Chord (p. 187) A segment that joins two points on a circle.

Circle (p. 187) A plane figure made up of all points that are the same distance from a given point in the plane.

Circumference (p. 188) The perimeter of a circle.

Collinear points (p. 182) Two or more points that lie on the same line.

Combination (p. 401) An arrangement of a group of things in which order does not matter.

Complementary angles (p. 195) Two angles whose measures have a sum of 90°.

Conditional probability (p. 424) The probability that an event B will occur given that an event A has occurred.

Cone (p. 331) A closed figure formed by a circular region and a curved surface that comes to a point.

Congruent figures (pp. 182, 191, 217) Figures that have the same size and shape.

Coordinate (p. 12) The number paired with a point on the number line.

Coordinate plane (p. 272) A plane marked with two perpendicular number lines, used to graph ordered pairs of numbers.

Coplanar (p. 183) Lying in the same plane.

Corresponding angles (p. 200) One of four pairs of angles formed when two lines are cut by a transversal, for example, $\angle 1$ and $\angle 5$, $\angle 2$ and $\angle 6$, $\angle 3$ and $\angle 7$, and $\angle 4$ and $\angle 8$.

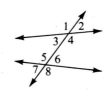

Cosine of an angle (p. 378) If $\angle A$ is one of the acute angles in a right triangle, the cosine of $\angle A$ (cos A) is the ratio of the length of the side adjacent to $\angle A$ to the length of the hypotenuse.

Cylinder (p. 327) A geometric solid with two parallel bases that are congruent and one curved surface joining the bases.

Density (p. 344) The mass per unit volume of a substance.

Dependent events (p. 424) Two events in which the result of the first affects the result of the second.

Diagonal (p. 210) A segment that joins two nonconsecutive vertices of a polygon.

Diameter (pp. 187, 340) A chord that contains the center of a circle or a sphere. Also, the length of such a chord.

Endpoint (p. 182) The point at the end of a line segment or ray.

Equation (p. 9) A mathematical sentence with an equals sign to indicate that two expressions name the same number.

Equilateral triangle (p. 205) A triangle in which all sides are congruent.

Equivalent equations (p. 146) Equations that have the same solution.

Equivalent fractions (p. 110) Fractions that name the same number.

Equivalent inequalities (p. 159) Inequalities that have the same solutions.

Evaluate an expression (p. 3) To replace a variable in an expression with one of its values and then complete the indicated arithmetic.

Expanded form (p. 44) The method of representing a number as the sum of products of each digit and powers of 10.

Exponent (p. 40) A number indicating how many times the base is used as a factor.

Extremes of a proportion (p. 230) The first and last terms of a proportion.

Faces of a polyhedron (p. 326) The parts of planes that make up the sides and bases of a polyhedron.

Factor (p. 40) Any of two or more whole numbers that are multiplied to form a product.

Frequency (p. 453) The number of times that one item appears in a set of data.

Frequency distribution (p. 453) A table that pairs each item in a set of data with its frequency.

Frequency polygon (p. 457) A line graph of frequencies, connected to the horizontal axis at each end to form a polygon.

Function (p. 277) A set of ordered pairs in which no two different ordered pairs have the same x-coordinate.

Geometric construction (p. 184) A geometric drawing for which only a compass and a straightedge may be used.

Graph of an equation (p. 280) The line consisting of all points whose coordinates satisfy the equation.

Graph of a number (p. 12) The point on the number line paired with the number.

Grouping symbols (p. 5) Symbols such as parentheses, ( ), and brackets, [ ], that are used to group expressions.

Height (p. 306) The perpendicular distance between the bases of a geometric figure. In triangles, cones, and pyramids, the perpendicular distance from the base to the opposite vertex.

Histogram (p. 457) A bar graph that shows a frequency distribution.

Hypotenuse (p. 364) The side opposite the right angle in a right triangle.

Improper fraction (p. 111) A positive fraction whose numerator is greater than or equal to its denominator, or the opposite of such a fraction.

Independent events (p. 420) Events that have no effect on each other.

Inequality (p. 12) A mathematical sentence formed by placing an inequality sign between two expressions.

Integers (p. 72) The whole numbers and their opposites: $\ldots, {}^-2, {}^-1, 0, 1, 2, \ldots$.

Interest (p. 174) The amount of money paid for the use of money.

Interpolation (p. 361) A method of approximation.

Inverse operations (p. 16) Operations that undo each other, such as addition and subtraction or multiplication and division.

Irrational number (p. 133) All real numbers that are not rational.

Isosceles triangle (p. 205) A triangle with at least two sides congruent.

Lateral area (p. 335) The surface area of a solid, not including the bases.

Lateral surface (p. 335) The faces other than the bases of a solid.

Least common denominator (LCD) (p. 115) The least common multiple of two or more denominators.

Legs of a right triangle (p. 364) The two sides forming the right angle.

Like terms (p. 56) Terms in which only the numerical coefficients are different.

Line (p. 182) A figure determined by two points and extending in both directions without end.

Line segment (p. 182) Two points on a line and all the points between them.

Linear equation in two variables (p. 281) An equation with two variables that can be written in the form $ax + by = c$, where a and b are not both 0.

Lowest terms (p. 111) A fraction is in lowest terms when the numerator and the denominator have no common factor but 1.

Mass (p. 344) The measure of the amount of matter an object contains.

Mean (p. 449) The value found by dividing the sum of a group of numbers by the number of numbers in the group. Also called *average*.

Means of a proportion (p. 230) The second and third terms of a proportion.

Median (p. 449) The number that falls in the middle when data are listed from least to greatest. If the number of data is even, the median is the mean of the two middle items.

Midpoint (p. 182) The point of a segment that divides it into two congruent segments.

Mixed number (p. 111) A whole number plus a proper fraction.

Mode (p. 449) The number that occurs most often in a set of data.

Number sentence (p. 9) An equation or inequality indicating the relationship between two mathematical expressions.

Numerical coefficient (p. 3) In an expression such as $3ab$, the number 3 is the numerical coefficient of ab.

Numerical expression (p. 2) An expression that names a number, such as $2 + 3$.

Obtuse angle (p. 191) An angle with measure between $90°$ and $180°$.

Obtuse triangle (p. 204) A triangle that has one obtuse angle.

Odds (p. 409) A ratio that compares the probability of an event occurring and the probability of the event not occurring.

Open sentence (p. 9) A mathematical sentence that contains one or more variables.

Opposites (p. 72) A pair of numbers such as $^-4$ and 4.

Ordered pair of numbers (p. 272) A pair of numbers whose order is important.

Origin (pp. 12, 272) The graph of zero on a number line or in a rectangular coordinate plane.

Outcome (p. 404) The result of an event.

Parallel lines (p. 200) Lines in the same plane that do not intersect.

Parallelogram (p. 209) A quadrilateral with both pairs of opposite sides parallel.

Percent (p. 241) A ratio of a number to 100, shown by the symbol %.

Percent of change (p. 249) The amount of change divided by the original amount.

Percentage (p. 245) The number that results from taking a percent of another number.

Perfect square (p. 356) A number whose square root is an integer.

Perimeter (p. 188) The distance around a plane figure.

Permutation (p. 396) An arrangement of a group of things in a particular order.

Perpendicular lines (p. 195) Two lines that intersect to form four right angles.

Plane (p. 183) A flat surface extending infinitely in all directions.

Point (p. 182) The simplest figure in geometry, representing an exact location.

Polygon (p. 213) A closed plane figure made up of line segments.

Polyhedron (p. 326) A three-dimensional figure formed of polygonal parts of planes.

Prime number (p. 111) A whole number greater than 1 that has only two whole-number factors, itself and 1.

Principal (p. 260) An amount of money on which interest is paid.

Prism (p. 326) A polyhedron that has two parallel, congruent faces called bases. The other faces are parallelograms.

Probability (p. 404) The ratio of the number of outcomes favoring an event to the total number of possible outcomes.

Proper fraction (p. 111) A positive fraction whose numerator is less than its denominator, or the opposite of such a fraction.

Proportion (p. 230) An equation stating that two ratios are equal.

Protractor (p. 191) A device used to measure angles.

Pyramid (p. 331) A polyhedron that has a polygonal base and three or more triangular faces.

Quadrilateral (p. 209) A polygon with four sides.

Radical (p. 373) An expression such as $\sqrt{5}$ or $\sqrt{a}$.

Radius (pp. 187, 340) A line segment joining any point on a circle or sphere to the center. Also the length of that segment.

Random variable (p. 461) A variable whose value is determined by the outcome of a random experiment.

Range (p. 449) The difference between the greatest and the least numbers in a set of data.

Rate (p. 234) A ratio that compares quantities of different kinds of units.

Ratio (p. 230) An indicated quotient of two numbers.

Ray (p. 182) A part of a line with one endpoint.

Real number (p. 133) Any number that is either a rational number or an irrational number.

Reciprocals (p. 126) Two numbers whose product is 1.

Rectangle (p. 209) A quadrilateral with four right angles.

Regular polygon (p. 213) A polygon in which all sides are congruent and all angles are congruent.

Relation (p. 294) A set of ordered pairs.

Relatively prime numbers (p. 111) Two or more numbers that have no other common factor but 1.

Rhombus (p. 209) A parallelogram in which all sides are congruent.

Right angle (p. 191) An angle with measure 90°.

Right triangle (p. 204) A triangle with a right angle.

Rigid motions (p. 217) Motions such as rotation, translation, and reflection, used to move a figure to a new position without changing its shape or size.

Sampling (p. 428) A method used to estimate probability by selecting a part of a larger group.

Scalene triangle (p. 205) A triangle with no two sides congruent.

Scientific notation (p. 98) A method of expressing a number as the product of a power of 10 and a number between 1 and 10.

Segment (p. 182) *See* line segment.

Semicircle (p. 187) Half of a circle.

Sides of an equation (p. 9) The mathematical expressions to the right and to the left of the equals sign.

Sides of a figure (pp. 191, 212) The rays that form an angle or the segments that form a polygon.

Similar figures (p. 368) Figures that have the same shape but not necessarily the same size.

Simple form (p. 111) A mixed number is in simple form if its fractional part is expressed in lowest terms.

Simplify an expression (p. 2) To replace an expression with its simplest name.

Sine of an angle (p. 378) If $\angle A$ is an acute angle of a right triangle, the sine of $\angle A$ (sin A) is the ratio of the length of the side opposite $\angle A$ to the length of the hypotenuse.

Slope of a line (p. 288) The steepness of a line; that is, of the change in the y-coordinate to the change in the x-coordinate when moving from one point on a line to another point.

Solid (p. 326) An enclosed region of space bounded by planes.

Solution (p. 9) A value of a variable that makes an equation or inequality a true sentence.

Solving a right triangle (p. 382) The process of finding the measures of the sides and angles of a right triangle.

Sphere (p. 340) A figure in space made up of all points equidistant from a given point.

Square (p. 209) A rectangle with all four sides congruent.

Square root of a number (p. 356) One of the two equal factors of the number.

Statistical measures (p. 449) Measures including the range, mean, median, and mode used to analyze numerical data.

Supplementary angles (p. 196) Two angles whose measures have a sum of $180°$.

Surface area (p. 335) The total area of a solid.

Symmetric (pp. 321, 322) A figure is symmetric with respect to a line if it can be folded on that line so that every point on one side coincides exactly with a point on the other side. A figure is symmetric with respect to a point O if for each point A on the figure there is a point B on the figure for which O is the midpoint of $\overline{AB}$.

System of equations (p. 284) A set of two or more equations in the same variables.

Tangent of an angle (p. 378) If $\angle A$ is an acute angle of a right triangle, the tangent of $\angle A$ (tan A) is the ratio of the length of the side opposite $\angle A$ to the length of the side adjacent to $\angle A$.

Terms of an expression (p. 3) The parts of a mathematical expression that are separated by a $+$ sign.

Terms of a proportion (p. 230) The numbers in a proportion.

Transform an equation or inequality (pp. 146, 159) To rewrite an equation or inequality as an equivalent equation or inequality.

Transversal (p. 200) A line that intersects two other lines.

Trapezoid (p. 210) A quadrilateral with exactly one pair of parallel sides.

Triangle (p. 204) A polygon with three sides.

Trigonometric ratios (p. 378) Any of the sine, cosine, and tangent ratios.

Value of a variable (p. 2) Any number that a variable represents.

Variable (p. 2) A symbol used to represent one or more numbers.

Variable expression (p. 2) A mathematical expression that contains a variable.

Vertex of an angle (p. 191) The common endpoint of two intersecting rays.

Vertex of a polygon or polyhedron (pp. 204, 331) The point at which two sides of a polygon or three or more edges of a polyhedron intersect.

Vertical angles (p. 197) The angles opposite each other when two lines intersect to form four angles.

Volume (p. 326) A measure of the space occupied by a solid.

x-axis (p. 272) The horizontal number line on a coordinate plane.

x-coordinate (p. 272) The first number in an ordered pair of numbers that designates the location of a point on the coordinate plane. Also called the *abscissa*.

y-axis (p. 272) The vertical number line on a coordinate plane.

y-coordinate (p. 272) The second number in an ordered pair of numbers that designates the location of a point on the coordinate plane. Also called the *ordinate*.

Index

Credits

Mechanical art: ANCO. Cover concept: Kirchoff/Wohlberg, Inc., cover photograph:
Balthazar Korab. Page 1, Gregory Heisler/Gamma-Liaison; 30, Milt & Joan Mann/The
Marilyn Gartman Agency; 39, © Peter Menzel/Stock, Boston; 62, Ben Rose © 1982/The
Image Bank; 71, W.K. Almond/Stock, Boston; 83, Clyde H. Smith/Peter Arnold Inc.; 87,
Gary Milburn/Tom Stack & Associates; 98, NASA; 105, © Paulo Bonino 1982/ Photo
Researchers, Inc.; 114, Judy Gibbs; 120, © Alvis Upitis/The Image Bank; 129, Greig
Cranna; 136, Rainbow; 143, Courtesy of French National Railroads; 172, Miguel/The
Image Bank; 174, Thomas Hovland/Grant Heilman Photography; 181, © Ted
Kawalerski/The Image Bank; 190, 222, NASA; 229, Peter Arnold, Inc.; 237, Benn
Mitchell © 1981/The Image Bank; 239, © 1980 Al Satterwhite/The Image Bank; 253, ©
John Lee/The Image Bank; 266, Greig Cranna; 271, Photo Courtesy of LEXIDATA; 292,
© Lou Jones 1981/The Image Bank; 305, Runk/Schoenberger/Grant Heilman
Photography; 310, © Joe Munroe/Photo Researchers, Inc.; 342, © Van Bucher
1982/Photo Researchers, Inc.; 348, © Dick Davis 1972/Photo Researchers, Inc.; 355, ©
Eunice Harris 1983/Photo Researchers, Inc.; 363, Milt & Joan Mann/The Marilyn
Gartman Agency; 377, © 1979 Stuart Cohen/Stock, Boston; 388, © C.B. Jones
1982/Taurus Photos; 395, © David W. Hamilton/The Image Bank; 403, Mike
Mazzaschi/Stock, Boston; 419, David Muench Photography; 430, © 1982 Arnold
Zann/Black Star; 439, Animals Animals/Robert C. Fields; 448, © Werner H.
Müller/Peter Arnold, Inc.; 455, © Gordon E. Smith 1980/Photo Researchers, Inc.; 460,
© Tom McHugh 1979/Photo Researchers, Inc.; 464, Russ Kinne/Photo Researchers, Inc.

Answers to Selected Exercises

1 Introduction to Algebra

PAGE 4 WRITTEN EXERCISES **1.** 48
3. 105 **5.** 14.15 **7.** 4.5 **9.** 25 **11.** 4 **13.** 12
15. 27 **17.** 2 **19.** 47 **21.** 26 **23.** 512 **25.** 9
27. 24 **29.** 2.5 **31.** 112.5 **33.** 680.805
35. 3.15 **37.** 2

PAGE 4 REVIEW EXERCISES **1.** 51.87
3. 45.93 **5.** 0.27 **7.** 6.3

PAGES 7–8 WRITTEN EXERCISES **1.** 92
3. 51 **5.** 2 **7.** 126 **9.** 7 **11.** 36 **13.** 10
15. 70 **17.** 36 **19.** 196 **21.** 3 **23.** 1512
25. 91 **27.** 84 **29.** 0.5 **31.** 4.1 **33.** 5827.248
35. 14.6 **37.** $2x \times (y - 4) + 2x$; or
$2x \times y - (4 + 2)x$
39. $x \times (y + z \div 3 + 1) - z$

PAGE 8 REVIEW EXERCISES **1.** 24
3. 13.2 **5.** 2040 **7.** 1.3 **9.** 0.63

PAGE 8 CALCULATOR KEY-IN **1.** 288
3. 16.5 **5.** 6048

PAGES 10–11 WRITTEN EXERCISES
1. True **3.** False **5.** False **7.** True **9.** False
11. 6 **13.** 85 **15.** 29 **17.** 8 **19.** No solution
21. No solution **23.** 1518 **25.** 17 **27.** 11
29. 51 **31.** 12 **33.** 9 **35.** 2 **37.** No solution
39. 4 For exercises 41 and 43, answers will
vary. An example is given. **41.** $3x - 25 = 5$
43. $400 \div x + 16 = 20$ **45.** $+, -$ **47.** $+, \div$
49. $-, -, +$; or $+, \div, -$; or $\div, -, \times$
51. $-, +, \div$

PAGE 11 REVIEW EXERCISES **1.** 588
3. 8 **5.** 60 **7.** 172

PAGES 13–15 WRITTEN EXERCISES

1.

3.

5.

7. $>$ **9.** $>$ **11.** $>$ **13.** $>$ **15.** $<$ **17.** $>$
19. $18 < 32 < 46$, or $46 > 32 > 18$
21. $103 < 130 < 310$, or $310 > 130 > 103$
23. $689 < 698 < 986$, or $986 > 698 > 689$

25.

27.

29.

31. No solution

33.

35.

37. 0, 1, 2, 3, . . . , 11 **39.** 6, 7, 8, and so on
41. 25, 26, 27, and so on **43.** 66, 67, 68, and
so on **45.** 11, 12, 13, 14, 15, 16, 17, 18 **47.** 22,
23, 24, 25, 26, 27, 28 **49.** 104, 105, 106, 107,
108, 109, 110, 111, 112, 113, 114, 115, 116, 117
51. 5, 10 **53.** No solution **55.** 23 **57.** 4, 10
59. 14 **61.** No solution **63.** 5, 6, 7, 8, 9
65. 5, 6, 7, 8, 9, 10 **67.** 3, 4, 5, 6

PAGE 15 REVIEW EXERCISES **1.** 21.9
3. 6.17 **5.** 91.5 **7.** 0.9 **9.** 0.00644

PAGES 18–19 WRITTEN EXERCISES
1. $x = 15 - 8$; 7 **3.** $f = 74 - 38$; 36 **5.** $y = 14 + 9$; 23 **7.** $b = 32 + 25$; 57 **9.** $c = 27 \div 3$;
9 **11.** $m = 108 \div 9$; 12 **13.** $n = 9 \times 6$; 54
15. $g = 7 \times 16$; 112 **17.** $a = 17 - 17$; 0
19. $n = 42 \div 14$; 3 **21.** $h = 297 \times 11$; 3267
23. $d = 110 + 87$; 197 **25.** $q = 465 \div 31$; 15
27. $p = 358 - 208$; 150 **29.** $c = 536 - 511$; 25
31. $g = 401 + 19$; 420 **33.** $r > 12 - 8$; all the
numbers greater than 4 **35.** $p \geq 36 \div 4$; all
the numbers greater than or equal to 9
37. $q \leq 59 + 24$; all the numbers less than or
equal to 83 **39.** $a < 340 \times 17$; all the numbers
less than 5780 **41.** $c \leq 177 - 113$; all the
numbers less than or equal to 64 **43.** $t \geq 9 +$
55; all the numbers greater than or equal to 64
45. $y < 20 \times 80$; all the numbers less than
1600 **47.** $x > 86 \div 43$; all the numbers greater
than 2 **49.** 5 **51.** 11 **53.** 46 **55.** 67.5
57. 56 **59.** 63 **61.** All the numbers less than
or equal to 10.8 **63.** All the numbers greater
than or equal to 8 **65.** All the numbers less
than 32

PAGE 19 SELF-TEST A **1.** 25.8 **2.** 5.75
3. 2.46 **4.** 7.6 **5.** 46 **6.** 15 **7.** 168 **8.** 50
9. 6 **10.** 2 **11.** 9 **12.** 4 **13.** 6 **14.** 29
15. 8 **16.** No solution **17.** 3 **18.** $>$ **19.** $<$
20. $=$ **21.** 0, 1, 2, 3, 4 **22.** 85, 86, 87, and so
on **23.** 19, 20, 21, 22, 23, 24, 25, 26, 27
24. $g = 12 + 32$; 44 **25.** $d < 112 \div 7$; all the

numbers less than 16   **26.** $5a = 49 - 4$; $a = 45 \div 5$; 9

PAGES 22–23 WRITTEN EXERCISES
1. $8b$ **3.** $53 - d$ **5.** $30 + t$ **7.** $g + 9$
9. $78 - m$ **11.** $19 + n$ **13.** $d \div 11$
15. $12 - z$ **17.** $15 + 11t$ **19.** $(m + n) \times 91$
21. $r \div (83 - 10)$ **23.** $c(3 + 9 + 12)$
25. $(60 + 40 + 10) \div d$ **27.** $b + 3$ **29.** $x + 6$
31. $0.25q$ **33.** $x \div 60$ **35.** $x - 10$

PAGE 23 REVIEW EXERCISES   **1.** 27
3. 576   **5.** All the numbers greater than 72
7. All the numbers less than or equal to 14

PAGES 25–26 WRITTEN EXERCISES
1. $5d > 20$ **3.** $3w - 7 = 8$ **5.** $5 + 6r < 42$
7. $n - 1 < 5$ **9.** $2n \div 3 = 15$ **11.** $(4 + x) \div 2 = 34$ **13.** $a(6 - 1) = a$ **15.** $59 - x > 2x + 3$
17. $(y + 12)5 = 100$ **19.** $(b \div 8) + 9 < 30$
21. $2n = (n + 4)8$ **23. a.** $2x = 32$ **b.** 16
25. a. $10y - 6 \geq 25$ **b.** 4, 5

PAGE 26 REVIEW EXERCISES   **1.** 22
3. 108   **5.** 2   **7.** $\frac{23}{7}$, or $3\frac{2}{7}$ **9.** 33.66

PAGES 29–31 PROBLEMS   **1.** 11.65 m
3. $2824.80   **5.** $41,520   **7.** 936 people
9. $78.87   **11.** $1596   **13.** $89,336   **15.** $23.29
17. $12.75

PAGE 31 SELF-TEST B   **1.** $12 \div y$
2. $x - 5$ **3.** $9g - 21$ **4.** $15 = 9 + 2x$
5. $25(b + 7) > 11 \div 4$ **6.** $24 - 4n \leq 12$
7. $114.15   **8.** 49 passengers

PAGE 33 ENRICHMENT   **1.** Answers vary.

PAGE 34 CHAPTER REVIEW   **1.** B   **3.** A
5. True   **7.** True   **9.** True   **11.** True   **13.** True
15. B   **17.** D   **19.** d

**PAGES 36–37 CUMULATIVE REVIEW
EXERCISES**   **1.** 809   **3.** 3.1   **5.** 351.9   **7.** 27
9. 25   **11.** 2   **13.** 55   **15.** 8.6   **17.** 28   **19.** 7
21. 3   **23.** 19   **25.** 13, 14, 15, and so on   **27.** 0,
1, 2, 3, 4, 5, 6, 7, 8   **29.** 8, 9, 10, 11, 12
31. $g = 20 - 18$; 2   **33.** $z < 65 \div 5$; all the
numbers less than 13   **35.** $7f \leq 13 + 1$;
$f \leq 14 \div 7$; all the numbers less than or equal
to 2   **37.** $t - 31$ **39.** $4 + 2k$
41. $n - 15 = 24$ **43.** $2n - 3 = 9$

**PAGE 37 CUMULATIVE REVIEW
PROBLEMS**   **1.** 6780 words

3. 81 certificates   **5.** 761 people   **7.** 72 m

2 The Decimal System

PAGE 43 WRITTEN EXERCISES   **1.** 64
3. 100   **5.** 14   **7.** 225   **9.** 1   **11.** 3^2 **13.** 9^2
15. $(16 \times 4)^2$ **17.** 2^7 **19.** 10^5 **21.** n^{11}
23. 100   **25.** 81   **27.** 576   **29.** 1   **31.** 1875
33. 225   **35.** 1   **37.** 1000   **39.** 96   **41.** 52
43. 4   **45.** $\frac{1}{8}$ **47.** $n = 1$

PAGE 43 REVIEW EXERCISES   **1.** $<, <$
3. $>, >$ **5.** $>, >$ **7.** $<, <$

PAGES 46–47 WRITTEN EXERCISES
1. $(3 \times 10) + 8$ **3.** $(8 \times 1000) + (9 \times 10) + 1$
5. $(4 \times 0.1) + (7 \times 0.01)$ **7.** $(6 \times 0.01) + (3 \times 0.001)$ **9.** $(1 \times 0.1) + (8 \times 0.01) + (7 \times 0.001)$ **11.** 54.57   **13.** 9002.146   **15.** 7.43
17. 19.005   **19.** 0.0048   **21.** 6.025   **23.** $<$
25. $>$ **27.** $>$ **29.** $>$ **31.** $<$ **33.** $<$ **35.** $>$
37. $=$ **39.** $=$ **41.** $>$ **43.** $<$ **45.** $3.08 < 3.16 < 3.97$ **47.** $0.07 < 0.08 < 0.2$ **49.** $7.028 < 7.0862 < 7.11$ **51.** $0.406 + 0.215 < 0.27 + 0.81 < 1.62 + 0.09$ **53.** $(5 \times 10^3) + (2 \times 10^2) + (8 \times 10^1) + (0 \times 10^0)$ **55.** $(1 \times 10^2) + (8 \times 10^1) + (3 \times 10^0) + \left(0 \times \frac{1}{10^1}\right) + \left(8 \times \frac{1}{10^2}\right)$
57. $\left(0 \times \frac{1}{10^1}\right) + \left(9 \times \frac{1}{10^2}\right) + \left(1 \times \frac{1}{10^3}\right)$
59. $(7 \times 10^0) + \left(4 \times \frac{1}{10^1}\right) + \left(8 \times \frac{1}{10^2}\right) + \left(2 \times \frac{1}{10^3}\right)$ **61.** $(2 \times 10^2) + (0 \times 10^1) + (4 \times 10^0) + \left(5 \times \frac{1}{10^1}\right)$ **63.** $(3 \times 10^1) + (8 \times 10^0) + \left(0 \times \frac{1}{10^1}\right) + \left(0 \times \frac{1}{10^2}\right) + \left(3 \times \frac{1}{10^3}\right)$

PAGE 47 REVIEW EXERCISES   **1.** 90   **3.** 5
5. 250   **7.** 27   **9.** 0.2

PAGES 49–50 WRITTEN EXERCISES   **1.** 30
3. 290   **5.** 650   **7.** 160   **9.** 72.46   **11.** 0.06
13. 0.01   **15.** 18.17   **17.** 0.001   **19.** 401.090
21. 250.341   **23.** 8.100   **25.** b   **27.** a   **29.** b
31. c

PAGE 50 SELF-TEST A   **1.** 16   **2.** 512
3. 9   **4.** 3125   **5.** a^{11} **6.** $>$ **7.** $>$ **8.** $<$
9. 80   **10.** 3.18   **11.** 300

PAGE 50 CALCULATOR KEY-IN   **1.** 56,
56   **3.** 3243, 3243

PAGES 54–55 WRITTEN EXERCISES
1. 14.6; associative   **3.** 14.24; distributive
5. 18.97; commutative and associative   **7.** 0.21;
commutative and associative   **9.** 0; associative
and multiplication property of zero   **11.** 72;
distributive   **13.** False   **15.** True   **17.** False
19. 0   **21.** 3.2   **23.** 0   **25.** 9   **27.** 15.9   **29.** 3
31. 1565   **33.** 0   **35.** 3.88   **37.** 400   **39.** 900
For exercises 41 and 43, answers will vary. An
example is given.   **41.** $a = 1$, $b = 2$, $c = 3$;
$(1 \times 2) + (2 \times 3) \neq 2(1 \times 3)$ **43.** $a = 4$,
$b = 6$, $c = 10$; $(6 + 10)(4 + 10) \neq 10(6 \times 4)$

PAGE 55 REVIEW EXERCISES   **1.** 31
3. 74   **5.** 13   **7.** 40

PAGES 57–58 WRITTEN EXERCISES
1. 54   **3.** 177   **5.** 247   **7.** 0.55   **9.** 73
11. $54m^6 + 7$ **13.** 29.9   **15.** $17x + 14y$
17. $36d$ **19.** $280m + 160$ **21.** 18.752   **23.** 1
25. 103.04   **27.** 128   **29.** 101.76
31. $(4^2 - 3) \times 5 - 2 = 63$
33. $12 - 10 \div 2 + 3 \times 8 = 31$
35. $4.2 + 3 \times (3.6 \div 0.4 + 9.6) = 60$

PAGE 58 REVIEW EXERCISES   **1.** 0.006
3. 200   **5.** 6   **7.** 30

PAGE 58 COMPUTER BYTE   **1.** 800
3. 7000   **5.** 17   **7.** 0.0   **9.** 75

PAGES 62–63 PROBLEMS   **1.** $113.70   **3.** 22
bonus points   **5.** 41 points   **7.** $488.75
9. 12,948 shares   **11.** $1.90

PAGE 63 SELF–TEST B   **1.** 102   **2.** 93
3. 21   **4.** 67.96   **5.** 36   **6.** 189   **7.** $16a + 14$
8. 6.25   **9.** 13   **10.** $43b + 37$ **11.** $182.24

PAGE 65 ENRICHMENT   **1.** Answers will
vary.

PAGE 66 CHAPTER REVIEW   **1.** $=$ **3.** $<$
5. $=$ **7.** $<$ **9.** True   **11.** True   **13.** False
15. B   **17.** C   **19.** E   **21.** b

PAGE 68 CUMULATIVE REVIEW
EXERCISES   **1.** 7.5   **3.** 23   **5.** 124   **7.** 57.2
9. 0   **11.** 36.7   **13.** 101.38   **15.** 24.5   **17.** 5
19. $15 < 26 < 48$, or $48 > 26 > 15$
21. $115 < 125 < 225$, or $225 > 125 > 115$
23. $2^2 < 5^3 < 3^5$, or $3^5 > 5^3 > 2^2$ **25.** a
27. a   **29.** True   **31.** True   **33.** False
35. False   **37.** True

PAGE 69 CUMULATIVE REVIEW
PROBLEMS   **1.** $3010   **3.** $42.95   **5.** $20
7. $17

3 Positive and Negative Numbers
PAGES 73–74 WRITTEN EXERCISES
1.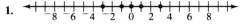
3.
5.
7.
9.

11. $>$ **13.** $>$ **15.** $<$ **17.** 3   **19.** 0   **21.** 9
23. 8   **25.** $^-15, ^-2, 0, 6$ **27.** $^-12, ^-8, ^-1, 1, 7$
29. $^-14, ^-10, 4, 8, 14$ **31. a.** $^-6, 6$ **33. a.** $^-4$,
4   **35. a.** 0   **37. a.** $^-1, 0, 1$ **39. a.** $^-4, ^-3, ^-2$,
$^-1, 0, 1, 2, 3, 4$ **41. a.** $^-7, ^-6, ^-5, ^-4, ^-3, 3, 4$,
5, 6, 7   **43.** positive   **45.** $|n|$ represents the
distance n from the origin.

PAGE 74 REVIEW EXERCISES   **1.** $>$
3. $>$ **5.** $<$ **7.** $>$ **9.** $<$

PAGES 77–78 WRITTEN EXERCISES
1.   **3.**
5.   **7.**
9.   **11.**

13. 2.36   **15.** 16   **17.** 3.03   **19.** $<$ **21.** $<$
23. $<$ **25.** $>$ **27.** $<$ **29.** $^-8, ^-7.6, ^-1.75$,
6.03, 6.3   **31.** $^-100.5, ^-46.8, ^-2.1, ^-2, 3.11$
33. $^-3.3, ^-0.33, ^-0.3, 30.3, 33$
35.
37.
39.

41. $^-4.1, 4.1$ **43.** $^-26.3, 26.3$ **45.** $^-1.19, 1.19$
47. $^-4.5$ **49.** $^-12$ **51. a.** $^-4, ^-3, ^-2, ^-1, 0, 1, 2$,
3, 4   **53. a.** $^-5, ^-4, ^-3, ^-2, ^-1, 0, 1, 2, 3, 4, 5$

PAGE 78 REVIEW EXERCISES 1. 11.14; distributive 3. 27.18; multiplication property of one 5. 132.3; distributive 7. 1075; commutative and associative 9. 0; associative property and multiplication property of zero

PAGE 82 WRITTEN EXERCISES
1.

3.

5. ⁻19 7. ⁻13 9. ⁻0.3 11. 0 13. 16.2
15. 4.17 17. ⁻84 19. 10.5 21. ⁻18.72
23. ⁻26.1 25. 0 27. ⁻0.12 29. 6.3 31. ⁻10.8
33. ⁻7.25 35. 12 37. ⁻12 39. ⁻18.5
41. ⁻2.4 43. ⁻19.8 45. ⁻25.9 47. a. ⁻6.7
b. ⁻9 49. < 51. > 53. a. = b. < c. <
d. < e. = f. < g. $|x + y| \le |x| + |y|$

PAGE 83 PROBLEMS 1. ⁻7 + 13 + ⁻3;
3°C 3. 3.5 + ⁻11 + 2; lost; 5.5 lost
5. ⁻4.30 + 2.50 + 2.60; gain

PAGE 83 REVIEW EXERCISES 1. 156.1
3. 64.9 5. 44.89 7. 4.2 9. 285

PAGES 85–86 WRITTEN EXERCISES
1. 7 + (−19) 3. 6.2 + 8.3 5. −12 7. 14.5
9. −6 11. −27 13. 42 15. 15 17. −43
19. 20 21. 44 23. −1.1 25. 2.2 27. −24.6
29. −24.6 31. 3.37 33. 24.8 35. −41.3
37. 1.8 39. −5.9 41. 8 43. 6.2 45. −4.5
47. −1.7 49. 10.7 51. −10.7 53. −1.7
55. −8 57. −5 59. −13 61. 4 63. 9
65. 14

PAGES 86–87 PROBLEMS 1. −3 − (−11);
8°C 3. 1226 − 1455; −229 m
5. (1100 − 200) − 350; 550 m 7. $10.25

PAGE 87 SELF–TEST A 1. > 2. >
3. < 4. = 5. = 6. ⁻54, ⁻4.52, ⁻0.25, 0,
5.4 7. ⁻7.3, ⁻3.79, ⁻0.37, ⁻0.09, 37 8. 33
9. 0 10. ⁻1.44 11. 35 12. 0 13. ⁻36
14. 11.6 15. −11.6 16. −11.6

PAGES 90–91 WRITTEN EXERCISES
1. 27 3. −56 5. 96 7. 0 9. −12 11. 5.1
13. −2.9 15. 15.4 17. −5 19. 459
21. −66.69 23. 0 25. 3.42 27. −111.24
29. 37.875 31. 61.38 33. −1.054 35. 0

37. 361.9 39. −40.81 41. −8.2 43. 66.0156
45. −100 47. 9m − 11 49. 2 51. −5a
53. 5b 55. −2 57. −2 59. 0 61. 2
63. −30 65. 0

PAGE 91 REVIEW EXERCISES 1. 56
3. 154 5. 13 7. 26

PAGES 93–94 WRITTEN EXERCISES
1. −6 3. 3 5. 0 7. −12 9. −7.5 11. 3.6
13. −35 15. −5.3 17. 8 19. 0 21. −0.5
23. −9.5 25. −2.2 27. 13.8 29. 0.1545
31. −6.3 33. 4.7 35. −1.85 37. −3.2
39. 0.625 41. −4.2 43. −1.2 45. −2
47. −72 49. −8

PAGE 94 REVIEW EXERCISES 1. 49
3. 784 5. 112 7. 1 9. 37

PAGE 94 CALCULATOR KEY–IN 1. 1.1
3. −28.201 5. 5101.015

PAGE 96 WRITTEN EXERCISES 1. $\frac{1}{-32}$
3. $\frac{1}{1000}$ 5. 1 7. $\frac{1}{25}$ 9. $\frac{1}{64}$ 11. $\frac{1}{49}$ 13. 1
15. $\frac{1}{27}$ 17. $\frac{1}{256}$ 19. $\frac{1}{-8}$ 21. 1 23. −3
25. 5 27. −2 29. −2 31. 8 33. 0 35. 1
37. −4 39. −3 41. $\frac{1}{x^5}$ 43. $\frac{1}{a^5}$ 45. $\frac{1}{w^8}$

PAGE 97 SELF–TEST B 1. −47.46
2. −136.68 3. 378 4. −11 5. −31 6. 8
7. $\frac{1}{16}$ 8. $\frac{1}{-216}$ 9. $\frac{1}{343}$ 10. $\frac{1}{81}$

PAGES 98–99 ENRICHMENT
1. 5.798×10^3 3. 8.915673×10^6 5. 1.75
7. 5.01×10^{-2} 9. 3790 11. 301,000
13. 0.056 15. 0.0000000399 17. 7.4×10^{-4}
19. 1.5×10^{11}

PAGE 100 CHAPTER REVIEW 1. <
3. > 5. = 7. < 9. > 11. > 13. False
15. True 17. True 19. False 21. True
23. False 25. False 27. True 29. True
31. True 33. True 35. True 37. c 39. b

PAGES 102–103 CUMULATIVE REVIEW
EXERCISES 1. 6 3. All the numbers less than 180 5. 3 7. 17 9. $p + 42$
11. $w^3 + 17$ 13. $59y^3$ 15. $3m = 33$
17. $x − 77 \le x + 5$ 19. 68.5 21. 190
23. 37.55 25. 175.8 27. 3248 29. $17n − 5m$
31. $8a^5b^2$ 33. $4w^5 + 3w^3$ 35. 6 37. 100
39. −20, −7, 0, 6, 12, 15 41. −5, −3, 0, 1, 7, 9

PAGE 103 CUMULATIVE REVIEW
PROBLEMS **1.** $59.46 **3.** 4 **5.** Deli Delights

4 Rational Numbers

PAGES 108–109 WRITTEN EXERCISES

1.

number line from -2 to 3

3.

number line from -1 to 2

5.

number line from -2 to 2

7. $\frac{-1}{2}, \frac{1}{-2}$ **9.** $-\frac{1}{11}, \frac{1}{-11}$ **11.** $-\frac{2}{9}, \frac{-2}{9}$
13. $\frac{-13}{6}, \frac{13}{-6}$ **15.** $\frac{-3}{4}, \frac{3}{-4}$ **17.** 6 **19.** $\frac{1}{4}$ **21.** 3
23. -3 **25.** $-\frac{7}{8}$ **27.** -1 **29.** $-\frac{1}{3}$ **31.** -3
33. -9 **35.** $\frac{7}{6}$ **37.** $\frac{3}{7}$ **39.** $-\frac{1}{9}$ **41.** $-\frac{2}{7}$
43. $-\frac{3}{8}$

PAGE 109 REVIEW EXERCISES
1. 3, 4, 8, 18, 36 **3.** 1, 5, 6, 10, 15, 30, 45 **5.** 6, x

PAGES 112–113 WRITTEN EXERCISES
1. 4 **3.** 5 **5.** 7 **7.** 3 **9.** 125 **11.** $\frac{3}{5}$ **13.** $2\frac{3}{4}$
15. $-\frac{1}{9}$ **17.** $-5\frac{2}{3}$ **19.** $\frac{-2}{5}$ **21.** $10\frac{5}{12}$
23. $-6\frac{1}{13}$ **25.** $-42\frac{6}{7}$ **27.** $1\frac{1}{2}$ **29.** $30\frac{11}{15}$
31. $\frac{13}{4}$ **33.** $\frac{38}{7}$ **35.** $\frac{43}{4}$ **37.** $-\frac{31}{8}$ **39.** $-\frac{65}{9}$
41. 2 **43.** 1 **45.** 4 **47.** -4 **49.** $\frac{1}{3}$ **51.** $\frac{1}{c}$
53. $\frac{x}{5y}$ **55.** $\frac{2}{3k}$

PAGES 113–114 PROBLEMS
1. $\frac{1}{3}$ of the apartments **3.** Yes **5. a.** $\frac{1}{2}$ of the class **b.** $\frac{2}{5}$ of the class **c.** $\frac{30}{30}$, or $\frac{1}{1}$ of the class **d.** $\frac{9}{10}$ of the class **7. a.** $\frac{1}{6}$ of the bulbs **b.** $\frac{1}{2}$ of the total collection **9.** $\frac{1}{5}$ of the families

PAGE 114 REVIEW EXERCISES
1. 49 **3.** 1296 **5.** 1 **7.** 5184 **9.** 243

PAGES 116–117 WRITTEN EXERCISES
1. $\frac{4}{12}, \frac{1}{12}$ **3.** $\frac{6}{8}, \frac{5}{8}$ **5.** $\frac{6}{27}, -\frac{1}{27}$ **7.** $\frac{70}{147}, \frac{6}{147}$
9. $-\frac{20}{30}, \frac{7}{30}$ **11.** $\frac{16}{300}, \frac{21}{300}$ **13.** $-\frac{48}{112}, -\frac{7}{112}$
15. $\frac{35}{294}, \frac{30}{294}$ **17.** $\frac{70}{80}, \frac{25}{80}, \frac{42}{80}$ **19.** $\frac{108}{252}, \frac{441}{252}, \frac{112}{252}$
21. $\frac{2}{130}, \frac{78}{130}, \frac{45}{130}$ **23.** $-\frac{60}{72}, \frac{16}{72}, -\frac{63}{72}$ **25.** $\frac{2a}{6}, \frac{b}{6}$
27. $\frac{20h}{500}, \frac{5h}{500}, \frac{4h}{500}$ **29.** $\frac{3}{3c}, \frac{2}{3c}$ **31.** $\frac{3yz}{xyz}, \frac{xz}{xyz}, \frac{5xy}{xyz}$ **33.** $<$ **35.** $<$ **37.** $>$ **39.** $=$ **41.** $>$
43. $>$

PAGE 117 REVIEW EXERCISES
1. 25.76 **3.** 4.87 **5.** -11.8 **7.** 23.4 **9.** 14.5

PAGE 117 CALCULATOR KEY-IN
1. $<$ **3.** $>$

PAGES 119–120 WRITTEN EXERCISES
1. $1\frac{1}{2}$ **3.** 0 **5.** $\frac{3}{8}$ **7.** $-\frac{11}{12}$ **9.** $1\frac{11}{12}$ **11.** $-\frac{41}{72}$
13. $3\frac{3}{8}$ **15.** $\frac{1}{4}$ **17.** $\frac{13}{24}$ **19.** $1\frac{1}{6}$ **21.** $-2\frac{1}{12}$
23. $-16\frac{23}{42}$ **25.** $\frac{19}{20}$ **27.** $1\frac{7}{12}$ **29.** $-6\frac{2}{3}$
31. $47\frac{11}{24}$ **33.** $-7\frac{29}{60}$ **35.** $\frac{b+5}{6}$ **37.** $\frac{2}{g}$
39. $\frac{6b+1}{2}$ **41.** $\frac{-5a-3}{a}$ **43.** $\frac{3t}{2}$ **45.** $-\frac{2n}{r}$
47. $\frac{7y}{4}$ **49.** $\frac{5x}{3}$

PAGES 120–121 PROBLEMS
1. $2\frac{7}{24}$ cups **3.** $14\frac{11}{16}$ yd **5.** $\frac{5}{6}$ mi **7.** Right: $1\frac{5}{16}$ in.; bottom: $\frac{11}{16}$ in.

PAGE 121 SELF-TEST A
1. $\frac{1}{8}$ **2.** $-\frac{1}{3}$ **3.** $\frac{7}{9}$
4. $\frac{2}{-3}$ **5.** $\frac{1}{4}$ **6.** $-2\frac{2}{5}$ **7.** $\frac{16}{21}$ **8.** $-1\frac{23}{48}$ **9.** $4\frac{1}{4}$
10. $\frac{11}{5}$ **11.** $-\frac{11}{3}$ **12.** $\frac{94}{15}$ **13.** $\frac{19}{3}$ **14.** $-\frac{69}{8}$
15. $\frac{56}{72}, \frac{63}{72}$ **16.** $-\frac{30}{147}, \frac{14}{147}$ **17.** $\frac{27}{450}, \frac{12}{450}$
18. $-\frac{16}{30}, -\frac{1}{30}$ **19.** $\frac{7}{12}$ **20.** $-\frac{2}{15}$ **21.** $-\frac{7}{10}$
22. $15\frac{7}{8}$ **23.** $22\frac{4}{9}$ **24.** $-4\frac{5}{24}$

PAGES 124–125 WRITTEN EXERCISES
1. 7 **3.** -2 **5.** $\frac{1}{28}$ **7.** $-\frac{1}{60}$ **9.** $\frac{10}{27}$ **11.** $-\frac{1}{4}$
13. $-\frac{2}{27}$ **15.** $\frac{5}{8}$ **17.** 0 **19.** $\frac{15}{64}$ **21.** 1
23. $43\frac{11}{12}$ **25.** $-22\frac{1}{7}$ **27.** $3\frac{10}{27}$ **29.** $\frac{1}{24}$ **31.** $\frac{1}{72}$
33. $-4\frac{1}{2}$ **35.** $6n$ **37.** $-\frac{y}{2}$ **39.** $\frac{2}{5}$ **41.** 3

PAGE 125 REVIEW EXERCISES
1. 60 **3.** -36 **5.** 8 **7.** $-3\frac{1}{9}$

PAGES 128–129 WRITTEN EXERCISES
1. $\frac{2}{3}$ **3.** 25 **5.** $\frac{25}{72}$ **7.** $3\frac{8}{9}$ **9.** 6 **11.** $5\frac{1}{5}$
13. $-\frac{9}{16}$ **15.** 7 **17.** $5\frac{23}{64}$ **19.** -2 **21.** -9
23. $\frac{1}{3}$ **25.** $-\frac{1}{2}$ **27.** $-8y$ **29.** $1\frac{1}{7}$ **31.** $\frac{-2}{c^2}$
33. $\frac{3e}{4d}$ **35.** $\frac{4}{5}$ **37.** $\frac{5}{12}$ **39.** $\frac{2}{5}$

PAGES 129–130 PROBLEMS
1. $9\frac{7}{9}$ packages **3.** 225 balloons **5.** $\frac{1}{19}$ **7.** $7500 **9.** $40\frac{1}{2}$ ft; $12\frac{1}{4}$ ft by $8\frac{5}{6}$ ft **11.** $\frac{1}{6}$ of the class **13.** $\frac{3}{20}$ of the workers

PAGE 130 REVIEW EXERCISES
1. $n = 240 - 135$; 105 **3.** $y = 156 \div 4$; 39 **5.** $x = 432 \div 12$; 36 **7.** $m = 418 \div 38$; 11

PAGES 134–135 WRITTEN EXERCISES
1. 0.25 **3.** $0.\overline{2}$ **5.** 0.9 **7.** $-0.\overline{6}$ **9.** -0.375

11. -0.12 **13.** 1.1 **15.** $0.58\bar{3}$ **17.** $0.2\bar{6}$
19. $-1.3\bar{8}$ **21.** 0.15 **23.** $3.\overline{285714}$ **25.** $\frac{1}{20}$
27. $-\frac{3}{5}$ **29.** $2\frac{7}{100}$ **31.** $5\frac{1}{8}$ **33.** $-1\frac{3}{8}$ **35.** $12\frac{5}{8}$
37. $\frac{9}{40}$ **39.** $-1\frac{413}{500}$ **41.** $-\frac{5}{9}$ **43.** $-1\frac{1}{90}$
45. $\frac{5}{33}$ **47.** $\frac{35}{99}$ **49.** $-1\frac{4}{33}$ **51.** $2\frac{121}{900}$
53. $\frac{41}{333}$ **55.** Rational **57.** Rational **59.** 3.0,
$3.00\bar{9}$, $3.0\bar{9}$, 3.1 **61.** 1, $=$ **63.** $-\frac{5}{4}$, $=$

PAGE 135 SELF–TEST B **1.** $3\frac{3}{4}$ **2.** $-\frac{1}{24}$
3. $1\frac{1}{5}$ **4.** $1\frac{41}{64}$ **5.** 15 **6.** $-8\frac{1}{7}$ **7.** $1\frac{1}{2}$ **8.** $-\frac{1}{8}$
9. 14 **10.** $\frac{1}{20}$ **11.** $-4\frac{1}{2}$ **12.** $2\frac{2}{29}$ **13.** 0.625
14. $0.\overline{18}$ **15.** -0.0125 **16.** $1.1\bar{6}$ **17.** $\frac{7}{8}$ **18.** $1\frac{2}{3}$
19. $-2\frac{213}{1000}$ **20.** $\frac{7}{30}$

PAGE 135 COMPUTER BYTE **1.** $0.\overline{142857}$
3. $0.\overline{90}$ **5.** $0.\overline{76}$ **7.** $0.\overline{51}$

PAGE 138 CHAPTER REVIEW **1.** False
3. True **5.** False **7.** False **9.** True
11. False **13.** C **15.** K **17.** D **19.** H
21. B **23.** E **25.** 0.3125 **27.** $-\frac{1}{8}$

PAGE 140 CUMULATIVE REVIEW
EXERCISES **1.** 58 **3.** 7 **5.** 5 **7.** 0.12
9. 225 **11.** 0.08 **13.** 10.24 **15.** 750 **17.** $75.70 >$
$75.40 > 75.06$ **19.** $0.33 > 0.30 > 0.03$ **21.** -7,
7 **23.** $-5, -6, -7$, and so on; also $5, 6, 7$,
and so on **25.** $-5, 5$ **27.** $-32, -33, -34$,
$-35, -36, -37, -38, -39, 32, 33, 34, 35, 36$,
$37, 38, 39$ **29.** $y = 18$ **31.** $b = 12$ **33.** $n = -4$ **35.** $-\frac{4}{5}$ **37.** $\frac{2}{5}$ **39.** $-1\frac{3}{7}$ **41.** $-\frac{2}{7}$ **43.** $\frac{2}{5}$
45. $-5\frac{5}{8}$ **47.** $8\frac{23}{136}$

PAGE 141 CUMULATIVE REVIEW
PROBLEMS **1.** $\$196.88$ **3.** No **5.** $\$787.50$
7. $\$444.75$

5 Equations and Inequalities
PAGE 145 WRITTEN EXERCISES
1. Addition property of equality
3. Multiplication property of equality
5. Addition property of equality
7. Multiplication property of equality **9.** 11
11. -5 **13.** 21 **15.** 3 **17.** -3 **19.** 7
21. 1.2 **23.** -9 **25.** 12 **27.** 0

PAGE 145 REVIEW EXERCISES **1.** 103
3. 35 **5.** 1.5

PAGES 147–148 WRITTEN EXERCISES
1. $b + 7 = 22$ **3.** $72 = 20 + u$ **5.** $2 = -12 + v$ **7.** $10 + f = 36$ **9.** $33 = 10n - 7$ **11.** $11q - 2 = 20$ **13.** $15 = 5z + 5$ **15.** $10x + 7 =$

-13 **17.** $4j + 8 = 36$ **19.** $20 = 2e - 10$
21. $-18 - 6w = 48$ **23.** $14 = 16 + 2b$
25. $15n + 30 = 45$ **27.** $3.2 = 15.6 + c$ **29.** $24 = k + 2$ **31.** $20g + 4.3 = 24.3$ **33.** $-\frac{8}{7} = \frac{6}{7} - v$ **35.** $6.6 = 3.3 - 3x$ **37.** $2h - 5 = 17$
39. $-22m - 15 = 6$ **41.** $25n + 6.3 = 26.3$
43. $\frac{10}{3}d + \frac{3}{8} = 33$

PAGE 148 REVIEW EXERCISES **1.** -6
3. -17 **5.** -8 **7.** 8 **9.** 20

PAGE 151 WRITTEN EXERCISES **1.** 15
3. -26 **5.** 23 **7.** -24 **9.** 7 **11.** -16
13. -1 **15.** -38 **17.** 40 **19.** -38 **21.** 13
23. -22 **25.** $3\frac{5}{8}$ **27.** $9\frac{1}{4}$ **29.** 6.4 **31.** $10\frac{1}{7}$
33. -6 **35.** 16.2 **37.** -2 or 2 **39.** -11 or 11

PAGE 151 REVIEW EXERCISES **1.** $\frac{1}{3}$ **3.** $\frac{1}{8}$
5. $\frac{1}{12}$

PAGE 154 WRITTEN EXERCISES **1.** 6
3. -38 **5.** -49 **7.** 99 **9.** 128 **11.** -528
13. -17 **15.** -4131 **17.** 972 **19.** -4896
21. 84 **23.** 158.5 **25.** 15.2 **27.** -400 **29.** $\frac{35}{16}$,
or $2\frac{3}{16}$ **31.** $-\frac{1}{6}$ **33.** 280 **35.** -1.4
37. -124 **39.** 3.15

PAGE 154 REVIEW EXERCISES **1.** $6, 5, 4$,
$3, 2, 1, 0$ **3.** $22, 23, 24$, and so on **5.** $9, 8, 7$,
$6, 5, 4, 3, 2, 1, 0$ **7.** $4, 5, 6, 7, 8, 9, 10, 11$

PAGES 157–158 WRITTEN EXERCISES
1. Simplify both sides; divide both sides by 6
3. Subtract 4 from both sides; divide both sides
by -3 **5.** Simplify the right side; add 12 to
both sides; divide both sides by 4 **7.** 2 **9.** 6
11. 3 **13.** 6 **15.** 56 **17.** -30 **19.** -180
21. -9 **23.** -6 **25.** $\frac{10}{9}$, or $1\frac{1}{9}$ **27.** -15
29. 3 **31.** $-\frac{12}{5}$, or $-2\frac{2}{5}$ **33.** 1 **35.** 4.7 **37.** 40
39. 1 **41.** 5 **43.** 1 **45.** $\frac{81}{2}$, or $40\frac{1}{2}$ **47.** -29
49. $\frac{9}{6} = 4(4 - y)$; $\frac{29}{8}$, or $3\frac{5}{8}$ **51.** $\frac{1}{3}y - \frac{5}{18} = 2y$;
$-\frac{1}{6}$

PAGE 158 SELF–TEST A **1.** 12 **2.** -8
3. $17 = 8x - 17$ **4.** $8 = 5m - 45$ **5.** 5
6. 47 **7.** -26 **8.** -7 **9.** 162 **10.** 32
11. 20 **12.** $-\frac{33}{2}$, or $-16\frac{1}{2}$ **13.** -4

PAGES 161–162 WRITTEN EXERCISES
All the numbers: **1.** less than 12 **3.** greater
than 42 **5.** less than 3 **7.** greater than or
equal to 20 **9.** less than -18 **11.** less than 7
13. less than -7 **15.** less than or equal to 12
17. less than or equal to 15 **19.** less than -26

21. less than or equal to 60 **23.** less than or equal to -11 **25.** less than -168 **27.** greater than 21.3 **29.** less than $5\frac{3}{7}$ **31.** less than or equal to -3.87 **33.** less than or equal to 47 **35.** less than or equal to -10.8 **37.** greater than or equal to 3 **39.** greater than 21 **41.** greater than -4.1 **43.** less than or equal to -92.4 **45.** greater than $22\frac{13}{15}$ **47.** greater than or equal to -9 **49.** greater than $\frac{1}{5}$ **51.** less than -1.7

PAGE 162 REVIEW EXERCISES 1. -2.6, -1.4, 1.2, 3.2 **3.** -12.2, -12.09, -11.2, 12, 112 **5.** -30.05, -5.3, -5.03, 0.35, 3.05 **7.** -2.89, -2.8, 2.089, 2.89, 28.9

PAGES 165–166 WRITTEN EXERCISES All the numbers: **1.** less than -6 **3.** greater than or equal to -9 **5.** less than -30 **7.** greater than or equal to -42 **9.** greater than $5\frac{2}{5}$ **11.** greater than or equal to -10 **13.** greater than 2 **15.** greater than or equal to 3 **17.** greater than -4 **19.** less than or equal to 5 **21.** less than 8 **23.** less than or equal to $-3\frac{1}{13}$ **25.** less than or equal to -3 **27.** greater than 1 **29.** less than or equal to -2 **31.** greater than 15 **33.** less than 2 **35.** greater than 24 **37.** less than -7.2 **39.** greater than or equal to -10.3

PAGE 166 REVIEW EXERCISES 1. $n + 9$ **3.** $n - 16$ **5.** $n + 3$ **7.** $\frac{n}{5}$, or $n \div 5$

PAGE 166 CALCULATOR KEY-IN 852

PAGE 168 WRITTEN EXERCISES
1.–16. Answers will vary. **17.** E **19.** D **21.** B

PAGE 168 REVIEW EXERCISES 1. $\frac{9}{2}$, or $4\frac{1}{2}$ **3.** 44 **5.** -18 **7.** 6

PAGES 172–173 PROBLEMS 1. Neon **3.** Osmium **5.** Osmium **7.** 11 plants **9.** $45 **11.** Byrne: $300,000; Chang: $60,000; Weinstein: $317,000 **13.** 12 nickels

PAGE 173 SELF-TEST B 1.–8. All the numbers: **1.** greater than 46 **2.** greater than or equal to -98 **3.** greater than 71 **4.** greater than or equal to 5 **5.** less than or equal to $-25\frac{1}{2}$ **6.** less than -68 **7.** less than -1 **8.** less than or equal to 6 **9., 10.** Answers will vary. **11.** 15 min

PAGE 175 ENRICHMENT 1. $125.86;

$162.75; $20.00 **3.** $249.75; $323.80; $35.00 **5.** $665.61; $676.09; $90.00

PAGE 176 CHAPTER REVIEW 1. False **3.** True **5.** False **7.** False **9.** True **11.** False **13.** True **15.** D **17.** A **19.** C **21.** c **23.** c

PAGE 178 CUMULATIVE REVIEW EXERCISES 1. True **3.** False **5.** False

7.
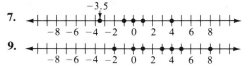

9.

11. $\frac{5}{40}$, $\frac{16}{40}$ **13.** $\frac{4}{6}$, $\frac{1}{6}$ **15.** $-\frac{48}{88}$, $-\frac{33}{88}$ **17.** $\frac{20}{24}$, $-\frac{21}{24}$ **19.** -78.51 **21.** -120 **23.** -16.867 **25.** $\frac{3}{4}$ **27.** $46\frac{11}{20}$ **29.** $6\frac{22}{25}$ **31.** $4\frac{2}{25}$ **33.** $99\frac{11}{25}$ **35.** 6.09 **37.** 5.657 **39.** 4000 **41.** 12 **43.** All the numbers greater than $1\frac{1}{2}$ **45.** All the numbers less than or equal to $\frac{1}{4}$ **47.** 7 **49.** $\frac{14}{3}$, or $4\frac{2}{3}$

PAGE 179 CUMULATIVE REVIEW PROBLEMS 1. $2.97 **3.** 220,000 or 0.22 million readers **5.** $418.50 **7.** $656.38 **9.** 100 inquiries

6 Geometry

PAGES 185–186 WRITTEN EXERCISES
1. $\overrightarrow{AN}$, or $\overrightarrow{AK}$ **3.** $\overleftrightarrow{AN}$, $\overrightarrow{NK}$, $\overrightarrow{AK}$, $\overrightarrow{NA}$, $\overleftrightarrow{KN}$, $\overrightarrow{KA}$
Answers to 5–12 will vary.

5. **7.** $\bullet R$

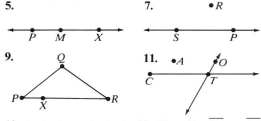

9. Q **11.** $\bullet A$

13. P, R, T; or P, Q, S **15.** Yes **19.** $\overline{EF}$, or $\overline{FE}$ **21.** $\overrightarrow{DG}$, or $\overrightarrow{DE}$, or $\overrightarrow{DF}$ **25.** 24 **27.** 10 **29.** 4 **31.** 7

PAGE 186 REVIEW EXERCISES 1. 56.0 **3.** 1.201 **5.** 2842.35 **7.** 0.863 **9.** 7.455

PAGES 189–190 WRITTEN EXERCISES

1. **3.**

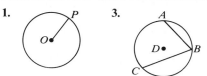

7. 2360 m **9.** 157 cm **11.** 4 **13.** 132 **15.** 17.5
17. 0.07 **19.** 18,800 km

PAGE 190 REVIEW EXERCISES **1.** $<$
3. $<$ **5.** $<$ **7.** $>$

PAGE 190 CALCULATOR KEY-IN
3.14084507; 3.14285714

PAGE 194 WRITTEN EXERCISES **1.** 50
3. 34 **9.** 45° **11.** 90° **15.** They form a right
angle.

PAGE 194 REVIEW EXERCISES **1.** 114
3. 112 **5.** 84 **7.** 60 **9.** 72 **11.** 138

PAGES 198–199 WRITTEN EXERCISES
1. 38° **3.** 67° **5.** 73° **7.** 52° **9.** 28° **11.** 152°
13. 80° **15.** 128° **17.** 33°, 57° **19.** 60°, 30°
21. 30°, 150° **23.** 72°, 108° **25.** 90°

PAGE 199 REVIEW EXERCISES **1.** 343
3. 6 **5.** 21.25 **7.** 10 **9.** 10.5

PAGES 202–203 WRITTEN EXERCISES
1. $\angle 5$, $\angle 7$ **3.** $\angle DBC$, $\angle 9$ **5.** $\angle 2$, $\angle 7$
7. $\angle DBC$, $\angle 11$ **9.** 58° **11.** 32° **13.** 122°
15. 90° **19.** Supplementary angles **21.** $\angle 2 \cong$
$\angle 3$ **23. a.** Construct an angle congruent to
$\angle 1$ with vertex P. **b.** $\angle 1$ and the constructed
angle are congruent alternate interior angles.
25. $\angle 2 \cong \angle 3$ because they are alternate
interior angles. Therefore, $\angle 1 \cong \angle 3$. Because
corresponding angles 1 and 3 are congruent,
$\overline{AB} \| \overline{DC}$.

PAGE 203 SELF-TEST A
1.
2.
3.
4.
5.
6. 154 **7.**

8. 82° **9.** m$\angle ARQ = 54°$, m$\angle QRT = 36°$
10. m$\angle ABC = 63°$, m$\angle XYZ = 117°$
11. YQS **12.** TQR

PAGES 206–208 WRITTEN EXERCISES
1. 67° **3.** 112°; 34° **5.** 62°; 62°

11. Yes **13.** 90°, 45°, 45° **15.** x is 65,
y is 25 **17.** x is 72, y is 36 **19.** x is 84,
y is 126 **21. d.** Each side appears to be three
times as long as the corresponding side of
$\triangle DEF$. **23.** A right triangle **25.** 125° **27.** 30°

PAGE 208 REVIEW EXERCISES
1. $d - 9 = 5$ **3.** $-4 = x + 20$ **5.** $14z > 98$
7. $2m - 10 = 2$

PAGES 211–212 WRITTEN EXERCISES
1. 115° **3.** 115° **5.** 12 **7.** $\overline{AB}$, $\overline{EC}$, $\overline{DC}$
9. $\angle BCE$, $\angle D$ **11.** True **13.** True **15.** True
23. 44 **25. b.** The median is parallel to the
parallel sides.

PAGE 212 REVIEW EXERCISES **1.** -9.175
3. 97.96 **5.** -35.36 **7.** 9 **9.** -6.24

PAGES 214–216 WRITTEN EXERCISES
1. 16 cm **3.** 50 m **5.** 42.5 mm **7.** 71.2 mm
9. 6.25 in. **11.** 45.1 m **17.** 135° **19.** 144°
21. a. 360° **b.** 540° **c.** $n - 2$ **d.** $(n - 2)180°$

PAGE 216 REVIEW EXERCISES **1.** 3.81
3. -7.95 **5.** 49.82 **7.** -37.2

PAGES 219–221 WRITTEN EXERCISES
1. ASA **3.** SSS **7.** SAS **9.** $\triangle ABC \cong \triangle DBE$;
rotation; SAS **11.** $\triangle KLM \cong \triangle NML$;
reflection, or reflection and translation; SAS
13. $\triangle SXR \cong \triangle PXQ$, SAS; $\triangle SXP \cong \triangle QXR$,
SAS **15.** $\triangle GHK \cong \triangle FHK$, SAS; $\triangle GDK \cong$
$\triangle FEK$, SAS **17.** $\angle A \cong \angle D$, $\overline{AC} \cong \overline{FD}$; SAS
19. $\angle X \cong \angle S$, $\angle ROS \cong \angle YOX$; ASA

PAGE 221 SELF-TEST B **1.** 90°; right
2. 60°, 60°, 60°, acute **3.** 35°; obtuse **4.** 90°
5. 54° **6.** $\overline{WT}$ **7.** $\overline{XR}$ **8.** 30 **9.** 22
10. 64.2 cm **11.** True **12.** True **13.** False

PAGE 223 ENRICHMENT **3.** P and the
center of the circle

PAGE 224 CHAPTER REVIEW **1.** $\overrightarrow{OE}$
3. $\overleftrightarrow{AC}$, or $\overleftrightarrow{CA}$ **5.** Approximately 11.8 **7.** 0,
90 **9.** True **11.** False **13.** False **15.** True
17. False **19.** False **21.** True

PAGE 226 CUMULATIVE REVIEW
EXERCISES **1.** $12.45 **3.** $160.87
5. $821.10 **7.** $375.90 **9.** $54y$ **11.** $100r$
13. $24a$ **15.** $1.6n - 6.72$ **17.** -15.8
19. 5.218 **21.** 9.1 **23.** -14.805 **25.** 324

27. 2.5 29. $-\frac{21}{29}$ 31. $-\frac{29}{41}$ 33. $\frac{6}{37}$ 35. $\frac{9}{250}$
37. $11\frac{21}{25}$ 39. $0.\overline{6}$ 41. $3.8\overline{3}$ 43. $8.08\overline{3}$ 45. $\frac{5}{6}$
47. $2\frac{14}{33}$ 49. 22 51. 169 53. 19 55. 53.2

PAGE 227 CUMULATIVE REVIEW
PROBLEMS 1. 15 cm 3. 4.4 km 5. Up $4\frac{5}{8}$
points 7. Adult $4, student $2 9. 20 cm,
15 cm 11. 15.2 m

7 Ratio, Proportion, and Percent
PAGE 232 WRITTEN EXERCISES 1. $\frac{5}{4}$
3. $\frac{3}{7}$ 5. $\frac{2}{1}$ 7. $\frac{25}{8}$ 9. No 11. Yes 13. 12
15. 6 17. $10\frac{1}{2}$ 19. 3 21. $2\frac{4}{5}$ 23. $1\frac{1}{2}$ 25. $3\frac{1}{2}$
27. $6\frac{2}{5}$

PAGE 233 PROBLEMS 1. 8 cans 3. $11\frac{1}{4}$ oz;
$10\frac{2}{3}$ servings 5. 12 vests 7. $1333\frac{1}{3}$ ft² 9. 6955
votes for, 2782 votes against

PAGE 233 REVIEW EXERCISES 1. $\frac{1}{3}$ 3. $\frac{6}{7}$
5. $\frac{11}{14}$ 7. $11\frac{2}{7}$

PAGES 236–237 PROBLEMS 1. $0.17
3. $16 5. $5.25 7. 195 km 9. 240 km
11. Best Brand 13. Sparkle Window Cleaner
15. 5 gal 17. 62 km/h, 74 km/h

PAGE 237 REVIEW EXERCISES 1. 20 cm
3. 84 cm 5. 142.4 m 7. 57.4 m

PAGES 239–240 WRITTEN EXERCISES
1. 40 in. 3. 22.5 in. 5. 2 in. 7. 4 cm 9. 30 cm
11. 0.63 mm 13. b. 15 cm, 14.5 cm c. 70 cm

PAGE 240 REVIEW EXERCISES 1. 0.365
3. 46.775 5. 60.006 7. 99.901

PAGE 240 COMPUTER BYTE 1. 2 3. 13.5

PAGES 243–244 WRITTEN EXERCISES
1. 83% 3. 0.52% 5. 472% 7. 0.3% 9. 80%
11. 37.5% 13. 27.5% 15. $83\frac{1}{3}$% 17. 45.5%
19. 21.4% 21. 78.9% 23. 46.2% 25. a. $\frac{9}{25}$
b. 0.36 27. a. $2\frac{12}{25}$ b. 2.48 29. a. $\frac{9}{2000}$
b. 0.0045 31. a. $\frac{7}{250}$ b. 0.028 33. a. $\frac{23}{400}$
b. 0.0575 35. $\frac{3}{800}$ 37. $\frac{1}{120}$ 39. $\frac{4}{125}$ 41. $\frac{1}{6}$
43. $\frac{1}{9}$ 45. > 47. < 49. > 51. = 53. =

PAGE 244 PROBLEMS 1. $\frac{7}{10}$, 70% 3. $\frac{3}{5}$,
60% 5. $\frac{1}{3}$, 33.3%

PAGE 244 REVIEW EXERCISES 1. 15
3. 39.51 5. -10 7. 21.50

PAGES 246–247 WRITTEN EXERCISES
1. 132 3. 7% 5. 20 7. 40 9. $33\frac{1}{3}$%
11. 162 13. $\frac{17}{900}$ 15. $66\frac{2}{3}$% 17. 175%

PAGES 247–248 PROBLEMS 1. 52%
3. 68.1 g 5. $375 million 7. 150 customers
9. $18,200 11. a. 80 people b. 14 people

PAGE 248 SELF–TEST A 1. $\frac{3}{5}$ 2. $\frac{3}{1}$ 3. $\frac{2}{25}$
4. 3 5. 2.4 6. 54 7. $2.50 8. 110 km
9. 570 km 10. 1235 km 11. 2660 km
12. 66% 13. 32.7% 14. 250% 15. $16\frac{2}{3}$%
16. 4.44 17. 50 18. $33\frac{1}{3}$% 19. 1.77

PAGES 250–251 PROBLEMS 1. $253
3. 12.5% 5. 25 mi/gal 7. 450 Calories
9. 1352 people 11. $7000

PAGE 251 REVIEW EXERCISES 1. 9.72
3. 17 5. 520 7. 220.5 9. 0.04

PAGES 253–254 PROBLEMS 1. 16%
3. $3600 5. $5.50 7. $72 9. 3%
11. $79,800 13. $89,400 15. $9250

PAGE 254 CALCULATOR KEY–IN
1. 1.05×25

PAGE 257 WRITTEN EXERCISES 1. 5.12
3. 80% 5. 40

PAGES 257–258 PROBLEMS 1. 82.5% 3. 49
books 5. $34.80; $27.84 7. $36.50
9. a. 108° b. $3.6 million

PAGE 259 REVIEW EXERCISES 1. 0.5
3. $0.1\overline{6}$ 5. 2.25 7. 0.75

PAGE 259 COMPUTER BYTE
3. Delete lines 20, 30, 60, and 70.
   Add: 5 INPUT "NUMERATOR: ";B
       6 INPUT "DENOMINATOR: ";A
       60 GOTO 5

PAGES 261–263 PROBLEMS 1. $600
3. 12.5% 5. 5 years 7. $10,000 9. $3650.33
11. $4073.84 13. Steve 15. $7000
17. $319.84 19. After 1 year: 1000 +
1000(0.05) = 1000(1 + 0.05) = 1000(1.05);
after 2 years: 1000(1.05) + 1000(1.05)(0.05) =
1000(1.05)(1.05) = 1000(1.05)²; after 3 years:
1000(1.05)² + 1000(1.05)²(0.05) = 1000(1.05)³,
and so on

SELF–TEST B **1.** 20% **2.** 930 books **3.** $119.84 **4.** $20.85 **5.** $9.25 **6.** 42% **7.** $2106 **8.** $355.28

PAGE 265 ENRICHMENT **1.** 3; 21, 144, and 987 are divisible by 3; 5, 55, and 610 are divisible by 5. **3.** The new pattern is every other member of the Fibonacci sequence, beginning with 3. **5.** The new pattern is every other member of the Fibonacci sequence, beginning with 5.

PAGE 266 CHAPTER REVIEW **1.** 56 **3.** $\frac{12}{6}$, or $2\frac{1}{6}$, h **5.** 62.5 **7.** 77 **9.** 85 **11.** $16\frac{2}{3}$% **13.** 30% **15.** B **17.** False

PAGE 268 CUMULATIVE REVIEW EXERCISES **1.** 8 **3.** 7 **5.** 12 **7.** −19 **9.** 9 **11.** 45 **13.** −7, −2.5, −2.2, 0, 3, 6.4 **15.** −8.4, −3, −1.6, −1.0, 0.5 **17.** True **19.** True **21.** True **23.** $\frac{6}{9}, \frac{5}{9}$ **25.** $-\frac{88}{33}, \frac{27}{33}$ **27.** $\frac{28}{12}, \frac{9}{12}$ **29.** $\frac{68}{128}, -\frac{3}{128}$ **31.** All the numbers greater than or equal to 1

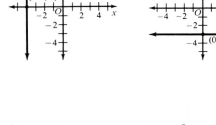

33. All the numbers less than −3

35. All the numbers greater than 3

37. Translation and rotation, ASA **39.** Rotation and translation, SSS

PAGE 269 CUMULATIVE REVIEW PROBLEMS **1.** $79.38 **3.** 23,500 ft **5.** 1230 lb **7.** 15 m, 5 m **9.** $616.13

8 The Coordinate Plane

PAGES 274–275 WRITTEN EXERCISES **1.** (−5, −5) **3.** (5, 1) **5.** (−3, −2) **7.** (−1, 4) **9.** *I* **11.** *V* **13.** *D* **15.** *W* **17.** *M* **19. c.** Rectangle **21. c.** Parallelogram **23. b.** (−5, 1), (−2, −2), (2, −2), (2, 1) **d.** Translation **25. b.** (−2, 3), (2, 3), (4, 1), (4, −1), (1, 1), (−1, 1), (−4, −1), (−4, 1) **d.** Translation **27. b.** (−6, −5), (−2, −1), (−9, −3) **d.** Reflection

PAGE 275 REVIEW EXERCISES **1.** 8 **3.** 27 **5.** −5 **7.** −15

PAGES 278–279 WRITTEN EXERCISES **1.** Yes **3.** Yes **5.** No **7.** No **9.** No **11.** No **13.** Yes **15.** Yes **17.** $y = -2x + 7$ **19.** $y = 4x + 16$ **21.** $y = \frac{2}{3}x - 2$ **23. a.** $y = x + 7$ **b.** (2, 9), (−5, 2), (7, 14) **25. a.** $y = \frac{1}{2}x + 5$ **b.** (4, 7), (0, 5), (6, 8) **27. a.** $y = -\frac{1}{4}x + 5$ **b.** (4, 4), (−8, 7), (0, 5) **29. a.** $y = \frac{3}{2}x - 3$ **b.** (4, 3), (−2, −6), (−8, −15) **31. a.** $y = \frac{1}{2}x + \frac{5}{2}$ **b.** (3, 4), (5, 5), (−1, 2) **33. a.** $y = \frac{5}{2}x + 3$ **b.** (2, 8), (1, 5$\frac{1}{2}$), (−3, −4$\frac{1}{2}$) Answers to Exercises 35, 37, 39, 41, and 43 may vary. Examples are given. **35.** (0, −1), (−1, 0), (1, −2) **37.** (−1, 1), (1, −1), (0, 0) **39.** (−1, 0), (0, 5), (1, 10) **41.** (6, 0), (0, −4), (3, −2) **43.** (0, 6), (−3, 0), (1, 8) **45.** $x + y = 0$ **47.** $x + y = -3$

PAGE 279 REVIEW EXERCISES **1.** 3 **3.** 28 **5.** 3 **7.** −56 **9.** −4

PAGES 281–283 WRITTEN EXERCISES **1.–33.** Each graph is a straight line through the points listed: **1.** (0, −7), (7, 0), (8, 1) **3.** (−8, 0), (−2, −3), (0, −4) **5.** (0, 10), (1, 8), (5, 0) **7.** (0, 0), (1, 1), (2, 2) **9.** (−2, −1), (0, 0), (2, 1) **11.** (0, −6), (6, 0) **13.** (−3, 0), (0, −3) **15.** (0, 4), (1, 0) **17.** (−2, 0), (0, 6) **19.** (−8, 0), (0, 2) **21.** (−4, 0), (0, 3) **23.** (−$\frac{5}{2}$, 0), (0, 1) **25.** (0, 6), (6, 0) **27.** (0, −6), (2, 0) **29.** (−12, 0), (0, 6) **31.** (0, −$\frac{1}{2}$), ($\frac{1}{3}$, 0) **33.** (0, −8), (6, 0)

35.
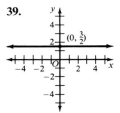

37.

39.

47. $-\frac{3}{4}$

PAGE 283 SELF–TEST A

1. $(-3, 6)$ **7.–12.**

2. $(4, -4)$

3. $(6, 6)$

4. C

5. T

6. P

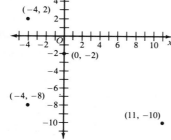

13. $(0, \frac{1}{2})$, $(-4, -\frac{1}{2})$, $(9, 2\frac{3}{4})$ **14.** $(-3, 12)$, $(\frac{1}{2}, 5)$, $(11, -16)$

15. 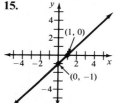 **16.**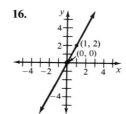

17.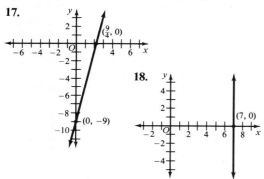

18.

PAGES 286–287 WRITTEN EXERCISES

1. Intersect at $(3, 3)$ **3.** Parallel **5.** Coincide
7. Parallel **9.** Intersect at $(0, 6)$
11. Coincide **13.** Intersect at $(-2, 4)$
15. Parallel **17.** Intersect at $(4, -1)$ **19.** 2

PAGE 287 REVIEW EXERCISES 1. $\frac{9}{8}$, or $1\frac{1}{8}$ **3.** $\frac{7}{8}$ **5.** $\frac{4}{5}$ **7.** $\frac{1}{13}$

PAGE 287 CALCULATOR KEY–IN
$13,107.20

PAGES 291–293 PROBLEMS 1. Slope $= \frac{3}{2}$
3. 4°C **5.** 245 mi **7. a.** $y = 4.5x + 2$ **c.** 7
9. a. $y = \frac{7}{12}x + \frac{1}{6}$ **c.** $\frac{32}{3}$, or $10\frac{2}{3}$, min **11.** 5.5 s

PAGE 293 REVIEW EXERCISES All the
numbers: **1.** greater than $1\frac{1}{3}$ **3.** greater than
or equal to -1 **5.** less than or equal to 0
7. greater than or equal to -1 **9.** greater than
41

PAGE 293 CALCULATOR KEY–IN 1, 121,
12321, 1234321; 123454321, 12345654321,
1234567654321, 123456787654321,
12345678987654321

PAGES 296–297 WRITTEN EXERCISES
1. $y = -3x - 6$ **3.** $y = x - 2$ **5.** $y = 3 - x$
7. Solid line through $(0, 9)$ and $(9, 0)$, shaded
region at right above line **9.** Solid line
through $(-1, 0)$ and $(0, 2)$, shaded region at
left above line **11.** Solid line through $(0, 4)$
and $(2, 0)$, shaded region at right above line
13. Solid line through $(-\frac{5}{2}, 0)$ and $(0, 5)$,
shaded region at left above line **15.** Dashed
line through $(0, -\frac{1}{3})$ and $(\frac{1}{2}, 0)$, shaded region
at left above line **17.** Solid line through $(0, 8)$
parallel to x-axis, shaded region below line
19. Solid line through $(-1, 0)$ and $(0, -1)$,
shaded region at left below line **21.** Solid line
through $(-3, 0)$ parallel to y-axis, shaded
region to left of line **23.** Dashed line through
$(-\frac{5}{2}, 0)$ and $(0, 5)$, shaded region at right below
line **25.** $x < 4$ **27.** $y \geq -3$

PAGE 297 SELF–TEST B
1. Intersect at $(4, 2)$

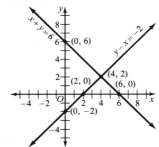

2. 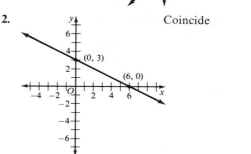 Coincide

3. Parallel

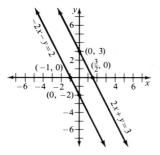

4. 4 weeks

5.

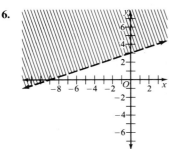

6.

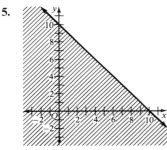

7.

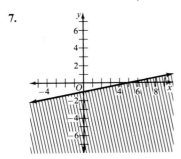

1. $y = 0.5x + 1.32$ Answers to Exercises 3, 5, and 7 may vary. Examples are given.
3. 2.97 kg **5.** $y = -3.3x + 20.8$ **a.** 15.85°C
b. 6.3 h **7.** $y = 0.59x + 7.39$; $10,930; $11,520

PAGE 300 CHAPTER REVIEW **1.** False
3. True **5.** C **7.** B **9.** Straight line through $(-2, 2)$ and $(0, 0)$ **11.** Straight line through $(-1, 0)$ and $(0, 2)$ **13.** C **15.** constant
17. dashed

PAGE 302 CUMULATIVE REVIEW
EXERCISES **1.** $5b$ **3.** $y + z - 12$
5. $3p + 7$ **7.** 288.01 **9.** 100.76 **11.** 4.8911
13. 554.09 **15.** 3.0088 **17.** -425.0612
19. -8.174 **21.** $-\frac{3}{14}$ **23.** $\frac{9}{8}$, or $1\frac{1}{8}$ **25.** $-\frac{247}{50}$,
or $-4\frac{47}{50}$ **27.** $t = -\frac{3}{4} \times \frac{1}{5}$; $-\frac{3}{20}$
29. $x + 12 > 2x$; the solutions are all the numbers less than 12. **31.** 20.7 m **33.** 1.6
35. 42 **37.** No **39.** Yes

PAGE 303 CUMULATIVE REVIEW
PROBLEMS **1.** $84.88 **3.** 7 times **5.** $9799; $10,038 **7.** 44.1% **9.** 0.5 kW·h

9 Areas and Volumes

PAGES 308–310 WRITTEN EXERCISES
1. $17\frac{1}{2}$ **3.** 30 **5.** 36 **7.** 1400 m; 105,600 m²
9. 70 cm; 210 cm² **11.** 72,900 **13.** 8 km
15. 4.8 **17.** 40, 100; 40, 96; 40, 36; 40, 19
19. area **21.** The greatest possible area for a rectangle with perimeter 20 is $(\frac{20}{4})^2 = 25$.

PAGES 310–311 PROBLEMS **1.** $2268
3. 600 m **5.** 225 m² **7.** 39.6 m² **9.** 48 m²
11. 448 tiles

PAGE 311 REVIEW EXERCISES **1.** 180
3. 88 **5.** 17 **7.** 60

PAGES 314–316 WRITTEN EXERCISES
1. 88 **3.** 36 **5.** 120 m² **7.** 59.28 km²
9. 14 cm **11.** 6 m **13.** 23.5 **15.** 16.5 **17.** 40
19. 80 cm² **21.** 54 **23. a.** $2 : 3$ **b.** $2 : 3$
c. $2 : 3$ **d.** $2 : 3$ **e.** $2 : 3$ **f.** $4 : 9$

PAGE 316 REVIEW EXERCISES **1.** 1 **3.** 64
5. 1.44 **7.** 7; -7 **9.** 0.6; -0.6

PAGES 318–319 WRITTEN EXERCISES
1. 1386 km² **3.** 1.54 cm² **5.** 50.2 m²
7. 78.5 cm² **9.** 707 m² **11.** 10 cm **13.** 14; 14π; 49π **15.** 4; 8; 16π **17.** 5; 10; 10π
19. 4 **21.** 18π **23.** $1050 + 50\pi$

PAGE 320 PROBLEMS **1.** 113 m²; 141 m²
3. 400 m **5.** 9540 m² **7.** 21.5%

PAGE 320   REVIEW EXERCISES
1. translation   **3.** reflection   **5.** rotation, or rotation and translation

PAGES 323–324 WRITTEN EXERCISES
1.   **3.**   **5.**
7. 452   **9.** 800   **11.** 103   **13.** 471
15. 12   **17.** 98.1

PAGE 325 SELF-TEST A   **1.** 1344   **2.** 18
3. 124   **4.** 4000 m   **5.** 7.5 cm   **6.** 29 cm
7. 180   **8.** 280   **9.** 19.6 cm²   **10.** 254 m²
11. 113 m²   **12.** 106   **13.** 15   **14.** 71.5

PAGES 328–330 WRITTEN EXERCISES
1. 90   **3.** 108   **5.** 22,600   **7.** 514   **9.** 50 L
11. 6330 L   **13.** 4π; 3   **15.** 5; 4   **17.** 3; 9π
19. 60   **21. a.** quadrupled   **b.** halved
c. doubled   **23.** 3

PAGE 330 PROBLEMS   **1.** 96 L   **3.** 7070 cm³
5. 1.62 cm

PAGE 330 REVIEW EXERCISES   **1.** 32
3. 0.845   **5.** 1256   **7.** 10; -10

PAGES 333–334 WRITTEN EXERCISES
1. 72   **3.** 301   **5.** 56   **7.** 0.16 L   **9.** 1000 L
11. 10   **13.** 6   **15.** 3   **17.** 15   **19.** 3   **21.** 18

PAGE 334 PROBLEMS   **1.** 2,592,100 m³
3. 14,700 cm³

PAGE 334 REVIEW EXERCISES   **1.** 36 m
3. 105 cm   **5.** 51.2 km   **7.** 580.8 km

PAGES 337–339 WRITTEN EXERCISES
1. 5700 cm²   **3.** 14.56 m²   **5.** 1660 cm²;
2560 cm²   **7.** 226; 283   **9.** 360; 468   **11. a.** 30
b. 72   **13.** 5 cm   **15.** 6   **17.** 72 m²; 120 m²
19. $n - 2$ **20. a.** 298   **c.** 440

PAGE 339 REVIEW EXERCISES   **1.** 6
3. 105   **5.** 35   **7.** 38

PAGES 341–343 WRITTEN EXERCISES
1. 36π; 36π **3.** 144π; 288π **5.** 400π; $\frac{4000}{3}\pi$
7. $\frac{16}{3}\pi$ **9.** 9.68π **11.** 51.84π; 62.208π **13.** 9;
324π **15.** 8; $\frac{2048}{3}\pi$ **17.** 324π m³   **19.** Earth's
volume is about 49.3 times that of the moon.
21. a. $2:3$ **b.** $2:3$ **c.** $4r:3h$, or $2:3$

PAGE 343 REVIEW EXERCISES   **1.** 2.1

3. 0.64   **5.** 3.5   **7.** 810

PAGE 343 CALCULATOR KEY-IN   **1.** 126

PAGES 345–346 WRITTEN EXERCISES
1. 6300   **3.** 4300   **5.** 810 g   **7.** 34 kg   **9.** 460 t
11. 180 g   **13.** 33.12 g   **15.** 72.7 g   **17.** 7460 kg

PAGES 346–347   **1.** 13.28805 kg   **3.** 81.12 g
5. 3.91 t

PAGE 347 SELF-TEST B   **1.** 41.8   **2.** 27,200
3. 9248; 9.248   **4.** 0.314 m³   **5.** 1200 m³
6. 10,816 cm³   **7. a.** 98   **b.** 122   **8. a.** 94.2
b. 251   **9. a.** 3024   **b.** 3672   **10. a.** 1296π cm²
b. 7776π cm³   **11. a.** 144π m²   **b.** 288π m³
12. 8240 g   **13.** 181.76 g

PAGE 349 ENRICHMENT   **1.** New York
3. Rio de Janeiro   **5.** Moscow   **7.** Casablanca
9. 40°N, 105°W   **11.** 55°N, 0°   **13.** 15°N,
15°W   **15.** 65°N, 165°W

PAGE 350 CHAPTER REVIEW   **1.** False
3. True   **5.** False   **7.** False   **9.** 3864 cm³
11. 45.2   **13.** 266   **15.** 2304; 18,432
17. 60.48 kg

PAGES 352–353 CUMULATIVE REVIEW
EXERCISES   **1.** 5   **3.** 10   **5.** 12.5   **7.** -22.5
9. $\frac{37}{12}$, or $3\frac{1}{12}$ **11.** $\frac{2}{5}$ **13.** $\frac{52}{3}$, or $17\frac{1}{3}$ **15.** $-\frac{37}{4}$,
or $-9\frac{1}{4}$ **17.** All the numbers greater than 3
19. All the numbers less than or equal to 40
21. All the numbers greater than or equal to 9
23. 7   **25.** 21   **27.** 45°; 45°   **29.** 8.1   **31.** 24%
33. 63,200   **35.** $y = 18 - 4x$
37. $y = -8\frac{1}{3} + x$ **39.** $y = \frac{20}{x}$ **41.** 196π cm²
43. $15,625\pi$ km²   **45.** $3,258,025\pi$ cm²
47. 256π; $\frac{2048}{3}\pi$ **49.** 5184π; $62,208\pi$

PAGE 353 CUMULATIVE REVIEW
PROBLEMS   **1.** 1929 stories   **3.** 25 m
5. $6075   **7.** 5%

10 Square Roots and Right Triangles
PAGE 357 WRITTEN EXERCISES   **1.** 6 and
7   **3.** -4 **5.** 1   **7.** -6 **9.** 7 and 8   **11.** 5 and
6   **13.** 3 and 4   **15.** 1 and 2   **17.** 3   **19.** 4 and
5   **21.** 9   **23.** $>$ **25.** $<$ **27.** $=$ **29.** $>$
31. 81   **33.** 11

PAGE 357 REVIEW EXERCISES   **1.** 6.57
3. 8.67   **5.** 11.95   **7.** 0.13

PAGE 360 WRITTEN EXERCISES   **1.** 3.3

3. 5.7 **5.** 2.8 **7.** 5.1 **9.** 7.5 **11.** 9.5 **13.** 2.3 **15.** 3.0 **17.** 2.8 **19.** 1.8 **21.** 12.3 **23.** 26.5 **25.** 3.9 **27.** 8.4 **29.** 0.6 **31.** 0.2 **33.** 1.41 **35.** 2.23

PAGE 360 REVIEW EXERCISES **1.** 58 **3.** 6.72 **5.** 3.89 **7.** 93.57

PAGE 360 CALCULATOR KEY–IN **1. a.** 1 **b.** 10 **c.** 100 **3. a.** 8.3666002 **b.** 83.666002 **c.** 836.66002 **5. a.** 0.7348469 **b.** 7.3484692 **c.** 73.484692

PAGES 362–363 WRITTEN EXERCISES **1.** 8.06 **3.** 7.48 **5.** 9.85 **7.** 64.03 **9.** 0.87 **11.** 22.25 **13.** 26.15 **15.** 59.40 **17.** 12.57 **19.** 0.37 **21.** 0.43 **23.** 2.43 **25.** 9.03 **27.** 2.95 **29.** 7.13 **31.** 27.15 **33.** 22.36 **35.** 19.46 **37.** 58.91

PAGE 363 PROBLEMS **1.** 9.22 m **3.** $21 **5.** 3.87 cm **7.** 5.92 m

PAGE 363 REVIEW EXERCISES **1.** 0.81 **3.** 0.0036 **5.** 13.69 **7.** 590.49

PAGE 366 WRITTEN EXERCISES **1.** 289 **3.** 400 **5.** Yes **7.** Yes **9.** Yes **11.** Yes **13.** No **15.** $c = 10$ **17.** $a = 3.32$ **19.** $c = 11.24$ **21.** $b = 70$ **23.** $a = 27, b = 36, c = 45$

PAGES 366–367 PROBLEMS **1.** 108.2 km **3.** 55.7 m **5.** 7.1 cm **7.** 17.3

PAGE 367 SELF–TEST A **1.** 7 and 8 **2.** -9 **3.** 8 **4.** 7 **5.** 9.3 **6.** 4.2 **7.** 7.1 **8.** 3.1 **9.** 2.4 **10.** $c = 5$ **11.** $a = 28$ **12.** $b = 16$

PAGES 371–372 WRITTEN EXERCISES **1.** RQ **3.** 9 **5.** 104° **7.** 25 **9.** 65 **11.** 5, 9 **13.** 25, 27 **15.** $46\frac{2}{7}$, 14 **17.** 180 cm **19. a.** 18 **b.** 18 **21.** $\triangle ADC$ and $\triangle ACB$ are right triangles; $\angle A \cong \angle A$; so $\angle B \cong \angle DCA$ **23.** Yes; angles congruent, sides proportional **25.** No. The lengths of the sides may differ.

PAGE 372 REVIEW EXERCISES **1.** 519 **3.** 1562 **5.** 2.2454 **7.** 4.878 **9.** 3741.36

PAGES 375–376 WRITTEN EXERCISES **1.** $\frac{3\sqrt{10}}{5}$ **3.** $\sqrt{3}$ **5.** $\frac{2\sqrt{x}}{x}$ **7.** $x = 3.2, y = 5.5$ **9.** $x = 7.4, y = 8.6$ **11.** $x = 3.2, y = 4.5$ **13.** $2\sqrt{2}$ **15.** $5\sqrt{3}, 10\sqrt{3}$ **17.** $AB = 5.4$

19. $BC = 6$ **21.** $BC = 1.7y$ **23.** $x = 6, y = 3$

PAGES 376–377 PROBLEMS **1.** 8.7 m **3.** 20 m **5.** 56.6 cm **7.** 40; 28.3 **9. a.** $0.9r$ units **b.** $0.4r^2$ units^2 **11.** 5.2 m

PAGE 377 REVIEW EXERCISES **1.** 1.25 **3.** $0.\overline{2}$ **5.** 1.1 **7.** $0.1\overline{6}$

PAGES 380–381 WRITTEN EXERCISES **1.** $\sin A = \frac{3}{5}$; $\cos A = \frac{4}{5}$; $\tan A = \frac{3}{4}$; $\sin B = \frac{4}{5}$; $\cos B = \frac{3}{5}$; $\tan B = \frac{4}{3}$ **3.** $\sin A = \frac{80}{89}$; $\cos A = \frac{39}{89}$; $\tan A = \frac{80}{39}$; $\sin B = \frac{39}{89}$; $\cos B = \frac{80}{89}$; $\tan B = \frac{39}{80}$ **5.** $\sin A = \frac{a}{c}$; $\cos A = \frac{b}{c}$; $\tan A = \frac{a}{b}$; $\sin B = \frac{b}{c}$; $\cos B = \frac{a}{c}$; $\tan B = \frac{b}{a}$ **7.** 5; $\tan A = \frac{5}{12}$ **9.** $\sqrt{21}$; $\sin A = \frac{\sqrt{21}}{11}$ **11.** 24; $\cos A = \frac{12}{13}$ **13. a.** $\frac{\sqrt{3}}{2}$; 0.866 **b.** $\frac{1}{2}$; 0.500 **c.** $\sqrt{3}$; 1.732 **15. a.** 6.4 **b.** 2.8 **c.** 0.4 **17. a.** 3.8 **b.** 8.2 **c.** 0.5

PAGE 381 REVIEW EXERCISES **1.** b **3.** a **5.** b **7.** b

PAGE 384 WRITTEN EXERCISES **1.** 0.4226; 0.9063; 0.4663 **3.** 0.9994; 0.0349; 28.6363 **5.** 0.6293; 0.7771; 0.8098 **7.** 0.9613; 0.2756; 3.4874 **9.** 0.6428; 0.7660; 0.8391 **11.** 0.9063; 0.4226; 2.1445 **13.** 81° **15.** 1° **17.** 76° **19.** 30° **21.** 60° **23.** 6 **25.** 58° **27.** 25° **29.** 70° **31.** $c = 9.4$, m$\angle A = 32°$, m$\angle B = 58°$ **33.** m$\angle B = 18°$, $a = 9.5$, $b = 3.1$ **35.** $a = 8.1$, m$\angle A = 64°$, m$\angle B = 26°$ **37.** m$\angle A = 70°$, $c = 43.9$, $a = 41.2$ **39.** m$\angle B = 32°$, $a = 19.2$, $c = 22.6$

PAGES 385–386 PROBLEMS **1.** 42.0 m **3.** 11° **5. a.** 42.5 m **b.** 10.7 m **7.** 39° **9.** 67°

PAGE 386 SELF–TEST B **1.** $\sim$ **2.** $\frac{TN}{TY}$ **3.** $7\frac{1}{2}$ **4.** $=$ **5.** $3.1\sqrt{2}$ cm **6.** $4\sqrt{3}, 8\sqrt{3}$ **7.** $\frac{p}{q}$ **8.** $\frac{r}{q}$ **9.** $\frac{p}{r}$ **10.** m$\angle P = 60°$, $p = 5.2$, m$\angle R = 30°$ **11.** $q = 24.1$, $p = 23.5$, m$\angle R = 12°$ **12.** m$\angle P = 67°$, $r = 3.4$, $q = 8.7$ **13.** m$\angle P = 33°$, $p = 13.1$, $r = 20.1$

PAGE 387 COMPUTER BYTE **1.** 3, 4, 5 **3.** 5, 12, 13 **5.** Output: THERE IS NO SUCH TRIPLE.

PAGE 389 ENRICHMENT **1.** 3 **3.** 2 **5.** 4
7. There is no square root because *a* is
negative and *n* is even. **9.** -10 **11.** 5 **13.** 6
15. 4 **17.** 2 **19.** 3 Calculator
Activity **1.** 2.1544347 **3.** 2.1867241
5. 1.4953488 **7.** About 9.4203395 ft

PAGE 390 CHAPTER REVIEW **1.** 2
3. 5.35 **5.** 4.899 and 5 **7.** False **9.** False
11. F **13.** 45 **15.** $7\sqrt{2}$ **17.** *A* **19.** *D* **21.** *F*

PAGES 392–393 CUMULATIVE REVIEW
EXERCISES **1.** $\frac{10}{27}$ **3.** 3300 **5.** $-3\frac{1}{3}$
7. Commutative **9.** Associative
11. Distributive **13.** -100 **15.** 0 **17.** -200
19. 2.5 **21.** -1 **23.** $>$ **25.** $<$ **27.** 38
29. 2.5 **31.** $7\frac{1}{3}$ **33.** 11.6 ft **35.** 4 **37.** 10
39. Straight line through $(0, \frac{7}{2})$ and $(7, 0)$
41. Straight line through $(0, 5)$ and $(1, 0)$
43. 55.545π **45.** $\frac{5\sqrt{2}}{2}$ **47.** $2\sqrt{n}$

PAGE 393 CUMULATIVE REVIEW
PROBLEMS **1.** 40 dimes, 52 quarters, 49
nickels **3.** $22.50 **5.** $2.17 **7.** 52 in. $\times$ 52 in.

11 Probability

PAGE 398 WRITTEN EXERCISES **1.** 120
3. 5040 **5.** 720 **7.** 40,320 **9.** 360 **11.** 74,046

PAGES 398–400 PROBLEMS **1.** 6 **3.** 24
5. 42 **7.** 24 **9.** 12 **11.** 5040 **13.** 720
15. 216 **17.** 20 **19.** 6

PAGE 400 REVIEW EXERCISES **1.** 7 **3.** 3
5. 12 **7.** 165

PAGES 402–403 PROBLEMS **1.** 15 **3.** 15
5. 210 **7.** 252 **9. a.** 4 **b.** 6 **c.** 4 **d.** 1
e. 15 **11.** 10,192

PAGES 407–408 WRITTEN EXERCISES
1. $\frac{1}{6}$ **3.** $\frac{2}{3}$ **5.** 0 **7.** $\frac{1}{4}$ **9.** $\frac{1}{5}$ **11.** $\frac{1}{2}$ **13.** $\frac{3}{4}$
15. $\frac{2}{5}$ **17.** $\frac{3}{5}$ **19.** $\frac{1}{3}$ **21.** $\frac{1}{2}$ **23.** $\frac{1}{3}$ **25.** $\frac{2}{3}$
27. $\frac{1}{12}$ **29.** $\frac{1}{6}$ **31.** $\frac{1}{18}$ **33.** $\frac{2}{9}$ **35.** $\frac{5}{12}$ **37. a.** $\frac{1}{9}$
b. $\frac{5}{9}$ **c.** $\frac{4}{9}$ **d.** $\frac{8}{9}$ **e.** $\frac{4}{9}$ **39.** $\frac{1}{2}$

PAGE 408 REVIEW EXERCISES **1.** 0 **3.** $\frac{1}{3}$
5. $\frac{1}{2}$ **7.** $\frac{3}{4}$

PAGES 411–412 WRITTEN EXERCISES
1. 1 to 1 **3.** 1 to 2 **5.** 5 to 1 **7.** 2 to 3 **9.** 3
to 2 **11.** 3 to 1 **13.** 1 to 1 **15.** 2 to 3 **17.** 5
to 1 **19.** 7 to 2 **21.** 7 to 5 **23. a.** 1 to 1 **b.** 1

to 1 **25.** 5 to 13 **27.** 1 to 3 **29.** 2 to 7 **31.** $\frac{5}{8}$

PAGE 412 SELF-TEST A **1.** 24 **2.** 60
3. 10 **4.** 105 **5.** $\frac{1}{8}$ **6.** $\frac{1}{2}$ **7.** $\frac{1}{4}$ **8.** 1 **9.** 1 to
3 **10.** 3 to 1

PAGES 414–415 WRITTEN EXERCISES
1. $\frac{13}{15}$ **3.** 0.3 **5. a.** $\frac{1}{3}$ **b.** $\frac{1}{2}$ **c.** $\frac{5}{6}$ **7. a.** $\frac{1}{6}$ **b.** $\frac{5}{6}$
9. a. $\frac{1}{2}$ **b.** $\frac{1}{3}$ **c.** $\frac{5}{6}$ **11. a.** $\frac{1}{5}$ **b.** $\frac{2}{5}$ **c.** $\frac{3}{5}$
13. a. $\frac{1}{4}$ **b.** $\frac{3}{10}$ **c.** $\frac{11}{20}$ **15. a.** $\frac{1}{9}$ **b.** $\frac{1}{6}$ **c.** $\frac{5}{18}$
17. 13 to 7 **19.** 1 to 4

PAGE 415 REVIEW EXERCISES **1.** $\frac{13}{15}$
3. $\frac{1}{2}$ **5.** $\frac{5}{8}$ **7.** 1.1 **9.** 0.3

PAGES 418–419 WRITTEN EXERCISES
1. 0.7 **3.** $\frac{7}{12}$ **5.** 0.5 **7. a.** $\frac{1}{4}$ **b.** $\frac{1}{3}$ **c.** $\frac{1}{12}$ **d.** $\frac{1}{2}$
9. a. $\frac{1}{2}$ **b.** $\frac{1}{3}$ **c.** $\frac{1}{6}$ **d.** $\frac{2}{3}$ **11.** $\frac{11}{20}$ **13.** $\frac{7}{10}$ **15.** $\frac{5}{18}$;
13 to 5 **17.** $\frac{13}{36}$; 23 to 13

PAGE 419 PROBLEMS **1.** 90% **3.** 80%
5. $\frac{3}{16}$

PAGE 419 REVIEW EXERCISES **1.** $\frac{5}{36}$
3. $\frac{1}{6}$ **5.** $\frac{6}{25}$ **7.** $\frac{12}{25}$

PAGES 422–423 WRITTEN EXERCISES
1. *A:* $\frac{1}{4}$ *B:* $\frac{1}{4}$ *C:* $\frac{1}{2}$ **3.** *A:* $\frac{1}{16}$ *B:* $\frac{9}{16}$ *C:* $\frac{5}{8}$ *D:* $\frac{3}{8}$
5. *A:* $\frac{1}{9}$ *B:* $\frac{2}{9}$ *C:* $\frac{4}{9}$ **7.** *A:* $\frac{1}{16}$ *B:* $\frac{9}{16}$ *C:* $\frac{7}{16}$ *D:* $\frac{3}{8}$
9. *A:* $\frac{1}{16}$ *B:* $\frac{1}{16}$ **11.** *A:* 0.216 *B:* 0.064
13. *A:* $\frac{1}{2}$ **15.** *A:* $\frac{1}{64}$ *B:* $\frac{9}{64}$ *C:* $\frac{27}{64}$

PAGE 423 REVIEW EXERCISES **1.** 6
3. 10 **5.** 15 **7.** 56

PAGES 426–427 WRITTEN EXERCISES
1. a. *A:* A red marble is drawn. *B:* A red
marble is drawn. **b.** $\frac{1}{3}$ **3. a.** *A:* A blue marble
is drawn. *B:* A red marble is drawn. **b.** $\frac{4}{9}$
5. $\frac{1}{15}$ **7.** $\frac{7}{30}$ **9.** $\frac{7}{15}$ **11.** $\frac{2}{11}$ **13.** $\frac{3}{10}$ **15.** $\frac{3}{5}$
17. $\frac{5}{14}$ **19.** $\frac{4}{91}$

PAGE 427 REVIEW EXERCISES **1.** 0.75
3. 0.875 **5.** 0.3125 **7.** 0.04 **9.** 0.054

PAGES 429–431 PROBLEMS **1.** 0.32
3. 0.22 **5.** 0.54 **7.** 460 **9. a.** 0.35 **b.** 14 hits
11. no **13. a.** 5 to 7; 1 to 2; 1 to 3 **b.** about
13,333 cars **15.** 0.9965

PAGE 431 SELF-TEST B **1.** $\frac{7}{12}$ **2.** 0.2
3. 0.5 **4.** $\frac{4}{5}$ **5. a.** $\frac{1}{36}$ **b.** $\frac{5}{36}$ **c.** $\frac{11}{36}$ **d.** $\frac{25}{36}$
6. a. $\frac{5}{18}$ **b.** $\frac{1}{6}$ **7. a.** 0.04 **b.** 56 plants

PAGE 432 ENRICHMENT
1. $P(\text{sum} = 2) = \frac{1}{36}$; $P(\text{sum} = 4) = \frac{1}{12}$;

530 *Answers*

$P(\text{sum} = 6) = \frac{5}{36}$; $P(\text{sum} = 7) = \frac{1}{6}$;
$P(\text{sum} = 8) = \frac{5}{36}$; $P(\text{sum} = 9) = \frac{1}{9}$;
$P(\text{sum} = 10) = \frac{1}{12}$; $P(\text{sum} = 11) = \frac{1}{18}$;
$P(\text{sum} = 12) = \frac{1}{36}$

PAGE 434 CHAPTER REVIEW 1. false
3. false **5.** false **7.** mutually exclusive **9.** $\frac{5}{6}$
11. $\frac{2}{9}$ **13. a.** $\frac{35}{132}$ **b.** $\frac{35}{66}$

**PAGES 436–437 CUMULATIVE REVIEW
EXERCISES 1.** 49.5 **3.** 7.475 **5.** $m + 3n$
7. $1\frac{6}{35}$ **9.** $\frac{21}{32}$ **11.** $-3\frac{2}{3}$ **13.** 20 **15.** all numbers
greater than or equal to -2 **17.** 42 **19.** 13.3
21. 46.8 **23.** 20% **25.** 36 **27.** 4, -7; $-\frac{1}{2}$
29. 468 m; 13,308.75 m² **31.** 144 m; 756 m²
33. no **35.** 2 **37.** 6 **39.** 1

**PAGE 437 CUMULATIVE REVIEW
PROBLEMS 1.** no **3.** 30% markup **5.** $\frac{41}{80}$
7. about 5.6 lb

12 Statistics

PAGES 442–444 WRITTEN EXERCISES
1. Percent of students employed
3. Babysitting; store sales **5.** Babysitting
7., 11. See graphs below.

PAGE 444 REVIEW EXERCISES 1. a. 0.18
b. $\frac{9}{50}$ **3. a.** 0.09 **b.** $\frac{9}{100}$ **5. a.** 0.825 **b.** $\frac{33}{40}$
7. a. $0.\overline{3}$ **b.** $\frac{1}{3}$ **9. a.** 0.255 **b.** $\frac{51}{200}$

PAGES 447–448 WRITTEN EXERCISES
1. 5 P.M. **3.** 4 P.M.–5 P.M.

5. United States Population

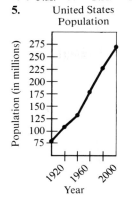

9. United States Energy Consumption

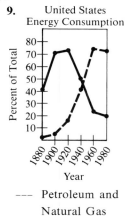

--- Petroleum and Natural Gas
—— Coal

PAGE 448 REVIEW EXERCISES 1. -18.2
3. 9.3 **5.** 50.96

PAGES 451–452 WRITTEN EXERCISES
1. 10, 6, 4, 3 **3.** 54, 88.2, 87, none **5.** 4.3,
10.1, 9.9, none **7.** 34, 1.4, 0, -9 **9.** 6, 99.6,
100, 101 **11.** 18 **13.** 10.5 **15.** 190 cm
17. 15 **19.** It is decreased by 5.

PAGE 452 SELF–TEST A 1. California
2. $4.5 billion **3.** See graph below. **4.** 5,
102.25, 102, 102 **5.** 16

PAGE 443
Ex. 7

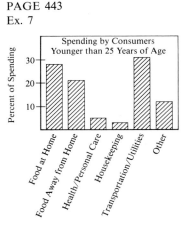

PAGE 443
Ex. 11

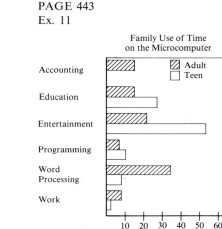

PAGE 452
Ex. 3

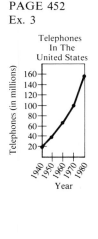

1.

x	f	$x \times f$
5	1	5
6	4	24
7	3	21
8	3	24
9	1	9
Total	12	83

7. a. 4 **b.** 7.8 **c.** 8 **d.** 8 **9. a.** 10 **b.** 7.12 **c.** 8 **d.** 4, 8 **11.** 6; 5; 4.5; 4 **13.** 5; 2.6; 2; 1, 2 **15.** 6, 7, 2, 3, 3, 3

17. Frequency distributions will vary depending on the intervals chosen. An example is given.

Scores	Frequency
51–60	1
61–70	4
71–80	8
81–90	6
91–100	5

19. 150 **21.** 73.75

PAGE 456 REVIEW EXERCISES
1. a. $y = \frac{1}{2}x - \frac{3}{2}$ **b.** $(0, -1\frac{1}{2})$, $(2, -\frac{1}{2})$
3. a. $y = -x - 3$ **b.** $(0, -3)$, $(2, -5)$
5. a. $y = -\frac{1}{2}x + 2$ **b.** $(0, 2)$, $(2, 1)$
7. a. $y = 2x - 4$ **b.** $(0, -4)$, $(2, 0)$

PAGES 459–460 WRITTEN EXERCISES
1. 9 **3.** 58 **5.** 8 **7.** 7 **9.** 226
11. a. 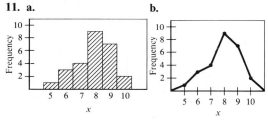 **b.**

13. a. 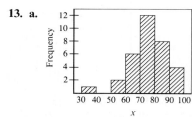 **b.**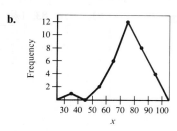

17. Graphs will vary depending on the intervals chosen. **19.** Each red triangle is congruent to a blue triangle.

PAGE 460 REVIEW EXERCISES **1.** $\frac{11}{36}$
3. $\frac{3}{4}$ **5.** $\frac{1}{18}$ **7.** $\frac{1}{12}$

PAGE 463 WRITTEN EXERCISES **1.** $26\frac{1}{4}$, or 26.25 **3.** 5.1 **5.** $2\frac{1}{2}$, or 2.5 **7.** 50 points

PAGE 463 SELF-TEST B
1.

x	f	$x \times f$
10	2	20
11	3	33
12	5	60
13	3	39
14	2	28
Total	15	180

range = 4
mean = 12
median = 12
mode = 12

2. 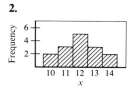 **3.**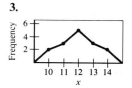

4. $8\frac{8}{9}$, or $8.\overline{8}$

PAGE 465 ENRICHMENT **1. a.** 12 gal **b.** $-1, 1, -3, 3$ **c.** 5 gal² **d.** 2.24 gal
3. a. 22.8 mi/gal **b.** $-2.8, -3.8, -2.8, -0.8, 10.2$ **c.** 26.96 (mi/gal)² **d.** 5.19 mi/gal

PAGE 466 CHAPTER REVIEW
1. True **3.** 1924 **5.** 10 **7.** 14.5 **13.** $5\frac{1}{2}$, or 5.5
11.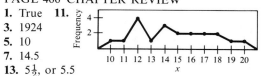

PAGES 468–469 CUMULATIVE REVIEW EXERCISES **1.** 3.79 **3.** 1.301 **5.** 100.01 **7.** $\frac{7}{12}$ **9.** $\frac{2}{11}$ **11.** $\frac{g}{2} + 12 = -6$; -36 **13.** $x - 9 = 5 - x$; 7 **15.** 62° **17.** 35° **19.** 40% **21.** $\frac{3}{5}$% **23.** 125% **25.** Intersect at $(7, 0)$ **27.** Parallel **29.** 0.243 L **31.** 6.86 **33.** 3.33 **35.** $\frac{1}{3}$ **37.** 0 **39.** 59, 48.4, 38, 26 **41.** 20, 99.8, 99.5, 99

PAGE 469 CUMULATIVE REVIEW PROBLEMS **1.** $129.46 **3.** 92 km **5.** 82

Skill Review

PAGE 470 ADDITION **1.** 57.8 **3.** 9.2 **5.** 92.167 **7.** 34.5051 **9.** 55.81 **11.** 153.69 **13.** 325.277 **15.** 46.119 **17.** 902.78 **19.** 61.17

21. 16.931 23. 91.67 25. 308.4564
27. 12.1013 29. 152.51 31. 55.708
33. 47.863 35. 119.46 37. 46.63 39. 442.166
41. 211.1826 43. 61.134 45. 660.353

PAGE 471 SUBTRACTION 1. 5.201
3. 11.744 5. 55.2 7. 2.137 9. 1.892
11. 150.745 13. 435.54 15. 46.291 17. 0.074
19. 1.0876 21. 51.8 23. 245.8 25. 573.78
27. 5.516 29. 147.09 31. 190.79 33. 485.6
35. 162.381 37. 358.88 39. 16.7
41. 567.4144 43. 2.92 45. 211.489
47. 7.2521 49. 281.712

PAGE 472 MULTIPLICATION 1. 942
3. 13,897.6 5. 44.53 7. 142.576 9. 1.3344
11. 0.06444 13. 49.248 15. 0.42966
17. 357.56334 19. 0.001505 21. 446.716
23. 10,580.075 25. 962.06 27. 0.00015
29. 26.2683 31. 14.884 33. 50.21088
35. 453.7533 37. 1871.574 39. 327
41. 4366.26 43. 355.4443 45. 41.03488
47. 162.873515 49. 8633.99913

PAGE 473 DIVISION 1. 35.2 3. 7.6
5. 15.7 7. 88.7 9. 3.6 11. 250 13. 548.1
15. 49.6 17. 2.6 19. 0.6 21. 146.7 23. 1.9
25. 2.5 27. 0.1 29. 47.9 31. 35.2 33. 1.0
35. 36.98 37. 46.55 39. 125.56 41. 17.47
43. 0.03 45. 7.49 47. 0.99

Extra Practice

PAGES 474–475 CHAPTER 1 1. 42.63
3. 0.16 5. 1 7. 24 9. 9 11. $\frac{1}{6}$ 13. 40.8
15. 14 17. 2 19. 47 21. 13 23. no solution
25. 3 27. < 29. $6 < 18 < 35$, or $35 > 18 > 6$
31. $208 < 280 < 802$, or $802 > 280 > 208$

33.

35.

37. 0, 1, 2, 3, 4, 5, 6 39. 1, 2, 3, 4 41. 732
43. 52 45. 36 47. 76 49. All the numbers
greater than or equal to 110 51. All the
numbers greater than 18 53. 9 55. $18 - t$
57. $40 \div m - 16$ 59. $3y + 11$
61. $k - 20 = 36$ 63. $y + (8 \times 6) \leq 50$
65. $20 - 6x < 12$ 67. $129.75 69. $806.90

PAGES 476–477 CHAPTER 2 1. 81 3. 89
5. 1 7. 36 9. 3^{12} 11. k^{18} 13. 1080
15. 128 17. 192 19. 0 21. 144 23. 1536

25. $(7 \times 100) + (3 \times 10) + 4$
27. $(2 \times 0.01) + (4 \times 0.001)$
29. $(2 \times 1000) + (1 \times 100) + (3 \times 10) + 8$
31. $(3 \times 0.1) + (8 \times 0.01)$ 33. 18.21
35. 242.6 37. 0.085 39. > 41. > 43. <
45. 900 47. 1.004 49. 380 51. 3.428
53. 75.0 55. 10.8; commutative and associative
properties 57. 0; associative property and
multiplication property of zero 59. 141.2;
distributive property 61. 0 63. 3.4 65. 1
67. 0 69. 158 71. 20.6 73. 0.305
75. $15k^2 + 30$ 77. 11.05 79. 54.9 81. 2.43
83. 18 85. $3230 87. $217.80

PAGES 478–479 CHAPTER 3 1. 3 3. 1
5. 6 7. 2 9. 9 17. ⁻8, ⁻2, 0, 5, 6 19. ⁻7, ⁻4,
⁻1, 3, 5 21. ⁻5, ⁻4, 0, 4, 5 23. ⁻2, 2 25. ⁻4,
4 27. ⁻3, ⁻2, ⁻1, 0, 1, 2, 3 35. ⁻8.83, ⁻8.3, ⁻8,
8.03, 8.3 37. ⁻5.5, ⁻5.05, ⁻0.5, 0.05, 5
39. ⁻42.6, ⁻4.26, ⁻0.42, 4.206, 42.06 45. ⁻12.5
47. ⁻7.6 49. 3.8 51. 19.78 53. ⁻6.7
55. ⁻4.81 57. 19.45 59. 12.5 61. -0.6
63. 20.3 65. -13.5 67. -20.3 69. 5.2
71. 5.7 73. -3.2 75. -2.5 77. -8.9
79. 2.5 81. -4.76 83. 50.02 85. 32.86
87. -25.434 89. -13.345 91. -15.66
93. 0 95. -31 97. -20 99. -95
101. 0.434 103. 410 105. 0 107. $\frac{1}{343}$
109. $\frac{1}{32}$ 111. $\frac{1}{8}$ 113. $\frac{1}{625}$ 115. $\frac{1}{729}$ 117. $\frac{1}{64}$
119. 1 121. 1 123. 216

PAGES 480–481 CHAPTER 4 1. $\frac{-3}{5}$, $\frac{3}{-5}$
3. $\frac{-8}{7}$, $\frac{8}{-7}$ 5. $-\frac{9}{14}$, $\frac{9}{-14}$ 7. 1 9. $-\frac{1}{5}$
11. $-\frac{2}{7}$ 13. 8 15. 5 17. 4 19. $\frac{1}{3}$ 21. $1\frac{2}{5}$
23. $-1\frac{1}{2}$ 25. $\frac{3}{5}$ 27. $-1\frac{3}{4}$ 29. $\frac{-7}{9}$ 31. $\frac{17}{3}$
33. $-\frac{43}{10}$ 35. $-\frac{57}{8}$ 37. $\frac{25}{4}$ 39. $\frac{20}{24}$, $\frac{9}{24}$ 41. $\frac{6}{12}$,
$\frac{5}{12}$ 43. $-\frac{33}{84}$, $\frac{34}{84}$ 45. $\frac{9}{36}$, $\frac{21}{36}$, $\frac{10}{36}$ 47. $\frac{56}{210}$, $\frac{48}{210}$,
$\frac{21}{210}$ 49. $-1\frac{1}{2}$ 51. $-\frac{1}{15}$ 53. $-\frac{7}{16}$ 55. $-\frac{179}{224}$
57. $-1\frac{17}{60}$ 59. $3\frac{35}{48}$ 61. $-5\frac{7}{12}$ 63. $\frac{143}{150}$
65. $-1\frac{31}{110}$ 67. $\frac{3}{10}$ 69. $-\frac{9}{35}$ 71. $\frac{7}{20}$ 73. $2\frac{4}{19}$
75. 2 77. $\frac{7}{30}$ 79. $-\frac{5}{27}$ 81. $-5\frac{1}{2}$ 83. $1\frac{21}{23}$
85. 0.6 87. -0.3125 89. $-0.\overline{5}$ 91. $-0.8\overline{51}$
93. $3.41\overline{6}$ 95. $4.0\overline{5}$ 97. $-\frac{1}{25}$ 99. $-4\frac{11}{50}$
101. $\frac{2}{3}$ 103. $1\frac{7}{9}$ 105. $-2\frac{1}{6}$

PAGES 482–483 CHAPTER 5 1. 7 3. 4
5. 23 7. $n + 7 = 7$ 9. $47 = 8v + 7$
11. $3h + 24 = 39$ 13. 15 15. 20 17. 20
19. -26 21. $3\frac{1}{3}$ 23. 16.6 25. 7 27. -5
29. -54.6 31. 8.4 33. 48 35. -15

37. -370 **39.** $1\frac{1}{5}$ **41.** $-4\frac{1}{3}$ **43.** 36 **45.** $\frac{25}{3}$, or $8\frac{1}{3}$ **47.** -24 **49.** -14 **51.** 10 **53.-79.** All the numbers: **53.** less than or equal to -22 **55.** greater than $4\frac{5}{6}$ **57.** less than 7 **59.** greater than 7 **61.** less than -4 **63.** less than -63 **65.** greater than or equal to -55 **67.** less than 70 **69.** less than or equal to $-4\frac{2}{7}$ **71.** less than or equal to $11\frac{1}{5}$ **73.** greater than -5 **75.** greater than or equal to -24 **77.** less than -9 **79.** less than or equal to -3 **81.-87.** Answers will vary. **89.** 14 tables **91.** 5 postcards

PAGES 484–485 CHAPTER 6
3. **5.**

7. 91.1 m **9.** 22.1 m
13. 66 **15.** 50°
17. 90° **19.** 18°, 72°
21. $\angle 3$, $\angle 6$; $\angle 4$, $\angle 5$
23. $m\angle 1 = m\angle 4 = m\angle 5 = 100°$;
$m\angle 2 = m\angle 3 = m\angle 6 = m\angle 7 = 80°$ **25.** 35°, 35° **27.** Acute triangle **29.** True **31.** True
33. False **35.** 260 mm **37.** 149.2 mm
39. 2.9 cm **41.** $\triangle ABC \cong \triangle ABD$; SSS

PAGES 486–487 CHAPTER 7 **1.** $\frac{1}{4}$ **3.** $\frac{3}{7}$
5. $\frac{3}{4}$ **7.** 9 **9.** 6 **11.** 1 h 51 min **13.** 52 km/h
15. 25 cm **17.** 173% **19.** 5% **21.** 60%
23. 25% **25.** $66\frac{2}{3}$% **27.** 55.6% **29.** 46.7%
31. a. $\frac{7}{1000}$ **b.** 0.007 **33. a.** $\frac{13}{1000}$ **b.** 0.013
35. a. $1\frac{7}{20}$ **b.** 1.35 **37. a.** $\frac{3}{1000}$ **b.** 0.003
39. $\frac{1}{800}$ **41.** $\frac{5}{6}$ **43.** 30 **45.** 18.4 **47.** 40%
49. 81 **51.** 128.6% **53.** 10 **55.** 51 boxes
57. 40% **59.** 351 people **61.** $40,000
63. $55.65 **65.** $762.25

PAGES 488–489 CHAPTER 8 **1.** $(-6, 2)$
3. $(4, 4)$ **5.** $(-2, 4)$ **7.** G **9.** I **11.** J
13. c. Rectangle **15. c.** Triangle **17. c.** Right triangle **19.** Yes **21.** No **23.** Yes **25.** Yes
27. Yes **29.** Yes **31. a.** $y = 3x + 4$
b. $(-5, -11)$, $(0, 4)$, $(5, 19)$
33. a. $y = \frac{3}{2}x + 3$ **b.** $(-2, 0)$, $(0, 3)$, $(2, 6)$
35. a. $y = x - 3$ **b.** $(6, 3)$, $(-1, -4)$, $(-3, -6)$ **37.-47.** Each graph is a straight line through the points listed: **37.** $(0, 1)$, $(-3, 0)$
39. $(0, 3)$, $(4, 0)$ **41.** $(0, -1)$, $(1, 0)$
43. $(0, -3)$, $(1, 0)$ **45.** $(0, 2)$, $(-1, 0)$
47. $(0, 3)$, $(-4, 0)$ **49.** Intersect at $(2, -4)$
51. Parallel **53.** Intersect at $(-1, -3)$

55. $y = 5x + 25$; Slope = 5; 60¢ **57.** Dashed line through $(0, 2)$ and $(4, 0)$, shaded region at left below line **59.** Solid line through $(0, 7)$ and $(1, 1)$, shaded region at right above line **61.** Solid line through $(0, 1)$ and $(1, -1)$, shaded region at right above line

PAGES 490–491 CHAPTER 9 **1.** 256 cm² **3.** 484 m² **5.** 144 m **7.** 2400 mm²
9. 2106 cm² **11.** 15 m **13.** 15,400 cm²
15. 16 mm **17.** 22 m **19.** Both; 32.6
21. 865 m³ **23.** 1260 mm³ **25.** 30 cm
27. 3536 cm³ **29. a.** 1350 cm² **b.** 1890 cm²
31. a. 900 cm² **b.** 1350 cm² **33.** 1296π cm²
35. 12 m **37.** 2.64 kg **39.** 8530.2 g

PAGES 492–493 CHAPTER 10 **1.** 3 **3.** -6, -5 **5.** 4, 5 **7.** 9 **9.** 7, 8 **11.** 5 **13.** 4 **15.** 9, 10 **17.** 4.8 **19.** 9.5 **21.** 7.1 **23.** 3.1 **25.** 6.0
27. 2.3 **29.** 2.83 **31.** 2.24 **33.** 4.90 **35.** 6.25
37. 5.57 **39.** 7.62 **41.** 3.97 **43.** 4.63 **45.** No
47. No **49.** No **51.** Yes **53.** Yes **55.** 6.40
57. 9 **59.** 9.90 **61.** 15 **63.** $x = 20$, $y = 40$
65. $x = 12$, $y = 12$ **67.** $x = 20$, $y = 10$
69. $\frac{2\sqrt{3}}{3}$ **71.** $\frac{x\sqrt{2a}}{2a}$ **73.** $\frac{x}{y}$ **75.** $\frac{y}{z}$ **77.** $\frac{x}{z}$
79. 0.4540, 0.8910, 0.5095 **81.** 0.9998, 0.0175, 57.2900 **83.** 26° **85.** 53° **87.** 23°

PAGES 494–495 CHAPTER 11 **1.** 720
3. 3,628,800 **5.** 120 **7.** 24 **9.** 210 **11.** 30
13. 6 **15.** 20 **17.** 252 **19.** 1326 **21.** $\frac{1}{7}$ **23.** $\frac{3}{7}$
25. 0 **27.** $\frac{4}{7}$ **29. a.** 1 to 7 **b.** 1 to 11
c. 1 to 3 **31. a.** $\frac{1}{6}$ **b.** $\frac{1}{18}$ **c.** $\frac{2}{9}$ **33.** 0.76
35. 0.40 **37.** Yes, $\frac{1}{12}$ **39.** $\frac{1}{22}$ **41.** $\frac{1}{11}$ **43.** $\frac{3}{65}$
45. 0.416

PAGES 496–497 CHAPTER 12
3. a. $19 billion **b.** $38 billion **c.** Japan
d. $16 billion **5. a.** 1941; 1961 **b.** 1901
7. 25; 39.7; 38.5; none **9.** 8.7; 13.4; 12.4; none **11.** 27 **13.** 5; 9.2; 9; 9 **15.** 292 kg
17. 8; 10.4; 10; 12 **19.** $13\frac{3}{4}$, or 13.75 **21.** $4\frac{1}{2}$, or 4.5